ENCYCLOPEDIA OF
Agricultural Science
Volume 2   E-L

EDITORIAL ADVISORY BOARD

ENCYCLOPEDIA OF

Agricultural Science

Volume 2   E-L

Editor-in-Chief

Charles J. Arntzen

Institute of Biosciences and Technology
Texas A&M University
Houston, Texas

Associate Editor

Ellen M. Ritter

Department of Agricultural
Communications
Texas A&M University
College Station, Texas

Academic Press

San Diego   New York   Boston   London   Sydney   Tokyo   Toronto

Copyright © 1994 by ACADEMIC PRESS, INC.
All Rights Reserved.
No part of this publication may be reproduced or transmitted in any form or by any
means, electronic or mechanical, including photocopy, recording, or any information
storage and retrieval system, without permission in writing from the publisher.

Academic Press, Inc.
A Division of Harcourt Brace & Company
525 B Street, Suite 1900, San Diego, California 92101-4495

United Kingdom Edition published by
Academic Press Limited
24-28 Oval Road, London NW1 7DX

Library of Congress Cataloging-in-Publication Data

Encyclopedia of agricultural science / edited by Charles J. Arntzen,
    Ellen M. Ritter.
        p.   cm.
    Includes index.
    ISBN 0-12-226670-6 (set) -- ISBN 0-12-226671-4 (v. 1)
    ISBN 0-12-226672-2 (v. 2) -- ISBN 0-12-226673-0 (v. 3)
    ISBN 0-12-226674-9 (v. 4)
    1. Agriculture--Encyclopedias.   I. Arntzen, Charles J.
II. Ritter, Ellen M.
S411.E713   1994
630'.3--dc20
                                            94-3143
                                              CIP

PRINTED IN THE UNITED STATES OF AMERICA
94   95   96   97   98   99   QW   9   8   7   6   5   4   3   2   1

CONTENTS OF VOLUME 2

CONTENTS OF OTHER VOLUMES

CONTENTS OF VOLUME 3

CONTENTS OF VOLUME 4

HOW TO USE THE ENCYCLOPEDIA

The *Encyclopedia of Agricultural Science* is intended for use by both students and research professionals. Articles have been chosen to reflect major disciplines in the study of agricultural science, common topics of research by professionals in this realm, areas of public interest and concern, and areas of economics and policy. Each article thus serves as a comprehensive overview of a given area, providing both breadth of coverage for students and depth of coverage for research professionals. We have designed the *Encyclopedia* with the following features for maximum accessibility for all readers.

Articles in the *Encyclopedia* are arranged alphabetically by subject. A complete table of contents appears in each volume. Here, one will find broad discipline-related titles such as "Agroforestry" and "Plant Pathology," research topics such as "Transgenic Animals" and "Photosynthesis," areas of public interest and concern such as "Plant Biotechnology: Food Safety and Environmental Issues" and "World Hunger and Food Security," and areas of economics and policy such as "Macroeconomics of World Agriculture" and "Consultative Group on International Agricultural Research."

Each article contains an outline, a glossary, cross references, and a bibliography. The outline allows a quick scan of the major areas discussed within each article. The glossary contains terms that may be unfamiliar to the reader, with each term defined in the context of its use in that article. Thus, a term may appear in the glossary for another article defined in a slightly different manner or with a subtle nuance specific to that article. For clarity, we have allowed these differences in definition to remain so that the terms are defined relative to the context of each article.

Each article has been cross referenced to other articles in the *Encyclopedia*. Cross references are found at the end of the paragraph containing the first mention of a subject area covered elsewhere in the *Encyclopedia*. We encourage readers to use the cross references to locate other encyclopedia articles that will provide more detailed information about a subject. These cross references are also identified in the Index of Related Titles, which appears in Volume 4.

The bibliography lists recent secondary sources to aid the reader in locating more detailed or technical information. Review articles and research articles that are considered of primary importance to the understanding of a given subject area are also listed. Bibliographies are not intended to provide a full reference listing of all material covered in the context of a given article, but are provided as guides to further reading.

Two appendices appear in Volume 4. Appendix A lists United States colleges and universities granting degrees in agriculture. Appendix B lists United Nations organizations concerned with agriculture and related issues. Both appendices provide address and telephone information for each institution listed.

The Subject Index is located in Volume 4. Because the reader's topic of interest may be listed under a broader article title, we encourage use of the index for access to a subject area. Entries appear with the source volume number in boldface followed by a colon and the page number in that volume where the information occurs.

Edible Tree Nuts: Pecan and Other Hickories

BRUCE W. WOOD, *USDA-Agricultural Research Service, Georgia*

Glossary

Cultivar Any plant type deemed worthy of cultivation and given a non-Latin name
Hickory Any member of the genus *Carya* of the Juglandaceae (walnut) family
Rootstock Rooted plant on which a scion is grafted
Scion Detached plant part grafted or budded onto a rootstock

Edible nuts are produced by the many hickory species that are natural components of much of the hardwood forests of central North America and eastern Asia. As one of the 20 known hickory species, pecan [*Carya illinoinensis* (Wangenh.) K. Koch] is regarded throughout much of the world as a major tree-nut crop. Chinese Hickory (*Carya cathayensis* Sarg.) is the second most important crop of this group and is a popular nut in southeastern Asia.

I. General Crop Characteristics of Hickories

A. Botanical Organization

The hickories are the sole genus of the Hicoreae tribe of the Juglandaceae family and are native to the hardwood forests of the eastern half of North America and eastern Asia. This group comprises 20 species (Table I) subdivided into the sections of *Apocarya* (pecan hickories; 10 species), *Carya* (true hickories; 9 species), and *Rhamphocarya* (1 species). All species of the pecan hickories are diploid (two sets of chromosomes or 16 total), whereas the species of the true hickories include both diploids (32 chromosomes) and tetraploids.

B. Tree Form and Growth

All *Carya* (hickory) species are long-lived deciduous upright forest-type trees. Most are capable of growing to substantial heights (10–50 m), thus exhibiting excellent tree form. Growth on adapted sites ranges from slow to moderate, depending on the species. Growth is such that most of the energy goes into vegetative rather than into reproductive structures.

C. Production

Hickories typically produce fewer nuts per volume of canopy than do most other major tree-nut crops (such as Persian walnut, almond, or pistachio). Because of their vegetative growth strategy and the high oil content of nuts, hickories typically exhibit strong cycling in fruit production. These cycles are such that little or no fruit production occurs for periods ranging from alternate to as many as 5 years. Trees growing under near optimal conditions for fruiting usually exhibit at least a moderate biennial tendency. This characteristic causes major problems for commercial producers of pecan. Maximum sustained "in-shell" (nut meat and shells) commercial production of United States pecan ranges 1700–2300 kg/ha, depending on cultivar, location, and management practice. There

TABLE I

World Hickories (*Carya* spp.), Origin, and Flavor of Nut Meats

Scientific name	Common name	Botanical section	Origin	Flavor
C. aquatica (Michx.) Nutt.	Water hickory	*Apocarya*	N. America	Bitter
C. carolina-septentrionalis (Ashe) Engl. and Graebn.	Southern shagbark hickory	*Carya*	N. America	Sweet
C. cathayensis Sarg.	Chinese hickory	*Apocarya*	Asia	Bitter
C. cordiformis (Wangenh.) Koch	Bitternut hickory	*Apocarya*	N. America	Bitter
C. floridana Sarg.	Scrub hickory	*Carya*	N. America	Sweet
C. glabra (Mill.) Sweet	Pignut hickory	*Carya*	N. America	Sweet
C. hunanensis Cheng and R. Cheng	Hunan hickory	*Carya*	Asia	Bitter
C. illoinensis[a] (Wangenh.) Koch	Pecan	*Apocarya*	N. America	Sweet
C. kweichowensis Kuang and Lu	Guizhou hickory	*Apocarya*	Asia	Bitter
C. laciniosa (Michx.)	Shellbark hickory	*Carya*	N. America	Sweet
C. myristiciformis (Michx.) Nutt.	Nutmeg hickory	*Apocarya*	N. America	Bitter
C. ovalis (Wangenh.) Sarg.	Red hickory	*Carya*	N. America	Sweet
C. ovata (Mill.) Koch	Shagbark hickory	*Carya*	N. America	Sweet
C. pallida (Ashe) Engl. and Graebn.	Sand hickory	*Carya*	N. America	Sweet
C. palmeri Manning	Mexican hickory	*Apocarya*	N. America	Bitter
C. poilanei (Chev.) Leroy	Poilane's hickory	*Apocarya*	Asia	Bitter
C. sinensis Dode	Beak-like hickory	*Rhamphocarya*	Asia	Bitter
C. texana Buckley	Black hickory	*Carya*	N. America	Sweet
C. tomentosa (Poir) Nutt.	Mockernut hickory	*Carya*	N. America	Sweet
C. tonkinensis Lecomte	Vietnam hickory	*Apocarya*	Asia	Bitter

[a] A nonofficial spelling is *C. illinoensis*.

is no commercial cultivation of the other North American hickories.

D. Flowering

Nut maturity varies greatly within and among species but is generally from August to November in the Northern Hemisphere. Mature trees produce male and female flowers at different locations on the shoot, with the period of relative maturation differing on the same tree (dichogamy) and with the order of maturity of male and female flowers differing among trees (heterodichogamy). This results in some trees shedding pollen before female flowers are receptive (termed protandrous or Type I) whereas others present mature pistillate flowers prior to pollen shed (termed protogynous or Type II). It is therefore necessary to plant complementary cultivars to insure adequate fertilization and fruit set. Female flowers are borne on florets produced on current season shoots and consist of 1–8 + fruit per cluster. Pollen is wind disseminated from clusters of catkins that droop from 1-year-old shoots.

E. Fruit

The hickory fruit is a nut consisting of a hard four-valved shell encasing an edible kernel. Nuts produced from all 20 species are major food sources for several wildlife species. Although the nut meats of all hickory species are edible, only those within the section *Carya* and one in *Apocarya* are nonastringent (sweet) as raw nuts, although all species can be made sweet tasting with proper processing. The best tasting nuts of the group are pecan, shellbark hickory, and the two shagbark hickories. Chinese Hickory is the only astringent species that is of much economic importance. The other hickories are of little or no economic importance as human food because of the following characteristics: strong astringency, low kernel content, excessively thick and hard shells, and difficulty of extracting the kernel due to its convolution within the shell.

F. Status as Food Crop

Four species of hickories merit crop status. Chinese Hickory is grown largely in the southeastern provinces of The People's Republic of China (P.R.C.) and is of only regional interest. Beak-like Hickory and Hunan Hickory receive a slight degree of cultivation in portions of Taiwan (Republic of China) and Hunan (P.R.C.), respectively. Pecan is by far the most important and widely grown crop of the Hicoreae with "farm-gate" value of production (ca. $310 million) in the United States exceeding that of Persian walnut (ca. \$280 million), hazelnut (ca. \$19 million), macadamia (ca. \$45 million), and pistachio (ca. \$140 billion), but being about one-half that of almond (ca. \$600 million).

Pecan is one of the relatively few food crops indigenous to North America. It is also the only tree crop indigenous to the continent that is cultivated beyond North America. Pecan was historically a favorite food of many tribes of Native Americans from the south-central United States. In fact, the name "pecan" is an Algonquin Indian word used to designate "nuts requiring a stone to crack." This nut was used by some Indians to produce a fermented intoxicating drink termed "Powcohicora," from which was derived the term "hickory." Pecan's popularity among Indians later spread to colonists and settlers who began its cultivation and development as a food crop.

G. Usage and Composition

The kernel, or nut meat, of pecan and the other hickories is generally consumed as a dessert item. Nut meats are eaten raw, roasted, or salted and are commonly used in baked goods, ice cream, liqueurs, mixed nuts, meats, vegetables, salads, and flavorings. Market outlets for United States shellers of pecan are such that about 25% goes to bakers, 22% to retail grocers, 14% to wholesale distributors, 12% to confectioners, 10% to the gift pack trade, 7% to ice cream manufactures, and 4% to food services.

Kernels are highly nutritious, being sweet and oily; are composed of about 74% fat, 13% protein; and are an excellent source of phosphorus and potassium. The fats are tricyglycerols and are composed primarily of oleic (55–83%), linoleic (14–38%), and linolenic (3–7%) fatty acids. Oils from the hickories are considered to be healthier than those of most other oil crops. Kernels are semiperishable; their high oil content causes rancidity after 3–6 mo at room temperature; however, flavor can be retained indefinitely if stored frozen.

II. Geographical Distribution of Pecan and Chinese Hickory

A. Native Range

Pecan is indigenous to the floodplains of many of the rivers and streams in east-central North America. Forest trees are common along much of the length of the Mississippi, Ohio, Red, and Missouri Rivers and many of the associated rivers and streams from the Gulf of Mexico in Louisiana to northern Iowa. Large pecan forests are also found along the rivers and streams of central and eastern Texas (for example, Brazos, Nueces, Colorado, Guadalupe, Neches, Trinity, and Sabine). The native range extends from latitude $+43°$ near Bellevue, Iowa, to about $+28°$ in south-central Texas. Many isolated and possibly native populations occur throughout Mexico and extend at least as far south as $+17°$ at Zaachila, Oaxaca, Mexico.

Of the three cultivated Asian hickories, Chinese Hickory is indigenous to the mountain slopes of the Tian Mu mountains at elevations of 400–1200 m in Zhejiang and Anhui Provinces of the P.R.C. Hunan Hickory is indigenous to the river valleys of the central portion of the Nan Ling mountain range (Hunan, Guizhou, Guangxi, and Yunnan Provinces of the P.R.C.). These regions are around 29–31° north latitude. "Beak-like Hickory" occurs in valleys and lower slopes of the mountains in northern Vietnam and in the Guizhou, Guanxi, and Yunnan Provinces in the P.R.C.

B. Location of Cultivated Production

Nuts from pecan are classified as "improved" (from cultivars) or "seedling" [from wild (often termed "native") or feral trees from obscure cultivars]. The vast majority of the worldwide commercial pecan nut production is from the United States (~130,000 t), Mexico (~40,000 t), and Australia (~5,000 t). Token production (a total of less than 7,000 t) originates from Brazil, Israel, South Africa, Argentina, P.R.C., Egypt, Peru, and Uruguay. Most of the United States crop is produced from the southeastern quadrant of the country; southwestern Georgia is the area of primary production (Table II). Although the United States "Pecan Belt" spans from North Carolina to California, production of "improved" nuts is concentrated in the general areas of Albany (Georgia), El Paso (Texas), Las Cruces (New Mexico), Tucson (Arizona), and Visalia (California), whereas production of "seedling" nuts (about one-third of the United States total) is mostly from east central Texas, eastern Oklahoma, and northern Louisiana.

The Mexican and Australian "Pecan Belts" produce almost entirely "improved" nuts from relatively young trees. Mexican production is expected to soon rival "improved" production from the United States. This production is mostly in the desert regions of the northern states of Chihuahua, Durango, Coahuila, and Sonora. Centers of production are in the vicinity of the cities of Jimenez, Torreon, Chihuahua and Her-

TABLE II

In-Shell Nuts Produced from States within the United States "Pecan Belt"[a]

State	Improved cultivars (t)[b]	Natives and seedlings (t)	All (t)	Percentage of total (%)
Alabama	3405	2838	6242	5
Arizona	8172	0	8172	7
Arkansas	409	414	823	1
California	1056	0	1056	1
Florida	1294	987	2281	2
Georgia	33,708	7151	40,859	33
Louisiana	1248	6583	7831	6
Mississippi	2134	1067	3201	3
New Mexico	13,393	0	13,393	11
North Carolina	783	590	1373	1
Oklahoma	601	8932	9533	8
South Carolina	908	624	1532	1
Texas	15,209	11,464	26,672	22

[a] In-shell (weight of nut meats and shells) production average from 1881–1991. Trivial production originates from Kentucky, Illinois, Missouri, Kansas, Nebraska, Iowa, Utah, Virginia, Indiana, and Tennessee.
[b] Metric tons.

mosillo. Australian production is concentrated at Moree in New South Wales.

The Asian hickories are cultivated in portions of southeastern P.R.C. and Taiwan. The P.R.C. has about 19,000 ha of cultivated Chinese Hickory. Most of this production is from Linan county (Zhejiang Province) and accounts for about 60% of the country's cultivated production. Maximum in-shell nut production is about 2,400 kg/ha; however, yields of 800–1,000 kg are typical.

III. Natural Habitat

A. Biotic Environment

Pecan naturally grows in a riverine environment rich in flora. Light competition is therefore severe, resulting in a growth habit that produces a fast growing tree that is a dominant component of overstory canopy. Pecan is moderately shade tolerant as a young tree but rather intolerant as an older tree. Associated forest types are "sycamore/pecan/American elm," "cottonwood," "sweetgum/nuttal oak/willow oak," "sugarberry/American elm/green ash," and "blackwillow."

B. Abiotic Environment

Pecan naturally grows in a relatively humid climate throughout most of its natural range. Rainfall typically ranges 75–210 cm per annum with most falling during spring and early summer. Native trees grow in regions ranging from 160 to about 365 continuous freeze-free days. The summer months are generally warm and frequently dry.

The soils of the pecan's native habitat are usually stratified and deep alluvials. The water table is typically high during the late winter and early spring and low during the rest of the year. Trees grow best on riverfront ridges and on well-drained flats, but grow slowly on heavy clay soils.

IV. Genetic Resources

A. Scion Cultivars

Most pecan orchards are composed of compound trees consisting of a root system (stock or rootstock) of one genetic type and a crown (scion) of another type. There are over 1,000 scion cultivars. However, most commercial production originates from about 30 cultivars; the remainder are essentially obsolete or untested (Table III). About 75% of the orchard land within the United States Pecan Belt is composed of the following nine cultivars: 'Stuart' (22%), 'Western Schley' (15%), 'Desirable' (11%), 'Wichita' (10%), 'Schley' (5%), 'Cheyenne' (5%), 'Success' (2%), 'Cape Fear' (2%), and 'Moneymaker' (2%). The scion cultivars grown in the Mexican Pecan Belt and in Australia are predominantly 'Wichita' and 'Western Schley.' The primary cultivars grown in other countries are largely 'Bester' (South Africa), 'Mahan' (Brazil and Peru), 'Delmas' (Israel), 'Curtis' (Egypt), and 'Stuart' (Uruguay). The following cultivars have po-

TABLE III
The Most Common Pecan Scion Cultivars and Their Characteristis

Cultivar	Flowering type	Ripening date[a]	Nuts per kg	Percent kernel
Alley	I	–	165	50
Burkett	II	–	112	54
Cape Fear	I	–	119	54
Cheyenne	I	–	117	55
Curtis	II	– –	187	54
Delmas	II	– –	108	46
Desirable	I	–	104	52
Elliott	II	+	163	53
Farley	II	– –	132	53
Forkert	II	+	104	62
Ideal	II	– –	152	57
Kiowa	II	–	106	58
Mahan	II	– –	108	54
Maramec	II	+	97	58
Mobile	I	– –	145	38
Mohawk	II	– –	86	58
Moneymaker	II	+ +	145	64
Pawnee	I	+ + +	108	57
Schley	II	+	143	58
Stuart	II	–	115	47
Sumner	II	– –	106	54
Tejas	II	–	148	54
Van Deman	II	+ +	132	42
Western Schley	I	+	141	57
Wichita	II	+	126	60

[a] Date of nut maturity relative to 'Stuart' cv. 'Stuart' is the most common cultivar in the southeastern United States. Days before (+) and after (−): 1–5 days, − or +; 6–10, − − or + +; 11–15, − − − or + + +.

tential in specialized commercial operations: 'Sumner,' 'Mohawk,' 'Sioux,' 'Pawnee,' 'Oconee,' 'Kiowa,' 'Choctaw,' 'Shawnee,' 'Shoshoni,' 'Apache,' 'Tejas,' 'Curtis,' 'Ideal,' 'Elliott,' 'Caddo,' 'Forkert,' 'Owens,' and 'Maramec.' Cultivars most suitable for cold climates are 'Giles,' 'Pawnee,' 'Osage,' 'Peruque,' 'Colby,' 'Starking Hardy Giant,' 'Caddo,' and 'Major.' The current most popular cultivars in the United States are 'Desirable,' 'Cape Fear,' 'Western Schley,' 'Wichita,' and 'Stuart.'

There are a hundred or more scion cultivars of Chinese Hickory. About 90% of the cultivated production originating from cultivars comes from 'Yuanguo' and 'Bianguo.' [See ORCHARD MANAGEMENT SYSTEMS.]

B. Rootstock Materials

Rootstocks (stocks) are open pollinated seed originating from one of a variety of scion cultivars or from seedling or native trees. The preferred rootstock source varies with geographical region. The most

common stocks for acidic soils are 'Curtis,' 'Elliott,' 'Waukeenah,' and 'Owens' whereas 'Riverside,' 'Apache,' and 'Burkett' are typically used in alkaline soils. Stocks from local wild trees and from 'Giles,' 'Peraque,' and 'Colby' are best for scions grown in the cold climate typical of the northern portion of the natural range.

The scion cultivars of Chinese Hickory and other Asian and North American hickories are typically grown on rootstocks composed of open-pollinated seed from wild trees. There are no clonal rootstocks for these species.

V. Climatic Adaptability

A. Length of Growing Season

Most pecan cultivars require 180–210 freeze-free days to mature their nuts, although cultivars exist that require as little as 110–120 days. Those with the shortest fruit development periods are usually the most cold hardy and the best adapted to the northern extreme of the natural range, and have the smallest nuts (180–330 nuts/kg).

B. Temperatures

Pecan can grow well in hot, warm, or cold climates. Productivity is, however, very sensitive to "heat units" received during the growing season. Heat units are calculated by the equation $\Sigma n(mt)$, where n is the number of days in growing season, m is the mean daily temperature during the growing season, and t is the minimum growth temperature for pecan (about 10°C). Most commercial cultivars perform poorly if the growing season is below about 4000 units, even if the growing season is long (in excess of 220 freeze-free days). In fact, most production areas in the United States and Mexico exhibit units ranging from 5000 to 7000. Most cultivars perform best in areas with a long growing season having hot days and warm nights. Environments with low heat unit levels facilitate excellent vegetative growth but little reproductive growth. At the lower latitudes of Mexico, pecan produces well at elevations up to at least 2000 m. Low heat units during the growing season apparently can be partially offset if sunlight levels are high. Commercial orchards in sunny environments are more productive than those in environments with much cloud cover.

C. Water Relationships

Pecan is a relatively heavy user of water and good yields require good water availability. Sufficient water is nearly always the most important factor for inducing rapid tree growth and for realizing early economic returns in orchards. Even in the southeastern United States, where annual rainfall is in excess of 125 cm, orchards with no supplemental irrigation usually suffer substantial yield losses. A large tree with a canopy diameter of 24 m can require as much as 1777 liters of water on a typical July day. A rule of thumb for estimating water use by pecan orchards is that they have at least 140 ha-cm (55 acre-inches) per growing season (usually about 210–225 days) or about 5 cm per week. Commercial operations supply water via one of several irrigation methods: flood, drip, sprinkler, or microsprinkler. Flood irrigation is most commonly used in arid climates such as the southwestern United States and Mexico whereas sprinkler and drip are most commonly used in the southeastern United States. [See IRRIGATION ENGINEERING: FARM PRACTICES, METHODS, AND SYSTEMS.]

A deficiency of water has profound effects on production, nut quality, return fruiting, and pest tolerance. For example, a deficiency during the later stages of fruit enlargement (July–August) greatly reduces nut size whereas a deficiency during the period of fruit filling (September–early October) suppresses kernel development and can cause a severe yield loss. Water deficiencies (or excessive water) during late August and September predispose trees to being especially susceptible to defoliation by black aphids and fungal pathogens (causing leaf scorch). Excessively dry conditions at the time of fruit ripening (shuck split) will prevent the shuck from opening and can cause major harvesting problems.

D. Salinity Tolerance

Salinity problems are the most prevalent causes of poor tree performance in orchards in arid climates. Salinity causes poor vigor, small leaves, stunted trees, and marginal leaf burn on older leaves during the latter portion of the growing season. Pecan is susceptible to damage by chlorine, boron, and sodium and is much less tolerant to salts than is cotton, but is more tolerant than are salt-sensitive vegetable crops such as peppers and carrots. Pecan is less tolerant to sodium than is alfalfa, but is comparatively more sensitive to saline conditions.

Problems can be avoided by not planting on clay, silty clay, or silty clay loam soils or on soils with clay substrata near the ground surface. For surface irrigation of clay or silty clay soils, salinity of water exceeding 0.50–0.75 mmho/cm is considered unsafe, whereas values up to 2.0 mmho/cm can likely be safely used on sandy soils. Boron levels of irrigation water should not exceed 1–2 ppm and sodium should not exceed a "sodium absorption ratio" (mmol Na/ mmol Ca + mmol Mg) of 3–5. [See ORCHARD MANAGEMENT: SOIL ENVIRONMENT AND RESOURCES.]

E. Chilling Requirements

Pecan typically requires about 700 hr of cold temperatures between 0 and 7°C during dormancy for uniform vegetative budbreak and flowering; however, some cultivars require less than 300 hr. The amount of heat received after the chilling requirement also determines the time and uniformity of fruit ripening. Pecan and most hickories are usually the latest species to break bud in the spring because of their high heat requirement. Extended cool spring temperatures can disrupt pollination and cropping. Pecan can be grown in areas with insufficient chilling by using hydrogen cyanamide to induce and accelerate budbreak.

F. Climatic Types Suitable for Growing Pecan

Pecan is a highly adaptable crop capable of being productive in a variety of environments. These include the cool uplands of tropical savannah, tropical and subtropical steppe, Mediterranean (or dry summer tropics), and humid subtropical (where pecan probably evolved) climate types. Some cold hardy cultivars can be cropped in humid continental climates with hot summers. Fruiting problems can be encountered in the dry desert regions because of the rapid drying of the stigma of female flowers by strong warm dry winds during the pollination period. The best locations for commercial production are probably warm sunny arid sites where plenty of water can be economically supplied.

G. Climate Types for Other Hickories

The genus *Carya* is composed of species adapted to climates ranging from very dry (Scrub Hickory) to very wet (Water Hickory) and from very warm (Beak-like Hickory) to very cold (Shagbark and Pignut Hickories). This variation results in some members of the genus being adapted to almost any climate on the planet.

VI. Principal Pests

A. Insects and Mites

Most pests of commercial and yard pecan trees have coevolved with pecan (Table IV). When introduced

TABLE IV

The Most Important Insect, Mite, and Disease Pests of Pecan Grown in the United States

Name	Scientific name	Level of economic importance General[a]	Level of economic importance Potential[b]
Insects and mites			
Black pecan aphid	*Melanocallis caryaefoliae* (Davis)	+ + + +	+ + + +
Black-margined aphid	*Monellia caryella* (Fitch)	+ + + +	+ + + +
Brown stinkbug	*Euschistus servis* (Say)	+ + +	+ + + +
Dusty stinkbug	*Euschistus tristigmus* (Say)	+ +	+ +
Fall webworm	*Hyphantria cunea* (Drury)	+	+ +
Green stinkbug	*Acrosternum hilare* (Say)	+	+ +
Hickory shuckworm	*Cydia caryana* (Fitch)	+ + +	+ + +
Hickory shoot curculio	*Conotrachelus aratus* Germar	+	+ +
Leaf-footed bugs	*Leptoglossus phyllopus* (Linnaeus)	+ +	+ + +
Nut curculio	*Conotrachelus hicoriae* Schoof	+ +	+ + +
Northern leaf-footed bug	*Leptoglossus oppositus* Say	+ + +	+ + + +
Pecan bud moth	*Gretchena bolliana* (Slingerland)	+	+ +
Pecan nut casebearer	*Acrobasis nuxvorella* Neunzig	+ + +	+ + + + +
Pecan phylloxera	*Phylloxera devastrix* Pergande	+ +	+ + + +
Pecan leaf phylloxera	*Phylloxera notabilis* Pergande	+	+ +
Pecan leaf casebearer	*Acrobasis caryivorella* LeBaron	+ +	+ + + +
Pecan cigar casebearer	*Colephora laticornella* Clement	+	+ +
Pecan nursery casebearer	*Acrobasis caryivorella* Ragonot	+	+ +
Pecan leaf scorch mite	*Eoteranchyus hicoriae* (McGregor)	+ + +	+ + + +
Pecan spittlebug	*Clastoptera achatina* German	+ +	+ + +
Pecan weevil	*Curculio caryae* (Horn)	+ + + +	+ + + +
Shoot curculio	*Conotrachelus caryae*	+	+ + +
Southern pecan leaf phylloxera	*Phylloxera russellae* Stoetzel	+	+ +
Southern green stinkbug	*Nezara viridula* Linnaeus	+ + +	+ + + +
Serpentine leafminer	*Stigmella juglandifoliella* (Clemens)	+ +	+ + +
Walnut caterpillar	*Datana integerrima* Gore & Robinson	+ + +	+ + + +
Yellow pecan aphid	*Monelliopsis pecanis* Bissell	+ + +	+ + + +
Diseases			
Anthracnose	*Glomerella cingulata* (Ston.) Spauld. and Schrenk	+ +	+ + + +
Cotton root rot	*Phymatotrichopsis omnivora* (Duggar) Hennebert	+ + +	+ + + +
Leaf scorch	Probably *Glomerella cingulata* (Ston.) Spauld. and Schrenk and/or *Phomopsis* spp.	+ + + +	+ + + +
Pecan scab	*Cladosporium caryigenum* (Ell. et Lang) Gottwald	+ + + +	+ + + +
Shuck and kernel rot	*Phytophthora cactorum* (Lebert. and Cohn) Schroeter	+ +	+ + + +
Shuck dieback	Unknown	+ + +	+ + + +
Sooty mold	*Capnodium* spp.	+ + + +	+ + + +
Stem-end blight	Probably *Glomerella cingulata* (Ston.) Spauld. and Schrenk, *Phomopsis* spp., and/or *Botryosphaeria* spp.	+ + + +	+ + + +
Zonate leaf spot	*Gnomonia caryae* Waterman and Marshall	+ +	+ + + +

[a] Approximate level of general economic importance to the United States pecan industry: +, essentially none; + +, slight; + + +, moderate; + + + +, great.

[b] Approximate level of potential economic importance to individual orchards: +, essentially none; + +, slight; + + +, moderate; + + + +, great.

as an exotic crop to other countries, natural pests such as the pecan aphids have sometimes been co-introduced and have subsequently become major pests. Pests endemic to areas outside the native range have transferred to pecan when cultivated in nonnative regions and can cause major problems. The most severe of these are usually root-boring insects that attack roots or stems. [*See* ENTOMOLOGY, HORTICULTURAL.]

The relative importance of the various insect and mite pests varies greatly with orchard location; however, from an overall industry perspective the pests of most importance are probably (in decreasing order) black pecan aphid, pecan weevil, hickory shuckworm, yellow aphids, pecan nut casebearer, stinkbugs, and phylloxeras. The aphids, pecan weevil, and stinkbugs are especially destructive in the southeastern United States whereas in the southwestern United States, Mexico, Australia, South Africa, and Israel the aphids are usually of most economic importance. Most insect pests can be controlled by insecticides or partially controlled using other predatory and parasitic insects. [*See* PEST MANAGEMENT, BIOLOGICAL CONTROL; PEST MANAGEMENT, CHEMICAL CONTROL.]

B. Diseases

Several coevolved disease pests (Table IV) can cause severe pecan yield losses. Most of these are fungal diseases. The pests of primary economic importance, especially in the humid southeastern United States, are pecan scab, anthracnose, and leaf scorch. All three can greatly influence tree productivity, nut quality, and return bloom. Orchards grown in arid climates do not exhibit significant problems with foliage or nut diseases; however, they can exhibit substantial tree losses due to cotton root rot. The other diseases of pecan can cause severe crop losses at some locations in some years but are not generally widespread problems. Diseases in commercial orchards are currently only controllable by choice of cultivar and cultural practices, and use of chemical fungicides. [*See* FUNGICIDES; PEST MANAGEMENT, CULTURAL CONTROL; PLANT PATHOLOGY.]

VII. Barriers to the Expansion of Hickory Cultivation

Because of the difficulty of removing kernels, low nut production per area of land, competition from other major nut crops, and in some cases astringent taste, all hickory species except pecan have little possibility of increasing in relative importance as tree-nut crops. Pecan is likely to continue increasing in relative importance because of its excellent food characteristics and increasing popularity among consumers in industrialized societies. The primary barriers to the expansion of the popularity of pecan is its short shelf life at room temperature, its cyclic production, the low yield per hectare, the high production costs, the high water requirements, the susceptibility to pecan aphids and pecan scab, the lack of early season ripening of cultivars with excellent nut quality, and the absence of organized marketing.

Bibliography

Goff, W. D., McVay, J. R., and Gazaway, W. S. (eds.) (1989). "Pecan Production in the Southeast: A Guide for Growers." Alabama Cooperative Extension Service, Auburn, Alabama.

McEachern, G. R., and Stein, L. A. (1993). "Texas Pecan Handbook," TAEX Hort. Handbook No. 105. Texas Cooperative Extension Service, College Station, Texas.

Sparks, D. (1992). "Pecan Cultivars: The Orchard's Foundation." Pecan Production Innovations, Watkinsville, Georgia.

Thompson, T. E., and Grauke, L. J. (1991). Pecans and hickories. *In* "Genetic Resources of Temperate Fruit and Nut Crops," pp. 839–904. International Society of Horticultural Science, Wageningen, The Netherlands.

Wood, B. W., and Payne, J. A. (1991). Pecan—An emerging crop. *Chron. Hort.* **31(2),** 21–23.

Wood, B. W., Payne, J. A., and Grauke, L. J. (1990). The rise of the U.S. pecan industry. *HortScience* **25(6),** 594, 721–723.

Yong-ling, R., Wood, B. W., and Payne, J. A. (1991). Chinese hickory: An emerging nut-tree crop. *Fruit Var. J.* **49(1),** 16–22.

Edible Tree Nuts, Walnuts

G. STEVEN SIBBETT, *University of California Farm Advisor, Tulare County*

Glossary

Cultivar Plant worthy of cultivation without a Latin name
Rootstock Plant onto which a scion is grafted
Scion Plant part grafted or budded onto a stock

All *Juglans*, 21 species, produce edible nuts from hardwood trees native to Central Asia, the Andean mountains, and parts of North America. The Persian or English walnut, *J. Regia*, is the best known member. Its edible nuts are cultivated and sold in many areas of the world.

I. General Crop Characteristics of Walnuts

A. Botanical Organization

The walnuts are the sole genus of the tribe Juglandeae of the family Juglandaceae (Table I). The genus includes 21 species divided into four sections: (1) *Juglans* Mann., Persian walnuts (1 species), consists solely of the commercially valuable Persian or English walnut, *Juglans regia* L. Persian walnuts are native to the mountains of Central Asia. The edible nut is four-celled, smooth, and thin shelled, having a husk that dehisces from the shell at maturity. (2) *Rhysocaryon* Dode (16 species) are "Black" walnuts native to North and South America, having a four-chambered nut with an indehiscent husk. (3) *Cardiocaryon* Dode (3 species) are Black walnuts native to eastern Asia, have heavily "ridged" nuts with two chambers and indehiscent husks, and are borne in racemes of 5–25 nuts. (4) *Trachycaryon* Dode ex. Mann. (1 species) is the "Butternut", *J. cinerea* L., also referred to as the "White Walnut" or "Oil Nut," native to north America. It has a heavily ridged nut with two chambers and an indehiscent husk. It is of little commercial value. All *Juglans* species contain 32 diploid chromosomes and many species readily hybridize with each other. [*See* EDIBLE TREE NUTS: PECAN AND OTHER HICKORIES.]

B. Tree Form and Growth

All *Juglans* species are large shrubs or moderately sized deciduous to almost evergreen trees growing from between 10 and 30 m in height. These are forest trees, and, as such, generally exhibit good tree form. Woods of the species vary in durability, with most species being highly regarded for their timber. Some Black walnuts, with extremely hard and fine-grained wood, are excellent for fine furniture and wood products. Most *Juglans* have softer wood not suitable for such purposes.

C. Flowering

All walnut species are *monoecious*, bearing catkins (male staminate flowers) and female pistillate flowers (nutlets) separately on the same tree. Catkins are borne on the previous season's shoot or spur growth, whereas pistillate flowers occur on the current season's growth, being differentiated within a mixed bud that contains both vegetative and reproductive initials.

Some level of *dichogamy*, that is, inconsistent overlap of bloom between male and female flowers, usu-

TABLE I

List of Species of Juglandeae

SUBFAMILY II. JUGLANDOIDEAE	
TRIBE A. JUGLANDEAE	
2. *Juglans* L. 21 spp.	
Sect. a. *Juglans*	
J. regia L.	Southeastern Europe, Iran to Himalayas, and China
subsp. *turcomanica* Popov	
subsp. *fallax* (Dode) Popov	
Sect. b. *Rhysocaryon* Dode	
J. australis Griseb.	Argentina
J. boliviana (C. DC.) Dode	Western South America
J. californica S. Wals.	California
J. hindsii (Jeps.) Rehder	California
J. hirsuta Mann.	Northeastern Mexico
J. jamaicensis C. DC.	West Indies
J. major (Torr. ex Sitsgr.) Heller	
var. *major*	Southwestern United States, Northwestern Mexico
var. *glabrata* Mann.	South-central Mexico
J. microcarpa Berl.	
var. *microcarpa*	Southwestern United States, northwestern Mexico
var. *stewartii* (Johnston) Mann.	Northern Mexico
J. molis Engelm. ex Hemsl.	Central Mexico
J. neutropica Diels	Northwestern South America
J. nigra L.	Eastern United States
J. olanchana Standl. & L. O. Williams	
var. *olanchana*	Guatemala
var. *standleyi* Mann.	Southwestern Mexico
J. pyriformis Liebm.	Southeastern Mexico
J. soratensis Mann.	Bolivia
J. steyermarkii Mann.	Guatemala
J. venezuelensis Mann.	Venezuela
Sect. c. *Cardiocaryon* Dode	
J. atlantifolia Carr.	
var. *atlantifolia*	Japan
var. *cordiformis* (Makino) Rehd.	Japan
J. cathayensis Dode	Eastern China, Taiwan
J. mandshurica Maxim.	Manchuria, northeastern China, Korea
Sect. d. *Trachycaryon* Dode ex Mann.	
J. cinerea L.	Eastern United States

ally occurs. Overlap ranges from complete (*homogamy*) to nonexistent (complete dichogamy) between walnut cultivars and many times between seasons. Walnut cultivars are also *heterodichogamous*; some shed pollen before all female flowers are receptive, that is, *protandrous* cultivars, whereas *protogynous* cultivars shed pollen following female flower receptivity. For commercial walnut production, a small percentage of a pollinizing cultivar should be included in the planting for optimal production.

Pistillate walnut inflorescences usually contain a maximum of three flowers. Singles and doubles are also common. Some Persian cultivars can contain four or five pistillate flowers depending on the climate where they are grown. In China and Middle Eastern countries, "cluster" or "grape-type" flowering has been reported in some Persian seedlings.

D. Bearing Habit

Walnuts are borne on the current season's shoot growth. Persian walnut cultivars include those that bear a portion of their crop on shoots that emerge from both lateral and terminal buds. These are termed *lateral-bearing cultivars*. *Terminal-bearing cultivars* are those that bear the crop only on the shoot emerging from the terminal bud. Lateral bud fruitfulness is an important trait for the Persian walnut; it relates directly to precocity and the earliest economic bearing in commercial plantings (Table II includes the lateral fruitfulness of Persian cultivars).

E. Fruit

1. Nut, Kernel Weight, and Percentage Kernel

Dry nut weight varies with shell thickness, kernel fill, and degree of drying during processing (Table II). Cultivar has a strong influence over kernel weight and percentage, which is further effected by cultural practices such as water and harvest management. High kernel percentages are desirable. However, once more than 60% kernel occurs, shell thickness is reduced to the point where hulling and drying following harvest results in kernel damage. Also, shipping and handling damage the in-shell product.

2. Nut Size

Potential nut size is strongly influenced by cultivar. Within any given year and cultivar, ultimate nut size is a function of nut load on the tree, that is, a high nut load has an adverse influence on nut size. Nut size is not necessarily related to percentage of kernel. Some cultivars with large nuts (e.g., the Carpathian types of Persian walnut, "Carmelo," "Wilson Wonder," etc.) have low kernel percentage.

3. Shell Strength and Seal

Shell thickness is highly cultivar dependent. Thick shells often preclude kernel extraction whereas thin

TABLE II

Comparison of Old and New Walnut Cultivars[a]

Variety	Percentage nursery sales (1982–1983)	Time of leafing (days after Payne)	Lateral buds producing pistillate flowers (%)[b]	Average kernel weight (g)	Average kernel percent	Percentage light kernels	Shell seal grade[c]	Crop estimate[d]	Harvest date (1982)
Old cultivars									
Payne	18	0	80	5.2	48	50	2.0	3.0	9/20
Hartley	35	16	5	5.9	45	90	2.2	2.4	9/21
Franquette	3	31	0	5.2	46	70	2.0	2.0	10/6
New cultivars									
Serr	5	−1	50	7.6	58	60	2.2	2.1	9/18
Ashley	1	−1	90	5.3	50	50	2.0	2.7	9/20
Sunland	2	2	80	9.9	58	60	1.8	2.7	10/2
Chico	4	2	90	5.0	47	70	2.0	3.8	9/18
Vina	12	7	90	5.6	48	60	2.3	3.2	9/19
Tehama	1	11	80	6.7	50	70	2.2	1.6	9/19
Amigo	<1	12	80	6.0	52	90	2.0	3.3	9/19
Howard	<1	15	80	6.5	50	90	2.2	3.6	9/19
Pedro	<1	18	80	6.5	48	50	2.4	2.3	9/19
Chandler	15	19	80	6.3	49	90	2.6	3.3	9/23
UC68-104		13	80	6.6	56	80	2.2	2.7	9/21
Tulare		20	80	7.3	54	80	2.4	3.1	9/24
UC66-178		31	80	6.6	47	60	2.0	1.2	10/6

[a]At the orchard at University of California, Davis. Five-year averages based on 10-nut or 4-tree sample each year.
[b]Percentage most often observed. May vary considerably from year to year.
[c]Shell seal: 1, very well sealed; 2, well sealed; 3, moderately well sealed; 4, poor; and 5, very poor.
[d]Crop estimate: 1, poor; 2, fair; 3, good; 4, heavy; and 5, very heavy.

shells promote it. Nuts with extremely thin shells are not suitable for shipping as in-shell product.

4. Kernel Quality

Light-colored kernels are considered the highest quality. Although ability to produce light-colored kernels is highly cultivar dependent, the climate where the cultivar is grown also effects it; extremes in weather conditions, particularly heat during the kernel development period, darken kernels. Improper cultural management, such as irrigation management and harvest timing, also affects kernel color.

5. Flavor and Oil

Some walnut cultivars have distinctly differing flavors, especially those originating in different countries. However, only subtle differences exist between those Persian cultivars grown commercially in California.

F. Status as a Food Crop

Both Persian and some Black walnuts are used as an edible food source; Persian walnuts comprise the vast majority of walnuts cultivated for food production.

The United States is, by far, the number one commercial producer. China, Turkey, Chile, and France also have Persian walnut production (Table III). Within the United States, essentially all Persian walnuts are commercially grown in California; a small acreage exists in the state of Oregon.

Two-thirds of the U.S. shipments are to the domestic market, and one-third is exported (Table IV). The domestic market is primarily a "shelled product" market, whereas those exported are "in-shell." Walnuts are generally used as a dessert item eaten dry, either alone or included in confectionery items such as candies, cookies, pies, and ice creams. In some countries, mature, wet walnuts are consumed, as are immature walnuts that are pickled prior to shell hardening, and the liquor is used to flavor ice creams and other confections. An alcoholic walnut liquor can also be made.

Walnuts are a high-energy food rich in oil, vitamins, and minerals and are an excellent source of nutrition (Table V). A 50-g serving is an excellent source of copper and a significant source of protein, magnesium, phosphorous, zinc, and vitamin B6. They are also quite low in sodium. A diet containing walnuts has also been shown to lower serum choles-

TABLE III
World Persian Walnut Production (Metric Tons)[a]

Country	1979–1981	1989	1990	1991
World	788,407	933,821	899,764	898,913
Africa				
Morocco	5467	6200	6300	6400
North America				
Mexico	2559	3600	3600	3700
United States	190,511	207,700	205,900	227,000
South America				
Argentina	9233	7500	7800	8000
Bolivia	1183	1945	2000	2000
Chile	5248	7020	7707	8500
Asia				
Afghanistan	5467	4500	5100	5000
China	105,667	160,054	149,580	153,000
Cyprus	186	180	180	180
India	17,333	17,000	20,000	17,000
Iran	7333	64,009	43,000	44,000
Iraq	2467	2350	2400	2000
Jordan	9	15	15	15
Lebanon	700	600	650	500
Pakistan	15,174	20,500	21,000	21,000
Turkey	131,333	113,000	115,000	115,000
Yemen	4	22	22	23
Europe				
Austria	7856	7557	12,348	10,000
Bulgaria	19,893	33,346	25,406	23,650
Czechoslovakia	9509	11,385	10,799	10,274
France	25,867	25,845	24,600	13,000
West Germany	8585	11,801	12,217	5071
East Germany	1000	1200	1000	1000
Greece	23,421	25,100	24,284	22,000
Hungary	13,305	8106	8473	8500
Italy	44,617	16,990	15,200	11,400
Portugal	6513	7300	6200	8000
Romania	37,328	24,400	26,000	28,000
Spain	9707	9329	9000	9000
Switzerland	4333	3720	2700	1225
Yugoslavia	23,006	35,610	30,031	30,000
Oceania				
Australia	75	60	92	94
New Zealand	106	80	80	80
Former USSR	51,267	90,000	95,000	96,000
Developed, all	476,899	519,529	509,330	506,294
North America	190,511	207,700	205,900	227,000
Europe	234,941	221,689	208,258	181,120
Oceania	181	140	172	174
Former USSR	51,267	90,000	95,000	96,000
Developing, all	311,508	414,292	390,434	392,618
Africa	5467	6200	6300	6400
Latin America	18,224	20,065	21,107	22,200
Near East	147,499	184,676	166,367	166,718
Far East	140,319	203,351	196,660	197,300

[a]*Source:* FAO Production Yearbook 15, Food and Agriculture Organization of the United Nations, Rome, Italy (1990).

TABLE IV
Primary California Walnut Markets for Crop Years 1992 and 1993[a]

In-shell walnut markets		Shelled walnut markets	
Country	In-shell pounds	Country	Shelled Pounds
Germany	27,967,906	United States	104,804,128
United States	25,960,945	Japan	8,092,405
Spain	23,136,585	Germany	3,095,776
Italy	11,794,328	Canada	1,716,170
Netherlands	2,682,784	Israel	1,667,230

[a]*Source:* Walnut Industry Fact Sheet, Walnut Marketing Board, Sacramento, California (1993).

terol; daily consumption of 28 g of Persian walnuts can decrease serum levels of total and LDL cholesterol by 4 and 6% respectively. Walnuts are a good source of dietary fiber, potassium, essential fatty acids (including "omega-3" linolenic acid), and many micronutrients.

Black walnuts are highly prized as a confectionery and are sold for high prices. They are only available in limited quantities and mainly from seedling trees. There is little intense commercial production of Black walnut; its low productivity usually makes it a poor choice for "best use" of land capable of producing other crops.

II. Geographical Distribution of Walnut

A. Native Range

Juglans spp. are native to Central Asia, the Andean Mountains of South America, and parts of North America. *Juglans regia*, the commercial Persian walnut, is native to the mountainous regions of Central Asia, extending from Xinjiang Province of western China, parts of Kazakhistan, Uzbekistan, and southern Kirghizia in the previously Central Asian USSR, and from the mountains of Nepal, Tibet, northern India, and Pakistan west through Afghanistan, Turkmenia, and Iran to portions of Azerbaijan, Armenia, Georgia, and eastern Turkey.

B. Cultivated Range

Black walnuts for food purposes are rarely produced in cultivated plantings. Some small areas of cultivation exist in the midwestern sections of the United States, but the ultimate objective of these plantings is for timber purposes; the nuts are collected as a

TABLE V
Composition of Persian Walnuts[a]

Walnuts		Walnut oil			
Nutrients	Amount in 100-g edible portion	Nutrients		Amount in 100-g edible portion	
Food energy	630.00 kcal	Lipids			
Proximate					
Protein	14.10 g	Fatty acids, total		61.2 g	(100%)
Total lipid (fat)	68.00 g	Saturated, total		7.6 g	(12%)
Carbohydrate (total)	3.20 g	Palmitic	16:0	5.4 g	(9%)
Dietary fiber	9.70 g	Stearic	18:0	2.2 g	(4%)
Ash	1.80 g	Arachidic	20:0	0.1 g	(<1%)
Water	3.20 g				
Minerals		Mono-unsaturated, total		11.0 g	(18%)
Calcium	89.00 mg	Oleic	18:1	10.8 g	(18%)
Copper	1.30 mg	Gadoleic	20:1	0.2 g	(<1%)
Iron	2.40 mg				
Magnesium	113.00 mg	Polyunsaturated, total		42.6 g	(70%)
Manganese	2.10 mg	Linoleic	18:2	35.2 g	(58%)
Phosphorus	348.00 mg	Linolenic	18:3	7.4 g	(12%)
Potassium	391.00 mg				
Sodium	10.00 mg	Cholesterol		0.0 mg	
Zinc	2.90 mg				
Vitamins					
Ascorbic acid	0.88 mg				
Thiamin	0.30 mg				
Riboflavin	0.10 mg				
Niacin	0.82 mg				
Pantothenic acid	0.45 mg				
Vitamin B6	0.44 mg				
Folacin	56.00 μg				
Vitamin A	146.00 IU				

[a] *Source:* Walnut Marketing Board 1986 Nutrition Study, Walnut Marketing Board, Sacramento, California (1986).

sideline to the timber operation. In areas where seedling trees exist, nuts are often collected when prices are high enough to make the venture economical. Approximately 18,000 metric tons are collected annually in the United States, about 10% of the Persian walnut production.

Persian walnuts have been introduced from their native range into a number of countries and districts for commercial cultivation. Areas of western Europe, North and South Africa, China, North America (primarily California), South America, Australia, New Zealand, and Japan now cultivate Persian walnuts for food purposes (see Table III).

III. Natural Habitat

A. Environment

Native *Juglans* species grow in widely diverse environments. They are forest trees or large shrubs and almost all grow in riparian, well-drained soils proximal to water courses. *Juglans* spp. are relatively intolerant of continually saturated soils.

Species native to mountainous regions go through an annual dormancy period and are completely deciduous, being tolerant to cold winter temperatures. Several species are native to more tropical districts where subfreezing temperatures rarely occur. These latter species can be essentially non-dormant and nearly "evergreen."

Most Persian walnuts cannot be cultivated under extremely adverse weather conditions. Early fall and late spring frost kills new vegetative growth and excessively cold winter temperatures can kill older wood of some species. The exceptions are *J. regia* selections that originated from the former USSR and the Carpathian Mountains of Poland. These can tolerate winter temperatures as low as −40°C. California cultivars cannot tolerate winter temperatures lower than −10°C. Persian walnuts require a dormancy period of at least 800 hr of winter temperatures below 7°C to leaf out and bloom normally. A growing season from leaf-out until nut maturation of 175–200 frost-free days is required, depending on the cultivar. Excessive heat in summer (>40°C) sunburns kernels, thus reducing quality.

IV. Genetic Resources

A. Scion Cultivars

Cultivated walnut trees include a scion cultivar grafted or budded onto a seedling "rootstock." There are only a few Black walnut cultivars identified with superior nut characteristics for cultivation. Those of note include Thomas, Elmer Myers, Ohio, Snyder, Sterling, and Bowser. In very limited circumstances these have been grafted onto Black walnut seedling rootstocks for orchard planting.

Persian walnut cultivars have been selected from native stocks or from breeding programs. Selection has been reported since the first century and breeding for genetic excellence began in the late 1940s. Breeding programs are actively in progress now.

Although numerous cultivars of Persian walnut exist, most acreage comprises only those few that possess excellent production and quality traits. For example, the California acreage is essentially composed of only nine cultivars: Hartley, 30%; Serr, 13%; Payne, 12%; Franquette, 10%; Vina, 6%; Ashley, 6%; Eureka, 5%; Chandler, 4%; and Tehama, 3% (see Table II for Persian walnut characteristics). In France, Lara and Franquette are the predominant cultivars. Current breeding programs are incorporating insect and disease resistance with production and quality parameters into new cultivars.

B. Rootstock Materials

Rootstock materials are grown from open-pollinated seeds. Seed sources are selected that promote disease resistance, tolerance to marginal soils, tolerance to salinity, and that enhance vigor. Although clonal propagation is being widely researched, there is no current commercially acceptable method.

Selected cultivars of Black walnut are grown on Black walnut seedlings, usually those species that grow locally. Persian walnut cultivars are grown on Black walnut seedlings of *J. hindsii (Jeps)*, the northern California Black walnut; *J. nigra L.*, the eastern Black walnut; and *J. californica* S. Wats, the southern California Black walnut. A hybrid rootstock, *J. hindsii* × *J. regia*, is popular as it enhances vigor and is more tolerant of marginal walnut soils than the Black species. All of these rootstocks are more tolerant of salts and diseases than *J. regia*. *Juglans regia* seedlings are used as rootstock in areas where Blackline virus occurs because these seedlings tolerate the virus. *Juglans regia* seedlings are intolerant of salinity and the phytophthora crown and root rot fungus.

V. Principal Pests

A. Insects and Mites

Concern for insect and mite pests occurs only where walnuts, primarily Persian walnuts, are cultivated for food purposes and profit is reduced by their influence on production and/or quality.

A number of insect and mite pests cause economic damage to Persian walnuts (Table VI). Pest management programs have been developed that integrate less disruptive insecticides and miticides, cultural practices, and introduced or native predators and parasites for the control of these pests. Conventional insecticide/miticide programs are also available.

TABLE VI

Insect and Mite Pests of Persian Walnuts

Common name	Latin name
Insect Pests	
Lepidopterous pests	
Codling moth	*Cydia pomonella*
Navel orangeworm	*Ameylois transitella*
Fall webworm	*Hyphantria cunea*
Red-humped caterpillar	*Shizura cuncinna*
Aphid and scale pests	
Walnut aphid	*Chromaphis juglandicola*
Dusky-veined aphid	*Callaphis juglandis*
Walnut scale	*Quadraspidiotus juglangregiae*
Fruited scale/European fruit lacanium	*Lecanium pruinosum/Partheno lecanium corni*
San Jose scale	*Quadraspidiotus perniciosus*
Other insects	
Pacific flatheaded borer	*Chrysobothris mali*
Walnut huskfly	*Rhagoletis completa*
Mite pests	
Web-spinning mites	
Twospotted mite	*Tetranychus urticae*
Pacific mite	*Tetranychus pacificus*
European red mite	*Panonychus ulmi*

B. Diseases

Bacterial, fungal, viral, and mycoplasmalike organism diseases cause economic damage to walnuts. Most concern is with Persian walnut, as disease problems influence orchard profitability.

1. Bacterial Diseases

a. Walnut Blight Walnut blight causes major damage to nuts and foliage of Persian walnut trees. It is caused by the bacterium *Xanthomonas campestris* pv. *juglandis* (Pierce) Dowson. The bacteria overwinter in dormant buds and are spread to emerging leaves, shoots, and nuts with spring rains. Cultivars that leaf out early in spring are most commonly infected as their tissue emergence is coincident with spring rainfall and heavy dew. In growing districts with intermittent rainfall during the growing season, walnut blight is a major factor in yield reduction.

The disease is controlled with frequent, topical applications of saftened copper. In districts where walnut blight is prevalent, the causal bacterium has built up considerable resistance to copper, making the disease difficult to control. Walnut breeding and selection programs are currently searching for cultivars that will be resistant to this disease.

b. Deep Bark Canker Deep bark canker is caused by the bacterium *Erwinia rubrifaciens* Wilson et al. The causal bacteria is systemic in the tree and infects the outer phloem and cambial cells, resulting in large quantities of bacterial exudate oozing from limbs and branches. It is usually not lethal but vascular damage weakens the tree, making limbs and branches more susceptible to sunburn and other insect and disease damage. The mechanical shaker, birds, and insects spread the bacteria from tree to tree.

This disease is most prevalent and virulent in the Persian cultivar "Hartley." Although other cultivars are often infected, damage is minimal. Management of deep bark canker requires attention to maintaining optimal conditions for best tree vigor. Any stress predisposes the tree to infection.

c. Crown Gall Crown gall, caused by the soilborne bacterium *Agrobacterium tumefaciens* (Smith and Town) Conn., causes galls to develop at the point of infection. As these grow the infected organ is girdled and then becomes weakened and dies. The bacterium requires an opening or wound to gain entry into the tree; commonly hoeing to eliminate weeds around the base of the tree injures the tree, resulting in infection. It also infects nursery trees as roots are cut when they are "dug" from the growing grounds. The Paradox hybrid rootstock is extremely susceptible to crown gall. Crown gall is best managed by preventing injury to the tree. When infection takes place, topical application of Gallex to the gall kills the infected tissue.

2. Fungal Diseases

a. Phytophthora Root and Crown Rot At least 13 species of the water mold fungus *Phytophthora* de Bary cause tree death or decline by killing roots and crowns of walnut trees. It is the most important disease of cultivated walnuts, and the fungus is primarily spread by farm implements and water. Infection is dependent on soil moisture and temperature and rootstock genotype; the Black walnuts are quite sensitive to infection, whereas the Paradox hybrid is more tolerant. Persian walnut seedlings are very sensitive to *Phytophthora* spp. infection.

Phytophthora-infected trees initially have chlorotic, thin foliage and poor vigor. Root and crown symptoms include dead roots and cankers on bark tissue. Tree death ultimately occurs. Water management and rootstock choice are the only reliable methods of preventing infections from some, but not all, *Phytophthora* spp.

b. Anthracnose Anthracnose is a foliar disease caused by the fungus *Gnomonia leptostyla* (Fr.) Ces & de N. that has an asexual stage, *Marssonina juglandis* (Lib.) Magn. The fungus overwinters in leaf debris and infects developing leaves in cool, wet weather in spring. This infection serves as a source of inoculum for subsequent infection of nuts during the growing season. It has been reported in the eastern United States, Canada, Europe, and South Africa on both Black and Persian walnut. It has never been reported in California. Copper fungicides are recommended for control of this disease.

c. Oak Root Fungus Oak root fungus is caused by the fungus *Armilleria mellea* (Vahl ex Fr.). This fungus infects the root system under conditions of high soil moisture, being more prevalent along river courses. It reduces tree vigor as the root system becomes increasingly damaged, and the tree ultimately dies. Symptoms include white mycelial "fans" between the bark and wood of the root and crown area of the tree, a distinct "mushroom" smell from infected tissue, "honey-colored" clumps of mushrooms at the base of infected trees, and rhizomorphs on the bark surface. Differential sensitivity exists; Persian walnut, Paradox hybrid, and Black walnut are ranked in increasing order of tolerance.

d. Butternut Canker Butternut canker is a disease of Butternut caused by the fungus *Sirococcus clavigignenti-juglandacearum* Nair et al. The disease, which decimates native stands of Butternut, is characterized by dying branches, discolored bark, and twig, branch, and trunk canker. When cankers grow and join together, death of the portion terminal to infection occurs. Butternut canker has not been found in commercial Persian walnut producing areas.

3. Viral Diseases
a. Blackline Disease Blackline disease is a lethal graft union disorder of Persian walnut caused by the walnut strain of the cherry leaf roll virus. The virus is spread by infected pollen and moves slowly down the tree to the graft union. Persian walnuts are tolerant of the virus but when grafted onto a hypersensitive rootstock species, such as *J. hindsii*, necrosis occurs at the union, resulting in death of the scion cultivar. In areas where the Blackline virus is prevalent, Persian walnuts should be grafted onto Persian walnut stock to avoid the hypersensitive reaction.

4. Mycoplasmalike Organisms
a. Walnut Bunch Disease Walnut bunch disease is caused by a mycoplasmalike organism that causes bunching of the twigs ("witches broom") on trees and limbs. The disease is widespread in the eastern and central United States, but has not been reported elsewhere. Removal of infected limbs is recommended for control.

VI. Dynamics of Walnut Cultivation

Black walnut cultivation will continue to have minimal importance. Economic constraints of low productivity and difficulty in processing will limit commercial growth. Static production of Black walnut is expected.

Persian walnut cultivation will continue to increase worldwide. Substantial acreage is being planted in China, Turkey, and Chile and that production will contribute significantly to the world supply. In California, currently the leader in world production, slight increases in acreage are expected; high costs of developing expensive land, urbanization, and alternative crop choices will preclude dramatic increases in Persian walnut acreage.

Bibliography

Anon. (1993). "Walnut Industry Fact Sheet." Walnut Marketing Board, Sacramento, CA.

Batchelor, L. D., and Braucher, O. Lee. *Walnut Culture in California,* Bulletin No. 379. University of California.

Chandler, W. H. (1957). "Deciduous Orchards." Lea & Febiger, Philadelphia.

Manning, W. E. (1979). The classification within the Juglandaceae. *Ann. Missouri Botanical Garden* **65**(4).

Moore, J. N., and Ballington, J. R. (1990). *Genetic Resources of Temperate Fruit and Nut Crops,* Vol. 2, Chap. 19. International Society for Horticultural Science, Wageningen.

Ramos, D. E., Ed. (1985). *Walnut Orchard Management,* Publication No. 21410, 1985. University of California, Division of Agriculture and Natural Resources, Oakland, CA.

Thompson, B. (1976). Black Walnut for Profit. Timber Press, Forest Grove, OR.

Education: Children and Youth

GARY E. MOORE, *North Carolina State University*

I. Public School Education in Agriculture
II. Postsecondary Education in Agriculture
III. Cooperative Extension Service
IV. Other Agricultural Programs for Youth and Adults

Glossary

Agribusiness Education Term used to describe high school programs of agriculture during the mid-1960s through the 1970s; still in use today but not as popular

Agricultural Education Term used to globally define all programs of education in agriculture for youth and adults; also commonly used in describing high school programs of agriculture today

Agriscience Integration of scientific principles and theories into the curriculum and teaching of agriculture

Cooperative extension service Education agency that conducts educational programs in agriculture and natural resources, home economics, community development, and youth development; this agency was created by the Smith-Lever Act of 1914 and is a cooperative venture of federal, state, and local governments

4-H Youth organization of children from 9 to 19 years of age; this organization is operated by the Cooperative Extension Service

FFA The student organization for students enrolled in high school agriculture courses

Smith-Hughes Act of 1917 Federal legislation that provided federal funds to support the teaching of agriculture in the public schools

Supervised agricultural experience (SAE) programs Hands-on learning activities participated in by high school agriculture students outside of normal class hours; in the past this involved growing crops or raising livestock but the scope of SAE programs now includes conducting agricultural experiments and working in agricultural firms

Vocational agriculture Term used to describe high school agricultural programs when job training was the primary emphasis; this term is not commonly used today

Vocational Education Act of 1963 Federal legislation that broadened the scope of high school agriculture programs to include all areas of agriculture, not just farming

Agricultural education is a far-reaching, multifaceted endeavor providing education in agriculture for children and adults. Agricultural education programs are offered by a variety of groups such as the public schools, community and technical colleges, universities, the Cooperative Extension Service, farm organizations, and youth programs such as 4-H and Scouting. Educational programs offered by these groups range from highly structured and formal programs to loosely structured and fragmentary programs. While there is little formal coordination between the various groups offering educational programs for youth and adults in agriculture they have all contributed to improving agriculture.

I. Public School Education in Agriculture

In the United States, structured programs of agricultural education are offered in about 10,000 public schools by some 12,000 teachers. The objectives of these school-based agricultural education programs are to acquaint students with agriculture and to prepare students for careers or further education in agri-

Encyclopedia of Agricultural Science, Volume 2   Copyright © 1994 by Academic Press, Inc.   All rights of reproduction in any form reserved.   **17**

culture. The majority of agricultural education courses are offered in comprehensive high schools but there are agricultural programs in elementary schools, junior high/middle schools, area vocational schools, and specialized agricultural high schools.

The term "vocational agriculture" has commonly been used to describe the public school educational program in agriculture. However, during the 1960s and 1970s "agribusiness education" was used to describe the program because the scope of what was taught expanded to include agricultural areas other than just farming. During the 1980s the term agricultural education was used to describe the high school program because there was a change in the scope of the program, content of the curriculum, and program objectives. The objective of preparing students to enter an agricultural career immediately after high school remained, but additional importance was placed on teaching agricultural literacy, emphasizing the scientific principles involved in agriculture, and preparing students for further education in agriculture. Thus, the broader term of agricultural education is now typically used instead of vocational agriculture or agribusiness education.

A. The Development of Agricultural Education in the Public Schools

At the end of the 19th century and the start of the 20th century, there was widespread criticism of public education. The critics charged that education was out of touch with the common person. Both the subjects being taught and the teaching methods used were under scrutiny. The teaching methods of lecturing, rote memorization, and verbatim recitations were widely used and abused. The classical subjects being studied such as Latin and Greek were viewed as largely irrelevant to an agrarian nation. Editors of farm publications, administrators of agricultural colleges, and other leading agriculturists and educators called for the inclusion of practical subjects such as agriculture in the public school curriculum.

The movement to teach agriculture in the public schools started slowly at the turn of the century but quickly gained momentum. Starting as early as 1903 legislators in Georgia and Louisiana required agriculture to be taught in the common schools. In the 1908 to 1913 era numerous states passed laws establishing the teaching of agriculture in the public schools. By 1915 agriculture was being taught across the nation in 4665 schools to 90,000 students. The agricultural subjects taught and the quality of the instructional

program varied widely from community to community and state to state.

As the teaching of agriculture in the public schools became established, there was a national movement to pass federal legislation to provide federal support for the teaching of agriculture and other vocational subjects. This movement culminated in the passage of the Smith-Hughes Act in 1917. This legislation provided federal funds to support the teaching of home economics, trades and industry, and agriculture in the public schools and provided funds for the training and supervision of teachers. The Smith-Hughes Act also created a Federal Board for Vocational Education. The Federal Board established national standards of uniformity for agricultural programs, verified that agricultural programs were meeting the provisions of the Smith-Hughes Act, and provided national leadership for the program.

B. The High School Agricultural Curriculum

At one time, the high school program in agriculture could have been nicknamed the "sow, cow, plow" program. The Smith-Hughes Act of 1917 stated the purpose of vocational agriculture was to train people "who have entered upon or who are preparing to enter upon the work of the farm." Thus, the early curriculum concentrated on preparing students to become farmers. The early vocational agriculture programs were found primarily in rural high schools and the students were typically boys. A traditional 4-year curriculum consisted of Agriculture I, II, III, and IV. In Agriculture I the boys were introduced to Animal Science, Soils, Plant Science, Record Keeping, and Agricultural Mechanics. In the first year they learned about the different breeds of livestock and how to select them, were taught basic soil science, were introduced to crop production, and learned how to use hand tools found on the farm. They also had instruction in leadership skills such as parliamentary procedure and public speaking. In subsequent years, the different areas of agriculture were studied in more depth. Considerable time was spent on livestock health, feeds and feeding, crop production, livestock housing, and farm mechanics. Economics and farm management were emphasized in the latter years. These agricultural classes were offered just like any other school subject, one period a day for the school year. The "sow, cow, plow" description of agricultural education was fairly consistent until 1963.

In 1963, there was a major change in the agricultural education curriculum due to new federal legislation.

The Vocational Education Act of 1963 stated that "any amounts allotted. . . for agriculture may be used for vocational education in any occupation involving knowledge and skills in agricultural subjects, whether or not such occupation involves work on the farm." As a result of this new federal legislation, the curriculum in agricultural education was expanded to include new courses in areas such as horticulture, forestry and natural resources, agricultural sales and services, food processing, small animal care, and agricultural mechanics. No longer was agricultural education just for farming. These nonfarm agricultural courses were well received in suburban and urban school districts. These new courses were typically one period in length and lasted for a semester or for a year. Production agriculture (farming) was still taught in many schools, especially in rural areas. More female students started enrolling in high school agriculture because of the changing curriculum and the emphasis on civil rights and equity during the 1960s.

The authority of the federal government in prescribing how to operate agricultural education programs was limited by the Vocational Education Act of 1963. States were given considerable latitude in determining program requirements and curricular issues.

The Vocational Education Act of 1963 also provided funding for the development of area vocational schools. One county or several counties would jointly build a centrally located school where a comprehensive array of vocational education courses would be offered. Junior and senior students in local high schools who desired specialized vocational training would be transported to this centrally located facility where they would spend a half day immersed in the study of a particular vocation. Specialized horticulture and agricultural mechanics programs were often found in these vocational schools. Depending upon the needs of the community, other specialized agricultural programs such as forestry, horse care and training, farm management, small animal care, and meat processing could be found at the vocational schools. Many area vocational schools established during the 1960s are still in operation today with a variety of specialized agricultural subjects being taught.

One by-product of the area vocational school idea was the establishment of specialized agricultural high schools. The Saul High School of Agriculture in Philadelphia, the Chicago High School of Agricultural Sciences, and the East Environmental Science and Agri-business Magnet School in Kansas City are three examples. These magnet high schools offer a wide array of agricultural courses in addition to academic subjects. Students come to these high schools for indepth study of various agricultural disciplines.

During the 1980s the agricultural education curriculum evolved even further. The educational reform movement starting with the publication of *A Nation at Risk* in 1983 followed by new vocational education legislation (Carl Perkins Act of 1984) and a 1988 National Research Council study of high school agricultural education (*Understanding Agriculture New Directions for Education*) all combined to cause additional curriculum changes in agricultural education. These changes resulted in greater emphasis on biotechnology and the scientific principles involved in agriculture. In a number of states science credit was awarded for completion of agricultural courses. High school agricultural students conducted experiments in plant growth, genetic engineering, and tissue culture. In addition to making the curriculum more scientific, new areas of study such as aquaculture and global agriculture were added to the curriculum. There was also a trend toward changing agricultural classes from year-long courses to semester-length courses.

Today the high school agricultural education curriculum varies greatly from state to state. In some states, such as Texas, there are 27 different semester-length agriscience and technology courses that can be offered. In other states, such as North Carolina, there are a smaller number of year-long agriculture courses that are taught. Regardless of the length of the course, there is typically an introductory course to agriculture titled "Introduction to Agriscience" or something similar. The introductory course provides a survey of agriculture with an emphasis on the scientific basis of agriculture. After the introductory course, the student may select from a variety of agricultural classes. A wide variety of courses may be taught such as biotechnology, horticulture, aquaculture, animal physiology, agricultural research, animal science, horse production, natural resources, crop science, forestry, agricultural sales, farm management, and agricultural mechanics. The actual courses taught in a school depend upon the size of the school and number of agriculture teachers, agricultural needs of the local community, and state curriculum guidelines. In some agrarian states, there is still a strong emphasis on production agriculture (farming) courses. There is a greater emphasis on horticulture and natural resources in the more urban states. Regardless of the type of state, there has been a marked increase on emphasizing biotechnology and agriscience in recent years. The curriculum in agricultural education today is far different from that called for in the Smith-Hughes Act of 1917.

C. Supervised Agricultural Experience Programs

One of the unique components of high school agricultural education programs is the Supervised Agricultural Experience (SAE) program. Students in the agricultural education program are expected to conduct a hands-on experiential learning program outside of the classroom. This program is supervised by the agriculture teacher and provides the student with the opportunity to apply skills and knowledge learned in the classroom to real world situations.

The supervised experience concept originated in 1908 with Rufus Stimson, Director of Smith's Agricultural School in Northampton, Massachusetts. Students in his school were required to grow farm crops or raise livestock on their home farm using practices taught to them in the agriculture classes. The agriculture teacher visited the students and supervised the program. When the results obtained by the students using improved farming methods were compared with standard farming practices of the day the value of the agricultural instruction was readily apparent. Based upon the success of the farming projects in Massachusetts, the authors of the Smith-Hughes Act included language in their bill requiring all agriculture students to have this "supervised practice." Over the years this concept has been know as a farming project, a supervised farming program, and a supervised occupational experience program. Originally, students grew crops or raised livestock.

Today there are a variety of ways in which students may conduct SAE programs. Placement programs involve the placement of students on farms and ranches, in agricultural businesses, in school laboratories, or in community facilities to provide a "learning by doing" environment. This is done outside of normal classroom hours and may be paid or nonpaid. Students keep records as to hours worked, type of work activities performed, and wages. Examples of placement SAE include working after school at a farm supply store, placement in a florist shop, working on Saturdays at a riding stable, and working in the school greenhouse after school and on weekends. A written agreement and training plan identify what is to be learned during the placement period.

Students may participate in exploratory activities, especially if they are first year students. Students spend short amounts of time working with, observing, or interviewing agricultural workers to learn about the type of activities they do. Students could also explore various agricultural opportunities by participating in field days, collecting materials, and engaging in similar exploratory activities. This type of SAE is appropriate for beginning agricultural students but is not restricted just to beginning students. This SAE activity is designed primarily to help students become literate in agriculture and/or become aware of possible careers in agriculture. Examples of exploratory SAE activities might include observing and/or assisting a florist, interviewing an agricultural loan officer in a bank, preparing a scrapbook on the work of a veterinarian, growing plants in a milk jug "greenhouse," assisting on a horse farm for a day, or attending an agricultural career day at the university.

In entrepreneurship SAE programs the student plans, implements, operates, and assumes financial risks in a farming activity or agricultural business. The students own the materials and other required inputs and keep financial records to determine return to investments. An SAE entrepreneurship program provides students the opportunity to develop the necessary skills to become established in their own business or gain employment. Examples of entrepreneurship activities include growing corn, operating a Christmas tree farm, growing bedding plants in the school greenhouse, raising pigs, and owning and operating a lawn care service. Many students have become established in farming through their entrepreneurial SAE programs.

An experimental SAE activity is where the student plans and conducts a major agricultural experiment using the scientific process. The purpose of the experiment is to provide students "hands-on" experience in verifying, learning, or demonstrating scientific principles in agriculture, discovering new knowledge or using the scientific process. In conducting an experimental SAE the student follows the scientific process. Examples of experimental SAE activities include comparing the effect of various planting media on plant growth, determining the impact of different levels of protein on fish growth, and comparing rooting hormones on plant root development.

Students who choose an analytical SAE must identify an agricultural problem that is not amenable to experimentation and design a plan to investigate and analyze the problem. The student gathers and evaluates data from a variety of sources and then produces some type of finished product. The product could be a marketing display or marketing plan for an agricultural commodity, a series of newspaper articles, a land use plan for a farm, a detailed landscape design for a community facility, an advertising campaign for an agribusiness, and so forth.

D. FFA—The Youth Organization

One component of the Agricultural education program that is synonymous in the minds of many people with agricultural education is the FFA. The FFA is an organization composed of students who are enrolled in agricultural education. Originally the letters FFA stood for Future Farmers of America. But since agricultural education has evolved into an educational program much broader than just farming, the organization changed its official name in 1988 to the National FFA Organization.

The FFA was started in 1928 and was patterned after the Future Farmers of Virginia. The purpose of the organization is to provide an avenue for students to develop abilities in leadership, citizenship, and cooperation. Local FFA chapters, working through a committee structure, develop an annual program of activities they follow. This plan includes monthly meetings, often using agriculturists in the community as speakers. A typical plan of activities includes community service projects, recreational and social activities, and fund raising, and culminates in an awards banquet at the end of the school year.

The FFA has an incentives and awards program that ties in with classroom instruction and the supervised agricultural experience program. There are four degrees of membership; greenhand, chapter, state, and American. To advance to higher degrees the student must participate in FFA activities, demonstrate leadership skills, and conduct a quality SAE program. Proficiency awards, based on the students' SAE program, are presented at the local, state, and national levels. Students who have outstanding SAE programs in areas such as agricultural mechanics, livestock production, and placement in sales and services compete for these awards. There are more than 35 different categories of proficiency awards.

Along with degrees and proficiency awards, the FFA sponsors competitive events in areas such as parliamentary procedure, livestock judging, agriscience student of the year, public speaking, marketing, and farm management. FFA activities are conducted on the local and regional level within a state, and at the state and national levels. The top level of competition occurs at the National FFA convention which is held every year in November in Kansas City, Missouri.

The colors of the FFA are national blue and corn gold. When schools in the South were segregated there was a parallel organization for black vocational agriculture students, the New Farmers of America (NFA). The FFA and NFA merged in 1965. The constitution of the FFA was amended in 1969 to allow girls to join. In 1971 a national FFA Alumni organization was formed. The Alumni organization has local and state affiliates and provides support to the FFA. For more information about the FFA or the FFA alumni organization, contact the National FFA Organization (5632 Mt. Vernon Memorial Highway, Alexandria, VA 22309). [See WOMEN IN AGRICULTURE.]

E. Adult Education

Since the inception of agricultural education, many high school agriculture teachers have also taught night courses for adults in the community. The wording of the Smith-Hughes Act of 1917 stated that agricultural education was for those "who have entered upon or who are preparing to enter upon the work of the farm." The phrase those "who have entered upon" was interpreted to mean adults and out-of-school youth who may have dropped out of school to farm. During the 1920s and 1930s it was common for an agriculture teacher to offer instruction to three distinct groups of students. The first group of students were those enrolled in high school and were called the all-day students. Instruction of this group occurred during the normal school day. The second group of students were called part-time students and were young men from 16 to 25 years of age who might not have completed high school or had not been enrolled in agriculture while in high school. They met immediately after school was out for the day or at night. The third group were the adult farmers in the community and they were enrolled in the evening program.

Agriculture teachers took two primary approaches in teaching the evening program. One approach was to offer a course that contained a variety of topics. One week the lesson might be on dairy production, the next week on corn varieties, and the following week on tractors. An advisory group of farmers helped the agriculture teacher choose the topics to be studied. The teacher either taught the lesson or arranged to have a guest speaker.

The second approach to teaching in the evening program was to offer a more systematic course concentrating on one topic such as dairying. Each meeting would concentrate on some aspect of dairying such as disease control, feeding, or facilities. The agriculture teacher taught most of these classes.

Classes for adults were typically taught during the late fall and winter months when activity on the farm was not as intense. There would be 10–15 class sessions. During the 1930–1950 era, over half of the agriculture teachers in the United States offered adult classes.

The pattern for teaching adults established in the early days is still in operation today. Today, about 1200 agriculture teachers in different communities and states offer educational program for adults. However, the subject matter has changed, especially in the more urban areas. The agriculture teacher may teach courses on landscaping, floriculture, or gardening. The courses may be of a vocational or avocational nature. In the more agrarian regions of the country, the emphasis is still on production agriculture. Both general courses and specialized courses are taught.

In many school districts, especially the rural school districts, a special adult education program is organized just for young farmers. The educational and social needs of those getting established in farming is different from those who have already become established in farming. The educational program conducted for these 18 to 35 year olds has several unique characteristics. Both the husband and wife are generally involved in the educational program. The classes may meet in the school but often are conducted in the home of the young farmers on a rotating basis. Social events such as pot-luck suppers, volleyball games, and parties are an important component of the program. The young farmers play an active role in determining the topics to be covered in class and often help arrange for speakers. The agriculture teacher may teach some of the classes but often serves more as an advisor to the group. In some Midwestern states such as Indiana, it is not uncommon for a high school to have two or three different young farmer groups.

In 21 states (AL, CA, CO, CT, GA, IA, IL, IN, KY, KS, MO, NE, OH, OK, PA, SC, TX, UT, VA, WA, WY) statewide young farmer associations exist. These associations have annual conventions where they have educational and social functions and compete in various activities such as debates, public speaking, and chapter competition. These 21 state associations comprise the National Young Farmer Educational Association. The National Association provides assistance to state and local affiliates, conducts an annual convention, and sponsors an incentives and awards program for members. The address of the National Young Farmer Educational Associa-

tion is 5632 Mt. Vernon Memorial Highway, Alexandria, Virginia 22309.

A third type of school-based adult education in agriculture is found in a number of midwestern and western states. Besides having the typical adult classes and young farmer programs mentioned previously, some school systems hire teachers whose sole responsibility is to teach adults. These teachers visit adult farmers during the day and provide consultation and assistance to the farmers. Night classes are also conducted. The primary emphasis of these adult programs is farm management. While some of the specialized adult teachers may be hired by local school systems as is the case in Minnesota and Ohio, the majority of the adult farm management teachers operate through the community or technical college system of the state. In the United States there are about 400 adult farm management teachers (found in NE, CO, SD, ND, ID, WA, OR, AZ, NM, UT, WI, MO, OH, and MN).

Special adult programs in agriculture were offered after World War II and the Korean War for veterans under the provisions of the GI Bill. The objective was to prepare the returning serviceman for the farm. High school agriculture teachers would teach veterans 3–4 nights a week. The veterans received money for attending the classes and the teachers were paid extra.

During the late 1950s and 1960s several events combined that resulted in less emphasis being placed on school-based adult education in agriculture. The high school curriculum in agriculture changed from just farming to include other areas of agriculture such as food processing, forestry, and natural resources. Different types of students (and parents) were associated with the high school agriculture program. This group had not experienced adult education in the past and the need for adult education in some of the new curriculum areas was not as evident as that in farming. In many states, schools in rural areas were consolidated. Instead of having readily identifiable community schools, one or two schools might serve the entire county. There was a loss of community identity and adults lost the feeling that the local school was "their school." Also, television and other forms of communication emerged during this era to compete for the attention of the adults. Today evening classes, young farmer programs, and specialized adult teachers still operate in the pubic schools, but the availability, extent, and type of adult education programs offered vary greatly from community to community and from state to state.

F. Middle School Programs of Agricultural Education

Agricultural instruction is provided in some middle schools. The purpose of the instruction is to provided a general overview of agriculture and to acquaint students with the types of careers available in agriculture. Students are enrolled in the agricultural class for one or two grading periods and then rotate on to other courses such as art, industrial arts, or home economics.

G. The Teacher of Agriculture

The minimum requirement to be a high school teacher of agriculture is to have a baccalaureate degree in agricultural education. There are approximately 90 universities in the United States with teacher training programs in agriculture. Teacher education programs are found in land-grant colleges and in some regional universities. In order to offer a degree in agricultural education a university must offer courses in both education and agriculture. Students preparing to be agriculture teachers complete a variety of courses in both of these areas plus general education courses. Masters degrees in agricultural education are offered in most universities that have baccalaureate programs. Doctoral degrees in agricultural education are offered in about 10 land-grant universities.

H. The Governance of Agricultural Education

Each state has one or more individuals in the state department of education who have supervisory and administrative responsibilities for agricultural education. These individuals are called supervisors or consultants and they provide guidance and direction to the agricultural programs within their states. Working cooperatively with the teachers, they determine the curriculum and program standards, and help coordinate FFA activities.

At the national level, two agricultural education specialists are located in the United States Department of Education. These specialists interact with state agricultural education officials, serve in a liaison position with other educational and agricultural groups at the national level, and work with the FFA. Prior to the passage of the Vocational Education Act of 1963 there were 10–12 agricultural education specialists at the federal level. They ascertained that the provisions of the Smith-Hughes Act were being followed in the various states and provided leadership in areas such

as adult education, farm mechanics, and curriculum development on a national level.

In the early 1980s the various constituent groups (teachers, supervisors, teacher educators, young farmers, alumni, etc.) involved in public school education in agriculture saw the need to develop a national organization to provide leadership and serve as a voice for the agricultural education profession. Accordingly, the National Council for Agricultural Education was established in 1984. Representatives of the various groups involved in public school education in agriculture comprise the Council. The Council serves as a think tank and advocate for agricultural education at the national level.

I. Professional Organizations in Agricultural Education

High school, post-secondary, and middle school agriculture teachers belong to the National Vocational Agriculture Teachers Association (NVATA). State supervisors belong to the National Association of Supervisors of Agricultural Education (NASAE). Teacher educators belong to the American Association for Agricultural Education (AAAE). Most teachers, supervisors, and teacher educators also belong to the American Vocational Association (AVA). The three agricultural education organizations hold their annual meetings in conjunction with the annual meeting of the American Vocational Association. Adult farm management instructors belong to the National Farm and Ranch Business Management Education Association. They may also belong to the NVATA.

II. Postsecondary Education in Agriculture

Education in agriculture for youth and adults is not limited to the public high schools and middle schools. Community and technical colleges offer a variety of courses in agriculture. Also 4-year agricultural colleges offer short courses and 2-year associate degree programs in agriculture. Baccalaureate and graduate programs in agriculture are described in another article. [See EDUCATION: UNDERGRADUATE AND GRADUATE UNIVERSITY.]

In the United States between 500 and 600 community and technical colleges offer agricultural courses. These courses can be taken as stand along single courses, be part of a 1-year certificate program or 2-

year associate degree program, and in some cases be transfer courses to a 4-year college. Students can enroll in a single course just to learn more about a specific agricultural topic or they can enroll in program for career preparation purposes. Courses and curricula exist in a variety of agricultural areas such as agricultural mechanics, floriculture, swine management, agricultural sales, veterinary technology, nursery management, horse production and care, farm management, and greenhouse production.

The national Postsecondary Agricultural Student (PAS) association is a student organization for agricultural students in the community and technical colleges. It was formed in 1979 and is loosely patterned after the FFA.

Several universities have special educational programs in agriculture for adults. One example is the winter short course at Purdue University in Indiana. Ten to twelve courses focusing on animal agriculture, plant agriculture, and general agriculture are taught. The courses are offered during an 8-week span starting in January and extending through March. The courses are taught on the main campus by university faculty members but the courses do not carry academic credit. The structure of the program is like a miniature semester; students enroll in several different courses, do homework, and have exams. The emphasis of the short course is on practical application of the latest technology and research. Young farmers and adults enroll in the winter school. A similar program is offered at the University of Wisconsin.

North Carolina State University offers a 2-year program called the Agricultural Institute. The Institute is a 2-year, terminal academic program that provides education and training in food science, agriculture, horticulture, turf grass management, and agribusiness. Students in this program enroll in specialized courses in agriculture that emphasize application and hands-on activities. The courses are taught on the main campus of the university by university faculty members. These courses do not transfer to a 4-year program. Virginia Tech, the University of Maryland, and the University of Massachusetts have similar programs.

The Ohio State University offers a program similar to that of North Carolina State but the program has its own campus and faculty. The Agricultural Technical Institute (ATI) is located in Wooster, Ohio. Specialized 2-year courses of study are offered in a wide variety of agricultural fields. However, a number of the courses at the ATI can be transferred to 4-year agricultural colleges.

Some universities offer 2-year associate degrees in agriculture but the courses are primarily the same as those taken by 4-year students. After 2 years the students may take their associate degree and enter the labor market or they may transfer into a 4-year academic program. Some of the universities with this type of program are the Pennsylvania State University, Michigan State University, University of Minnesota, Ohio State University, Purdue University, and the University of New Hampshire.

III. Cooperative Extension Service

The organization that has the largest agricultural educational program in the world is the Cooperative Extension Service (CES). The Cooperative Extension Service is a cooperative venture of federal, state, and local governments. [See COOPERATIVE EXTENSION SERVICE.]

In the early 1900s America was predominately an agrarian nation and farmers needed help in improving their farming practices. The findings of the agricultural research being conducted at the land-grant colleges was not readily available to the farmers. A method for transferring agricultural research findings and scientific knowledge about farming from the universities to the farmer was needed. In many states various activities such as traveling railroad car exhibits, demonstration farms, farmers institutes, agricultural fairs, and meetings of agricultural societies were sponsored by universities, federal and state departments of agriculture, and private citizens in an attempt to disseminate agricultural knowledge. In 1914 the federal government passed the Smith-Lever Act which established a nationwide extension system that operates at the state and county level. The purpose of the extension service was to transmit information from the agricultural colleges to the people. Today, the cooperative extension service still transmits information to people but the type of information disseminated and the people served have been expanded.

The Cooperative Extension Service is found in nearly every county in the United States. The county extension office is staffed by one or more extension agents. A common model is to find an agricultural agent, a home economics agent, and a 4-H agent. In more populous counties there could be several additional agents such as community development agents and horticultural agents. In less populous counties, there may not be a 4-H agent. The agricultural agent and home economics agent would then handle 4-H activities. The type and number of agents employed in a county depend upon the needs of the county.

The educational programs and services offered by the extension service at the county level are varied. The extension service publishes a large number of educational brochures on a variety of topics that are available to the public. Classes and meetings are held in local communities. Examples of meetings could be lawn care, nutrition, raising children, handling agricultural wastes, pesticide safety, and rural zoning. Advisory committees in each county provide advice as to the type of education programs needed. Extension agents are also available for individual consultation. If a farmer or homeowner was having a disease or insect problem, the agricultural agent would visit the farmer or homeowner, identify the problem, and provide suggestions for solving the problem.

County extension agents are supported by a state extension staff. The state extension staff is located at the land-grant college in each state. Besides performing administrative and leadership functions, the state staff develops the educational publications used at the county level and develops educational aids such as slide programs and displays. The state staff also includes subject matter specialists who assist county agents in conducting education programs and in solving problems.

A widely recognized component of the extension service is the 4-H program. The 4-H program is an educational and leadership development program for young people between the ages of 9 and 19. The 4-H members are generally organized into clubs. The clubs may be community based or can be composed of individuals from throughout a county who have common interests such as a horse club or beef cattle club. The clubs meet regularly, have educational programs, plan and conduct service activities, and hold social functions.

IV. Other Agricultural Programs for Youth and Adults

A. Ag in the Classroom

The United States Department of Agriculture (USDA) provides leadership for a program called Ag in the Classroom. This is an educational program that operates in the elementary schools. The objective of this program is to acquaint elementary students with agriculture. While the USDA provides leadership for the program, the implementation of the program varies from state to state.

Typically, sets of instructional materials are provided to elementary teachers. The instructional materials include lesson plans, student activities, and visual aids. The lessons are on agricultural topics but are integrated with the state curriculum guides for each grade level. For example, if a unit on plant growth is to be taught at a certain elementary grade, the Ag in the Classroom materials would contain all the information that would normally be taught about plant growth but the illustrations and examples would be on agricultural crops grown in that state. Agricultural coloring books, agricultural videos, and an agricultural newspaper similar to the "Weekly Reader" are also used. Trips to agricultural colleges and community agricultural expositions may be conducted.

Workshops are held in the summer for elementary teachers to teach them how to use the materials. In some states, such as Idaho, special "hands-on" programs are held for elementary teachers at the state agricultural college. Teachers actually perform agricultural tasks.

The administration and funding of the Agriculture in the Classroom program varies from state to state. In Iowa, the state department of agriculture coordinates the program. In North Carolina, the Farm Bureau operates the program with financial support from other agricultural industries. In Idaho, an educational foundation has been established to operate the Ag in the Classroom program and funds are provided by private donations and the state legislature.

B. Boy Scouts of America

While the Boy Scouts are not thought of as an agricultural education program, they do offer several merit badges related to agriculture. If a scout desires to work on an agricultural merit badge, he obtains a merit badge booklet that contains information about the subject. He studies this information and then completes a number of required projects or activities related to the merit badge. All of this is done under the supervision of an adult who has expertise in the agricultural field being studied. Boy scout merit badges are available in agribusiness, animal science, bee keeping, botany, farm mechanics, forestry, gardening, horsemanship, landscape architecture, plant science, rabbit raising, soil and water conservation, and veterinary science.

Historically, agricultural education programs in the high school and educational programs conducted by the Cooperative Extension Service were the primary sources of education in agriculture for youth and adults. These two groups are still vitally involved in this task, but the scope and content of what they teach have expanded. Other groups have also joined in the educational effort.

Bibliography

Dormody, T. (1992, Oct.). Integrating science and agriculture. *The Agricultural Education Magazine* 12–13.

Dwyer, D. A. (1992, Jan.). The agri-business magnet high school: A new approach to agricultural education. *The Agricultural Education Magazine* 15–17.

Hughes, M., and Barrick, R. K. (1993, Fall). A model for agricultural education in public schools. *J. Agricult. Educ.* 59–67.

Knebel, E. H., and Richardson, W. B. (1982). "Terminology in Agricultural Education." American Association for Vocational Instructional Materials, Athens, GA.

National Research Council (1988). "Understanding Agriculture: New Directions for Education." National Academy Press, Washington, DC.

Phipps, L. J., and Osborne, E. W. (1988). "Handbook on Agricultural Education in Public Schools." Interstate, Danville, IL.

"The Status of Adult Education in Agriculture" (1992). National Council for Agricultural Education, Alexandria, VA.

Stimson, R. W., and Lathrop, F. W. (1942). "History of Agricultural Education of Less than College Grade in the United States." U.S. Government Printing Office, Washington, DC.

Education: Undergraduate and Graduate University

J. DAVID MCCRACKEN, *The Ohio State University*

Glossary

Agriculture Knowledge base that is a composite of disciplines that broadly link basic sciences, natural systems, economics, business, and human resources to the more traditional production agriculture and food enterprises; it encompasses the production of food, fiber, wood products, horticultural crops, and other plant and animal products; and includes the financing, processing, marketing, and distribution of agricultural products; farm production supply and service industries; health, nutrition, and food consumption; and use and conservation of land and water resources; development and maintenance of recreational resources; and related economic sociological, political, environmental, and cultural characteristics of the food and fiber system; educational programs in food, agriculture, and natural resources tend to be interlinked.

Cultural diversity Involvement of individuals of different or varied backgrounds relating to ethnicity, gender, location, and inherited ideas, beliefs, values, and knowledge as students, faculty, and staff

Distance education Process of conducting educational programs within states and across state lines through the use of correspondence and telephone and satellite communications to reach people who are unable to participate at the location where the instruction originates

Graduate education, agriculture Postgraduate education in a specialized discipline of agriculture usually leading to a Master of Arts, Master of Science, or Doctor of Philosophy Degree from a comprehensive university; study at the Masters level prepares students as researchers and/or professionals within their disciplines; the doctoral degree is awarded for original research within one's specialized field

Undergraduate agricultural education, associate degree level Educational programs offered in a 2-year postsecondary vocational–technical schools, in junior and community colleges, as 2-year programs within agricultural colleges and universities, and in technical schools with either a vocational or technical education emphasis or a more general education designed for transfer to a 4-year university

Undergraduate agricultural education, baccalaureate level General and professional education in agriculture of at least 4 years providing content, context, and practice for undergraduate liberal study within the context of a comprehensive college or university which lays a foundation for understanding professional life in the discipline

This article examines general and professional education in a broad range of food, environmental, and agricultural specialties, including agricultural business and management, natural resources, agricultural education and/or communication, animal science, entomology, plant and/or soil science, agricultural engineering and/or mechanization, food science and/or human nutrition, horticulture, plant pathology, rural sociology, general agricultural studies, and related biological and/or physical sciences within the context of a comprehensive college or university, a 2-year postsecondary vocational–technical school, or a junior or community college at associate degree, baccalaureate degree, and graduate degree levels.

I. Introduction

The concept of "education as a public service," initiated with the Morrill Act of 1862, marked a unique

U.S. contribution to higher education. While the teaching of agriculture was given primary emphasis when the act was initiated, research and extension missions and funding were added later. Every state established at least one agricultural college under the act, funded from both federal and state sources. These colleges have contributed to an adequate and high-quality food supply for the American public.

As the nation changed from an agricultural society to an industrial society, and more recently to a knowledge-based professional society, questions have been raised about the public need for the agricultural college system. The population has shifted from rural to urban areas. The economy is no longer national but international in character, and agriculture is no longer the strong social or political factor that it once was. However, most of the land, water, and natural resources in the United States continue to be devoted to the production of agricultural commodities. Natural resources of soil, land, and water support not only the farm, but also nonfarm uses, and call forth a complex set of problems and political issues that transcend agriculture, and require a high degree of knowledge in both natural and social sciences. There have been major changes in the societal setting: a decrease in the number of farmers, a migration of rural America to the cities, and voicing of major public concerns for the nutritive value of food and the quality of the environment. [See RURAL SOCIOLOGY.]

The traditional mission of agricultural colleges has been expanding. The focus has been broadened from agriculture to agricultural systems. Included are most aspects of food and fiber production, food safety and human health, environmental quality, and conservation and use of natural resources. As the focus of agricultural colleges has been changing, students and curricula have also been in a state of transition. Efforts have been made to diversify the student body and prepare students as more generally educated professionals with less emphasis on technical specialization.

An understanding of the broadened mission of agriculture within the American society, of undergraduate education at the associate degree and baccalaureate degree levels, and of graduate education provides a basis for a treatise on the topic of education: undergraduate and graduate university.

A. Agriculture

As one considers the field of agriculture, one must be cognizant of the changes taking place within the environment in which agriculture operates, and how these changes might influence agricultural systems. Five key anticipated characteristics of agriculture in the year 2002 identified by an Agricultural Strategic Planning Task Force (1992) follow:

1. *Scientifically advanced.* Throughout the 20th century agriculture has been buffeted by scientific advances. New advances over the next 10 years will require even more scientific expertise on the part of agribusiness operators. Moreover, agribusiness operators will need to express their scientific literacy in ways which reassure the public of the safety and quality of their products. Successful agribusiness operators will be ambassadors, not just users, of science.

2. *Consumer driven.* Agribusiness operators, whether they be input suppliers, farm producers, or output processors and merchandisers, will be attuned to the needs of consumers. Traditional commodity markets increasingly will be relegated to export markets in less developed countries, and bulk processing markets in the United States. Specialized products, most aimed at small markets, will be engineered to meet the diverse life style needs of economically well-off consumers in the United States and other developed countries. These specialized products will service both food and nonfood markets.

3. *Environmentally accountable.* The public no longer perceives that agriculture is unique and thus warrants special treatment with respect to environmental regulation and utilization of natural resources. Therefore, irrespective of its wishes, agriculture will be accountable for its impact on the quality of life in surrounding communities. Given this inevitability, agriculture may become proactive in developing a good neighbor policy.

4. *International.* Agriculture currently sells products into worldwide markets, but in 10 years international dimensions also will influence agriculture's scope and ownership as well as its managerial perspectives and attitudes. The role of national boundaries as determinants of policy will diminish as multinational restrictions on policy alternatives grow. These changes will place new strains and challenges upon the market-oriented change process confronting agriculture.

5. *Dynamically managed.* Successful agribusiness operators will: (a) efficiently use resources, (b) capture the advantages of change, and (c) focus energy on being good neighbors by minimizing the nuisances associated with their business. Management of the external environment will be as important to a firm's long-term success as management of its internal environment. Management of the internal environment will be more about managing change than efficiently using resources.

On many campuses, colleges of agriculture and related disciplines are undergoing programmatic changes and, more important, are reexamining the philosophy underlying their missions. They are developing a unique knowledge base that is much broader than is generally perceived—a knowledge base that is a composite of disciplines that broadly link basic sciences, natural systems, economics, business, and human resources to the more traditional production agriculture and food enterprises.

A definition developed by the Committee on Agricultural Education in Secondary Schools recognizes the changing nature of agricultural systems:

> Agriculture encompasses the production of agricultural commodities, including food, fiber, wood products, horticultural crops, and other plant and animal products. Agriculture also includes the financing, processing, marketing, and distribution of agricultural products; farm production supply and service industries; health, nutrition, and food consumption; and use and conservation of land and water resources; development and maintenance of recreational resources; and related economic sociological, political, environmental, and cultural characteristics of the food and fiber system. (1988, p. vi)

B. Education, Undergraduate

Undergraduate education in agriculture has been offered at both the associate degree and baccalaureate degree levels. These programs have offered both general education and occupational preparation in a broad range of agricultural specialties in a variety of institutional settings.

1. Associate Degree Level

Associate degree programs in agriculture have included those with a vocational education emphasis, those with a technical education emphasis, and those emphasizing transfer to a 4-year university. One significant variant in determining the type of program has been the number of credits or courses in general education (mathematics, science, communications, human relations, etc.) versus the number of credits or courses in a technical specialty in agriculture that have been required. The range of offerings in agriculture in these 2-year programs has paralleled programs at 4-year universities. These programs have been offered in 2-year postsecondary vocational–technical schools, in junior and community colleges, as 2-year programs within agricultural colleges and universities, and in technical institutes.

2. Baccalaureate Level

Undergraduate general and professional education in agriculture provides content, context, and practice for undergraduate liberal study. It lays a foundation for understanding professional life in a broadly defined agricultural environment. Preparation of agriculturalists at this level occurs within the context of a comprehensive college or university. A minimum of 4 years of study beyond the secondary level is usually required to complete a curriculum of study at this level. Majors vary by institution, but are generally available in the areas of agricultural business and management, natural resources, agricultural education and/or communication, animal science, plant and/or soil science, agricultural engineering and/or mechanization, food science and/or human nutrition, general agriculture, related biological and/or physical sciences, and other areas.

C. Education, Graduate

Graduate education in agriculture has been available at both the masters and doctoral levels. These programs have been designed to fit within the requirements of the graduate schools of the colleges and universities where they are found. Graduate education in agriculture has offered the opportunity for students to develop a greater degree of specialization than is normally possible at the undergraduate level. Students usually specialize within one of the disciplines within agriculture, supplementing their education with courses which provide professional support to the agricultural specialty.

1. Doctoral

A doctorate is the highest academic degree in any field of knowledge. In agriculture doctorates are usually awarded for study in such fields as agricultural economics, agricultural education, agricultural engineering, agronomy, animal science, food science, horticulture, natural resources, and rural sociology. The Doctor of Philosophy is the doctoral degree awarded for original research within one's specialized field.

2. Masters

A Master of Arts or Master of Science degree is awarded for graduate study beyond the baccalaureate but at less than the doctoral level. In agriculture the Master of Science degree is the usual one offered at this level. Fields of study are similar to those offered for doctoral work. At most colleges and universities this degree is offered for students pursuing one of two options. The first option prepares the student as a researcher in the discipline. The major emphasis is often considered to be preparation for study at the doctoral level in the same discipline. The second option is intended to prepare the student as a professional in the discipline. In the second option a thesis may not be required.

II. Education at the Associate Degree Level

Two-year postsecondary education in agriculture developed rapidly in the 1960s and 1970s. Two-year educational programs provided a way for students to prepare for agricultural occupations at the mid-management and technician levels without completing a 4-year college degree.

A. Nature of Programs

There has been a great deal of variance from institution to institution in the nature of the program offered. Some institutions have emphasized transfer programs, providing the basic courses in general subjects required for transfer to a 4-year college or university. Other institutions have emphasized the preparation of students for entry into specialized, technical or mid-management positions in agricultural business and industry. Some of the programs at less than the baccalaureate level which have been offered in the vocational–technical institutes and centers have not been Associate Degree programs but instead have provided certificates or diplomas. In these programs the emphasis has been on technical skills rather than general education. These differing outcomes have resulted in differing curricula. Regardless of these differences, there have been some commonalities in the curricula provided by these 2-year institutions.

B. Enrollment Trends

There have been no solid data on enrollments at the 2-year or Associate Degree level in agriculture. The data that are available indicate a decline in enrollment during the 1980s. The general impression is that enrollments have stabilized in the early 1990s. Very few of the students at this level have been enrolled in 2-year programs within 4-year universities. Only 4621 students were enrolled in the National Association of State Universities and Land Grant Colleges and the American Association of State Colleges of Agriculture and Renewable Resources colleges. The comparable enrollment 1 year earlier was 4442 students. The

vast majority of enrollments have been in community and technical colleges, including area vocational–technical institutes and centers. These institutions have not been involved in the reporting of statistics relating to their agricultural student enrollment.

C. Curriculum and Instruction

Curriculum and Instruction in 2-year postsecondary institutions may be characterized as more practical and applied than curriculum and instruction at the baccalaureate level. Industry advisory committees usually have provided strong input concerning curricula and program decisions; practice and "hands-on" instruction usually has been provided in laboratories and on internships in industry; and faculty usually have possessed strong industry experience, often at the expense of having had degrees at the doctoral level.

The 2-year and the 4-year curricula have been integrated in some states but maintained as separate entities in others. The articulation of 2-year and 4-year programs has been a continuing issue in many states, but some progress has been evident. The problem has been that 2-year programs have attempted to serve multiple purposes, involving preparation for immediate employment as well as preparation for further education. Persons making academic decisions in 4-year universities have sometimes been reluctant to accept credits from 2-year institutions because the purpose for and level of the instruction has been viewed as different than that offered at the baccalaureate level.

III. Education at the Baccalaureate Level

Undergraduate education in agriculture may be essential to any strategy of meeting the new forces in world competition and should be a key factor in harnessing inventive genius in the marketplace. Undergraduate education serves the multiple roles of preparing generally well-educated people, professionals who are general agriculturalists, professionals in specific disciplines within agriculture, and preparatory education for graduate education in agriculture and related disciplines.

A. Nature of Programs

Through a variety of programs, colleges of agriculture have been drawing on the wealth of their sciences to address the general issues facing society, contributing special expertise to other curricula in the university, and providing a general education to students in colleges other than colleges of agriculture.

B. Enrollment Trends

There were 12,762 baccalaureate degrees in agriculture awarded in 1970–1971, 23,748 in 1983–1984, and 17,030 in 1991–1992. The growth that has occurred has been mainly in majors linked with high technology, including disciplines such as agricultural and food engineering, biotechnology, agricultural economics, agribusiness, and environmental sciences.

A trend that probably will continue is the fact that more students choosing agricultural careers will come from suburban and urban backgrounds. Enrollment from these populations have been increasing at a much faster rate than enrollment from rural populations. The pool of rural youth who traditionally have gone into agriculture will not be sufficient to supply the work force needed.

During the past 10 years, U.S. college of agriculture and natural resources undergraduate enrollments fell by 9%. Since 1979, the annual number of U.S. high school graduates, who serve as the potential enrollees in colleges of agriculture, declined by more than 20%. However, the number of high school graduates is expected to increase by 20% in the next decade.

More than 55% of the total student enrollment growth in colleges of agriculture during 1987–1991 was in natural resources curricula, which accounted for only 17% of the undergraduate enrollment. This growth in natural resources curricula may be due to interest by students in the environment, safe food and water, land use planning, and other related concerns.

Byler reported findings from a study of undergraduate agricultural students in Tennessee universities: (1) female and minority enrollment was low, (2) declining numbers of students had agricultural background or experience, (3) parents heavily influenced students' choice of major, and (4) students needed current and accurate information about career opportunities in agriculture.

Christmas reported factors students considered important in their choice of an agricultural major in college: agricultural experiences, perceived opportunities in agriculture, interest in agriculture, involvement in the secondary agriculture program, and a feeling of usefulness. Parents were the most influential persons in the students' choice of a course of study.

Other influential factors included students' secondary programs and participation in 4-H clubs.

Decreasing student enrollment in seven California 4-year agricultural schools was reported by Thompson. He discussed the loss of student interest in relation to agriculture's negative image and the national agricultural economic crisis. Increased enrollment was noted in some agriculturally related fields.

C. Curriculum and Instruction

The curriculum should provide for the needs of industry in a changing world. Graduates with agricultural degrees should think globally, act creatively, value diversity, behave responsibly, respond flexibly, and interact cooperatively.

> In the food, agricultural, and natural resource sciences, curriculum revitalization is essential to the survival of higher education as we know it. Over the years, our curricula have undergone significant changes, from the pre-1970s emphasis on production agriculture to a strong business approach in the 1970s. This was followed by greater attention to the underlying sciences of agriculture in the 1980s. . . and in the 1990s, we find ourselves in a new wave of transformation that emphasizes the educated person and a broader and more philosophical approach to preparing people for life. In colleges of agriculture and natural resources, we are now giving greater attention to the global perspective: systems models, problem-solving techniques, environmental ethics, social issues, and the critical area of oral and written communications. (Hess, 1992, p. 21).

Zimmerman indicated that many college campuses are responding to the need to improve the communication and thinking skills of graduates by implementing a "writing-across-the-curriculum" program. This program is based on the concept that all teachers should both require students to use a variety of writing techniques and help teach writing. The program emphasizes writing as a process and puts it at the center of the curriculum.

Expected levels of learning for undergraduate students in agriculture were identified by Ellington and Hartung as follows:

1. *Scientific literacy*. Literate in the agricultural, physical, biological, and mathematical sciences
2. *Communications*. Competent in written communications, literate/competent in oral communications, literate in interpersonal communications, and aware/literate in graphic communications
3. *Appreciation and comprehension*. Literate in social and behavioral sciences and aware/literate in arts and humanities

4. *Lifelong skills*. Competent in problem solving and literate in reasoning and logic, leadership, management, synthesis, and information systems

5. *Economics and business principles*. Literate in economics and business principles.

6. *Appreciation of worldwide interdependence*. Literate in agriculture and aware/literate in society.

Goecker suggested 10 things which must be done by colleges of agriculture: (1) provide agricultural, food, and environmental literacy, (2) offer a more flexible undergraduate program, (3) mentor students more effectively, (4) focus on problem solving, (5) package instruction in creative ways, (6) achieve a more diverse student body, (7) update at least 10% of each course each year, (8) build new educational teams, (9) change the faculty incentive structure to give greater reward to effective teaching, and (10) take time to assess and reflect upon accomplishments.

A desired outcome for college of agriculture graduates is a broad understanding of the agricultural industry. Eleven areas of study identified in a study by Frick, Kahler, and Miller were agriculture's important relationship with the environment, the processing of agricultural products, public agricultural policies, agriculture's important relationship with natural resources, production of animal products, societal significance of agriculture, production of plant products, economic impact of agriculture, and marketing of agricultural products, the distribution of agricultural products, and the global significance of agriculture.

The principal international thrusts in undergraduate education today are foreign language studies, the inclusion of international content in courses, study abroad opportunities, and the implementation of area studies programs. However, progress in these areas has been inconsistent. Most institutions have not determined what the optimum level of international competence should be. While some institutions have provided opportunity for some students to study international issues in depth, the typical undergraduate in colleges of agriculture is given little to aid his or her understanding of the impact of trade, global environmental impacts, and the nature of international agricultural research.

Hertford and Hartley reported the development of 12 new international courses and cross-cultural simulations undertaken by Cook College, the agricultural and environmental unit of Rutgers, The State University of New Jersey. Reasons for international program activities were identified as program enrichment, the self-interest of the university, and humanitarianism.

IV. Education at the Graduate Level

Students who desire a career as an agricultural scientist or who wish to work at a professional level which requires a graduate degree may specialize within one or more of the agricultural disciplines. Graduate education has been provided by universities in the agricultural sciences at both the masters and doctoral levels.

Gelinas advocated that agricultural colleges should focus less on the undergraduate program and more on the graduate program. Emphasis on the graduate program would allow faculty members to specialize within their disciplines and keep the focus of agricultural colleges on agriculture. Others have argued that efforts to expand the breadth of undergraduate offerings has kept agricultural colleges relevant, and that graduate programs can only be built on a strong foundation of undergraduate studies.

A. Nature of Programs

Graduate majors are generally offered in specializations similar to those of the baccalaureate degree programs. Programs in most majors use professional support courses outside of agriculture to supplement and enhance the curriculum. Areas of professional support include the biological, physical, and mathematical sciences, economics, and education.

B. Enrollment Trends

Goecker has indicated that during the past 10 years, graduate student enrollments declined by 10%, but this finding has been somewhat difficult to interpret. Enrollments were low in the early 1970s and increased in the late 1970s and early 1980s before the more recent decline. The number of graduate degrees at the masters level awarded in 1970–1971 was 2457; in 1983–1984 the number awarded was 5478; and in 1991–1992 the number awarded was 4119. At the doctoral level the number awarded in 1970–1971 was 1086; in 1983–1984 the number awarded was 1981; and in 1991–1992 the number awarded was 1827. Graduate enrollment is expected to remain fairly stable over the next decade.

C. Curriculum and Instruction

Even though graduate programs have prepared students to meet the demand for agricultural scientists, some voices have been asking that programs be refocused in various ways. Goecker has suggested that doctoral degree programs be refocused to better prepare graduates for professions outside of academe. Hess has suggested that graduate students be prepared for their probable future role as faculty in colleges and universities.

> Graduate students' education in any discipline should not merely be a time to develop research skills and produce a dissertation. They should have the opportunity to teach and to learn the skills of instruction to ensure the perpetuation of effective instruction in colleges and universities. (p. 22)

Steele reported graduate student curriculum recommendations from a conference of foreign students as follows: the development of documentation to explain the role and activities of participant training contractors; creation of small research award programs to support early professional development in home countries; internationalization of United States universities' curricula in agriculture, incorporating relevance of agricultural education to home country situations; and the development of a central clearinghouse to provide relevant information and resources for international student advising.

Francis and Youngquist suggested that graduate students desiring a career in international agriculture plan for that eventuality as they structure their graduate programs. Technical competence, language capability, cultural sensitivity, awareness of gender roles, and broad knowledge of geography, history, political science, and economics were suggested as essential for a well-prepared scientist. It was indicated that young scientists abroad often have administrative and program organization challenges that would come much later in a domestic career.

V. Problems and Issues

Major problems and issues facing colleges of agriculture in the preparation of undergraduate and graduate students for agricultural careers related to preparation for college, student recruitment, cultural diversity, social/ethical responsibility, global educational context, educational delivery systems, and the balance of teaching, research, and service.

A. Preparation for College

Many states and universities have been prescribing a set college-preparatory curriculum for students who plan to matriculate in college. This curriculum has upgraded the preparation of students in foreign language, science, mathematics, and communication. However, it has made it more difficult for students to enroll in agricultural science or other agricultural education courses in high school and still meet the expectations of the college-preparatory curriculum. Agricultural science in high school has served effectively for many years as a means of encouraging students to maintain their interest in agriculture and enroll for advanced work in a college of agriculture.

Kunkel identified three aspects of precollege education in agriculture. First was the program of vocational agriculture, which has been in the process of being updated with an agricultural science emphasis. A related program is the 4-H clubs and youth programs of the Cooperative Extension Service. The second precollege preparation, one that may be receiving additional attention, has been the science programs in secondary schools. The third precollege preparation, which may be the most important in the long run, is the recent emphasis on the intregration of agriculture into the elementary school curriculum to provide agricultural literacy for all students. [See COOPERATIVE EXTENSION SERVICE; EDUCATION: CHILDREN AND YOUTH.]

Riesenberg and Lancaster found no difference between secondary agricultural program completers and noncompleters in high school grade point average, class rank, college entrance examination scores, college grade point average, and graduation rate. It was concluded that high school agricultural education graduates were well prepared for college and that agricultural credits should be accepted for admission to colleges.

Raven and Warmbrod reported that the vast majority of freshmen who completed 3 to 4 years of vocational agriculture indicated that vocational agriculture enrollment did not affect their ability to complete college preparatory requirements.

B. Student Recruitment

In the past decade undergraduate education in agriculture has experienced some stress. Fewer students have graduated from secondary schools nationally, and the decline in the number of students graduating has been most pronounced in rural areas, a traditional source of students entering colleges of agriculture. In addition, agricultural positions have been filled, not only by 2-year and 4-year graduates in agriculture, but also by people prepared in other disciplines and by people who hold a graduate degree. Some of this stress is expected to disappear due to a projected increase in the number of secondary school graduates in the next decade and a stronger employment market for students prepared in agricultural disciplines.

Efforts given to recruitment of minorities and women have proved to be successful. Current trends will need to continue. Between 1986 and 1992, enrollment of women increased by 11.9% at the baccalaureate level and by 14.4% at the graduate level. During the same time period, enrollment of minorities increased by 44.2% at the baccalaureate level and by 25.8% at the graduate level. [See WOMEN IN AGRICULTURE.]

The impressions from the media about the farm crises of recent years have not encouraged prospective students to consider careers in agriculture. However, there is expected to be a shortage of graduates to fill the number of positions available for employment.

A study was conducted at the University of Idaho by Lancaster and Riesenberg to assess the perceptions of students concerning agriculture and careers in agriculture. A large majority of the students perceived agriculture as concerned only with production and did not indicate they knew the breadth of the agricultural industry and associated careers. It was suggested that if university students enrolled in majors in colleges other than agriculture become the recruitment target population, colleges of agriculture will have some major information hurdles to overcome. Information would need to overcome negative or false perceptions of the image of agriculture and of agricultural careers.

There are at least three ways to enhance enrollments in colleges of agriculture. First, expand the range of course offerings, especially in those disciplines that are part of the agricultural system but that are pertinent to other elements of society, such as business management, personal enterprise, communications, engineering, and the biological, biomedical, and environmental sciences. Second, the student body should be expanded to include those other than the typical enrollees, including those at an age above the age of the usual undergraduate. Third, the attraction of minority students to colleges of agriculture must be enhanced. While the percentage increases in minority enrollment have been impressive, the proportion of minorities remains small compared to minority percentages in the population at large.

A 2-year agricultural technical institute reported nine activities used to increase enrollment: college night programs, direct mail, telemarketing, individualized campus visits, specialized print and video mate-rials, computerized student follow-up, special events, alumni network, and periodic evaluation and reviews.

Some agricultural colleges have attempted to build their 4-year undergraduate enrollment by recruiting transfer students from 2-year programs. Research has indicated that significant differences exist between students beginning their collegiate career at 2-year institutions and those initially enrolling at 4-year institutions. Two-year college transfer students generally have lower achievement test scores and quality point averages than students beginning college at 4-year institutions. In addition, research has indicated that once enrolled in a senior college, transfer students are less likely to complete a baccalaureate degree than are students who initially enroll at 4-year institutions. Finally, students transferring to 4-year institutions and earning a baccalaureate degree require a longer period of time to complete the degree requirements. Johnson, Taylor, and Kohler reported that, in a study of Mississippi State University agricultural students, those initially enrolling as freshmen, rather than as transfers, had a stronger academic record prior to attending the university. However, native and transfer students were equal in academic performance at Mississippi State University. Native students were more likely to persist and complete a degree than were transfer students.

Hoover and Houser reported a 5-week intensive program for academically outstanding high school sophomores and juniors who had demonstrated exceptional ability in the sciences or who had a high interest in some phase of agriculture. This Pennsylvania Governor's School for the Agricultural Sciences (PGSAS) involved over 300 students in a residential agricultural enrichment program at the University Park campus of the Pennsylvania State University. The PGSAS program appeared to reinforce students aspirations to pursue agricultural careers and slightly increase their knowledge base about agricultural careers. It was concluded that the program lacked efficiency as a way to inform all students about agricultural careers.

C. Cultural Diversity

Demographers predict that by the year 2000, women, minorities, and immigrants will account for 80% of the growth in the U.S. labor force. . . . The changing ethnic, racial, and social composition of the U.S. work force, coupled with the need for food, agricultural, and natural resource professionals to work with people from different lands and different cultures, requires that students and faculty become sensitive to the issues of cultural diversity. Closely linked to this is the importance of markedly increasing recruiting efforts, with scholarship support for ethnic and racial minorities needing financial assistance. (Hess in Board on Agriculture, p. 23)

Of the 17,030 baccalaureate degrees awarded in 1991–1992, 11,739 went to males and 5291 went to females; 905 went to minority students. The number of degrees at the graduate level in 1991–1992 awarded to males was 4225 and to females was 1721. There were 371 degrees awarded to minority students.

Hytche recommended that colleges of agriculture develop and implement early intervention programs, reaching minority students even before high school and continuing with them through college. The programs might include: special skill sessions, Saturday academy, motivational sessions, an adopt a high school program, research apprenticeships, summer scholars programs, summer internships, re-evaluation of entrance requirements, high-profile recruitment and marketing initiatives, creation of agricultural high schools, more relevant curricula, effective mentoring, financial assistance, liaison relationships, and post-baccalaureate programs.

Jaschik reported that the traditionally black land-grant colleges were being forced to reevaluate their missions, develop new student recruitment strategies, and forge new relationships with predominantly white colleges and state legislatures in an effort to survive and to serve their clientele.

D. Social/Ethical Responsibility

In recent years, agricultural and natural resources technology has been labeled as suspect by many in the media and the general populace. We are viewed by some as having little or no concern for the environment, health, safety, or conservation. It is imperative that we change these negative perceptions by providing students at our colleges and universities with ethical decision-making tools for addressing those issues. We must ensure that our graduates, many of whom will become scientists and leaders, acquire an appropriate sensitivity and perspective. (Hess in Board on Agriculture, 1992, p. 23) [*See* ETHICS.]

E. Global Educational Context

The world economy is becoming ever more closely linked, and agriculture in the United States of America, which already is a significant player in world

markets, will continue to feed and educate a developing, expanding, and needy world population. The challenge to agricultural educators in the United States is how to prepare students for future competition in the global economy brought about by complex changes in the global agricultural system. McCracken and Magisos recommended that a well-educated student should have an understanding of (1) geographical, political, and economic factors influencing agriculture, (2) agricultural production and consumption areas of the world, (3) trends in the production and consumption of food and fiber, (4) agricultural practices in different countries, (5) agricultural trade and banking practices, (6) communications, transportation, and other technological development influencing agriculture, and (7) cultural and religious differences with implications for agriculture.

F. Distance Education

The Agricultural Satellite Corporation (AG*SAT) was formed by 27 land-grant universities in October of 1989. Shared programs among the universities began in the fall of 1990. Since that time more than 120 extension programs and 13 college credit courses have been shared nationally (*Downlink,* 1992). In 1992 AG*SAT included 40 land-grant universities and two government agencies joined to share agricultural education programming via satellite and other technologies. AG*SAT provided the mechanism for interstate programming and distance education in agriculture. In the future, video and audio telephone communication is expected to surpass satellite communication as a viable technology for distance education.

Distance education is expected to increase access to unique educational programming, unique educational resources, and cutting edge research and other developments in a timely fashion. It should maximize optimal use of available resources among participating institutions by providing an economy of scale and sharing faculty and staff resources. Distance education via AG*SAT has provided for cooperative funding, national and international visibility, and extension of centers of excellence. The future of the AG*SAT system will require administrative support, faculty development and support, learner support, technical support and equipment, course development, and funding. Even though this type of instruction limits personal interaction between teachers and their students and restricts the ability of instructors to provide relevant local examples relating to instructional content, Goecker believes it is likely that significantly more courses will be shared by several universities in the future to utilize the available faculty resources more effectively.

G. Balance of Teaching, Research, and Service

Relevant curricula, a good learning environment, excellent student advising, and faculty interest in teaching are required to attract the brightest and best undergraduate students from both urban and rural communities. The major problem is how to reward faculty interest as the key resource for preparing broadly educated undergraduates with sufficient professional competence. There has been a shortage of rigorous generalists compared to specialists among the faculty. The current reward system and the competition of research may be working against achieving an appropriate balance of mission and discipline-oriented research, teaching, and extension programs. Teaching and extension have been moving toward a broader, more comprehensive approach for agriculture; however, researchers in agriculture have been moving toward a more narrow and specialized view of agriculture.

Lichtenberg wrote that faculty mentors and department heads have been reported to counsel against spending time on textbook authorship, portraying it as something of "no academic value" that may even work against success in promotion and tenure. These attitudes, which favor the creation of specialized new knowledge that benefits other specialists over the synthesis of a discipline for a larger audience of learners, has become a factor in higher education's "teaching versus research" debate. The low regard for textbook authorship is seen as further evidence of the devaluing of teaching itself.

Colleges of agriculture have a reputation for placing more value on teaching than other colleges within major universities; however, even within agricultural disciplines the trend has been toward valuing research above teaching. Newcomb, however, argued that universities are giving renewed emphasis to the teaching function because of public pressure for increased attention to the education of undergraduates and the need to treat students as consumers. [See AGRICULTURAL EXPERIMENT STATIONS.]

VI. Conclusion

Educators in higher education in agriculture will need to respond to the major changes in the societal setting, such as the significant decrease in the number of farms and farmers, the migration of rural American to the cities, the highly visible public concerns for the nutritive value of food, and the quality of the environment. If the colleges whose roots are in agriculture are able to bring about structural, organizational, and programmatic changes to meet the concerns that are likely to become critical in the future, they will continue to have an essential role in educating undergraduate and graduate students as professionals and scholars influencing the future of food, fibre, and renewable natural resources in the United States.

Bibliography

Agricultural Strategic Planning Task Force (1992). "Phase I Report" Unpublished working paper. The Ohio State University, Ohio Cooperative Extension Service, Futuring Panel, Columbus.

Board on Agriculture, National Research Council (1992). "Agriculture and the Undergraduate, Proceedings." National Academy Press, Washington, DC.

Byler, B. L. (1987). "A Study of Undergraduate Students Enrolled in Agriculture Majors at Tennessee Universities." ERIC Document Reproduction Service #ED287006.

Christmas, O. L. (1989). "Why Enroll? Student Enrollment Strategy in the College of Agriculture and Home Economics." ERIC Document Reproduction Service #ED314608.

Committee on Agricultural Education in Secondary Schools. (1988). "Understanding Agriculture: New Directions for Education." National Academy Press, Washington, DC.

Downlink (1992, November). Downlink: The Agricultural Satellite Corporation Newsletter 1(2), 1–3.

Food and Agricultural Education Information System (1993). "1992 Degrees Awarded and Placement for Agriculture and Natural Resources." Texas A&M University, Mailstop 2124, College Station.

Food and Agricultural Education Information System (1992). "Fall 1991 Enrollment in Agriculture and Natural Resources." Texas A&M University, Mailstop 2124, College Station.

Food and Agricultural Education Information System (1993). "Fall 1992 Enrollment in Agriculture and Natural Resources." Texas A&M University, Mailstop 2124, College Station.

Francis, C. A., and Youngquist, J. B. (1991). Developing a career in global agriculture. NACTA J. 35(2), 33–37.

Frick, M. J., Kahler, A. A., and Miller, W. W. (1992). Agricultural literacy: Providing a framework for agricultural curriculum. NACTA J. 36(1), 34–37.

Gelinas, D. A. (1988). To survive, agricultural colleges may need to abandon their undergradutae programs, Chron. Higher Education 34(31), 56.

Goecker, A. D. (1992). Undergraduate preparation for agricultural, food and environmental science careers. *NACTA J.* **36**(3), 9–12.

Hertford, R., and Hartley, M. P. (1987). "Strengthening International Agricultural and Environmental Programs: Four Key Ingredients. "Paper presented at the Annual Conference of the Association for International Agricultural Education, Chevy Chase, MD.

Hoover, T. S., and Houser, M. L. (1991). Participant perceptions about agricultural careers. *NACTA J.* **35**(2), 14–18.

Jaschik, S. (1987). For the nation's 17 Black land-grant colleges, unique difficulties and new strategies, *Chron. Higher Education* **34**(9), 31–32.

Johnson, D. M., Taylor, W. N., and Kohler, E. T. (1991). A comparison: Native and transfer students, *NACTA J.* **35**(2), 41–44.

Kreps, G. M. (1991). Implementing a successful enrollment program in a two-year agricultural college. *NACTA J.* **35**(2), 30–33.

Lancaster, L. L., and Riesenberg, L. E. (1992). University of Idaho students' perceptions of agriculture and careers in agriculture, *NACTA J.* **36**(1), 53–57.

Lichtenberg, J. (1992). Rigor, partisanship, and multiculturalism; destain for writing college textbooks; laughter in the the theater. *Chron. Higher Education* **39**(11), B2.

Litzenberg, K. K., Whatley, S. S., and Scamardo, J. (1992). 1991 U.S. enrollment for agriculture and renewable natural resources. *NACTA J.* **36**(2), 4–7.

McCracken, J. D., and Magisos, J. H. (1989). Integrating international concepts into the curriculum. *Agricult. Education Magazine* **61**(10), 9–11.

Meyer, J. H. (1992). "Rethinking the Outlook of Colleges Whose Roots Have Been in Agriculture." University of California, Chancellor Emeritus Office, Davis.

Newcomb, L. H. (1991). Restoration of teaching emphasis in the university. *In* "Strategies for Teaching and Learning, Proceedings, North Central Regional Teaching Symposium" (F. H. Buelow, ed.), pp. 72–81. The University of Wisconsin, Madison.

North Central Region RICOP Committee (1987). "National Curriculum Revitalization—2005 Conference, Proceedings." U.S. Department of Agriculture, Cooperative State Research Service, Washington, DC.

Raven, M. R., and Warmbrod, J. R. (1990). Influence of enrollment in vocational agriculture on admission to a college of agriculture. *J. Agricult. Education* **31**(4), 15–21.

Riesenberg, L. E., and Lancaster, L. L. (1990). High school agriculture program completers and their success in college. *J. Agricult. Education* **31**(4), 27–31.

Sledge, G., Gibson, C., Gibson, T., and Meadowcroft, J. (1992). "AG*SAT: Potentials and Processes, Items for Consideration." Unpublished working paper. University of Wisconsin, Madison.

Steele, R. (1990). "Winrock/NAFSA Workshop on Improving Academic programs in agriculture for students from developing Countries, NAFSA Working Paper #19." ERIC Document Reproduction Service #ED331367.

Thompson, O. E. (1989). The crisis in agricultural education. *California Agriculture* **43**(1), 25–27.

Zimmerman, A. P. (1991). Journal writing for technical courses in writing-across-the-curriculum. *NACTA J.* **35**(2), 24–29.

Egg Production, Processing, and Products

WILLIAM J. STADELMAN, *Purdue University*

Glossary

Albumen White of the egg
Albumin One of the principal proteins of albumen
Blood spot Bright red drop of blood usually on the yolk surface or in the chalaza
Cages Confinement areas for one or more hens
Chalaza Layer of albumen closest to the yolk and mucin fibers extending from it to the other albumen layers
Crack Shell is broken with the shell membranes still intact
Dub Remove tips of points on single comb birds to prevent freezing in cold climates
Egg products Liquid, frozen, or dried whole egg, yolk or albumen
Pullets Immature female chickens
Leaker Shell and shell membranes are broken so the liquid contents of the egg are exposed or leaking from the opening
Meat spot Inclusion of mucous tissue from the oviduct or a denatured blood clot
Shell eggs Eggs in the shells
Yolk Yellow portion of the egg

Eggs are the female gamete in reproduction. As used in this discussion eggs of chickens (*Gallus domesticus*) will be considered. In some cultures eggs of other species are eaten including eggs from ducks, guinea, quail, goose, and turkey hens. Production, processing, and products of eggs from these species may vary significantly from material presented for chicken eggs.

I. The Egg Industry

Eggs are eaten throughout the world. Therefore, an egg industry is present in all countries. China has the largest industry with a reported production of over 158 thousand million eggs in 1990. By comparison, production in the United States was almost 68 thousand million and United Kingdom was only 12 thousand million. In 1990 over 550,000 thousand million eggs were produced in countries with production records. This amounts to an average of about 100 eggs per person.

Production practices vary widely from the large units with over a million laying hens on each farm as found in the United States and some other countries to small flocks of only a few hens. With the layer commercial units hens are usually kept in cages. For the small flocks, floor pens and outside runways are often used. The breeds and strains of chickens grown vary with areas of the world. In most countries, Leghorn type hens are used. These hens produce white-shelled eggs. Depending on environment, management, and feeding practices, these hens will produce over 270 eggs each per year. In parts of the world brown-shelled eggs are preferred, so breeds of hens that produce brown eggs are utilized.

The industry is divided into primary breeders, multiplying breeders, hatcheries, feed manufacturers, pullet growers, commercial laying flocks, and egg marketing groups. With some organizations, several of these divisions are under a single manager. The marketing groups may be limited to shell egg handling but can include conversion of eggs into a number of products.

The success of the egg industry is dependent on a number of segments each working to do its part in having a healthy hen kept in an environment that is least stressful so that the hen can perform to most nearly maximize her genetic potential for egg production of high-quality eggs. [*See* POULTRY PROCESSING AND PRODUCTS; POULTRY PRODUCTION.]

A. Breeders

While the total number of hens kept for egg production has increased significantly during the last half-century, the number of breeders has decreased. The modern breeder must keep a number of pure lines each selected for one or more desirable characteristic. These birds are the great grandparents of commercial layers. These pure lines must be maintained and these are crossed to find combinations which will impart as many of the desired characteristics as possible. These crosses make up the grandparent stock from which relatively large numbers of parent stock can be produced. The parent stock is distributed to multiplier breeders to produce the chicks that will make up the laying flock.

Breeders have been successful in achieving small improvements in livability, feed conversion, egg production, egg quality factors, and temperament of the hens so that during the last 50 years average egg production has increased about 100 eggs per hen. The percentage of marketable eggs of all eggs laid has also increased because of improvements in egg shell quality and reduction in numbers of eggs with inclusions such as blood spots or meat spots. With this, the feed required to produce a dozen eggs has been reduced from about 4.5 to 3.5 pounds.

B. Hatcheries

Most hatcheries are operated by the multiplier breeder. The hatchery receives fertile eggs from the breeders and incubates them for 21 days to produce a chick. Improvements in hatchery management during the last 50 years have resulted in the hatchery being able to get a quality chick from most of the fertile eggs. Hatchery personnel then segregate the chicks into male and female group by either the Japanese method of cloaca examination or the most used method of examining development of primary flight feathers on the wing of the day-old chick. Breeders have developed strains of birds in which there is an easily discernable difference in feather development between the sexes. The hatchery also vaccinates, clips toe, clips beak, and dub comb if the customer desires these services.

C. Pullet Growers

The objective of the pullet grower is to convert the day-old female chick into a healthy pullet at an age of about 18 weeks so that it can be sold to the egg producer. A good pullet grower will be able to market over 95% of all chicks purchased. In addition to caring for the feed, water, heat, and other necessities of the chicks, the pullet grower will vaccinate the birds and trim beaks as needed during the growing period. The major costs of pullet production are feed, chick, and labor. Housing and medications costs can also be significant factors. No program of reducing growing costs should impair the quality of the mature bird. The productivity of the hen in the house or cage is due in great part to the quality of the pullet at the time she reaches sexual maturity.

Pullet growers adapt their operations to meet the needs of their customers, the egg producers. For this reason there are four combinations of brooding–growing management with respect to type of floor. These are:

1. Wire brooding (to 6 weeks), litter growing.
2. Litter brooding (to 6 weeks), wire growing.
3. Two house, wire brooding and growing.
4. Brooding-growing continuous cage.

Pullets to be kept in cages are usually grown on litter.

D. Supporting Industries

For all segments of the egg industry there are supporting industries. Two of the more important ones are the feed manufacturers and the equipment suppliers.

The feed manufacturers formulate feeds to meet the specific needs of the birds being fed. The nutritive requirements of the chicken at all stages of life are well known. Feed mill operators produce special feeds for starting the chicks, for development of the pullets, and for the hens in the laying house with variations depending on the age of the hens and even the temperature. They also produce feed especially for the breeder hens. Generally the protein requirement of the chick is higher than for older chickens. For laying hens the calcium content is of great importance. For breeder hen feeds it is essential that there is adequate vitamins, especially B_{12}, to support good hatchability of all fertile eggs. [*See* ANIMAL NUTRITION, NONRUMINANT; FEEDS AND FEEDING.]

The equipment suppliers have designed special equipment for handling the feeding and watering needs of birds of all ages. They have also mechanized many of the operations in management so that one person frequently cares for all needs of 100,000 laying hens and even more chicks or growing pullets. This group has also developed housing so that complete environment control is possible. There are also a number of other possible applications with a lesser degree of environmental control such as fans, lights, and evaporative coolers.

II. Egg Production

Laying hens have been increasing annual production rates at a rather steady pace over the last 50 years from an average of about 150 eggs to about 250 eggs per hen per year in the United States. The increase in productivity has been the result of improvements in breeding and selection, nutrition, housing, and management. In many developing countries the rates of lay are still near the low end of this scale.

The management of layers involves maintaining the environment in the house so as to minimize any stress on the hens from lack of fresh air, heat or cold, or availability of feed and water. Space requirements for layers vary with the strain of bird being used for egg production and housing arrangement. The trend has been toward housing commercial layers in cages, but there is still a good percentage of commercial layers kept on a floor of litter, slats, or wire. This is particularly true in the lesser-developed countries.

A. Cage Operations

Over 90% of all layers in the United States are kept in cages. The dimensions of the cages vary depending on numbers of hens per cage. When cages were first used, almost all were single bird units. In more recent times, the multiple hen cages have become more popular. Each cage has a sloped floor so that eggs laid will roll, usually to the front of the cage, onto an egg collection system. Each cage has adequate water and feeder space to allow hens room to eat and drink sufficient for maximum egg production.

Cages are generally arranged in tiers so as to maximize hen density per unit of floor space. The cages are frequently offset so that droppings from top tiers fall into deep pits below the floor level of the building. Other cages are built with belts between tiers for removal of droppings on a regular basis.

Ventilation in these houses is maintained by high-volume fans. Air movement is directed to keep fresh air for the hens and to dry manure in the deep pit houses. Temperature is maintained at near optimal,

about 21°C, by the use of evaporative coolers during hot weather and regulated ventilation during cold weather periods.

B. Floor and Range Operations

There are still a few floor pen operations used in egg production. For breeding flocks to produce eggs for replacement pullets, floor pens are the usual operation. Many of these houses will have feeders, waterers, and roosts over dropping pits with about 30% of the total floor space devoted to litter. Depending on location geographically, the litter may be straw, wood shavings, bagasse, peanut hulls, rice hulls, or other similar materials that are locally available.

Floor pens with range area are still used in many areas for growing replacement pullets to about 18 to 20 weeks of age when they are moved to cages or layer house floor pens. When range areas are used they should be well drained soil to eliminate muddy spots around waterers. If such birds are moved to cages the move should be made at 16 to 17 weeks of age to allow the pullets to adapt to wire floors before onset of egg production.

There is a niche market for eggs from hens kept in floor pens with outside range areas. The size of this market in different localities varies widely. Some persons believe such eggs are more nutritious and others buy them as they believe the hens are treated more humanely. In Switzerland keeping of hens in cages has been banned. The cost of producing eggs in floor pens is greater than in cages.

C. Layer Nutrition

Poultry nutrition has been extensively researched so the nutritive requirement of laying hens is well known. The degree of sophistication is such that different strains of laying hens have feeds formulated to meet their specific requirements. The basic requirements are for protein, carbohydrates, fats, vitamins, and minerals. The protein requirement is met by including soybean meal, corn gluten meal, meat and bone meal, low-fat fish meal, and other protein rich ingredients. Carbohydrates are supplied by cereal grains most readily available in the locality. The fat content of laying rations is usually limited to the oils in the cereal grains. For some niche markets, low levels of omega-3-rich fish oils are included in the laying hens diet to produce omega-3 enriched eggs. In all laying hen rations a significant amount of minerals is needed, especially calcium to meet the needs of

TABLE I

Breeder—Layer Rations

	Phase 1[a]: 5% production 36 weeks	Phase 2[b]: 36 to 52 weeks	Phase 3: 52 weeks to end of cycle
	----Percentage----		
Ingredient			
Ground yellow corn	69.75	70.20	70.50
Soybean meal (48%)	15.00	14.05	13.70
Corn gluten meal (60%)	3.00	2.80	2.25
Meat and bone meal (50%)	2.50	2.50	2.50
Limestone[c]	7.50	8.50	9.40
Dicalcium phosphate	1.20	0.95	0.65
Salt	0.35	0.35	0.35
Vitamin mix (Table II)	0.50	0.50	0.50
Trace mineral mix (Table III)	0.10	0.10	0.10
Methionine, DI	0.10	0.05	0.05
	100.00	100.00	100.00
Calculated analysis			
Metab. energy (kcal/kg)	2915	2915	2893
Protein (pct.)	16	15.5	15
Fat (pct.)	3	3.1	3.2
Fiber (pct.)	2.5	2.5	2.4
Calcium (pct.)	3.4	3.7	4
Available phosphorus (pct.)	0.45	0.4	0.35
Total phosphorus (pct.)	0.64	0.58	0.53
Ash (pct.)	11.8	13.4	13.1

[a] Do not go to Phase 2 while egg production exceeds 85%.
[b] Do not go to Phase 3 while egg production exceeds 80%.
[c] A course or granulated limestone or oyster shell is recommended for amounts in excess of 100 lbs (45.3 kg).

the hen in forming egg shells. The rations are also supplemented with premixes containing vitamins and trace minerals. An example of layer rations fed at various stages of production is given in Table I. Frequently for layers, not breeders, the meat and bone meal will be omitted. Table II gives the vitamin mix

and Table III the trace mineral mix indicated in Table I. The rations shown in Table I were developed for farms in a corn and soybean production area. The principle sources of carbohydrates and proteins will vary with locality based on ingredient costs.

An important consideration in layer feed formulation is the availability of nutrients from different ingredients. Methionine is included in the formulations listed in Table I as it is the limiting amino acid in soybean meal.

Often, with very small flocks allowed an outside range area, a much less complete diet is supplied in

TABLE II

The Vitamin Mix

Vitamin	Amount per pound of mix	Amount per kilogram of mix
Vitamin A	900,000 IU	1,980,000 IU
Vitamin D₃	150,000 ICU	330,000 ICU
Vitamin E	750 IU	1,650 IU
Choline	50,000 mg	110,000 mg
Niacin	3,000 mg	6,600 mg
Pantothenic acid	750 mg	1650 mg
Riboflavin	400 mg	880 mg
Thiamine	200 mg	440 mg
Vitamin K (msb)[a]	200 mg	440 mg
Folic acid	40 mg	88 mg
Biotin	10 mg	22 mg
Vitamin B₁₂	800 mcg	1,760 mcg

[a] Menadione sodium bisulfite.

TABLE III

The Trace Mineral Mix

Mineral	Percentage per pound of mix	Amount per kilogram of mix
Manganese	28.48 mg	62.66 mg
Zinc	28.48 mg	62.66 mg
Iron	13.64 mg	30.00 mg
Copper	1.36 mg	3.00 mg
Iodine	0.262 mg	0.58 mg
Selenium	0.045 mg	0.099 mg

the feed. Such hens obtain a number of nutrients from insects, green plants, and the soil.

D. Egg Composition

The fresh shell egg and the components albumen and yolk have composition as shown in Table IV. The proteins of the egg have all of the essential amino acids needed by humans in almost perfect alignment with requirements. For this reason egg proteins are often used as the reference standard against which other proteins are evaluated.

The extremely low level of lipid material in the albumen makes egg albumen a valuable protein source for special diet formulation. There are 12 separate proteins in egg albumen with ovalbumin being the predominant one. Several of the proteins are effective in inhibiting bacterial growth. Lysozyme actually digests the cell wall of microorganisms. Ovotransferrin chelates multivalent metallic ions making them unavailable for bacterial use. Avidin binds biotin so this vitamin is not available for bacterial growth. Ovoflavoprotein binds riboflavin so it, also is not available. Upon cooking all of the binding of these nutrients is destroyed so the cooked egg furnishes the minerals and vitamins for nutritional needs.

The yolk consists of about one-third lipid material. There are natural antioxidants in the yolk to keep the polyunsaturated fatty acids present from becoming rancid due to oxidation. The fatty acid composition of the yolk lipids can be changed significantly by modifying the fatty acids in the hen's diet. Vitamin and mineral content of the egg can be modified by raising or lowering the content of the nutrient in the hen's diet.

Color of the egg yolk in determined by the level of caratenoid pigments in the feed. It is possible to produce eggs with a variety of colors by feeding hens feeds with nontoxic fat-soluble dyes.

III. Egg Processing

The consumers of eggs expect to purchase eggs free of defects, clean, and packaged to protect the egg from damage. To market such eggs it is necessary to put each shell egg through several operations. For liquid egg products shell eggs must have all shell and shell membranes removed. The edible contents are then given various treatments to assure the user a wholesome product.

A. Shell Eggs

Eggs as produced by a flock of hens vary in size, shape, shell quality, interior quality, and freedom from defects. Commercial egg farms in the United States produce over 90% of all eggs. These are flocks of 30,000 hens or more.

The first operation is the gathering of eggs. In most cage operations there is an egg gathering belt in front of the cages arranged so the eggs shortly after production will roll onto the belt. At intervals the belt is activated to move eggs to a central gathering station. A typical egg production facility is located in close proximity to the egg processing areas so that egg gathering and transport to the processing area is all on conveying belts. Such a production facility is called an "in-line" operation. In other facilities eggs are conveyed to a packing area where eggs are placed on filler flats to be taken to a remote egg processing plant. These units are referred to as "off-line."

In those few units without mechanical egg-gathering equipment egg collections is a hand operation. Usually eggs are gathered and placed on filler flats but in some instances wire baskets are used. These are usually found only in relatively small egg production facilities.

1. Cleaning Shell Eggs

Eggs coming from a production facility are usually clean but some few eggs will have wire marks from cage floors, adhering dirt, or, if an egg is broken in the cage or on the collection system, egg yolk on the shells. In most countries of the world these egg shells are cleansed by washing. In those few countries where washing is banned by regulations, eggs are cleaned by using dry abrasive techniques. The rationale for

TABLE IV

Composition of Liquid Whole Egg, Albumen, and Yolk

Egg Component	% Water	% Protein	% Lipid	% Carbohydrate	% Ash
Whole egg	74.5	12.8–13.4	10.5–11.8	0.3–1.0	0.8–1.0
Albumen	88.5	9.7–10.6	0.03	0.4–0.9	0.5–0.6
Yolk	49.0	15.7–16.6	31.8–35.5	0.2–1.0	1.1

banning washing is the dry shells are less likely to aid bacterial invasion of the egg contents.

In the United States almost all eggs are washed using detergents, and antibacterial agents such as chlorine or iodine compounds are used to sanitize the eggs. With the use of proper procedures washing of eggs results in eggs with smaller bacterial populations than dry cleaning. The wash water should always be at least 10°C warmer than the eggs with a minimum water temperature of 40°C. All eggs should be dried in warm air as soon as possible after washing.

2. Grading Shell Eggs

Grading of eggs is accomplished by a process called candling. This consists of passing the egg in front of a bright light so as to illuminate the interior as well as the surface of the egg. In this way the condition of the shell, the albumen, and the yolk can be determined. Equipment manufacturers have developed handling equipment so that one person is able to grade eggs at rates up to 250 cases per hour with each case holding 30 dozen eggs.

Grade standards for eggs have been established in most countries. The standards are based on shell cleanliness, shape, smoothness, and freedom from defects such as calcium nodules and cracks. Also considered are interior quality including viscousness of the albumen, yolk mobility, yolk color, and freedom from defects such as mottled yolks, blood, or meat spots. The terminology for different grades may differ in various countries and emphasis placed on the various external and internal quality characteristics will vary but two or more grades of eggs are usually found.

In the United States consumer grades of eggs are AA, A, and B. For AA quality the shell must be clean, unbroken, and practically normal. The air cell must not exceed $\frac{1}{8}$ in. (3.175 mm) in depth, may show unlimited movement, and may be free or bubbly. The white must be clear and firm so that the yolk is only slightly defined when the egg is twirled before the candling light. The yolk must be practically free from apparent defects.

For A quality, the shell must be clean, unbroken, and practically normal. The air cell must not exceed $\frac{3}{16}$ in. (4.76 mm) in depth, may show unlimited movement, and may be free or bubbly. The white must be clear and at least reasonably firm so that the yolk outline is only fairly well defined when the egg is twirled before the candling light. The yolk must be practically free from apparent defects.

For B quality, the shell must be unbroken, may be abnormal, and may have slightly stained areas. Moderately stained areas are permitted if they do not cover more than $\frac{1}{32}$ of the shell surface if localized, or $\frac{1}{16}$ of the shell surface if scattered. Eggs having shells with prominent stains or adhering dirt are not permitted. The air cell may be over $\frac{3}{16}$ in. (4.76 mm) in depth, may show unlimited movement, and may be free or bubbly. The white may be weak and watery, so that the yolk outline is plainly visible when the egg is twirled before the candling light. The yolk may appear dark, enlarged, and flattened, and may show clearly visible germ development but no blood due to such development. It may show other serious defects that do not render the egg inedible. Small blood spots or meat spots (aggregating not more than $\frac{1}{8}$ in. (3.175 mm in diameter) may be present.

Grading of eggs is done by visually checking each egg. The egg is rotated in front of an intense light so that internal as well as external quality factors can be evaluated. In modern egg grading rooms mechanical equipment is utilized so a person can effectively grade up to 72,000 eggs per hour. Such equipment uses computers and electronics to assist the visual grading of eggs. A summary of grading standards used in the United States is given in Table V.

3. Egg Sizing

Sizing of eggs is a mechanical operation in a modern shell egg processing facility. The eggs are generally moved over a series of scales set so that the largest eggs are removed first on through the several sizes to the smallest. The size categories used in United States market channels for consumer grades of eggs are given in Table VI. Terminology used in the trade in describing weights of eggs is in ounces per dozen. Grams per average egg are included. Weight tolerances are allowed as eggs lose weights over item in storage or in market channels. Sizing of eggs so that there is uniformity in a package aids in packaging. The package has better appearance and can be designed to give greater protection to the eggs.

4. Packaging Shell Eggs

The standard 30 dozen egg case is used in the United States. For domestic trading fiber board cases are generally used. There is some handling of eggs in dozen-cartons packed in plastic or wire frames holding 15 dozen. The carton used for egg distribution is usually a 2 × 6 design. There is still some usage of 3 × 4 cartons but these are limited to small operations where eggs are hand packed.

TABLE V

Summary of U.S. Standards for Quality of Individual Shell Eggs: Specifications for Each Quality Factor

Quality factor	AA Quality	A Quality	B Quality
Shell	Clean, practically normal	Clean, practically normal	Clean to slightly stained[a] Unbroken, abnormal
Air cell	$\frac{1}{8}$ in. or less in depth Unlimited movement and free or bubbly	$\frac{3}{16}$ in. or less in depth Unlimited movement and free or bubbly	Over $\frac{3}{16}$ in depth Unlimited movement and free or bubbly
White	Clear, firm	Clear, reasonably firm	Small blood and meat spots present[b]
Yolk	Outline, slightly defined; practically free from defects	Outline, fairly well defined; practically free from defects	Outline, plainly visible Enlarged and flattened Clearly visible germ development but no blood Other serious defects

[a] Moderately stained areas permitted ($\frac{1}{32}$ of surface, if localized, or $\frac{1}{16}$, if scattered).

[b] If they are small (aggregating not more than $\frac{1}{8}$ inch in diameter).

Note. For eggs with dirty or broken shells, the standards of quality provide two additional qualities. These are:

Dirty	Check
Unbroken. Adhering dirt or foreign material, prominent strains, strains, moderate stained areas in excess of B quality	Broken or cracked shell, but membranes intact, not leaking[c]

[c] Leaker has broken or cracked shell and membranes, and contents leaking or free to leak.

The 2 × 6 carton varies in size with a oversized carton for jumbo sized eggs, the standard carton for large and extra-large sizes, and a reduced size carton for the smaller sized eggs. When only a few medium sized eggs are being produced, these eggs are frequently packed in the standard size of carton. When pullets first start laying eggs, sizes are in the smaller size bracket. With most commercial egg producing strains of hens the egg size increases quickly so that a few weeks after production commences most eggs produced are large size. The size of eggs then increases slowly so that after months of production extra-large eggs may be the normal size.

Eggs after sizing are usually mechanically packed into dozen carton for retail sales. For some markets eggs per carton may be varied. An 18 egg carton is quite popular. In European markets carton sizes vary from 2 eggs to 10 eggs in most countries. For commercial trade eggs are packaged in 30-egg filler-flats or trays and then into either half-case, 15 dozen, or case, 30 dozen, fiber-board cases. Wooden cases are frequently used for export trading of eggs.

The interior quality of the egg is at its maximum at the time of production. From that point on the quality will deteriorate. The rate of quality loss is affected by the temperature of the egg, humidity of

TABLE VI

Minimum Weights of Eggs in Consumer Grades Sold in the United States

Size category	Ounce/dozen	Grams/egg	Pounds/30 dozen case
Jumbo	30	70.9	56.25
Extra large	27	63.8	50.63
Large	24	56.7	45.00
Medium	21	49.6	39.52
Small	18	42.5	33.75
Peewee	15	35.4	28.13

the atmosphere, shell texture of the egg, and handling conditions. As the solids content of the yolk is over 50% and the albumen is only about 13% at the time of lay, there is a great osmotic pressure difference across the vitelline membrane surrounding the yolk. Due to the pressure difference there is a slow migration of water from the albumen to the yolk. This water distends the yolk membrane so that it breaks more easily in an old egg. The shell contains a large number of pores of various size as respiration of the embryo during incubation requires available oxygen. In infertile eggs these pores allow the passage of gases including water vapor so that as the egg ages the total liquid content of the egg decreases resulting in an enlarged air cell. Handling conditions affect egg quality in two ways. Rough handling will usually result in some cracked shells and in extreme conditions even broken shell membranes. With less rough handling the shells may remain intact but the structure of the albumen is disrupted so that when broken on a flat surface the white runs covering a considerable area. A high-quality egg should have a high percentage of thick albumen which remains around the yolk when the egg is broken on a flat surface.

In order to minimize rate of interior quality loss as well as moisture loss with a resultant increase in air cell size eggs are frequently sprayed with a light coating of edible mineral oil just prior to carton closing. After packaging all eggs should be handled at temperatures of 45°F (7°C) or less to maintain internal quality and retard growth rate of most microorganisms.

B. Liquid Egg

All eggs are washed and sanitized and excess water is blown from the shell surfaces. The eggs are then candled prior to breaking of the eggs to remove dirty eggs or eggs with interior defects.

1. Breaking

Equipment is available that is capable of breaking and separating shells, albumen, and yolks at rates in excess of 75,000 eggs per hour. Individual eggs are picked up by grips holding the egg so the long axis is parallel to the direction in which the equipment is arranged. The grips are attached to a moving chain which is moving synchronously with a series of small cups moving on a chain below the grips. The egg is broken with the yolk dropping on a small cup. The albumen drains from the yolk giving a separation of the two distinct edible portions. The shells are dropped onto a belt or into an auger system for re-

moval from the breaking unit. In this way the liquid products of albumen, yolk, and whole egg can be produced. The processing of each of these is somewhat different.

2. Pasteurization

For albumen, the product is pumped through a strainer to remove bits of shell and heavy chalaza. This process also helps to mix thick and thin white portions of the albumen. The next step in processing is pasteurization. This is accomplished by passing the albumen through a heat exchanger and into holding tubes. Albumen is heated to 134° to 138°F, (57° to 59°C). This temperature is maintained for at least 3.5 min. The exact temperature used varies with pH of the albumen. Older eggs, with higher pH albumen, can be pasteurized at lower temperatures. Immediately following pasteurization the albumen is cooled to about 40°F (4.5°C).

As the pasteurization temperatures are sufficient to cause coagulation of some proteins of the albumen, processes to reduce the denaturation have been developed. Most proteins of the albumen are most heat stable at near neutral pH. However, conalbumin is most labile. The conalbumin can be stabilized by adding aluminum sulfate and lactic acid to the product prior to pasteurization. The stabilized albumen can be pasteurized with temperatures of 140°F (60°C) for 3.5 min with minimal heat damage.

Following pasteurization and cooling the albumen may be homogenized. This is an optional procedure. The liquid is then packaged and frozen or shipped in refrigerated transport.

For egg yolks the processing steps are similar but conditions are changed. The strainer for yolks assures that all vitelline membranes are broken. Pasteurization temperatures are higher with a minimum of 141.8°F (61°C) for 3.5 min for plain yolk. Salt is frequently added to yolk so the frozen-thawed yolk will be more fluid than plain frozen-thawed yolk. For salted yolks a temperature of 145.4°F (63°C) is required in the United States. The yolks must be homogenized to maintain a stable product as some albumen is included. Homogenization blends the albumen and yolk so they will not separate when held as a refrigerated product. Other handling is similar to liquid or frozen albumen.

With whole eggs or various blends of albumen and yolk the only variation from yolk processing is in the temperature required for pasteurization. A minimum temperature of 140°F (60°C) for 3.5 min is required in the United States. With blends of albumen and yolk or when more than 2% of non-egg ingredients are added the required temperature for pasteurization is 143.6°F (62°C).

3. Ultrapasteurization

Extended refrigerated shelf–life whole egg products were marketed first in 1990 in the United States. Pasteurization times and temperatures for these products are greater than for products with no guaranteed shelf-life. To be effective the extended shelf-life products must be processed under the best manufacturing procedures possible. The quality of eggs used, particularly with respect to bacterial quality, must be very high.

All liquid egg products should be maintained at temperatures of less than 4°C at all times after pasteurization. The liquid product may be distributed to users in refrigerated, frozen, or dehydrated form.

4. Dehydration

Most dried products are manufactured using spray drying equipment. There are, however, some dryers using pan drying, belt drying, freeze drying, and modifications of these procedures. Spray dried egg products are prepared by atomizing of the eggs into a warm air flow so that moisture is quickly removed. Air temperature to be used for different products are specified by the various equipment manufacturers. The spray dried products are frequently instantized for quick rehydration. The process for instantizing is known as agglomeration and is the same as used for dry milk products. This is done by adding back moisture under controlled conditions to get fine particles to stick together, loosely, and is then redried.

With all dried egg products the drying must be done at low enough temperatures to prevent cooking or rapidly enough at high temperatures to minimize heat damage to any of the functional properties of the egg product.

a. Dried Whole Egg   The products include standard whole egg, stabilized whole egg (glucose free), and free-flowing whole egg. Spray drying is the common method of dehydration. A modified belt drying having a foam drying in a fluidized bed has also been used successfully. For stabilized whole egg the glucose is removed from the liquid whole egg by bacterial fermentation, yeast fermentation, or the addition of glucose oxidase. For free-flowing whole egg either 2% silicoaluminate or 1% silicon dioxide is added to the whole egg. There are also dried whole egg products with carbohydrates added. These include whole

egg plus sucrose, whole egg plus corn syrup, and a whole egg plus yolk blend plus corn syrup. Any of the whole egg products should be dried to a moisture content of less than 5% water. Reducing moisture levels below 2% results in a dry whole egg with superior storage shelf–life.

There is a small volume of whole egg products dehydrated by freeze drying. The advantage of this process is ease of rehydration but costs of equipment and its operation are far higher than for spray drying.

b. Dried Yolk   Dried yolk products include standard egg yolk, stabilized egg yolk (glucose free), free-flowing egg yolk, and egg yolk plus corn syrup. While salted yolk is the most common form of frozen yolk there is very little salt yolk dried. Yolk for drying is, therefore, usually from the raw product. The various yolk products are processed under conditions similar to those for dried whole egg products.

c. Dried Albumen   Albumen is more heat sensitive than whole egg or yolk, and so requires special handling. The majority of albumen is spray dried. The glucose in albumen must be removed prior to drying to prevent a reaction between free amino acids and the reducing sugar. Bacterial or yeast fermentation and the addition of glucose oxidase are the methods of preference for glucose removal.

The most important types of dried egg white products include spray dried egg white, whipping type; spray dried egg white, nonwhipping type, pan dried egg white; and instant dissolving egg white.

The whipping type of dried egg white has a whipping agent such as sodium lauryl sulfate added. For the nonwhipping type the whipping agent is not added. Pan dried egg white comes in three forms (a) flakes, (b) powder, or (c) granules. To use flaked pan dried egg white it is recommended that the flakes be soaked overnight for convenience. Instant egg white is an agglomerated product.

5. Packaging

Packaging of liquid or frozen egg products varies depending on the market. For the retail trade the container sizes vary from about 2 ounces to a quart. For institutional users containers from 4 to 30 pounds are used. For the food manufacturer many eggs are distributed in insulated liquid tankers.

Packaging of dry egg products requires as nearly moisture proof materials as possible as the dry egg products are very hygroscopic. A common package for commercial handling of dried egg products is a fiber drum with a polyethylene liner. In this package the rate of moisture transfer through the liner is slow and there is little moisture pickup when the product is stored. The humidity in the packaging area should be kept very low.

After packaging the dried whole egg, products should be stored at refrigerated temperatures if they are to be held for more than 30 days. The fats in the whole egg will undergo oxidative changes to produce off flavors and odors.

IV. Egg Products

A. Conventional Products

The egg products of commerce include shell eggs, liquid and frozen eggs, and egg solids or dried eggs. The shell eggs and liquid and frozen products have been discussed. The dried egg products take all forms of liquid egg and remove the moisture to produce the desired product.

B. Specialty Egg Products

Specialty products come as shelf stable, refrigerated, frozen, and dried products. This class of products is prepared so as to be more convenient for the user. Many of the products are for institutional use as well as for the retail trade. The products fitting this category vary widely depending on formulation of egg products for different ethnic populations. A few of the products now in the market in the United States are listed with an attempt to include some from other cultures.

1. Scrambled Eggs

Scrambled egg mixes are packaged in frozen and dried forms. Additionally, precooked scrambled eggs are sold as frozen and freeze dried products.

A scrambled egg mix consists of whole egg and milk with seasonings added. The raw frozen product is packaged in cartons varying in size from two egg equivalent for the retail market to about 2-kg cartons for the institutional trade. Another packaging form for the institutional user is a flexible film, such as Cry-O-Vac, a product of W. R. Grace of Duncan, South Carolina, that will maintain strength in the freezer and also in water temperatures to 90°C. This product is cooked in the bag in a water bath at from 85° to 90°C. For the institutional user package sizes containing 36 or 72 servings are available. With this

package the problem of washing cooking utensils is eliminated.

For dry mixes, dried standard whole egg is mixed with nonfat dry milk. The freeze dried precooked scrambled egg is taken from the grill where it was cooked to the freezer and then lyophilized under high vacuum. This product has found a market in some military rations, as well as for campers. It is reconstituted merely by pouring a measured amount of hot water over the dry product. The frozen precooked scrambled egg is used in warm-and-serve retail meal packages.

2. Hard-Cooked Egg Products

The starting material for these products is clean, sound-shelled eggs that have been aged for from 24 to 72 hr until the albumen pH is at least 8.9, and are then cooked in the shell either in steam or in hot water at about 90° to 95°C for about 15 min.

The cooked eggs are cooled slightly and the shells are then removed. In many plants this is all hand labor but in others there is some degree of mechanization for shell removal. The peeled eggs may be packed in a dilute citric acid, less than 2%, with a small amount of ~0.1% benzoic acid solution. Such eggs are sold to institutional feeding establishments. The eggs may also be used in pickled eggs, deviled eggs, Scotch eggs, diced eggs, or ground eggs.

Pickled eggs are produced by packing hard cooked peeled eggs in a 5% acetic acid solution, vinegar. For variations it is possible to add a variety of seasonings or red beet juice for color to the pickled egg.

Deviled eggs are hard cooked eggs cut in half with the yolks removed. The yolks are then mixed with salad dressing or cream cheese along with seasoning. This mixture is then placed in the open pocket in the half of egg albumen. It is sold to caterers for special parties as a hors-d'oeuvres item.

Scotch eggs are prepared by wrapping a hard-cooked peeled egg in a thin layer of sausage. A turkey sausage is preferred to pork sausage because of the lower fat content. The wrapped product is then cooked for about 4 min in deep fat to a temperature of about 160°C.

Diced eggs or ground eggs are hard-cooked eggs, frequently imperfect in peeling, that are diced or ground to be used in egg salads or as an item on salad bars.

Another form of hard cooked egg is the "long egg." This is an egg product prepared from egg yolk hard-cooked as a center core surrounded by albumen cooked over the yolk core. Preparation equipment is available. Each slice of the product looks like a center cut of a whole hard cooked egg. The market for this product is either caterers or top quality restaurants where the slices of egg are used to decorate salads.

3. Fried Eggs

It is possible to precook fried eggs and freeze them for sale in warm and serve meals. The fried egg must be prepared in a containing ring to minimize very thick layers of albumen which could burn on reheating the egg. Freezing requires cryogenic procedures.

4. Omelets, Frittatas, Quiches, and Souffles

This group of products are prepared as frozen mixes, dry mixes and as precooked frozen items. They are sold to institutional feeders and the retail market. The formula for each is similar to that used for individual preparations.

5. Egg Drinks

For quick nutrition in a drink, liquid whole egg can be added to orange juice, apple juice, or cranberry juice. It is preferable to use pasteurized liquid egg rather than fresh shell egg for these drinks.

6. Egg Substitutes

The desire for the quality proteins of the egg without the high level of cholesterol has led to a number of formulations based on egg albumen as the primary ingredient. Other constituents of egg substitutes may be vegetable oil, starches, coloring agent, and vitamins.

7. Other Products

Egg-rich products that are also being marketed include French toast, pancakes, waffles all as warm-and-serve frozen items. Albumen rings have been cooked in a mold then battered, breaded, and deep fat fried to cook the coating. This is a high-protein snack food.

C. Eggs as a Source of Complex Chemicals

Egg albumen is a relatively rich source of lysozyme. Extraction proceedings have been developed to remove lysozyme from egg white leaving the remaining albumen in an edible form. Lysozyme has found a market as an antimicrobial agent in food processing and in the pharmaceutical industry. Two other egg components are being extracted on a commercial basis, aviden from albumen and lecithin from the yolk.

Still in a developmental state, IgY an anti-diarrheal compound, has been extracted from egg yolk without affecting the potential use of the remaining yolk for food.

V. Summary

Egg production and marketing are commercial enterprises throughout the world. In addition to food uses eggs have an important place in the history of art and religion. While originally the hen produced only a few eggs during the spring months each year, through improvements in breeding, feeding, and care the flocks of the United States average over 250 eggs per hen per year. Many individual flocks average over 300 eggs per hen each year. The production of eggs is now quite uniform throughout the year.

The egg is one of the most versatile of all food products. Its functional properties include coagulation, foaming, emulsifying, contributing nutrients, and minimizing sugar crystallization in candies. The egg is truly an incredible, edible product.

Bibliography

Austic, R. E., and Nesheim, M. C. (1990). "Poultry Production," 13th ed. Lea Febiger, Philadelphia, PA.

North, M. O., and Bell, D. D. (1990). "Commercial Chicken Production Manual," 4th ed. Van Nostrand Reinhold, New York, NY.

Parkhurst, C. R., and Mountney, G. J. (1988). "Poultry Meat and Egg Production." Van Nostrand Reinhold Co., New York, NY.

Stadelman, W. J., and Cotterill, O. J. (1990). "Egg Science and Technology," 3rd ed., Haworth Press, Binghamton, NY.

Stadelman, W. J., Olson, V. M., Shemwell, G. A., and Pasch, S. (1988). "Egg and Poultry Meat Processing." Ellis Horwood Ltd., Chichester, England.

Stadelman, W. J., and Pratt, D. E. (1989). Factors influencing composition of the hen's egg. *World's Poultry Sci. J.* **45**, 247–266.

Embryo Transfer in Domestic Animals

ROBERT H. FOOTE, *Cornell University*

Glossary

Artificial insemination (AI) Deposition of preserved semen by catheter into the female reproductive organs

Blastocyst Stage in early development when the embryo has developed a cavity and has differentiated into an outer layer (trophectoderm) which will become the placenta and the inner cell mass which will become the fetus

Corpus luteum (CL) Endocrine gland which secretes progesterone that is essential for maintaining pregnancy

Embryo transfer (ET) In simplest terms it is the transfer of an embryo from one source (donor) to a recipient

Estrous cycle Reproductive cycle of female domestic animals in which ovulation and sexual receptivity (estrus) recur on a regular basis

***In vitro* fertilization (IVF)** Fertilization of an oocyte in a "test tube"

Morula Early embryo forming a ball of cells as a result of several cleavage divisions

Oocyte Female gamete yet to be fertilized by a sperm cell; often referred to as an egg

Superovulation Induction of a large number of follicles to develop and ovulate oocytes more or less in synchrony

Zona pellucida Tough coat surrounding the oocyte which protects the oocyte and plays an important role of usually allowing only one sperm in to cause fertilization

Embryo transfer heralded a new era for animal breeding with the potential for identification, selection, and transfer of naturally produced or engineered special or superior genotypes. While embryo transfer simply signifies the transfer of one or more embryos from donor females to suitable recipients, the technique provides an opportunity to apply many biotechnologies resulting ultimately in the transfer of embryos produced. These include the following: (1) embryo splitting to increase the number of progeny per original embryo available; (2) embryo freezing; (3) embryo sexing; (4) *in vitro* fertilization; (5) sperm microinjection; (6) cloning production of transgenic animals; (7) preservation of endangered species; and (8) development of new genetic selection programs, such as velogenics, whereby oocytes are obtained from preuberal animals, fertilized *in vitro,* and cultured with genetic markers to prescreen the embryo for genetic potential. All techniques ultimately require embryo transfer to produce new offspring and this overview incorporates these developing technologies.

I. Introduction

In domestic animals embryo transfer (ET) is most successful and widely used in cattle. This stems from the fact that a substantial body of knowledge and repertoire of techniques relative to artificial insemination (AI), synchronization of estrus with control of ovulation, essential for successful embryo transfer, were previously established in cattle on a practical basis. Artificial breeding in cattle has proven to be of great economic importance because of its impact upon both genetic improvement and control of many serious infectious diseases. One great sire can easily have more than 100,000 progeny through AI, and this is important to recognize in considering the application of embryo transfer.

Embryo transfer, per se, is not as powerful a genetic tool as AI because the intensity of donor selection is much less with the limited number of embryos available per donor female and less is known about the genetics of the female than progeny tested sires. However, emerging biotechnologies which permit oocytes, zygotes, embryos, and possibly stem cells to be modified in various ways to produce highly valuable embryos for ET with superior progeny, are exciting. Highly selected naturally produced or engineered embryos could bring major changes in one generation.

The potential power to direct rapid genetic change brings a special challenge to scientists and practitioners of the art to apply principles of ethics and wisdom as fully as is humanly possible. This is not different, in principle, from the past where the quality of life achieved in any society stemmed from knowledge and its proper application. Now the potential rapidity of change requires that benefits and risks be carefully scrutinized before new programs are widely applied. [*See* ETHICS.]

II. Historical Perspective

The first reported successful ET was by Walter Heape in Cambridge in 1891, when he produced young in rabbits. Successful rat and mouse ET was reported in 1933 and 1942, respectively. Laboratory animals have served as models for similar domestic animal research. The first cattle eggs were seen in 1931 and the first calf was produced following ET in 1951. Another 20 years passed before the first commercial ET organization was established in 1971. Sheep and goats were used successfully for ET in 1934. Horse eggs were seen in 1939 and the first successful transfer was in 1974. Successful pig ET was reported in 1951. Along the way, ferret, baboon, cat, and dog have been used in ET studies. The list is expanding rapidly, particularly in exotic species of mammals.

The technique of ET has far more ramifications than the simple transfer of embryos from one donor female to multiple female recipients. It is an essential component of a variety of biotechnology–genetic engineering techniques that result in an embryo which must be transferred to a sexually mature recipient female in mammals to develop into young.

Prior to 1970 nearly all of the embryo transfers were experimental to study various aspects of fertility and embryo mortality. When European breeds of dual-purpose cattle became a wanted item in North America, especially, the limited pool of cattle and the international health restrictions caused money to become available commercially to multiply Simmental, Limousin, and other breeds by ET. The selection emphasis was on famous pedigrees rather than on individual performance. During the 1970s exotic breed demand decreased, and the introduction of nonsurgical transfer procedures from Japan simplified ET, especially in cattle, during early lactation. By far the largest application of ET to any breed has been with Holstein cattle and several hundred thousand progeny have been produced. The availability of prostaglandin $F_2\alpha$ and several analogs to synchronize estrus and development of nonsurgical collection and transfer techniques reduced the cost, increased the convenience, and made on farm ET practical. Also, in the 1980s, freezing of cattle embryos was perfected so that high-quality embryos gave good pregnancy rates after freezing and thawing them before transfer. The first calf born from a frozen embryo was in 1974. Sexing, twining by splitting embryos, *in vitro* fertilization (IVF), development of probes as genetic markers in embryos, and the hope for improved cloning with stem cells have continued to keep the commercial cattle industry involved with ET. Because of its cost ET will continue to be a procedure with special applications, in contrast to AI, until true cloning of stem cells on a repeatable and efficient basis is accomplished.

III. Advantages and Limitations

Some of the potential advantages of ET for cattle and most other species follow:

1. Obtain more progeny from selected females, thus increasing the opportunity for more intensive selection on the female side of the pedigree.
2. Obtain progeny from outstanding old cows no longer able to sustain a pregnancy.
3. Provide an opportunity to introduce new genotypes into any country without the cost and other problems of shipping live animals.
4. Better control of disease when carefully washed embryos rather than animals are transported.
5. Provide opportunities for special genetic testing such as for a bull suspected of being a carrier of an undesirable trait controlled by one pair of genes.

6. Establish controlled twinning in beef cattle through transfer of two embryos or one transfer plus a natural conceptus to increase the number of progeny and pounds of meat produced per beef cow per year.

7. Possibly obtain progeny from prepuberal females to decrease the generation interval required to get milk production information. Also, with many progeny one could progeny test females.

8. Devise new schemes of multiple ovulation and embryo transfer (MOET) to accelerate genetic gain through more accurate appraisal of individual animals and with a reduced generation interval. This includes prepuberal superovulation and the use of genetic markers to detect genetic potential of the embryo.

9. Store a diversity of germplasm frozen in liquid nitrogen.

10. Facilitate research on reproduction such as fertilization, embryonic death and aging.

11. Provide opportunities to modify the oocyte or zygote genetically so that new or unusual types of individuals might be synthesized or reproduced with the formation of clones, chimeras, or transgenic stem cells and animals of the desired sex and other characteristics.

12. Preservation of exotic or endangered species through IVF, embryo culture, cryopreservation, and finally ET.

13. Allow racing mares to produce embryos that can be transferred to a recipient, allowing the mare to continue to race.

The list of advantages of ET is impressive. However, it is a costly program, despite the fact that improvements in procedures described in this chapter have reduced the costs from a few thousand dollars per embryo to a few hundred dollars. It will become clear, as the procedures required for successful ET are described, that drugs, labor, travel, animals, and animal transportation, given the variability in response of donor cows, make this process expensive compared to artificial insemination. Unless one has a market for specific animals, such as bulls produced for artificial insemination or selected dams that have unusually appealing pedigrees or type that a few individuals will pay large premiums for, ET usually does not pay for the commercial dairyman. Money invested in the program will not be repaid by the milk check.

This technique has made possible the development of new types of breeding programs referred to as MOET (multiple ovulation, embryo transfer). In such a program embryos from the best bull × dam combinations are produced and brought into a central breeding establishment for transfer. Bulls produced in this system can be proven more rapidly than in

the usual progeny test system and cows can obtain a progeny test. By combining multiple types and sources of information in this system superior bulls can be detected and placed into service with a reduced generation interval and superior females sold to breeders.

The many advantages of ET must be weighed against the cost. The successful application of ET procedures has generated interest in many related areas of gamete biology with a knowledge explosion which would not have occurred otherwise. This has led to splitting, sexing, and cloning of embryos. Eventually, it may lead to development of highly tested superior lines of stem cells.

IV. Current Embryo Transfer Practices in Cattle

An ET program involves the following components: (1) selection of healthy donor cows possessing the desired characteristics, (2) superovulation of the donor, (3) insemination of the donor at the proper time, (4) collection of embryos, (5) embryo evaluation, (6) embryo culture, freezing, or transfer, (7) selection of healthy recipients at the right stage of their estrous cycle for transfer of embryos synchronized in development with this stage, and (8) pregnancy checking. Obviously a high degree of planning and management and technical skills are required to have donors and recipients coordinated reproductively if high pregnancy rates are to be achieved. The principles outlined here for cattle also apply to other species. Details vary to accommodate the differences in reproductive anatomy and physiology among species.

A. Selection of Donors

Donor cows should be reproductively normal with a history of good fertility, except when ET is used to overcome certain infertility problems. Each donor should be examined carefully by palpation of the reproductive organs and should have normal estrous cycles of around 21 days to qualify. Milk production should be the primary genetic trait selected for in dairy cattle. Lactating cows should not be superovulated within the first 60 days after calving, as the best cows are producing so much milk during this time that they are in a negative energy balance and embryo yields and quality may be reduced. If Holstein heifers with outstanding pedigrees are used they should weigh at least 350 kg and be cycling normally. Beef cows are selected on a variety of traits as there is a great diversity of opinion in the beef cattle industry regarding the relative importance of different traits. All donors should be well fed and managed and free from known diseases. They should be observed daily.

B. Superovulation

It is very important to release as many oocytes (eggs) as possible at one time. Donors should receive a series of subcutaneous injections of follicle stimulating hormone (FSH) starting about midcycle (Days 9–13 of the estrous cycle). The cycle can be a naturally occurring one or one induced by the use of prostaglandin $F_2\alpha$, or an analog, to regress the corpus luteum (CL) and start a new cycle. The FSH is administered at 12-hr intervals for 4 days to induce superfollicular growth. On the last day prostaglandin is given to functionally destroy the animal's CL so it will come into estrus and be inseminated. The dosage varies depending upon the FSH preparation used. A typical schedule would be to inject subcutaneously a total of 35 mg of FSH given as eight injections, starting with 5 mg and gradually reducing the dosage to 3 mg on the fourth day. Prostaglandin $F_2\alpha$ or an analog at the seventh FSH injection is administered to regress the CL. A single injection of long-acting pregnant mare's serum gonadotrophin (PMSG) has been used to stimulate follicular growth, but the superovulatory response has been a little higher with FSH. An antibody to PMSG given along with the prostaglandin inhibits further stimulation by the long-acting PMSG. This part of the program can be all done on the farm where donors are kept and embryos can be recovered.

C. Insemination

Animals should be observed several times daily for estrus. Estrus should occur about 36 to 48 hr after the prostaglandin injection. Skilled observers should be assigned to this important job. Cows are inseminated as soon as they are seen in estrus with frozen semen from the desired bull. To insure highest fertilization rates insemination should be repeated at 12-hr intervals until animals go out of estrus to cover the range of times that oocytes are ovulated. Semen should be of high quality. Sperm are not transported to the site of fertilization after insemination of a superovulated cow as readily as in a natural cycle without exogenous hormones. With frozen semen it is desirable to have at least 20 million sperm per insemina-

tion, with a high proportion of sperm being motile. [*See* ANIMAL REPRODUCTION, NONPREGNANT FEMALE; ANIMAL REPRODUCTION, PREGNANCY.]

D. Embryo Recovery

In the early days bovine embryos were collected from the oviducts by surgical procedures about 3 days after insemination and transferred surgically to the oviducts of recipients. With nonsurgical transfer, the embryos are in a later stage of development (morula and blastocyst, Fig. 1) and usually are collected 6 to 8 days after insemination. The animal is held in a convenient restraining stall and given an epidural block to relax the reproductive tract area. The external genitalia is thoroughly washed prior to recovering the embryos.

A special cannula (Foley catheter) is inserted into the vagina through the cervix into the horn of the uterus. A balloon is inflated to fit firmly in the uterine lumen to block any exit from the uterus. Through another channel in the catheter a compatible warm flushing medium, such as phosphate-buffered saline containing bovine serum albumin, is injected by syringe or gravity flow until the uterine horn is filled. The flow is shut off and an outflow channel opened. The uterus is massaged gently and the recovered fluid filtered to retain embryos. About 50 ml per time with 6 to 10 replications per horn are done to insure that every possible embryo is recovered.

The opposite uterine horn also is flushed in a similar manner. The balloon is deflated, the catheter is with-

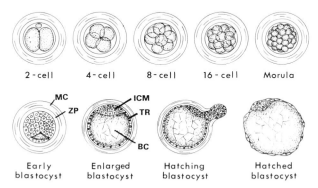

FIGURE 1 Stages in early embryo development. The one-cell fertilized egg or zygote (not shown) divides through a series of cleavage divisions to form a ball of cells, the morula. This differentiates into a blastocyst which is composed of an inner cell mass (ICM), trophectoderm (TR), and a blastocoele cavity (BC). Through all these initial stages the embryo is surrounded by a protective coat, the zona pellucida (ZP). The rabbit embryo shown here also is surrounded by a mucin coat (MC).

drawn slightly and placed forward in the other uterine horn. The process for embryo recovery is repeated.

The donor is infused with an antibiotic as insurance against possible infection and with a luteolytic injection of a prostaglandin to eliminate CL's, so that the cow does not have multiple pregnancies should some embryos be retained after flushing.

The next step is searching for tiny embryos in the fluid and uterine mucus and tissue debris. This is also critical. Personnel experienced with embryo identification and handling are essential. By carefully manipulating the debris with needles, while viewing the field using a dissecting microscope, the embryos can be located, aspirated with a pipet, and moved to a new dish of sterile culture medium. Care should be taken to avoid evaporation of the culture medium and temperature shock (cooling from body temperature to the laboratory temperature of 20–25°C is satisfactory).

E. Embryo Evaluation

Technicians highly experienced in examining embryos within a species can rather accurately estimate their quality subjectively. These estimates are positively correlated with pregnancies achieved and survival of embryos when frozen. A good quality microscope also is essential for this morphological evaluation. This evaluation is based upon (a) development of each embryo in comparison with the expected stage of normal development on the day of embryo recovery, (b) the uniformity of blastomeres, (c) the distinctness of membranes, (d) the presence of vesicles, (e) clear signs of embryo degeneration and dissolution, and (f) any damage to the zona pellucida. Cleavage patterns for bovine embryos obtained from healthy cows have been carefully analyzed and these serve as a guide. An advantage of employing these criteria is that they can be performed rapidly without damage to the embryo. The final test of embryo quality is its ability to develop into a normal young.

Many other tests have been employed such as (1) dye exclusion, (2) live–dead stain, (3) glucose utilization, and (4) measurement of enzymes. These and other tests are more suited for research where the treated embryo will not be transferred to produce a pregnancy.

F. Embryo Culture

Embryos used for transfer are seldom cultured, but they may be held while waiting for recipients to be prepared or to check embryo appearance after being frozen and thawed. Embryo culture is a major component of research studies where zygotes are produced by various procedures and study of development *in vitro* is very important. The usual precautions of handling any delicate material are followed. These include gentle handling, proper media, appropriate gas environment, avoidance of drying of media, sterility of all materials, and avoidance of temperature shock.

During early development *in vivo* the embryo undergoes several cleavage divisions in the oviduct. The oviduct contains a complex fluid, but presumably many components are not essential for the embryo. During this time the embryo has a substantial store of ingredients that are utilized during the early divisions. Extensive studies have been done on culture requirements of embryos of many species. There are species differences. Also, within a species the need for metabolic substrates changes as the embryo develops. During the first few cleavage divisions control of development shifts from maternal to embryonic genome control and there is considerable protein synthesis as the embryo develops into a blastocyst. Following is a list of factors known to influence embryo development in culture.

1. *Temperature.* Incubation at the same temperature as the physiological temperature of the species, about 39°C for cattle.

2. *Sterility.* Avoid any microbiological contamination.

3. *Water quality.* Media should be prepared with deionized water of the highest quality, as it is the major component of any medium.

4. *Ions.* Provide a balance of the major inorganic ions as Na^+, K^+, Ca^{2+}, and Mg^{2+}.

5. *Osmolarity.* Total concentration of ingredients should not exceed physiological levels as measured by osmometry and the response of the embryo.

6. *pH.* This should be neutral or a little higher. The intracellular pH of bovine embryos is not known.

7. *Bicarbonate, CO_2, and O_2 levels.* Bicarbonate is a precursor of components in the energy transport system and so plays a role in addition to pH control. The bicarbonate–CO_2 ratio affects pH, but plays a role not duplicated by adjusting pH. Oxygen tension in oviduct fluid is less than 10%. The gaseous environment in culture should be around 5 to 10% CO_2, 5% O_2, and the remainder N_2.

8. *Carbohydrate energy substrates.* As the embryo develops from a one-cell zygote to an expanding blastocyst it utilizes pyruvate and lactate and finally glucose. Glucose can inhibit development of the early embryo of some species. Intra-embryonic stores of substrate undoubtedly are used initially.

9. *Few amino acids are needed initially.* Glutamine, glycine, and taurine appear to be most important. Glutamine is also used as an energy source.

10. *Nucleic acid precursors*. Adequate intracellular stores appear to be available initially.

11. *Growth factors and vitamins*. As knowledge of growth factors and their receptors unfolds these substances appear to be important in normal development.

12. *Hormones*. Gonadotrophic hormones can stimulate embryo development in cumulus cell coculture studies. The effect may result from an interaction between the coculture and the embryo.

13. *Macromolecules*. Serum in large quantities, bovine serum albumin, or polyvinyl alcohol usually has been beneficial in culture media. However, with the optimal balance of all ingredients it is quite possible to promote good embryo development without them.

There are dozens of major formulations and minor modifications which have been published on culture media. One need only consult the current literature in the field. Catalogs of suppliers give details of many media such as Whittens, TCM 199, Hams F10, CZB, and KSOM, and many others. Many supplements to basic media are available.

Embryos of many species could not be cultured *in vitro* a few years ago without blocking at some stage of development. In cattle this was at the 8- to 16-cell stage which is a transitional stage of development between maternal and embryonic genome control of development. This block can be overcome by culturing the embryos with oviduct cells, cumulus cells, or media conditioned by these cells. Also, defined media providing amino acids are included, having been developed to culture zygotes to the blastocyst stage, but the percentage success is low. The best pregnancy rates are obtained by coculture of embryos with oviduct cells, or other cocultures.

G. Embryo Storage and Freezing

Embryos can be stored in culture up to the blastocyst stage, but any long-time storage is accomplished by freezing and storage in liquid nitrogen. Mouse embryos have been stored for 20 years without a detectable decrease in viability. Pregnancy rates of high-quality frozen–thawed bovine embryos are about 10% lower than comparable embryos that are transferred fresh. Freezing of embryos has had a tremendous impact upon the cattle ET industry. A majority of the transfers today are done with frozen–thawed embryos. Because of the importance of cryopreserved embryos, it is important to consider advantages and procedures. Among the advantages are:

1. A herd of synchronized recipients is not needed. Surplus embryos collected on any occasion can be preserved and not wasted.

2. A bank of embryos of desired types can be accumulated to be delivered at the desired time and place.

3. In beef cattle, embryos could be collected during seasons when beef cattle usually are not bred and used in a short breeding season to synchronize calving.

4. ET would be done in the whole herd when it is most economic to produce a calf crop.

5. The holding of cryopreserved embryos permits various health checks to be completed on the donors so that worldwide shipments can be done cheaply and with the assurance that the embryos will pass a battery of specific health checks.

6. Freezing also permits the banking of selected types of germplasm. This would provide diploid material of wide genetic diversity to be maintained while intensive breeding and selection programs are conducted.

7. Controls for genetic experiments would be available. The Jackson Laboratories are an example of this as several hundred strains of mice are preserved as frozen embryos in liquid nitrogen tanks, without the cost and hazards of maintaining all stocks as live animals.

Critical principles to be observed in freezing and thawing are to avoid thermal and osmotic shock. Osmotic changes induced by the cryoprotectants include shrinkage and swelling of the embryo. The latter can be especially lethal if the embryo swells to the bursting point. The details of many procedures are described in general texts on the subject. The embryos are treated with glycerol in a medium such as Dulbecco's phosphate-buffered saline containing serum or bovine serum albumin. Embryos are placed in 0.25-ml straws, sealed, and cooled moderately slowly from room temperature to about −5° to −7°C. They are held and seeded (indication of ice formation) at that temperature to avoid damage due to supercooling. After further cooling to −30° to −40°C the straws containing the embryos are transferred to liquid nitrogen at −196°C for storage or transport.

Other methods, as vitrification, are successful in some species. With a high concentration of cryoprotectant and serum the embryos are plunged into liquid nitrogen. Under these conditions the glassy state prevails and no damaging intracellular ice should be formed.

Thawing of frozen-cryoprotected embryos is critical as they can swell. This is due to water rushing in because of the accumulation of cryoprotectant and other substances inside the embryo during freezing. Sucrose often is included in the straw as a separate component. Embryos are impermeable to sucrose so swelling is reduced as the embryo is mixed with the sucrose solution during thawing.

H. Embryo Splitting

Embryos harvested at the morula or blastocyst stage can be cut in half with a microsurgical blade. The morula can be cut in any direction into two equal halves. However, the blastocyst is organized into an inner cell mass that will become the fetus and the trophectoderm which will become the placenta (see Fig. 1). Thus, it is necessary to divide a blastocyst into equal left and right halves. When this is done the two halves can be placed in two zona pellucidae (one in the original and one in a zona pellucida saved from an unfertilized egg or even in a foreign zona pellucida such as from a pig). Under some conditions, demi-embryos can be transferred directly without placing them back into a protective zona pellucida. The zona pellucida reduces the chance that cells become loose and lost from the demi-embryo, which would reduce the probability of survival. If embryos are to be cryopreserved, best results are obtained when the whole embryo is frozen and then split after thawing. The pregnancy rate per transfer is reduced about 10% by splitting, but as the total number of potential transfers is doubled, the number of progeny may be increased by at least two-thirds.

Because splitting is relatively easy to do, once a person has the training, it has economic advantages when costs per embryo are high. For research the use of identical twins also has substantial value in decreasing the number of replicates per two-treatment experiment needed to detect differences at a predetermined probability.

I. Recipient Selection and Synchronization

A high-quality embryo will only develop into a viable newborn animal if it is provided with a good environment to develop in. Selection of healthy recipients is essential. If the ET plan is to use fresh embryos transferred directly to recipients, synchronization of donors and recipients is essential. This requires careful planning to have a large pool of healthy recipients synchronized to ovulate at the same time as the donors, or a day later, so that the reproductive systems of the two groups will be undergoing nature's program of reproductive cyclicity in synchrony. This is expensive because a substantial number of recipients may be wasted if the yield of good embryos is much

less than expected. Freezing of embryos has greatly simplified this problem. Either all the embryos may be frozen for transfer at some other time and/or place or embryos equal to the number of good recipients can be transferred fresh and the rest frozen. Those frozen embryos then are available for transfer when the owner has suitable recipients or, if highly valuable, they may be marketed.

Synchronization of recipients and donor estrous cycles is required to provide a pool of recipients of adequate size. Too few recipients would be available from animals cycling naturally to match the donor unless a huge recipient herd was available. Two general procedures are available to provide synchrony. The donor schedule is planned, based on natural cycles and detected estrus or estrus is induced by an injection of prostaglandin $F_2\alpha$ or analogue. Then recipients can be programmed. Recipients with a good CL can be given a progestin, such as Synchro-Mate B (a progestagen) to extend the estrous cycle, or prostaglandin at the appropriate time (between Days 6 and 16 of the recipients' cycle) to induce estrus and ovulation in synchrony with the donor. Injection of slightly asynchronous recipients by giving progesterone, starting with estrus, also can be used. With frozen embryos, the required number of recipients is prepared in the same way.

J. Transfer of Embryos

In early work with cattle oviductal collections and transfers were the standard procedure. All transfers were done surgically with the animal under general anesthesia. Later some embryo transfer specialists used local anesthesia and transferred later stage embryos (a morula or blastocyst) to the uterine horn adjacent to the corpus luteum through a flank incision on the same side.

Today essentially all cattle transfers are made by a modification of the procedure for inseminating sperm. A "7-day" blastocyst would be transferred to a recipient 7 days after estrus. The "French gun" for holding 0.25-ml straws, in which the embryo is placed, or special equipment for inserting the straw into the uterus, may be used.

Epidural anesthesia to relax the rectal musculature, the same as for embryo collection, is recommended. The external genitalia of the cow should be cleaned and the "gun" inserted so as not to touch any external skin or tissue. It is extremely important to be aseptic as the animal's resistance to infection is less at this stage than during estrus. Also the "gun" must be worked through the cervical canal into the uterine horn adjacent to the corpus luteum to deposit the embryo. This contrasts with insemination of sperm just barely past the cervix. Also, the cervix is more rigid and dry at this stage than when the female is in estrus, making passage of the "gun" through the cervical canal more difficult.

The embryo should be gently expelled into the uterus. If the "gun" has been properly loaded with a small volume of fluid and air behind the embryo it should be expelled from the "gun" every time. The "gun" should be checked upon withdrawal to be sure that all fluid was expelled.

Animals should be watched carefully for recurring estrus about 2 weeks after transfer. If no estrus occurs this is a preliminary sign that a pregnancy was established. Experts with ultrasound equipment can check for pregnancy soon after this. However, because some early embryonic death occurs in cattle under good management conditions, a final pregnancy check by palpation of the reproductive organs per rectum about 60 days after embryo transfer is standard practice. Animals pregnant at that stage almost always produce young under normal circumstances. Surveys of the ET industry indicate that progeny and the sex ratio are normal.

K. Success Rates

Success for the total process from superovulation to transfer of the embryo varies greatly, depending upon the quality of the animals, embryos, environmental conditions, and especially the careful planning and skill of the people involved. An example of the results of flushing Holstein cows under good conditions is given in Table I. Not all cows selected as embryo donors have normal estrous cycles and not all respond to hormones to superovulate. Perhaps 90 out of 100 cows will respond. The nonresponders should not be flushed for embryo recovery. The number is further reduced to about 75% which yield embryos (14% of the healthy cows in Table I did not yield embryos). For subfertile cows the results are lower (Table I). If one could select only high-quality semen a fertilization rate of 85 to 90% is possible. However, with semen from the bulls breeders select for commercial ET, only 66% of the eggs collected are fertilized (Table I). The variability of individual donors is great, ranging in large studies from 0 to >40 ova or embryos per donor.

High-quality embryos represent about 60 to 70% of the embryos collected under these good conditions

TABLE I

Summary of Results Obtained in a Large-Scale Embryo Transfer Program

Item	Reproductive status		Healthy plus infertile
	Healthy	Infertile	
Animals, number	666	318	984
Total eggs, number	6828	1943	8771
Mean eggs/donor	10.3	6.1	8.9
Mean fertilized eggs/ donor	6.7	2.6	5.4
Mean embryos/donor	6.4	2.4	5.1
Eggs fertilized, %	66	42	61
Donor with no eggs, %	4	21	10
Donor with no embryos, %	14	51	26
Embryos transferred, no.	3707	604	4311
Pregnant recipients, %	68	58	67

Source: Adapted with permission from Hasler, J. F., McCauley, A. D., Schermerhorn, E. C., and Foote, R. H. (1983). Superovulatory response of Holstein cows. *Theriogenology* **19**, 83–99.

versus 50% under poorer conditions. Such embryos can yield a pregnancy rate in excess of 70%. The fair and poor quality embryos yield around 60 and 40% pregnancies, respectively. Under adverse conditions the values given here should be reduced by at least 10%.

L. Sanitation, Diseases, and International Marketing

The importance of using sterile equipment and aseptic techniques is obvious. Contamination could kill the embryo and/or promote disease transmission. At the same time sterilization of equipment must be done by procedures which leave no harmful residues. It is a good practice to rinse all equipment which will come in contact with the embryo with sterile medium before use. The disease status of prospective donor cows should be carefully determined. All countries have specific requirements relative to health checks on the donor animal. Fortunately the embryo is surrounded by a protective barrier, the zona pellucida (Fig. 1). Pathogens in the reproductive tract seldom penetrate this barrier. If they adhere to the surface most pathogens can be removed by repeated washing with a 0.25% trypsin solution.

It is possible that sperm could serve as a vector to carry pathogens into the embryo. All the major artificial breeding studs in North America and many other countries have stringent health test requirements. Their bulls are free of known pathogens and all semen collected is tested for a host of pathogens. Freezing of sperm allows regular tests to be completed and certified to be negative before sperm are used for insemination.

Shipment of cryopreserved embryos is worldwide. The procedures provide a means of distributing new genetic material throughout the world where it is needed and technology is available to use it without the threat of disease introduction.

M. Record Keeping

Detailed accurate record keeping is essential to maintain the integrity of the data, identification of genetic material, and records of procedures used. With modern computer technology such inventory and procedural records can be analyzed easily as a means of quality control and retrospective analysis of factors associated with high success rates or failures.

V. Synopsis of Embryo Transfer in Other Species

The principles described for cattle have been modified for use with other domestic species, exotic species, and laboratory animals. The nonsurgical procedure for embryo collection and transfer in the horse is very similar to the procedure used for cattle. All smaller species require surgical procedures where palpation of the reproductive system per rectum is not possible because of smaller size.

Much less is known about the culture requirements of embryos of most species. Exceptions are sheep and laboratory animals, such as the mouse and rabbit. Because the rabbit is being used as a laboratory model for domestic animals a few details will be given for it.

This field is rapidly advancing. In a few years it is likely that successful culture systems will have been identified for most species of interest and where sufficient material is available. This is important for human reproduction to provide knowledge to clinics assisting couples with reproductive problems, where the technologies described here could be helpful.

A. Horse

The ovary of the mare, with only one small area on the surface through which ovulation can occur (ovulation fossa), cannot be superovulated to any major extent. Therefore, only one embryo usually is available per attempted collection. The careful selection of donors and recipients and flushing and transfer techniques are similar to those used for cattle. In the mare it is easier to insert a catheter into the uterus because the cervix is much more open and the channel larger than in the cow.

Because mares do not superovulate well, no FSH is given. Donors and recipients are synchronized by the use of prostaglandin $F_2\alpha$ or analogs. Two injections 14 to 15 days apart are given to both groups. Also, synchronization of ovulation in the donor mare is improved by administering an ovulating hormone preparation, human chorionic gonadotropin. Synchronization of donors and recipients within ±2 days gives good results. A band of recipient mares also can serve as recipients by ovariectomizing them and injecting them with progesterone at the appropriate time to simulate development of the CL.

The horse embryo can be seen using ultrasound as early as the 12th day of pregnancy, and ultrasound by 20 days (2 weeks after transfer of the embryo) frequently is used to test for pregnancy. A pictorial record also can be made at that time. Pregnancy rates range from 50 to 70%, using the nonsurgical procedure. Because one embryo is recovered only about 60% of the time and 60% of those transferred produce pregnancies, approximately three attempts are required per pregnancy. An average of five attempts is needed per pregnancy when infertile donor mares are used.

Some breeds of horses do not allow progeny resulting from embryo transfer (or even AI) to be registered. Where this is allowed, ET is useful not only to obtain progeny from racing donor mares that can then continue to race, but also to obtain progeny from injured or older infertile mares. Experiments can also be performed to increase understanding of reproduction and enhance man's ability to manage animals so as to maintain normal function. An example of experimental ET, with human implications for miscarriages, is the study of immune reactions and differences in leukocytic infiltration of the placenta when donkey, mule, and horse embryos are transferred to heterologous recipients.

B. Sheep and Goats

Early workers utilized sheep, goats, and embryo transfer to study species hybrids and placentation. The cost of the procedure relative to the value of each female has limited commercial application. Because of the small size of these animals and difficult cervices to pass catheters, surgical recovery and surgical ET are necessary. Both species can be superovulated with eight injections of FSH or a single injection of PMSG. FSH gives a higher ovulation (16 vs 11 in one study) in goats, but similar averages of 8 per ewe with either gonadotrophin were obtained in sheep. Individual donors vary greatly in response, as is true with all species. Recovery rates of 75 to 80% are typical when the number of embryos recovered is compared with ovulation rates. Fertilization of oocytes is about 80%, depending on the time after estrus embryos are recovered, location of the embryos flushed, and many environmental and management factors. A pregnancy rate of 60% can be expected when two embryos are transferred to a recipient with two or three CLs. With only one CL, inadequate progesterone may be produced and fetal survival is reduced.

Pregnancies and young were achieved more than 30 years ago after embryo transfer by sheep embryos that had been shipped in oviducts of live rabbits. Considerable effort has been made to develop simple defined media for culturing sheep zygotes to blastocysts. Sheep embryos tolerate a considerable range in media composition, but typical sheep culture media contain 10 to 20% serum. Alternatively embryos may be cocultured with oviduct cells plus serum or BSA and fibronectin. Recent studies indicate that lymphocyte inhibiting factor may promote development of more functional embryos in culture. Transfer of embryos to tightly synchronized recipients or recipients 1 day behind gives the best results in sheep.

C. Pigs

The natural high prolificacy of this species limits the commercial application of ET except to produce specific pathogen-free herds. ET has been used to study embryo migration and crowding and in the production of transgenic pigs. Embryo culture has been studied successfully. Incubating pig zygotes in organ culture (mouse oviducts) or coculture with oviduct cells results in embryos passing the so-called 4-cell development block in pigs. Taurine, hypotaurine, and glutamine included in complex media all stimulate development of embryos in culture into blastocysts. Transfer of embryos is done surgically. Synchrony between embryo age and recipient is important.

D. Laboratory Animals

The rabbit has been useful as a model for studying domestic animals because sperm can be evaluated,

females inseminated, and all phases of ET in domestic animals tested in the rabbit. Superovulated oocytes have the same fertilization potential as naturally ovulated oocytes and development of embryos in culture and following transfer to recipients gives equivalent results. Rabbits are superovulated by injecting FSH at 12-hr intervals for 4 days followed by an injection of LH. Superovulation occurs about 10–15 hr later. All embryo recoveries and transfers must be done surgically.

Embryo culture with complex media and various cocultures have led to a defined macromolecule-free medium simpler thn TCM 199. This medium promotes nearly 100% of the zygotes cultured to develop into blastocysts. Cell numbers (rate of mitosis) are increased when the oxygen level for culture is reduced from 20 to 5% and CO_2 is increased to 10%.

E. Exotic Animals

Various aspects of the superovulation and ET procedures have been attempted with wild animals in zoos. Superovulation has been successful in several species of antelope and different members of the cat family, including domestic cats as a model. White-tailed deer have been tested in a complete ET program, demonstrating feasibility as a model for endangered deer species. However, limited resource material has resulted in sporadic attempts in zoo animals. Increased emphasis is being placed on obtaining ovaries to increase the number of oocytes which possibly can be matured, then fertilized *in vitro,* cultured, and transferred. Limited successes with primates (other than man) also are encouraging, but it is premature to attempt to codify results to date.

VI. Emerging Technologies and Research Using ET

A. Improving Superovulation

The use of pregnant mare serum gonadotropin (PMSG), a follicle stimulating hormone, was used extensively in the development of ET as only one injection was required. However, there was considerable batch to batch variation in purity and potency as well as some problems of obtaining a good synchronized superovulation with the long biological half-life of PMSG. However, this problem can be surmounted by administering an antiserum against PMSG 4 to 5 days after injecting PMSG to induce a rapid decrease in available PMSG. Other researchers are attempting to regulate the endogenous release of FSH by immunizing animals with inhibin. The latter normally suppresses release of FSH and if the inhibin effect could be blocked the individual potentially could release enough FSH to cause superovulation.

Improvement in the repeatability of superovulation when treating animals with FSH is possible through greater purification of FSH. Products are available today with most of the contaminating LH removed. Then a small amount of LH can be added back to the FSH to provide a standard FSH-LH product.

B. Sexing Embryos

Development of Y chromosome specific probes and the polymerase chain reaction have made it possible to sex a few cells removed from a blastocyst by microsurgery. The embryo is not damaged and may be transferred or used for other studies such as cloning. With proper controls the sexing is essentially 100% accurate. The extra cost of sexing under special test situations is worth it as only female embryos in a dairy herd or male embryos to produce bulls for AI would be transferred, for example.

C. *In Vitro* Fertilization (IVF)

Several organizations are offering commercial service to produce embryos by IVF. Superior cows which fail to superovulate can have ovarian oocytes aspirated by ultrasound guided probes. Oocytes can be fertilized *in vitro* and some embryos (currently about 40%) will develop into blastocysts during culture. At this point they are ready for transfer. Another advantage of this system is that few sperm are required for IVF and an expensive straw with semen for routine insemination of one cow can be divided among many dishes of oocytes for IVF. With repeated ovarian aspirations every few days a single donor may produce many offspring. Another approach is to obtain slaughterhouse ovaries. Oocytes by the hundreds can be removed from dozens of ovaries and fertilized *in vitro* by sperm from the most highly selected sires. Embryos produced would be less expensive than other types and could be used to upgrade native cattle in developing countries. Improved techniques for IVF, such as oocyte maturation, also are useful in producing oocytes for nuclear transfer.

Oocytes can be recovered from superovulated prepuberal (sexually immature) females and fertilized *in vitro*. These zygotes produced can be cultured and transferred to mature recipients, thus reducing the generation interval. Also various genetic markers may be used to provide a basis for selecting embryos on the basis of their genetic potential. Only a few markers are currently available, but this field is progressing rapidly.

Procedures developed with cattle and other domestic animals could have direct application with zoo animals on the endangered species list. Females of any endangered species could have oocytes removed periodically from their ovaries. These could be matured and fertilized *in vitro*, cultured to some embryonic stage suitable for transfer, and transferred or frozen. Successful techniques for many species await development.

D. Sperm Microinjection

Under normal circumstances the sperm is capable of penetrating oocytes. If a situation arose where this did not happen or sperm numbers were low and oocytes were not penetrated, sperm could be microinjected. Only one sperm is required per oocyte. While such techniques may have limited commercial application, if sperm could be sexed, even very inefficiently, oocytes could be inseminated with sperm of the desired sex, thus producing embryos with the desired sex. The technique is being used to overcome some forms of male infertility in humans. The technique also serves as a powerful research tool to determine the effect a specific type of sperm has on early embryo development.

E. Cloning

More details are presented elsewhere in this book. It is important to note here that any embryos produced by cloning or genetic engineering must be transferred into recipients to finally establish viability and economic benefits. [See TRANSGENIC ANIMALS.]

Many cattle clones have been produced. It is expensive and the overall procedure is inefficient. Also, giant calves have been produced, requiring surgical intervention at parturition. This provides an intriguing model to study maternal cytoplasmic components as they interact with the nucleus.

Stem cell lines could provide unlimited cloning of "animals" of the desired sex and other traits. These stem cell lines are lines of cells that can be cultured to provide millions of genetically identical cells in the undifferentiated state, frozen, and still maintain their totipotency to produce identical sexed progeny when placed in a suitable environment for culture after thawing. This procedure also could serve as a vector for reproducing a single high valuable transgenic animal and multiply the progeny. At the present time only a few isolated cases have been reported that cultured stem cells were prepared which maintained their totipotency to form multiple new identical individuals. These studies need to be repeated and results verified. However, the technique would be of great value, if an efficient procedure can be developed.

VII. Current Status of ET and Conclusions

Cattle and to some extent horses are the only species in which ET is established on a commercial basis. Studies are being pursued in the rabbit because in some countries, such as France and Italy, rabbit meat production is a substantial food item. Also, embryo transfer techniques are available for sheep, goats, pigs, and many exotic species. Nonsurgical procedures are useful in large animals, but surgical procedures are required in small animals.

The technique of ET to simply transfer an embryo from one animal to another has limited value. It does not pay the commercial cattle farmer to do this. Use of AI is the most cost-effective biotechnology for cattle improvement. However, as the various biotechnologies are perfected their application depends upon the final step of ET. Collectively, these new technologies provide a basis for posing questions, formulating hypotheses, and designing experiments to test the hypotheses. The resulting studies, in turn, are bound to lead to discoveries which already have the potential of revolutionizing the breeding of some species of economically important or rare animals. The use of IVF and ET, including use of sexed sperm to prevent male specific genetic lethal diseases, is a major medical industry used to overcome selected medical problems.

Bibliography

Adams, C. E. (1982). "Mammalian Egg Transfer." CRC Press. Boca Raton, FL.

Betteridge, K. J. (1981). An historical look at embryo transfer. *J. Reprod. Fertil.* **62**, 1–13.

Betteridge, K. J. (ed.) (1977). "Embryo Transfer in Farm Animals." Monograph 16, Agriculture Canada, Ottawa.

Brackett, B. G., Seidel, G. E., Jr., and Seidel, S. M. (ed.) (1981). "New Technologies in Animal Breeding." Academic Press, Orlando, FL.

Foote, R. H. (1987). In vitro fertilization and embryo transfer in domestic animals: Applications in animals and implications for humans. *J. In Vitro Fertilization Embryo Transfer* **42**, 73–88.

Foote, R. H., and Yang, X. (1992). Cloning of bovine embryos. *Reprod. Dom. Anim.* **27**, 13–21.

Hare, W. C. D. (1986). "Diseases Transmissible by Semen and Embryo Transfer." Office International des Epizootics, 12 rue de Prony, F-75017, Paris.

Hasler, J. F., McCauley, A. D., Lathrop, W. F., and Foote, R. H. (1987). Effect of donor–recipient interactions on pregnancy rate in a large-scale bovine embryo transfer program. *Theriogenology* **27**, 139–168.

International Embryo Transfer Society (1987). Manual. 309 W. Clark Street, Champaign, IL 61820, 87 pp.

Seidel, G. E., Jr., and Seidel, S. M. (1991). "Training Manual for Embryo Transfer in Cattle." FAO paper, Vol. 77, pp. 1–164.

Theriogenology. January issues of this journal each year are devoted to new developments in the field of embryo transfer and embryo biotechnologies.

Energy Utilization

MARIO GIAMPIETRO, *Istituto Nazionale della Nutrizione, Rome, Italy*

DAVID PIMENTEL, *Cornell University*

Glossary

Agro-ecosystem Human-managed ecosystem in which crops and domesticated animals are dominant populations of the biotic community; this altered configuration is stabilized because of a continuous flow of applied power from humans which prevents the return of the system toward a more natural occurrence of populations

Direct energy inputs Flow of energy directly consumed by the farmer in the management of the agro-ecosystem (such as gasoline consumed by tractors or by irrigation pumps)

Endosomatic energy or power Energy converted into power within the human body (or more in particular, within the muscles); alternatively called "metabolic" energy or power ("endosomatic" means inside the human body)

Exosomatic energy or power Supplementary source of power for human work ("exosomatic" means outside the body); in developed societies, exosomatic energy is converted into power via mechanic devices, such as engines and machines, and is generally referred to as commercial energy

Indirect energy inputs Flow of energy sequestered (embodied) in the inputs used by the farmer to sustain agricultural activities, such as the energy spent in the manufacturing of fertilizers, pesticides, tools, and mechanic devices

Nonrenewable (fossil) energy Flows of energy derived from the depletion of stocks; fossil fuels are limited in their stock dimension (we will run out of them) but virtually unlimited in their flow dimension (the flow of power obtained from fossil fuels can be increased further and further, by simply increasing the level of technological capital)

Renewable energy Flows of energy generated at a constant rate by natural processes (such as solar energy driving biomass production, wind, photovoltaics). Renewable energy can be assumed to be unlimited in its stock dimension (it will be available for a very long period of time), but limited in its flow dimension (the density at which this energy can be concentrated and transformed into a flow of useful power is subject to biophysical constraints)

Sustainable agricultural production Agricultural production that, in the long term, maintains biodiversity at the regional scale, preserves soil productivity, does not obtain its water supply from the mining of ground water, does not cause pollution to the surrounding ecosystems, and has a reduced dependance on fossil energy

This article provides (1) basic concepts of Energy analysis and its ability to describe agriculture as an interface between economic and biological processes; (2) numerical examples, mainly taken from U.S. agriculture, to illustrate the pattern of energy use in agricultural production in relation to the technological development of society; (3) a discussion, from an energetic perspective, of the historical trends in agricultural performance and population in relation to future changes and sustainability.

I. Basic Concepts of Energy Analysis Applied to Agriculture

A. Definition of Agriculture and Related "Costs" and "Benefits"

Agriculture can be defined as the alteration of biota, to obtain crop plants and/or livestock at densities different from those that are typical of wild ecosystems. This alteration of natural ecosystems to increase harvestable biomass requires a flow of applied power from humans, that during the year with several interventions prevents the system from returning toward a more natural occurrence of populations (e.g., by tilling the soil, weeding, applying pesticides, fertilizers, irrigating). Thus, agricultural management costs human society in terms of labor, machinery, and fossil energy for irrigation, fertilizers, pesticides, etc. In principle, the greater the change generated in the natural system to increase the yield of crops and livestock, the greater the flow of power (total energy input consumed) that must be applied by humans (Tables I and II).

On the other hand, managing agricultural ecosystems can be considered a "benefit" from the human point of view, because the manipulation of natural biota and the physical/chemical environment provides a larger percentage of harvestable biomass for food, fuel, and shelter compared with the wild situation.

It should be noted that these "costs" and "benefits" of agriculture relate only to the human perspective and are therefore not the only parameters that should be considered in optimizing the management of ag-

TABLE I

Energy Inputs and Output per Hectare for U.S. Corn Production (1985)

Item	Quantity/ha	10^3 kcal/ha
Labor	10 h	—
Machinery	55 kg	1018
Gasoline	40 l	400
Diesel	75 l	878
Electricity	100 10^3 kcal	100
Nitrogen	152 kg	3192
Phosphorus	58 kg	365
Potassium	75 kg	187
Lime	426 kg	134
Seeds	21 kg	520
Insecticides	0.6 kg	60
Herbicides	3.5 kg	350
Irrigation	18 %	2250
Drying	3800 kg	760
Transport	322 kg	89
Total inputs		10303
Yield	7400 kg	29600
Energy input/kg of corn	1392 kcal/kg	

Source: Pimentel, D., Dazhong, W., and Giampietro, M. (1990). "Agroecology: Researching the Ecological Basis for Sustainable Agriculture" (S. Gliessman, ed.), pp. 305–321. Springer Verlag, New York.

TABLE II

Energy Inputs and Output per Hectare for Swidden Agriculture (Corn) in Mexico

Item	Quantity/ha	10^3 kcal/ha
Labor	1144 h	589.2
Axe and hoe	16.6 10^3 kcal	16.6
Seeds	10.4 kg	36.6
Total inputs		642.3
Yield	1944 kg	6901.2
Energy input/kg of corn	285 kcal/kg	

Source: Reprinted with permission from Pimentel, D. (1984). Energy flow in the food system. *In* "Food and Energy Resources" (D. Pimentel and C. W. Hall, eds.), pp. 1–24, Academic Press, New York.

ricultural ecosystems. A different set of costs and benefits referring to agricultural activities can be defined by adopting an environmental perspective: a dramatic increase in the flow of harvested biomass can result in a deterioration of the natural processes sustaining the environment, such as soil erosion, loss of biodiversity, pollution, etc.; these ecological costs can eventually lead to a decrease in the productivity of the managed agro-ecosystem in the long-term and other costs to society due to the deterioration of environmental services.

Energy analysis can provide an enlargement of the perspective on the assessment of agricultural production, since it can describe and quantify constraints and performances related to both the ecological (= biophysical) and economic (= human) side of agro-ecosystem management.

On the ecological side, energy analysis can be used to deal with (i) physical boundary conditions limiting productivity, such as the availability of natural inputs (e.g., solar energy, rainfall, useful biota, and soil characteristics); (ii) physical constraints limiting agricultural activities, generally represented by bottlenecks in the supply of power for agro-ecosystem management, such as the availability of human and machine power, availability of fertilizers, pesticides, and limits to the expansion of irrigation; and (iii) the assessment of the ecological impact of agricultural production, since energetic indicators can be used to describe the alteration of the pattern of energy flowing in biophysical systems (e.g., the transformation of a forest into a corn field reduces the ability of that ecosystem to use solar energy to maintain biomass on a yearly basis).

On the economic side, energy analysis can be used to assess the flows which determine the return of agricultural activities, that depends on the value of inputs consumed and outputs obtained. The value of the output produced (e.g., kilograms of crops and/ or livestock) can be compared to the costs related to the requirement of land, hours of human labor, and investment in technological capital.

Clearly, energy analysis does not represent an alternative to economic or ecological analyses, but is a useful tool to integrate findings derived from economic and ecological analyses. Moreover, it can be used to examine biophysical constraints affecting the feasibility of technical changes that are not normally considered by either of these two disciplines. [*See* BIOMASS; LABOR; QUANTITATIVE METHODS IN AGRICULTURAL ECONOMICS.]

B. Boundaries and Embodied Energy

Land, water, labor, energy, genetic resources, and technological capital are often needed to generate the inputs used by the farmer; therefore, they can be considered embodied in the flow of inputs such as animal feed, fertilizers, pesticides, etc., used in farming systems. The decision to take into account embodied requirements can significantly affect the assessment of a production system. For example, the land area requirement for the production of milk can be calculated considering only the area of the dairy farm where the cows are kept, or it can be calculated including also the area needed to produce the feed imported by the dairy farm.

Although the economic boundaries for a farm are easily defined, the ecological boundaries are more difficult to assess. For example, agricultural yields are calculated on the basis of hectares of cultivated land, despite the fact that a farm is not a self-sustained ecosystem. The flows of nutrients through the agricultural ecosystem are related to biogeochemical cycles (C, O, N, P, K, H_2O, etc.) that are only in part sustained by the agro-ecosystem under analysis. Agriculture, to be sustainable, must leave a part of the ecosystem in wild configuration, in order to maintain biological diversity and stability of biogeochemical cycles. However, theoretical ecology has not developed sufficiently to define the minimum size of landscape that is required for community equilibrium. Therefore, data referring to the production actually achieved on a particular plot (kg/ha) can be quite different from data assessing the level of production (kg/ha) that can be sustained in steady state by farming (as a regional value) without losing soil fertility or decreasing the genetic diversity of the managed and natural ecosystems.

C. Farmers around the World Adopt Different Optimization Strategies

Since agriculture is an interface between processes operating in natural ecosystems (the ecological side) and processes operating in human societies (the economic side) (Fig. 1), it is subject to different, and sometimes contrasting, optimizing strategies. Thus, the farmer's final choice of which optimizing strategy to adopt depends on the characteristics of the society in which the farming system is operating, as well as the characteristics of the ecosystem that is altered to produce crops and/or livestock. For example, in affluent societies with temperate ecosystems the main farming strategy is aimed at the maximization of the return of human investment by increasing the yield per hour of labor and/or the yield per hectare. In these societies the individual life of farmers is protected against boundary fluctuations (drought, floods, and other possible natural catastrophes on the biophysical side and severe consequences of market adversities on the economic side), and technical activities are regulated by economic mechanisms. However, this strategy aimed at a high labor productivity of farmers with heavy use of technology also implies that the number of farmers be limited; for example, in the United States farmers currently comprise only 2% of the working force, compared to 80% around the year 1850.

On the other hand, farming strategies in tropical or fragile ecosystems (usually concerning societies in developing countries) are generally aimed at maximizing the stability and sustainability of the agroecosystem. Here, the farmer is still concerned with the very survival of his family (minimization of risk), and the incomplete monetarization of farming systems makes the total regulation of agricultural activities via economic mechanisms impossible. As already noted, the maximization of human return is a strategy different than and often contrasting with the maximization of the stability of the farming system in response to fluctuations of boundary conditions.

Farming systems within developed countries, such as the United States, tend to save human labor and minimize the use of land. Table III shows that the amount of corn produced per hour of labor has increased 343-fold compared to swidden agriculture, and the yield per hectare has increased 3.6-fold. However, this increase in yield is due to large injections of fossil energy and machine power (the flow of exosomatic power input in U.S. agriculture—1392 kcal/ kg of crop—is 50 times higher than in swidden agri-

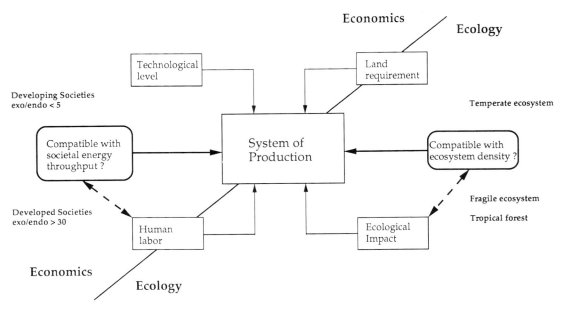

FIGURE 1 Parameters describing a system of agricultural production. Agriculture as an interface between economy and ecology.

culture—27 kcal/kg of crop) and implies a substantial reduction of the output/input ratio (a 4.3-fold decrease in the U.S. system). This solution therefore requires that in developed societies fossil fuel and technology are inputs relatively inexpensive and abundant compared to human labor and space. This type of production strategy results in a low energy efficiency for agriculture (output–input ratios can often result lower than 1 for nongrain crops).

Moreover, agricultural production is just the first step to guarantee food security to the population;

TABLE III

Indicators of Performance of Corn Production for Different Agricultural Systems

	United States[a] (1985)	Swidden agriculture[b] (Mexico)	China[c] (1980)
Yield in kg/ha	7400	1944	2700
Yield/hr of labor (kg/hr)	740	1.7	3.8
Exosomatic energy input (kcal/kg)	1392	27	825
Ratio energy output/input	2.9	12.5	3.6

[a] From Table I.
[b] Using manpower only. From Table II.
[c] Hailuen County, Heilongjiang Province. Data from Dazhong, W., and Pimentel, D. (1984). Energy use in crop systems in northeastern China. *In* "Food and Energy Resources" (D. Pimentel and C. W. Hall, eds.), pp. 91–120. Academic Press, New York.

food security means guaranteeing a flow of food that matches the demand of the population in time and in space in terms of both quantity and quality of nutrients (in rich countries this includes an acceptable level of accessibility (convenience) of food products). Food processing, packaging, distribution, and home preparation are supplementary activities required in the food system, implying that the overall performance of the food system in developed countries is characterized by an energy output/input ratio below 1 (Table IV). Put another way, in the U.S. food system more energy input is consumed in the form of fossil energy than is provided to the final U.S. consumers in the form of food calories (the ratio is about 10 kcal of exosomatic energy per food kcal). As noted earlier, in developed societies characteristics of food products other than the metabolic energy content (e.g., improvements in convenience and food safety) are responsible for this increase in energy cost. [*See* WORLD HUNGER AND FOOD SECURITY.]

On the contrary, in developing countries fossil energy and technology are scarce. Therefore, these societies are predominantly based on biological processes, and tend to apply less power in agricultural activities. This implies a more extensive use of the land area, with an associated lower yield per hectare, and human time (Table III). In terms of energy, this results in a higher return for agricultural activities (measured as Joules of harvested biomass per Joule

TABLE IV

Energy Use in Agriculture as Percentage of Total Energy Use in the U.S. Food System

	1950		1960		1970		1982	
	10^{12} kcal	%	10^{12} kcal	%	10^{12} kcal	%	10^{12} kcal	%
Agriculture	303	27	374	26	526	24	687	24
Rest of food system (processing, packaging, transportation, distribution and home preparation)	561	73	1066	74	1646	76	2253	76
Total food system	1134	100	1440	100	2172	100	2940	100
Energy use in agriculture as % of total US energy use		3.6		3.4		3.1		3.8
Energy use in food system as % of total US energy use		13.6		13.1		13.0		16.5

Source: 1950, 1960, and 1970 data from Hall *et al.* (1986). "Energy and Resource Quality—The Ecology of the Economic Process." Wiley, New York. 1982 data from Fluck (1992) "Energy in World Agriculture," Vol. 6, Elsevier, Amsterdam; and Pimentel, D., and Hall, C. W. (eds.) (1984). "Food and Energy Resources." Academic Press, New York.

of energy input), but a relatively low standard of living for the society (low energy return per hour of labor). In fact, the low density of energy output obtained by these societies in the form of harvested biomass per year per hectare (measured as W/m^2), can support only a limited population density at a limited per capita energy expenditure (clearly, "limited" refers to a comparison with values and standards typical of developed countries). [*See* PRODUCTION ECONOMICS.]

D. Agricultural Production as a Part of the Food System

As agriculture relates human society to the natural ecosystem, it follows that the performance of a particular form of agricultural management should be assessed by considering the constraints imposed by the structure and organization of human society as well as by those of the natural ecosystem that was displaced. Following the inputs and outputs of the agricultural sector in its interaction with the ecosystem and society it is possible to describe the whole food system cycle within which agricultural production takes place (Fig. 2).

The density of flows (the speed at which resources flow through a single step) in the food system cycle emerges as a fundamental parameter in defining the terms of reference of agricultural processes. In fact, four related activities are required to sustain food security (Fig. 2): (1) food production (food = energy and matter compatible with human metabolism); (2) making the food accessible to the consumers (accessible food = meals ready to be consumed according to a

defined pattern of consumption); (3) generation of wastes (wastes = energy and matter no longer compatible with human needs); and (4) recycling of wastes into the form of agricultural inputs (agricultural inputs = energy and matter compatible with the agricultural process).

The major problems faced in the exploitation of agroecosystems can be seen in terms of lack of harmony among flows within the cycle. In fact, if

F1 > F4 there is depletion of biophysical capital (e.g., soil degradation);
F2 < F3 there is a failure in food security (malnutrition);
F2 > F3 there is mismanagement (stress of natural ecosystems to produce useless surplus);
F4 > F1 there is pollution (the flow of waste is too dense to be recycled).

Figure 2 also emphasizes three points concerning the concept of efficiency in agriculture:

(i) It could be misleading to focus only on the efficiency of a single step of the cycle. Since all steps are interconnected, the definition of a flow as an input, available resource, accessible resource, or waste is often arbitrary, depending on the point of view from which the system is analyzed (i.e., an increase in evapotranspiration due to the introduction of trees can be considered negative in terms of less accessible water in the soil, but at the same time positive in terms of more water vapor in the atmosphere that can generate rain clouds);

(ii) The efficiency must be related to the system's level of energy throughput (= the speed at which energy flows through the system). The more the agricultural flows differ in density from the natural ones,

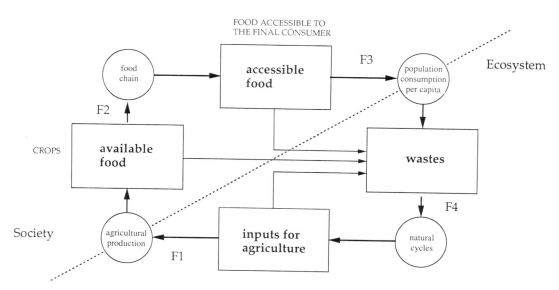

FIGURE 2 Flow diagram of energy and matter in the food system. F1, [water, air, nutrients, biota, soil, solar energy] × SPACE and TIME; F2, crops after production and harvest; F3, food after processing, packaging, transport, and cooking; F4, wastes recycled in the ecosystem.

the more energy input is required in the agricultural production (e.g., comparing Tables I and II we can see that a 3.8-fold increase in agricultural yields per hectare implies a 19-fold increase in energy inputs per hectare). Hunter–gatherers need no fossil energy subsidies to produce their food and can be considered to have a very "efficient" agricultural system if the energy output/input ratio is considered. On the other hand, a hunter–gatherer system can support only a society with a limited population density (i.e., in the range of hundreds to thousands of ha per capita) at a low standard of living, which compromises the chance of technical development of such a society. The per capita energy expenditure of preagricultural societies can be estimated to be lower than 9000 kcal/day, implying a ratio exosomatic energy/endosomatic energy of 3/1 (in these societies exosomatic energy is obtained by the use of biomass for fire, clothes, and shelter). To have a fair comparison between the energy efficiencies of different agricultural systems, we have to compare human societies operating at similar levels of energy throughput (in the United States the per capita energy expenditure is higher than 230,000 kcal/day; that means a ratio exosomatic/endosomatic energy of about 90/1 !).

(iii) Flows have to be analyzed not only in terms of average values in steady state but also in terms of stability (resilience of the system in the case of perturbations); for example, in order to define how much food surplus is useless, we have to assess first how reliable the food supply is for a given system in the case of droughts, pest outbreaks, or man-made perturbations.

E. Energy Throughput (Power Level) in Society and the Meaning of Agro-Food Systems

In subsistence societies where the level of exosomatic power is low (exosomatic/endosomatic energy ratio < 5/1), production and consumption activities referring to the economic process are based on the physiological conversion of biomass energy input into work, via human and/or animal muscles. This means that in preindustrial societies both the flow of energy input used to sustain societal activities and the flow of power used to manage the ecosystem are driven by the agro-food system. This implies that the performance of agricultural activities is basically concerned with increasing the energy return of the process. In terms of energy output/input ratio, agriculture must therefore have a positive return to society (the energy output provided by agriculture has to be greater than the energy input consumed).

In contrast, in developed countries the bulk of societal activities is made possible because of a flow of fossil energy input and the use of exosomatic, mechanical devices—e.g., thermic engines. Exosomatic power is responsible for the economic activities of production and consumption, in fact, in developed countries the ratio exo/endo is always higher than

30/1 (about 30 to 50/1 in Western Europe, and about 90/1 in the United States and Canada). This means that in these societies humans can apply power for a particular task at a level that is a thousand times higher than that provided by their muscles. A farmer who drives a 100 HP tractor is delivering 1000 times more power than a farmer working manually in the field (the average power delivered by manual workers in agriculture is 0.1 HP).

This change in the mechanism of power generation due to industrialization dramatically reverses the relationship between the densities of energy flows consumed by society and the densities of food and biomass obtained by agricultural production. For example, in Japan the density of energy use (energy consumption of the country divided by its surface) amounts to 2.1 W/m^2, while in Tanzania the average density of energy consumption is only 0.02 W/m^2. These values can be compared with the energy flow obtainable by traditional agricultural production (rice under intense cultivation, but without heavy fossil energy subsidies) which can supply a flow in the order of 0.1 W/m^2 (= yield of 1950 kg/ha/yr). Farming rice in Tanzania can be considered an activity making available a "high density energy flow" for the rest of society, whereas in developed countries the picture is completely different. When technological development increases the speed of energy throughput in a society and the exosomatic/endosomatic energy ratio, more energy and power are spent in the food system than are obtained. In these societies fossil fuel, technology and other imported resources are used to offset the deficiency.

F. From the Maximization of the Output/Input Ratio (Preindustrial Agriculture) to the Maximization of Energy Throughput (Industrial Agriculture)

The development of technology in agricultural production can be related to changes in the type of interaction between human society and ecosystem. The industrial revolution has led to a nearly unlimited flow of exosomatic power available to power society's activities, which is therefore constrained only by a nation's ability to buy more oil and further develop technology. Clearly, the dramatic change in the speed of economic processes has changed the perception of costs and benefits related to agricultural activities. This is illustrated by the striking difference between preindustrial and industrial agriculture.

1. Agriculture of Preindustrial Societies Maximizes the Energy Output/Input Ratio

In preindustrial societies the "fuel" used to sustain societal activities consists mainly of food calories produced by agriculture, as well as the "energy converters" of the economic system are workers and draft animals, which are sustained because of the nutrients made available by agriculture. Since in these societies agricultural activity supplies the energy input and maintains the "converters" of energy into power, the more output is obtained from the energy invested in agriculture, the better off will be the rest of society, in terms of both stability and complexity. In preindustrial societies the energy surplus provided by agriculture is practically the only energy available for developing a service sector and improving the standard of living. Since this energy surplus is generally low in preindustrial agriculture, it is clear why preindustrial societies have a limited service sector.

2. Agriculture in Industrial Societies Maximizes the Speed of Energy Throughput

Industrial societies are no longer driven by human or animal labor, they are mainly fueled by fossil energy. Exosomatic energy flows, fed by fossil energy and driven by engines, represent the major component of society's energy budget. Alternatively, we can consider the total U.S. consumption of commercial energy per capita as an "expanded metabolism" of U.S. citizens, which, due to the use of exosomatic energy, amounts today to 90 times the human metabolism. A high ratio of exosomatic to endosomatic energy means that the opportunity cost of human time is high in industrial societies. We will illustrate this by a calculation of the opportunity cost of human labor in the United States.

In the United States only 51% of the population is economically active, and this value is further reduced to 47% because of actual unemployment. The average U.S. labor charge amounts to 1800 hr/yr (based on a 36 hr work-week, and 50 weeks of work a year); however, this value is reduced to 1750 hr/yr because of work-days lost for various reasons (e.g., illness, strikes, etc.). This means that a worker works for only about 20% of the total time in a year. Thus, considering the total population, less than 10% of the average human time (20% of the 47%) in the United States is spent working, while more than 90% is spent in nonworking activities. As the per capita energy consumption in the United States is 230,000 kcal/day = 9600 kcal/hr (referring to the total population, both working and nonworking), one hour of labor has to maintain also the consumption of 9 hr of non-working human time, that is, one hour of labor, as average, gives back to society about 100,000 kcal!

This huge "energy opportunity cost" of human time can explain the apparently bizarre evolution of agricultural performance. That is, technical evolution implies a continuous increase in the energy cost of a calorie of food produced. Since in the United States 1500 liters of oil equivalents are utilized per person to supply food for one year ($\approx 14 \; 10^6$ kcal/yr per capita), the energy cost of the diet is approximately 38,000 kcal/day per capita (about a gallon of oil equivalent). Considering that 3500 kcal/day per capita of food are currently available for consumption in the United States, this means that more than 10 kcal of oil is spent for each kcal of food. Comparison of this energy cost with the productivity of human labor shows that this quantity of fossil energy is made available by about 20 min of labor. Making a similar calculation for the diet of subsistence societies, reveals that the total energy cost of the daily diet in subsistence societies is certainly much lower in absolute terms—approximately 7000 kcal/day per capita, as-

suming a level of embodied energy of 3/1 for a per capita food supply of 2000 to 2500 kcal/day—but, because of the much lower productivity of human labor, this quantity of energy is made available by more than 3 hr of human labor (calculated as average energetic productivity of societal labor). This example stresses the importance to put in perspective any assessment of agricultural performance to include the interface with the economic process of the society in which the farmer is operating.

II. Current Pattern of Energy Use in Agriculture

A. Changes in Energy Use in U. S. Agriculture and Comparison with Agriculture in Other Countries

Table V shows the trend of fossil energy use in the United States. Exosomatic power, fueled by fossil energy, has increased while human labor inputs have been reduced dramatically. Whereas in 1950 only

TABLE V

Trends in Energy Inputs and Output per Hectare for U.S. Corn Production

Item	10^3 kcal/ha						
	1910	1950	1954	1959	1964	1970	1985
Machinery	278	555	648	777	907	907	1,018
Draft animals	886	ND	ND	0	0	0	0
Gasoline	0	1,350	1,500	1,550	1,250	1,200	400
Diesel	0	275	342	399	741	912	878
Electricity	ND	16	24	36	60	80	100
Nitrogen	0	357	630	966	1,555	2,478	3,192
Phosphorus	0	69	82	113	227	454	365
Potassium	0	28	50	85	70	170	187
Lime	3	61	39	50	64	69	134
Seeds	44	322	421	470	520	520	520
Insecticides	0	7	13	20	27	40	60
Herbicides	0	3	7	20	40	200	350
Irrigation	ND	125	250	375	625	1,125	2,250
Drying	0	10	15	54	145	376	760
Transport	25	58	67	79	89	84	89
Total inputs	1,236	3,236	4,088	4,994	5,920	8,615	10,303
Labor input[a] (hours/ha)	120	44	42	35	27	22	10
Yield	7,520	9,532	10,288	13,548	17,060	20,320	29,600

Source: Data are taken from Pimentel, D., Dazhong, W., and Giampietro, M. (1990). "Agroecology: Researching the Ecological Basis for Sustainable Agriculture" (S. Gliessman, ed.) pp. 305–381. Springer Verlag, New York.

Note: ND, no data.

a Labor inputs are expressed in hours/hectare as the opportunity cost of human time differs widely in the time span considered.

54 kg of corn was produced per hour of labor, in 1985 this had increased to 740 kg per hr! In the United States only 10 hr of human labor is required per hectare for corn production. Whereas in labor-intensive Chinese agriculture about 700 hr of human labor is required per hectare (Table III). Again the low density of the energy throughput in the Chinese society (in China the ratio exo/endo is about 8/1, almost 1/10th that in the United States) implies that the opportunity cost of human time is much lower in this system.

The population density—the availability of arable land per capita—of the society in which the farming system is operating also determines the optimizing strategy in allocating energy in agricultural production. This is illustrated by comparing the performance of agricultural systems in the United States and Western Europe, in both of which the energy throughput is maximized by heavy fossil energy subsidies (Table VI). The quantity of energy yield per hour of labor in Western Europe is almost twenty times higher than in China or Africa, but less than one fourteenth of that in the United States. However, the difference in land availability per farmer between the United States and Western Europe (almost 15-fold) implies that European agriculture uses twice as much energy as U.S. agriculture, while getting a much lower productivity of labor. Land constraints can explain the high consumption of fossil energy per hectare in China (in the same order of magnitude as in the United States), this high use of fossil energy subsidies is due to the need of boosting the yield per hectare and does not generate a dramatic increase in farmers' income, as indicated by the low productivity per hour of labor. In general, where the population density is high, fossil energy-based inputs are used in higher quantity to save land-area by increasing the yield per hectare. In Europe, the economic return of saved land area pushes for the use of more fossil energy, while in the United States the use of fossil energy is mainly driven by the effort to keep high the productivity of labor.

Finally it should be noted that the data of Table VI are from a different author and refer to the consumption of commercial energy. These assessments do not include the energy sequestered in machinery and other facilities, and therefore the ratios between output and input of energy calculated on these data can result different than the ones presented in the previous tables. This example should make the reader aware of a general problem concerning data found in the energy analysis literature. Since a generally accepted methodology for measuring energy balances is not available, assessments of energy flows and quantities are always affected by the assumptions made by the author (in particular, the decision of what is considered embodied in the flows of energy accounted for). This does not mean that data reporting different assessments are wrong, but simply that it is possible to describe the same system adopting different boundaries. Data provided by a single author are meaningful and can be used to study the performance of an agricultural system, but the methodology used to obtain data has to be always carefully checked before comparing them with data from different authors.

TABLE VI

Current Pattern of Energy Use in Different Agricultural Systems Producing Cereals

	United States	Africa	China	West Europe
Energy Throughput in society (ratio exo/endo)	90/1	≈ 5/1	8/1	≈ 40/1
Arable land (ha/worker)	92.0	1.4	0.4	6.1
Cereal yield (kg/worker)	340,300	1300	1300	23,300
Cereal yield (kg/ha)	3,700	900	3300	3,800
Cereal yield (10^6 kcal/ha)[a]	12	3	11	13
Cereal yield (kcal/hr labor)[a,b]	623,600	2400	2400	42,700
Cereal yield (kcal/kcal commercial energy input)	4.2	15.9	3.8	1.7
Commercial energy input (10^6 kcal/worker per year)	267.5	0.3	1.1	45.5
Commercial energy input (10^6 kcal/ha per year)	2.9	0.2	2.9	7.4
Commercial energy input (kcal/hour labor)[b]	149,000	150	611	25,300
Commercial energy input (kcal/kg cereal)	784	208	872	1,957

Source: Data from Faidley, L. W. (1992). Energy in farm production. *In* "Energy in World Agriculture," (R. C. Fluck, ed.), Vol. 6, pp. 1–12. Elsevier, Amsterdam.

[a] Assuming 3300 kcal/kg cereal.

[b] Assuming 1800 hr/year for agricultural workers.

B. Energy Inputs for Crops Production

This section discusses the energy inputs of agricultural production. Data referring to U.S. corn production are used as examples. [See CORN PRODUCTION.]

1. Machinery and Power

The tremendous difference made by engine power can be illustrated by analyzing the manpower equivalent of a gallon of fuel. One gallon (3.79 liters) of fuel fed to a small gasoline engine will convert 20% of the energy input into power. That is, 38,000 kcal (the energy in a gallon of gasoline) can be transformed into 8.8 kWhr. Thus, 1 gallon of gasoline can provide about 3 weeks of human work equivalents (human work output in agriculture is assumed to be 0.1 HP ≈ 0.074 kW, and the labor charge is assumed to be 40 hr/week).

Interestingly, the total amount of fuel consumed has declined from about 160 liters/ha in 1950 to about 120 liters/ha in 1985. The reason for the decline has been improved engine performance, and changes from gasoline to diesel fuel. Another reason for the reduced fuel consumption per hectare has been the use of large farm equipment that allows more operations to be performed over less time. The weight of the machinery per hour of labor, for example, has grown from about 0.4 kg in 1950 to about 5.5 kg in 1985—about a 14-fold increase. Hence, where liquid fuel inputs (direct energy consumption) have declined, fossil energy input for producing machinery (indirect energy consumption) has risen dramatically.

Initially in corn production, the principal fuel used in tractors was gasoline (85%), whereas diesel counted for only 15% of the fuel. With time, there was a shift toward diesel, and today at least 65% of tractor fuel is diesel. Diesel can provide 20 to 25% more power per gallon or greater efficiency per unit of fossil energy.

2. Commercial Fertilizers

In early slash and burn agriculture, vegetation was cut and burned to release the nutrients to the soil. Usually, the land had to lay fallow for about 20 years before sufficient nutrients would accumulate in the soil. The land could then be tilled and planted to crops for 2 years out of 22.

Early U.S. agriculture was primarily organic; that is, nutrients for crop production were provided mostly by livestock manure and green manures. In most cases, the farming system required 2 ha of land to produce 1 ha of crop. For example, 1 ha would be planted to a legume crop, such as clover or vetch, and the following year this legume would be plowed under and planted to corn. This 2-yr rotation system did provide an adequate amount of nitrogen for the corn crop; however, the soils were slowly depleted of phosphorous, potassium, and calcium.

In 1945, only 8 kg/ha of nitrogen and phosphorous and 6 kg/ha of potassium were applied. By 1985, nitrogen rates had reached a high of 152 kg/ha, this was nearly a 20-fold increase. Note that in 1985 the energy input for nitrogen alone was greater than the total energy inputs for all items combined in corn production in 1945. This is a clear example of a change in energy use in agriculture related to change in technologies.

During this 40-yr period a 30% improvement in efficiency of producing nitrogen fertilizers was reported. Although the amounts of phosphorous and potassium applied per hectare rose significantly from 1945 to 1985, these quantities clearly did not grow as rapidly as occurred with nitrogen, and both potassium and phosphorous require significantly less energy per kilogram to produce. [See FERTILIZER MANAGEMENT AND TECHNOLOGY.]

The quantity of lime applied to agricultural land also rose about three-fold from 1945 to 1985, but lime is, in the United States, the least costly in terms of energy of the fertilizers that are used in corn production.

3. Pesticides

Little or no pesticide was used in corn production in 1945. The quantity of insecticide applied to corn rose from 0.1 kg/ha in 1950 to 3 kg/ha by 1985. The insecticides used in the early 1950s and 1960s were primarily chlorinated insecticides. Starting with the ban of some chlorinated insecticides in the early 1970s, there was a gradual shift to carbamate and phosphate insecticides. With this change in the chemical makeup of insecticides, the energy inputs per kilogram of pesticide produced increased about 50%, and the total inputs for chemical insect control rose 45-fold. [See PEST MANAGEMENT, CHEMICAL CONTROL.]

Changes in herbicide use also occurred in corn production starting in 1950. The first herbicide used in corn production was 2,4-D, a phenoxy herbicide that was relatively efficient to produce in terms of energy input per kilogram. The newer triazines and other herbicides that were added during the 1960s and later were 50% more energy costly to produce. The total input for chemical weed control increased 267-fold from 1950 to date. Hence, changes affecting the requirement of energy input occurred not only in the quantities of pesticides applied, but also in the kinds of insecticides and herbicides used. [*See* HERBICIDES AND HERBICIDE RESISTANCE.]

4. Irrigation

The application of irrigation water for corn production has increased steadily over the years. Irrigation of corn acreage has increased from less than 1% in 1945 to an estimated 18% today. Water applied per irrigated hectare has increased from 1.8 million liters to about 3 million liters today. The energy input for irrigation water during the period 1945 to 1985 rose nearly 20-fold. [*See* IRRIGATION ENGINEERING: FARM PRACTICES, METHODS, AND SYSTEMS.]

C. Different Crop Production

1. Other Crops and Feed Crops

Until now we focused mainly on corn production to illustrate the general trend of changes in energy use and the methodological approach of energy analysis. Data for the energy input and output for different crops (other grains, legumes, vegetables, and fruits) are presented in Table VII for those who are interested to study in detail the performance of other techniques of production. Because of limited space, we only provide an overview of the range of values (energy input

requirement, hours of labor, and return of the cultivation) that can be found in U.S. agriculture for different types of crops.

D. Livestock Production

1. Livestock

The amount of energy expended in livestock production systems depends not only on the animal but also on the type of feed. Animals vary in the efficiency with which they convert plant energy and protein into animal protein. In addition, they vary in their ability to utilize different plant foods. Table VIII shows energy inputs and returns per hectare for various livestock production systems in the United States.

III. Future Energy Use in Agriculture in Relation to Sustainability

A. Trends in Agricultural Performance and Demographic Pressure

In the early phase of human evolution the population size was so small that, practically, the planet was void of human civilization and new frontiers were available all around. The problem of feeding more people was

TABLE VII

Energy Input and Return per Hectare for Various U.S. Crop Production Systems

Crops (food and feed)	Yield (kg)	Yield in protein (kg)	Yield in food energy (10^6 kcal)	Commercial energy input (10^6 kcal)	Labor (hr)	kcal food-feed/ kcal commercial energy input
Corn (U.S. average)	7,000	630	24.5	6.9	12	3.5
Wheat (North Dakota)	2,022	283	6.7	2.5	6	6.0
Oats (Minnesota)	2,869	423	10.9	2.1	3	5.1
Rice (Arkansas)	4,742	272	14.0	12.5	30	1.1
Sorghum (Kansas)	1,840	202	6.0	1.5	5	4.0
Alfalfa (Minnesota)	11,800(dry)	1845	47.2	3.6	12	13.1
Tame hay (New York)	2,539(dry)	160	5.5	0.6	7	8.6
Corn Silage (Northeast)	9,400(dry)	753	29.1	5.2	15	5.6
Soybean (Illinois)	2,600	885	10.5	2.3	8	4.5
Beans, dry (Michigan)	1,176	285	4.1	3.1	19	1.3
Peanuts (Georgia)	3,720	320	15.3	10.9	19	1.4
Potato (New York)	34,468	539	21.1	15.5	35	1.4
Lettuce (California)	31,595	284	4.1	19.7	171	0.2
Tomato (California)	49,620	496	9.9	16.6	165	0.6
Cabbage (New York)	53,000	1060	12.7	16.8	289	0.8
Apples (East)	41,546	83	23.3	26.2	176	0.9
Oranges (Florida)	40,370	404	19.8	11.8	210	1.7

Source: Adapted from Pimentel, D. (1984). Energy flow in food system. *In* "Food and Energy Resources" (D. Pimentel and C. W. Hall, eds.), pp. 1–24. Academic Press, New York.

TABLE VIII

Energy Input and Return per Hectare for Various U.S. Livestock Production Systems

Livestock	Yield (kg)	Yield in protein (kg)	Protein as food energy (10³ kcal)	Commercial energy input (10³ kcal)	Labor (hr)	kcal protein/ kcal commercial energy input
Broilers	2,000	186	740	7,300	9.8	0.14
Eggs	910	104	416	7,400	17.8	0.05
Pork	490	35	140	6,000	42.9	0.09
Sheep (grass-fed)	7	0.2	0.8	70	87.5	5
Dairy	3,270	114	457	5,400	11.8	0.02
Beef	60	6	24	600	25.0	0.5
Dairy (grass-fed)	3,260	114	457	5,400	7.2	0.02
Beef (grass-fed)	54	5	20	500	25.0	0.5
Catfish	2,783	384	1,536	52,500	34.2	0.02

Source: Adapted from Pimentel D., and Hall, C. W. (1984). "Food and Energy Resources." Academic Press, New York.

solved by simply putting more land under agricultural production.

After the introduction of fossil energy and machines, humans grew fast, terms of both in population size and in per capita resource consumption. The consequent demographic and economic growth saturated the available land and pushed agricultural production techniques toward higher densities of withdrawal of net primary productivity per unit of land.

The increasing use of fossil energy to augment yields implied a decreasing return per unit of input. Moreover, the more saturated the land, the more marginal areas, less suitable for agricultural production, were put in production, further exacerbating the effect of decreasing returns. However, despite the continuous increase in the energetic cost of production, the trend toward increasing productivity per unit of land is forced by the continuous decrease in arable land per capita, induced by demographic growth.

When the stress induced by human activity on natural and managed ecosystems becomes excessive, environmental degradation can appear as an unwanted side effect. This occurs when too little energy is left in the natural compartment to sustain those processes that have no economic return, but that nevertheless are required to maintain the ecosystems' structure and functions.

B. Limits to the Intensification of Agriculture

Stable ecosystems have the ability to use solar energy to sustain their own process of self-organization. Agriculture has an impact on the pattern of energy flows in ecosystems, and in general reduces the capability of a defined ecosystem of using solar energy for evapotranspiration, gross primary production, and recycling nutrients. In fact, human alteration is aimed at increasing the fraction of useful biomass produced and harvested per year, and the "side" effect is a reduction of the flow of solar energy that a biological community uses to stabilize its structure and functions. In spite of the fact that this "ecological cost" of agriculture has been systematically overlooked by modern economic analysis, the long-term productivity of agro-ecosystems depends on the stability of natural systems (biological, soil, and water resources). In order to be sustainable agriculture should not disrupt the natural processes that maintain a stable supply of those inputs.

Therefore, there exists an upper limit to the increase in productivity provided by the (in)stability of the agroecosystem (land degradation, loss of topsoil, pollution from agriculture, groundwater mining). We should care about the quality and productivity of our agroecosystems since their productivity is finite. In this century, technological development basically enabled us to convert fossil fuel into food, but we must be aware that technology has not lowered our dependence on fossil fuels nor our dependence on natural services to obtain our food supply.

Natural factors are still fundamental for the sustainability of food production and all are deeply related to the energetics of agricultural production: (1.) biodiversity, more species means more ability to use solar energy for environmental services and a wider range of biological functions which could result indispensable to human survival in the future. At the ecological level, all species are useful and once they are lost, they are lost forever. (2.) Soil fertility determines the ability of soil to retain nutrients, water, and to support plant activity. Agricultural soil is a very valuable capital which can be lost when humans intensify too much agricultural production. Today, top soil is lost at a rate of 40–70 tons/ha per year in China and India, and at an annual rate of 16 tons/ha in the United States. The level of sustainable loss is estimated at about 1 ton/ha per year, since 500 years are required to replace 2.5 cm of lost topsoil (2.5 cm = 1 in.; 1 hectare-inch of topsoil weighs 400 tons). (3.) Water supply: the requirement of fresh water for agricultural production is huge in the United States. In total, U.S. agriculture uses 400 10^{12} liters water/year (= 85% of the total consumption of fresh water ≈ 1.6 million liters per capita/year ≈ 4000 liters per capita/day). In many areas, more water is used than is naturally supplied. Pumping groundwater is used to offset the difference and, again, fossil energy and mechanical power are used to overcome the limitation provided by natural cycles. Groundwater resources are renewed, but at an extremely slow rate (about 1% per year). However, in the United States the average overdraft is 25% higher than the replacement, and in some locations like the Ogallala aquifer, overdraft amounts to 130 to 160% over the replacement. Finally, agriculture can negatively affect the supply of fresh water to society, by polluting the water table with residues of fertilizers and/or pesticides.

In many cases, technological solutions exist to increase productivity while preserving the essential capital of nature, but this requires that future trends in energy use in agriculture should be directed not only toward increased rates of harvest (optimization of economic variables), but also toward the sustainability of vital agricultural and ecological processes (optimization of the stability of natural processes and the environment). However, it should be noted that, in spite of any technological evolution, environmental concerns push toward a slow down of the speed of energy flows, which clashes with the economic perspective of pushing toward higher returns for agricultural activities.

C. Future Energy Use in Agriculture?

The adoption of the economic point of view aiming at an illimited growth explains the current heavy use of energy inputs in agriculture (high energy intensity of cultivation). On the other hand, concern for sustainability seems to question this "growth-mania." Agriculture, being at the interface between two systems (economic and ecological) going at increasingly different speeds, is experiencing the resulting increasing friction.

When the economic perspective is the only parameter considered for optimization (with the goal: more goods and services have to be produced and consumed to achieve a higher standard of living) the role of agriculture is to increase the population density. Because of the multiplicative effect that exosomatic energy has on human labor, increasing the number of people means the possibility to expand the activity of the economic process; in ultimate analysis the food supply has as effect to enable the society to pump oil out of the ground and transform it in useful work for humankind at a faster rate.

When the ecological side is considered we can see the reverse of the medallion of this pattern of technological evolution: human expansion means a decrease of the energy used by natural systems (loss of biodiversity, desertification, loss of fertility, soil erosion, reduction of biomass present on a yearly basis, reduction of evapotranspiration per unit of area); and industrial agriculture becomes a dangerous tool for altering as much as possible what is left of the original endowment of natural ecosystems around the world.

The issue of sustainability in agricultural production implies that the aspiration toward economic growth should be balanced by a concern for the stability of natural processes that guarantee environmental equilibria. In this perspective a reduction of energy intensity in agriculture should be searched for in many areas of the world. However, the saved energy should not be used for further boosting the productivity (at continuously decreasing return) of the already overstressed agroecosystem, but rather for enhancing natural capital, restoring the areas where the human impact generated major damages. This should and we hope will be the future trend in energy use in agriculture.

Unfortunately, the actual trend of demographic growth (doubling of the population every 40 to 45 years) and the consequent shrinking of land availability (0.28 ha of arable land per capita with 5.5 billion people, will become 0.15 ha/capita with a population of 8 to 10 billion) makes a reduction of the intensity in agricultural production unlikely. The threat provided by population growth is further stressed by the following considerations: (i) most countries of the world are now dependent on imports to match their food demand. The world grain supply is basically maintained by a few countries with low population density (United States, Canada, Australia, and Argentina); what will happen when an increase in population within these countries will consume the current surplus available for export? (ii) Many developing countries use more fertilizer per hectare than the United States; this is not for boosting income but for survival, just for producing more food on a shrinking area per capita. What would a future restriction of the oil supply mean to the agriculture of these countries?

The dilemma of human return versus environmental stability can no longer be ignored by the public: continuous population growth, increasing dependency of our food supply on rapidly depleting stocks of oil, and degradation of the productivity of agroecosystems will force us to focus again and it is hoped under new, more holistic perspectives on agriculture and on its fundamental role in sustaining human development.

Bibliography

Giampietro, M., Cerretelli, G., and Pimentel, D. (1992). Energy analysis of agricultural ecosystem management: human return and sustainability. *Agricult. Ecosystems Environ.* **38**, 219–244.

Giampietro, M., Cerretelli, G., and Pimentel, D. (1992). Assessment of different agricultural practices. *Ambio* **21**(7), 451–459.

Hall, C.A.S., Cleveland, C.J., and Kaufmann, R. (1986). "Energy and Resource Quality—The Ecology of the Economic Process," Chap. 6, pp. 115–142. Wiley, New York.

Pimentel, D. (ed.) (1980). "Handbook of Energy Utilization in Agriculture." CRC Press, Boca Raton, FL.

Pimentel, D., Dazhong, W., and Giampietro. M. (1990). Technological changes in energy use in U.S. Agricultural production. *In* "Agroecology: Researching the Ecological Basis for Sustainable Agriculture" (S. Gliessman, ed.), pp. 305–321. Springer Verlag, New York.

Pimentel, D., and Hall, C. W. (eds.) (1984). "Food and Energy Resources." Academic Press, New York.

Stout, B. A. (Editor-in-Chief). "Energy in World Agriculture," Vols. 1–6. Elsevier, Amsterdam.

Entomology, Horticultural

KENNETH A. SORENSEN, *North Carolina State University*

Glossary

Biological control Pest control strategy that employs methods such as conservation, introduction, augmentation, and mass release of parasites, predators, and disease organisms

Bacillus thuringiensis (BT) Bacterium that causes disease in many insects; in the past, BT has been directed toward certain Lepidopterous plant feeders; now BT has effectiveness against beetles and flies, with a great deal of specificity

Good laboratory practices (GLPs) Specific actions in the conduct of a research study that allow assurances about the integrity of the data; involving written documentation of standard operating procedures, uses, master schedules, and quality assurance

Insect sex pheromone Chemicals emitted by one sex of a species (usually a female) to call a mate (usually a male) to it for mating and propagation; these intraspecific communication compounds attract insects of the opposite sex for the purpose of mating and reproduction

Integrated pest management (IPM) Economic, ecological, environmental, and social strategy that focuses on long-term prevention or suppression of pest problems through a combination of techniques such as encouraging biological control, use of resistant varieties, or adaption of alternative cultivating, pruning, or fertilizing practices or modification of habitat to make it incompatible with pest development; pesticides are used based on trap monitoring and field scouting and on need according to pre-established guidelines or thresholds

IR-4 Federally sponsored interregional research program to support registrations and obtain residue tolerances for minor use pesticides and biorationals on major crops and on minor crops such as most vegetables, fruits, nuts, herbs, ornamentals, trees, and turf; this program also includes registration of animal health drugs

Mating disruption Technique of insect control based on the premise that males are unable to locate females when the environment around the females is permeated with a sex pheromone; this is a preventive measure that has been successful only when insect populations are relatively low and mated females do not migrate

Microbial insecticides Insecticides that contain microorganisms or their by-products and comprise microscopic living organisms (viruses, bacteria, fungi, protozoa, or nematodes); they are safe, since their toxicity to nontarget animals and humans is extremely low

Reregistration All pesticides registered before November 1, 1984, are to be reregistered by 1997; this process has five phases and involves industry, growers, and governmental agencies

Resistance management Strategy to overcome or retard the ability of species, races, or biotypes to withstand normally lethal doses of pesticides due to genetic or behavioral selection

Semiochemicals Chemicals that mediate interactions between organisms of the same or different species; pheromones are the type that excite or stimulate an organism of the same species

Sustainable agriculture System of production agriculture that employs any and all techniques that are environmentally compatible and usually involves low input renewable resources; this system is often associated with organic gardening

Tomato spotted wilt virus (TSWV) Virus disease of plants that has a wide host range and variable symptoms; TSWV is spread by an insect vector, usually the Western flower thrips

Horticultural entomology is that specialized area in entomology that deals with insects and related arthropods associated with horticultural crops. These crops include the general areas of pomology (fruits), olericulture (vegetables), floriculture (flowers), herbs, nuts, shade trees, ornamentals, and turf. The rural and urban audience consists of commercial producers, homeowners, greenhouse growers, garden center operators, agribusiness, and various practitioners. Diversity, intensity, specialty, and complexity are realistic attributes of horticultural entomology programs.

I. New and Old Insect Pests

A. Traditional Pests

Such traditional arthropod pests as corn earworm, European corn borer, cabbage looper, armyworm species, cutworm species, leafminer, flea beetle, vegetable weevil, and mites continue to plague growers of horticultural crops. However, some of the older pests have resurged. These include aphids (new biotypes), whitefly (greenhouse and sweetpotato), *Diabrotica* (rootworm) species, wireworms, and white grubs. [*See* PLANT PATHOLOGY.]

B. New Pests

Some new pests of economic concern to growers of horticultural crops are the strain B (silverleaf whitefly) whitefly and the western flower thrips. Both these pests are small, have a wide host range, complete a generation in a short time, are usually grouped with a common species, have adapted to changes in cultural practices and pesticides, and cause direct and indirect damage. The direct damage is feeding on plant tissue, whereas the indirect damage is associated with plant viruses (tomato spotted wilt viruses and others). Increased movement of plants has favored the spread of whitefly and thrips. [*See* PLANT VIROLOGY.]

C. Soil Insects

Soil insects in general are on the increase. Wireworms, white grubs, whitefringed beetle, and the sweetpotato weevil all cause chronic damage to plants by feeding on seed, seedlings, tubers, or roots. The loss of the persistent chlorinated hydrocarbon insecticides, the setting aside of land not in production, and the movement to no-till or minimum tillage are some reasons for the resurgence of soil insects.

D. Pests Resistant to Insecticide

Two other pests, the Colorado potato beetle and the diamondback moth, have established themselves as pests of the first order. Not only are they destructive, but through the development of resistance to insecticides they have become most difficult to control.

II. Insect Sex Pheromones

A. Monitoring and Mating Disruption

Insect behavioral studies have contributed a novel approach to pest control. Through studies of insects searching for mates, chemists have identified, synthesized, field tested, and commercialized semiochemicals. One type of semiochemical that is useful is determining where, when, and how many insects of a single species are present is called an insect sex pheromone. Males locate a mate by following a sex attractant called a pheromone.

Insect sex pheromones, once synthesized, undergo extensive laboratory and field studies to determine their purity, the type of slow release medium to use, the dosage, and the trap type. With commercialization, the attractant lure and trap are selected and promoted. Presently, about 100 insect pheromones are available; several companies produce and distribute insect sex pheromones.

B. Uses of Insect Sex Pheromones

Two uses of sex pheromone are detection and control. Detection is easy, since the approach is, for the most part, specific. The control approach is further divided into mass trapping and mating disruption. Mass trapping as a control tactic has not been effective. However, the mating disruption approach has been more successful. Some programs in various stages of development target tomato pinworm, codling moth, tufted apple bud moth, Oriental fruit moth, cranberry girdler, pink bollworm, and gypsy moth.

III. Minor Use Registration and Pesticide Reregistration

A. The IR-4 Program

Minor crops such as most vegetables, fruits, nuts, herbs, ornamentals, and trees and minor uses such as the use of a biorational material on stored grain do not have the volume of "pesticide use" required to economically justify registration through traditional and expensive manufacturer procedures as mandated by the Environmental Protection Agency (EPA). Hence, needs by a commercial enterprise at any level exists, so some assistance is required in conducting field and laboratory studies to obtain residue tolerances and efficacy data, and to document any adverse affects to the crop, the applicator, or the environment.

The Interregional Research Project No. 4 (IR-4 project) was established in 1963 by directors of the State Agricultural Experiment Stations, located at land grant universities throughout the United States, to obtain residue tolerances for minor-use pesticides on food and feed crops. In 1977, the program was expanded to include registrations of pesticides needed for the protection of nursery and floral crops, forestry seedlings, and turf grass. The program was further expanded in 1982 to include the registration of animal health drugs, antibiotics, and anthelminthics for minor animal species. Another addition to the program in 1982 was the inclusion of an initiative to register biorationals for agricultural pest control. These substances include microbial and biochemical pest control agents that can be an important adjunct to integrated pest management (IPM) systems.

IR-4 cooperates with state and federal research scientists, growers, and agricultural chemical and biotechnology companies to register pest control agents for use in pest management programs on minor crops and for minor uses on major crops. Since 1964, IR-4 has worked to register pesticide uses for minor crops; some 3500 pesticides and biorationals had been registered by 1992. With Centers this program will assess local needs, prioritize limited resources, and, with good laboratory practices, help provide the efficacy and residue data needed to support registrations.

B. Pesticide Reregistration

In October 1988, Congress amended the Federal Insecticide, Fungicide, and Rodenticide Act (FIFRA 88).

As amended, FIFRA requires that all pesticides and their uses registered before November 1984 be reregistered, complying with certain human health and environmental risk standards by the end of 1997. This requires that some 10,300 tolerances be obtained; of these, some 8,000 would involve minor uses. This legislation has most serious implications for minor crops (nuts, fruits, vegetables, ornamentals, flowers, trees, and turf grass) since minor crops are of major importance in the United States. Agrichemical companies will decide about reregistering the pesticides they manufacture after considering the market potential, the cost of supporting reregistration, and the potential adverse effects on public health and the environment. As a result, the availability of pesticides used on minor crops will be greatly reduced, and their loss will jeopardize the American farmer's ability to grow and market these very important crops. The 1990 Farm Bill also addresses pesticides and food safety, and includes worker safety standards, IPM, and sustainable agriculture.

IV. *Bacillus thuringiensis:* A Wave of Biological Insecticides

A. What Is It?

Bacillus thuringiensis (BT) is a naturally occurring bacterium commonly found in the soil. First identified in the early 1900s, BTs did not develop commercially until the 1940s. Their use in the 1950s and 1960s was directed at cabbage looper, imported cabbageworm, and other Lepidopterous larvae of crucifers. Limited knowledge of BT genetics and mode of action inhibited their development. An improved BT strain, BT *kurstaki,* was discovered in the late 1960s that was consistently active against caterpillars and was easier to produce. Expanded use on vegetables and against gypsy moth resulted in increased markets. More recently, many companies have identified and increased BT potency against targeted insects using genetic manipulation. IPM, organic farming, and sustainable agriculture offer additional markets. BT specificity and effectiveness against such resistant insect pests as Colorado potato beetle and diamondback moth have further synergized BT development and use around the world (see Table I).

BT products, for the most part, are exempt from residue tolerances and, as such, pose no hazard or risk to humans and the environment. Also, there are no time limitations to harvest or re-entry restrictions.

TABLE I

Available *Bacillus thuringiensis* products

Strain	Name®	Formulation[a]	Pest controlled[b]	Manufacturers
kurstaki	Biobit	FC, WP	Lepidopterous larvae	Dupont
	Dipel	2X, 4L, WP	Lepidopterous larvae	Abbott
	Javelin	WG	Lepidopterous larvae	Sandoz
	Cutlass	WP	Lepidopterous larvae, esp. diamondback moth	Ecogen
	Foil	L	esp. diamondback moth, Colorado potato beetle, some European corn borer	Ecogen
	MVP	L	Diamondback moth	Mycogen
san diego	M-Trak	L	Colorado potato beetle	Mycogen
tennebrionis	Trident II	L	Colorado potato beetle	Sandoz
	Novodor	FC	Colorado potato beetle	Novo Nordisk
aizawai	Xentari	WDG	Diamondback moth	Abbott
	Agree	WP	Diamondback moth	Ciba-Geigy
israelensis	Gnatrol	L	Fungus gnats	Abbott

[a] FC, Flowable concentrate; WP, wettable powder; 2X, 2-concentrate; 4L, 4-liquid; WG, wettable granules; L, liquid; WDG, water dispersible granule.

[b] BT products may also have relative effectiveness against other pests such as armyworms, cutworms, webworms, hornworms, earworm, pickleworm, and leaf rollers. Be sure to check label for crop and pests controlled, as well as university specialists and county extension agents for specific recommendations. Other BT products may be available and include Bactospene, Larvo, and Thuricide. Still other formulations may exist or will be available in the near future.

These products are also safe on such beneficials as honey bees, predaceous and parasitic insects (Neuroptera, Coleoptera, Diptera, Hymenoptera), and predaceous mites and spiders. [*See* PLANT BIOTECHNOLOGY: FOOD SAFETY AND ENVIRONMENTAL ISSUES.]

B. Mode of Action

BT products act as stomach poisons and must be ingested by larvae to be effective. Also, BT products are most effective against small larvae. BT products contain spores and active protein crystals, produced by the naturally occurring bacterium. In some cases, BT are conjugated or encapsulated to afford effectiveness and stability. On ingestion by an insect larva, spores and protein crystals enter the midgut where they are dissolved and toxins are released. This event causes a disruption of the membranes and cell walls. Feeding stops within hours and larval mortality occurs over a 2- to 5-day period. Enzyme and pH activity are critical because these activities dissolve the crystals. Several protoxins may be converted and bound to specialized receptor molecules in the insect gut lining.

C. In the Future

BTs have a definite market niche. Companies are directing attention to those markets in which efficacy of BT products is as good as or superior to that of other products. Where no alternatives exist, or when insecticide resistance is a major concern, BT products offer a new chemistry and a new approach. The issue of safety opens new areas, new audiences, and new crops. As a result, specialty crop areas such as potato for Colorado potato beetle and collards for diamondback moth have received and will continue to receive much attention.

The future of BTs will extend well beyond the year 2000. In fact, with over 2000 strains of BT available and with genetic engineering, the combinations and permutations are many. New formulation technology, increased understanding of mode of action, custom design of BT toxins in transgenic plants (potatoes with BT could be available in 1995) or in other organisms (cell cap technology), and the integration of cultural, biological, natural, and chemical control methods will bring BTs to the forefront in IPM and sustainable agriculture.

V. Best Management Practices

Best management practices comprise any and all strategies and tactics employed with a plant or animal to help optimize production and marketing efficiency. In horticultural and field crops, this system may be referred to as Integrated Crop Management (ICM).

A. Integrated Pest Management

IPM emerged in the 1960s and 1970s and is an economic, ecological, environmental, and social strategy that focuses on long-term prevention or suppression of pest problems through a combination of techniques. IPM seeks maximum use of naturally occurring pest controls including weather, disease agents, predators, and parasites. In addition, IPM utilizes various biological, physical, and chemical control and habitat modification techniques. Artificial controls are imposed only as required to keep a pest from exceeding predetermined and periodic assessments of population levels. This all-inclusive decision-making approach strives for pest control while minimizing hazards to human health and the environment. [See INTEGRATED PEST MANAGEMENT.]

Various levels of IPM are utilized for horticultural crops grown in the field, greenhouse, and garden. The more successful programs employ pest monitoring and field scouting by professional consultants, whose sole purpose is to provide timely advice based on economic and action thresholds. Every state and most countries have specific programs and such resources as training manuals, sources of monitoring traps and natural enemies, and slides and videotapes. These resources are available through local county extension offices, State University specialists, and various state agencies.

B. Resistance Management

The development of resistance to insecticides is common among pests of horticultural crops. Historical records document the wide variety of insects that have developed resistance to insecticides. Insects and mites on the list include corn earworm, fall armyworm, cabbage looper, diamondback moth, tomato pinworm, aphids, whiteflies, leafminers, spider mites, Colorado potato beetle, and various soil insects. The list of insecticides to which resistance has developed includes Sevin,® malathion, Lannate,® Furadan,® Guthion,® parathion, Vydate,® *Bacillus thuringiensis,* diazinon, Cygon,® Ambush,® Pounce,® Asana,® and Kelthane.® Resistance to BT by diamondback moth, Colorado potato beetle and gypsy moth has been reported.

What can be done to slow, prevent, or manage insecticide resistance? First is a recognition that insects may already be resistant to specific insecticides. Next is an understanding of how insects develop resistance to insecticides. Finally, the steps that can be taken to address the problem constitute resistance management.

A good indication of insecticide resistance is control failure with an insecticide that has worked previously. However, improper mixing or poor application

methods are common reasons for failure of insect control. On-farm tests with different insecticides, insect counts, and damage assessment will confirm resistance. Verification procedures consist of using a bioassay that compares a known susceptible insect colony to a "suspect colony" using dosage response curves. The method is leaf discs, slide dips, vials, traps or direct topical application of insecticides to the target insect. Mortality is checked usually after 24 or 48 hr. LD_{50} values (dosage necessary to kill 50% of the insect population) are determined. When these values from susceptible and suspect insect populations are compared, the relative degree of resistance is determined.

Insects develop resistance from exposure to insecticides over time by a combination of physiological and genetic means. The insect metabolizes the toxicant and, thus, renders a dose sublethal. Hence, the next insect generation can be resistant to an insecticide it has never contacted directly. Similarly, with "cross resistance," once resistance to an insecticide occurs, that insect population may possess resistance to other insecticides in the same or different chemical classes. Hence, pesticide users need to know what insecticides are carbamates, organophosphates, pyrethroids, and so on. This resistance can develop on a single farm in a single year. Insects introduced into an area from areas further south also are likely to be resistant because of previous and frequent exposure to insecticides.

Managing insect resistance with BTs must be considered. BTs are ideal for controlling insects that are resistant to chemical insecticides, because they offer new chemistry and a unique mode of action. However, when used wrongly or overused, resistance to BT toxins has resulted. An approach to resistance management consists of minimizing the development of BT resistance by alternating or rotating BT products that have different toxins, using BTs when resistance to other chemicals exists, and using BTs in alternating programs with different classes of insecticides to prevent development of resistance. Obviously, rotation of crops, the use of high pressure sprayers, the timely use of BTs and other insecticides, and resistance monitoring (in field scouting and records) will aid in pest and pesticide management.

What can be done to manage insecticide resistance? A few suggestions for consideration follow.

1. Practice crop rotation within season and between years.
2. Do not grow small plants next to older plants over a long period of time.

3. Isolate plantings.
4. Use insect-resistant varieties.
5. Plant insect-free transplants.
6. Rotate chemical classes of insecticides (organophosphates, carbamates, biologicals, etc.).
7. Follow good horticultural practices to reduce plant stress.
8. Monitor for insects and spray only when needed.
9. Avoid low rates and long spray intervals.
10. Use tank mixes.
11. Use a synergist such as piperonyl butoxide.
12. Obtain good coverage to help insure good control.
13. Monitor for insecticide resistance (on-farm comparisons).
14. Contract to have dose–response curves developed.
15. Use biological control and IPM practices.
16. Keep good records.

C. Sustainable Agriculture

Sustainable agriculture is a system of production agriculture that has gained popularity and support at all levels in recent years. This system employs any and all techniques that are environmentally compatible and usually includes low input renewable resources and, as such, has been associated with organic gardening. Strict interpretation and practices in sustainable agriculture avoid all synthetic fertilizers, pesticides, and chemicals and many natural materials that are not environmentally friendly. This practice relies exclusively on natural amendments, green manures, composting, and cultural and natural control methods that maintain soil structure, manage pests, and produce horticultural crops in a sustainable manner. [See Sustainable Agriculture.]

Low input and environmental compatibility are important elements in sustainable agriculture. The 1990 Farm Bill specifically directs resources to research and development in this arena. Other attention is being directed at the state level to the development, implementation, and inspection requirements that will allow for organically certified crops and animals.

VI. Conclusion

The fields of horticultural entomology and crops face several challenging issues in the decade ahead. First is the delicate task of maintaining agricultural competitiveness in global marketing with declining resources. The North American Free Trade Agreement (NAFTA) and General Agreement on Tariffs and Trade (GATT) will have significant impacts on fruit and vegetable producers. Downsizing in government, landgrant universities, county extension offices, and agribusiness will restrict free flow of capital, research development, and transfer of technology. Second is the production of a stable, economical, and safe food supply. With instability in weather, pests, and governments, any shift in horticultural production and markets will influence the supply and demand of raw and processed products. Increased regulations and public pressure will affect produce at the farm gate. New or revised legislation on pesticides and worker safety standards will impact growers and consumers alike. Interpretation of the Delaney Amendment and its application will have implications for processed foods and raw agricultural products. Our collective task in the future will center on our continuous ability to research, understand, and apply scientifically based knowledge to improve the quality of life for all and to sustain the environment.

Bibliography

Beroza, M. (1975). "Pest Management with Sex Attractants and Other Behavior-Controlling Chemicals." American Chemical Society, Washington, D.C.

Jutsum, A. R., and Gordon, R. F. S. (1989). "Insect Pheromones in Plant Protection." Wiley. New York.

Knight, A. L., and Norton, G. W. (1989). Economics of agricultural pesticide resistance in arthropods. *Annu. Rev. Entomol.* **34,** 293–315.

Mitchell, E. R. (1982). "Management of Insect Pests with Semiochemicals." Plenum Press, New York.

Nordlund, D. A., Jones, R. L., and Lewis, W. J. (1981). "Semiochemicals: Their Role in Pest Control." Wiley, New York.

Ridgeway, R. L., Silverstein, R. M., and Inscoe, M. (1990). "Behavior-Modifying Chemicals for Insect Management Applications of Pheromones and Other Attractants.". Marcel Dekker, New York.

Rodriguez, B. A., and Trumble, J. T. (1989). "El Manejo Integrado de las Placas en el Cultivo de Tomate en Sinawa." University of California, Riverside.

Scentry (1992). "Nomate Gusano en el Gusano Alfiler del Tomate." Scentry, Buckeye. Arizona.

United States Department of Agriculture (1992). "New Crops, New Uses, New Markets." Yearbook of Agriculture. Office of Publishing and Visual Communications, U.S. Department of Agriculture, Washington, D.C.

University of California Statewide IPM (1990). "Integrated Pest Management for Tomatoes." University of California, Davis.

Entomology, Veterinary

R. W. SUTHERST, *CSIRO Division of Entomology, Australia*

Glossary

Density dependent mechanisms Influences which have an effect on the fecundity or mortality rates of a species that varies with the density of the population
Endemic Permanent occupation by a parasite or disease
Equilibrium population density Density to which a population tends to return following perturbation
Expert system Computer software based on artificial intelligence and used to provide easy access to advice on diagnosis or management of a problem
Host resistance Acquired partial immunity to a parasite
IPM Integrated pest management
Moderation Minimum possible use of pesticides
Myiasis Infestation with a disease caused by fly maggots
Pest risk analysis Process of defining risk of introduction and establishment of an exotic pest or outbreak of an endemic pest
Population regulation Process by which populations return to equilibrium in response to negative feedback mechanisms.
Saturation Use of pesticides at concentrations high enough to kill heterozygous resistance strains

The taxonomy, ecology, behavior, damage, and vector roles of veterinary arthropods are described together with control methods and management strategies to reduce the impacts of those arthropods on livestock and domestic pets. Other aspects of veterinary entomology such as insect physiology and structure are not considered. [*See* INSECT PHYSIOLOGY.]

I. Introduction

Veterinary entomology is mainly concerned with the management of arthropods, including insects, ticks, and mites, which attack livestock, domestic pets, or wildlife. Some of these arthropods also act as vectors of disease or cause problems by breeding in animal waste. Most are parasites, but some, such as houseflies, cause a nuisance without parasitizing their host. Damaging species of arthropods are found throughout the world, either alone or together with other species on the same host, and are more prevalent in the tropics. They affect almost every type of wild and domesticated animal. The control of veterinary arthropod pests involves a variety of techniques based on chemical pesticides, vaccination, natural enemies, animal breeding, grazing management, trapping, release of sterilized populations of pests, and other methods. The frequent presence of mixed infestations of parasites means that it is desirable to adopt an integrated pest management (IPM) approach. In IPM, a combination of measures is used to attack the complex of pests present while emphasising the need to be compatible with overall management of the agricultural enterprise. Quarantine measures are used to protect against the spread of pests around the world and eradication measures are applied under special circumstances. [*See* INTEGRATED PEST MANAGEMENT.]

II. Taxonomic Groups

Veterinary entomology covers a large number of taxonomic groups, including several insect genera and

TABLE I

Taxonomic Groups Considered in Veterinary Entomology

Diptera
    Muscidae (house fly, stable fly, horn fly, buffalo fly)
    Calliphoridae (myiasis flies, screwworm fly, and sheep
      blowfly)
    Ceratopogonidae (biting midges)
    Culicidae (mosquitoes)
    Glossinidae (tsetse fly)
    Hemiptera (bugs)
    Hippoboscidae (keds, louse flies)
    Oestridae, Hypodermatidae, Gasterophilidae, Cuterebridae
      (bot, nasal, warble flies)
    Psychodidae (sandflies)
    Simuliidae (black flies)
    Tabanidae (horse, deer, or March flies)
Phthiraptera [sucking (Anoplura) and chewing (Mallophaga)
    lice]
Siphonaptera (fleas)
Acari (mange and blood-sucking mites)
Ixodida
    Argasidae (soft ticks)
    Ixodidae (hard ticks)

acarines. A summary of these groups is given in Table I.

Most species can be separated by traditional taxonomic keys based on morphological characters that are visible under a light microscope, especially when supported by information on the geographical distribution, host range, and behavior of each species. More sophisticated methods involving electron microscopy or molecular biology are sometimes applied to distinguish between morphologically indistinguishable species.

III. Ecological Principles

Arthropods need energy, water, food, and shelter from their environment. Their hosts may supply some or most of these needs. The individual needs of each species vary widely and determine its geographical distribution, the animals on which it is found, and its relative abundance. Within the field of veterinary entomology the whole range of variation is to be found. While many arthropods such as biting or myiasis flies attack a wide range of hosts, others such as lice and some ticks and mites feed only on a single host species. Some arthropods are cosmopolitan while others have very limited geographical distributions. Important species such as screwworm flies are quite rare but very damaging to their host while others such as mosquitoes are abundant and can cause

distress simply by their numbers. Some are highly mobile while others are sedentary and rely on hosts contacting them. Ecologists need appropriate tools to study each of these extremes. This is only possible if they have sound ecological principles on which to base their studies.

A. Geographical Distribution—Concept of Limiting Factors

An arthropod's first requirement is a suitable climate. Each species has characteristic requirements for daylength, temperature, and available moisture which is the balance of rainfall and evaporation. In any one location a species will be subjected to periods of varying duration of favorable and unfavorable conditions each year. The balance of these conditions determines the relative abundance of a species in each location, other things being equal.

The essential requirements of each species can be captured using computer programs such as the CLIMEX model. It integrates the response of a species to weekly temperatures and moisture into an "Ecoclimatic Index" which is a measure of the favorableness of that location for the relative abundance and permanent persistence of the species. An example of a CLIMEX-generated global projection is given in Fig. 1, using the New World screwworm fly, *Cochliomyia hominivorax*, as an example. It shows the fly's present geographical distribution and the relative favorableness of representative locations around the world for the species, and so provides a measure of vulnerability of each area to colonization by the fly. Similar maps can be produced to indicate the nature of the effects limiting the range of a species in a given region and the seasonal limits for species which annually migrate into warmer areas as the season progresses. The weekly temperature and population "Growth Indices" for the screwworm fly in Austin, Texas, are shown in Fig. 2. They reveal the season during which the fly is able to multiply.

Naturally, arthropods need more than a suitable climate in which to live. They need an adequate supply of hosts on which to feed and appropriate shelter in which to rest. In the case of the New World screwworm fly, fairly dense thickets of bushes or trees are essential and a supply of livestock or wildlife must always be present. These conditions can be mapped using modern computer packages, called Geographical Information Systems or GIS. Overlays of each environmental component can be built up into a com-

TABLE V
Diseases of Poultry

Disease	Cause	Nature
Aspergillosis, thrush	*Aspergillus fumigatus*	A respiratory disease of chickens, turkeys, and sometimes wild birds with signs of respiratory distress
Blackhead, histomoniasis	Protozoan, *Histomonas* species	A serious disease of liver of turkeys transmitted by a worm of the turkey's caecum; causes weakness, diarrhea, and death
Chlamydiosis	*Chlamydia psittaci*	Acute or chronic infection of domestic or wild birds with diarrhea, weakness, and inflammation of respiratory organs; man is susceptible
Coccidiosis	Protozoan, *Emieria* species	Very serious and common disease of poultry with blood in the caecum and droppings of young birds and decreased growth and egg production of older birds
Colibacillosis	*Escherichia coli*	Strains of the organism cause acute to chronic enteritic disease
Duck plague	A herpesvirus	An acute, severe, and fatal disease of ducks, geese, and swans characterized by hemorrhages and sudden deaths
Eastern encephalitis	Specific virus	An acute disease of pheasants and other birds with staggering and paralysis
Encephalomyelitis	Not clearly shown	A viral disease of chickens, quail, and turkeys manifested by tremors of the neck and limbs and paralysis
Erysipelas	*Erysipelothrix rhusiopathiae*	An acute disease of turkeys with diffuse, multiple hemorrhages in the large muscles
Fowl cholera	*Pasteurella multocida*	An acute to chronic disease of domestic and wild birds; strains of the organism from nonavian hosts do not infect birds
Fowl pox	Specific virus	A slow-spreading infection of chickens and turkeys manifested by blisters on the skin that progress to heavy scabs
Infectious bronchitis	Specific virus	An acute, rapidly spreading, respiratory disease with coughing, sneezing, and decreased egg production
Infectious coryza	*Hemophilus gallinarum*	An acute respiratory disease of chickens manifested by signs of respiratory distress
Infectious laryngotracheitis	Specific virus	An acute disease of chickens causing severe respiratory distress
Influenza, fowl plague	Strains of influenza virus	Wide range of responses from none to very high mortality; fowl plague is an eradicable disease in the United States
Listeriosis	*Listeria monocytogenes*	An acute or chronic disease of chickens and turkeys; often sporadic in adult birds with necrosis of liver and muscles of heart
Lymphoid leukosis	A specific retrovirus	Infection may be congenital; causes diffuse or nodular lymphoid tumors in liver, spleen, and elsewhere
Marek's disease	A specific herpesvirus	Very widespread infection manifested by depression, paralysis, and death with lymphoid tumors of nerves and organs
Mycoplasmosis	*Mycoplasma gallisepticum*	A chronic respiratory disease of chickens
	Mycoplasma meleagridis	A venereal disease of turkeys with inflammation of the air sacs
	Mycoplasma synoviae	Acute to chronic disease of chickens and turkeys with inflammation of tendons and the respiratory tract
Mycotoxicosis	Aflatoxin	Ingestion of the toxin produced by *aspergillus* species growing in feeds
Newcastle disease	Specific virus	An acute, rapidly spreading disease of domestic poultry and other birds with nervous and respiratory signs
Necrotic dermatitis	*Clostridium septicum*	Causes acute necrosis of the skin
Necrotic enteritis	*Clostridium perfringens*	An acute, explosive, enterotoxemic disease with necrosis of intestines and organs
Salmonelloses	*Salmonella pullorum*	Causes pullorum disease, an acute, fatal disease of young chickens and turkeys; now controlled
	Salmonella gallinarum	Causes fowl typhoid, a chronic disease of adult birds
	Salmonella arizona	Causes paracolon or arizona disease, an indistinct infection of turkey flocks
	Salmonella species	Indistinct infection of all domestic birds; mortality varies
Spirochetosis	*Borrelia anserina*	An acute to chronic disease of all birds with fever, weakness, and diarrhea
Tuberculosis	*Mycobacterium avium*	A chronic, slowly spreading disease of chickens and captive wild birds with emaciation and weakness
Viral hepatitis of ducks	A picornavirus	An acute, very contagious disease of young waterfowl
Viral hepatitis of geese	A parvovirus	An acute, highly fatal infection of young geese
Viral hepatitis of turkeys	An adenovirus	Acute or subclinical infection of turkeys with inflammation of the liver and pancreas

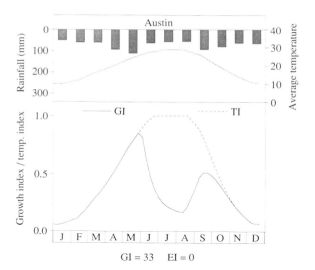

FIGURE 2 The weekly Temperature (TI) and Growth (GI) indices, generated by CLIMEX, for the New World screwworm, *Cochliomyia hominivorax*, at Austin, Texas. The indices are measures of the favorableness of the temperature and temperature combined with moisture, respectively, for population growth of the species.

prehensive picture of the resources available to a species in different locations.

B. Abundance

Populations of animals usually fluctuate about a long-term average density in any given set of circumstances. This number can be thought of as the carrying capacity of that environment for that species. Following perturbation, a population will return to its "equilibrium population density" in response to negative feedback mechanisms. The extent to which the population fluctuates or tends to return to the equilibrium density depends both on the inherent properties of the species and on the constancy of the outside environment. Some species have evolved a "boom or bust" strategy by which they rapidly exploit new resources after migrating into a new locality or after a change in the state of their environment. These are called *r* selected species. Screwworm flies, some ticks, horn flies, and lice fall into this category. The species usually have high reproductive rates and short generation times. The other strategy, referred to as *K* selected, relies on steady growth rates and longer generation times with much smaller fluctuations in numbers. The tsetse fly in Africa is a good example of a *K*-selected species. It produces only one offspring at a time and its numbers vary little over long periods.

The size of fluctuations in population density is dampened to varying degrees by a variety of negative-feedback mechanisms in different species. These mechanisms work by decreasing population growth rates at high population densities and increasing them at low densities. This can come about through reduced fecundity or increased mortality. Some examples of such density-dependent mechanisms are the increased immunological or behavioral responses of animals to feeding by the parasite. For example, cattle express their immunologically based resistance to tick feeding more strongly when larger numbers of ticks attach to them, and they respond to an increased frequency of feeding attempts of biting flies by increasing their defensive reactions. Cattle detect and avoid areas of pasture with large clusters of tick larvae on them. The result of these mechanisms is to slow population growth rates when the density is high and to increase the chances of success of each individual when the population density is very low. The process is termed *population regulation*. Where populations are regulated the equilibrium population density will be equivalent to the long-term average population density. In the case of some chaotic populations whose sizes vary in response to the dynamics of their internal population processes, the equilibrium density can vary greatly over time.

At any one time there is usually a small proportion of hosts in a given herd or flock which is more heavily infested than the other animals. This is a characteristic feature of parasitism and can result from unequal numbers of parasites attacking each animal as a result of aggregation of parasites in the environment or, more often, from varying susceptibility of the host. This phenomenon has important consequences for both host and parasite populations. When parasite numbers increase to high levels, a small proportion of hosts, usually about 15–20% with lower resistance, die first. The resultant impact on the parasite population is much greater, with up to 50% of the parasites commonly being removed with those hosts. The average resistance level of the surviving hosts is consequently increased. This is another negative feedback mechanism which is triggered when the earlier ones fail to suppress population growth rates sufficiently.

In searching for unifying themes in parasite ecology we need to concentrate on the ecological processes rather than on the individual variations observed in the life cycles of different species. While there is a vast array of different life-cycle patterns exhibited by different veterinary arthropods, there are only three underlying processes to consider. These are free-living development, host finding, and survival and reproduction of parasitic stages.

The usual concern of humans with parasites affecting their stock distracts us from the fact that for most parasites, most of the time is spent away from the host in a free-living state. During this period the parasite is subject to the effects of climate and is prone to predation. There is a wide range of suitable habitats for different species. Horn flies lay their eggs in the freshly dropped dung of their cattle host, ticks lay their eggs in pastures, and lice and myiasis flies lay their eggs on the coat of their host. In each case the eggs must develop through to the infective or host-finding stage in very different environments.

The host-seeking stages in the life cycle have to find a host. Their success in doing so depends on how long they can survive while awaiting a host and how many hosts are within their range. Some species like screwworm flies are highly mobile and have very sensitive host-seeking behavior as they cue into odors from long distances. Other species, like ticks and fleas, await more or less passively until a suitable host approaches when they respond to short range cues like exhaled breath or vibration and attach to the animal.

Once the parasite has found a host it adopts a strategy which again varies widely depending on the species concerned. Biting flies, such as horse or March flies (Tabanidae) and tsetse flies, make fleeting visits to their hosts and take rapid and large blood meals. On the other hand, horn flies remain on their host for the duration of their life as adults feeding up to 18 times a day, with female flies leaving only to lay eggs in their host's freshly deposited dung. Ticks, lice, keds, and fleas also remain on their host for the whole of their feeding period. The choice of feeding site on the host varies with the species and often appears to be an adaptation, either to avoid the host's grooming behavior, excessive heat from direct sunlight, or to minimize competition and interference with other species. Different species of horse flies feed on different parts of the body, at different times of the day or in different seasons. Ticks in Africa show similar sharing of resources between species, where up to five species may often be found on a host at any one place. Some ticks feed within the ear canal of bovines, others attach inside the nostrils of camels, or around the anus or on the hooves of antelope. Myiasis flies show temporal separation with primary species initiating strikes, secondary species following, and tertiary species only arriving when the host is almost dead. Where temporal or spatial separation is inadequate to segregate closely related species, reproductive interference may occur and result in one or other species being excluded, such as in a hybrid zone.

The success of an arthropod in feeding depends on its ability to circumvent the host's immunological and behavioral defences. Typically, hosts become sensitized to the feeding of the arthropod and mount immune responses of varying effectiveness against them. The response often involves an immediate hypersensitivity reaction and is expressed in various grooming behaviors and immune reactions at the feeding site. An understanding of the host–parasite relationship is vital to any attempt to control parasite populations by means which rely on altering the host's resistance to attack.

Once the life cycle of an arthropod has been defined, the behavior of field populations needs to be investigated. Once again we are faced with a variety of strategies used by the arthropods to survive in different circumstances. Some species such as horn flies can undergo one generation in 2 weeks, while temperate species of ticks require 1 to 3 years to complete a single generation. It is common to observe a single generation each year, with or without a diapause or dormant stage being involved to assist overwintering. On the other hand, some species such as lice are more successful under cold conditions. Naturally, the shorter the generation time the faster the species can respond to change and the quicker it will reach equilibrium in a new set of circumstances. We will see later how the generation time is so important in determining the useful life of pesticides.

In the face of this great diversity of life styles it is essential to refocus on the ecological processes themselves and address the problem of what veterinary arthropods do. Ways to interfere with those behaviors for the purpose of control are then easier to devise in order to control pests.

IV. Damage

Veterinary arthropods directly affect livestock, domestic animals, and wildlife in a variety of ways, with results that conflict with the objectives set by humans for the use of those animals. The effects, summarized in Table II, vary from disturbance of milking cows by houseflies to death from excessive infestations of ticks or blackflies (Simulium). In addition to these direct effects, many arthropods also act as vectors of diseases, as described in the next section. Effects not listed in Table II include the disruption to animal movements that are necessary to avoid the spread of veterinary arthropods from farm to farm or country to country. In order to move animals, it is common to

TABLE II
Some Types of Damage Caused by Veterinary Arthropods to Domestic Pets and Livestock

Arthropod	Effect							
	Disturbance	Anemia	Reduced growth	Reduced milk	Damaged wool/hides	Allergy	Paralysis	Death
Lice chewing	+		+		+			
Lice sucking	+	+	+		+			+
Biting flies	+	+	+	+		+		+
Myiasis flies	+		+	+	+			+
Nuisance flies	+							
Fleas	+	+	+			+		
Soft ticks	+	+	+					
Hard ticks	+	+	+	+	+	+	+	+
Mites	+		+		+	+		

have to undergo quarantine treatments which involve expensive delays, feeding, and chemical treatment facilities, in order to prevent the spread of the parasites.

Veterinary arthropods have enormous social impacts around the world. They affect human health and our ability to keep the very limited number of different types of livestock that we usually maintain in every environment, viz., sheep, cattle, and horses. Some of the most spectacular impacts have been caused by the New World screwworm fly. In the southern United States deer populations were kept low by the high mortality caused by attacks by the screwworm fly. They have increased dramatically since the eradication of the fly in the 1970s and are now rated as a very important economic resource. While beneficial to farmers in the short term the increase in deer numbers now threatens the ability of that area to maintain its eradication of the cattle ticks, *Boophilus microplus* and *Boophilus annulatus*, which feed on both cattle and deer. The ticks had been eradicated while deer were rare but are continuously being reintroduced from Mexico. Local eradication was feasible when deer were rare but that is now becoming much more difficult. Another example of the impact of the screwworm fly is illustrated by the result of a survey of villagers in Mexico who were asked to rank improvements in their life styles resulting from technological development. They rated the eradication of the fly as one of the most significant. The interaction between the control of screwworm flies and ticks in the United States highlights the need to take a holistic view of veterinary entomological problems. Control of one species may not improve the situation for farmers if they still have to treat their animals for other species.

V. Disease Transmission

Frequently the need to study a veterinary arthropod arises not from any direct detrimental effect of the species on an animal, but from the role that the arthropod plays in transmitting disease between domesticated animals or from animals to humans. The arthropod is studied in order to provide options apart from treatment of the pathogen, to control the disease. We often forget that many pathogens live in hosts other than the animals we are interested in. They can have detrimental effects on these intermediate hosts as well. Conversely, some potential vectors are refractory to infection by the pathogens which are unable to survive in them, and some have been shown to develop immune reactions to the pathogens in a manner more commonly associated with mammals. As we have already seen in relation to other attributes of veterinary arthropods, a wide range of pathogen groups are transmitted by these vectors, and examples of the most important ones are listed with their vectors in Table III. [*See* ANIMAL DISEASES.]

The rate at which vectors transmit diseases depends on the infection rate in the vector, the success of the vector in finding a host, the suitability of the host for multiplication of the pathogen, and the ability of the pathogen to infect another vector.

Vector-borne diseases greatly limit the productivity of livestock in every country. In Africa in particular trypanosomiasis transmitted by the tsetse fly and East Coast fever transmitted by the tick *Rhipicephalus appendiculatus* have prevented the widespread introduction of more productive but less well-adapted breeds of cattle. Mosquitoes transmit debilitating equine encephalitis virus in the United States. In Europe, Asia, and Australia the vector-borne diseases of most sig-

TABLE III
Vector-Borne Diseases and Their Arthropod Vectors

Pathogen	Vectors
Trypanosomiasis	
Americas	Triatomid bugs
Africa	Tsetse fly
Asia	Stomoxys (mechanical)
Babesia (cattle, dogs)	Ticks
Theileria (cattle)	Ticks
Borrelia—Lyme disease	Ticks
Leishmania	Sandfies (Phlebotomus)
Rickettsia	
Coxiella, Rickettsia	Ticks
Anaplasma (cattle)	Ticks, biting flies
Cowdria—Heartwater	Ticks
Sweating sickness	Ticks
Viruses	
Equine encephalitis (U.S.)	Ticks
Ephemeral fever, bluetongue	Midges (Culicoides)
African swine fever	Soft ticks

nificance are transmitted by ticks. In South America Hemipteran bugs transmit protozoan parasites, such as trypanosomes causing anemia in horses, while ticks transmit *Babesia* and *Anaplasma* spp between cattle.

VI. Control Methods

Humans control veterinary arthropods to minimize the impacts on livestock production, pets, or humans themselves. In the former case, decisions are usually made using economic criteria but in the latter cases cost often takes second place to emotional issues. Considerations in relation to livestock include the costs of chemicals, vaccinations, traps, or other management practices used to reduce arthropod or arthropod-borne diseases. There are also less obvious costs associated with use of capital and labor, and the side effects on public health and the environment. There is also a cost associated with the loss of chemicals due to the development of resistant strains of arthropods. Each control method has a unique mixture of benefits, constraints, and adverse consequences. For example, chemical pesticides are often a health and environmental hazard, breeding livestock for parasite resistance is usually at the cost of other productive attributes, traps may need more effort from management, and use of sterilized insects is limited to situations where the insect population is already at low levels and is being eradicated. On the positive side, pesticides usually work almost instantly, breeding for resistance minimizes other de-

mands on management, traps avoid problems of resistance and pollution but some types may have adverse effects on nontarget insects, and sterilized insects offer advantages when dealing with large heterogeneous areas containing low population densities of otherwise inaccessible pests.

Over the past half century there have been a succession of natural and synthetic chemical pesticides developed for use on livestock or domestic animals. The main chemical groups have been based on arsenic, natural pyrethrum, organochlorins, organophosphates, carbamates, amidines, synthetic pyrethroids, avermectins, and arthropod growth regulators. [*See* PEST MANAGEMENT, CHEMICAL CONTROL.]

Each of the chemical groups has characteristic strengths and weaknesses. The attributes of most significance are the degree of specificity of the chemical and its persistence after application. Specificity refers to the extent to which the chemical's effects are restricted to a target group of arthropods. Chemicals such as DDT, an organochlorin, were hailed as miracle solutions to many arthropod problems because they had a broad spectrum of activity and very long persistence in the environment after application. Experience showed that these advantages were not in fact long lasting and led to severe, adverse side effects, such as the rapid emergence of resistant strains of insects, accumulation in other animals which fed on treated insects, and persistent chemical residues which accumulated in the soil and water. The avermectin group of chemicals has similarities to the organochlorins in having a broad spectrum of activity and persistence for long periods in the soil or in animal manure. Avermectins are extremely active compounds and kill arthropods and helminths at very low concentrations while having low toxicity to mammals. At the other extreme, amidines are very selective and kill only acarines such as ticks and mites, and do not persist long after use, although weight for weight they are much more active than organochlorins.

Chemical pesticides have many different modes of action. Some chemicals such as DDT and some organophosphates are contact poisons and are applied topically to the animal. Others such as the avermectins have systemic effects which means that they work by circulating in the body fluids of the host animal and are taken up by the arthropod during feeding. Residues of avermectin remain in animal manure where they can be used to control dung breeding flies such as *Haematobia* spp. Unfortunately they also affect beneficial insects such as dung burying beetles and so should be used only when side effects can be avoided, such as in seasons when dung beetles are not active.

The range of pesticide delivery systems include: hand spraying, mechanical spraying in "spray races," timed space sprays in dairy sheds, immersing livestock in dipping vats, pouring small amounts of concentrate mixed with various oils onto an animal's back and letting it spread through affinity of the mixture with the animal's skin oils using the pour-on method, automatic chemical dispensing devices such as back-rubbers for use in control of horn fly, impregnated ear-tags, injections, and sustained-release boluses impregnated with pesticide and implanted into the stomach of an animal where the chemical is released at a fixed slow rate.

Chemical pesticides have one major advantage over other control methods—they often act almost instantaneously. This means that they are invaluable for treating livestock prior to movement in order to prevent the spread of the pests to new places or countries. As usual there is a down side to this in that residues of the chemicals often remain in the body tissues of livestock for some days after use and can contaminate animal products such as meat or milk. Regulations usually define the length of the so-called with-holding period needed after treatment before livestock can be slaughtered.

Apart from the disadvantages caused by chemical residues, the main problem with relying only on chemical pesticides for control of arthropods is the rapidity with which many pests are able to develop resistance to each new product. Resistant pests emerge as a result of initially rare individuals with lower sensitivity to the chemical becoming more frequent in the population as their more susceptible siblings are killed by the pesticide. When their frequency reaches about 5% a decline in efficiency of control starts to become apparent and the pesticide has to be replaced with a different type of chemical. The time from the introduction of a new product until resistance develops depends on the genetic nature of the resistance gene—whether it is dominant or recessive—and on many ecological and operational factors. Ecological factors include the number of generations that the species undergoes each year; the extent to which treated and untreated populations intermix; and the number of individuals sheltered from exposure to the chemical by being in a state of "refugia" away from the treated hosts. Operational factors include the concentration of the pesticide, the frequency of its use, and the extent to which the concentration on the animal is allowed to decline between treatments. A strat-

egy of moderation in the use of pesticides applied at saturation concentrations has been advocated to delay the development of resistance. However, the necessary price for delaying resistance is to accept greater levels of damage or to rely on integration of pesticides with other methods of control. The cost of pesticides has to take into account the long-term value of pesticide susceptibility which, once lost, is lost forever. In this sense a pesticide should be seen as a nonrenewable resource to be carefully husbanded, preferably by restricting its use to situations where other options are not available, for cleansing livestock of pests prior to movement, and where possible to win permanent gains by eradication of the pest.

Control methods which exploit the natural abilities of animals to defend themselves against arthropods have many advantages. Two such approaches are first to select and breed genetically resistant animals and second to vaccinate animals against arthropod parasite antigens. Host resistance is defined as the ability of an animal to reduce the fecundity or increase the mortality of the parasite. Various mechanisms exist to damage parasites, but the most frequent is based on immediate hypersensitivity which triggers reactions such as grooming or blister-like lesions which displace the arthropod. The ability of an animal to resist parasites is affected by its physiological state and is reduced during lactation and by nutritional and other stresses. Vaccination against ticks and some biting flies has been shown to be possible using genetically engineered antigens from body tissues to immunize the host. When ingested in blood, host antibodies attack the tissues of the arthropod. No practical use has yet been made of the technology.

Host resistance has been used to control parasites of domestic animals. Reliance on host resistance minimizes the need for management or for use of pesticides. The average level of resistance of a herd or flock can be increased by either culling or segregating animals with low resistance in order to win immediate but short-lived benefits, or more effectively by long-term breeding programs. The best practical example of such an approach is given by the control of the cattle tick *B. microplus* in Australia. It has resulted in a change of cattle breeds away from European breeds toward zebu breeds in tropical areas with large reductions in the use of acaricides. Unfortunately cattleowners still spray their cattle for control of the buffalo fly so reducing the benefits gained from the use of tick resistant cattle.

Trapping is becoming a more popular means of control of veterinary arthropods in order to reduce the use of pesticides. The design of each type of trap depends greatly on the behavior of the species concerned. In Africa, traps baited with cattle urine and placed in a grid pattern across large grazing areas have led to the suppression of the tsetse fly. Attempts were made to control the horn fly in North America using darkened boxes filled with curtains through which the cattle walked. Acceptance of these "Bruce" traps has been low and the traps have not been very effective. Recently much more effective traps have been developed in Australia using the principle of curtains borrowed from the Bruce trap but employing an opposite concept in relation to light. Instead of a darkened box which inhibits the entry of both the flies and the cattle, the Australian trap is based on a transparent tunnel. The trap is being used to control the closely related buffalo fly on dairy cattle in Australia. It has been proven to work on horn fly so there are good prospects for reducing the amount of pesticide used to control *Haematobia* on cattle. The next step will be to find alternatives for control of the other flies pestering dairy and feedlot cattle, especially houseflies and the stable fly *Stomoxys calcitrans*. The first priority is to address hygiene deficiencies to reduce the opportunities for fly breeding.

Some of the most dramatic successes in the control of veterinary arthropods have been achieved using the sterile insect release method, known as SIRM. Male New World screwworm flies *C. hominivorax* were bred using artificial diets in massive numbers in factories in north America, sterilized with low levels of irradiation, and then released from aircraft into the wild to mate with wild females. The number of sterilized males was designed to greatly outnumber the wild males and so prevent them from mating with female flies which only mate once. If the ratio of sterilized to wild flies is sufficiently high, eradication is possible and has been achieved over the southern United States and Mexico and more recently in Libya following an accidental introduction of flies with live sheep imports. Economic analyses have shown benefits of up to $300 for every dollar spent in the program.

VII. Management Strategies

Sustainable management strategies for control of veterinary arthropods rely on successful integration into normal agricultural practices. Control strategies which require major changes will not be widely adopted unless either they can be fitted into current practices or there is no acceptable alternative and the

pest is very severe. Such constraints demand that veterinary entomologists adopt a holistic view of each problem and define the industry and wider context of the problem before recommending solutions. A major contribution to widespread adoption and sustainability is provided by biological methods of control. [*See* PEST MANAGEMENT, BIOLOGICAL CONTROL; PEST MANAGEMENT, CULTURAL CONTROL; SUSTAINABLE AGRICULTURE.]

Management strategies are adopted at the national level through quarantine services or through eradication programs. At the farm level the need is for integrated pest management approaches which make the best use of all available methods and adopt a holistic view to cover all pests present, taking into account the specific needs, resources, and constraints of the individual farmer.

Quarantine is the first line of defence for any country. It has traditionally been based on a concept of minimum risk but the trend is currently toward adoption of the concept of acceptable risk in order to facilitate free trade. Risks are evaluated using procedures known as pest risk analyses. In such a study the country of origin, mode of transport, and destination of a commodity is examined to define risks associated with proposed importations. The trend is toward quantifying the risks where possible and involving wide consultation with all community groups that are likely to be affected. A variety of computer-based techniques are being adopted including expert systems, geographic information systems, databases, climate-matching models such as that used to produce Figs. 1 and 2, and elaborate simulation models. International efforts are being made to develop the concept of global harmonization of quarantine pest risk assessment procedures.

Eradication of very expensive pests is an option in situations where special circumstances warrant the vast expense involved. Both cattle ticks and screwworm flies have been eradicated from the United States and North America, respectively. Success with the former species depended on adequate funds, staff, motivation, and legislation. It was achieved using very inefficient chemicals compared with modern pesticides and was only possible because of the relative rarity of alternative hosts for the ticks. Ironically, the later successful eradication of the screwworm fly using the sterile insect release method (SIRM) enabled populations of white-tailed deer to build up to numbers which would make eradication of cattle ticks impracticable. The inability of the United States to secure its border with Mexico is a major weakness in the tick eradication approach as it requires continuous surveillance and eradication of local outbreaks of ticks associated with movement of cattle from Mexico to the United States. In Africa attempts have been made to eradicate tsetse fly from many areas with mixed success. The development of cheap and efficient traps offers improved prospects of success but raises the whole question of the value and sustainability of wild animal populations which could be displaced by cattle and sheep once tsetse flies have been removed. A possible future candidate for eradication is the warble fly which is very susceptible to systemic pesticides.

The costs and risks associated with eradication are very high and the benefits need to be large to warrant eradication rather than an IPM-based approach. Two of the benefits are the preservation of pesticide susceptibility for future generations and the avoidance of long-term exposure of consumers to pesticide residues.

At the farm level it is rarely possible to maintain an arthropod-free status and management strategies have to be employed to minimize the economic impact of the pest on the farm. The most popularly espoused, but rarely implemented, approach is integrated pest management (IPM). Biological, cultural, and chemical methods are employed in combination to suppress pests. Ideally, control programs which address all pests simultaneously are preferred. Compatibility of recommendations with the other management requirements of the farmer is an important consideration.

VIII. Education

The role of veterinary entomologists means that they have to understand not only entomology but also the livestock or domestic animals that are attacked by the arthropods. Entomologists have been in the forefront of moves to adopt holistic approachs to pest management. Their education should reflect that need by being based on the systems approach to pest management, which emphasizes the inter-relatedness of each component of the host–parasite–environment system. New approaches to education will rely more and more on computer-based training where the taxonomic, ecological, management, and economic skills are learned from computer software programs. Simulation models and expert systems will guide students

through exercises and games to let them learn by experience how best to manage veterinary pests while at the same time integrating their practices into the total farm management system.

IX. Future Directions

The future trends in the practice of veterinary entomology will be driven largely by regulations in relation to the use of pesticides and the availability of such chemicals. The development of resistant strains of arthropods poses an immediate threat. Lower tolerance levels are very likely for synthetic chemicals in livestock products. Further spread of some severe pests will occur and the status of existing pests is likely to change with changing knowledge and market conditions. Biological control methods, including biotechnology products, and cultural practices are likely to increase in popularity. In order to adapt to such changes there is a need for continuous alertness and the maintenance of a capacity to respond to new situations. The future developments in veterinary entomology in theory and practice will depend heavily on the type of education that is given to the next generation of students and farmers. New teaching tools based on computers can play an important part in teaching taxonomy, diagnosis, ecological principles, control strategies, and management of environmental impacts. Suitable tools include expert systems and simulation models as well as simple graphics packages.

Bibliography

Anonymous (1992). "The New World Screwworm Eradication Programme North Africa 1988–1992." FAO, Rome.
Kettle, D. S. (1984). "Medical and Veterinary Entomology." Croom Helm, London.
Kunz, S. E., Murrell, K. D., Lambert, G., James, L. F., and Terrill, C. E. (1991). Estimated losses of livestock to pests. In: "CRC Handbook of Pest Management in Agriculture," Vol. I, pp. 69–98.
Sutherst, R. W., and Maywald, G. F. (1985). A computerised system for matching climates in ecology. *Agricult. Ecosystems Environ.* **13**, 281–299.
Sutherst, R. W., and Utech, K.B.W. (1991). Controlling livestock parasites with host resistance. In: "CRC Handbook of Pest Management in Agriculture" (Pimentel, ed.) Vol. II, pp. 379–401.

Environmental Horticulture

TERRIL A. NELL, *University of Florida*

Glossary

Cultivar Man-made plant variety; from the words "cultivated" and "variety"

Floriculture Science and practice of growing, harvesting, storing, designing, marketing, and exporting of cut foliage or container-grown foliage and flowering plants, ornamental bulb crops, and bedding plants

Landscape horticulture Science and practice of growing, harvesting, storing, designing, marketing, and exporting shrubs, trees, and turfgrass for exterior landscapes

Turfgrass science Production and use of turfgrasses for residential and commercial landscapes, sports fields, roadsides, parks, and gardens

Environmental horticulture, also known as ornamental horticulture, is the science and art of growing and using plants to enhance the environment, both indoors and out, by applying traditional methods and advanced technology. The field includes floriculture, landscape horticulture, turfgrass science, and therapeutic and recreational horticulture. Grown for their aesthetic value, ornamental plants include flowers, foliage, landscape plants, and turfgrasses.

I. Introduction/Historical Overview

The earliest recorded civilizations cultivated plants for food and medicinal value, and soon began to seek and tend plants valued for their flowers or foliage. In the time of the ancient Egyptians, elaborate plantings of trees and flowers attest to the importance of ornamental plants in that culture. The lotus, a sacred flower in Egypt, is incorporated into much of the art and architecture of the period.

But it is Imperial Rome which is credited as the true birthplace of "ornamental horticulture." Gardens created purely for pleasure appeared for the first time in Italy sometime prior to the first century A.D. In 62 A.D. Pliny described gardens containing sycamore, fig, mulberry, cypress and pine trees, shrubs such as boxwood, laurel, and myrtle, groundcovers such as ivy, rosemary, and fern, blooming vines and a host of flowering plants including 12 varieties of roses, bulbs (hyacinths, lilies, narcissi, crocuses), violets, irises, anemones, poppies, and oleanders.

Specimen plants and flowers were included among the commodities acquired by early explorers venturing into new lands. Commercial trade in plants and flowers began soon after. By the 17th century, people were paying enormous prices for a single tulip bulb. Wealthy homeowners began converting orangeries to houses for the maintenance of ornamental plants, such as laurel and myrtle. In the late 1700s and early 1800s, European botanic gardens introduced people to "new" plants from throughout the world. Around 1830, commercial nurseries were born and replaced botanic gardens as the source of plant material. As the Victorian period began in England, large greenhouse conservatories at botanic gardens educated citizens about plants acquired from various climatic areas of the world.

The first American colonists cultivated plants only for food and medicine. But by the mid-1600s, survival

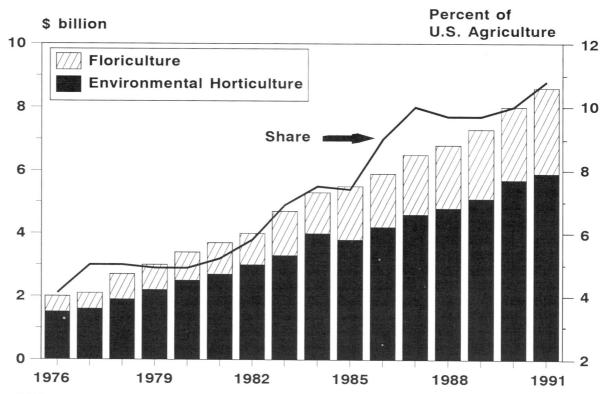

FIGURE 1 Value of environmental horticulture and floriculture crops and percentage share of U.S. agriculture, 1976–1991. (*Source:* Financial Performance of U.S. Floriculture and Environmental Horticulture Farm Businesses, 1987–1991. Statistical Bulletin 862, U.S. Department of Agriculture, Washington, DC.)

became more certain in the larger settlements, and, strongly influenced by memories of gardens in their native lands, colonists began to incorporate flower beds around their dwellings and among their herbs and vegetable plots. The Dutch who settled in America brought with them considerable horticultural experience, and by 1700, shipments from Europe included bulbs, seeds, dwarf box, and garden tools, among the other necessities imported by the colonies.

II. Production

A. Market Value and Plants Produced

Ornamental horticulture crops are produced in every state in the United States, and were the most rapidly expanding segment of crop agriculture from 1976 to 1991, with total wholesale value increasing from $2 billion in 1976 to $8.7 billion in 1991. In 1991, the environmental horticulture industries represented nearly 11% of crop agriculture in the United States and was the sixth largest agriculture commodity after cattle and calves, dairy products, corn, hogs, and soybeans (Fig. 1). Twenty-one states had a whole-

sale value over $100 million in ornamental horticulture, with three states—California, Florida, and Texas—exceeding $500 million in grower cash receipts (Fig. 2). In 1990, average net farm income for green industry farm enterprises was $53,589, the highest among all farm production specialties.

The ornamental horticulture industry in the United States comprises more than 50,000 small businesses—growers, wholesalers, and retailers. Ornamental plants include cut flowers and fresh foliage, potted foliage and flowering plants, bedding plants (annuals and perennials), woody ornamental landscape plants (trees, shrubs, and ground covers), and turfgrass (seed and sod). [*See* FLORICULTURE; TURF-GRASSES.]

Americans buy flowers and plants as gifts, to decorate home and work areas, and to create attractive landscapes outside homes, apartments, institutions, and commercial buildings. A recent study revealed that during a 3-month period, 25% of American households purchased flowers or plants. Consumer purchases and utilization of flowers and plants vary widely throughout the world. Per capita consumption of flowers and foliage plants ranged from $18.52 in

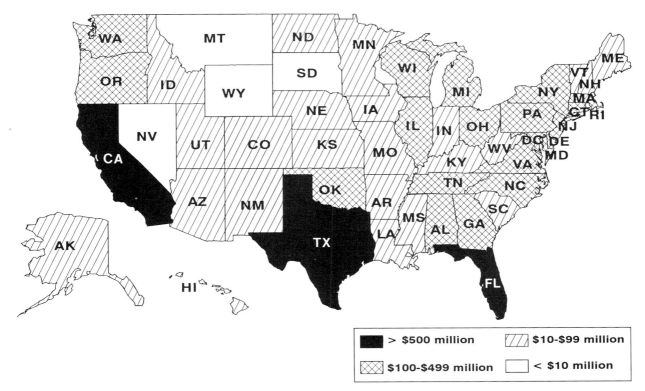

FIGURE 2 Wholesale value of floriculture and environmental horticulture crops in the United States, 1991. (*Source:* Financial Performance of U.S. Floriculture and Environmental Horticulture Farm Businesses, 1987–1991. Statistical Bulletin 862, U.S. Department of Agriculture, Washington, DC.)

Czech Republic to $126.75 in Norway (Table I). Consumers in Norway, Switzerland, Sweden, and Denmark purchased more potted plants than cut flowers, while cut flowers were more popular in other parts of the world.

III. Plant Use

Whether in a city apartment windowbox or a suburban garden, flowers and plants enhance the aesthetic quality of the environments where people live, work, and relax in and out of doors. Exposure to living plants has been shown to have positive human psychological and physiological benefits. For instance, patients assigned to hospital rooms with window views facing natural scenes had shorter postoperative hospital stays and took less pain medication than matched patients facing a wall. Other studies have pointed to the positive role of plants in reducing stress.

Plants are beneficial in maintaining the environment by reducing energy consumption and preserving natural resources. Plants are the most economical way to modify the microclimate around structures.

TABLE I

Per Capita Consumption of Flowers and Foliage Plants (U.S. Dollars)

Country	Flowers	Plants	Total
Norway	$58.09	$68.66	$126.75
Switzerland	$55.45	$63.37	$118.83
Sweden	$40.67	$62.85	$103.51
Denmark	$33.27	$68.13	$101.40
Italy	$67.07	$26.93	$ 94.01
Germany	$45.95	$43.83	$ 89.78
Japan	$64.29	$18.37	$ 82.66
Austria	$35.38	$33.80	$ 69.18
Netherlands	$40.67	$25.35	$ 66.02
Belgium	$31.16	$29.57	$ 60.73
France	$26.93	$24.29	$ 51.23
United States	$23.77	$19.54	$ 43.31
United Kingdom	$20.60	$ 7.39	$ 27.99
Spain	$12.15	$ 8.98	$ 21.12
Czech Republic			$ 18.52

Source: Reprinted with permission from "Key Facts about the World of Floriculture Production" (1993). Floriculture International, Batavia, IL.

Proper placement of trees, shrubs, and ground covers around homes and buildings can lower heating and cooling costs by managing the influence of sun and wind. Tree shade can decrease the amount of electricity required to operate air conditioners by 10–50%, thereby reducing subsequent carbon dioxide emission.

Preliminary studies have demonstrated that foliage plants properly placed and maintained in buildings and homes can also improve indoor-air quality by reducing pollutants. In addition, trees absorb pollutants from smog.

Gardening has been recognized as the nation's foremost hobby. New plant species are more durable and pest resistant, making it easier than ever before to be successful in growing plants for personal enjoyment. The individual satisfaction gained from caring for living plants has led to the development of horticultural therapy activities for those who are wheelchair-confined, emotionally and physically challenged, injured, terminally ill, and imprisoned. Horticultural therapy provides exercise, fresh air, creative outlets, stress reduction, and boredom relief.

Interior plants are common elements in the design of homes, offices, shops, shopping malls, and restaurants. Lush green foliage and flowers help to create an appealing setting. Indoor plants are used as art, to accent other objects, as traffic channelers, noise buffers, privacy screens, and space fillers. The burgeoning interest in the effective uses of indoor plants has led to the establishment of a new horticultural specialty area—commercial interior landscaping. Also called interiorscaping, interior plantscaping, or plantscaping, this discipline has emerged as a multibillion-dollar industry, which encompasses interior design, plant rental, and maintenance in public and commercial areas.

Another fast-growing segment of ornamental horticulture involves the incorporation of native plants into landscapes. Most widely utilized in Florida and California, these new plant specialists work to incorporate existing native plant materials into landscape designs, so that these plants are preserved through the site development and construction process. Native plants are advantageous because they are adapted to local pests, diseases, and weather, and are often considered more drought tolerant than nonnative plants. The cultivation and production of native plants for sale has led to the development of nurseries which specialize in indigenous plant materials.

Developers, mining companies, zoos, aquaria, and tourist attractions are using native plants for restoration and reclamation of upland areas, wildlife habitats, and retention ponds. Native plants have been appearing around governmental buildings and parks for quite some time because many city, county, and state ordinances require that landscapes include native plants. Due to increased awareness, more homeowners are also planting natives.

With more than 50 million lawns and over 14,000 golf courses in America, turfgrass production, use, and maintenance are a major agricultural industry. Three-quarters of all turfgrass is in lawns. Other uses include recreational and athletic fields, along roads and airport runways, cemeteries, parks, and around commercial and institutional buildings. Turfgrass is attractive, durable, decorative, stabilizes soil, absorbs many toxic vehicle emissions, and reduces dust. Another important benefit of turfgrass is that it provides optimum footing for athletes and a relatively soft cushion for falls onto field surfaces.

IV. Fresh and Potted Flowers

A. Production

Fresh cut and potted flowers and bedding plants are grown and marketed based on their aesthetic value and consumer appeal indoors and in landscapes rather than their foliage plants. Total value of floriculture crops in the United States was nearly equally divided between flowering and foliage plants, bedding plants and cut foliage, and greens in 1987 (Fig. 3). Economic value of U.S. produced cut flowers was greatest for roses, followed by carnation, chrysanthemum, and gladiolus. The most valuable flowering potted plants in the United States are poinsettia, chrysanthemums, azaleas, lilies, and african violets. Primarily grown

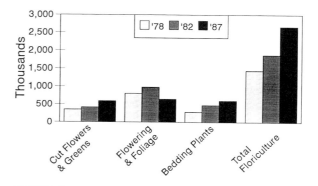

FIGURE 3 Value of floriculture crops in the United States. (*Source:* Miller, M., George J. Ball Co., W. Chicago, and U.S. Census.)

FIGURE 4 Mass market retailers offer a wide assortment of plants and flowers. (Photograph provided by Ball Publishing Co., Batavia, IL.)

in greenhouses, these crops may also be cultivated outdoors year-round in the U.S. sunbelt states (Florida, Hawaii, California, and Texas) and elsewhere during the summer months. Outdoor production in modified shadehouses or greenhouses is common year-round in areas of Central and South America, Southern Europe, and Asia. Production of flowering bulbs (geophytes) is an important segment of the industry in The Netherlands, United States, United Kingdom, and France. In the United States, annual sales of flowering bulbs exceeded the value of potted chrysanthemums in 1987. Production of bulb flowers for cut and potted plants is common in Europe and the United States and other locations throughout the world (Fig. 4).

Floriculture is competitive, highly technical, and requires knowledge, skill, and large amounts of capital. Greenhouse floriculture is, in many respects, the most sophisticated kind of plant agriculture because it is very specialized by crop. Growers must provide precise environmental control and constantly strive for pest- and blemish-free crops. Also, exact production scheduling is a must because most floral crops are subject to seasonal demand. Because these products are perishable, market channels must function smoothly to avoid losses.

To achieve precise environmental control, flowers are grown in greenhouses that incorporate glass, plastic, lath, or shade cloth, and artificial heating and cooling. As a result, energy costs represent a significant portion of production costs in greenhouse grown crops.

Water quantity and quality concerns have necessitated major changes in the way water is supplied to ornamental potted plants. Fueling these changes have been mandates by regulatory agencies requiring either all or portions of the drainage of water be retained on the producer's property and to prevent it from leaching through the soil and into the groundwater. The major concern with drainage and irrigation runoff exists with the fertilizer salts that may be in the water and could potentially move into the groundwater supplies, rivers, and lakes. Drip-tube systems, ebb-and-flow benches, flood floors, trough systems, and capillary-mat watering systems can conserve, retain, and reuse irrigation water.

Flowering plants are propagated primarily by cuttings, seeds, or tissue culture (plant propagation from nearly microscopic portions of parent plants). Growing media comprise a variety of ingredients, including peat moss, perlite, vermiculite, styrofoam beads, and calcined clay and are sterilized to control weeds, disease organisms, insects, and nematodes. Soil fertility and pH are precisely controlled with appropriate fertilizer amendments. [*See* PLANT PROPAGATION; PLANT TISSUE CULTURE.]

Greenhouse atmospheres are enriched with carbon dioxide and watering is automatically regulated. Temperatures are also regulated by steam heating and evaporative cooling with mist and fan-and-pad. Day length is controlled by combining shade cloth and illumination to extend the day or interrupt a dark period. Computers control irrigation and the environment in some greenhouses. [*See* HORTICULTURAL GREENHOUSE ENGINEERING.]

Insect control practices have changed from routine use of pesticides to integrated pest management (IPM) in which sprays are employed only when insects are present, with pesticides specifically designed and approved for controlling a specific insect. Biological controls, such as insect growth regulators and naturally occurring bacteria lethal to insects, are playing a bigger role in pest control. Natural predators are particularly effective in greenhouses devoted to a single crop. [*See* INTEGRATED PEST MANAGEMENT; PEST MANAGEMENT, BIOLOGICAL CONTROL.]

B. Geography/Distribution

Over the last 50 years, the floriculture industry has relocated from eastern urban areas in the United States to locations in the western and southern United States and Latin America, which offer lower tax rates, larger rural labor pools, and more favorable climates. Air freight has allowed for the rapid movement of flowers from production sites around the world to markets in the United States, Europe, and Asia. Domestic production of fresh flowers has declined dramatically in the last two decades as imports from Central and South America, Europe, and Israel have increased. Today three out of every four carnations and chrysanthemums, and slightly more than half the roses sold in the United States are grown in other countries.

C. Harvesting/Shipping/Storage

The quality of fresh and potted flowers is affected by harvesting practices, because they remain alive after harvest and can deteriorate quickly. Harvesting must occur within a narrowly defined time frame to assure peak quality. Timing factors include: optimal equipment and labor use, an orderly marketing sequence, and ultimate product quality, and appearance. Actual harvest date depends on cultivar, planting or flow-

ering date, and environmental factors present during the growing season.

For many high-value floricultural crops, hand harvesting is still the only practical method although mechanized and semi-mechanized harvesting can sometimes be used. After harvest, most floricultural crops require special preparation, such as leaf stripping and refrigeration to prolong flower life. Ethylene is a colorless, odorless gas produced by plants and decaying fruits and vegetables. Ethylene acts to accelerate aging in leaves and flowers. Exposure to ethylene during shipping and holding periods adversely affects many flowers and plants. Leaf and bud drop, premature aging, and leaf yellowing are typical symptoms of ethylene injury. The extent of injury depends on ethylene concentration, temperature during exposure, exposure duration, and cultivar. Proper temperature control and use of anti-ethylene solutions can minimize damage on some susceptible plants.

Proper treatment of flowers after harvest is necessary to maximize flower longevity. Pulsing freshly harvested flowers with supplemental sugar, hydration, anti-bacteria, and/or anti-ethylene solutions is effective in extending fresh flower longevity. Refrigeration of fresh flowers after treatment reduces metabolism and respiration, minimizes transpiration, and reduces the detrimental effects of ethylene.

Providing supplemental sugars to flowering potted plants during flowering is not possible. These plants produce carbohydrates naturally through photosynthesis in the greenhouses but light levels are generally so low in most interiors that photosynthesis does not take place, and stored carbohydrate reserves are depleted. Carbohydrates also can be depleted through respiration during shipping, the rate of depletion being directly proportional to shipping temperature, with higher temperatures increasing both respiration rate and carbohydrate depletion.

Proper packaging is important and necessary to assure safe transport. Flowers and plants are placed in paper, plastic, or mesh sleeves and boxed to prevent bruising and mechanical damage to leaves, flowers, and bracts during shipping. Proper transport temperature is dependent on plant species with some flowers and plants requiring cool temperatures (35–40°F, 2–5°C) and tropical flowers and plants requiring temperatures of 55–60°F (13–16°C). Sleeves are removed at the retail market, and ideally, fresh flower stems are recut and placed into a sugar-based preservative. Potted plants should be removed from the box and sleeves removed.

D. Marketing

Fresh flowers are marketed through full-service retail florists and mass markets such as supermarkets, shopping malls, airports, and large discount stores. Almost 36,000 American florists offer flower arrangements, plants, and greenery and related products: ribbons, pots, and accessories. Flower shop purchases are primarily for weddings, funerals, hospitalizations, and holidays. Computers and toll-free numbers enable florists to provide national and international flower delivery.

Floral mass markets focus on high-volume business and spontaneous purchases. It is not uncommon for larger supermarkets to offer mixed bouquets of cut flowers, floral arrangements, potted flowering plants, and delivery in and out of state.

Flowering-plant sales occur through retail florists and mass market outlets year-round. Sales peak around holiday seasons, although routine purchases for personal use and gifts are increasing.

E. Competition

Flower production is becoming more and more competitive because the industry now spans the globe. The American public receives flowers and plants from worldwide growers. Colombia, the Netherlands, Mexico, Ecuador, and Costa Rica together export over $350 million worth of floral products to the United States annually. While imports continue to increase, domestic producers are developing new ways to compete in the world market. The passage of the North American Free Trade Agreement may encourage the production of fresh flowers in Mexico, while relaxation of Quarantine 37, which restricts the importation of plants in soil, is necessary before flowering potted plants can be imported from Europe or other parts of the world.

V. Cut and Potted Foliage

A. Background

Tropical in origin, foliage plants are grown primarily for their overall appearance and use in interior decoration or landscaping. Potted foliage plant popularity increased dramatically in the 1970s in the United States as their use in homes and offices became commonplace. Use of foliage plants in commercial interiorscapes has increased the use of foliage plants significantly.

Prominent groups of foliage plants, some of which are in constant demand because of attractive new cultivars, are aglaonema, dieffenbachia, dracaena, fern, ficus, palm, philodendron, schefflera, palm, and peperomia. Cut foliage, such as leatherleaf fern, is used to complement fresh flowers in arrangements and bouquets. In 1990, potted foliage plant production exceeded one-half million dollars in the United States, while cut foliage was valued at $110 million. Ninety-six percent of the cut foliage production was in Florida (85%) and California (11%). Leatherleaf fern production represented 66% of the value of cut foliage produced.

B. Production

Potted and cut foliage plants need a mild climate and high temperature, humidity, and light conditions. Potted foliage plants are usually produced in greenhouses in nontropical regions, and in shade houses or outdoors in tropical/semi-tropical areas. A wide range of potted foliage plant sizes are grown. Small container plants (less than 2 in. in diameter) are grown for incorporation into decorative containers while large trees are produced for use in interiorscapes of malls and offices. Large trees cannot be produced economically in greenhouses, and are generally grown outdoors in the southernmost areas of the United States, primarily in Florida or California. In Europe, some large foliage plants are produced in the Netherlands or in southern France or Spain while other plants are imported from the United States. Cut foliage is grown in shade houses or outdoors under tree canopies.

Foliage plants are propagated from cuttings, seed, air layers, spores, division, rhizomes, and tissue culture. The most common propagation system for potted foliage involves a mist area where unrooted cuttings are stuck in a cell-pak or tray system on a bench. After rooting, cuttings are pulled and potted. Transplanting is done as soon as possible after root development to minimize root damage. Many growers are now placing cuttings directly into the pots in which they will be sold (direct-stick), a procedure that reduces total production time and labor required for transplant. Common in southern areas where plant growth is rapid, direct-stick propagation is dependent on a high rooting percentage and large area equipped with misting and irrigation systems. Sanitary conditions are necessary to avoid disease contamination and the spread of insects. The most common propagation mixes contain sphagnum peat moss amended with dolomite for proper pH adjustment.

Interrelationships among environmental conditions, fertilization, and irrigation practices must be effectively managed in order to produce a marketable crop which will perform satisfactorily under indoor home and office conditions. Over the last 20 years, research has demonstrated that foliage plants can be "acclimatized" to interior conditions by subjecting them to a period of reduced fertilizer and water, and low light levels prior to sale. Such plants lose fewer leaves when moved indoors, and will survive longer under interior conditions.

Mechanization and computerization have been incorporated into modern foliage plant production facilities. Crop scheduling and inventory control, nursery design and organization, materials flow, and organization of labor and equipment to meet production plans are used to increase the efficiency and profitability of foliage plant operations.

C. Geography/Distribution

Florida, California, and Texas produce over 70% of the potted foliage plants in the United States, including large tropical plants and trees found in shopping malls and commercial and institutional buildings. Secondary production areas include the Gulf Coast states, Hawaii, the Northeast and Midwest. Currently, federal regulations prohibit importation of crops grown in soil into the United States to prevent introduction of harmful pathogens and insects. So, finished plants are not imported, but foliage plant cuttings are often produced in the Caribbean or Latin and Central America, and then shipped to the United States or Europe for propagation and production.

Foliage plants are distributed primarily by truck for domestic markets and shipped by boat to international markets. Cut foliage may be shipped by airplane or boat to international markets.

D. Shipping and Storage

Plant quality and performance are significantly affected by environmental conditions during transport and/or storage. Plant preparation begins during the production period, by systematically reducing light and fertilizer levels.

Plants grown under high light will not ship as well as those grown under low light, and may exhibit excessive leaf drop or other quality loss. Plants grown in high light and warm temperatures are not as likely to tolerate cool shipping temperatures without sustaining chilling injury. Plants grown with higher-than-recommended nutritional regimes are also likely to drop leaves once moved indoors.

Shipping temperatures are often in the range of 55–65°F, but will vary with plant species, shipping duration, and season of the year. Shipping temperatures are generally lower in winter than in summer. Duration of exposure to a specific temperature can also affect plant quality. A temperature that might be optimum for 2-week shipments might cause damage when plants are exposed for 3–4 weeks.

Plants should have adequate soil moisture at shipping time. Too much moisture can cause leaf drop, whereas too little increases plant-tissue desiccation and increases leaf drop and injury potential. Foliage plants shipped or stored for long durations need a relative humidity level around 85–90% for maintenance.

Ethylene is probably the only contaminant that can occur in containers during shipping unless there is pollution from an outside source. Foliage plants, however, are somewhat tolerant of ethylene and require fairly high levels (1–2 ppm) at relatively high temperatures (18°C or higher) for long durations before causing damage. Ethylene does not seem to be a major problem when plants are shipped at cooler (16°C or lower) temperatures.

E. Marketing/Competition

The foliage plant market has expanded throughout the world because of the demand for tropical plants. Ecological awareness, more apartment dwellers, increased plant availability, commercial applications, and new cultivars have spurred interest in foliage plants.

Once available only through retail florists, cut and potted foliage are now marketed through distributors, interstate greenhouse operators, wholesale florists, local growers, supermarkets, retail florists, department and plant stores, garden centers, brokers, and plant-scaping services.

VI. Woody Ornamental Landscape Plants

A. Nurseries/Geography

Woody ornamental plants include evergreen and deciduous trees and shrubs most commonly used for permanent planting in landscapes. More than 15,000 independent U.S. nurseries produced over $4 billion worth of nursery plants in 1987. The nursery industry comprises propagators, growers, and distributors.

The nursery industry is concentrated in Florida, California, the Great Lakes and Middle Atlantic states. Nursery sales for home and commercial landscapes represent nearly 40% of the horticulture retail trade. Nurseries are equally divided among the production of coniferous evergreens (yew, juniper, spruce, pine), broad-leaved evergreens (rhododendron, camellia, holly, boxwood), deciduous plants (*Forsythia, Viburnum,* barberries, privets, lilacs, flowering vines), roses, and ornamental trees.

In some cases, temperature tolerances of woody ornamental plants limit production to certain geographical regions. For instance, yews will not tolerate warm production conditions in the south and evergreen azaleas will not survive cold northern winters.

B. Production/Market Preparation/Storage

Ornamental shrub nurseries can be specialized. Some produce "lining out" stock—seedlings and rooted cuttings for use in production of finished plants. Also, these nurseries sell bare-root liners—small plants started in propagation flats or containers—and small grafted plants of expensive and/or rare cultivars. Lining-out stock eliminates the need for every grower to have propagation facilities.

Nursery growers may only produce plants for wholesale sales. In most cases, plants are produced outdoors, although overwintering structures may be used in the mid-western United States to protect plants from temperature extremes and wind injury. Until plants reach a marketable size, they are watered and fertilized, treated for insect and disease pests, and pruned to develop proper form. Production time may be as short as 9–12 months for plants sold in a one-gallon container.

The last 20 years has seen a move from plants grown in native soils in the field to plants grown in containers filled with organic soilless substrates. Production of containerized plants allows growers to select growing medium and to control fertilizer and water to the plant more accurately. Also, digging of field grown plants (often a manual operation) is eliminated.

Mechanization has reduced manual labor requirements for filling containers and for watering and fertilizing plants. More growers are also using herbicides to control weeds and using transplanting equipment and conveyors to reduce labor costs.

Plants such as hollies and junipers may be grown to maturity in southern nurseries or propagated and grown for one year in a warm climate before being transported to northern nurseries for finishing. This arrangement takes advantage of the optimum southern conditions for propagation and early growth, with good finishing conditions of northern climates. Also, shipping costs for prefinished plants are less than for finished plants.

C. Marketing

Garden centers, nurseries, and mass market outlets sell trees, shrubs, and ground covers. Today's retail nursery manager is likely to have a broad range of skills involving merchandising and landscape services in addition to horticultural expertise. Diversified garden centers sell many different kinds of horticultural products and maintain display areas for trees, shrubs, and roses, many of which come from wholesale growers. Many of these businesses also have landscaping services, which offer advice, installation, and/or maintenance services to homeowners.

VII. Turfgrass

A. Industry Overview

Turfgrass is the primary ornamental plant in landscapes. The turfgrass industry is a multibillion-dollar business in the United States and Canada, including the production of sod and seed and utilization. Sod production in the United States in 1987 was valued at $392 billion from slightly more than 1400 farms.

Rapid expansion of the housing market since 1950 and increased numbers of parks, recreational/sports facilities, and golf courses have increased the demand for turfgrasses. Commercial lawn maintenance firms offering turfgrass maintenance, pest control, and landscape design have emerged as a major service-oriented industry associated with turfgrass.

B. Geography

Seed and sod are the two basic commodities of the turfgrass industry. Kentucky bluegrass (*Poa pratensis*), red fescue (*Festuca rubra*), and bentgrass (*Agrostis* species) are the major turfgrasses grown in the northern two-thirds of the United States. Grass species adapted to the south are bermudagrass (*Cynodon dactylon*), bahiagrass (*Paspalum notatum*), carpetgrass (*Axonopus compressus*), centipedegrass (*Eremochloa ophiuroides*), *Zoysia* species, and St. Augustinegrass (*Stenotaphrum secundatum*).

With climates ideal for seed production, Washington, Oregon, Idaho, and western Canada produce most cool-season grasses. Florida, Texas, and Arizona have a large number of sod producers for warm-season turfgrasses.

C. Seed Production/Harvesting

Established in either the spring or fall, seeds are planted very lightly in weed-free rows 16 in. apart. Seed rows are covered with a band of activated charcoal and sprayed with a pre-emergence herbicide to control weeds. The charcoal absorbs the herbicide near the seed and protects the seedling from injury. A more traditional method involves tilling the field in the fall, letting it lie fallow over the winter, applying a herbicide treatment, and planting in the spring. Vigorous postplanting weed control ensures that only the desired cultivar's seeds are harvested.

In late June or early July harvesting begins when upper stems are mowed and windrowed (arranged for drying). Large combines pick up and thresh the seeds after they have dried in the field for several days. Then the seed is shipped to seed companies for cleaning, testing, and packaging. Seed cleaning is as important as field production. Equipment such as vibrating screens, shakers, and air jets remove chaff, soil, weed seeds, and other impurities.

Burning fields after harvesting results in much greater seed production in subsequent years. Burning destroys straw left from harvesting, reduces insect, disease, weed, and thatch problems, and increases tillering (production of stems that develop at the parent plant's crown and grow upward within the parent plant's leaf sheath). Seed fields are only in production for 5 years or less.

D. Sod Production/Harvesting

In recent years, because of the popularity of "instant" turf, sod production has increased steadily. Farms that produce sod (pieces or strips of live grass and adhering soil used for vegetative planting) must be located near prospective markets because sod should be installed within 48 hr of harvest. Successful sod production requires deep soil and a good water supply. The best soils are organic muck because they are lighter than mineral soils. Sod grown on muck soils do not have to be as well knit and can be harvested in a shorter

time. The most satisfactory mineral soils are well-drained sandy loam, silt loam, or loam.

Profits increase as the time between planting and harvesting is shortened. Harvesting cannot occur, however, until sod is strong enough to hold together well when handled. Species and cultivars producing aggressive rhizomes (spreading underground stems that produce new shoots and roots at nodes) and stolons (surface spreading stems that produce new shoots and roots at nodes) are preferred. Species with limited spreading ability, like fine fescue, knit sod together slowly and are less desirable.

Sod production usually takes 18 to 24 months although sod produced in netted seedbeds may be harvested in 100 days or less. Netting helps reinforce sod strength during harvesting and installation. Another way to speed up strengthening is to grow sod over plastic.

Producing quality sod quickly requires intensive maintenance. Adequate fertilization, constant irrigation, and correct mowing are essential. Pesticides keep the sod totally free of weeds, insects, and diseases. Sodded turfgrasses should have vigorous spreading ability, be attractive, resist diseases, and perform under local conditions.

Large harvesting machines cut sod. Some of these machines cut, roll, and stack sod on pallets in one operation. Sod pieces of cool-season grasses are generally 12–18 in. wide and 4–6 feet long. Sod pieces of warm-season grasses are generally 16 by 24 in. in size. Big roll technology has now made it possible to harvest both cool- and warm-season grasses in strips 4 by 45 feet in size. To minimize soil loss, make the sod lighter and easier to handle, and encourage rapid rooting, sod is cut as thin as possible.

E. Environmental Issues

Turfgrass requires water to survive and grow. Turfgrasses also need fertilization, pesticides, fungicides, nematicides, insecticides, and regular mowing to sustain quality. Such chemicals are energy-intensive, using nonrenewable fossil fuels (coal, petroleum, or natural gas) in production, packaging, distribution, and application. However, turfgrasses can filter fertilizers and pesticides from underground aquifers, provided maintenance procedures prevent runoff from the site. Increasingly, turf managers are now applying integrated pest management (IPM) techniques. By combining all pest-control methods, rather than relying solely on pesticides, pest populations can be reduced below injury levels. Growing healthy grass is the foundation of IPM, because healthy grass is less susceptible to diseases, insects, and weeds. Proper fertilization, mowing, and watering contribute to successful IPM. IPM decreases reliance on pesticides and ensures that they are applied correctly when no other alternatives exist.

F. Artificial Turf

Introduced and installed at a number of major U.S. sports stadiums in the 1960s, artificial turf is made of nylon fibers. This man-made grass became popular because it provided a permanent, uniform playing surface that was relatively maintenance free. A foam pad underneath the grass cushions the impact of a fall; an asphalt layer is under the pad. Vacuuming and water-removal machines are the primary maintenance equipment.

Experience over the years has revealed serious drawbacks to the use of artificial turf. During the 1970s oil prices rose sharply, and the cost of artificial turf increased since nylon is a petroleum derivative. Injuries are more prevalent and surface temperatures are extremely high during hot weather. The nylon is not permanent; it can be damaged by oil leaking from equipment, cigarette burns, and other accidents. Colors fade. Cleaning and repair costs were considerably higher than originally anticipated. Artificial turf is, however, still used in covered stadiums and for heavily used fields.

VIII. Student Opportunities in Environmental Horticulture

A. Education

Environmental horticulture students are given the skills, abilities, and experiences to prepare them for competitive, viable job markets, productive citizenship, and lifelong learning as it impacts food/agricultural suppliers, natural resources, and communities. Leading undergraduate programs include international and multi-cultural dimensions that produce graduates who understand and are able to participate meaningfully in a global industry.

Graduates have skills in technical, oral, and written communication; computer applications, personnel management, professional ethics, international studies, and leadership development. Curricula include the study of safety, health, and environmental impact issues, as well as technical courses.

Quality academic programs emphasize the integration of the physical, biological, social, and business sciences. Internships and other hands-on experiences enable students to apply what they have learned.

B. Environmental Horticulture Careers

The environmental horticulture field employs thousands of people in hundreds of job specialties. Landscape horticulture employs growers, designers, maintenance personnel, researchers, garden center staff, and retail and wholesale salespersons. Nonproduction industry careers include those in botanical gardens, arboretums, municipal park and street tree programs, and utility companies.

Career opportunities in turfgrass include sod producers and seed specialists, institutional and commercial grounds supervisors, golf course, cemetery, highway, athletic and recreational fields, and lawn maintenance personnel. Turfgrass equipment, irrigation supply, fertilizer, and seed and pesticide companies also hire professionals as researchers, writers, evaluators, marketers, and advertisers.

Floriculture employs growers, researchers, salespeople, and wholesale, retail, and mass-market florists, such as those who work in the floral sections of supermarkets. The commercial interiorscaping field requires professionals to be horticulturists and designers.

Horticultural therapists use gardening in substance abuse and mental health recovery programs, with active and sedentary senior citizens, the terminally ill, high-achieving and troubled children, those individuals with temporary or permanent injuries, and prisoners. Several colleges and universities now offer programs in horticultural therapy.

Federal and state cooperative extension services hire environmental horticulture specialists as researchers, writers, and agents who share the latest information with the public and the industry. Vocational agricultural teachers in middle and high schools introduce students to horticulture. College and university faculty educate undergraduate and graduate students, and conduct basic and specialized research.

IX. The Future

A. Vision of the Future Required

Environmental horticulture will increasingly focus on the issues of global production and marketing, product quality and diversity, environmental issues like water and pesticides, more basic and specialized research, and educational programs which teach students to become competent and environmentally sensitive professionals.

Producers, distributors, and retailers attempting to capitalize on expanded consumer demand for plants and flowers will face new challenges as the 21st century nears: global marketing competition, increased federal and state regulations on natural resources, and emphasis on environmental preservation. The pressure to remain competitive will continue in the 1990s but external forces may have a much greater impact than previously seen by the environmental horticulture industries. Benefits to the consumer (user), the economy (money), and the environment (shared habitat) will drive the decisions of policy makers as to where public funds will be allocated.

B. Global Production and Marketing

Global production and marketing of ornamental plants and flowers will increase in the 1990s as production and labor costs and environmental regulations play a more dominant role in site selection for production. Imports of numerous ornamental plants may increase, but the countries producing these plants and flowers will probably change during the next decade. For instance, flower growers have expanded into Costa Rica, Peru, and Mexico as a result of political instability in Colombia. Production areas may also shift in response to international trade agreements that reduce or eliminate tariffs on flowers. Potted plant and nursery plant importation will continue to be conducted by domestic producers if Quarantine 37 restrictions are maintained.

As American green industries compete in the global market, they are restrained by more expensive labor, environmental standards that will become even more stringent, and pesticide limitations. Nevertheless, the U. S. floral and environmental horticulture industry will work to identify effective marketing strategies to increase domestic sales. Also, domestic growers must pursue opportunities to export domestically grown plants. Opportunities for domestic growers to expand sales will be realized only if growers use new production technology and market their products aggressively domestically and globally.

C. Product Quality, Diversity, and New Crops

The "Green Industry" should focus greater attention on product quality and consumer satisfaction, so lo-

cally grown products may be favored over imported crops which are subject to mishandling during shipping and storage. Increasingly, consumers are demanding a selection of plants and flowers offering diversity in flower color, leaf color, texture, and form, as well as good performance in an interior environment or exterior landscapes. Impulse sales will continue, but plants that do not provide lasting customer satisfaction will not sell. Growers and distribution facilities will face increased pressure to produce and handle flowers and plants properly.

Potted plant growers will attempt to select and grow high-performance, long-lasting varieties and alter production conditions to maximize interior longevity. Industry standards defining "quality" will change to include optimum product performance for the consumer and physical dimensions and characteristics at sale.

D. Environmental Issues

Water is in limited supply and concerns over contamination of drinking water supplies are increasing. In the next decade, expanding flower, foliage, and woody ornamental plant production and the turfgrass industry in many parts of the United States may be limited by federal, state, and local environmental restrictions. These regulations will limit water amounts and usedwater disposal procedures to prevent runoff problems. Maintaining sufficient quantities of good quality water to meet basic human needs and agricultural requirements, therefore, is a primary global concern.

The environmental horticulture industry must address the water issue from three perspectives—quality of water used, conservation of applied water, and reduction of the amount of impure water leaving the production facility and contaminating the remaining water supply.

Because of concerns about the effect of pesticides and other chemicals on water quality and worker safety, growers need to rethink traditional insect and disease control methods. Weekly preventive pesticide applications should be eliminated or significantly reduced and replaced with integrated pest management and biological control practices. Nonchemical measures are likely to become the norm as governmental agencies remove pesticides from the market and registration requirements for new pesticides become more difficult.

E. Research

To meet the technological challenges of the future, the environmental–horticulture industry must join with government, universities, and associations to support research and development.

Research priorities for the "Green Industry" are: (1) pest management and marketing/consumerism; (2) crop production, resource management, and post-production; (3) biotechnology and recycling/environment; (4) new plants/germplasm; and (5) people–plant interactions. Focusing on these priorities will further the competitiveness, environmental sensitivity, and sustainability of the U.S. green industries and associated services. The research objectives link societal issues to science, technology, and community development advances that can occur through basic and multi-disciplinary research of plant production systems and their influences and impacts on the environment.

Bibliography

Anon. (1991). "Floriculture Crops, 1990 Summary." United States Department of Agriculture, Washington, DC.

Berrall, J. S. (1966). "The Garden, An Illustrated History." Viking Press, New York.

Cathey, H. M. (1993). "Priorities for Research Opportunities for Optimism." U.S. Department of Agriculture, Washington, DC.

De Hertogh, A. A., and Le Nard, M. (1993). "The Physiology of Flower Bulbs." Elsevier, Amsterdam.

Johnson, D. C., and Johnson, T. M. (1993). "Financial Performance of U.S. Floriculture and Environmental Horticulture Farm Businesses, 1987–1991." Statistical Bulletin Number 862. United States Department of Agriculture, Washington DC.

Joiner, J. N. (1981). "Foliage Plant Production." Prentice Hall, Englewood Cliffs, NJ.

Janick, J. (1986). "Horticultural Sciences." Freeman, New York.

Larson, R. A. (1992). "Introduction to Floriculture," 2nd ed. Academic Press, New York.

Rice, L. W., and Rice, R. P., Jr. (1993). "Practical Horticulture." Regents/Prentice Hall, Englewood Cliffs, NJ.

Turgeon, A. J. (1991). "Turfgrass Management." Prentice Hall, Englewood Cliffs, NJ.

Ethics

Paul B. Thompson, *Texas A&M University*

Glossary

Analytical agricultural ethics Review and investigation of concepts, arguments, and implicit norms as they are deployed in developing an understanding of agricultural practice

Burdens of proof Criteria that must be met in order for a particular ethical judgment to be made or reversed

Ethical reductionism Reduction of ethical concepts and phenomena to statements about individual and subjective experiences; it promotes a strong division between fact and value

Informed consent Burden of proof often applied to risk issues: When parties that must bear risks voluntarily agree to do so under conditions of full disclosure, risks may be found acceptable without regard to risk benefit ratios; when informed consent is lacking, even low level beneficial risks may be rejected

Reductionism Reduction of a complex system or set of phenomena to a formal set of interrelated rules

Rights Justified or enforceable claims that may be made on behalf of right-holding parties; typically thought to provide absolute protection of individual interests against social benefits

Scientific reductionism Reduction of a system or complex set of phenomena to a set of rules solely based on scientific principles; for example, one could reduce the functioning of the human organism to chemical principles and completely disregard psychological principles

Substantive agricultural ethics Prescribes specific action plans, practices, and policies for persons and organizations involved in agricultural issues; the aim of substantive ethics is to present arguments for or against a proposed course of action that apply those concepts, rules, and standards with clarity, rigor, and logical coherence

Utilitarianism Nineteenth century approach to ethics which has greatly influenced 20th century public policy, particularly in the arena of cost benefit and risk benefit management; the term was first used by Jeremy Bentham and then by John Stuart Mill; the Utilitarian maxim states that the correct action is the one which produces the greatest amount of good for the greatest number of people

The word ethics is often used interchangeably with the word morality to indicate goals, norms, and values that are taken to guide human action. A common, but far from universal, distinction is to define ethics as the systematic study of moral codes, particularly with regard to the criticism, justification, and acceptability of social norms. Since critical evaluation of moral norms itself implies the application of norms, scholarly work on ethics has perennially been accused of circularity, dogma, relativism, and begging precisely the question it attempts to answer. Scholarly study of morality has, nevertheless, made it possible to provide considerably more explicit, logically coherent, and rigorous arguments on goals, norms, and values than are typically found in ordinary life.

Agricultural ethics is the criticism, analysis, and justification of systematic moral codes and the acceptability of social norms that exist or are applied to practices of food and fiber production, distribution, and consumption. Two methodological approaches are common in agricultural ethics. *Analytic agricultural ethics* undertakes review and investigation of concepts, arguments, and implicit norms as they are employed in developing an understanding of agricultural practice, its goals, and the secondary social and environmental consequences of food and fiber networks. Analytic ethics aims to improve understanding of concepts, rules, and standards that are commonly used to frame and defend moral judgments and prescriptions for action. *Substantive agricultural ethics* prescribes specific action plans, practices, and policies for persons and organizations involved in agricultural issues. The aim of substantive ethics is to present arguments for or against a proposed course of action that apply those concepts, rules, and standards with clarity, rigor, and logical coherence.

Given this definition, agricultural ethics can be understood as an interdisciplinary research and education area. Research and teaching on ethics take place to some degree in all disciplines of the social sciences and humanities, though some practitioners of these disciplines have disavowed work on ethics. The most typical disciplinary home for work in ethics has been philosophy, though departments of theology, religious studies, and political science also typically have specialists in ethics. Recent work in agricultural ethics emphasizes (1) unintended health, safety, and environmental impacts of agricultural technology; (2) the structure of agriculture, including distribution of benefits from agricultural production; and (3) questions of conduct, character, and professional ethics. In addition, special attention has been given to the moral standing of agricultural animals, and to ethics as it relates to agricultural biotechnology.

I. History of Agricultural Ethics

Normative or ethical implications of agriculture were a common topic for scholars of philosophy, society, and biology for most of the 3000-year history of Western thought. Aristotle discussed the configuration of agriculture he thought necessary for fulfilling human promise. More recently, Thomas Jefferson was both a scientifically informed practitioner of agriculture at his Monticello plantation and a philosopher of agriculture who contributed enduring analysis of how farm structure is related to problems of governance in a democracy.

Ethical reflection on agriculture carried over into the 20th century through the efforts of scientists and agricultural leaders such as Liberty Hyde Bailey and Henry Wallace, but the systematic discussion of agriculture was virtually absent in the writings of late 19th and early 20th century philosophers and moralists. The last generation of philosophers to discuss agriculture as a philosophical topic is the one that included John Stuart Mill, Ralph Waldo Emerson, and Karl Marx. Each of these three wrote extensively on agriculture, but no one recognized as a leading contributor to philosophical or religious ethics since them has done so.

After World War II, agricultural scientists and leaders gave little systematic attention to ethical issues. Agricultural ethics was not included in the curriculum of agricultural colleges. Ethics became increasingly marginalized through the 1950s and 1960s, with only a handful of social scientists undertaking normative evaluation of agriculture. Even in these studies, the role of ethics was largely implicit in that the norms or values on which evaluations had been based were seldom stated and almost never defended on philosophical grounds. Significant exceptions to this rule can be found in the work of agricultural economists John Brewster, Harold Breimyer, and Glenn Johnson. These works were almost totally ignored by professionals in liberal arts disciplines such as philosophy, religious studies, and political science. Indeed, the decline of attention to ethics in agriculture reflects a general decline in attention to ethics throughout all departments of the university in the decades following World War II.

In 1962, Rachel Carson published *Silent Spring*. While not in itself a philosophical book, Carson's critique of agricultural chemicals was arguably the first in a series of criticisms of the agricultural practices that had emerged following World War II. Frances Moore Lappe's *Diet for a Small Planet*, Jim Hightower's, *Hard Tomatoes, Hard Times*, Wendell Berry's *The Unsettling of America*, and the republication of Walter Goldschmidt's 1947 study *As You Sow*, were among the most influential and most enduring of critical works published before 1980. Books by critics of agriculture have since proliferated, with at least a dozen published every year in the decade between 1982 and 1992. While these books seldom present rigorous empirical or philosophical arguments for their conclusions, they typically make an explicit statement of the goals, values, and norms on which their evaluations of agriculture depend. They have in this way provided the source material for a resurgence of interest in careful scholarly attention to the philosophical foundations of agricultural practice.

As public criticism and mistrust of agricultural practices grew under the influence of these critics, agricultural institutions showed a renewed interest in the study of agricultural ethics. Courses were offered in some agricultural colleges, and a limited amount of research by philosophers and social scientists has been undertaken. Ethics and values issues have also become topics for symposia at disciplinary meetings of agricultural scientists and at consensus conferences intended to establish priorities for research and for policy change. Attempts to extend work on ethics to producer groups have thus far been limited. While agricultural ethics remains somewhat marginal in the agricultural disciplines, the role of ethics in curriculum, research, and public policy has been increasingly accepted.

II. Unintended Consequences

Many criticisms of modern agriculture have noted unwanted and unintended consequences of agricultural chemicals. Pesticides have had documented effects upon wildlife populations, and some are known carcinogens. Nitrogen fertilizers can pollute ground- and surfacewater. Many agricultural chemicals have long been known to have toxic effects when improperly handled, stored, or applied. It is clear that neither manufacturers nor producers intended or wanted these consequences, and both groups have made efforts to mitigate and control unintended consequences. Nevertheless, unintended consequences of agricultural chemicals pose ethical problems in that it is impossible to eliminate the risk of an unwanted event entirely. Furthermore, there is often disagreement about the degree of risk associated with agricultural chemicals. Some individuals express far greater concern about exposure to pesticides than do others. Producers, scientists, and chemical manufacturers thus face the problem of managing concern for unwanted effects, even when the empirical evidence for such effects is scant, controversial, and even nonexistent. Whether real or imagined, unwanted consequences of chemicals have significantly affected the reception of many agricultural technologies, including mechanization and biotechnology, among producers and food consumers since 1962.

An analysis of ethical issues associated with unintended consequences surveys the assumptions and implicit norms that have guided action contributing to the unintended outcomes. Public claims expressing a rationale or justification of such action are scrutinized, and the pattern of reasoning is exposed. In many cases, disagreement over agricultural practices can be traced to incommensurable assumptions in the way that antagonists view the world and the relation of moral norms to human action. This is a disagreement that is both more subtle and more longlasting than simple disagreement over values. Alternative approaches to the problem of unintended consequences provide an example. Many people, especially those associated with the agricultural sciences, exhibit behavior and speech that is most consistent with a *utilitarian* approach to ethics. Environmentalist, agrarian, and consumer critics have rejected this basic approach, sometimes assuming a pattern of thought more consistent with *rights*.

The utilitarian strategy adopts an ethical norm which requires decision makers to anticipate the consequences of their actions and policies to the fullest extent possible, and to weigh the costs associated with unintended consequences against the acknowledged benefits of technology accruing in the form of increased food availability, increased profitability of farming, and decreased consumer food cost. This strategy presents a series of methodological and philosophical problems, in that unwanted costs are often difficult to quantify, and in that there are philosophical disagreements over when to accept trade-offs. A severe distributive inequality, for example, might provide a reason to reject technologies that clearly produce more aggregate benefits than harms. The strategy has been called utilitarian, because it shares key philosophical features with the ideas of utilitarian philosophers Jeremy Bentham and John Stuart Mill.

The alternative strategy assumes that individuals may be accountable for predictable, though unintended, consequences of their action. Rights provide criteria for accountability because acts that do not interfere with others' rights will be judged ethically permissible. When individuals and organizations act within their rights, their actions are ethically acceptable without regard to whether they optimize the trade-offs of cost and benefit. However, virtually all of the unintended consequences associated with agriculture constitute interference in some form. A strict application of rights constraints implies that all such actions should be prohibited. A more adequate determination of accountability requires one to see that many individuals have acted in ways that collectively produce the unintended consequence. As such, the accountability of individuals and groups depends upon how their activity is related to the activity of others who may share or wholly assume responsibility for consequences.

In application, the rights approach to agricultural ethics often establishes *burdens of proof* that must be satisfied before an action is undertaken, rather than absolute constraints. A burden of proof is a criterion that establishes which party can be held accountable for consequences. A key burden of proof in evaluating unintended consequences is *informed consent*. Individuals who use an agricultural technology or product under conditions of informed consent can be understood to have accepted responsibility for the consequences of use. Scientists, extension agents, and private sector firms that introduce technology under conditions that secure the informed consent of affected parties satisfy ethical norms, and may not be held accountable for unintended consequences. The criterion of consent transfers accountability to the affected parties. Consent criteria present a series of philosophical problems not unlike utilitarian approaches, in that the conditions for expression of consent are complex. Consent implies that people have meaningful options, that there are commonly recognized practices that imply consent, and that those giving consent have full knowledge of the unintended consequences that might ensue. Since such criteria are seldom fulfilled completely, burdens of proof are often satisfied in the same idealized fashion that utilitarians perform optimizing calculations.

Although both strategies are idealizations, each establishes a general conceptual approach to problems in agricultural ethics at cross purposes with the other. The utilitarian strategy begins with an assessment of the likely consequences associated with an agricultural technology or practice. In the case of a chemical pesticide, the consequences would include risks to the health of farm labor and to food consumers, as well as benefits to producers in the form of increased profitability. If a proposed activity will have a significant impact upon consumer food prices, it will also be important to anticipate indirect effects upon the availability of food for the poor. When all the relevant consequences have been assessed, the proposed activity can be compared to one or more alternatives. At a minimum, alternatives include simply using and not using the proposed pesticide, but the array of possible strategies for use is always complex, include licensing for restricted vs general use, notification, rules that may or may not be included, etc. The comparison allows one to make a fairly sophisticated judgment about the trade-offs between two choices.

Trade-offs themselves can be complex. A simple-minded decision rule for utilitarian ethics is to allow an action whenever benefits outweigh costs, but there may be alternatives that produce a more attractive ratio of benefit to cost. One may also face a choice

between one option that has a high benefit to cost ratio, yet returns few total benefits, and another with a less attractive ratio of benefit to cost that produces more benefits (at higher cost). Distributive issues also make trade-offs difficult to compare. For example, one chemical may pose a low-level risk of cancer to many food consumers, while another may pose little or no risk to consumers, but may be far more dangerous to handle in the field. One may thus be comparing a low-level risk to all food consumers against a high level risk to a small group of agricultural laborers. A question of fairness arises, particularly if the laborers are comparatively less well off as a group than are food consumers. Here, costs (in the form of risk) are not comparably distributed by each option.

The alternative strategy for dealing with unintended consequences would approach the decision to use an agricultural chemical by examining a series of burdens of proof. Here, the beginning assumption is that agents are responsible for unintended consequences of their action. However, a manufacturer of a chemical may shift responsibility to the actual users of the chemical, provided that criteria for informed consent have been met. Similarly, a producer may shift responsibility for unintended consequences to employees or consumers when these groups are informed of the potential consequences, and when they have meaningful opportunities to make alternative choices. On this view, the food residue of agricultural chemicals poses no ethical problem as long as consumers have both a reasonable opportunity to get information about unintended consequences and an alternative choice in the form of organic foods. If these conditions are met, then it is reasonable to conclude that consumers have consented to risk the possibility that there may be chemical residues, and to bear the responsibility for any consequences for their choice of foods.

The burdens of proof that must be met in developing and promoting an agricultural technology may seem heavy when described abstractly. In practice, they are consistent with the general structure of a free market economy, provided that two conditions are met. Sellers must provide full information, and sellers' economic power must not become so concentrated that buyers are effectively denied a meaningful opportunity to choose alternatives. It is important to note that consent criteria do not necessarily produce a socially optimal outcome from a utilitarian perspective. One reason it may not is that buyers may have faulty preferences. They may, for example, choose foods that are unhealthy, or they may place too much emphasis upon immediate gratification. Many economists assume that consumers' actual preferences constitute the norm for determining a social optimum. If immediate gratification and consumption of unhealthy food are defined as a benefit in virtue of the fact that such activities satisfy consumer preferences, there will be less divergence between utilitarian and consent criteria than would be the case when costs and benefits are defined according to criteria that are independent from existing preferences.

The economic concept of *market failure* is also an instance where consent and utilitarian criteria diverge. Resource economics identifies a number of situations in which buyers and sellers making voluntary exchanges will reach outcomes that all would regard as suboptimal. The American dust bowl has frequently been analyzed as an instance of market failure. Under utilitarian criteria, market failure provides a justification for regulation, the coercive application of state power to ensure that individuals and organizations do not engage in practices that produce the unwanted outcome. Such state actions can come into direct conflict with ethical criteria associated with property rights. The result is a philosophically based political conflict between those who advocate government regulation of unintended consequences based upon utilitarian analysis, and those who evaluate such action on the part of government as a violation of consent criteria implied by common notions of property rights.

III. The Structure of Agriculture

Ethical issues associated with the structure of agriculture overlap with those of unintended consequences to the extent that changes in the size distribution or number of farms can be understood as an unwanted consequence of technological change. The general relationship between means of agricultural production and norms for land entitlement and property rights has been an enduring philosophical question, however. As noted above, Aristotle thought that achievement of moral virtue in the elite of society depended upon a release from labor of agricultural production that could only be provided through a system of agricultural production based upon human slavery. In the 18th century, John Locke defended the enclosure movement that removed English lands from common pastoral use and converted them to privately controlled croplands on the grounds that enclosure returned far more benefits in the form of

increased food availability. At about the same time, Jean Jacques Rousseau argued that the primary impact of privatization of agricultural lands was to *create* scarcity, by creating a privileged class of land-holding aristocrats.

This pattern of divergent philosophical views has continued. Some, such as economist Luther Tweeten, evaluate changes in the distribution of farms by size and by type of ownership in terms of criteria that stress efficiency and aggregate benefits of farm production. Others, such as sociologist Jack Kloppenburg, stress how changes in agricultural practice have favored the interests of a few influential individuals, generally working behind the scenes.

The dispute is particularly relevant for planning and evaluation of agricultural development. Agricultural development programs such as the Green Revolution have been based on the view that carefully managed increases in agricultural productivity are a necessary condition for improved conditions in the developing world. On the opposing view, dependency theorists have argued that underdevelopment has been caused by exploitative encouragement of sugar, tobacco, coffee, tea, and other stimulant production in developing countries, as well as "luxury," crops such as fruits, oilseeds, and spices. This group sees little hope for development until the developing world's cycle of dependency upon developed countries (first for production technology and expertise, then for export markets) is broken.

One way to analyze the contrast between the two philosophies is to return to the distinction between utilitarian and rights-based ethics. On a utilitarian view, changes in farm structure create costs in the form of financial and emotional consequences for those who exit farming. There may also be more abstract costs in the form of esthetic and historical values associated that link a given farm structure to broader patterns of culture. The key question is whether production efficiencies achieved through new technology and the resulting farm structure produce benefits that outweigh these costs. For a rights theorist, the comparison of cost and benefits is largely irrelevant. The key question is whether affected parties were adequately involved in the events that cause a change in structure. Dependency theory, for example, may be interpreted as resting on the claim that affected parties in the developing world have been denied any meaningful opportunity to reject the offer of Green Revolution technology. As such, the resulting changes in farm structure do not satisfy burdens of proof that relate to the participation, representation, and consent of affected parties.

It is likely that those who defend the record of change in farm structure would be willing to accept a utilitarian characterization of their ethical rationale. Luther Tweeten has done so explicitly. While some critics would base their objections on rights claims, others diagnose a more fundamental problem. Like utilitarians, critics such as Kloppenburg or Wendell Berry (discussed below) would concentrate on the consequences of farm structural change. They would, however, argue that the relevant consequences are far more comprehensive and systematic than utilitarian defenders have recognized. This form of criticism has emphasized the *reductionism* implicit in the defense of the status quo, a tendency to evaluate action in terms of criteria that fail to account for holistic or systematic effects.

Reductionism is seldom defined precisely in critics' writings. Two themes that recur are *scientific reductionism* and *ethical reductionism*. Scientific reductionism is the belief that obtaining knowledge is an additive process. The building blocks of this process are specific facts or observations that are localized in time and space. Scientific theories consist in generalizations or laws that aggregate data. Critics argue that this approach to knowledge can never capture the systematic interrelationships of natural and social phenomena, and hence will tend to overlook important environmental and social consequences. Spokesmen for the status quo often attempt to meet these criticisms by arguing that the critics' claims are not adequately supported by data. A vicious circle of claim and counterclaim ensues. Scientific reduction is also associated with the philosophical view that science is value-free. The claim is asserted in two district senses. One is that the process of conducting research and establishing facts through experiment is not influenced by values. The second is that data and theoretical generalizations produced scientifically do not, in themselves, entail value judgments. In application, the alleged value-free nature of science functions very much like an ethical norm, instructing scientists to avoid overt expressions of value judgments in their scientific practice. It is in such applications that scientific reductionism has tended to stifle research, teaching, and public discussion of agricultural ethics.

Ethical reductionism (sometimes called methodological individualism) is the belief that all ethical significance derives from impact upon or action of individuals. Costs, benefits, and rights violations alike are, for the reductionist, significant only when they affect individuals, rather than groups, or, more abstractly,

culture as a whole. Critics argue that changes in farm structure can produce broad cultural patterns that transform the values and world view of future generations. These changing world views may lead future individuals to evaluate farm structure very differently. The ethical individualist does not find the change significant, precisely because individuals living in the future culture are unlikely to perceive themselves as victims. From the reductionist perspective, if no one complains, nothing is wrong. Ethical reduction is influential because many rural social scientists assume that value is a function of individual preferences. One of the most effective criticisms (unrelated to agriculture) is Aldous Huxley's novel *Brave New World,* in which citizens of the future are totally content with lives in which they have been genetically, chemically, and behaviorally conditioned to take pleasure in circumstances that present generations would find totally devoid of meaning and morally intolerable.

Scientific reductionism is relevant to ethical analysis of changes in farm structure because some critics believe that changes in farm structure which produce broad scale environmental, social, and cultural changes are not amenable to analysis and identification by the methods of reductionist science. If choices or policies cannot be justified scientifically, the reductionist concludes that they cannot be justified at all. Ethical reductionism is relevant because, to the extent that these changes affect culture and the transmission of values from one generation to another, it may be difficult to identify harms or rights violations that apply to specific individuals. This theme in the criticism of farm structure overlaps with the next area, conduct and professional ethics.

IV. Conduct and Professional Ethics

The third area of concentration in agricultural ethics has to do with conduct. Agricultural producers and those employed in agribusiness should adhere to standards of professional conduct, and the standards of conduct for agricultural research form a related category. Critics and representatives of the agricultural establishment alike have raised concern over the conduct of those involved in pesticide sales and in certifying the safety and efficacy of input chemicals and agricultural products. Professional conduct is, perhaps, the most obvious area of relevance for agricultural ethics, and one where violations of legal and ethical norms can stir significant public attention. Philosophical questions arise in determining the precise role responsibilities of agricultural professionals, but in general, these ethical issues are far less contentious than those that arise in the first two categories. While the enforcement of norms for good professional conduct can be a difficult practical problem, there is often a broad consensus of opinion even among practitioners on what the norms are.

The writings of Wendell Berry and his followers provide one exception to the generally noncontroversial nature of issues involving ethical conduct. Berry has argued that changes in farming practice and in rural communities have produced a situation in which all persons are less able to engage in virtuous conduct. Specialization in food production and distribution has, in Berry's view, fractured the integrity of family-based production and consumption, and has made it difficult to perceive social responsibilities to family members and to others in the community. Similarly, this specialization has made it difficult to perceive human dependency upon nature and upon natural cycles for restoring the environment and replenishing the resource base. Berry thus argues that industrialized agriculture necessitates unethical conduct, not only on the part of agricultural producers, but on the part of society at large. Berry's concerns with personal conduct, thus, overlap with the criticism of reductionism discussed above.

Berry's sweeping claims aside, the most serious problems arise in constructing procedures for enforcing what would commonly be regarded as acceptable norms for professional conduct. Farmers may have incentives to abuse chemicals, to adulterate products (spraying water into a grain truck to increase weight is a well-known abuse), or to cheat on Federal programs. Similarly, agribusiness firms producing inputs may have incentives to misrepresent the safety and effectiveness of their products, and food processing firms may have incentives to pass contaminated or adulterated products on to consumers. Finally, public officials, including research scientists, may have incentives to favor special interests, including industry and producers, over the public good. Philosophical questions arise in how government should regulate such activities, and when penalties should be applied for noncompliance. This area of agricultural ethics becomes closely involved with agricultural law.

V. Research Ethics in Agricultural Science

The conduct and professional ethics of agricultural scientists deserves special attention. Whether basic or applied, science is an activity dedicated to the production of knowledge. Scientists have long recognized that the success of this enterprise depends upon strict adherence to the norms of honesty in reporting results, and openness in being willing to consider alternative hypotheses. First order issues in research ethics stress the importance of these norms to the research enterprise, and decry the occurrence of fraud, deceit, and coercion in science. These norms can be described as an element of professional ethics for the scientist. The doctrine of academic freedom was advanced in the 19th century to protect the openness of scientific enquiry, and to protect scientists from reprisal when they reported unpopular results. Historically, scientific organizations have relied upon a process of socialization to enforce norms of honesty. During recent years, however, it has become clear that scientists can advance their careers, as well as commercial products, through fraud and deceit, and new concerns have been raised about the integrity of the scientific community.

Recent work in the philosophy of science by Steve Fuller and in the sociology of science by Bruno Latour has established the basis for understanding second order issues in research ethics. These authors have shown how scientists are taught to believe that science is founded on value-free objective procedures, while ethical norms are based on emotion or mere opinion. Belief in the value-free nature of science is often expressed as scientific and ethical reductionism, discussed above. Belief in the value-free nature (e.g., objectivity) of science does not strictly entail that ethical questions about the choice of a scientific research project, or about the unintended consequences of a scientific finding, are inimical to the methods and practice of science. Nevertheless, practices in many agricultural research organizations discourage deliberation of ethical issues as unscientific. Although these beliefs represent value judgments themselves, they have allowed scientists to project a public image of being neutral parties, committed only to the facts, and unmotivated by value judgments or norms.

When the belief that science should always produce more knowledge is combined with a belief that applying ethical standards to research choice is inimical to science, scientists and scientific organizations become may become committed to a goal of always increasing knowledge, while rejecting the legitimacy of other interests that may oppose the creation of new knowledge (or may feel that resources are better invested in other goals). Scientists who adopt this posture pursue funding and freedom to conduct research, but refuse to participate in debate over the goals or value of research on the grounds that doing so will compromise objectivity. In this situation, scientists are an interest group whose interests depend upon being thought to have no interests. The situation creates incentives for duplicity and self-deception within the scientific enterprise, and may ultimately erode scientists' commitment to the norms of honesty and openness. The alternative is to reject either the norm of advancing knowledge or the belief that science is value-free. Either way, scientists have a responsibility to review and defend the value of their research programs, and to at least consider the significance of unintended consequences. The conclusion is that second order ethical deliberation should be accepted as an intrinsic element of scientific practice.

VI. Animal Well-Being

The legal and ethical protection of animals has long standing in the United States. Anticruelty statutes were enacted in some colonies before the Revolutionary War. More recently, animal protectionists have noted concern for the well-being of farm animals in confinement settings, especially since the publication of Ruth Harrison's *Animal Machines* in 1966. However, the principal focus of the recent animal rights movement has been to oppose the use of animals in product testing and biomedical research. The biomedical debate has become quite acrimonious, with some parties on both sides taking extreme positions. Few in agriculture would deny that caregivers have ethical responsibilities to assure the well-being of farm and food animals.

Farmers and ranchers have traditionally thought to be especially respectful of the well-being of food and farm animals. They have been thought to possess personal moral concern for animals. Also, animal health and well-being have been thought to correspond closely to a producer's interest in efficiency and marketability of animal products. The correlation between producer and animal interests fails to obtain when any one of three conditions obtains. First, some products, such as *foie gras* or pale veal, may require production methods contrary to animal well-being. Second, some elements of animal well-being may be realizable only under ideal conditions seldom realized in either wild or domesticated settings. Third, with large operations or high stocking rates, the management cost of attending to the needs of a few individual animals will not always be matched by returns based on average or aggregated sales of animal products. Animal protection organizations have criticized ag-

ricultural producers on each of these three points. The political rhetoric of the animal experimentation debate influences criticisms of agriculture and ambiguous terminology presents a barrier to any clear presentation of ethical issues. Multiple uses for the terms *animal welfare* and *animal rights* are especially confusing. For some, the term "animal rights" implies an extreme reformist position, while "animal welfare," is taken to imply an attitude favoring moderate or no reform in animal agriculture. Popular use suggests that those who express support for animal rights merely feel that individual animals' interests deserve consideration, and do not propose radical change in animal agriculture. More formal uses of these terms have been introduced into the literature by two influential philosophers, Peter Singer and Tom Regan.

Peter Singer advocates an animal welfare philosophy in a series of articles and in his book *Animal Liberation*. Singer is a utilitarian philosopher who believes that the morality of an action is to be evaluated by assessing its consequences. The key to the animal welfare philosophy is the belief that comparable interests deserve equal consideration without regard to species. This means that comparable experience of physical pain, for example, would be given equal consideration without regard to whether the pain is experienced by a pig, a monkey, or a human being. Singer explicitly notes that many interests do not admit of meaningful cross-species comparisons, and that the complex cognitive interests of human beings establish bases for evaluating consequences to humans in a manner that is unparalleled for other species. Hence, Singer's view admits of many opportunities in principle where human interests will be favored over animals', and even where animal pain or suffering may be justified by compensating benefits to humans. However, Singer is also of the opinion that animals in confinement settings suffer to a degree that makes it impossible to justify human consumption of food animals. As such, he is commonly associated with the so-called animal rights group advocating radical change.

Tom Regan has made numerous public appearances on behalf of animal interests, especially since publication of his book *The Case for Animal Rights* in 1983. Regan advocates an animal rights philosophy that is opposed to the animal welfare philosophy of Singer. In summary, Regan's view states that Singer's utilitarian position does not provide adequate reason for protecting the interests of individual animals. Aggregation of costs and benefits to human and nonhuman animals leaves open the possibility that significant harms to a few individual animals can be compensated by relatively insignificant benefits to a large number of human beings. This argument has been especially relevant to the cases of product testing and scientific research. According to Regan, animals are "subjects of a life." Accordingly, humans must respect their interests. While Regan's view would allow priority to comparable human interests (e.g., one might sacrifice animal lives to save human lives) his animal rights philosophy prohibits the aggregation of relatively low level interests (such as gustatory pleasure) to compensate for harms of an ethically fundamental sort.

Although the writings of Singer and Regan represent the philosophical distinction between animal welfare and animal rights, both have advocated vegetarianism. For Singer, vegetarianism is a specific response to the use of confinement systems and high stocking rates. For Regan, vegetarianism is a general moral responsibility that would apply at all times and places. Since both Singer and Regan are sharply critical of animal agriculture, the more moderate views of Bernard Rollin have had more influence within animal science and veterinary medicine. Rollin has written several influential works such as his 1987 book *The Unheeded Cry,* but a paper entitled "Animal Welfare, Animal Rights and Agriculture," provides a particularly concise statement of his views. For Rollin, the idea of animal rights represents the consensus judgment of society that the interests of individual animals matter, and that producers may be required to sacrifice financial gains in order to assure that vital interests are met. Rollin thinks that this idea is generally consistent with traditional notions of animal husbandry, but that emphasis upon narrow scientific or economic measures of productivity and animal health have caused an erosion of moral concern for food animals. Rollin urges animal rights as a philosophy that is, in effect, a return to more humane and responsive practices of traditional husbandry.

VII. Agricultural Biotechnology

The rapid growth of recombinant DNA transfer techniques and their application to agricultural science has created a situation in which agricultural biotechnologies present excellent case studies for many of the ethical issues discussed above. Unintended consequences of agricultural biotechnology have stimulated the most acrimonious debate. In the early 1980s, Jeremy Rifkin's Foundation for Economic Trends filed lawsuits designed to ensure that those undertaking re-

search and development of agricultural biotechnology assume responsibility for all social and environmental consequences. The first round of debate focused on ice-nucleating bacteria that could provide crop protection against freezing temperatures as low as 30°F (-1°C). Rifkin delayed experiments with these bacteria by raising questions about whether scientists had undertaken adequate review of potential environmental consequences. [*See* PLANT BIOTECHNOLOGY: FOOD SAFETY AND ENVIRONMENTAL ISSUES; TRANSGENIC ANIMALS.]

The second round of debate has focused on recombinant bovine somatotropin (BST), a genetically engineered version of the hormone that can be used to stimulate milk production in dairy cows. The unintended consequences that raised concern with BST stressed social impact upon the structure of the U.S. dairy industry. Economic analysis predicted that the technology would accelerate a shift from small to large dairies, and from the Northeast to the South and Southwest as principal production regions. Concern over the impact on the health of dairy cows has been raised, largely associated with mastitis problems associated with the increased volume of milk production. Finally, consumer groups expressed reluctance to accept milk produced using recombinant BST, despite scientific evidence documenting safety and quality. [*See* DAIRY CATTLE PRODUCTION.]

In addition to these problems associated with unwanted consequences, recombinant techniques have been associated with ethical questions about property rights and about the religious and metaphysical implications of biotechnology. Property rights issues concern the question of whether newly discovered or assembled segments of genetic code qualify as patentable or ownable material. The issues have been most hotly debated for animal patents. On the side of animal patents is the incentive effect of property rights for potential producers of recombinant technologies. Against animal patents are the claims that genetic sequences are "nature's handiwork," and that biotechnologies should be regarded as scientific discoveries (which are traditionally not patentable) rather than as inventions. Religious and metaphysical considerations enter the discussion of property rights when people express the view that life forms should not be owned or, perhaps, manipulated. In this regard, the emergence of biotechnology has apparently brought longstanding practices of genetic manipulation and breeding into the public consciousness for the first time.

Biotechnology is religiously significant because for some people, at least, the ability to move genetic material from one animal to another raises questions about the ethical significance of species boundaries. These questions are of two sorts. First, theologies that propose a difference in kind between human and nonhuman animals are challenged by the new molecular biology. Second, some religious views interpret the existing distribution of species as God's handiwork, and interpret genetic modification as a violation of absolute constraints on human action. Religiously based concerns often enter debates indirectly, being expressed along with secular ethical concerns about property rights or unwanted consequences. The U.S. tradition of separating church and state may make religiously based arguments seem less legitimate in the public policy context.

Bibliography

Aiken, W. (1986). On evaluating agricultural research. *In* "New Directions for Agriculture and Agricultural Research: Neglected Dimensions and Emerging Alternatives." (K. Dahlberg, ed.), pp. 31–41. Rowman and Allanheld, Totowa, NJ.

Berry, W. (1977). "The Unsettling of America." Sierra Club Books, San Francisco, CA.

Blatz, Charles V. (ed.) (1991). "Ethics and Agriculture: An Anthology on Current Issues in World Context." Univ. of Idaho Press, Moscow, Idaho.

Burkhardt, J. (1992). On the ethics of technical change: the case of bST. *Technol. Soc.* **14,** 221.

Comstock, G. (ed.) (1987). "Is There a Moral Obligation to Save the Family Farm?" Iowa State Univ. Press, Ames, IA.

Haynes, R., and R. Lanier (eds.) (1983). "Proceedings of the Agriculture, Change, and Human Values Conference." Univ. of Florida, Gainesville, FL.

Kloppenburg, J., Jr. (1988). "First the Seed: The Political Economy of Plant Technology." pp. 1492–2000." Cambridge University Press, Cambridge.

Regan, T. (1983). "The Case For Animal Rights." Univ. of California Press, Berkeley, CA.

Rollin, B. (1981). "Animal Rights and Human Morality." Prometheus, Buffalo, NY.

Rollin, B. (1989). The Unheeded Cry: Animal Consciousness, Animal Pain, and Science. Oxford University Press, New York, NY.

Rollin, B. E. (1990). Animal welfare, animal rights, and agriculture. *J. Anim. Sci.* **63,** 34–56.

Shepard, P., and Hamlin, C. (1993). "Deep Disagreement in U.S. Agriculture: Making Sense of Policy Conflict." Westview Press, Boulder, CO.

Singer, P. (1975). "Animal Liberation: A New Ethics for Our Treatment of Animals." Random House, New York.

Thompson, P. B., Matthews, R., and Van Ravenswaay, E. (1994). "Ethics, Public Policy, and Agriculture." Macmillan, New York, NY.

Thompson, P. B., and Stout, B. (eds.) (1992) "Beyond the Large Farm." Westview Press, Boulder, CO.

Tweeten, L. (1983). Food for people and profit: Ethics and capitalism. "The Farm and Food System in Transition—Emerging Policy Issues, No. FS5," Cooperative Extension Service, Michigan State University, East Lansing, MI.

Evolution of Domesticated Plants

KHIDIR W. HILU, *Virginia Polytechnic Institute and State University*

Glossary

Crop plant A plant genetically modified by human practices, grows in disturbed habitats, and depends on the grower for its survival
Gene pools Groups of species and populations that include the crop, its wild ancestral species and weedy form, and various related species; gene pools are grouped into three categories according to their degree of interfertility with the crop from fertile to sterile
Germplasm resources Plant material potentially useful for the improvement of the crop; it may come from its various cultivars, the weedy biotypes, the direct and indirect ancestors, or other closely or distantly related species
Plant domestication Genetic fixation of characters in wild plant populations that results in morphological–anatomical alterations suitable for agricultural practices
Weedy plant Plant that grows in disturbed habitats but maintains its natural means of dispersal and relies on humans only for maintaining habitat disturbance

Plant domestication is the genetic fixation of characters in wild plant populations that results in morphological–anatomical alterations suitable for agricultural practices. Domestication of wild plants may result from repeated cycles of harvesting and sowing accompanied by cultivation of the field. During these practices, automatic (natural) selection and intentional (artificial, human imposed) selection operate on the population, resulting in the introduction of traits that mark domesticated plants. The morphological–genetic traits that accompany domestication include changes from shattering (breaking off of fruits and seeds) to nonshattering, indeterminate (continuous) to determinate growth, nonuniform to uniform maturation at the individual plant and population levels, and dormant to nondormant seeds, as well as increase in size, texture, shape, and changes in chemical contents.

I. Plant Evolution

A. Plant Groups and Their Contribution to Domestication

Organisms that are traditionally considered as plants are divided now among three kingdoms: Protista (includes Algae), Fungi (different types of fungi), and Plantae (includes bryophytes, seedless vascular plants called Pteridophytes, and seed plants of both Gymnosperms and Angiosperms classes). Algae includes plants that range from the microscopic diatoms to the giant kelps; fungi encompasses heterotrophic plants of various structural complexities such as the unicellular yeasts and mushrooms; bryophytes encompasses a diverse group of plants such as mosses and liverworts; pteridophytes consists of the primitive, seedless land plants with vascular tissue (conductive tissue of xylem and phloem) such as ferns, horsetails, and club mosses; gymnosperms includes nonflowering seed plants such as pines, hemlocks, ephedra, and bold cypress; and angiosperms encompasses flowering plants such as petunias, legumes, roses, grasses, magnolia, and oak trees.

Plants of economic importance (whether domesticated or not) come from these various plant groups. However, plant domestication is more widely spread in flowering plants. Two reasons may account for the widespread domestication of flowering plants. One, they are the most diverse, widely spread, and dominant species in terrestrial biological communities on earth. Two, they are the only plants that produce fruits, and only gymnosperms share, with them, the seed production trait (thus called seed plants).

B. Major Events in Plant Evolution

It is commonly believed that plants evolved and first diversified in aquatic habitats. Thus, the movement of plants from an aquatic to terrestrial habitat was one of the major evolutionary events. The terrestrial habitat required and enforced a number of structural and physiological modifications, such as the production of a covering layer (cuticle), development of a well-structured vascular system for the conduction of raw material (xylem tissue) and food (phloem tissue), establishment of roots well specialized for absorption of raw supplies and for anchoring the plant, and leaves specialized in harvesting the sun's energy for photosynthesis and in transpiration to help cool the plant and to assist in the movement of material in the vascular tissue. [See PHOTOSYNTHESIS; PLANT PHYSIOLOGY.]

Another major event in plant evolution involved the evolution of the flower, fruit, and seed. The flower enhanced various aspects of reproduction including plant–pollinator interaction and varying degrees of self- and cross-fertilities. The fruit and seed allowed for wider dispersal of the reproductive propagules via physical means of dispersal, such as wings and hooks. They also contributed to the physical protection of the embryo, and provided nutrition and control of germination, resulting in the seed dormancy phenomenon. The latter gave the seed a longer opportunity and more efficient methods for dispersal. [See DORMANCY.]

Current information from fossils and molecular studies point to the origin of flowering plants at the Cretaceous period (about 120 million years ago) or earlier. The area of origin of flowering plants is believed to be the seasonal tropics. From that area, flowering plants invaded new regions in different directions by adaptive radiation, where new evolutionary lines emerged as a response to the new environments. Two major environmental events, continental drift and the recent glaciers, enhanced and significantly contributed to the diversity and dominance of flowering plants. Continental drift, the process of separation of the continental land masses, started around 110 million years ago during the middle Cretaceous period, which is the time marking the first appearance of flowering plants in fossil records. This drift of continents, which continued for about 30 million years, resulted in physical separation between plant species and produced changes in the environment as the continents moved away. The combined isolation and changes in the environment enhanced the rate of plant evolution from the species to the community levels.

The glaciers pushed the ranges of distribution of plant species and communities to new ranges, and resulted in bringing together species that had been physically isolated. In addition, glaciers disturbed the physical characteristics of the environment, generating new habitats. As consequences of the glaciers, hybridization, polyploidy (doubling of part or the whole chromosome set in an organism), and weediness in plants were enhanced. The first two are major factors in plant evolution while the third is a prime contributor to the process of plant domestication. It is believed that the progenitors of domesticated plants were aggressive colonizers of new and disturbed habitats.

C. Major Processes Governing Plant Evolution

One of the first points to raise here is that plants should be treated somewhat differently from animals in terms of their responses to the processes governing evolution. They are structurally different from animals (perhaps simpler), reproduce differently, more apt to accommodate genetic phenomena such as polyploidy and hybridization, and stationary in the community. Plants evolve via mutations that occur at the gene level (point mutation), chromosomal rearrangement, doubling of part or the whole genome complement (polyploidy), and hybridization. Unlike most animal species, polyploidy is a prominent factor in flowering plant evolution, with the frequency of polyploidy estimated to be around 80%. Hybridization between closely and distantly related species is also a widespread phenomenon in plants. Polyploidy and hybridization, when combined with various asexual means of reproduction, result in considerable amounts of genetic diversity at the population and higher taxonomic levels. These two processes have been important in the postdomestication evolution of domesticated plants, providing further diversity and various means of breeding. Plasticity in plants is also a prominent feature where a genetic type (genotype) can be expressed as different physical or physiological forms under different environments. This is an adaptive trait in widespread species against environmental changes, and for the exploitation of different niches. Studies have also shown that some simple genetic changes in plants, such as single gene mutations, can result in an amplified effect in the morphology. This attribute makes plants capable of evolving at faster rates than animals, and was perhaps one of the factors that contributed to the success of plant domestication. The evolution of corn from the wild ancestor teosinte represents a classic example of the effect of single gene mutations in crop evolution, where a few single-genes mutations can account for the major morphological changes from the wild ancestor teosinte to the domesticated corn.

II. Domestication of Plants

A. Time of Domestication

Hunting and gathering of wild species had been the prominent food acquiring practice throughout the majority of human history. Remains of domesticated plants in the Old World did not appear in the archaeological record until around 1000 B.C. The oldest record of a domesticated plant comes from the Middle East. In the New World (the Americas), archaeological records of plant domestication were dated to about 8700 B.C. Excavations of historic settlements worldwide continue to take place and an earlier date for plant domestication might yet be uncovered. The procedure for dating plant remains follows the estimation of the ratio $^{13}C/^{14}C$ in plant remains. Both ^{13}C and ^{14}C are found at a constant ratio in the atmosphere and in plants. Once plants die, ^{14}C starts decaying, presumably at constant rate, into nitrogen. Since the half time of the ^{14}C isotope is known (about 5730 years), the age of the plant remains can be calculated by using a special formula. This procedure can be used for intact plant remains as well as charred or cooked remains, but reliable dating can only be provided for plants that are no older than 50,000 years.

B. Centers of Domestication

The domestication of plants was not diffused uniformly throughout the world. There were centers for domestication on some continents, but others such as Australia and North America, have few records of crop domestication. For instance, sunflower and artichoke were the only major crops domesticated in North America. The Russian geneticist N. I. Vavilov studied the patterns of variation in crops to determine their areas of origin. When he mapped the geographic distribution of the areas of crop origin, he found that eight centers and four subcenters could be recognized in Asia, Africa, Europe, and the Americas, and called them Centers of Origin. Vavilov also recognized that the area of highest diversity for a crop is not necessarily the area of origin, and thus he proposed the concept of "Secondary Center" of diversity. J. R. Harlan further refined Vavilov's idea by making distinctions between well-defined centers and larger geographic regions with diffused areas of crop domestication. He called the former "centers" and the latter "noncenters" of plant domestication. Three centers (Near East, North China, and Mesoamerica) and three noncenters (Africa, South Pacific, and South America) were recognized by Harlan. The major, and some minor, food crops domesticated in these regions are listed in Table I.

The geography of plant domestication was further examined by Harlan in the context of ecological settings. Of the 10 climatic regions compared, the Mediterranean woodlands and the tropical savannas were the formations that have provided most of our crops, including many of the 30 crops that feed the world (Fig. 1). These two climatic regions are characterized by long dry seasons that constituted ecological settings promoting annual growth which is characteristic of the major crop plants that nourish the human race.

C. Practices and Processes That Led to Domestication

The practices and processes that led to the evolution of a domesticated plant from a wild or weedy ancestor require the introduction of a suit of genetic changes that are manifested in morphological modifications. The changes must satisfy the requirements of efficient harvesting and high yield. The essence of the practices and manipulations by humans of these wild plant populations is not well known, but it is believed that the practices of repeated cycles of harvesting and sowing harvested seeds, cultivation of fields, and the processes of natural and artificial selection pressures on plants could have led to their domestication, at least in the Middle East. Successive cycles of harvesting and sowing of the population are believed to have

TABLE I

Major and Some Minor Food Crops and Their Areas of Origin Following Harlan (1992)

Scientific name	Common name and area of origin
Cereals	
Triticum aestivum L.	Bread wheat; Transcaucasia–Caspian
T. dicoccum Schrank	Emmer; Near East
T. monococcum L.	Einkorn; Turkey
T. timopheevi Zhuk.	Very minor wheat; Soviet Georgia
T. turgidum L.	Tetraploid wheat; derived from emmer, Near East
Zea mays L.	Indian corn; Mesoamerica
Oryza sativa L.	Rice; S. China to India
Oryza glaberrima Steud.	African rice; W. Africa savanna
Secale cereale L.	Rye; Anatolian plateau–N. Europe
Hordeum vulgare L.	Barley; Near East
Sorghum bicolor (L.) Moench	Sorghum; savanna zones Sudan–Chad
Pennisetum glaucum (L.) R. Br.	Pearl millet; dry savanna Sudan to Senegal
Eleusine coracana L.	Finger millet; Highlands, Ethiopia–Uganda
Eragrostis tef Trott.	Tef; Ethiopia
Digitaria exilis (Kipp.) Stapf	Fonio; W. Africa, Nigeria to Senegal
Brachiaria deflexa (Schum.) Hubb.	Guinea millet; Guinea highlands
Panicum miliaceum L.	Proso, broomcorn millet; N. China
Panicum miliare Lam.	Slender millet; Himalayas–Upper Burma
Setaria italica (L.) Beav.	Italian, foxtail millet; N. China
Echinochloa frumentacea Link.	Japanese millet; E. China
Paspalum scrobiculatum L.	A millet; Nilgiris of S. India
Coix lachryma-jobi L.	Job's tears, adlay; Indochina–Philippines
Pseudocereals	
Amaranthus species	Amaranth, the Americas
Chenopodium species	Huaozontle; the Americas
Legumes (pulses)	
Cicer arietinum L.	Chickpea; Near East
Lens esculenta Moench	Lentil; Near East
Pisum sativum L.	Garden pea; Near East with addition from the Mediterranean
Vicia faba L.	Broadbean, fava beans; Near East
Vigna unguiculata (L.) Walp.	Cowpea; W. Africa
Arachis hypogaea L.	Peanut, South America
Phaseolus vulgaris L.	Common bean; South America
Phaseolus acutifolius A. Gray	Tepary bean; Mesoamerica and North America
Phaseolus lunatus L.	Lima bean; Mesoamerica
Vigna radiata (L.) Wilczek	Mung bean; India or S. China
Voandzeia subterranea (L.) Thouars	Bambara groundnut; W. African savanna
Glycine max (L.) Merill	Soybean; N.E. China
Cajanus cajan (L.) Millsp.	Pigeonpea from *Atylosia* India
Cyamopsis tetragonolobus (L.) DC	Guar; India
Psophocarpus tetragonolobus (L.) DC	Winged Bean, also has tubers; New Guinea
Vegetable crops	
Allium species	Onion, garlic, leak; Mediterranean
Allium bakeri Regel	Chinese shallot; China
Brassica oleracea L.	Cabbage, cauliflower, brussels sprouts, kale, kohlrabi, broccoli, Near East, addition from W. Europe
Lactuca sativa L.	Lettuce; Mediterranean
Petroselinum sativum Hoffm.	Parsley; Mediterranean
Daucus carota L.	Carrot; Mediterranean
Raphanus sativus L.	Radish; Near East, China, wild and weed races widespread
Beta vulgaris L.	Beet; Mediterranean, W. Europe
Brassica rapa L.	Turnip; Mediterranean (also maybe China)
Capsicum species	Pepper; Mesoamerica and South America

(continues)

TABLE I (*continued*)

Major and Some Minor Food Crops and Their Areas of Origin Following Harlan (1992)

Scientific name	Common name and area of origin
Cucurbita maxima Lam.	Squash; South America
Cucurbita pepo L.	Squash–pumpkin; Mesoamerica
Cucumis sativus L.	Cucumber; N.E.?, India? (possible domestication in both areas)
Lycopersicon esculentum Mill.	Tomato; South America
Physalis species	Tomate; Mesoamerica and South America
Brassica rapa L.	Turnip; N. China (Mediterranean? possible independent domestication)
Solanum melongena L.	Eggplant; India
Starchy crops	
Solanum tuberosum L.	Potato; South America
Dioscorea trifida L.f.	Yam; Mesoamerica
Dioscorea cayenensis Lam.	Yam; Ivory Coast to Cameroon
Dioscorea esculenta (Lour.) Burk.	Chinese yam; S. China
Alocasia macrorrhiza Schott.	An elephant-ear; Indonesia–Melanesia
Ipomoea batatas (L.) Lam.	Sweet potato; Mesoamerica
Manihot esculenta Crantz	Manioc; Mesoamerica
Artocarpus communis Forst.	Breadfruit; S.W. Pacific Islands
Artocarpus integrifolia L.	Jackfruit; S. Pacific and S.E. Asia
Fiber and oil crops	
Brassica napus L.	Rapeseed; E. Mediterranean
Brassica nigra (L.) Koch	Mustard, mustard oil; E. Mediterranean
Carthamus tinctorius L.	Safflower; Near East
Linum usitatissimum L.	Flax, linseed; Near East
Olea europea L.	Olive; Mediterranean
Elaeis guineensis Jacq.	Oil palm; W. Africa
Ricinus communis L.	Castor bean, castor oil; Africa, widespread
Brassica campestris L.	Rapeseed; temperate China
Cocos nucifera L.	Coconut; S. Pacific Islands
Sesamum indicum L.	Sesame; India
Helianthus annuus L.	Sunflower; North America
Arachis hypogaea L.	Peanut; South America
Gossypium species	cotton; Africa and South America
Cannabis sativa L.	Hemp, widespread Eurasian
Fruit crops	
Ficus carica L.	Fig; Turkey–Iraq–Iran
Juglans regia L.	English walnut; Balkans to Pakistan
Phoenix dactylifera L.	Date palm; Near East
Pistacea vera L.	Pistachio; Turkey–Iran
Prunus amygdalus Stokes	Almond; Turkey to Pakistan
Prunus armeniaca L.	Apricot; Turkey–Iran
Prunus avium L.	Cherry; Balkans to Caspian
Prunus domestica L.	Plum; Balkans to E. Europe
Punica granatum L.	Pomegranate; Transcaucasia–Caspian
Pyrus communis L.	Pear; Turkey–Iran
Pyrus malus L.	Apple; Balkans–Transcaucasia–Caspian
Vitis vinifera L.	Grape; Mediterranean
Blighia sapida Koenig	Akee apple; W. Africa
Colocynthis citrullus (L.) O. Kuntze	Watermelon; S. and E. Africa
Chaenomeles spp.	Chinese quinces; temperate China
Eriobotrya japonica Lindl.	Loquat; S.W. China
Citrus species	Orange, lemon, lime, grapefruit, citron, tangerin, etc.; S.E. Asia and S. China
Mangifera indica L.	Mango; Indo-Malaysia
Musa species	Banana; Southeast Asia
Ananas comusus (L.) Merrill	Pineapple; Mesoamerica
Anacardium occidental L.	Cashew; South America
Carica papaya L.	Papaya; Mesoamerica

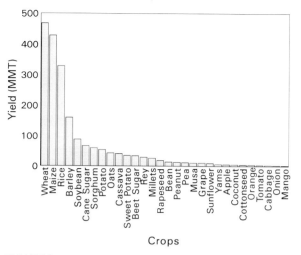

FIGURE 1 Annual yield in million metric tons of the 30 leading crops that feed the world. (Data were obtained from the Food and Agricultural Organization Year Book, Vol. 33.)

imposed strong automatic selection pressures that favored loss of natural mechanisms for seed dispersal, better adaptation to man-made habitats, larger seeds and earlier emerging seedlings, shortening or loss of seed dormancy, and uniformity at the individual plant and population levels. This practice was also accompanied by intentional selection by the earlier farmers for agriculturally desirable mutants such as free-threshing seeds, larger plant parts, fewer sterile flowers, inflorescences with larger number of flowers and fruits, as well as convenience in harvesting underground and above-ground parts, and superior plant products in terms of taste, texture, and food product.

However, not all plants that were harvested in the wild or those humans attempted to domesticate lend themselves to domestication. Success in plant domestication was confined to only a small fraction of wild plants. For instance, among the hundreds of species of grasses that were harvested in the wild, only about 34 species were domesticated. Genetic responses to the processes and practices which lead to domestication appear to have been unique features of a limited number of species. Ability to colonize new and disturbed habitats might have been a factor, but polyploidy has been excluded as a factor in the initial process of plant domestication. It appears that polyploid and diploid plants are equally domesticable in seed, fruit, vegetable, and tree crops, as well as in annual and perennial crops.

III. Evolutionary Changes Associated with Domestication

The kinds of genetic–morphological changes associated with the evolution of domesticated plants can be grouped into two categories: (1) primary changes which constitute the prerequisite modifications for the emergence and establishment of a crop plant, and (2) the secondary and postdomestication changes which refine the emerging crop species.

A. Basic Changes

Wild species possess natural means of dispersing their reproductive propagules, by the free shattering of the individual seeds or fruits, or by the dehiscence of the fruit and subsequent release of the seeds, as in legumes. These mechanisms are assisted by various dispersal agents such as animals, wind, and water. Wild plants also acquired indeterminate growth to continue producing new parts throughout the season. These parts, especially the reproductive ones, mature at different times, as a safeguard against losing all of them at one time due to stochastic environmental events. Seed dormancy is essential for plants that grow in a seasonal environment because germination may be detrimental prior to the favorable growing season. However, these wild type traits are not particularly attractive to a farmer. A one-time harvest and a maximum yield without losing some or most of the seeds via shattering is essential for a farmer's investment. Thus, nonshattering seeds and fruits, uniform growth, and synchronized maturity are basic genetic–morphological changes that define a domesticated plant and provide convenient crop harvesting and adequate yield. These mutations are desirable and were under strong selection pressure.

Natural plant communities, although dominated by one or a few species, are often diverse in species composition where the various species tend to exploit different niches in the community. Thus, the ability of plants to adapt and become productive when grown in mostly monospecific cultivated fields with intense intraspecific (within species) competition, is another trait essential for the selection of a successful crop. Contrasted with the natural habitat of the wild species, disturbing the habitat by plowing, irrigating, cultivating and fertilizing adds yet other selection factors. Therefore, a wild progenitor of a perspective crop should have some ability to colonize such habitats and adapt to the increasing and continuous disturbances by the grower.

B. Secondary and Postdomestication Changes

These changes include selection for increasing the size of the desired part such as the seed in various legumes, the fruit in fruit crops, the inflorescence in corn and rice, the buds in brussels sprout and cabbage, the stems in kohlrabi and potato, and the roots in cassava and beets, to cite a few. To increase yield, selection of plants that have regained fertility in otherwise sterile flowers was also practiced. This can be exemplified by the selection for the six-row barley from the two-row crop. In wild and primitive domesticated barley, only two of the six rows of florets around the axile of the inflorescence are fertile (producing seeds); the remaining rows are sterile. Early farmers observed and selected a mutant in domesticated two-row barley in which the sterile florets regained fertility, resulting in seed heads with six rows of fertile flowers. Selection for dwarfness of cultivars, reduction in certain plant parts to facilitate harvesting, increase in the tissue of edible parts, and manifestation of the number and size of flower parts in horticultural plants are also examples of postdomestication evolution. In addition to these traits, traditional and biotechnology-oriented breeding for different agronomic traits including disease and pest resistance are ongoing changes in the process of crop evolution. [See CULTIVAR DEVELOPMENT.]

IV. Crop–Wild–Weed Complex

A. Definitions of the Crop, Weed, and Wild Plants

For each crop species there is a corresponding wild ancestor. Crops are also accompanied in the field by weedy plants. This weedy species is genetically related to both the crop and the wild ancestral species. Other nonrelated weedy species also might be present in the field, but often are not of significance in the history of evolution of the crop and its future differentiation. A simple definition of a crop plant is a plant genetically modified by human practices, grows in disturbed habitat, and depends on the grower for its survival. A wild species is a plant that grows in natural habitat and does not rely on humans for its future survival. In contrast to these two, a weed is a plant that grows in disturbed habitats, but maintains its natural means of dispersal and relies on humans only for maintaining the disturbance of the habitat. Weeds could originate as a specialized genetic line of a wild species that has the capability to invade and colonize man-made

habitats. It also could arise as a result of hybridization between the wild and domesticated species, or as a result of some cultivated plants regaining their natural means of dispersal (i.e., the shattering of the seed and the dehiscence of the fruit). [See WEED SCIENCES.]

B. Dynamic Interactions between the Crop–Wild–Weed Plant Complex

The domestication process, although resulting in various degrees of morphological changes, has not enforced genetic isolation between the crop and its wild progenitor. Similarly, the allied weedy form can generally cross freely with both the crop and the wild form. As a result, gene flow between the triad is not uncommon in the field, and natural hybrids are often spotted in the field. This hybridization can be duplicated in the laboratory. There are positive and negative consequences to this lack of reproductive isolation. Due to the gene flow between the crop and the weedy species, the latter starts resembling the crop more closely, creating a problem in eradicating the weed from the field. Weeds have maintained natural means of seed dispersal and, in many cases, they cannot be recognized in the field until the seeds reach maturity and start shattering. Thus, such weeds can maintain themselves at a certain equilibrium in the field for a long period of time. A positive consequence of this reproductive compatibility is the possible use of the weedy and wild forms as sources of desirable genetic material in the breeding programs of the crops.

C. Gene Pools of Domesticated Plants

The importance of wild species in the improvement of crops has long been recognized. Crop plants represent subsets of the total genetic diversity of the wild and weedy species since often they were domesticated from very limited number of populations. Therefore, desirable agricultural traits needed for the improvement of the crop can be sought from wild or weedy species closely or distantly related to the crop. The species that can be used as a source of genetic material for the crop constitutes its gene pools. These gene pools have been classified into primary, secondary, and tertiary pools depending on the degrees of fertility between the crop and its related species.

The primary gene pool represents the crop and species that can cross freely with it and produce highly fertile hybrids; members of this gene pool include the various races of the crop, the direct wild ancestor, and the weed form. It can possibly include other species interfertile with the crop. The secondary gene pool consists of species that can cross with members of the primary gene pool with at least some fertility in the first generation. Gene transfer from the secondary gene pool to the crop is possible, but may be difficult. The tertiary gene pool represents genetically distant species that maintain strong reproductive isolation barriers between them and members of the primary gene pool. In this case, gene transfer can be achieved only by radical techniques such as embryo culture, *in vivo* hormone treatments, and bud pollination. It is evident that the gene pool system is based on conventional crossing and breeding. However, recent advances in biotechnology can overcome these breeding boundaries between the gene pools and, thus, will significantly expand the gene pools to include taxonomically unrelated species. [*See* PLANT GENETIC ENHANCEMENT.]

V. Taxonomy of Domesticated Plants

A. Taxonomy of the Crop–Wild–Weed Complex

The crop–wild–weedy types differ in morphology and habitat. The process of domestication has often resulted in pronounced changes in the morphology of the wild plants. The wild ancestor of peanut, for instance, is a weak vine, grows in forest understory, and has small seeds and fruits as compared with the open-field peanut crop, that is more erect and relatively stout and produces much larger seeds. The wild species of corn has much different branching patterns of their culms (grass stems) and in reproductive parts from the corn crop, having ears that are only a few inches long, about half an inch wide, and containing two rows of small seeds that are enclosed in stony cups.

The morphological differences between the wild species and its domesticated counterpart have impacted the taxonomic treatment of these species. The treatments have varied from giving each form a species status to merging them all into one species. The majority of these changes and differences are, however, due to simple genetic changes controlled by one or few genes. In addition, the complex triad of wild–crop–weedy plants did not become genetically isolated, and natural hybridization between them occurs in the field and can be enforced artificially.

The biological species concept has been applied to the taxonomy of this group. This concept promotes the inclusion of all taxa (taxonomic units) in one species if they hybridize freely and the hybrids are highly fertile. Since these criteria apply to the crop–wild–weedy forms, it seems appropriate to include them in one species. The three forms could be given subspecific ranks under the specific name of the crop, with the crop acquiring the type name (the specific epithet for the species) since it is the popular type. For instance, finger millet, and its direct progenitor, used to be named *Eleusine coracana* and *Eleusine africana*, respectively. Following the biological species concept, they are named *E. coracana* subspecies *coracana* for the crop, and *E. coracana* subspecies *africana* for the wild ancestor.

B. Taxonomy of the Crop Plant

Due to human's intense selection for a variety of traits in crops, these plants tend to be morphologically highly variable. This variation has resulted in considerable difficulties in the classification of domesticated plants. Overclassification and the creation of a large number of intraspecific categories are the prominent difficulties in the taxonomy of cultivated plants. The sorghum crop was once divided among 52 species, 28 of them domesticated. At present all domesticated, wild, and weedy types of sorghum are lumped under one species, *Sorghum bicolor*. More than 65 intraspecific categories have been reported in the literature for domesticated plants. However, considering the nature of the genetic bases of the morphological variation and the artificial selection imposed on them, a simpler system of classification can be followed. The system is illustrated in Table II.

TABLE II

An Example of the Classification of Domesticated Plants, Their Related Weedy Types, Direct Ancestral Species, and Indirect Species (Diploid Species that Hybridized to Produce the Polyploid Direct Ancestral Species)

Biological species *Eleusine coracana* (crop, wild, and weedy types)
    Subspecies *coracana* (domesticated type)
        Race highland
            subrace
                Cultivar
                    Line, Clone, Genotype
    Subspecies *africana* (direct wild ancestor)
        Variety Verticillata
Biological species *Eleusine indica* (one of the ancestors to the tetraploid ancestral subspecies *africana*)

The specific, subspecific, and race names are Latin names while names below the race do not need to be written in Latin. The species and the subspecies categories are already defined above. A race is a group of cultivars that occupy a recognizable geographic area and display a morphological identity. Races are expected to hybridize at zones of contact and, thus, the morphological boundaries among races might be blurred, as is the case of the sorghum races in Africa. The race is equivalent to a botanical variety in the classification of the wild and weedy species. Races that occupy large geographic areas and/or tend to be morphologically variable can be classified into subraces that include morphologically distinct groups of cultivars. Races and subraces encompass various numbers of cultivars which represent morphological and agronomic units. Within cultivars are breeding lines, clones, and genotypes which may be defined to represent selections within germplasm (gene banks) collections or breeding programs. The clone and genotype categories are especially useful for crops that are asexually propogated via stem cuttings, tissue culture, and apomixis (a sexual production of seeds) since they are genetically more uniform, as opposed to sexually reproducing plants.

VI. Major and Minor Crops

A. Types of Crops

Wild plants have been selected for domestication for a variety of objectives, such as food (cereals, legumes, vegetables, and fruits), oil, drugs, fiber, ornamental plants, and a number of utility crops such as gums, rubber, fiber, and balatas (see Table I for examples of these crops). Selection in the various crops was directed toward the specific, desirable part(s) of the plant. In the species *Brassica oleraceae,* selection for food in different populations of the same species was directed toward the terminal bud to produce cabbage, the lateral bud to generate brussels sprouts, the inflorescence to domesticate broccoli and cauliflower, and the stem to produce kohlrabi. In flax, two types of cultivars exist, one selected for oil and the other for fiber. In some cases, two or more species within a genus were selected for domestication for the same or different purpose. Several species were domesticated as food crops in the grass genus *Triticum,* the legume genus *Phaseolus,* and the rose genus *Prunus.* In the family Cannabaceae, the species *Cannabis sativa* (marijuana) was domesticated for fiber and a drug,

while *Humulus lupulus* (hops) was selected for brewing.

B. Major Crops and Their Botanical Distribution

The more than 300 domesticated plant species come from over 60 monocot and dicot families, with 30 being most important to feed the world (Fig. 1). The crops belong to 17 angiosperm plant families. They were domesticated in six centers and noncenters primarily in Asia, the Americas, and Africa. The grass family (Poaceae, Gramineae) leads the list with eight cereal crops and over seven species included under the millets group; the four most widely grown crops are cereals (Fig. 1). The legume family (Fabaceae, Leguminosae) comes second to cereals and is represented by four species, although beans and peas include several pulse species. In terms of total production, the grass family by far surpasses all the other families, accounting for about 80% of the total world food supply of the 30 crops (Fig. 1). Some families like the Rosaceae, although having only apples on the list of the 30 leading crops, includes a large number of fruit crops (such as pears, plums, cherries, apricots, etc.) and ornamental plants (such as roses and flowering cherries). The same principle applies to the Liliaceae (onion family) and a number of other flowering plant families. Thus, domestication appears to have cut across a wide range of plant families with some contributing more significantly than others.

C. Minor Crops

In addition to the major crops that reach the world trade centers, there are a large number of crops that are considered minor because they are grown and consumed locally, or are exported on a minor scale. Examples of these crops are the less known tropical fruit crops (such as the star fruit), plants that provide starch products (like the bread fruit), and the millet crops (small grain cereals). Some of these crops are domesticated from native wild species and tend to be very well adapted to the climate of their geographic region. The millets, for instance, were domesticated from wild species native to semi-arid regions and, thus, those species and the crops that evolved from them tend to be very well adapted to the drier environments of the semi-arid areas and to the existing poor soil conditions. The millets have good potential in drought-struck regions and other areas that are expected to face similar environmental conditions, particularly with the predicted changes resulting from the greenhouse effect.

VII. Germplasm Resources and the Future of Domesticated Plants

A. Germplasm Resources

Germplasm resources constitute all the genetic material from domesticated and wild forms available for the improvement of crops. These materials may be stored in national or international gene banks, grown in traditional farming systems, or found in wild populations. There are several national and international agencies that are involved in the collection, maintenance, and characterization of these plant materials. The International Board for Plant Genetic Resources (IBPGR) is one of the leading international organizations for this purpose. The United States Department of Agriculture and the National Japanese centers are known for their large collections of genetic materials. There are also a number of germplasm centers in various parts of the world that are specialized in the deposition and breeding of particular crops. These centers include Centro International de Papas (CIP) in Peru for potato, the International Rice Research Institute (IRRI) in the Philippines specializes in rice, the International Crop Research Center for the Semi-Arid Tropics (ICRISAT) emphasizes sorghum millets and peanut, and the Centro Internacional de Mejoramiento de Maiz y Trigo (CIMMYT) in Mexico specializes in maize and wheat genetic resources collection and breeding. Plant breeders, geneticists, and other scientists can obtain seed and plant material from these centers for research. [See INTERNATIONAL AGRICULTURAL RESEARCH; PLANT GENETIC RESOURCES; PLANT GENETIC RESOURCE CONSERVATION AND UTILIZATION.]

B. Genetic, Evolutionary, and Agronomic Impact of Germplasm Resources

Postdomestication evolution of crop plants is an ongoing process. Selection from existing cultivars and introduction of various genetic traits from diverse gene pools result in altering the genetic make-up of the crops. Wide crosses between domesticated plants and some distantly related species (gene pools 2 and 3) have been attempted on a number of crop species, such as hybrids generated from crossing gamma grass (*Tripsacum*) with maize, and wheat with members of

the tribe Triticeae. A relatively recent crop has been synthesized from hybrids between wheat (*Triticum*) and rye (*Secale*) to produce Triticale. The crop combines several good agronomic qualities of both parental species, but has a low gluten level, a protein important in producing leavened bread (bread that rises during fermentation).

A number of crops, such as soybean, tomato, coffee, banana, and maize, have very narrow genetic bases. This status could be the result of introducing a very limited number of cultivars from the area of domestication, or breeding for a few genetic lines in the large-scale breeding programs, or both. This situation is rather alarming since it highlights the vulnerability of these crops to various diseases. Because of the genetic uniformity of the cultivars grown, damage will be inflected if they are susceptible to a pathogen or an insect. The male–sterile derived cultivars of corn were susceptible to the fungus *Helminthosporium maydis,* causing a major infestation of corn leaf blight in the United States in 1970. In Ireland, the potato crop was devastated by the potato blight in 1845. These incidents attest to the problems that could arise from the narrow genetic bases of a number of crops.

Germplasm resources provide the material for increasing the genetic diversity of crops and for the introduction of genes that confer disease resistance, drought tolerance, and higher food quality, among other desirable agronomic traits. Genetic resources important for plant breeding, genetics, and evolution of crops are threatened in some areas. For example, the natural habitat for teosinte, the wild form of corn, has been disappearing. The tropics, that contain a large array of genetic resources, are also facing the same future. Similar situations are found outside the tropics because of the increase in human population. Therefore, concerted efforts have to be made to collect genetic material, particularly for crops that are poorly represented in the world germplasm collections.

C. Ethics and Politics Governing Utilization of Germplasm Resources

A look at the geography of the origin of domesticated plants reveals that the vast majority of the crops come from the developing countries. However, most of the research involved in the development of modern, high yield, and resistant cultivars is conducted in the developed world. As a consequence, traditional cultivars and populations of wild species, that represent the raw material for the breeding of crop plants in the developed countries, are found in the developing countries. This situation has resulted in a dilemma, where genetic resources obtained from the developing countries, resulted in the release of new cultivars sold back to the developing countries. This situation prompted the developing countries to consider the genetic resources of their crops as national property and, thus, have the right to control the dispensing of the material and to put monetary value on the germplasm resources. This is in contrast with the view of the developed countries, who consider the germplasm resources as a common human heritage with no one country having the right to control its utilization. The two sides have been discussing these issues for a possible compromise and solution.

Bibliography

Bailey, L. H. (1977). "Manual of Cultivated Plants." Macmillan, New York.

Harlan, J. R. (1992). "Crops and Man," 2nd ed. American Society of Agronomy, Madison, WI.

Hilu, K. W. (1993). Polyploidy and the evolution of domesticated plants. *Am. J. Bot.,* **80,** 1494–1499.

Purseglove, J. W. (1987). "Tropical Crops, Dicotyledons." Wiley, New York.

Purseglove, J. W. (1988). "Tropical Crops, Monocotyledons." Halstedd, New York.

Simpson, B. B., and Conner-Ogorzaly, M. (1986). "Economic Botany, Plants in our World." McGraw-Hill, New York.

Farming Systems

JOHN S. CALDWELL, *Virginia Polytechnic Institute and State University*

Glossary

Domain Group of farm households with a common constraint or problem associated with a common farming system or a common element in different farming systems

Environments Activities outside the control of the farm household unit managing a particular farming system; these include the biophysical environment (soils, rainfall), sociocultural environments (social structure, status, and roles, culture), economic environments (input, output, and consumer product markets), and institutional environments (research and extension services, political institutions)

Farming system Unique, relatively stable pattern, continuing from year to year, of agricultural and non-agricultural activities that a household unit manages using well-defined practices within the constraints imposed by the internal functioning of the system and by the biophysical, sociocultural, economic, and institutional environments outside the system, in accordance with household unit members' goals, preferences, and resources; the variability of the system as a whole is less than the variability of its components

Farming systems research/extension (FSR/E) Methodology for conducting interdisciplinary, on-farm, user-based adaptive agricultural research targeting defined groups of relatively homogeneous farming system types characterized by similar constraints

Farming system type Farming system which is characteristic of a number of household units

Mixed linear models Analysis of variance models which divide farms into fixed and random effects to examine interactions of treatments with farm types representing defined differences in environments and/or farming systems types

Modified stability analysis Regression of treatments over an environmental index representing the mean of all treatments on each farm, where farms are chosen across as wide a range of variation as possible, to determine what potential treatment by environment interactions may exist

Participatory research Research designed to facilitate farmers' own analyses of and experimentation in their farming systems; it includes participatory rural analysis (PRA) and farmer participatory research (FPR)

Rapid rural appraisal (RRA) Any of a number of open-ended, participatory techniques, in large part derived from anthropological field research methods, for obtaining information on farming systems

Systems interaction Directional movement of resources from a source component within or without a system to a destination component within or without the system, and the effects that such movement has on the functioning of each component; at least one component, either the source or the destination, must be within the system; these systems interactions are distinguished from the interactions of factors in statistical analysis

Farming systems are both units of analysis of agricultural production and methodologies for user-based agricultural research and development. As units of analysis, farming systems are defined by their components and boundaries and by the types of interactions among their components and with the environments outside their boundaries. Farming systems include all activities, both agricultural and nonagricultural, under the control of farm household units. Farming systems types may be identified at the level of regions within a country, or at a global level. Farming systems research methodologies deal with the identification of priority constraints and opportunities, and the carrying out of research with farm household members in their farming system designed to reduce or eliminate the constraints and utilize opportunities to achieve their goals and preferences.

I. Characteristics of a Farming System

A. Components, Boundaries, and Interactions

A farming system is a relatively stable pattern of agricultural and nonagricultural activities that a household unit manages. Those activities that the household unit controls are components of the farming system; those activities which occur outside their control are parts of the environments of the farming system. The boundary of the farming system is the physical, temporal, or conceptual demarcation between components that make up the farming system, and the environments of the farming system.

A system is a set of components that exhibit a stable pattern of interrelationships in their functioning. Activities occur within individual components of the system, between different components within the system, and between components of the system and components outside the system. Activities that occur within a component are considered to be the internal functioning of the component, and are not the focus of analysis at the systems level. Activities which involve the movement of resources from one component to another are termed systems interactions. Movement is from a source component to a destination component. Either the source or the destination component may be outside a system, but at least one, either the source or the destination, must be within the system.

Interactions affect the functioning of the source and the destination components. When an interaction in one direction produces a second interaction in the reverse direction, the second interaction is termed a feedback. For example, the production of maize may depend, in part, on the quantity of manure from cattle, but the quantity of manure may also depend on the amount of maize stover fed to the cattle. A reduction in the quantity of stover resulting from a change to a shorter maize variety may lead to a reduction in the production of manure, and this in turn may negatively affect the yield of maize. The change of maize variety has generated a feedback through the two interactions between the maize and the cattle.

These patterns are termed systems because the variance of the pattern as a whole is less than the variance of its component activities. They are also termed systems because the different component activities are all manifestations of an underlying, integrated set of goals and preferences of their users, the farm household unit members.

B. Goals and Continuity

Farming systems differ from purely biological or physical systems in that they are goal-oriented. Farm household members create and continue a given farming system to meet their goals. It is these goals, rather than a particular biological or physical process or principle, which integrate the functioning of the different components of the farming system and give the farming system its stability and continuity.

Continuity in the pattern of a farming system can be observed from year to year. This pattern is evidenced in the continuity of both the types of activities and the practices used by the household unit to carry out those activities. Farm households in a sorghum/cowpea-based system, for example, will produce sorghum each year intercropped with cowpea at a low density. Sorghum yield may vary from year to year depending on rainfall, and cowpea yield may likewise vary depending on pests. Cattle may have more or less cowpea forage depending on both sorghum and cowpea yields in the association. The farm household may sell excess sorghum in good years, and be obliged to purchase sorghum by selling an animal in a bad year. Nevertheless, from year to year, the farm household continues to produce sorghum and cowpea in association by mixing the two types of seeds in a gourd in about the same ratio each year, continues to use sorghum as its main source of food, and continues to feed cowpea forage to its cattle.

C. Subsystems and Environments

Four major components make up a farming system. Each component is in itself a subsystem of the overall farming system. Two subsystems involve agricultural production activities: the crop subsystem and the animal subsystem. The other two subsystems involve nonagricultural activities: the household subsystem and the nonfarm subsystem.

Farming systems have a complex nature that combines physical, biological, and sociocultural processes. Each subsystem is a pattern of activities that follow one or more of these three types of processes.

The crop subsystem is a primarily biological subsystem. The elements of the crop subsystem are types of crops. Each type of crop is a population of individual plants in a given field. Within the crop subsystem there may be both spatial and temporal interactions among different types of crops. Spatial interactions occur when intercropping, the growing of more than one crop in the same field, is practiced. Temporal interactions occur through multiple cropping, where more than one crop is grown in the same field during one year, or through rotations, where the crop in one year has an effect on the crop that succeeds it the following year.

The animal subsystem is also primarily biological. The elements of the animal subsystem are types of animal herds, flocks, or fish. Each type of animal herd, flock, or fish is a population of individual animals, birds, or fish. Interactions within the animal subsystem are usually less important than interactions of elements in the animal subsystem with other subsystems or with environments outside the farming system.

The household subsystem is both biological and sociocultural in nature. The elements of the household subsystem are the individual household members. These are distinguished by gender and age. Because of the importance of household member goals in integrating the functioning of the system as a whole, interactions among different members of the household subsystem have major implications for the functioning of the two agricultural production subsystems. Interactions with other subsystems or with environments often vary depending on gender and age. [See Rural Sociology; Women in Agriculture.]

The nonfarm subsystem is primarily physical. The elements of the nonfarm subsystem are nonagricultural production activities such as handicrafts or tool manufacturing. The importance of this subsystem varies, and it is not always present in all farming systems.

Activities not under the control of the farm household make up the environments of the farming system. The biophysical environment includes types of soils, rainfall, and diseases and pests of crops and animals. The sociocultural environment includes other persons in the community or village of which the farm household considers itself a member. The economic environment consists of markets and market channels for the purchase of inputs for agricultural or nonagricultural production and of goods and services consumed by the household,

and markets and market channels for the sale of agricultural and nonagricultural products and labor of the farm household. The institutional environment includes sources of information, such as research and extension services and media, and institutions at a larger level of functioning, such as religious organizations, political parties, and governmental policy-making organs. This can be envisioned as an encompassing environment which affects the more immediate economic and sociocultural environments that farming systems interact directly with.

Figure 1 is a conceptual depiction of the four types of subsystems making up a farming system and of the environments outside its boundary.

II. Farming Systems Types

A. Levels of Farming Systems Types

In one sense, each farming system is unique. The biophysical environment of a given farm household is never exactly the same as that of its neighbor, since each uses different pieces of land. The members of

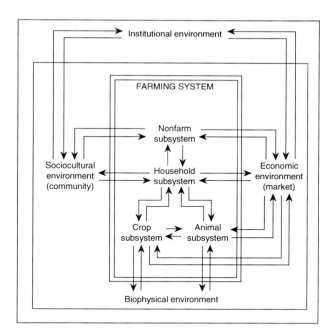

FIGURE 1 Conceptual model of a farming system. (———) Boundaries between systems outside the farming system; (═══) boundary enclosing the farming system; (----->) interaction. [From Gittenger, J. Price, Leslie, J., and Hoisington, C. (eds.) (1987). An overview of farming systems research and development: Origins, applications, and issues. *In* "Food Policy: Integrating Supply, distributions and Consumption," p. 177. Johns Hopkins Univ. Press.]

two different farm household units are different individuals, and even in a small, highly homogeneous community, it is unlikely that they will have exactly the same goals. Similarly, it is unlikely that agricultural production practices will be exactly the same from one farm household unit to the next.

Treating each farming system as a unique case is sometimes done in public and private extension or consulting work, but this is an expensive approach. To be more efficient in the use of resources, public research and extension institutions look for similarities among individual farming systems, and seek to develop technology valid for farming systems that can be grouped together as a single farming systems type. Research uses the farming system type as a unit of analysis to assess variation among many individual farming systems, and to arrive at explanations valid for farming systems types that group many household units with similar farming systems.

The grouping of farming systems into farming systems types is most often done at two levels of analysis: the regional level within a country, sometimes extended to the whole country; and the cross-national or global level. The objectives of analysis differ between the two levels.

Analysis at the level of a region of a country is usually done by a research or extension organization or institution with the practical objective of providing better information to the farm household units of the region. Both quantitative and qualitative data on individual farming systems are gathered directly from farm household units in a number of communities or villages selected as broadly representative of the region. When similar grouping has been done in more than one region of a country, farming systems types may also be identified across the entire country. [See COOPERATIVE EXTENSION SYSTEM.]

At the global level of analysis, grouping is done with the objective of creating general typologies of farming systems types. These general typologies are created indirectly based on results of studies done in many individual countries. They serve both to organize the conception and understanding of worldwide agricultural production and to assess broad historical trends of change across farming systems types. Such broad typologies can also be useful in setting priorities for basic research at international agricultural centers, and in providing information to policy makers. [See INTERNATIONAL AGRICULTURAL RESEARCH.]

B. Farming Systems Types at the Regional Level

Factors for distinguishing farming systems types vary depending on the level of analysis. At the level of a region within a given country, farming systems types are distinguished based on one or more of the following factors:

1. Characteristics of their biophysical environments, such as soil types, land area, annual precipitation, or access to irrigation.

2. Characteristics of the components of the farming system, such as the type of crop produced on the largest proportion of the household unit's land area, presence or absence of animals, and household size and resources.

3. Practices used in agricultural production in the crop and/or animal subsystems, including interactions between these two subsystems, such as method of soil preparation (manual, animal traction, tractor), method of planting (mixed intercropping, row intercropping), and fertilization (natural soil fertility only, collection and use of animal manure, use of chemical fertilizers).

4. Degree of integration into sociocultural, economic, and political environments outside the farming system boundary, such as extent of labor sharing, land tenure status, proportion of harvest or animals sold, participation in cooperatives or farmers' associations, and off-farm employment.

Which factors are most important for grouping farm household units into meaningful farming systems types is highly specific to the region where the grouping is done. For example, in West Africa, where hand tillage is widespread and animals are a source of wealth, but land is relatively plentiful, held communally, and allocated by village custom, use of animal traction and numbers of animals owned may be key factors. In the Philippines, in contrast, where land preparation is done by buffalo or in some cases by hand tiller but land is scarce, ownership is private, and the area available to each farm household unit is variable, land tenure status and total area may be key factors.

C. Farming Systems Types at the Global Level

At the global level, several factors have been used to group farming systems into farming types. From a broad historical perspective, one key factor is the intensity of land use. As population increases, land use becomes more intensive. Cultivating a piece of land for only a couple of years and then abandoning it, moving to a different piece of land, and allowing natural vegetation to reclaim and occupy the abandoned land for one or even several decades is land use at a very low level of intensity. At the opposite extreme, land in parts of China has been in permanent annual cultivation for centuries, with multiple cropping (more than one crop following another in the same year) typical.

A simple measure of land use intensity is the ratio of the number of crop years divided by the number of crop plus fallow years, called the R value:

$$R = \frac{C}{C + F} \times 100,$$

where C = number of crop years, and F = number of fallow years.

The R value also indicates the proportion of land in cultivation in a given year.

The R value can be used to distinguish three farming systems types:

Value of R	Farming system type
<33	Shifting systems (also called slash-and-burn or swidden)
33–66	Fallow systems
>66	Permanent systems

Within shifting and fallow systems, where natural fallow remains an important part of the system, distinctions can be made based on the type of fallow vegetation (forest, bush, savanna, or grass). A further distinction can be made between systems where no use is made of fallow vegetation, and systems where the fallow is used for livestock production. When the fallow is in grass or legumes planted or used naturally for animal production, the system is termed a ley system. Ley systems are more prevalent in temperate areas and some highland areas of the tropics, than in the lowland tropics.

Nomadic grazing and ranching are farming systems types without a crop subsystem. They are found primarily in regions where rainfall is too low for cropping, and in some regions with adequate rainfall for cropping but low population density.

Water use intensity is an important distinguishing factor in systems with permanent cropping. In rainfed systems, crops receive water only when rain falls through natural precipitation, whereas irrigated systems hold or supply water so that crops receive it at times when there is no natural precipitation. Within irrigated systems, a further distinction is made between wet rice systems, where the crop is grown in standing water during most of the period to harvest, and other irrigated systems, where water is supplied intermittently by furrows, sprinklers, or drip hoses.

In humid and semihumid areas, permanent cropping may be based on crops which occupy the land for more than one year. These are termed perennial systems. They include crops grown like field crops but over several years, and tree and shrub crops which have lifetimes of several decades.

Mixed systems are also common. These are farming systems where the farm household unit simultaneously manages different farming systems types on different pieces of land. For example, in the Philippines farm household units may combine irrigated wet rice in lowlands with banana- and coconut-based perennial and rootcrop-based fallow and shifting rainfed systems in uplands. In North America farm household units may grow maize and vegetables on 2–3 hectares of permanent fields in fertile valley bottoms, carry out extensive grazing on more rocky, sloping hillside areas, and hold other hillsides in forest as a form of savings, to be cut to meet emergency cash needs.

III. Historical Development of Farming Systems Research Methodologies

The term farming systems is also used to refer to several related methodologies for user-based agricultural research and development. Early antecedents were independently developed in the 1940s and 1950s in both the United States and Japan, although they were largely abandoned during the 1960s. Other antecedents can be seen in approaches developed in West Africa in the 1960s. The most widespread set of methodologies today grew out of work independently begun in Asia, Africa, and Latin America in the 1970s, and brought together in the 1980s. This set of methodologies is called Farming Systems Research-Extension (FSR/E). More recently, newer methodologies are appearing, particularly participatory research and sustainability research, which both build on the principles of FSR/E and move beyond the methodologies of the 1980s.

A. Early Antecedents

In the 1940s and 1950s, a number of similar approaches developed in the southeast United States that treated the farm as a system. These included the Balanced Farming Program of Missouri, the Farm and Home Development Program of Kentucky (later expanded to other states), and the Rapid Rural Adjustment Program of the Tennessee Valley Region. In all these approaches, technical scientists, economists, rural sociologists, and often home economists worked together to improve the entire farm. The systems-based conception of the farm and the use of interdisciplinary teams parallels FSR/E, but in contrast to FSR/E, these approaches were primarily extension-focused and prescriptive and generally did not have an explicit research orientation.

In Japan, a concept of systems research (called *sogo kenkyu,* or "comprehensive research") was developed in the Tohoku Region of northern Honshu in the late 1940s and early 1950s. This concept expanded ecological concepts to create the concept of a farm as a management system of people, crops, and animals. This early conceptual development was followed by the *einoshiken* national program of on-farm trials at 389 sites between 1952 and 1962. Similar to the U.S. approaches of the same period, the program had a strong extension focus, but at the same time there was also an experimental aspect that was more explicitly developed than in the U.S. programs.

In a number of countries in Francophone West Africa, systems research approaches appeared in the 1960s and 1970s. Many had an orientation toward *recherche-développement,* a concept that combines agricultural research and rural development. These approaches not only included the development of the concept of *systèmes de production,* but also the development of methods of *zonage* and *typologie* of systems. Trials were conducted both to improve existing systems and to transform them into fundamentally different systems. Finally, these approaches included a regionally based rural development orientation not as explicitly developed in either the earlier U.S. or Japanese approaches.

B. Origins of Farming Systems Research/ Extension (FSR/E)

The direct origins of FSR/E are multiple. One line of origins can be traced back to East and Southeast Asia. In the late 1960s, research began on multiple cropping at the International Rice Research Institute (IRRI), Philippines. This research drew its inspiration and much of its technology from the complex farming systems of Taiwan. Later, when IRRI researchers took rice production technology which they had adapted for the tropics in large part from technology first developed in Japan, they initially experienced failure under real farm conditions. These experiences led to the development of methodologies for on-farm experimentation, initially on double cropping and rotations, and later more broadly on rice-based farming systems.

These early efforts influenced other pioneering work in different South and Southeast Asian countries, especially Thailand and Indonesia. Much of this work focused on upland areas, where the package approach (fixed, complete set of production recommendations) of the Green Revolution was soon found to be less appropriate. The package approach was more successful in lowland irrigated areas where more uniform biophysical conditions exist, and a fixed set of recommendations can be applied by a large number of farm households. It is less useful in the more diverse conditions of rainfed uplands. Technology becomes more site and client specific.

In Africa, pioneering efforts were undertaken in both East and West African Anglophone countries. The Centro Internacional de Mejoramiento de Maíz y Trigo (CIMMYT, International Maize and Wheat Improvement Center), based in Kenya but working in a number of East and southern African countries, developed methods for identifying priorities for on-farm trials, and for the economic evaluation of results. A group of researchers at Ahmadu Bello University, Nigeria, developed methods of farming systems analysis and multidisciplinary team research.

In Latin America, the Instituto de Ciencia y Tecnologia Agricoles (ICTA) developed the first rapid team appraisal approach, called *sondeo,* or "sounding out." Other antecedents can be seen in different Latin American countries, including Peru, Mexico, and Costa Rica.

IV. Farming Systems Research/ Extension (FSR/E)

A. Characteristics

The FSR/E approach developed in the 1980s can be characterized as a client-diagnostic approach. Researchers identify needs of the clients, farm households, and based on those needs develop and test potential solutions. However, the parallel with medicine is not complete. FSR/E methodology does not assume that a "prescription" can be written just based on "diagnosis." Rather, a partcipatory, experimental process is deemed essential. Also, in medicine normally the patient seeks out the doctor, but in FSR/E researchers have usually been the initiators of the process.

FSR/E is a regional approach. A basic assumption is that agricultural technology is site and clientele specific. It is normally conducted by teams based in defined regions of a country.

FSR/E uses interdisciplinary teams. This reflects the nature of farming systems themselves, with biophysical, economic, and sociocultural aspects. Only a interdisciplinary team can provide the diversity of specialized knowledge necessary to comprehend all these aspects.

FSR/E is an interactive process that can be divided into four stages: diagnosis, design, testing, and extension. A basic principle is that diagnosis, or analysis of the farming systems of the region, precedes experimentation in design and testing, but experimentation frequently reveals new problems which call for further diagnosis.

B. Diagnosis

Diagnosis is the process of characterizing the farming systems of a region and identifying farm household constraints. Diagnosis can be divided into initial and on-going diagnosis.

Initial diagnosis refers to the process by which a new team characterizes a region and its farming systems. Since the principal objective of FSR/E is problem-solving rather than understanding *per se* of farming systems, the emphasis in reconnaissance is on cost-effective, efficient methods, called "rapid rural appraisal" (RRA).

RRA methods are largely informal and draw much from anthropological field research methods. Two key assumptions parallel the anthropological approach: that meaningful hypotheses can only be generated after first understanding the system, and that more accurate information is obtained through open-ended, participatory techniques than through formal, closed questionnaires. Detailed, closed questionnaires are biased toward the preconceived hypotheses of the interviewers. Quantitative, comprehensive baseline surveys are inefficient, because even when good data are obtained, by the time they are analyzed, either the team has already begun on-farm trials based on qualitative insights obtained during the collection of the quantitative data, or else one or more seasons are lost. Also, the results are already no longer fully valid by the time they are finally available.

Techniques used in RRA include transects, group walks, mapping, diagramming, matrices, ranking and scoring, ethnohistories, time lines, seasonal analysis, trend analysis, portraits, and key probes.

On-going diagnosis uses many of the same informal techniques of initial RRA. These are often complemented by formal, quantitative data gathering, such as monitoring of farmer practices and labor time in the on-farm trials, or collection of prices in local markets. This quantitative data collection has limited, specific objectives related to the priorities established for the trials by informal techniques.

C. Design

Design is the process of prioritizing the constraints identified in diagnosis and translating priority constraints into researchable problems. Design in FSR/E involves two key processes: stratification and prioritization. The two processes are linked, because an important basis for stratification is differences in priorities.

Stratification means dividing the farm households into homogeneous groups. Such groups are called domains. A domain is a group of farm households with a common constraint or problem associated with a common farming system or a common element in different farming systems. In design, which is prior to on-farm testing, domains are research domains: a group of farm households having a common constraint or problem and for whom hypothesized solutions to the common problem could have potential applicability and are therefore subjected to on-farm testing.

Initial diagnosis usually reveals a multitude of constraints and problems. Several criteria can be used for prioritizing these constraints and problems:

1. Extent of importance (proportion of farm households or individual farmers having the constraint or problem).
2. Importance of the problem to farmers and to society.
3. Potential for solution.
4. Potential farmer acceptability.
5. Necessity of inter-institutional cooperation and policy support.

D. Testing

Testing in FSR/E has been based on adaptation of agricultural research methods to the on-farm situation. The on-farm situation involves different types of systems, different objectives, and different populations of inference.

In agricultural research done in laboratories or on experiment stations, the system of focus is a passive biological system (for example, a population of plants). The population of inference is similar biological systems (other similar populations of plants). The objective is to learn how one aspect of the biological system functions, and why it so functions. One or at most only a couple of factors affecting that population are studied. Only variation in the factor or factors being studied is of interest. Variation in other factors is reduced to a minimum, so that any variation in the factor or factors studied can be clearly identified.

In on-farm testing, the system of focus is goal-oriented farming systems that combine biophysical, economic, and sociocultural aspects. The population of inference is a group of farm households or individual farmers making up the research domain. The objective is to test potential solutions to a perceived problem or constraint of the farm households or individual farmers managing the farming system. The potential solutions are assessed under the same farm conditions as under which the solutions would continue to be used after the test. Variability in factors other than those changed by the potential solution is accounted for and used to partition the population of inference.

With the above objectives, on-farm testing uses the farm as the unit of replication, rather than the individual parcel of a field or individual animal in a herd. Farms are chosen to reflect the range of variability among farm households or individual farmers belonging to the domain. Factors other than the factor or factors of the potential solutions are left at farmer level.

Two approaches have been developed for the analysis of data from such on-farm trials: modified stability analysis, and mixed linear models.

In modified stability analysis, an environmental index is first calculated as the mean of all treatments on each farm. Farms are chosen across as wide a range of variation as possible. The values of each treatment on each farm are then regressed on this index. If the resulting regression lines cross, this indicates a treatment by environment interaction. The treatment with the highest level within each interval of the index is taken as the best treatment for similar farms. Examination of soils, rainfall, and farmer management is done at each interval of the environmental index associated with a different highest treatment, to provide an explanation for the causes of the treatment by environment interaction.

In mixed linear models, farms are grouped into fixed farm types. Farm types may represent different environments where the same farming systems type exists (for example, sorghum in 800- and 1000-mm rainfall zones), or different farming systems types (with or without mechanized weeding). A number of farms within each type are included in the trial; these farms are considered random. The interaction of treatments with the fixed farm types is then tested in an analysis of variance model.

A modification of mixed linear models can also be applied in on-farm testing involving animals, where each farm only has one treatment, but within the same farm type, one set of farms receives one treatment, a second set a second treatment, and so forth.

Rather than judging whether differences are real or not based on conventional levels of significance, the probabilities of no real differences existing are compared with the risks associated with using the technology of the treatment being assessed. Confidence intervals can also be placed around means or differences. Decisions on whether a technology is worth the risk of its being no better than current practices can be left to each farm household or individual farmer.

Analysis of biological effects in mixed linear models is followed by various types of economic analysis, including net benefits, marginal rates of return, risk, and sensitivity analysis. Effects on different stakeholders disaggregated by gender are also examined.

E. Extension

At the end of on-farm testing, a research domain is often divided into several recommendation domains: a group of farm households or individual farmers managing a common element (type of crop, herd, flock, or fish) in farming systems for which a tested solution meets their (the users') biophysical, economic, and sociocultural requirements for adoption and use. Diffusion domains, or informal interpersonal communications networks through which newly acquired knowledge of agricultural technology flows, are also examined as part of the design of extension programs.

The technologies may be tested with extension personnel and other farmers prior to large-scale promotion. Such pre-extension may also include pilot credit programs.

A recent approach to extension in FSR/E is the "minimalist" approach. It is based on the recognition that there is more diversity of farming systems than either research or extension can handle given their limited resources. It expects that farmers themselves must complete the process of technology adaptation. The function of research is to generate sets of viable technologies, a "basket" of technologies, from which each farmer can pick and choose according to his or her needs and circumstances. The function of extension is to stimulate farmers to think critically and to experiment.

V. Toward a New Paradigm in the Application of Science to Agricultural Development: Participatory Research

Farming systems research continues to evolve in new directions. Although FSR/E has moved agricultural research off the experiment station and into farming systems in the real world, it is still based on the same fundamental paradigm as station-based agricultural research: study of agriculture by persons other than farmers, and the generation of new agricultural technology by specialists. This paradigm, called the transfer-of-technology paradigm, has assumed that the methods of science are necessary for improving agriculture, and that it takes special training to be able to apply them.

These assumptions are under question today. The alternate assumption is that the methods of science do not have a comparative advantage in understanding or improving complex farming systems, particularly when they are mixed systems encompassing several different farming systems types, with many systems interactions and feedback among the different components of each type, managed by farm households in risk-prone, marginal environments according to a mixture of economic and noneconomic goals. Underlying this alternative assumption is a conception of science as a reductionist process: one which studies individual factors in isolation, with other factors and interactions controlled. When science seeks to simulate such complex farming systems, it aggregates individual data gathered by the reductionist process into synthetic models, but the resulting models depart too far from reality to have much practical value.

Even when, despite its shortcomings, the formal scientific process does produce innovations that are found useful and adopted by farm households in complex, risk-prone farming systems, these innovations are too few to justify the human and financial resources expended. At best, formal science is a very inefficient process for improving these types of farming systems. The formal scientific process has its comparative advantage in simpler farming systems in more controlled environments, such as wet rice-based farming systems, or commercialized crop monoculture in areas of the temparate zones with favorable rainfall and good soils.

A related observation is that farmers already carry out experimentation on their own. Research and extension personnel may simply not have looked for farmer experimentation nor recognized it when seeing it, because of preconceived ideas that experimentation can only be done by those who have special training.

These assumptions and observations lead to a new paradigm for the relationship between farm households and outsiders, including persons with specialized training in formal science. Its premise is that as managers of complex systems over long periods of time, farmers in marginal environments have a comparative advantage in understanding the detailed workings of their systems, knowing where change is needed, assessing probable short- and long-term effects of change on the functioning of the system, and designing and evaluating realistic tests of changes. The function of outsiders is to serve as catalysts and resource persons. The objective of research and development activities in this paradigm is the enhancement of farmers' own capabilities for sustained, independent experimentation and development of their farming systems and rural communities.

New methods have begun appearing in the 1990s based on this paradigm, under the general rubric of participatory research, and including two related sets of methods that correspond roughly to diagnosis and testing in FSR/E: participatory rural analysis (PRA) and farmer participatory research (FPR).

In PRA, farmers conduct their own analyses using many of the same techniques as RRA, but with two key differences. First, the objective is not for outsiders to extract information, but for farmers to assemble and share among themselves the information they already possess. Second, the primary users of the information are not the outsiders, but the farmers. Farmers make the decisions about what to do based on the information.

In FPA, farmers begin changes in their systems based on the analyses they have done through PRA methods. Outsiders search out and supply the plant materials or animals, practices, and principles requested by farmers, and arrange for farmers to visit other farmers and experiment stations to widen their options. Outsiders also assist farmers in monitoring the changes that occur in their systems. New techniques for monitoring sustainability are currently being developed, particularly in North America.

Evaluation of FPA is based on observed change and adoption. Statistics are not needed to assess effects as a predictor of potential adoptability, because user change (the equivalent of adoption) occurs directly in the experimental process.

In this process, the role of formal biological science changes. It uses its comparative advantage in reductionist research to come up with new "pieces" of technology (such as resistant or short-cycled varieties, new methods of biological control, or even long-term station research on complex rotations to assess sustainability, using treatments designed by farmers) in response to farmer needs.

At this point, participatory research is just beginning. That it has a comparative advantage is a hypothesis for development that will be increasingly tested during the 1990s, especially by non-governmental development organizations that often have more institutional flexibility to experiment in these directions than do governmental institutions. Some preliminary assessments suggest that 5 to 8 years is necessary for farmers to develop enhanced capabilities for sustained, independent experimentation and development. If so, by the end of the 1990s there should be sufficient empirical data from the tests of the participatory research paradigm and methods to assess its performance in comparison with that of the more conventional research paradigm and methods, including client–diagnostic FSR/E.

Bibliography

Caldwell, J., Taylor, D., and Walecka, L. (eds.) (1987). "Analysis and Interpretation of On-Farm Experimentation," University of Florida, Gainesville, Florida.

Chambers, R., Pacey, A., and Thrupp, L. A. (1989). "Farmer First: Farmer Innovation and Agricultural Research." Intermediate Technology Publications, London.

Frankenberger, T., and Walecka, L. (eds.) (1987). "Diagnosis in Farming Systems Research and Extension, 2nd ed. Univ. of Florida, Gainesville, FL.

Fresco, L. (1984). "Comparing Anglophone and Francophone Approaches to Farming Systems Research and Extension." Farming Systems Support Project Networking Paper No. 1. Univ. of Florida, Gainesville, FL.

Ruthenberg, H. (1980). "Farming Systems in the Tropics," 3rd ed. Oxford Univ. Press, New York.

Sands, D. M. (1986). Farming systems research. *Exp. Agricult.* **22,** 87–104.

Shaner, W. W., Philipp, P. F., and Schmehl, W. R. (1982). "Farming Systems Research and Development." Westview Press, Boulder, CO.

Stroup, W. W., Hildebrand, P. E., and Francis, C. A. (1991). "Farmer Participation for More Effective Research in Sustainable Agriculture," Staff Paper SP91-32. Univ. of Florida, Gainesville, FL.

Suzuki, F. (1986). On the farming systems approach. *Int. Coop. Agricult. Forestry* **8**(3), 2–9. (in Japanese)

Fats and Cholesterol, Role in Human Nutrition

DONALD C. BEITZ, TRAVIS J. KNIGHT, *Iowa State University*

I. Chemical Nature of Fats and Cholesterol
II. Physiological and Biochemical Significance of Fats and Cholesterol
III. Essentiality of Fats and Cholesterol in the Diet
IV. Content of Fats and Cholesterol in Common Foods
V. Dietary Recommendations for Humans
VI. Degenerative Diseases

Glossary

Atherosclerosis A common degenerative process that involves lipid deposition in the intima of large and medium arteries; excessive development of atherosclerosis can result in total occlusion of arteries to cause strokes, heart disease, and impaired peripheral blood circulation

Bile acid Relatively water-soluble metabolites of cholesterol that are produced in liver and transported to the small intestine via bile to participate in the digestion and absorption of dietary lipids

Cholesterol A sterol with 27 carbons and four rings that serves as a precursor for bile acids and steroid hormones and as a structural component of animal cell membranes; cholesterol is found in bile and is most abundant in animal brain; cholesterol may be synthesized from metabolites of carbohydrates, other lipids, and proteins in animal cells

Eicosanoids Biologically active molecules that are synthesized from long-chain polyunsaturated fatty acids and include the prostaglandins, thromboxanes, and leukotrienes

Fat (1) Adipose tissue of animal bodies as in fat, lean, and bone of the carcass; (2) lipids of biological materials that are extractable with organic solvents and that consist largely of triacylglycerols and/or phospholipids

High-density lipoprotein An extracellular globular complex that consists of primarily cholesteryl esters and triacylglycerols in the core and primarily phospholipids, cholesterol, and specific proteins on the surface; the complex has a density that ranges from 1.063 g/ml to 1.210 g/ml and functions to transport water-insoluble compounds in animals

Low-density Lipoprotein An extracellular globular complex that consists of primarily cholesteryl esters and triacylglycerols in the core and primarily phospholipids, cholesterol, and specific proteins on the surface; the complex has a density that ranges from 1.019 g/ml to 1.063 g/ml; low-density lipoproteins function to carry water-insoluble compounds, such as cholesterol, from organ to organ in animals

Polyunsaturated fatty acid Long-chain hydrocarbon molecules that have a carboxyl group on one end, are usually linear, and contain two or more double bonds

Saturated fatty acid Hydrocarbon molecules that have a carboxyl group on one end, are usually linear, and possess only single covalent bonds between carbon atoms

Triacylglycerol A lipid composed of glycerol with a fatty acid esterifed to each of its three hydroxyl groups; triacylglycerol represents a major form of energy storage in animal bodies and some plant seeds; formerly, triacylglycerols were called triglycerides

Even among nutritionists, the word "fat" has many definitions. Nutritionists and food scientists frequently and broadly refer to the triacylglycerol-rich fraction of foods as fat. Adipose tissue of an animal body and the extractable oil from a plant crop or animal body commonly are called fat. Adipose tissue is made of fat-laden cells in a matrix of connective tissue. Fat and lipid, often incorrectly, are used interchangeably. When fat refers to adipose tissue, it consists of lipids, water, proteins, and other constituents.

In this article, the term "fat" will refer to those lipid-rich fractions derived from or present within plants or animals that are used for human food. Further, lipids will be those compounds related to fatty acids and sterols that are relatively insoluble in water and soluble in nonpolar solvents, such as diethyl ether and chloroform. The types of lipids in biological tissues include fatty acids, triacylglycerols, phospholipids (glycerophospholipids and sphingophospholipids), glycolipids (glycosphingolipids), waxes, cholesterol, cholesteryl esters, and vitamins A, D, E, and K.

I. Chemical Nature of Fats and Cholesterol

A. Fatty Acids

Fatty acids are long-chain hydrocarbons with a carboxyl group at one end and a methyl group at the other end (Table I). Most naturally occurring fatty acids are unbranched and have an even number of carbon atoms. Fatty acids vary in chain length from 4 to 24 carbon atoms but in meat, fish, and vegetable fats and oils they generally range from 14 to 22 carbons. Butterfat from ruminants contains significant amounts of fatty acids with 4–12 carbons, as well as the longer chain acids. Fatty acids may contain only single bonds between adjacent carbons, in which case they are fully saturated with hydrogen atoms and are known as the saturated fatty acids. In other fatty acids, one double bond or more may be present between

adjacent carbon atoms; because they are not fully saturated with hydrogen atoms, these are called unsaturated fatty acids. Fatty acids with one double bond are called monounsaturated fatty acids, whereas those with two or more double bonds are called polyunsaturated fatty acids. A commonly used denotation for the individual fatty acids is shown in Table I. [*See* FOOD BIOCHEMISTRY: LIPIDS, CARBOHYDRATES, AND NUCLEIC ACIDS.]

The presence of a double bond in the fatty acid enables the molecule to maintain two different geometric configurations. In the *cis* configuration, the molecule can be "folded back on itself" at the double bond (Fig. 1). In the *trans* configuration, the fatty acid molecule is extended fully to its maximal length at the double bond. The unsaturated fatty acids in foods and in the human body are predominantly those of the *cis* form. *Trans* fatty acids occur in relatively larger amounts in hydrogenated vegetable oils, such as shortenings and margarines.

Three classifications of unsaturated fatty acids predominate in food fats, namely ω-9, ω-6, and ω-3 acids. The ω designation is used to indicate the position of the last double bond. Thus, these double bonds are at the 9th, 6th, or 3rd carbon from the methyl group end of the fatty acid. The polyunsaturated fatty acids are composed of the ω-3 and ω-6 acids. Linolenic, eicosapentaenoic, and docosohexaenoic acids in Table I are ω-3 fatty acids. The latter two ω-3 fatty acids are especially abundant in the lipids of fish.

De novo synthesis of fatty acids in plants and animals terminates with palmitic acid, a saturated 16-carbon

TABLE I

Common Fatty Acids in Food Fats

Symbol	Common name	Structure
Saturated fatty acids		
$C_{4:0}$	Butyric acid	$CH_3(CH_2)_2COOH$
$C_{6:0}$	Caproic acid	$CH_3(CH_2)_4COOH$
$C_{8:0}$	Caprylic acid	$CH_3(CH_2)_6COOH$
$C_{10:0}$	Capric acid	$CH_3(CH_2)_8COOH$
$C_{12:0}$	Lauric acid	$CH_3(CH_2)_{10}COOH$
$C_{14:0}$	Myristic acid	$CH_3(CH_2)_{12}COOH$
$C_{16:0}$	Palmitic acid	$CH_3(CH_2)_{14}COOH$
$C_{18:0}$	Stearic acid	$CH_3(CH_2)_{16}COOH$
Unsaturated fatty acids		
$C_{16:1}$	Palmitoleic acid	$CH_3(CH_2)_5CH{=}CH(CH_2)_7COOH$
$C_{18:1}$	Oleic acid	$CH_3(CH_2)_7CH{=}CH(CH_2)_7COOH$
$C_{18:2}$	Linoleic acid	$CH_3(CH_2)_4(CH{=}CHCH_2)_2(CH_2)_6COOH$
$C_{18:3}$	Linolenic acid	$CH_3CH_2(CH{=}CHCH_2)_3(CH_2)_6COOH$
$C_{20:4}$	Arachidonic acid	$CH_3(CH_2)_4(CH{=}CHCH_2)_4(CH_2)_2COOH$
$C_{20:5}$	Eicosapentaenoic acid	$CH_3CH_2(CH{=}CHCH_2)_5(CH_2)_2COOH$
$C_{22:6}$	Docosahexaenoic acid	$CH_3CH_2(CH{=}CHCH_2)_6CH_2COOH$

Oleic acid

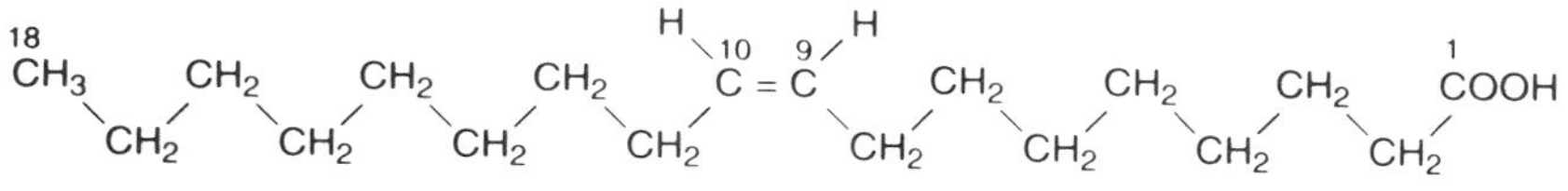

Elaidic acid

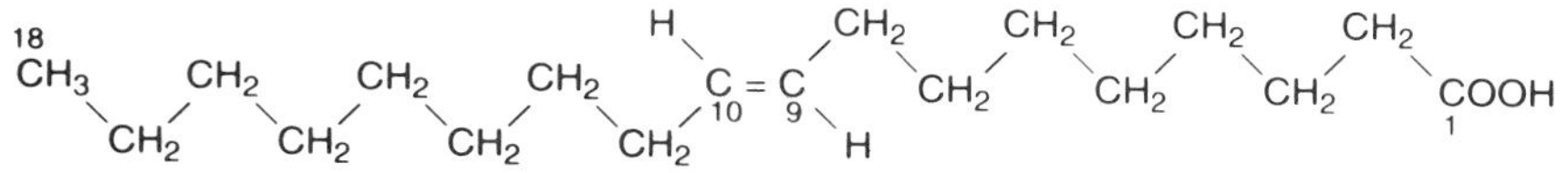

FIGURE 1 Geometric isomers of $C_{18:1}$ fatty acid. Oleic acid is the *cis* form; elaidic acid is the *trans* form.

fatty acid. Palmitic acid subsequently may be elongated by a separate metabolic pathway. In addition, desaturase enzymes form double bonds (form unsaturated fatty acids) at several positions in the chain. Animals cannot form double bonds at carbon positions beyond 9 (carboxyl carbon is position 1), whereas plants can form double bonds at carbons 12 and 15. Because of this inability, animals have a dietary requirement for linoleic and linolenic acids. The major polyunsaturated fatty acids in animals are either derived from the diet, especially in nonruminants, or from desaturation and elongation of linoleic, linolenic, or arachidonic acids. The synthesis of arachidonic acid from linoleic acid exemplifies synthesis of a polyunsaturated fatty acid from an essential fatty acid.

B. Triacylglycerols

Fatty acids in foods are not present in the free form but are combined covalently by ester linkage to a 3-carbon alcohol called glycerol to form triacylglycerols, also called triglycerides (Fig. 2). Glycerol may be esterified with one, two, or three fatty acids giving rise to mono-, di-, or triacylglycerols, respectively. Triacylglycerols are the predominant form of all lipids associated with fats in food. For example, over 98% of the fatty acids in meats, fish, and vegetable oils are in triacylglycerols. Nearly all the remaining fatty acids also are esterified components of the phospholipids, waxes, or cholesterol. Triacylglycerols usually con-

tain several combinations of the fatty acids. In summary, triacylglycerols differ according to the type and placement of the three fatty acids on the glycerol and are the primary storage form of lipids in the animal body and in many plant seeds, such as soybeans.

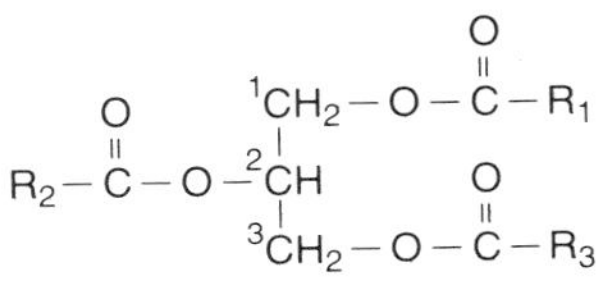

C. Phospholipids

Glycerophospholipids, which are the major phospholipids in food fats, contain two fatty acids esterified with two of the alcohol groups of glycerol (Fig. 3). The third alcohol group of glycerol is esterified with phosphoric acid, which, in turn, is esterified with another alcohol, such as choline. Glycerophospholipids are named according to the identities of these alcohol moieties, as in phosphatidylcholine, which commonly is called lecithin. Glycerophospholipids are the major lipid components of cellular membranes of plant and animal tissues and bacteria. Glycerophospholipids usually contain a high proportion of unsaturated fatty acids and, in animals, contain more unsaturated fatty acids than do triacylglycerols.

D. Cholesterol

Cholesterol is a steroid alcohol that is composed of four fused rings, as shown in Fig. 4. Cholesterol is present in animal tissues but is present in only trace

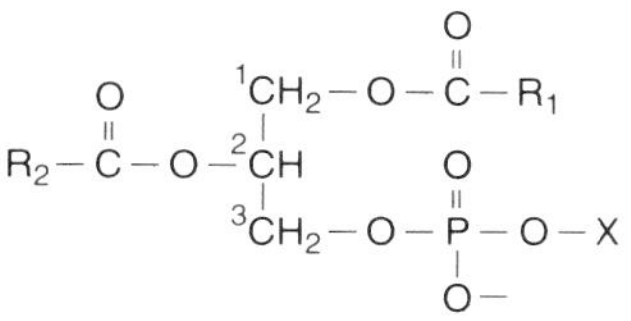

FIGURE 2 Generalized structure of triacylglycerol. R_1, R_2, and R_3 represent three fatty acids.

FIGURE 3 Generalized structure of a common glycerophospholipid. R_1 and R_2 represent two fatty acids; X may be ethanolamine, choline, serine, inositol, glycerol, or phosphatidylglycerol.

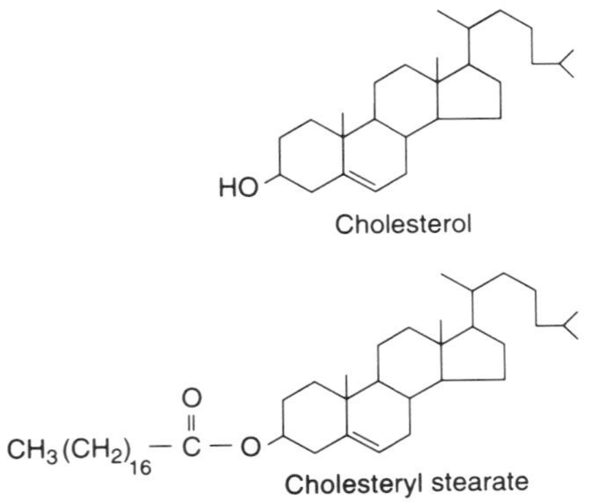

FIGURE 4 Structure of cholesterol and cholesteryl esters.

amounts in plant tissues. Cholesterol is an important component of cell membranes of animals. Because of its unique chemical structure, cholesterol is an important determinant of membrane fluidity. Cholesterol and cholesteryl esters, for example, cholesteryl stearate (Fig. 4), perform many vital functions such as serving as precursors for the synthesis of bile acids and steroid hormones. Because cholesterol has these important functions, the body synthesizes cholesterol daily in inverse proportion to the amount in the diet to maintain adequate cholesterol balance. Essentially, all the cholesterol in meat is associated with the cell membranes; that in adipose tissue is in the fat droplets of the fat cells as well as in the cell membranes. Because red muscle cells have more mitochondria, hence, more membranes, than do white muscles, the cholesterol content of red muscles is slightly greater than that of white muscles. This observation is readily evident when comparing the cholesterol contents of dark and light meat of poultry.

Most of the cholesterol in animal cell membranes is present as unesterified or free cholesterol, whereas about 70% of the cholesterol in lipoproteins in blood plasma is present as cholesteryl esters. Thus, most cholesterol in meat, milk, and separated animal fats, such as beef tallow and lard, is free cholesterol. Most cholesterol in eggs is present as cholesteryl esters.

II. Physiological and Biochemical Significance of Fats and Cholesterol

A. Biological Function of Fats and Cholesterol

The significance of fats and cholesterol to humans and other animals relates to structural, storage, and metabolic roles. Phospholipids and cholesterol are integral constituents of biological membranes. Phospholipids have the unique chemical property that one portion of the molecule interacts well with the aqueous phase of cells and another portion is highly hydrophobic, preferring to interact with other lipids in a nonaqueous environment. Thus, phospholipids orient into two layers to form a biological membrane. Fluidity of the membrane is determined, in part, by the composition of fatty acids in the phospholipids and, in animals, by the amount of cholesterol that intercalates among the phospholipids. The hydroxyl group of cholesterol projects into the aqueous cellular environment. In addition to their role in membrane structure, unique phospholipids function as surfactants in lung, preventing alveolar collapse. As an example, deficiency of surfactant causes respiratory distress syndrome in preterm infants. Lipids also provide protection of the skin of humans from external irritants.

Having about 9 kcal gross energy per gram, triacylglycerols represent an efficient storage form of energy in animals. Within a cut of meat, adipose tissue may be located around a muscle (subcutaneous), between muscles (intermuscular), and within muscles (intramuscular) as marbling fat. Adipose tissue usually contains greater than 90% triacylglycerols by weight. Triacylglycerols also serve as an energy store in the yolk of eggs and in butter fat of milk. Triacylglycerols and fatty acids also are forms by which high energy molecules are transported among organs of an animal.

In addition to structural and energetic functions, lipids participate in transmission of chemical messages in living organisms. For example, specific polyunsaturated fatty acids are converted to prostaglandins, thromboxanes, and leukotrienes (eicosanoids), which have a variety of physiological effects including involvement in smooth muscle contraction and platelet aggregation. Further, inositol-containing phospholipids of cell membranes are hydrolyzed in response to extracellular signals to form inositol triphosphate and diacylglycerol. Cells respond to changes in concentrations of these second messengers through their effects on intracellular calcium concentrations and protein phosphorylation.

Cholesterol is an integral component of all animal, but not plant, cell membranes. Further, cholesterol is a major component of myelin that surrounds the nerve cells of the peripheral and central nervous systems. Cholesterol can be converted in liver to bile acids, which are secreted via the bile into the small intestine to facilitate solubilization and absorption of dietary fats. Further, cholesterol functions as a precursor for the synthesis of steroid hormones. For example, adrenal glands synthesize glucocorticoids and aldosterone from cholesterol, the ovary synthesizes estrogen, and the testis synthesizes testosterone.

Quantitative relationships of the metabolic fates of cholesterol in a human are illustrated in Fig. 5. Diet and synthesis of cholesterol are the two inputs of cholesterol into the body pool of about 120 g, which is relatively constant. Cholesterol is not oxidized to carbon dioxide and water but is eliminated from the body as cholesterol or its derivatives. Most cholesterol is eliminated from the body via the feces as cholesterol and other sterols and as bile acids.

B. Interrelationships of Fats and Cholesterol among Organs of the Body

Triacylglycerol and cholesterol are highly insoluble in the aqueous blood of animals and, hence, are packaged in a minuscule "fat droplet" with a negatively charged hydrophilic surface provided by phospholipids and protein as illustrated by low-density lipoproteins (LDL) in Fig. 6. The droplets, known as lipoproteins, repel each other and remain in quasi-solution within blood plasma. Plasma lipoproteins are of variable sizes and composition. They commonly are classified according to density, and are abbreviated as shown in Table II.

A simplified scheme for the transport and storage of lipids in the human body is presented in Fig. 7.

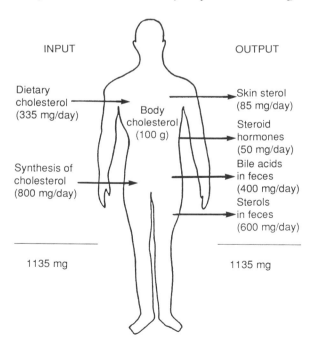

FIGURE 5 Overall cholesterol balance in a typical human.

INPUT

OUTPUT

Dietary cholesterol (335 mg/day)

Body cholesterol (100 g)

Synthesis of cholesterol (800 mg/day)

Skin sterol (85 mg/day)

Steroid hormones (50 mg/day)

Bile acids in feces (400 mg/day)

Sterols in feces (600 mg/day)

1135 mg

1135 mg

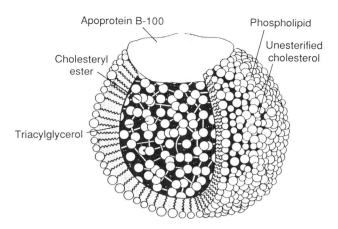

FIGURE 6 Model of the structure of a low-density lipoprotein.

Apoprotein B-100

Phospholipid

Unesterified cholesterol

Cholesteryl ester

Triacylglycerol

Chylomicron triacylglycerols, which are primarily of dietary origin, are removed rapidly from plasma by tissues other than liver. The mechanism involves a hydrolytic enzyme, lipoprotein lipase, which is anchored to the luminal side of the capillary wall and thereby functions extracellularly. Actions of lipoprotein lipase on chylomicrons result in loss of about 90% of triacylglycerols, forming the chylomicron remnant that then is taken up by the liver through endocytosis.

The very-low-density lipoproteins (VLDLs), synthesized primarily within the liver and to a lesser extent in the small intestine, transport triacylglycerol to tissues other than liver, where hydrolysis of triacylglycerol occurs through the action of lipoprotein lipase (Fig. 7). The liberated nonesterified fatty acids are absorbed rapidly and are reesterified to form triacylglycerols for storage or oxidation. Liberation of triacylglycerols from the VLDLs forms VLDL remnants or intermediate-density lipoproteins (IDLs), which then become converted, while still in blood plasma, to LDLs. Most LDLs seem to arise from VLDLs; some, however, are synthesized and secreted directly by liver. Liver is responsible for at least 80% of LDL removal from plasma. Control of LDL concentration in plasma is of great interest because the concentration of LDLs in plasma is correlated positively with the risk of development of coronary atherosclerosis.

The high-density lipoproteins (HDLs) are synthesized and secreted by both liver and intestine (Fig. 7). Lecithin–cholesterol acyl transferase, which catalyzes formation of cholesteryl esters and lysolecithin from cholesterol and lecithin (phosphatidylcholine) extracellularly, assists with the maturation in plasma of the newly secreted nascent HDL to form HDL_3 and then HDL_2. The major sources of the cholesterol in

TABLE II

Composition of Lipoproteins of Human Plasma

Fraction[a]	Source	Diameter (nm)	Density (nm)	Protein[b] (%)	Total lipid[b] (%)	Percentage of total lipid[b]				
						Triacylglycerol	Phospholipid	Cholesteryl ester	Cholesterol	Nonesterified fatty acids
Chylomicrons	Intestine	100–1000	<0.960	1–2	98–99	88	8	3	1	—
VLDL	Liver and intestine	30–90	0.960–1.006	7–10	90–93	56	20	15	8	1
IDL	VLDL and chylomicrons	25–30	1.006–1.019	11	89	29	26	34	9	1
LDL	VLDL and chylomicrons	20–25	1.019–1.063	21	79	13	28	48	10	1
HDL$_2$	Liver and intestine; VLDL? chylomicrons?	10–20	1.063–1.125	33	67	16	43	31	10	—
HDL$_3$	Liver and intestine; VLDL?	7.5–10	1.125–1.210	57	43	13	46	29	6	6
Albumin-free fatty acid	Adipose tissue		>1.281	99	1	0	0	0	0	100

Source: Murray et al. (1988).
[a] VLDL, very-low-density lipoproteins; IDL, intermediate-density lipoproteins; LDL, low-density lipoproteins; HDL, high-density lipoproteins.
[b] Expressed on a weight basis.

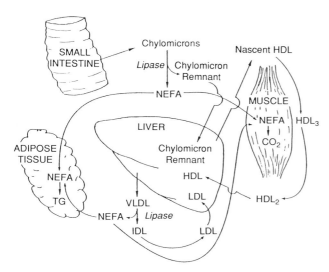

FIGURE 7 Metabolism of plasma lipoproteins by major animal organs. Lipases refer to lipoprotein lipase, diacylglycerol lipase, and monoacylglycerol lipase. For simplicity, only release of triacylglycerols (TG) from lipoproteins as nonesterified fatty acids (NEFA), not glycerol, is illustrated. VLDL, Very-low-density lipoproteins; IDL, intermediate-density lipoproteins; HDL, high-density lipoproteins; LDL, low-density lipoproteins.

HDLs are tissues other than liver. The mature HDLs ultimately become endocytosed by the liver, thus illustrating the scavenger role of HDLs in effecting a flow of cholesterol to liver. Unlike that of LDL, HDL concentration in plasma is related inversely to incidence of coronary atherosclerosis.

III. Essentiality of Fats and Cholesterol in the Diet

Triacylglycerols are not essential in the diet because they can be synthesized from other lipids, proteins, carbohydrates, and ethanol when dietary energy exceeds daily energy needs. Linoleic acid, a polyunsaturated fatty acid that may be a constituent of triacylglycerols, is essential to maintaining good health. Linolenic acid, another polyunsaturated fatty acid, is usually considered essential, although its essentiality is more difficult to demonstrate. No specific daily amount of either fatty acid for humans has been specified, although 1% of total dietary energy as linoleic acid has been suggested.

Why are specific fatty acids required? First, cell membranes contain relatively high proportions of the essential fatty acids or fatty acids produced from them. Second, eicosanoids (mentioned earlier) are synthesized directly or indirectly from linoleic acid.

Therefore, adequate amounts of the essential fatty acids are needed for all the physiological functions of eicosanoids.

As mentioned earlier, cholesterol fulfills many necessary physiological roles. Nevertheless, cholesterol is not a dietary essential because adequate amounts are synthesized from dietary lipids, carbohydrates, proteins, and ethanol.

IV. Content of Fats and Cholesterol in Common Foods

Americans consume diets that contain an average of 37% of calories from fat. About half comes from animals and about half comes from plants. The major constituent of fat in food is triacylglycerols. "Saturated" fats, such as beef fat and palm oil, contain relatively high proportions of saturated fatty acids and are semisolid at room temperature. Highly "unsaturated" or "polyunsaturated" fats, such as soy oil and fish oil, contain relatively high proportions of monounsaturated or polyunsaturated fatty acids and are liquid at room temperature. Total fat or lipid, fatty acid, and cholesterol contents of selected foods are presented in Table III. Only foods or food ingredients that are derived from animals contain cholesterol. Therefore, plant-derived foods are listed as containing 0 cholesterol in Table III.

V. Dietary Recommendations for Humans

Americans have available numerous publications from which to decide on diet composition that promotes optimal health. The National Research Council has used the scientific literature to recommend optimal daily intake of most of the known nutrients required for life. Moreover, the dietary guidelines for Americans that were published in 1990 by the United States Department of Agriculture (USDA) and by the United States Department of Health and Human Services (DHHS) are setting the standard for individual consumers who wish to change food intake and for food producers and processors who wish to alter composition of foods. Those guidelines are presented in Fig. 8.

With regards to recommendations on fats and cholesterol, the USDA–DHHS report suggests the following numerical goals for daily intake of fat and

TABLE III

Fat, Fatty Acid, and Cholesterol Composition of Selected Foods

Component	Milk[a]	Pink salmon[a]	Skinless chicken[a]	Lean beef[a]	Lean pork[a]	Palm oil[b]	Canola oil[b]	White safflower oil[b]	Egg yolk[b]
Total fat[c]	0–3.5	6.1	3.6	9.9	9.3	100	100	100	33
Fatty acids[d]									
$C_{4:0}$	3.6	—	—	—	—	—	—	—	—
$C_{6:0}$	3.3	—	—	—	—	—	—	—	—
$C_{8:0}$	1.3	—	—	—	—	—	—	—	—
$C_{10:0}$	2.5	—	—	0.1	0.1	—	—	—	—
$C_{12:0}$	2.9	—	0.3	0.1	0.1	Tr	—	—	—
$C_{14:0}$	10.4	0.9	1.0	3.4	1.5	1	Tr	—	Tr
$C_{16:0}$	30.4	25.0	23.0	27.1	26.0	42	4	6	29
$C_{16:1}$	1.9	8.7	5.0	4.2	4.8	Tr	Tr	Tr	4
$C_{18:0}$	12.1	2.6	8.3	14.7	12.2	4	1	3	9
$C_{18:1}$	24.2	19.8	34.7	45.8	48.4	43	54	15	43
$C_{18:2}$	2.6	1.1	19.7	3.3	5.2	8	23	13	11
$C_{18:3}$	1.7	1.1	1.0	0.4	0.1	Tr	10	1	Tr
$C_{20:4}$	—	1.5	2.0	0.5	0.4	—	—	—	Tr
$C_{20:5}$	—	15.7	—	—	—	—	—	—	—
$C_{22:6}$	—	15.0	—	—	—	—	—	—	—
Cholesterol[e]	15	65	85	86	80	0	0	0	0

[a] Data from Council for Agricultural Science and Technology (1991).
[b] Data from Gurr and Harwood (1991).
[c] Expressed as weight percentage of total food.
[d] Expressed as weight percentage of total fatty acids in food. Tr, trace amounts. Totals may not equal 100 because small amounts of other fatty acids were not included in the table.
[e] Expressed as milligrams of cholesterol per 100 grams of food.

saturated fat. The USDA–DHHS suggests that daily intake of total fat be limited to 30% of total caloric intake. Thus, if you consume 2000 kcal each day, 600 kcal of fat or 67 g (600 kcal ÷ 9 kcal per gram) would be the recommended daily limit of fat intake. With regard to saturated fat, an amount that provides less than 10% of total calories, or less than 22 g at 2000 kcal daily intake, is suggested. Complicating the practice of this guideline is that different dietary fats contain different mixtures of saturated and unsaturated fatty acids. Further, because people respond differently to dietary fats, total compliance with the aforementioned guidelines does not guarantee optimal health. No numerical goal is suggested for cholesterol, although the American Heart Association and other groups recommend cholesterol be limited to 300 mg per day.

VI. Degenerative Diseases

A. Cardiovascular Disease

1. Description of the Disease

Cardiovascular disease (CVD) is used as a general term to describe disease processes involving the heart, the large vasculature surrounding the heart (atherosclerosis), and the peripheral vasculature supplying blood to organs and limbs (arteriosclerosis). In 1985, 48% of all deaths resulted from a form of CVD such as stroke, heart attack, or vascular disease. Currently, the estimate is that 65 million Americans are in some way afflicted by CVD, resulting in medical costs that are approaching $100 billion per year. Despite these staggering figures, the rate of CVD has decreased over the last three decades. With the advent of advanced medical care and extensive nutrition research resulting in sound medical and nutritional advice, a 32% decrease has occurred since 1964 in coronary heart disease, the most prevalent form of CVD.

2. Risk Factors

CVD has been difficult to study and treat because it is a multifactorial process involving genetics, stress, diet, environmental factors, and other factors known and unknown. Historically, researchers have known for over 80 yr that feeding cholesterol to rabbits would cause atherosclerosis, although cholesterol is a vital component in normal cellular membrane function. However, according to some researchers, cholesterol can become a risk factor in the development of CVD

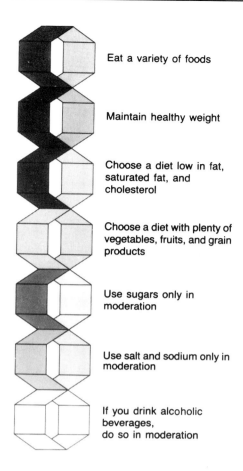

Eat a variety of foods

Maintain healthy weight

Choose a diet low in fat, saturated fat, and cholesterol

Choose a diet with plenty of vegetables, fruits, and grain products

Use sugars only in moderation

Use salt and sodium only in moderation

If you drink alcoholic beverages, do so in moderation

FIGURE 8 Dietary guidelines for Americans. *Source:* U.S. Department of Agriculture (1990).

if plasma cholesterol concentrations rise above 220–240 mg/dl. Before treatment for hypercholesterolemia begins, blood tests should be conducted more than once because plasma cholesterol concentrations can vary according to season of the year, time of day, mood, and other variations in individual living habits. Hypercholesterolemia is one of the primary risk factors named among 200 other identified risk factors for CVD. More important possibly than total plasma cholesterol is the concentration of cholesterol in LDL compared with the concentration in HDL. The LDL-cholesterol concentration is related directly to incidence of CVD, whereas HDL-cholesterol concentration is related inversely to incidence of CVD. Other primary risk factors with non-genetic components associated with CVD include cigarette smoking, high blood pressure, obesity, diabetes, and high plasma triacylglycerol concentrations.

3. Mechanisms

Researchers have defined three distinct phases in the progression of atherosclerotic disease: (1) initia-tion, (2) progression, and (3) thrombosis. The process of atherosclerosis, as diagrammed in Fig. 9, involves the interaction of LDLs, monocyte differentiation and LDL engorgement, and smooth muscle cell proliferation.

a. Initiation Currently, the most widely accepted mechanism for initiation is the response-to-injury theory. According to this theory, the inner wall of the blood vessel is damaged in a mechanism yet to be characterized completely. Some proposed

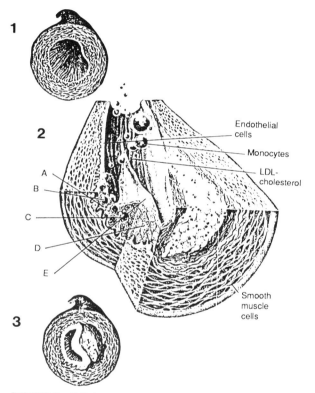

FIGURE 9 Cellular processes responsible for development of atherosclerosis. (1) Artery depicting early fatty streak development. (2) A. LDL becomes oxidized within the arterial subendothelial space. B. Circulating monocytes are recruited to the subendothelial space by chemoattractants including oxidized LDL. C. These monocytes undergo differentiation, becoming macrophages, which are scavenger cells that recognize and accumulate oxidized LDL. D. The lipid-laden macrophages then become foam cells, which cluster under the endothelial lining to form a bulge into the artery. E. This bulge is called a fatty streak and is the first overt sign of atherosclerotic change. (3) Macrophages can subsequently die, releasing cytotoxic oxidized LDL. Injury to and loss of endothelial cells over the fatty streak result. Platelets adhere to the site of injury and aggregate. They release growth factors that cause proliferation of smooth muscle cells, furthering the atherosclerotic process. The artery becomes increasingly narrowed, preventing normal blood flow.

situations that may damage the inner endothelial layer of vessels include physical means associated with increased blood pressure or, more probably, chemical oxidative stress by oxidized fatty acids or other oxidized lipid-like molecules in LDL, for example, cholesterol.

Oxidized compounds are produced naturally in the human body as a protection mechanism against pathogenic organisms. For example, oxidized products accumulate at the site of injury to skin to inhibit bacterial growth and to attract monocytes, which are special cells of the immune system that can differentiate and turn into protective cells. Under normal conditions, the body also has enzyme systems—such as superoxide dismutase, catalase, and glutathione peroxidase—to remove toxic oxidized products. These antioxidant enzymes systems may become overwhelmed when dietary fats are consumed that became oxidized before consumption. Oxidation of fats and lipid-like molecules has been associated with deep-fat frying, dehydration, and powdering of food. When the oxidized products accumulate in blood, they may damage the integrity of the lining of the vessel and the artery may become damaged in a manner that is not well understood. Clearly, oxidized molecules attract monocytes from the circulating blood and cause them to change into macrophages, which can accumulate LDLs.

b. Progression Progression includes plaque formation on the wall of the artery. The mechanisms involved usually are associated with macrophages that become imbedded at the site of arterial injury. Macrophages attempt to repair the injured arterial membranes by accumulating cholesterol and other cellular building blocks from blood to be placed in cellular membranes. To accomplish this repair, macrophages have receptors to remove oxidized LDL from circulation. The LDL receptors are not regulated and continue to cause oxidized LDL constituents to accumulate intracellularly, leading to a plaque containing primarily cholesteryl ester deposits. At the same time, macrophages activate platelets, which can initiate clot formation in an attempt to repair arterial damage. Platelets also secrete growth factors that cause smooth muscle cell proliferation in the underlying musculature, further decreasing the diameter of the arterial lumen.

c. Thrombosis The final stage occurs when vascular occlusion develops because a blood clot blocks an already restricted vessel. Tissues downstream of the blockage are unable to function as a result of the loss of oxygen-containing blood, causing tissue damage and/or tissue death. If the coronary arteries are occluded, the heart muscle fails and a loss of function occurs.

4. Recommendations

Obviously, to best control CVD, we must minimize as many risk factors as possible. To control some risk factors such as smoking, the recommendations are simple—quit smoking. For other risk factors, however, the recommendations are not as simple and, in fact, can become quite confusing. Often when one risk factor is decreased, other risk factors also decrease. For example, if obesity is addressed, blood pressure often will decrease as will plasma cholesterol and triacylglycerol concentrations. Also, as a patient loses weight, insulin insensitivity often improves and non-insulin-dependent diabetes improves. Usually, the first phase recommended in controlling risk factors includes diet modification.

a. Dietary Fat and Cholesterol Recently, the emphasis for controlling plasma cholesterol has switched from dietary cholesterol to type and amount of dietary fat. In the mid-1980s, the U.S. Surgeon General recommended that no more than 30% of calories be derived from fat, with up to 10% from saturated fatty acids. This change in emphasis has been based on clinical trials that demonstrate little change in plasma cholesterol because of changes in cholesterol intake. Some researchers indicate that two-thirds of the population readily regulates cholesterol synthesis to compensate for changes in dietary cholesterol.

The individual fatty acids have been re-examined with respect to their ability to increase (lauric, myristic, and palmitic acids) or decrease (linoleic and linolenic acids) plasma cholesterol. The ω-3 fatty acids (eicosapentaenoic and docosahexaenoic acids) present in marine fish oils also decrease plasma cholesterol concentrations. The general trends were in place in the mid-1960s when Keys and Hegsted developed equations that predicted changes in plasma cholesterol based on changes in type and amount of fatty acids in a given diet. Today, these equations have been updated to further define the actions of individual fatty acids and to consider *trans* fatty acids. As intake of processed foods containing hydrogenated fatty acids increases, so does the intake of *trans* fatty acids. Currently, *trans* fatty acids are receiving much attention in research trials, but minimal evidence has been collected to accurately define their effects on CVD risk.

b. Drug Therapy For those patients who have elevated plasma cholesterol concentrations despite diet therapy, several drugs that block cholesterol synthesis are available. Other useful drugs act in the small intestine to decrease absorption of bile acids and biliary or dietary cholesterol by increasing their rates of excretion. Soluble dietary fiber, as in oat bran, but not insoluble fiber decreases blood cholesterol by a similar mechanism. In large studies that tested cholesterol-lowering drugs, researchers found equal mortality rates in treatment and control groups. The treatment fatalities are not as often related to CVD, but the total death rate in the groups seems not to differ, making drug therapy a topic of further investigation.

c. Antioxidants A long-term preventative measure may be to include more antioxidants in the diet in the form of vitamin C, beta-carotene, or vitamin E. To date, the most promising antioxidant for CVD control seems to be vitamin E. In one large study in which health professionals were surveyed for several years, those who ingested vitamin E in excess of currently recommended concentrations had significantly fewer incidences of CVD. The general recommendation to increase intake of supplemental vitamin E is equivocal, and no strong recommendations are in place for large doses of vitamin E.

d. Summary Because of a positive association of blood cholesterol with CVD, use of effective nutritional and pharmacological methods to decrease plasma cholesterol concentrations will decrease the incidence of CVD in humans. Cholesterol concentrations can be decreased to differing degrees in different people by modifying the type and amount of fat in the diet, by exercising, and by drug therapy, but the most effective approach for decreasing total cholesterol while keeping an optimal HDL-cholesterol:LDL-cholesterol ratio remains controversial.

B. Cancer

1. Description of the disease

Cancers, as do most diseases, have multifactorial points of environmental and genetic origin. Currently, epidemiologists believe that 60–90% of human cancers are of environmental origin, for example,

from viruses, radiation, and chemicals. Strictly speaking, food we consume is chemical in nature and must be evaluated component by component. Of the natural food components, dietary fat has been given the most attention with respect to carcinogenesis. As early as 1940, fat had been demonstrated to influence tumor development in rat mammary tumor models.

Most dietary compounds are not carcinogenic in their natural state but can become carcinogenic when altered by the body, usually by the mixed-function oxidase system. This process results in molecules that are electro-chemically able to interact with DNA, making the molecules capable of interfering with DNA replication and resulting in DNA mutations. Certain regions of DNA are affected strongly by mutation, whereas other regions withstand many mutations that are never expressed at the phenotypic level. The more vulnerable regions of DNA are termed oncogenes and promote carcinogenesis when activated by mutation; alternatively, tumor suppressor genes are no longer able to inhibit carcinogenesis when they become mutated.

The process of carcinogenesis has two discrete stages—initiation and promotion. Clearly, cancer formation requires both stages and initiation must occur first. Initiators mutate the DNA, whereas promoters cause expression of the mutant DNA. Dietary fat currently is accepted to enhance the promotion stage of carcinogenesis but to have minimal effect on the initiation stage, except perhaps in liver tissue.

2. Risk factors

Information concerning diet-related issues associated with the risk for cancer development is equivocal. What can be said, however, is that certain cancers, such as colon and breast cancer, are more likely related to dietary fat intake, whereas pancreatic, ovarian, and prostate cancers are less likely related to dietary fat intake. This statement is based on epidemiologic studies conducted throughout the world. One study compared the United States and Japan, where the population consumes about half as much fat per capita as in the United States. In both countries, which share similar literacy rates and standards of living, about 0.2% of both populations die from cancer each year. However, a person in the United States is four times more likely to die of breast cancer and five times more likely to die of prostate cancer, whereas death from colon cancer is only slightly less common in Japan. However, a study in the United States compared nurses who consumed 32 or 44% calories as fat and found no differences in the incidence of breast cancer.

A similar study in Italy, where fat consumption is more divergent, found that fewer women consuming diets with 26% calories as fat died of breast cancer than those who were consuming diets with 46% calories as fat.

3. Mechanisms

Describing the precise mechanisms involved in the etiology of diet-induced carcinogenesis is difficult. One theory is the endocrine-based mechanism theory in which essential fatty acids, precursors to prostaglandin molecules, may affect rates of cancer development. Another theory related to fat intake involves increased bile acid secretion and the conversion of bile acids to secondary bile acids in the gut, which may be partly responsible for colon cancer. Fat-induced changes in membrane structure and lipid peroxidation are also plausible causes for carcinogenesis.

4. Recommendations

Giving sound dietary guidance to prevent cancer development is difficult because little is known about the mechanisms of initiation of carcinogenesis. Some experts contest the recommendations of the National Research Council of limiting calories as fat to 30% as still too great a fat intake to prevent development of cancer, whereas others adopt the philosophy of not being concerned with fat intake. Most experts advise following the recommendation of the National Research Council to consume diets with up to 30% calories as fat, which does not severely compromise the palatability of foods.

C. Obesity

1. Description of the Disease

Obesity is simply a condition in which the human has an excessive amount of body fat as measured by under-water weighing, skin-pinch calipers, or body mass index (BMI = weight/height^2). The cause for the accumulation of fatty tissue, however, is far from simple and has yet to be defined clearly. This complex condition affects 34 million Americans aged 20–74, with a large percentage in the poor or minority population.

2. Risk Factors

The major risk factor for obesity is simply greater caloric intake than caloric expenditure. The variability between individuals with different genetics is what makes predicting expenditure a complex issue. For example, some strains of rats can adjust to a high-calorie, high-fat diet without becoming obese, whereas other strains cannot adjust and quickly become obese, proving a genetic component to obesity. This type of study has been difficult to conduct in humans because of the length of time required for a good nutrition study and because of the inaccuracy associated with dietary recall by free-living individuals. The focus of obesity should be on its role as a risk factor for other diseases such as CVD, high blood pressure, and possibly cancer.

3. Mechanisms

The mechanisms regulating caloric intake have not been described thoroughly. From experimental trials, humans are better able to compensate by increasing caloric intake after times of caloric restriction than they are able to compensate by decreasing caloric intake after times of excess caloric intake. This differential compensation was demonstrated by increasing or decreasing the calories in the noon meal by 66%. Those given the caloric deficit compensated and maintained typical body weight, whereas those given the caloric excess at noon did not compensate and gained weight.

Because fat has more than twice the caloric density of carbohydrate and often increases palatability of foods, it is much easier for humans to overconsume fat. At the same time, the metabolic efficiency of storing dietary fat as fat is 93%, whereas the efficiency of converting dietary carbohydrate to fat for storage is 72%. In addition to biochemical explanations of obesity is a psychological pleasure component, for most people, that is associated with consuming food containing fat. The sensory characteristics of different types of fats also are significant.

4. Recommendations

For most individuals, removal of excess weight is a matter of energy balance. To lose weight, one must enter a negative energy balance for a period of time. This negative balance can be accomplished by increased combustion of fuels (exercise), by decreased intake of fuels, or by a combination of both. Body weight can be maintained when consuming a high fat diet; however, dietary fat, the most concentrated form of energy that humans consume, usually should be decreased when trying to lose body weight.

D. Diabetes

1. Description of the Disease

The two forms of diabetes are insulin-dependent diabetes mellitus (IDDM or Type I), which affects

1% of the population and requires exogenous insulin, and non-insulin-dependent diabetes mellitus (NIDDM or Type II), which usually occurs later in life and often is associated with obesity. Type I diabetes is characterized by an absolute need for insulin because of decreased pancreatic output of insulin, whereas type II diabetics have a relative need for extra insulin because their tissues are not responding to normal insulin concentrations in the blood.

2. Risk Factors and Mechanisms

The greatest risk for type II diabetes is obesity. The incidence of type II diabetes is increasing in minority populations as their metabolic systems try to adapt to a western life-style, including a diet rich in calories and fat. Further, both types of diabetes are a risk factor for CVD.

3. Recommendations

The best recommendations for dietary control of diabetes have not changed dramatically over the years. A heart-healthy, calorie-restricted diet rich in complex carbohydrates will help decrease the risk of obesity and will decrease the risk of furthering the progression of CVD. Blood pressure and plasma lipids should be monitored frequently and treatments should be imposed as necessary.

E. Disorders of the Immune System

1. Description of the Immune System

Immunity can be considered a protective mechanism against foreign bacteria and viruses. Moreover, the immune system represents components that are not always beneficial and components that recognize and dispose of foreign cells. The immune system can be classified functionally as specific and nonspecific. Nonspecific immune function includes general inflammation in response to injury, whereas specific immune function is defined more clearly. Specific immune functions include cellular immunity, which is represented by phagocytic lymphocytes and thymic cells (T cells), and humoral immunity, which is associated primarily with antibodies produced from B cells. Macrophages are considered accessory cells and assist in both specific and nonspecific immunity.

2. Risk Factors and Recommendations

Dietary practices that can influence the immune system recently have come under greater scrutiny. Dietary fat has received much attention in the last two decades because fat has been shown to have significant effects on immune function. The research that has been conducted until now, however, does not support the need to alter well-balanced diets to achieve changes in our immune system. People with disorders such as systemic lupus erythematosus, allergic encephalomyelitis, and multiple sclerosis may benefit from increased fat intake as a method of attenuating an overactive immune system. Ability to manipulate the immune system with dietary treatment is a very exciting possibility; however, the current recommendation for the average population to consume less than 30% of calories as fat remains sound advice. With further research, more specific immune-modulating diets may be formulated for patients suffering from immune deficiency or immune hyperactivity.

3. Mechanisms

In research trials utilizing experimental animals and, less frequently, humans, extremely high fat diets and diets rich in ω-6 polyunsaturated fatty acids are immunosuppressive. These diets, however, are extreme in fat content and are not representative of the average American diet. Many studies indicate that excessive fat intake results in a predictable decrease in T-lymphocyte activity and an unpredictable change in B-lymphocyte activity.

The changes in lymphocyte function can be accounted for by changes in fatty acid composition of immune cell membranes. Changes in linoleic acid concentration in membranes causes the most marked changes in immune function. Changes in immune function could be explained mechanistically by one of two major hypotheses: (1) changes in membrane fluidity/function or (2) changes in the production of eicosanoids from fatty acid precursors. Other mechanistic studies involve large dietary doses of oxidized lipids, which decrease immune function; hypercholesterolemia, which decreases immune function; and vitamin E, which enhances immune function when oxidatively unstable fatty acids are consumed.

F. Renal Disease

1. Description of the Disease

Basic renal function maintains fluid and electrolyte balance, regulates blood pressure, excretes waste, influences erythrocyte production via erythropoietin, activates vitamin D, and supplies the body with some glucose in times of starvation. If any of these systems is less than optimal, other organ systems quickly become involved and a patient's health can deteriorate quickly. Renal function can deteriorate chronically or acutely, depending on the causative agent. All types of kidney failure can be classified as (1) prerenal, including blood flow to the filtration apparati, (2) renal, including problems associated with the filtration apparati, or (3) postrenal, usually associated with some form of urinary blockage. The causative agent of failure in many instances has yet to be determined, but possibilities include compromised blood circulation associated with vascular disease or immune-mediated tissue damage.

For many years, protein intake was the primary dietary concern for patients with decreased kidney function. Recently, dietary lipids have come into question in the development and possibly even in the treatment of diseases that compromise kidney function.

2. Risk Factors

Currently, no established guidelines exist for dietary fat consumption with respect to kidney function. The risk factors that are associated with dietary intake are centered around maintenance of optimal blood flow. Improvements in cardiovascular health will improve blood supply to the kidneys as well. Research currently is being conducted to evaluate the effects of different dietary fatty acids on kidney function and to understand the mechanism of these effects.

3. Mechanisms

Little is known about the ability of dietary fatty acids to modulate and optimize kidney function. What is known is that most fatty acid effects are mediated via eicosanoid metabolism or changes in membrane fluidity, which may affect membrane permeability and function. Eicosanoids, which are synthesized from linoleic acid and linolenic acid, maintain normal kidney function by modulating vessel tone, altering blood viscosity, and controlling platelet aggregability. Under some disease states, the kidney synthesizes unusual ratios of the bioactive eicosanoids. On the basis of this information, researchers have investigated the possibilities of altering eicosanoid formation by altering the enzyme systems responsible for eicosanoid synthesis or by altering the precursor fatty acid inputs into the system.

Eicosanoids are not stored but are used immediately after synthesis. The rate-limiting step of synthesis is the enzymatically catalyzed release of fatty acid precursors from membrane phospholipids. Polyunsaturated fatty acids, which are eicosanoid precursors, are known to decrease blood pressure, which helps relieve complications associated with renal disease. Increased dietary linoleic acid alters fatty acid composition of kidney membranes, which changes membrane fluidity and increases prostaglandin E_2 synthesis. Eicosanoids synthesized from linoleic acid are vasodilatory and antiaggregatory. Further, ω-3 fatty acids, as in fish oil, decrease renal vascular tone and also decrease clotting time, which may prevent intraglomerular thrombosis. Additionally, blood viscosity is decreased and red cell deformability increases, allowing easier passage through capillaries. Saturated fatty acids seem not to affect renal function directly but may augment problems by contributing to arteriosclerosis. Although unproven, some researchers believe that certain fatty acids also may be nephrotoxic.

4. Recommendations

No general recommendations are in place for maintaining healthy kidney function other than normal recommendations for a healthy diet. Under medical supervision, however, certain diets will alleviate symptoms associated with particular forms of kidney disease. Most treatment regimes include decreased protein intake and increased intake of fats rich in polyunsaturated fatty acids. These diet modifications will alleviate unnecessary nitrogen excretion and increase eicosanoid synthesis in the kidney. The resulting eicosanoids have strong positive effects on vascular musculature, platelet aggregability, and inflammatory events associated with some renal diseases. However, more research is warranted to further evaluate influence of dietary fatty acids on kidney health.

G. Neuromuscular Disorders

1. Description of the Disease

Numerous disorders in function are caused by changes in fatty acid composition of the myelin sheath. The symptoms of several neural disorders such as Refsum's disease, peroxisome deficiency disorders, and Reye's syndrome can be minimized if the metabolic defect is recognized and dietary adjustments are made. Because these disorders are genetic defects, the best technology currently available is to treat the symptoms with changes in diet or, in some instances, with specific enzyme inhibitors. Further work must continue if a cure for these genetic neuronal disorders is to be found. Use of molecular biological techniques, such as gene therapy, seems highly promising.

2. Risk Factors

Because these diseases are all genetic in nature, there are no known risk factors.

3. Mechanisms and Recommendations

The symptoms of the previously mentioned neuronal disorders—loss of neural control and possibly even coma—usually are caused by changes in fatty acid composition of neural membranes. This change can occur because of (1) accumulation of peculiar fatty acids that are typically and quickly metabolized, as in Refsum's disease or (2) removal of components from the myelin sheath by circulating detergent-like free fatty acids that are abnormally high, as in Reye's syndrome.

Most symptoms of the neuromuscular disorders are irreversible, and dietary treatment must be initiated early to minimize progression of the symptoms. Patients with Refsum's disease, for example, must avoid dietary phytanic acid, the fatty acid metabolite that accumulates in their tissue. Products from ruminants— meat and milk products—have considerable amounts of phytanic acid and must be avoided. Rapid weight loss also should be avoided because of the possibility of mobilizing large amounts of phytanic acid from triacylglycerol stores. Patients with a defect in beta-oxidation because of defective peroxisomes, as in Zellweger syndrome or neonatal adrenoleukodystrophy, usually are prescribed to a diet that minimizes most long-chain fatty acid intake but maximizes oleic acid intake. When mitochondrial beta-oxidation is affected because of a deficiency of carnitine at the mitochondrial membrane, dietary carnitine and medium-chain triacylglycerols will relieve the symptoms of carnitine deficiency. Recently, Duchenne muscular dystrophy has been linked to a decreased ability of skeletal muscle to oxidize palmitic acid, as demonstrated by increased concentrations of long-chain fatty acyl CoA in muscle and a decreased ability for muscle homogenates to oxidize palmitic acid.

The neuronal diseases mentioned here are only a few of the diseases with compromised abilities to catabolize fatty acids. The dietary suggestions that have been made and tested are being implemented in some instances. However, as was stated earlier, special diets only treat the symptoms, not the disease. For these diseases to be conquered, gene therapy is needed to replace missing or dysfunctional genes.

Acknowledgment

Journal Paper No. J.15593 of the Iowa Agriculture and Home Economics Station, Ames, Iowa. Project No. 3037.

Bibliography

Chow, C. K. (ed.) (1992). "Fatty Acids in Foods and Their Health Implications." Marcel Dekker, New York.

Council for Agricultural Science and Technology (CAST) Task Force (1991). "Food Fats and Health," Report No. 118. Council for Agricultural Science and Technology, Ames, IA.

Gurr, M. I., and Harwood, J. L. (1991). "Lipid Biochemistry - An Introduction," 4th Ed. Chapman and Hall, New York.

Murray, R. K., Granner, D. K., Mayes, P. A., and Rodwell, V. W. (1988). "Harper's Biochemistry," 21st Ed. Appleton & Lange, Norwalk, CT.

Nelson, G. J. (ed.) (1991). "Health Effects of Dietary Fatty Acids." American Oil Chemists' Society, Chicago.

Surgeon General of the United States (1988). "Surgeon General's Report on Nutrition and Health," U.S. Department of Health and Human Services Pub. No. 88-50210. U.S. Department of Health and Human Services, Public Health Service, Washington, D.C.

Feeds and Feeding

WILLIAM E. KUNKLE, *University of Florida*

Glossary

Cellulose Carbohydrate abundant in plant cell walls; it is a glucose polymer with beta linkages that can be digested by microbial enzymes

Concentrate Feed that is high in digestible energy and contains less than 18% crude fiber

Crude protein Quantitative measure of nitrogen (kjeldahl procedure) in feeds calculated as nitrogen times 6.25; it includes proteins, amino acids, nitrate, urea, and amines

Digestibility Portion of a feed that is absorbed from the digestive tract of animals

Fiber Carbohydrate in plant cell walls that requires microbial enzymes to be digested

Forage Plant material such as pasture, hay, or silage that is fed to livestock

Heat increment Heat produced by microbial fermentation in the digestive tract and metabolism in the animal's body

Hemicellulose Carbohydrate abundant in plant cell walls; it contains hexoses, pentoses, and uronic acids that are digested by microbial enzymes

Lignin Group of compounds that are found in plant cell walls; they are resistant to enzymatic degradation and limit digestion of cellulose and hemicellulose

Nutrient Chemical substance necessary for maintenance, production, and health in animals; classes of nutrients include carbohydrates, fats, proteins, minerals, vitamins, and water

Rumen Largest compartment of the stomach; it has billions of microbes that anaerobically ferment feeds to volatile fatty acids

Silage High-moisture feed that has been stored in an air tight container such as a silo; sugars in the feed have been fermented to lactic acid, which lowers the pH and preserves the feed

Feeds contain nutrients that are used by livestock and poultry for maintenance and production. An objective of many producers feeding livestock and poultry is to provide a diet of different feeds and supplements that meet the nutrient requirements of the animal and produce meat, milk, fiber, or work at a profit or at a minimal cost. The level of production varies widely across species and management systems. Feeds available vary widely in different species, geographic regions, and seasons of the year. The principles involved in feeding livestock for efficient production at a reasonable cost can be applied across the different species and production systems.

I. Feed Supply

Livestock and poultry in the United States consumed an estimated 478 million tons of feed expressed on a feeding value equivalent to corn in 1990 (Table I). Forage represented 54% of the total feed supply, with 37% provided as grazed forage from pasture and 17% provided as forages harvested as hay and silage. Concentrates provided 46% of the livestock feed supply, with 75% of concentrates being provided by the grains corn, sorghum, oats, barley, wheat, and rye. Approximately 60% of the feed grains grown in the United States in 1990 were fed to livestock, 22% were exported to other countries, and 18% were used for

TABLE I
Feed Consumed (in Millions of Tons) by Livestock and Poultry
in the United States

Feed type	Year	
	1985	1990
Pasture[a,b]	191	178
Harvested forages[a,b]	83	79
Concentrates, all[a,b]	213	221
Grains, all[a]	161.00	165.40
Corn	115.20	130.70
Sorghum	18.60	11.30
Oats and barley	14.90	9.30
Wheat and rye	12.30	14.10
High-protein oilseed meals, all[a]	21.38	25.50
Soybean	19.09	22.91
Cottonseed	1.52	1.62
Linseed	0.11	0.13
Peanut	0.18	0.11
Sunflower	0.35	0.34
Canola	0.13	0.39
Animal proteins, all[a]	3.72	3.25
Tankage and meat by-products	2.80	2.53
Fishmeal and fish solubles	0.51	0.27
Milk products	0.41	0.45
Grain protein products, all[a]	2.27	1.42
Gluten feed and meal	1.16	0.18
Brewers dried grains	0.15	0.12
Distillers dried grains	0.96	1.12
Other, all[c]	11.79	13.61
Wheat millfeeds	5.82	6.60
Rice millfeeds	0.55	0.61
Beet pulp	0.77	1.16
Alfalfa meal	0.86	0.37
Fats and oils	0.84	1.10
Molasses	2.08	2.39
Misc. products	0.87	1.38

[a] Adapted from *Agricultural Statistics* (1992). United States Department of Agriculture, Washington, D.C.
[b] Expressed in feeding value equivalent to corn.
[c] Adapted from *Feed* (November 1991). United States Department of Agriculture, Washington, D.C.

human food, seed, and industrial purposes such as ethanol production.

Corn supplied over 79% of the grains and soybean meal supplied 89% of the high-protein oilseed meals (Table I) fed to livestock and poultry in 1990. The livestock and poultry industries also feed by-products from the processing industries, including wheat mill feeds from manufacturing of flour; gluten feed, brewers grains, and distillers grains from production of alcohol and high-fructose sweeteners; and molasses from sugar production. In addition, significant quantities of crop residue and vegetable and animal wastes are fed to livestock. Many of these feeds are fed near where they are produced because they are low in feeding value or high in moisture, which limits the distance they can be transported.

Feeds provide nutrients needed to sustain life. Feeds have been separated into classes based on the type of feed, their nutrient content, and method of harvest. Two general classifications are forages and concentrates. Forages are feeds from plants that are characterized as containing over 18% crude fiber (dry basis) and are fed largely to ruminants. Examples are bermudagrass pasture, alfalfa hay, and corn silage. Concentrates are feeds that have lower fiber content and usually have a higher digestibility than forages. Concentrates can be from plant or animal origin. Examples are corn, soybean meal, wheat middlings, and meat and bone meal. [*See* FORAGES.]

Forages are usually higher in fiber, calcium, potassium, and fat-soluble vitamins but lower in digestibility than concentrates. Forages have variable protein content with legumes ranging from 12 to 25% protein and grasses ranging from 4 to 15% protein. Forages have been further classified into pasture or range forages, hay, and silages. Pasture or range forages are grazed by livestock and include growing vegetation and plant residues left in the field. Hay is the aerial part of plants that is harvested during the growing season, preserved by drying, then mechanically made into bales or stacks that are stored outside or in barns for feeding at another location or during the winter. Approximately 152 million tons of hay were utilized in the United States during 1992.

Silages are made from high-moisture forages that are usually chopped at harvest and then stored in silos or other systems that limit oxygen penetration. Silages are preserved by the lactic acid that lowers the pH. Lactic acid is produced from an anaerobic fermentation of sugars by bacteria after storing in the silo. The forage is usually harvested at 50 to 75% moisture and ensiling is the method of choice for timely harvest of forages when rainy weather prevents rapid drying or for crops that are difficult to dry in the field, such as whole-plant corn or sorghum. An estimated 90 million tons of corn and sorghum silages were harvested in the United States during 1992.

Concentrates have lower levels of fiber and higher digestibilities than forages. Most concentrates are low in calcium but have higher levels of phosphorus than forages and are the predominant feeds used in swine and poultry diets. Concentrates are further classified into energy feeds and protein feeds. Energy feeds include the grains, several of the lower-protein (<20%) by-product feeds, and fats. Protein feeds have

20% or higher protein and many are by-products from the manufacturing or processing industries. Most protein feeds are named by their origin and method of processing, which helps characterize their nutrient content. Examples include soybean meal, solvent processed, without hulls, and meat and bone meal.

II. Nutrients in Feeds

Nutrients are components of feeds that are used for maintenance and production. These can be classified as follows:

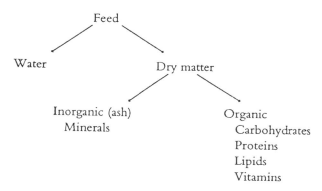

Water is essential for life and a clean supply of drinking water should be available for livestock and poultry at all times. Dry matter in feeds contains minerals, many of which are required in bone formation and normal metabolism, and the organic fraction, which includes carbohydrates, proteins, lipids, and vitamins. Carbohydrates and lipids are utilized mostly as energy sources, protein provides the amino acids used to synthesize protein in muscles and enzymes, and vitamins are needed in small quantities for essential metabolic processes. [See ANIMAL NUTRITION, PRINCIPLES.]

A. Energy

Energy is required for maintenance and production in all animals. Organic compounds contain energy stored in chemical bonds that is made available to the animal during metabolism. However, only part of the chemical energy in feeds is available for absorption and metabolism and this is schematically shown in Fig. 1. The gross energy is the total energy available from complete oxidation or burning (such as in a furnace). Digestible energy accounts for energy lost in the feces, which includes undigested feed and metabolic losses. Metabolizable energy accounts for en-

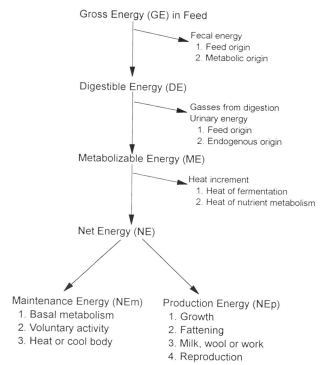

FIGURE 1 Scheme of feed energy utilization by animals.

ergy lost in gases such as methane during digestion and energy excreted in metabolism end products such as urea or uric acid. Ruminant animals may lose 5 to 10% of dietary energy as methane produced by rumen bacteria. Gaseous energy losses in monogastric animals are usually less than 1%. Net energy accounts for losses of energy in the heat of fermentation in the ruminant animals and the heat associated with nutrient metabolism after absorption. This heat can be used to maintain body temperature in cold weather, but dissipating heat during hot weather requires energy. Net energy is the energy that is available for maintenance, such as basal metabolism and breathing, and the energy stored during growth, fattening, or reproduction, and in the products produced such as milk, eggs, and wool. [See ANIMAL NUTRITION, NONRUMINANT; ANIMAL NUTRITION, RUMINANT.]

Grains are high in starch and have higher digestible, metabolizable, and net energy values than forages that have similar levels of carbohydrates but less starch and more fiber. Corn, alfalfa, and fescue hay have similar gross energy concentrations but the metabolizable energy varies from 40 to 87% of the gross energy depending on the feed and the animal (Table II). Digestion losses vary from 11 to 53% for these

TABLE II

Energy Losses of Feeds during Digestion and Metabolism by Swine and Beef Cattle

Feed and species	Gross energy (GE)	Digestible energy (DE)	Metabolizable energy (ME)	Net energy maintenance	Net energy growth
Corn grain					
Swine					
kcal/kg	4480	4000	3880	—	—
% GE	—	89.3	86.6	—	—
Beef					
kcal/kg	4480	3960	3250	2240	1550
% GE	—	88.4	72.5	50.0	34.6
Alfalfa hay, 17% CP					
Swine					
kcal/kg	4350	2040	1850	—	—
% GE	—	46.9	42.5	—	—
Beef					
kcal/kg	4350	2690	2210	1340	770
% GE	—	61.8	50.8	30.8	17.7
Fescue hay					
Beef					
kcal/kg	4300	2120	1740	900	350
% GE	—	49.3	40.5	20.9	8.1

feeds and the losses from digestible energy to metabolizable energy vary from 3 to 16% of the gross energy. Monogastric animals have lower losses of energy in gases than ruminants and this results in lower losses between digestible energy and metabolizable energy. The metabolizable energy of corn is 630 kcal/kg lower for beef than for swine, but this is reversed for alfalfa hay with beef having a 360 kcal/kg higher metabolizable energy value than swine. The net energy for production of the poor-quality forages such as fescue hay is low and these feeds are used mostly in maintenance diets for ruminants or as fiber sources in concentrate diets fed to ruminants.

B. Protein

Protein is made up of different proportions of 22 amino acids. Ten of the amino acids are essential, meaning they are not synthesized in the body and are required in the diet of monogastric animals. The other 12 amino acids are nonessential in monogastric diets. Four of these may limit performance under some situations and dietary levels are considered in diet formulation. The crude protein is often analyzed in feeds by determining the nitrogen concentration with the kjeldahl analysis procedure and multiplying by 6.25. This assumes the protein contains 16% nitrogen, which is the average nitrogen composition of several proteins. However, the kjeldahl procedure measures the total

nitrogen and some feeds contain nonprotein nitrogen that can be synthesized into the bacterial nitrogen in the ruminant but is of limited value for formulating diets for monogastric animals. Diets for monogastric animals are formulated to contain the required concentrations of each amino acid using different feeds and synthetic sources of amino acids. A diet with concentrations of some amino acids above the requirements is common, but large excesses of some amino acids may reduce feed intake or efficiency of utilization.

Protein can be classified into two types for ruminants: (1) rumen-degraded protein and (2) rumen-undegraded protein. Rumen-degraded protein is broken down to peptides, amino acids, and ammonia by bacteria in the rumen and nonprotein nitrogen (NPN) is degraded to ammonia. Ammonia from rumen-degraded protein and NPN needs to be synthesized into microbial protein to contribute amino acids needed for maintenance and production of the animal. When excess rumen-degraded protein is fed, the extra ammonia is absorbed from the rumen, metabolized to urea in the liver, and recycled to the rumen in saliva or across the rumen wall, or excreted in the urine. The rumen-undegraded or bypass protein is the protein in feeds that escapes digestion in the rumen but can be digested in the small intestine. The bypass protein from the feed plus the bacterial protein provide the amino acids for maintenance and production.

In ruminants at maintenance or with low growth rates the bacterial protein can usually meet the animal's amino acid requirements and dietary formulation emphasizes meeting the bacterial nitrogen requirements with nonprotein nitrogen. Feedlot diets for finishing cattle and sheep often have high levels of corn grain and approximately 50% of this protein escapes rumen degradation. These diets typically utilize NPN to provide most of the supplemental crude protein needed to meet animal requirements. Diets with added NPN need to have adequate levels of sulfur that is required for synthesis of the sulfur-containing amino acids in bacterial protein.

Formulating diets that contain higher levels of bypass protein is important in lighter-weight ruminants that are growing rapidly and for those producing high levels of milk such as the lactating dairy cow. In these situations, animal production is often improved when the diets contain rumen-degraded crude protein balanced with digestible energy and sufficient bypass protein to meet the total amino acid requirements of the animal.

C. Minerals

Minerals are inorganic compounds required for maintenance and production in livestock and poultry. Minerals are divided into two classes based on the concentrations required in the diet; macrominerals and microminerals. Macrominerals include calcium, phosphorus, potassium, magnesium, sodium, chlorine and sulfur. Calcium and phosphorus are required for the formation of bones, teeth, and egg shells. Required levels range from 0.15 to 3.5% in the diet depending on the animal and level of production. Other macrominerals are used in many essential functions and required levels range from 0.1 to 1.0% in the diet. Microminerals include cobalt, copper, iodine, iron, manganese, selenium, and zinc. Microminerals are used in many metabolic processes and required levels range from 0.1 to 100 mg/kg of diet.

Minerals in the diet are provided by feeds and from inorganic mineral supplements. A common source of sodium and chlorine is salt, phosphorus is often supplemented from dicalcium phosphate, and ground limestone is a good source of calcium. Most of the macro- and microelements can be supplemented in the diet from inorganic compounds. Microminerals are typically provided in trace element mixes that contain several of the microminerals mixed in the needed concentrations to supplement a typical diet. An example is a corn–soybean meal diet fed to a growing pig. Feed formulation and mixing can be simplified by adding a trace element premix to provide all the supplemental microminerals.

D. Vitamins

Vitamins are organic compounds that are essential for normal metabolic processes in animals. Vitamins are divided into two classes, fat-soluble vitamins, which are A, D, E, and K, and the water-soluble B-complex vitamins—thiamine, riboflavin, niacin, pyridoxine, pantothenic acid, cobalamin, biotin, choline and folacin—and ascorbic acid. Fat-soluble vitamins A and E are easily oxidized and concentrations in feeds decrease during storage. Carotene, a naturally occurring compound in plants, can be converted to vitamin A with different efficiencies in different animals. Poultry can synthesize approximately 1600 International Units (IU) of vitamin A from each milligram of carotene, but pigs synthesize only 100 to 300 IU of vitamin A for each milligram of carotene. Diets fed to ruminant animals usually do not contain supplemental B-complex vitamins or vitamin K because bacteria in the rumen usually synthesize enough to meet the animals' requirements. During periods of stress when feed consumption is low or in other special situations, B-complex vitamin supplements may increase performance in ruminants. B-complex vitamins are required in the diets of monogastric animals at levels ranging from 0.005 to 1300 mg/kg. B-complex vitamins and fat-soluble vitamins are typically added to a diet in a premix designed for a typical diet similar to trace element premixes.

E. Lipids

Lipids include both the fats and oils. Most fatty acids in lipids can be synthesized in the animal tissues but linoleic acid cannot be synthesized by some animals and is required in the diet. Current recommended levels of linoleic acid in the diet are 0.1% for swine, 0.5% for the horse, and 1% for poultry. Ruminant animals do not have a dietary requirement for linoleic acid.

III. Feed Composition and Analysis

Swine, poultry, and other monogastric animals are typically fed concentrates. These feeds have similar dry matter concentrations and the nutrient requirements of these animals are expressed as concentrations in the air-dry diet. In contrast, diets of cattle, sheep,

TABLE III

Typical Composition of Important Livestock Feeds: Energy Values, Protein, Fiber, and Linoleic Acid[a]

Feed name/description	Dry matter (%)	TDN (%)	ME (Mcal/kg)	NEM (Mcal/kg)	NEG (Mcal/kg)	Dairy cattle NEL (Mcal/kg)	Chickens MEN (kcal/kg)	Horse DE (Mcal/kg)	Swine ME (kcal/kg)	Crude protein (%)	Undegraded intake protein (% CP)	Cell walls (%)	Acid detergent fiber (%)	Crude fiber (%)	Linoleic acid (%)
Pasture or range forages															
Bermudagrass	100	60	2.22	1.31	0.65	1.35	—	2.38	—	12.0	20	72	35	26	—
Bluegrass, early bloom	100	69	2.62	1.55	0.94	1.57	—	1.78	—	16.6	—	65	32	27	—
Brome grass, immature	100	73	2.80	1.67	1.06	1.67	—	2.59	—	21.3	22	50	30	23	—
Clover, red, early vegetative	100	68	2.58	1.52	0.91	1.55	—	3.19	—	21.0	—	—	—	—	—
Fescue, vegetative	100	67	2.49	1.47	0.85	1.50	—	2.22	—	14.5	30	66	31	25	—
Orchardgrass, midbloom	100	57	2.09	1.23	0.55	1.28	—	2.02	—	11.0	25	68	41	34	—
Rye pasture	100	69	2.62	1.55	0.94	1.57	—	—	—	15.9	—	—	—	29	—
Ryegrass pasture	100	60	2.22	1.31	0.65	1.35	—	2.20	—	14.5	48	59	35	20	—
Wheatgrass, full bloom	100	61	2.27	1.33	0.69	1.38	—	—	—	9.8	—	—	36	30	—
Dry forages															
Alfalfa hay, early bloom	100	60	2.22	1.31	0.65	1.35	—	2.48	—	18.0	20	46	35	29	—
Alfalfa hay, full bloom	100	55	2.00	1.19	0.47	1.23	—	2.17	—	15.0	28	56	40	34	—
Alfalfa meal, dehydrated	100	62	2.31	1.36	0.72	1.40	1774	2.48	2099	22.0	59	42	31	23	0.45
Barley straw	100	49	1.73	1.05	0.23	1.08	—	1.62	—	4.3	—	80	59	42	—
Bermudagrass hay, immature	100	61	2.27	1.33	0.69	1.38	—	2.17	—	16.0	—	66	30	27	—
Bermudagrass hay, mature	100	54	1.96	1.16	0.43	1.20	—	1.87	—	16.5	—	78	43	27	—
Corn stover	100	59	2.18	1.28	0.62	1.33	—	1.62	—	6.6	—	67	39	34	—
Cottonseed hulls	100	45	1.55	0.98	0.06	0.98	—	1.89	—	4.1	45	90	73	48	—
Fescue hay, full bloom	100	58	2.13	1.26	0.58	1.30	—	2.06	—	12.1	35	72	40	29	—
Oat straw	100	50	1.78	1.07	0.28	1.11	—	1.62	—	4.4	—	70	47	41	—
Orchardgrass hay, early bloom	100	65	2.45	1.44	0.82	1.47	—	2.17	—	15.0	30	61	34	31	—
Pangola grass hay, immature	100	45	1.55	0.98	0.06	0.98	—	1.89	—	7.1	—	73	43	36	—
Sorghum stover	100	54	1.96	1.16	0.43	1.20	—	1.62	—	32.2	—	34	34	12	—
Wheat straw	100	44	1.51	0.96	0.01	0.96	—	1.62	—	3.6	70	85	54	42	—
Wheatgrass, crested	100	53	1.91	1.14	0.40	1.18	—	1.90	—	12.4	—	—	36	33	—
Silages															
Corn silage, few ears	100	62	2.31	1.36	0.72	1.40	—	—	—	8.4	—	—	—	32	—
Corn silage, well eared	100	70	2.67	1.58	0.97	1.60	—	—	—	8.1	31	51	28	24	—
Sorghum silage, dough stage	100	55	2.00	1.19	0.47	1.23	—	2.68	—	6.0	36	56	37	27	—
Energy feeds															
Barley	88	74	2.90	1.76	1.19	1.71	2502	3.24	2903	11.9	27	17	6	5	0.24
	100	84	3.29	2.00	1.35	1.94	2843	3.68	3299	13.5	—	19	7	6	0.27
Corn, shelled	88	75	2.94	1.79	1.21	1.72	3399	3.38	3420	8.8	—	8	3	2	1.80
Corn, high lysine	100	85	3.34	2.03	1.37	1.96	3862	3.84	3886	10.0	52	9	3	3	2.05
	90	80	3.16	1.94	1.32	1.85	3364	—	3429	10.2	—	10	4	3	—
	100	89	3.51	2.15	1.47	2.06	3738	2.86	3810	11.3	—	11	4	4	—
Corn and cob meal	87	72	2.83	1.71	1.15	1.66	2745	2.86	2794	7.8	9	22	9	8	—
	100	83	3.25	1.97	1.32	1.91	3155	3.29	3212	9.0	52	25	10	9	—
Fat, animal	99	223	9.47	6.54	4.19	5.34	8150	7.92	8260	0.0	0	0	0	0	4.26
	100	225	9.57	6.61	4.23	5.39	8232	8.00	8343	0.0	0	0	0	0	4.30
Fat, vegetable	100	195	8.23	5.25	4.02	4.66	8132	9.00	8047	0.0	—	0	0	0	66.00
	100	195	8.23	5.25	4.02	4.66	8132	9.00	8047	0.0	—	0	0	0	66.00
Hominy	90	85	3.37	2.08	1.43	1.96	2887	—	3371	10.4	—	23	6	5	3.34
	100	94	3.74	2.31	1.59	2.18	3208	—	3745	11.5	44	25	7	5	3.71
Sorghum grain	90	77	3.04	1.85	1.26	1.79	3322	3.20	3227	11.2	—	17	5	2	1.08
	100	86	3.38	2.06	1.40	1.99	3691	3.56	3585	12.4	54	19	5	3	1.20

Molasses, sugarcane blackstrap	75	54	2.07	1.23	0.77	1.23	1939	2.63	2213	4.4		0	0	0	—
	100	72	2.76	1.64	1.03	1.64	2585	3.50	2951	5.8	0	0	0	0	—
Oat grain	89	69	2.65	1.59	1.04	1.58	2547	2.85	2681	11.8		28	14	11	1.49
	100	77	2.98	1.79	1.17	1.77	2862	3.20	3012	13.3	17	32	16	12	1.67
Rice grain	89	70	2.73	1.65	1.09	1.62	2668	3.38	2726	7.9		—	—	9	—
	100	79	3.07	1.85	1.22	1.82	2998	3.80	3063	8.9		—	—	10	—
Rye grain	88	74	2.90	1.76	1.19	1.71	2641	3.38	2928	12.1		—	8	2	—
	100	84	3.29	2.00	1.35	1.94	3001	3.84	3327	13.8	20	—	9	3	—
Triticale	90	76	2.96	1.80	1.22	1.75	3169	—	3056	15.8		20	5	4	—
	100	84	3.29	2.00	1.35	1.94	3521	—	3396	17.6	25	22	5	4	—
Wheat grain	88	77	3.05	1.87	1.28	1.80	2993	3.40	3257	14.1		11	4	3	0.57
	100	88	3.47	2.12	1.45	2.04	3401	3.86	3701	16.0	22	12	4	3	0.65
Wheat middlings	89	61	2.33	1.38	0.84	1.40	2118	3.09	2732	16.4		33	11	7	2.48
	100	69	2.62	1.55	0.94	1.57	2380	3.47	3070	18.4	24	37	12	8	2.79
Whey, dried	93	75	2.94	1.78	1.18	1.74	1941	3.78	3103	13.2		0	0	0	0.01
	100	81	3.16	1.91	1.27	1.87	2087	4.06	3337	14.2	20	0	0	0	0.01
Protein feeds															
Blood meal, dried	92	60	2.25	1.32	0.75	1.35	2820	—	1950	85.8		14	2	1	0.09
	100	65	2.45	1.44	0.82	1.47	3065	—	2120	93.3	82	15	2	1	0.10
Brewers grains, dried	88	77	2.35	2.01	1.20	1.41	2192	2.42	2184	25.9		49	21	13	2.59
	100	88	2.67	2.28	1.36	1.60	2491	2.75	2482	29.4	56	56	24	14	2.94
Corn gluten feed	90	75	2.67	1.77	1.19	1.72	1732	—	2476	23.0		34	12	9	—
	100	83	2.93	1.97	1.32	1.91	1924	—	2751	25.6	25	38	13	10	—
Corn gluten meal	91	78	3.08	1.87	1.27	1.81	2983	—	3127	42.6		27	8	4	3.83
	100	86	3.38	2.06	1.40	1.99	3278	—	3436	46.8	55	30	9	5	4.21
Cottonseed meal	91	69	2.67	1.60	1.04	1.58	1939	2.74	2359	41.1		27	18	12	—
	100	76	2.93	1.76	1.14	1.74	2131	3.01	2592	45.2	43	30	20	13	—
Cottonseed, whole	92	88	3.52	2.18	1.51	2.05	—	—	—	22.0		48	39	26	—
	100	96	3.83	2.37	1.64	2.23	—	—	—	23.9	39	52	42	28	—
Distillers grains and solubles	92	81	3.19	1.95	1.33	1.88	2539	3.21	2824	23.0		40	17	9	—
	100	88	3.47	2.12	1.45	2.04	2760	3.49	3070	25.0	47	44	18	10	—
Feather meal, hydrolyzed	93	65	2.48	1.47	0.90	1.49	2426	—	2215	84.9		28	13	1	—
	100	70	2.67	1.58	0.97	1.60	2609	—	2382	91.3	71	30	14	1	—
Fish meal, menhaden	92	67	2.58	1.54	0.98	1.54	2861	2.94	2645	61.2		23	2	1	0.11
	100	73	2.80	1.67	1.06	1.67	3110	3.20	2875	66.5	60	25	2	1	0.12
Linseed meal	90	70	2.72	1.64	1.07	1.61	1409	2.74	2517	34.5		23	17	9	0.37
	100	78	3.02	1.82	1.19	1.79	1565	3.04	2797	38.3	35	25	19	10	0.41
Meat and bone meal	93	66	2.52	1.50	0.93	1.51	2079	—	2182	50.3		33	6	2	—
	100	71	2.71	1.61	1.00	1.62	2236	—	2346	54.1	50	35	6	2	—
Peanut meal	92	71	2.74	1.65	1.08	1.63	2694	2.99	3031	48.1		25	14	7	0.22
	100	77	2.98	1.79	1.17	1.77	2928	3.25	3295	52.3	25	27	15	8	0.24
Skim milk, dried	94	80	3.14	1.91	1.29	1.84	2534	3.81	3550	33.7		0	0	0	0.01
	100	85	3.34	2.03	1.37	1.96	2696	4.05	3777	35.8	—	0	0	0	0.01
Soybean meal, 49%	90	78	3.08	1.89	1.28	1.81	2457	3.36	3157	49.7		—	—	3	0.35
	100	87	3.42	2.09	1.42	2.01	2724	3.37	3500	55.1	35	—	—	4	0.39
Soybeans, whole	92	84	3.31	2.04	1.40	1.94	3380	—	3593	39.4		9	6	3	7.97
	100	91	3.60	2.22	1.52	2.11	3674	—	3905	42.8	26	10	6	3	8.66
Sunflower meal	93	60	2.28	1.34	0.76	1.37	2085	2.60	2651	46.3		37	20	11	1.48
	100	65	2.45	1.44	0.82	1.47	2242	2.80	2851	49.8	26	40	21	12	1.59
Urea	99	0	0.00	0.00	0.00	0.00	0	0.00	0	278.2		0	0	0	0.00
	100	0	0.00	0.00	0.00	0.00	0	0.00	0	281.0	0	0	0	0	0.00
Yeast, brewers dried	93	73	2.86	1.72	1.13	1.69	2045	3.07	2863	43.6		—	—	3	0.05
	100	79	3.07	1.85	1.22	1.82	2199	3.30	3078	46.9	42	—	—	3	0.05

[a] Adapted from Table 1 in *United States–Canadian Tables of Feed Composition,* 3rd edition, National Academy Press, Washington, D.C. (1982). TDN, Total digestible nutrients; ME, metabolizable energy; NEM, net energy maintenance; NEG, net energy gain; NEL, net energy gain; MEN, metabolizable energy corrected for nitrogen; DE, digestible energy; Mcal, mega calories; Kcal, kilo calories; Kg, kilograms; CP, crude protein.

TABLE IV

Typical Composition of Important Livestock Feeds: Minerals[a]

Feed name/description	Dry matter (%)	Calcium (%)	Chlorine (%)	Magnesium (%)	Phosphorus (%)	Potassium (%)	Sodium (%)	Sulfur (%)	Cobalt (mg/kg)	Copper (mg/kg)	Iodine (mg/kg)	Iron (mg/kg)	Manganese (mg/kg)	Selenium (mg/kg)	Zinc (mg/kg)
Pasture or range forages															
Bermudagrass	100	0.53	—	0.17	0.21	1.70	—	—	—	6	—	—	—	—	—
Bluegrass, early bloom	100	0.33	0.40	0.17	0.34	1.98	0.16	0.29	0.08	14	—	255	55	0.54	25
Brome grass, immature	100	0.50	—	0.18	0.30	2.30	0.02	0.20	0.14	9	—	200	—	—	—
Clover, red, early vegetative	100	1.64	0.77	—	0.36	2.44	0.20	0.27	—	—	—	300	104	0.31	22
Fescue, vegetative	100	0.51	—	—	0.37	—	—	—	—	—	—	—	—	—	—
Orchardgrass, mid bloom	100	0.37	—	0.29	0.39	3.33	0.04	0.26	—	24	—	470	—	—	—
Rye pasture	100	0.39	—	0.31	0.33	3.40	0.07	—	—	—	—	—	—	—	—
Ryegrass pasture	100	0.65	—	0.35	0.41	2.00	0.01	0.10	—	—	—	650	—	—	—
Wheatgrass, full bloom	100	0.39	—	—	0.28	2.00	—	—	—	—	—	—	—	—	—
Dry forages															
Alfalfa hay, early bloom	100	1.41	0.38	0.33	0.22	2.52	0.14	0.28	0.16	11	—	192	31	0.54	25
Alfalfa hay, full bloom	100	1.25	—	0.31	0.22	1.53	0.11	0.27	0.33	14	—	150	37	—	25
Alfalfa meal, dehydrated	100	1.74	0.51	0.36	0.30	2.73	0.14	0.29	0.28	12	0.15	415	39	0.31	22
Barley straw	100	0.30	0.67	0.23	0.07	2.37	0.14	0.17	0.07	5	—	201	17	—	7
Bermudagrass hay, immature	100	0.47	—	0.21	0.27	1.50	0.08	0.21	0.12	—	0.12	290	—	—	11
Bermudagrass hay, mature	100	0.26	—	0.13	0.18	1.30	—	—	—	—	—	—	—	—	—
Corn stover	100	0.57	—	0.40	0.10	1.45	0.07	0.17	—	5	—	210	136	—	22
Cottonseed hulls	100	0.15	0.02	0.14	0.09	0.87	0.02	0.09	0.02	13	—	131	119	—	—
Fescue hay, full bloom	100	0.30	—	0.19	0.26	1.70	—	0.23	—	—	—	—	—	—	—
Oat straw	100	0.24	0.78	0.18	0.06	2.57	0.42	0.26	0.46	10	—	175	37	—	6
Orchardgrass hay, early bloom	100	0.39	0.41	0.17	0.35	3.36	0.05	—	—	13	—	99	120	—	26
Pangola grass hay, immature	100	0.46	—	0.15	0.23	1.40	—	—	—	—	—	—	—	—	—
Sorghum stover	100	0.52	—	0.28	0.13	1.20	0.02	—	—	—	—	—	—	—	—
Wheat straw	100	0.18	0.32	0.12	0.05	1.42	0.14	0.29	0.05	4	—	157	41	—	6
Wheatgrass, crested	100	0.33	—	0.16	0.21	2.00	—	—	0.24	16	—	178	36	0.40	32
Silages															
Corn silage, few ears	100	0.34	—	0.23	0.19	1.41	—	0.08	—	—	—	—	—	—	—
Corn silage, well eared	100	0.23	—	0.19	0.22	0.96	0.01	0.15	0.06	10	—	260	30	—	21
Sorghum silage, dough stage	100	0.35	0.13	0.29	0.21	1.37	0.02	0.11	0.35	35	—	285	73	—	32
Energy feeds															
Barley	88	0.04	0.16	0.13	0.33	0.41	0.03	0.15	0.09	8	0.04	75	16	0.19	17
	100	0.05	0.18	0.15	0.38	0.47	0.03	0.17	0.10	9	0.05	85	18	0.22	19
Corn, shelled	89	0.03	0.04	0.12	0.26	0.33	0.03	0.11	0.04	4	0.00	27	4	0.07	12
	100	0.03	0.05	0.14	0.29	0.37	0.03	0.12	0.05	4	—	30	5	0.08	14
Corn, high lysine	90	0.04	0.05	0.13	0.20	0.35	—	0.10	—	—	—	—	—	—	—
	100	0.04	—	0.14	0.22	0.39	—	0.11	—	—	—	—	—	—	—
Corn and cob meal	87	0.06	0.04	0.12	0.23	0.46	0.02	0.14	0.27	7	0.03	79	12	0.08	12
	100	0.07	0.05	0.14	0.27	0.53	0.02	0.16	0.31	8	0.03	91	14	0.09	14
Hominy	90	0.05	0.05	0.23	0.51	0.59	0.08	0.03	0.05	14	—	68	14	0.10	3
	100	0.05	0.06	0.26	0.57	0.65	0.09	0.03	0.06	15	—	75	16	0.11	3
Sorghum grain	90	0.04	0.09	0.16	0.30	0.35	0.03	0.14	0.16	10	0.04	46	16	0.45	17
	100	0.04	0.10	0.18	0.33	0.39	0.03	0.15	0.18	11	0.04	51	18	0.5	19
Molasses, sugarcane, blackstrap	75	0.75	2.33	0.32	0.08	2.88	0.17	0.35	0.91	59	1.58	188	42	—	23
	100	1.00	3.10	0.43	0.11	3.84	0.22	0.47	1.21	79	2.1	250	56	—	30

Feed	%														
Oat grain	89	0.06	0.10	0.12	0.34	0.39	0.07	0.20	0.05	6	0.10	76	37	0.23	36
	100	0.07	0.11	0.14	0.38	0.44	0.08	0.23	0.06	7	0.11	85	42	0.26	41
Rice grain	89	0.06	0.08	0.13	0.28	0.32	0.05	0.04	0.04	3	0.04	51	18	—	15
	100	0.07	0.09	0.15	0.32	0.36	0.06	0.04	0.04	3	0.05	57	20	—	17
Rye grain	88	0.06	0.03	0.12	0.33	0.46	0.03	0.05	0.05	7	0.05	57	58	0.35	32
	100	0.07	0.03	0.14	0.37	0.52	0.03	0.15	0.05	8	—	61	66	0.4	36
Triticale	90	0.05	—	—	0.30	0.36	—	0.17	—	—	—	—	—	—	—
	100	0.06	—	—	0.33	0.40	—	0.17	—	—	—	—	—	—	—
Wheat grain	89	0.04	0.07	0.14	0.37	0.37	0.04	0.16	0.12	6	0.09	54	37	0.27	45
	100	0.04	0.08	0.16	0.42	0.42	0.05	0.16	0.14	7	0.1	61	42	0.3	50
Wheat middlings	90	0.12	0.36	0.36	0.89	1.02	0.17	0.18	0.20	20	0.11	84	113	0.75	104
	100	0.13	0.40	0.40	0.99	1.13	0.19	0.20	0.10	22	0.12	93	126	0.83	116
Whey, dried	93	0.86	0.07	0.13	0.76	1.14	0.65	1.04	0.75	47	—	168	6	—	3
	100	0.92	0.08	0.14	0.82	1.23	0.70	1.12	0.82	50	—	181	6	—	3
Protein feeds															
Blood meal, dried	92	0.29	0.25	0.21	0.23	0.10	0.29	0.45	0.09	6	0.02	2340	10	—	16
	100	0.32	0.27	0.23	0.25	0.11	0.32	0.49	0.10	7	0.02	2543	11	—	17
Brewers grains, dried	92	0.30	0.16	0.15	0.51	0.08	0.32	0.29	0.07	21	0.06	245	37	—	28
	100	0.33	0.17	0.16	0.55	0.09	0.32	0.32	0.08	23	0.07	266	40	—	30
Canola meal	90	0.65	—	—	1.06	1.17	0.03	0.25	0.07	—	—	—	—	0.70	63
	100	0.72	—	—	1.18	1.30	0.03	0.28	0.08	—	—	—	—	0.76	70
Corn gluten feed	90	0.32	0.23	0.32	0.74	0.58	0.95	0.21	0.09	47	0.06	424	23	—	65
	100	0.36	0.25	0.36	0.82	0.64	1.05	0.23	0.10	52	0.07	471	26	—	72
Corn gluten meal	91	0.15	0.06	0.05	0.46	0.03	0.10	0.23	0.07	27	—	385	7	0.27	173
	100	0.16	0.07	0.06	0.50	0.03	0.10	0.25	0.08	30	—	423	8	0.3	190
Cottonseed meal	91	0.20	0.04	0.50	1.10	1.26	0.04	0.35	0.08	18	—	203	21	1.01	63
	100	0.22	0.04	0.55	1.21	1.39	0.04	0.39	0.08	20	—	223	23	1.11	69
Cottonseed, whole	92	0.15	—	0.32	0.69	1.11	0.04	0.31	0.75	50	—	139	9	—	34
	100	0.16	—	0.35	0.75	1.21	0.04	0.34	0.82	54	—	151	10	—	37
Distillers grains and solubles	92	0.14	0.17	0.17	0.65	0.40	0.52	0.30	0.17	53	—	239	23	0.39	83
	100	0.15	0.18	0.18	0.71	0.44	0.57	0.33	0.18	58	—	259	25	0.42	90
Feather meal, hydrolyzed	93	0.26	0.28	0.20	0.67	0.29	0.71	1.50	0.05	7	0.05	75	13	0.84	69
	100	0.28	0.30	0.22	0.72	0.31	0.76	1.61	0.05	7	0.05	81	14	0.9	74
Fish meal, menhaden	92	5.20	0.55	0.15	2.91	0.70	0.40	0.45	0.16	11	1.09	482	34	2.21	149
	100	5.65	0.60	0.16	3.16	0.76	0.43	0.49	0.17	12	1.19	524	37	2.4	162
Linseed meal	91	0.39	0.04	0.60	0.81	1.39	0.14	0.39	0.19	26	—	322	38	0.83	55
	100	0.43	0.04	0.66	0.89	1.53	0.15	0.43	0.21	29	—	354	42	0.91	60
Meat and bone meal	93	10.29	0.74	1.01	5.10	1.43	0.72	0.25	0.18	2	1.31	684	13	0.26	89
	100	11.06	0.80	1.09	5.48	1.55	0.77	0.27	0.19	2	1.41	735	14	0.28	96
Peanut meal	92	0.27	0.03	0.16	0.63	1.13	0.07	0.30	0.11	16	0.06	142	27	—	20
	100	0.29	0.03	0.17	0.68	1.23	0.08	0.33	0.12	17	0.07	154	29	—	22
Skim milk, dried	94	1.28	0.90	0.12	1.02	1.60	0.46	0.32	0.11	1	—	1	2	0.12	39
	100	1.36	0.96	0.13	1.09	1.70	0.49	0.34	0.12	1	—	1	2	0.13	41
Soybean meal, 49%	92	0.27	0.05	0.29	0.64	2.12	0.03	0.44	—	20	0.11	136	38	0.10	56
	100	0.29	0.05	0.32	0.70	2.30	0.03	0.48	—	22	0.12	148	41	0.11	61
Soybeans, whole	92	0.25	0.03	0.27	0.60	1.67	0.02	0.22	0.31	18	—	84	36	0.11	57
	100	0.27	0.03	0.29	0.65	1.82	0.02	0.24	0.33	20	—	91	39	0.12	62
Sunflower meal	93	0.41	0.10	0.72	0.91	1.06	0.22	—	—	4	—	31	19	—	47
	100	0.44	0.11	0.77	0.98	1.14	0.24	—	—	4	—	33	20	—	50
Yeast, brewers dried	93	0.12	0.07	0.25	1.39	1.66	0.07	0.42	0.19	33	0.35	109	6	0.91	38
	100	0.13	0.08	0.27	1.49	1.79	0.08	0.45	0.20	35	0.38	117	6	0.98	41

[a] Adapted from Table 2 in *United States–Canadian Tables of Feed Composition*, 3rd edition, National Academy Press, Washington, D.C. (1982).

TABLE V

Typical Composition of Important Livestock Feeds: Vitamins[a]

Feed name/description	Dry matter (%)	Fat-soluble vitamins				Water-soluble vitamins										
		Carotene (mg/kg)	A (IU/g)	D2 (IU/g)	E (mg/kg)	K (mg/kg)	Biotin (mg/kg)	Choline (mg/kg)	Folic acid (mg/kg)	Niacin (mg/kg)	Pantothenic acid (mg/kg)	Riboflavin (mg/kg)	Thiamine (mg/kg)	Vitamin B6 (mg/kg)	Vitamin B12 (µg/kg)
Pasture or range forages															
Bermudagrass	100	310	—	—	—	—	—	—	—	—	—	11.0	8.8	—	—
Bluegrass, early bloom	100	248	—	—	—	—	—	—	—	66	—	7.7	3.1	—	—
Brome grass, immature	100	192	—	—	—	—	—	—	—	81	—	19.2	6.6	—	—
Clover, red, early vegetative	100	202	—	—	143	—	—	—	—	—	—	12.0	16.8	—	—
Fescue, vegetative	100	376	—	—	—	—	—	—	—	—	—	—	7.3	—	—
Orchardgrass, midbloom	100	302	—	—	436	—	—	—	—	—	—	—	—	—	—
Rye pasture	100	343	—	—	—	—	—	—	—	—	—	—	—	—	—
Ryegrass pasture	100	401	—	—	—	—	—	—	—	—	—	8.6	3.0	—	—
Wheatgrass, full bloom	100	213	—	—	—	—	—	2161	—	—	—	—	—	—	—
Dry forages															
Alfalfa hay, early bloom	100	140	—	1996	23	—	—	—	—	—	—	—	—	—	—
Alfalfa hay, full bloom	100	65	—	—	—	—	—	—	—	—	—	—	—	—	—
Alfalfa meal, dehydrated	100	174	—	—	165	15.5	0.39	1547	3.2	52	38.8	16.6	5.9	9.6	—
Barley straw	100	2	—	662	—	—	—	—	—	—	—	—	—	—	—
Corn stover	100	15	—	—	—	—	—	—	—	—	—	—	—	—	—
Fescue hay, full bloom	100	73	—	662	136	—	—	—	—	—	—	—	—	—	—
Oat straw	100	4	—	662	191	—	—	234	—	—	—	6.8	2.9	—	—
Orchardgrass hay, early bloom	100	22	—	—	—	—	—	—	—	—	—	—	—	—	—
Pangola grass hay, immature	100	62	—	—	—	—	—	—	—	—	—	—	—	—	—
Wheat straw	100	2	—	662	—	—	—	—	—	—	—	2.4	—	—	—
Silages															
Corn silage, well eared	100	45	—	119	—	—	—	—	—	—	—	—	—	—	—
Sorghum silage, dough stage	100	15	—	662	—	—	—	—	—	—	—	—	—	—	—
Energy feeds															
Barley	88	2	—	—	22	0.2	0.15	1036	0.5	83	8.0	1.6	4.4	6.4	—
	100	2	—	—	25	0.2	0.17	1177	0.6	94	9.1	1.8	5.0	7.3	—
Corn, shelled	89	3	—	—	22	0.2	0.07	505	0.3	25	5.9	1.2	3.4	4.7	—
	100	3	—	—	25	0.2	0.08	567	0.3	28	6.6	1.4	3.8	5.3	—
Corn, high lysine	90	—	5	—	—	—	—	518	—	20	4.7	1.1	—	—	—
	100	—	5	—	—	—	—	575	—	22	5.2	1.2	—	—	—
Corn and cob meal	87	3	—	—	17	—	0.03	358	0.3	17	4.2	0.9	2.9	6.0	—
	100	4	—	—	20	—	0.04	412	0.3	20	4.8	1.0	3.3	6.9	—
Hominy	90	9	—	—	—	—	0.14	1152	0.3	47	8.2	2.1	8.0	10.9	—
	100	10	—	—	—	—	0.15	1280	0.3	52	9.1	2.3	8.9	12.1	—
Molasses, sugarcane blackstrap	75	—	—	—	5	—	0.69	759	0.1	37	37.7	2.9	0.9	4.3	—
	100	—	—	—	7	—	0.92	1012	0.1	49	50.3	3.8	1.2	5.7	—
Oat grain	89	—	—	—	13	—	0.28	993	0.4	14	7.8	1.5	6.3	2.5	—
	100	—	—	—	15	—	0.31	1116	0.4	16	8.8	1.7	7.1	2.8	—

Feed														
Rice grain	—	—	—	10	—	0.08	958	0.4	35	8.1	1.1	2.8	4.5	—
	—	—	—	11	—	0.09	1076	0.4	39	9.1	1.2	3.2	5.0	—
Rye grain	—	—	—	15	—	0.05	422	0.6	18	8.0	1.7	3.7	2.6	—
	—	—	—	17	—	0.06	479	0.7	21	9.1	1.9	4.2	2.9	—
Sorghum grain	1	26	—	—	—	0.38	663	0.2	39	11.3	1.3	4.2	4.5	—
	1	29	—	—	—	0.42	737	0.2	43	12.5	1.4	4.7	5.0	—
Triticale	—	—	—	—	0.2	—	473	—	—	—	0.5	—	—	—
	—	—	—	—	0.2	—	514	—	—	—	0.5	—	—	—
Wheat grain	—	—	—	15	—	0.10	966	0.4	57	10.1	1.4	4.3	5.0	0.9
	—	—	—	17	—	0.11	1085	0.5	64	11.4	1.6	4.8	5.6	1.0
Wheat middlings	—	—	—	—	—	0.31	1006	1.1	116	13.7	2.2	15.3	11.0	—
	—	—	—	—	—	0.34	1118	1.2	129	15.2	2.4	17.0	12.2	—
Whey, dried	—	—	0	—	—	0.35	1787	0.8	—	46.1	27.3	4.0	3.3	18.6
	—	—	1	—	—	0.38	1921	0.9	—	49.6	29.4	4.3	3.6	20.0
Protein feeds														
Blood meal, dried	—	—	—	—	—	0.08	786	0.1	31	2.4	2.0	0.4	4.4	4.5
	—	—	—	—	—	0.09	854	0.1	34	2.6	2.2	0.4	4.8	4.9
Brewers grains, dried	—	—	—	27	—	0.63	1616	7.1	43	8.2	1.5	0.6	0.7	—
	—	—	—	29	—	0.68	1757	7.7	47	8.9	1.6	0.7	0.8	—
Corn gluten feed	6	—	—	13	—	0.32	1516	0.3	71	13.6	2.0	2.0	13.3	—
	7	—	—	14	—	0.36	1684	0.3	79	15.1	2.2	2.2	14.8	—
Corn gluten meal	16	—	—	31	—	0.18	352	0.3	50	10.1	0.2	1.6	7.9	—
	18	—	—	34	—	0.20	391	0.3	55	11.2	0.2	1.8	8.8	—
Cottonseed meal	—	—	—	15	—	0.96	2781	1.4	41	13.7	4.7	6.6	5.6	—
	—	—	—	17	—	1.06	3056	1.5	45	15.0	5.2	7.3	6.2	—
Distillers grains and solubles	3	552	—	40	—	0.78	2579	0.9	73	14.1	9.2	2.9	5.0	—
	3	600	—	43	—	0.85	2803	1.0	79	15.3	10.0	3.1	5.4	—
Feather meal, hydrolyzed	—	—	—	—	—	0.05	895	0.2	21	9.0	2.0	0.1	3.0	83.7
	—	—	—	—	—	0.05	962	0.2	23	9.7	2.1	0.1	3.2	90.0
Fish meal, menhaden	—	—	—	12	—	0.18	3126	0.2	55	8.6	4.8	0.6	4.7	122.4
	—	—	—	13	—	0.20	3398	0.2	60	9.4	5.2	0.6	5.1	133.0
Linseed meal	—	—	—	14	—	—	1390	1.3	33	14.7	2.9	7.6	—	—
	—	—	—	15	—	—	1544	1.4	37	16.3	3.2	8.4	—	—
Meat and bone meal	—	—	—	1	—	0.10	2042	0.4	49	4.1	4.6	0.2	8.7	107.9
	—	—	—	1	—	0.11	2196	0.4	53	4.4	4.9	0.2	9.4	116.0
Peanut meal	—	—	—	—	—	0.33	1950	0.6	173	46.6	9.0	5.7	6.3	—
	—	—	—	—	—	0.36	2120	0.7	188	50.7	9.8	6.2	6.9	—
Skim milk, dried	—	419	—	9	—	0.33	1391	0.7	11	36.3	19.3	3.7	4.2	50.8
	—	446	—	10	—	0.35	1480	0.7	12	38.6	20.5	3.9	4.5	54.0
Soybean meal, 49%	—	—	—	3	—	0.32	2749	0.7	22	14.8	2.9	3.1	5.0	—
	—	—	—	3	—	0.36	3054	0.8	24	16.4	3.2	3.4	5.5	—
Soybeans, whole	1	—	—	33	—	0.33	2645	3.5	22	15.6	2.8	9.5	—	—
	1	—	—	37	—	0.37	2939	3.9	24	17.3	3.1	10.6	—	—
Sunflower meal	—	—	—	11	—	—	4120	—	268	40.8	3.9	3.2	13.8	—
	—	—	—	12	—	—	4430	—	288	43.9	4.2	3.4	14.8	—
Yeast brewers dried	—	—	—	2	—	1.00	3931	9.6	448	110.1	35.4	92.3	37.0	0.9
	—	—	—	2	—	1.08	4227	10.3	482	118.4	38.1	99.2	39.8	1.0

[a] Adapted from Table 3 in *United States–Canadian Tables of Feed Composition*, 3rd edition, National Academy Press, Washington, D.C. (1982).

TABLE VI

Typical Composition of Important Livestock Feeds: Amino Acids[a]

Feed name/description	Dry matter (%)	Arginine (%)	Glycine (%)	Histidine (%)	Iso-leucine (%)	Leu-cine (%)	Lysine (%)	Methionine (%)	Cystine (%)	Phenyl alanine (%)	Tyrosine (%)	Serine (%)	Threonine (%)	Tryptophan (%)	Valine (%)
Dry forages															
Alfalfa hay, early bloom	90	0.73	0.68	0.34	0.60	1.07	0.81	0.19	0.31	0.71	0.48	0.65	0.60	—	0.79
Alfalfa hay, full bloom	90	0.67	0.69	0.32	0.61	1.05	0.78	0.20	—	0.68	0.46	0.64	0.55	—	0.77
Alfalfa meal, dehydrated	92	0.96	0.98	0.37	0.89	1.41	0.90	0.32	0.32	0.94	0.62	0.86	0.81	0.41	1.04
Energy feeds															
Barley	88	0.51	0.38	0.24	0.45	0.75	0.39	0.15	0.21	0.58	0.34	0.43	0.37	0.15	0.57
Corn, shelled	89	0.43	0.37	0.26	0.35	1.21	0.25	0.17	0.22	0.48	0.38	0.50	0.35	0.08	0.44
Corn, high lysine	90	0.66	0.48	0.35	0.35	0.99	0.42	0.17	0.20	0.43	0.40	0.47	0.37	0.11	0.50
Hominy	90	0.47	0.34	0.19	0.39	0.85	0.38	0.16	0.15	0.33	0.50	0.20	0.39	0.11	0.49
Oat grain	89	0.70	0.46	0.18	0.43	0.81	0.39	0.17	0.19	0.52	0.46	0.44	0.36	0.15	0.56
Rice grain	89	0.57	0.55	0.14	0.31	0.56	0.27	0.16	0.12	0.33	0.54	0.45	0.24	0.11	0.44
Rye grain	88	0.53	0.49	0.26	0.47	0.70	0.42	0.17	0.19	0.56	0.26	0.52	0.36	0.11	0.56
Sorghum grain	90	0.39	0.34	0.23	0.45	1.44	0.25	0.13	0.20	0.56	0.41	0.50	0.36	0.11	0.52
Triticale	90	0.86	0.70	0.40	0.61	1.18	0.52	0.21	0.29	0.80	0.51	0.76	0.57	0.18	0.84
Wheat grain	89	0.59	0.57	0.29	0.47	0.87	0.37	0.18	0.28	0.61	0.38	0.58	0.38	0.15	0.57
Wheat middlings	89	0.92	0.51	0.38	0.67	1.08	0.67	0.18	0.22	0.64	0.40	0.73	0.54	0.20	0.75
Whey, dried	93	0.34	0.49	0.17	0.79	1.18	0.94	0.19	0.30	0.35	0.25	0.47	0.90	0.18	0.68
Protein feeds															
Blood meal, dried	92	3.34	4.23	4.57	0.88	11.48	7.56	0.95	1.20	6.41	2.32	5.46	4.07	1.06	8.03
Brewers grains, dried	92	1.27	1.08	0.52	1.54	2.49	0.88	0.46	0.35	1.44	1.20	1.30	0.93	0.37	1.61
Corn gluten feed	90	0.78	0.85	0.61	0.88	2.20	0.64	0.37	0.44	0.81	0.72	0.85	0.78	0.15	1.10
Corn gluten meal	90	2.08	2.10	1.40	2.54	10.23	1.01	1.78	0.99	4.02	3.19	3.35	2.22	0.30	3.09
Cottonseed meal	91	4.21	1.98	1.11	1.52	2.33	1.69	0.59	0.77	2.24	1.03	1.75	1.38	0.56	1.88
Distillers grains and solubles	92	0.96	0.51	0.64	1.39	2.23	0.70	0.50	0.29	1.51	0.70	1.30	0.93	0.17	1.50
Feather meal, hydrolyzed	93	7.05	6.44	0.99	4.06	6.94	2.32	0.55	3.24	3.05	2.32	9.26	3.97	0.52	6.48
Fish meal, menhaden	92	3.75	4.19	1.45	2.88	4.48	4.74	1.75	0.56	2.46	1.94	2.23	2.50	0.65	3.22
Linseed meal	90	2.94	1.74	0.69	1.68	2.02	1.16	0.54	0.61	1.46	1.09	1.92	1.72	0.51	1.74
Meat and bone meal	93	3.49	6.45	0.96	1.64	3.06	2.90	0.65	0.50	1.70	0.79	1.81	1.65	0.30	2.45
Peanut meal	92	4.55	2.35	0.95	1.76	2.70	1.77	0.42	0.73	2.04	1.51	3.10	1.16	0.48	1.88
Skim milk, dried	94	1.15	0.29	0.86	2.18	3.32	2.53	0.90	0.45	1.56	1.14	1.67	1.52	0.43	2.28
Soybean meal, 49%	90	3.67	2.42	1.22	2.46	3.73	3.11	0.71	0.75	2.44	1.68	2.89	1.94	0.69	2.55
Soybeans, whole	92	2.85	1.52	0.97	2.12	3.00	2.44	0.54	0.55	2.03	1.02	2.14	1.66	0.54	2.06
Sunflower meal	93	4.42	2.82	1.23	2.25	3.83	1.92	1.16	0.74	2.36	1.39	2.20	1.93	0.61	2.60
Yeast, brewers dried	93	2.20	1.75	1.09	2.21	3.23	3.11	0.74	0.49	1.83	1.50	2.30	2.12	0.52	2.36

[a] Adapted from Table 4 in *United States–Canadian Tables of Feed Composition*, 3rd edition, National Academy Press, Washington, D.C. (1982).

and other ruminant animals often contain feeds with a wide range in dry matter concentration (silages have low dry matter) and their requirements are usually expressed as concentration in the dry matter. The nutrient concentrations in Tables III, IV, V, and VI are listed as the concentration in the dry matter for all feeds (used in formulating ruminant diets) and the air-dry concentration for feeds (concentrates) typically used in monogastric diets. The nutrient requirements of the horse may be expressed as the concentration in air-dry feed or dry matter depending on the reference source.

The nutrient concentrations in feeds vary depending on variety, climate, soil, storage, and maturity. The variation in nutrient concentration is larger in forages than in concentrates. Feeds should be analyzed for nutrient concentration when possible, but feed composition tables can be used as a guideline when analyses are not available.

The energy values used in formulating diets are different for each species. Swine and poultry nutritionists typically use the metabolizable energy (ME) concentration of feeds to formulate diets but the ME concentration of a feed will be different for each species. Differences in the digestive systems and experimental procedures used to determine requirements result in different ME concentrations for a feed. For dairy and beef cattle, typically the net energy content of feeds is used to formulate diets. There is less research data on net energy concentrations of feeds for sheep and goats, and typically the total digestible nutrients (TDN) or ME concentration of feeds are used in their diet formulation.

An important factor related to nutrient concentration of forages is the maturity, which is often included in the feed description used in tables. For instance, the nutrient concentration of alfalfa hay harvested at early bloom is higher in energy, crude protein, minerals, and vitamins than alfalfa hay harvested at full bloom (Tables III, IV, and V). The description of forages often includes the maturity, bloom, or days since last cutting. Corn and sorghum silages often include the maturity of the grain such as dough, or the proportion of grain in the feed, because this is related to the nutrient concentrations. Grains may include the test weight and the variety to provide additional information on nutrient concentration.

Forages vary widely in nutrient concentration. Laboratory analysis of each different field of hay or silage harvested under similar conditions is conducted routinely on many farms. A sample from 15 to 20 locations in several different bales or areas of the silo should be taken, and a representative sample sent to a feed analysis laboratory. A typical analysis would include dry matter, crude protein, fiber, and perhaps calcium, phosphorus, and other minerals. The fiber analysis is used to estimate the digestible energy (DE), metabolizable energy, or net energy (NE) in the forage. The proximate analysis system, developed in the nineteenth century, provided a chemical analysis system for describing feeds (Fig. 2). Crude fiber concentration in forages is used for estimating TDN. The Van Soest feed analysis system was developed in recent years and measures the cell wall portion of plants using the neutral detergent fiber procedure and the lignin–cellulose portion of the cell wall with the acid detergent fiber procedure. The Van Soest feed analysis system compared to proximate analysis has provided better estimates of the available energy in forages. Many analytical laboratories use the acid detergent fiber and crude protein concentrations in prediction equations to estimate the TDN, ME, and NE values for the forage analyzed. The equations to estimate energy are usually different for different types of forages.

The analytical procedures for dry matter, crude protein, fiber, and minerals require specialized laboratory equipment, facilities, and considerable labor to complete. This typically requires a week or longer to complete with a cost of $25 to $50 per sample. The high cost and time required for analysis led to the development of a near-infrared (NIR) feed analysis system. The NIR system requires that the forage be dried and finely ground. This technology utilizes the reflectance properties of chemical bonds in the feed to specified wavelengths of infrared light. Absorbance of the infrared light is quantitatively related to the chemical composition and biological availability of the forage. NIR feed analysis has proven to be accurate when properly calibrated with a diverse set of feeds that have been analyzed in the laboratory, and can significantly reduce the time and cost of analysis. NIR is routinely used when large numbers of similar samples such as alfalfa hay or corn silage need to be analyzed. Some laboratories have NIR equipment in a van that travels to local communities and provides analytical results the same day. Feed companies also utilize NIR analysis to routinely analyze feed ingredients and mixed feeds as part of their quality control programs.

IV. Nutrient Requirements

Nutrient requirements of livestock and poultry are established for each species at different sexes, weights,

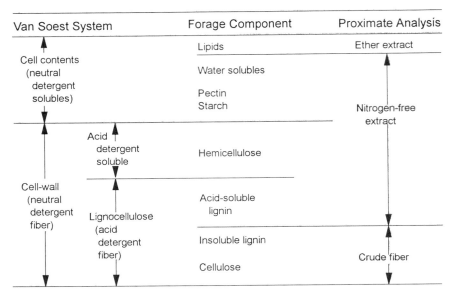

FIGURE 2 Forage analysis by proximate analysis and the Van Soest system.

and levels of production. These requirements are periodically reviewed, updated, and published by boards appointed by the National Academy of Sciences in the United States.

A listing of nutrient requirements in each species can be found in the bibliography. As young growing animals gain weight and get closer to physiological maturity, they deposit relatively less mineral and protein and more fat. This results in lower concentrations of protein, minerals, and vitamins required in the diet. The opposite trend occurs when an animal is lactating. As the relative milk production increases, the daily requirement and the dietary concentrations of protein, minerals, and vitamins increase. For accurate estimates of animal nutrient requirements it is important to know the species, sex, weight, and level of production.

V. Nutrient Availability

Although the nutrients may be present in feeds, their availability to the animal varies widely.

A. Energy

The energy available to the animal is well quantitated for many different feeds and estimating available energy is an important reason for feed analysis. The cell contents in plants (Fig. 2) contain sugars, starch, and much of the protein and these are readily digested by livestock and poultry. In contrast, the cell wall contains the structural carbohydrates (cellulose, hemicellulose, and lignin) not degraded by the animal's digestive enzymes, and these require bacterial enzymes for digestion and absorption. Plant cell walls are digested at slower rates than the cell contents and feeds with higher concentrations of cell wall tend to have a lower digestibility. The rate of cell wall digestion is important in determining the extent that it will be digested before passing out of the digestive tract and this rate varies across feeds. Within a feed, a higher concentration of acid or neutral detergent fiber usually results in a lower digestibility of the feed. This relationship is used to estimate available energy. However, the cell wall concentration alone across different feeds is not closely related to rate and extent of fiber digestion, therefore different equations are required for estimating metabolizable energy concentrations from the fiber concentrations for each feed.

B. Protein

Crude protein (total nitrogen) is easily measured in feeds, but part of this may be unavailable to the animal. During fermentation of silage the temperature of the silage may rise above 130° F, which can cause the protein to complex with the sugar, reducing its digestibility. This heat-damaged protein can be analyzed in silage by analyzing the acid detergent fiber nitrogen (ADF-N). Silages are routinely analyzed for ADF-N and the available crude protein is used in formulating diets for ruminant animals. By-product feeds such as blood and fish meals are dried during processing and high temperatures will reduce protein digestibility. ADF-N analysis can be used to determine if these feeds have heat-damaged protein.

Another example where protein availability varies is in feathers. Protein in feathers (80% protein) has a low digestibility, but steam hydrolysis improves the digestibility of this protein. Swine and poultry researchers have determined the availability of individual amino acids in different feedstuffs and will formulate rations for available amino acids when this information is available.

C. Minerals and Vitamins

Phosphorus in grains and by-product feeds is partially complexed in an organic form called phytate. Phytate phosphorus has a low digestibility in monogastric animals but has a higher digestibility in ruminant animals. Poultry and swine diets are usually formulated on the available organic phosphorus in the feeds and the requirements are listed as available phosphorus. Recent research has shown that a phytase enzyme added to poultry diets improves the availability of organically bound phosphorus and this may become a routine procedure in the future.

Minerals have different biological availabilities depending on their chemical form. For example, iron oxide has a low availability but iron sulfate has a high availability. The sulfate salts of most minerals have a high availability. Another factor affecting availability of minerals is the level of other minerals in the diet. One mineral may reduce the solubility or competitively inhibit absorption or utilization of another mineral. An example is copper, whose absorption and utilization are reduced by high levels of sulfur and molybdenum. This increases the required concentration of copper in the diet to meet the animal requirements. Vitamin bioavailability in feeds also depends on the chemical form. Carotene is converted to vitamin A with different efficiencies in different species.

Many factors influence nutrient availability and utilization. It is important to recognize the known relationships and formulate diets with higher nutrient concentrations above the recognized requirements when needed. These situations require an estimate of risk, cost of reduced performance from a deficiency, and added cost to determine the concentrations of nutrients in livestock diets.

VI. Diet Formulation

Diets fed to livestock and poultry are formulated by blending the needed amounts of different feeds to meet the nutrient requirements. Most nutrients have minimum requirements but moderate excesses are not usually detrimental to animal performance or health. Dietary levels of most vitamins and trace minerals can be included in the diet at 10 to 100 times the requirement without toxicities. This provides some flexibility using feeds that may have high levels of some nutrients.

A. Energy Density

Many diets are offered to livestock and poultry ad libitum and diet consumption is limited by natural regulatory processes. When the energy density of the ration is high (high ME concentration), the animal consumes the diet to meet their energy requirements and chemostatic feedbacks limit diet intake in most situations. However, when the energy density of the diet is low, the animal will eat to its physical capacity to consume and digest feed but this may be below their energy requirement for the desired level of production. Ruminant animals grazing low-quality forages often cannot consume enough of these forages to meet their requirements and they have lower weight gains or may lose weight. Moderate weight loss in mature animals is not detrimental if the body reserves are good, but when reserves are depleted, additional weight loss may be detrimental to the productivity and longevity of the animal.

Formulating a diet to meet animal requirements can be done by several methods. The first step is to determine the requirements of the animal, then determine the proportions of feeds and supplements that will meet these requirements at a low cost. The following examples will provide an example of the information needed and the approach to formulating the diet.

B. Trial and Error Method—Swine Diet

Step 1: Determine Animal Requirements. These can be found in reference books for each species by weight and level of production. The example in Table VII is for a 40-kg growing pig, which requires 3260 kcal/kg of ME, 15% crude protein, 0.75% lysine, 0.60% calcium, and 0.50% phosphorus in the

TABLE VII

Formulating a Swine Diet: Balancing Lysine, Phosphorus, and Calcium

Ingredient	Cost ($/100 lb)	% in diet	Concentration in air-dry feed				
			ME (kcal/kg)	Crude protein (%)	Lysine (%)	Calcium (%)	Phosphorus (%)
Corn	5.00	80.60	3420	8.8	0.25	0.03	0.26
Soybean meal, 49% CP	11.50	17.50	3157	49.7	3.11	0.27	0.64
Dicalcium phosphate	15.00	0.98	0	0.0	0.00	26.30	18.07
Limestone	4.50	0.72	0	0.0	0.00	38.00	0.00
Salt	5.00	0.00	0	0.0	0.00	0.00	0.00
Vitamin premix	50.00	0.00	0	0.0	0.00	0.00	0.00
Mineral premix	30.00	0.00	0	0.0	0.00	0.00	0.00
Diet composition	6.22	99.80	3309	15.8	0.75	0.60	0.50
Requirement in air-dry diet 40-kg pig			3260	15.0	0.75	0.60	0.50

air-dry diet. These requirements are concentrations in the diet from *Nutrient Requirements of Swine*.

Step 2: Select the Energy Feeds. The energy feed makes up a large portion of the diet and the cost of ME is a consideration. The lowest-cost energy feed can be determined by calculating the kilocalories of ME purchased for each dollar. If corn costs $2.80/bushel (56 lbs) and contains 3420 kcal ME/kg as fed (Table III), and wheat costs $3.50/bushel (60 lbs) and contains 3257 kcal ME/kg as fed, the lowest-cost source of ME is corn, where each dollar will purchase 31,091 kcal compared to wheat, where each dollar purchases only 25,386 kcal ME.

Corn: $2.80/bushel = $.05/lb (2.80/56)
= $.11/kg (.05*2.2)
$.11/kg with 3420 kcal ME/kg
= 31,091 kcal/$ (3420/.11)
Wheat: $3.50/bushel=$.0583/lb (3.50/60)
=$.1283/kg (.0583*2.2)
$.1283/kg with 3257 kcal ME/kg
=25,386 kcal/$ (3257/.1283)

Step 3: Select the Protein Feeds. Corn contains 8.8% crude protein (Table III) and 0.25% lysine (Table VI) as fed, which is below the requirements of 15% protein and 0.75% lysine for a 40-kg growing pig, therefore a feed high in protein is needed to increase the protein in the diet. Corn is known to be deficient in lysine, therefore a protein source high in lysine (percentage of total protein) may be a better value. Selecting the lowest-cost source of protein or lysine can be done as in the preceeding example. If soybean meal costs $11.50/100 lb and contains 49.7% crude protein (Table III) and 3.11% lysine (Table VI)

as fed, and fish meal costs $20.00/100 lb and contains 61.2% crude protein and 4.74% lysine as fed, then the lowest-cost source of lysine is soybean meal.

Soybean meal: $11.50/100 lb that contains
3.11 lb lysine (100*(3.11/100))
$1.00 buys 0.270 lb lysine (3.11/11.50)
Fish meal: $20.00/100 lb that contains
4.74 lb lysine (100*(4.74/100))
$1.00 buys 0.237 lb lysine (4.74/20)

Step 4: Balance Protein and Energy. Determine the amounts of corn and soybean meal needed to meet the protein and lysine requirements. The nutrient concentrations in corn and soybean meal can be found in Tables III, IV, V, and VI. The nutrient concentration of different mixtures can be determined using a calculator or putting the formulas into a microcomputer spreadsheet such as Lotus 123 or Quattro, which will calculate the answers as fast as they are entered and makes "trial and error" formulation easy. The protein and lysine requirements should be met with about 98% of the ration because the other 2% of the diet will be needed minerals and premixes that contain very little protein. The example in Table VII shows that a mixture of 80.6% corn and 17.5% soybean meal provided 0.75% lysine. A protein concentration of 15.8% was needed to meet the lysine requirement. In some situations other sources of protein higher in lysine may be more economical or lower levels of soybean meal could be used with synthetic lysine supplements added to meet the lysine requirement. The extra protein should not be detrimental to the animal. The energy concentration of the corn–soybean meal mixture is above the energy density requirement which should allow the pig to eat enough feed to meet its energy requirement (Table VII).

Step 5: Balance Phosphorus. Phosphorus is contained in natural feeds but most of the supplemental phosphorus in livestock diets is provided by one of five chemical sources manufactured for livestock feeds. The phosphorus concentrations in these sources range from 12 to 23%. Dicalcium phosphate (26.3% calcium and 18% phosphorus) was added at 0.98% of the diet to meet the 0.5% phosphorus requirement (Table VII).

Step 6: Balance Calcium. Ground limestone is often used to provide the extra calcium in the diet. It contains 38.0% calcium and negligible concentrations of other nutrients. Limestone was added at 0.72% of the diet to meet the 0.60% calcium requirement (Table VII).

Step 7: Add Other Ingredients and Adjust to 100%. Trace minerals, vitamins, and drugs are usually added to the diet from premixed packages that were formulated to provide the required levels for a particular species and grain-protein type such as corn–soybean meal for growing swine. Premixes eliminate the need for storing all the trace minerals and vitamins at each location, eliminate weighing out the small quantities, and facilitate a more uniform mixing of all nutrients in the diet. Salt added at 0.25% of the diet will meet the sodium and chlorine requirements. After adding the premixes (0.1% of diet) and salt the level of corn should be adjusted to make the total ingredients add to 100. In the swine diet the corn was adjusted to 80.25% and the soybean meal to 17.6% to make the total ingredients add to 100% and meet the nutrient requirements (Table VIII).

C. Trial and Error Method—Dairy Cow Diet

Step 1: Determine Animal Requirements. This example will formulate a diet for a 600-kg dairy cow producing 40 kg/day of 4% fat milk. The lactating cow requires 1.72 Mcal/kg of net energy of lactation (NEL), 17% crude protein with 5.9% of undegraded protein in the diet, 0.64% calcium and 0.41% phosphorus. These requirements are concentrations in the diet dry matter found in the *Nutrient Requirements for Dairy Cattle*.

Step 2: Select the Energy Feeds. Energy feeds used in this example include shelled corn, alfalfa hay, and corn silage and the composition of these feeds are listed in Tables III, IV, and V. Note that the requirements are concentration in the diet dry matter and the nutrient concentrations selected from the table for all feeds must be on a 100% dry matter basis. The nutrient concentrations in forages such as alfalfa and corn silage can vary considerably and a feed analysis is recommended to determine the composition of the forages available.

Step 3: Select the Protein Feeds. Feeds high in protein used in this example include soybean meal and urea. The undegraded protein and crude protein concentrations in all feedstuffs (Table III) are needed to formulate the diet to meet the requirements of the lactating cow.

Step 4: Balance Protein and Energy. In this example the alfalfa hay, corn silage, and urea have NEL concentrations below the NEL requirement and corn and soybean meal have NEL concentrations above the requirement (Table IX). Alfalfa, soybean meal, and urea have protein concentrations above the 17% required but only soybean meal has undegraded

TABLE VIII

Formulating a Swine Diet: Balancing Other Ingredients

			Concentration in air-dry feed				
Ingredient	Cost ($/100 lb)	% in diet	ME (kcal/kg)	Crude protein (%)	Lysine (%)	Calcium (%)	Phosphorus (%)
Corn	5.00	80.25	3420	8.8	0.25	0.03	0.26
Soybean meal, 49% CP	11.50	17.60	3157	49.7	3.11	0.27	0.64
Dicalcium phosphate	15.00	0.98	0	0.0	0.00	26.30	18.07
Limestone	4.50	0.72	0	0.0	0.00	38.00	0.00
Salt	5.00	0.25	0	0.0	0.00	0.00	0.00
Vitamin premix	50.00	0.10	0	0.0	0.00	0.00	0.00
Mineral premix	30.00	0.10	0	0.0	0.00	0.00	0.00
Diet composition	6.31	100.00	3300	15.8	0.75	0.60	0.50
Requirement in air-dry diet 40-kg pig			3260	15.0	0.75	0.60	0.50

TABLE IX

Formulating a Lactating Dairy Cow Diet to Meet Nutrient Requirements

Ingredient	Cost ($/100 lb as fed)	% in diet as fed	Dry matter (%)	Concentration in dry matter				
				NEL (mcal/kg)	Crude protein (%)	Undegraded protein (%)	Calcium (%)	Phosphorus (%)
Alfalfa hay, early bloom	5.50	15.00	85	1.35	18.0	3.6	1.41	0.22
Corn silage, well eared	1.40	45.45	33	1.60	8.1	2.5	0.23	0.22
Corn, shelled	5.00	29.40	88	1.96	10.0	5.2	0.03	0.29
Soybean meal	11.50	8.80	90	2.01	55.1	19.3	0.27	0.65
Urea	15.00	0.30	99	0.00	281.0	0.0	0.00	0.00
Dicalcium phosphate	15.00	0.39	97	0.00	0.0	0.0	26.30	18.07
Limestone	4.50	0.16	97	0.00	0.0	0.0	38.00	0.00
Salt	5.00	0.25	97	0.00	0.0	0.0	0.00	0.00
Mineral–vitamin premix	40.00	0.25	97	0.00	0.0	0.0	0.00	0.00
Diet cost or concentration								
As fed	4.17	100.00	62.9	1.08	11.3	3.7	0.40	0.26
Dry matter	6.63	—	100.0	1.72	18.0	5.9	0.64	0.41
Requirement in diet dry matter								
600-kg cow producing 40 kg/day of 4% fat milk				1.72	17.0	5.9	0.64	0.41

protein concentrations above the 5.9% required. The alfalfa hay was fixed at 15% of the diet and the corn silage, corn, soybean meal, and urea levels were changed by "trial and error" in the spreadsheet until the NEL, crude protein, and undegraded protein concentrations were met (Table IX). In this example, it required 15% alfalfa hay, 45.45% corn silage, 29.40% corn, 8.8% soybean meal, and 0.30% urea to meet the NEL, crude protein, and undegraded protein requirements. Other ingredient concentrations are possible that are above the required nutrient concentrations but these would increase the cost of the diet in this example.

Step 5: Balance Phosphorus. It required 0.39% dicalcium phosphate to meet the phosphorus requirements in this diet (Table IX).

Step 6: Balance Calcium. It required 0.16% limestone to meet the calcium requirements in this example (Table IX).

Step 7: Add Other Ingredients and Adjust to 100%. Salt and the mineral–vitamin premix were both added at 0.25% of the diet and the levels of corn, corn silage, and soybean meal adjusted slightly to meet all the nutrient requirements and make the ingredients total to 100% (Table IX). The diet contained 62.9% dry matter and the nutrient concentrations were calculated in the diet dry matter.

D. Least-Cost Feed Formulation

The diets formulated for a growing pig and a lactating cow balanced the requirements for five nutrients using a limited list of ingredients. Large livestock and poultry producers and commercial feed manufacturers purchase feed ingredients to formulate their diets. "Trial and error" calculation of diets when considering many feeds and nutrients is time-consuming and may not result in the lowest-cost diets. Least-cost diet formulation using many ingredients and balancing for several nutrients is possible using linear programming. Least-cost diet formulation was developed in the 1950s but required large computers and it was tedious and time-consuming to enter the information and interpret the results. Several least-cost diet programs are now available for microcomputers and are easy to use and interpret. The feed compositions and animal requirements are usually stored and can be easily retrieved to formulate a diet. It may require several minutes to select the feeds and set the nutrient constraints but the least-cost diet can be calculated in a few seconds.

A diet for a 700-lb feedlot steer gaining 2.7 lb/day was formulated from ingredients listed in Table X. The nutrient requirements for the diet were 0.97 Mcal/lb for net energy for maintenance, 12% crude protein, 0.57% calcium, and 0.35% phosphorus. Feed nutrient composition from the feed library in the computer program was used and the dry matter levels for the silage were adjusted to the concentrations in Table X. A premix supplement was added at 0.5% of the diet in this example. Many feeds and nutrients have minimum and maximum levels that must be considered when formulating the diet and limits of feeds in

TABLE X

Feed Prices and Limits in Least-Cost Diet for Finishing Steers

| Feed name | Feed prices ($/ton) | Limit in diet, % diet DM | |
		Minimum	Maximum
Corn grain, ground	115	—	100
Wheat, grain	110	—	50
Corn, hominy	110	—	50
Citrus pulp, dehydrated	110	—	50
Soybean hulls	87	—	—
Molasses, cane	83	4	7
Cottonseed, with lint	120	—	25
Wheat middlings	82	—	25
Brewers grains, dehydrated	120	—	—
Corn, distillers grains	150	—	—
Corn gluten feed	125	—	—
Cottonseed meal	153	—	—
Soybean meal	196	—	—
Urea, 45% nitrogen	260	—	1
Corn silage, well eared (32% DM)	22	—	—
Sorghum silage (25% DM)	17	—	—
Bermuda hay, mature	45	—	—
Bermuda hay, immature	60	—	—
Cottonseed hulls	55	—	—
Rice bran	75	—	—
Limestone	80	—	—
Dicalcium phosphate	300	—	—
Salt	80	0.5	0.5
Vitamin–mineral premix	400	0.5	0.5

this example are in Table X. Feeds in a diet may be limited for a variety of reasons, including palatability effects, toxicities, metabolic limits, physical characteristics limiting mixing and storage, moisture, and available supply. Nutrition references for each species give guidelines for ingredient and nutrient minimums and maximum levels for diets.

The least-cost steer diet included nine ingredients and cost $94.74/ton (Table XI). Both wheat and cottonseed were included at the maximum level. The feeds in the least-cost diet will change when feed prices change. The upper and lower critical price for each ingredient indicates the price range for this least-cost formula. For example, if corn silage price goes below $20.24/ton or above $22.54/ton the least-cost diet will change (Table XII). Wheat was in the diet at the maximum level allowed, therefore it does not have a lower critical price. Most least-cost diet formulation programs also give the opportunity price (the price at which these feeds will be used in the diet) for ingredients not included in the diet (Table XIII). The opportunity price considers all nutrients in each feed and provides valuable information in purchasing feeds. Many least-cost programs also calculate the nutrient concentration for nutrients that had minimum and/

or maximum limits and may also calculate the concentrations of other nutrients (Table XIV). These are useful to evaluate potential deficiencies or toxicities of other nutrients. Least-cost diet formulation is used daily by many livestock and poultry producers in feed purchasing decisions and diet reformulation. This tool helps many producers reduce production costs.

VII. Feed Processing

The nutritional value of many feeds can be improved by processing. Processing of feeds can include both physical changes, such as drying, grinding, and flaking, and chemical changes, such as deactivating trypsin inhibitor or treating forage with ammonia. Feed processing can result in nutritional changes, such as improved feed intake and digestibility, and improved handling characteristics, such as better mixing, storage, and bulk density.

Feed costs account for 50 to 70% of total production costs for many livestock and poultry production systems. Feed processing can often improve production efficiency 5 to 10% and occasionally improve production efficiency by 15 to 20%. Small improvements in

TABLE XI

Feeds in Least-Cost Diet for Finishing Steers

| Feed name | As fed basis | | Dry matter basis | | Limits in diet | |
	lb/day	%	lb/day	%	Minimum % DM	Maximum % DM
Wheat, grain	8.11	43.77	7.22	50.00	—	50.0
Cottonseed with lint	3.92	21.17	3.61	25.00	—	25.0
Corn silage, well eared	3.65	19.71	1.17	8.10	—	—
Corn grain, ground	1.59	8.59	1.40	9.70	—	—
Molasses, cane	0.77	4.16	0.58	4.00	4.0	7.0
Limestone	0.18	0.98	0.18	1.26	—	—
Soybean hulls	0.15	0.81	0.14	0.94	—	—
Vitamin–mineral premix	0.08	0.43	0.07	0.50	0.5	0.5
Salt	0.07	0.39	0.07	0.50	0.5	0.5
Total ration	18.52		14.44			
Cost ($/day)	0.88					
Cost ($/ton)	94.74		121.61			

feed utilization or handling costs can have a significant impact on profitability. A 10% improvement in feed efficiency for a feedlot steer finished from 650 to 1100 lb can save 300 lb of feed with a value of $18. Although part of the reduced feed cost may be spent for feed processing, feed processing can reduce the cost of production and is used widely in livestock and poultry production.

A. Concentrates

Most grains are processed prior to feeding to livestock and poultry. Processing grains usually improves feed efficiency and facilitates mixing and feeding grains with supplements containing protein, mineral, vitamins, and drugs. Grinding has been used extensively but other processing methods include pelleting, roll-ing, roasting, popping, extruding, reconstituting, steam flaking, cooking, and exploding. Each processing method has different effects depending on the grain and animal. Grain sorghum has a waxy coat that resists digestion and the seeds not broken during chewing may not be digested. Therefore, grain sorghum shows more response to processing than other grains. Steam-flaked and high-moisture grain sorghum has shown 10 to 15% better feed efficiency than dry ground grain sorghum in cattle finishing diets. In contrast, corn is often fed whole in feedlot finishing diets. Steam-flaking or roasting corn may

TABLE XII

Price Sensitivity of Feeds in Least-Cost Ration for Finishing Steers

Feed name	Current price ($/ton)	Lower critical price ($/ton)	Upper critical price ($/ton)
Wheat, grain	110.00	—	110.70
Cottonseed with lint	120.00	—	140.33
Corn silage, well eared	22.00	20.24	22.54
Corn grain, ground	115.00	114.26	115.20
Molasses, cane	83.00	57.55	—
Limestone	80.00	—	347.13
Soybean hulls	87.00	84.57	91.00
Vitamin–mineral premix	400.00	—	—
Salt	80.00	—	—

TABLE XIII

Price Sensitivity for Feeds Not Used in Least-Cost Diet for Finishing Steers

| Feed name | Price, as fed ($/ton) | |
	Current	Opportunity
Bermudagrass, immature	60.00	33.87
Bermudagrass, mature	45.00	9.57
Brewers grains, dehydrated	120.00	49.94
Dicalcium, phosphate	300.00	11.75
Citrus pulp, dehydrated	110.00	91.27
Corn distillers grains	150.00	115.69
Corn gluten feed	125.00	99.80
Corn, hominy	110.00	109.82
Cottonseed hulls	55.00	−19.30
Cottonseed meal	153.00	79.71
Rice bran	75.00	60.72
Sorghum silage	17.00	8.72
Soybean meal	196.00	100.83
Urea, 45% nitrogen	260.00	−111.23
Wheat middlings	82.00	55.73

TABLE XIV

Nutrient Composition of Least-Cost Diet for Finishing Steers (dry matter basis)

Nutrient	Nutrient concentration in diet	Nutrient level specified	
		Minimum level % DM	Maximum level % DM
Dry matter	77.90%	—	—
Net energy—maintenance	0.97 Mcal/lb	0.97	0.97
Net energy—gain	0.66 Mcal/lb	—	—
Crude protein	15.72%	12.0	—
Calcium	0.57%	0.57	2.0
Phosphorus	0.42%	0.35	1.0
Potassium	0.74%	—	—

improve feed efficiency 7 to 10% but the costs of processing limit its use. In swine, grinding corn usually improves feed efficiency 3 to 5% compared to feeding whole corn, but roasting and steam flaking do not improve feed efficiency.

Soybeans are usually processed to extract soybean oil and soybean meal is fed as a protein supplement in diets. In some situations the whole soybeans are fed to livestock but they need to be processed to destroy a trypsin inhibitor that reduces digestibility of protein in monogastric animals. Unprocessed soybeans also contain a urease enzyme that will hydrolyze urea to ammonia if soybeans and urea are mixed in the same diet. The trypsin inhibitor and urease enzyme are inactivated during oil extraction and can be inactivated by roasting or extruding soybeans prior to feeding.

B. Forages

As plants mature they have a lower digestibility. Mature forages and crop residues (straws and stovers) are usually low in quality and are used primarily to feed beef cattle and sheep during the winter. Many types of processing to improve the digestion rate and extent of low-quality forages have been researched. Treating forages with 3 to 5% sodium or calcium hydroxide improved the intake and digestion of low-quality forages but costs of grinding and environmental concerns (high levels of sodium) prevented adoption of this technology. Anhydrous ammonia treatment of forages has been used across the United States. Treating low-quality harvested forages with 3 to 4% anhydrous ammonia has improved forage digestibility 10 to 20%, increased forage consumption 5 to 40%, reduced wasted forage, and improved cattle performance. Anhydrous ammonia treatment can be done on the farm by covering bales with polyethylene

sheeting, releasing the ammonia under the plastic, and keeping the pile covered for 3 to 5 weeks before feeding. Ammonia treatment costs $10 to $15/ton, can be done with materials and equipment usually available, and is cost-effective in many situations.

VIII. Toxic Substances

Many types of toxic substances can be found in feeds, pasture or range forages, and water. These include minerals, nitrates, prussic acid, alkaloids, mycotoxins, and bacteria. Most toxicities can be prevented or managed by limiting the intake of the feed containing the toxin.

A. Water

Several minerals and compounds are occasionally found at toxic concentrations in water. A common problem in drinking water is salt. Salt levels up to 5000 mg/kg are usually safe and levels as high as 15,000 to 17,000 mg/kg can be tolerated in some situations. Nitrate concentrations can be high in some water supplies. Concentrations of 100 to 200 mg/kg are considered dangerous and concentrations of 3000 mg/kg can be lethal. Other contaminants in water that can be toxic include aluminum, arsenic, cadmium, chromium, cobalt, copper, fluorine, lead, mercury, nickel, selenium, vanadium, zinc, and fecal bacteria.

B. Forages

Many plants found in ranges and pastures contain substance that can be toxic to livestock. These plants often grow in isolated pastures or during limited seasons of the year. Grazing animals may not consume the toxic plants unless other forages are unavailable. As an example, plants grown on soils high in selenium may concentrate selenium and be toxic to the grazing animal. These species have been identified and livestock managers recognize these and manage the animals to avoid problems.

Nitrates are a common form of nitrogen utilized by plants and high levels can result in death. Nitrogen fertilization of forages can increase nitrate in plants and concentrations of nitrate above 9000 mg/kg can be toxic. Nitrate is converted to nitrite by bacteria in the rumen and binds with hemoglobin, causing tissue oxygen starvation. Nitrates usually are higher in young, fast-growing forages and in forages damaged by drought. Several forages, including cereal grains, sorghums, soybeans, beet tops, and several weeds, may have high concentrations of nitrates. Delaying grazing, gradual adaptation, and dilution with other feeds are management strategies that reduce risk and losses.

Prussic acid is a glycoside found in cultivated plants that breaks down to hydrocyanic acid and can cause death. Plants containing prussic acid include sorghums, Sudan grass, Johnsongrass, vetches, arrow grass, and wild cheery. Concentrations of prussic acid increase significantly in some plants after they have been damaged from frost or drought. Livestock managers need to be cautious under these conditions. Fields tests for prussic acid are useful in evaluating the risk of grazing forages with suspected problems.

Several fungi grow on plants and may produce toxins. Ergot is a purplish-black fungus that grows in the seed heads of grasses and grains. It can cause paralysis, abortion, lose of circulation, and necrosis in extremities of the animal. Toxicities can be prevented by observing grains and hays for the fungus. Another example is fescue toxicity, which is caused by a fungus that grows on the fescue plant and reduces forage intake and animal performance, especially during hot weather. The fungus is not visible on the plant but can be detected with laboratory tests. The fungus is spread with the seed and plants are infected for their entire life. Effects of fescue fungus can be reduced by grazing other forages during hot weather.

C. Concentrates

Mycotoxins are toxic metabolites produced by molds and can be present in concentrates and forages but are more likely to be found in grains. Visible mold in the feed is not a good indicator of mycotoxin content.

Most molds do not produce toxins, but *Aspergillus, Fusarium,* and *Penicillium* molds produce one or more toxins under some conditions. Mycotoxins can be produced while the crop is in the field or during harvest, storage, or feeding. Effects of mycotoxins on the animal include changes in nutrient absorption and metabolism, changes in hormonal function, and a suppression of the immune system. Symptoms such as reduced feed intake, unthrifty appearance, higher incidence of disease, and poor response to treatments, abortions, and diarrhea have been reported.

Aflatoxin, produced by *Aspergillus,* is a carcinogenic toxin often found in corn, peanut, and cotton products. The Food and Drug Administration limits aflatoxin to 20 parts per billion (ppb) in dairy feeds because some of the toxin is excreted in the milk. Beef cattle can tolerate higher levels in the total diet (300–400 ppb) than poultry or swine. Vomitoxin is produced by *Fusarium* and is common in many feeds. The most common symptom is a reduced feed intake or feed refusal. Other mycotoxins of concern in livestock include zearalenone, T-2 toxin, ochratoxin, patulin, tremorgens, and fumonisin. Field testing kits and laboratory analytical procedures are available to determine the levels present.

Bibliography

Church, D. C. (1988). "The Ruminant Animal." Prentice Hall, Englewood Cliffs, NJ

Ensminger, M. E. and Olentine, C. G. (1980) "Feeds and Feeding." Ensminger Publishing Company. Clovis, CA.

Lesson, S., and Summers, J. D. (1991). "Commercial Poultry Production." University Books, Guelph, Ontario, Canada.

National Research Council. (1978). "Nutrient Requirements of Laboratory Animals." 3rd ed. National Academy Press, Washington, D. C.

National Research Council. (1981). "Nutrient Requirements of Goats." National Academy Press, Washington, D.C.

National Research Council. (1982). "United States–Canadian Tables of Feed Composition." 3rd ed. National Academy Press, Washington, D. C.

National Research Council. (1984). "Nutrient Requirements of Beef Cattle." 6th ed. National Academy Press, Washington, D. C.

National Research Council. (1984). "Nutrient Requirements of Poultry." 8th ed. National Academy Press, Washington, D. C.

National Research Council. (1985). "Nutrient Requirements of Sheep." 6th ed. National Academy Press, Washington, D. C.

National Research Council. (1985). "Ruminant Nitrogen Usage." National Academy Press, Washington, D. C.

National Research Council. (1988). "Nutrient Requirements of Swine." 9th ed. National Academy Press, Washington, D. C.

National Research Council. (1989). "Nutrient Requirements of Dairy Cattle." 6th ed. National Academy Press, Washington, D. C.

National Research Council. (1989). "Nutrient Requirements of Horses." 5th ed. National Academy Press, Washington, D. C.

Pork Industry Handbook. (1992). Purdue University Cooperative Extension Service. West Lafayette, IN.

Fertilizer Management and Technology

GEORGE REHM, *University of Minnesota*

I. Economic Benefit to Production Agriculture
II. Predicting Nutrient Needs through Soil Testing and Plant Analyses
III. Managing Fertilizer with a Concern for the Environment
IV. Fertilizer Management for Farm Profitability

Glossary

Annual variable costs Price of inputs used in crop production that must be purchased each year; some examples of annual inputs are fertilizers, seeds, herbicides, and insecticides

Foliar application Application of fertilizers in fluid form to a variety of crops

Grid sampling Sampling scheme that can be followed in the collection of soil samples needed to define variability and nutrient needs; fields are divided into grids with some routine procedure and soil is collected from each individual grid for analysis and interpretation

Plant analysis Process that involves collection of plants or specific plant parts, analysis of the plant tissue, and interpretation of the data to classify nutrient concentrations as deficient, marginal, or sufficient

Pop-up application Method of fertilizer application that involves the placement of either fluid or dry fertilizer materials in direct contact with the seed at the time of planting

Ridge-till planting system Planting system that involves the construction of small ridges in a field during a growing season with a cultivator; the next crop in the planned crop sequence is planted on the top of these ridges

Slow release nitrogen fertilizers Fertilizer materials that are used to supply nitrogen to growing crops. These materials are manufactured so the nitrogen becomes available over the major part of the growing season

Soil testing Multi-step process that involves collection of soil samples from the field, analyses of these samples in the laboratory for nutrients of interest, the interpretation of the analytical results, and the writing of a fertilizer recommendation

Split application Multiple applications of fertilizer during a growing season; this practice is usually followed when mobile nutrients are applied to sandy soils

Fertilizer management and technology are a subdiscipline in the rather broad subject of Soil Science. Fertilizer management focuses on the effective and efficient use of a variety of sources of plant nutrients, both organic and inorganic, needed for production of a variety of species on a diversity of soils in highly variable environments. Fertilizer management involves decisions that relate to rate of application, selection of an appropriate source, most appropriate placement, and use of chemical additives and growth regulators. Fertilizer technology is a subject which deals with the manufacture, use, and evaluation of various fertilizer materials that have potential for supplying the nutrients needed for profitable crop production in the modern, diverse agricultural environment.

I. Economic Benefit to Production Agriculture

The economic importance of fertilizers for efficient and effective crop production in a wide variety of cropping systems is well documented. The return to the grower on investment in fertilizers can be substantial. The magnitude of this return is affected by such factors as nutrient supplying capacity of the soil, yield potential of individual crops, climate, the value of the crop grown, and the cost of the plant nutrients when purchased.

When the annual variable costs of crop production are considered, approximately 30% of the total is used to purchase fertilizer. Thus, cutting fertilizer costs is usually considered by growers to be one way to increase profit margins. However, underfertilization may reduce yields and these lower yields could have a negative impact on the profit margin. Maximum profit from fertilizer use is usually achieved when adequate, but not excessive, rates of needed nutrients are applied in a fertilizer program.

The economic importance of fertilization of crops can be demonstrated in a number of ways. The information summarized in Table I illustrates the economic value of the application of nitrogen fertilizer to corn. The benefit is especially impressive if calculations are expanded to a farm enterprise that might grow 200 hectares of this crop. Similar calculations can be used to illustrate the benefits of using other plant nutrients for a wide variety of crops.

The response to proper fertilization is not limited to improved yield. Fertilization is known to improve the quality of the crop produced, to enable crops to withstand infestation of some pathogens, and to speed crop recovery from several forms of stress.

In addition to the monetary benefits to the growers, proper use of fertilization can and will have a positive effect on the economy of a community, a state, and a country. Higher crop yields associated with fertilizer use have increased the global supply of food. The food produced is also of higher quality and this has had a positive effect on the diets of developing countries. The task of supplying adequate food for an expanding world population is awesome. The effective and efficient use of fertilizer will assist the producers of this food in meeting this challenge.

TABLE I

Economic Value of the Application of Nitrogen Fertilizer to Corn

N applied	Yield (1987–1989 average)	Return over no N Use	Fertilizer cost	Return to fertilizer
kg ha^{-1}	Mg ha^{-1}	\$ha^{-1}	\$ha^{-1}	\$ha^{-1}
0	5.4	—	—	—
84	9.4	73.71	4.56	69.15
168	11.0	93.96	9.11	83.84
252	10.7	85.86	13.67	71.19

Source: G. W. Randall, University of Minnesota.
Note: N price, \$.068 kg^{-1}; corn price, \$13.65 Mg^{-1}.

II. Predicting Nutrient Needs through Soil Testing and Plant Analyses

Much of the emphasis on fertilizer management revolves around decisions for rate of application of needed nutrients in a fertilizer program. The management tools of soil testing and plant analysis can both be used as a basis for logical decisions that pertain to rate of application. [*See* Soil Fertility.]

An understanding/knowledge of the nutrient status of the soil is needed before application rates can be determined. There are several techniques for evaluating the nutrient status of the soil. Among these are: (1) field plot fertilizer trials, (2) greenhouse pot experiments, (3) crop symptoms, (4) plant analysis, (5) rapid tissue or plant sap testing, (6) biological tests, and (7) rapid soil chemical analyses. There are advantages as well as limitations to each of these techniques. Rapid chemical analysis of soils can be used for a large number of samples at minimal cost. If the chemical analysis is related to nutrient response, it is then possible to arrive at a decision on nutrient needs with efficiency in time and cost. Of course, various chemical analyses are needed to predict the needs of a variety of essential plant nutrients. This collection of appropriate analytical procedures for analysis of soil samples is referred to as soil testing. [*See* Soil Testing.]

Simply stated, the objectives of soil testing are: (1) to accurately determine an index of the ability of soils to supply plant nutrients, (2) to indicate the degree of nutrient deficiencies that might exist, (3) to provide the basis for fertilizer recommendations, and (4) to report the results of the chemical analysis in a way that they permit an economic evaluation of the suggested fertilizer recommendation. These objectives recognize that the analytical results of the chemical analysis are only a part of the factual data needed for making fertilizer recommendations. Interpretation of the chemical analysis will vary with different crops. Therefore, fertilizer rate recommendations are based on an individual's interpretive judgment of the chemical analysis combined with the knowledge of crop response to various nutrients at defined soil test levels.

In general, soil testing is a program that may be divided into four phases: (1) collection of the sample, (2) appropriate chemical analysis of the sample, (3) interpreting the analytical results, and (4) the writing of the actual fertilizer recommendation. It is generally recognized that the success of any soil testing program depends as much on good individual judgment as accurate chemical analysis.

A. Sample Collection from the Field

All reliable soil testing programs start with the collection of soil samples from the field. There are several soil sampling schemes in use today. Regardless of the scheme used, the sample or samples collected should accurately reflect the true nutrient status of the field. This does not mean that the analytical results from all samples collected from an individual field will be the same. The results of the chemical analysis, however, should reflect the true variability that exists in the field. The accuracy of the entire soil testing program cannot be greater than the accuracy used in sample collection.

A single sample can seldom be used to accurately characterize the nutrient status of a given field. However, the collection of a single sample to represent an individual field, regardless of size, has become a common practice in today's agriculture. Written instructions for sample collection, usually state that atypical areas in a field should be avoided in the process of sample collection. This instruction is easy to follow if differences in soils across a field are visually obvious. However, there are numerous situations where variability exists in a field, but it is not immediately obvious. Consequently, it is relatively easy to mix variable soils together in situations where one sample represents one field.

Recognizing that hidden variability exists in most fields for a variety of reasons, consultants, fertilizer dealers, and researchers have developed two strategies which are thought to be more precise for collecting soil samples. In one strategy, a field is divided into smaller areas with a gridding process. Each part of the grid, which can vary in size, is sampled separately and fertilizer rate recommendations are made after the results of analyses from all grids have been considered. This grid system of sampling is popular where soil variability in any field is a major concern. This sampling system provides a process for identification of portions of a field that have varied in cropping history, received different rates of fertilizer in the past, or have a history of manure use.

The second strategy used to improve the sampling process is to sample by soil type. This sampling scheme can be used only if there is a modern Soil Survey of the field to be sampled. This Soil Survey provides an identification and description of the soils present. Using the map provided in the Soil Survey, the individual collecting the soil samples accumulates a sample that represents each of the major soil types in the field. As with the grid system, the results of the chemical analysis of all samples in the field are considered and fertilizer suggestions are made accordingly.

These two sampling systems offer several advantages when compared to the system where one sample represents one field. There are, however, major economic concerns. It is obvious that the grid sampling and sample by soil type schemes require the chemical analysis of more samples and added time is needed for sampling. Thus, these sampling schemes usually become more expensive. This added expense may or may not be offset by a savings in money spent for fertilizer. This economic question is the subject of current research projects which, as yet, have not produced definitive answers.

B. Laboratory Analysis of the Samples

Chemical analysis follows sample collection. There are numerous chemical procedures that can be used to analyze a soil sample for a specific nutrient. The chemical procedure must provide an accurate indication of the relative level of available nutrients. The results of the chemical analysis of a soil sample are usually indexes or indicators of the soil to supply particular nutrients to a specific crop. These analyses are not a measure of the total amount of nutrients present in a soil. The chemical procedures used must also be designed so that a large number of samples can be analyzed in a short period of time.

The analytical procedures used in soil testing are not uniform for all regions. For example, soil testing laboratories in the southeastern United States rely more on the procedures developed by Mehlich, while those in the Midwest use a combination of a variety of tests developed by various researchers.

Most soil testing laboratories offer analytical services for the measurement of all essential nutrients. Major emphasis, however, is placed on providing accurate tests for phosphorus (P) and potassium (K). In order to improve the efficiency in the operation of a soil testing laboratory, it would be ideal if nutrients could be extracted from the soil with one reagent. This single extract could then be analyzed for the nutrient or nutrients of interest. Although considerable research has been directed toward this goal, the search for the universal extractant continues. Those that have worked for acid soils do not give the most accurate indication of nutrient availability in calcareous soils (pH of 7.4 or higher). Conversely, those that have worked for calcareous soils, do not perform adequately when soils are acid. [See SOIL CHEMISTRY.]

C. Interpreting the Analytical Results

The collection of the analytical data is not the last step in the soil testing process. In order to be meaningful, these data must be interpreted to develop a rate recommendation for a specific nutrient for a specific crop. This interpretation is usually accomplished through some type of previously determined correlation between test results and known responses of a crop to a specific nutrient. These correlations are established in greenhouse and field experiments.

Human judgment is an important ingredient in this interpretation process. Individuals may interpret the analytical results in various ways and these differences in interpretation can lead to a disparity in fertilizer recommendations.

Human judgment is also affected by differences in philosophies or approaches to making fertilizer recommendations. The differences in philosophies are most obvious when recommendations for K and magnesium (Mg) are considered.

Two philosophies currently dominate the soil testing and fertilizer recommendation process. The "sufficiency level of available nutrient" (SLAN) approach is built on the concept that there are definable levels of individual nutrients in the soil below which crops will respond with some probability to added fertilizer. Likewise, there are also levels above which crops will not respond to fertilization. The "basic cation saturation ratio" (BSCR) philosophy promotes the idea that maximum yields can be achieved by creating an "ideal" ratio of calcium (Ca), Mg, and K in soils.

Currently, most public soil testing laboratories follow the SLAN approach to making fertilizer recommendations. Several private laboratories, on the other hand, tend to adhere to the BSCR concept. It is possible to identify past research projects that support both of these philosophies. The majority of the field response data collected, however, appears to favor the SLAN approach. There are several instances where the use of the BSCR concept has resulted in the use of excessive rates of plant nutrients.

D. Developing a Soil Test for Mobile Nutrients

From a soil testing perspective, the nutrients that are essential to crop growth can be categorized as either mobile or immobile. Much of the preceding discussion applied to those nutrients that are not mobile in soils. However, the search continues for analytical procedures that will lead to accurate fertilizer recommendations for those mobile nutrients. Because of both environmental and economic concerns, major emphasis is being placed on the development of a reliable soil test for nitrogen (N). [*See* SOIL, CHEMICALS: MOVEMENT AND RETENTION.]

It can be argued that N is the most transient of all nutrients in soils. It exists in several forms at any one time. Consequently, there is substantial difficulty in determining the most appropriate form to measure as well as the best time for collection of soil samples for analysis. In the Great Plains and western Corn Belt, where total growing season rainfall is usually limited, a soil nitrate test has been developed as a basis for making N fertilizer recommendations for numerous crops. Successful use of this test requires that both surface (0–15 cm) and subsoil (15–60 cm) samples be collected. These samples are analyzed for nitrate–nitrogen (NO_3-N). This information, when coupled with a realistic yield goal, provides for N fertilizer recommendations that have been accepted by a large number of crop producers. [*See* NITROGEN CYCLING.]

Efforts to develop a soil test for N have been less successful in more humid regions. Development of an appropriate test in these regions is also hindered by the frequent addition of organic sources of N (legumes, livestock manures) to the complex chemistry of N in soils. The amount of N released from these sources that is available for crop growth is difficult to predict using various laboratory procedures. There have been some attempts to use a measurement of NO_3-N in the surface soil (0–30 cm) as a basis for recommendations. These attempts have not been successful. It appears that a soil test for N, that will be useful in the more humid regions, must take potential contributions from organic sources as well as some measure of past environmental conditions into consideration.

Boron (B) and chloride (Cl) are micronutrients that are also mobile in soils. Neither nutrient has negative environmental implications and established soil testing procedures have been accepted over a broad geographical area. Responses to B fertilization are most numerous for alfalfa and vegetable crops. Some attention should be given to analyzing soil samples for B if growers intend to include these crops in the farming enterprise. To date, there has been an identified need for Cl in a fertilization program for wheat and, possibly, other small grain crops. A soil test for Cl has been developed and is accurate in predicting needs.

Efforts to develop a soil test for sulfur (S) have met with limited success. The need for S in a fertilizer program is not extensive and is limited to certain soil conditions and situations. In general, the need for this nutrient is greatest for sandy soils that have a low organic matter content and research has adequately defined the S requirements for these situations. Like B and Cl, S fertilization has not been identified as having a negative impact on the environment. Consequently, minimal attention has been devoted to developing a more accurate analytical procedure for measurement of S in soils.

E. Plant Analysis as a Predictor of the Nutrient Requirements of Crops

Plant analysis is frequently described as a management tool that can be used to either determine the nutrient status of various crops or predict nutrient needs in a fertilizer program. This analytical procedure is based on the principle that the concentration of a nutrient in a plant is a reflection of all factors that have interacted to affect the growth of that plant.

The interpretation of plant analysis information assumes there is some knowledge of the critical concentrations of an essential plant nutrient in various parts of a growing crop. This assumption is valid for a limited number of crops. For example, there is a limited data base that can be used to define the nutrient status of corn if the leaf opposite and below the ear is collected at silking. This assumption, however, is not valid for most agronomic crops. Plant analysis has not evolved or improved to the point that it can be used as a basis for fertilizer recommendations. At the present time, this tool can be used most effectively to classify nutrient concentrations as deficient, adequate, or excessive.

Considerable research efforts have also been devoted to a plant analysis interpretation system based upon the ratio of the concentration of one plant nutrient to another. This interpretive approach utilizing plant analysis has been referred to as the Diagnosis and Recommendation Integrated System or DRIS system.

In order to be effective as a diagnostic tool, the DRIS system requires that an extensive data base be developed for the crop of interest. This development requires the collection of a substantial number of plant samples representing a large number of environmental and nutritional situations. This approach is not usually any less expensive than the system of identi-

fying the deficient, marginal, and excessive categories for crops.

III. Managing Fertilizer with a Concern for The Environment

A. General Concepts

Managing fertilizer use for crop production is complex. The individual responsible for the management of this input must make decisions on rate of application, nutrient source, time of application, method of application, and placement. The potential for profitability and protection of the environment must also be considered when fertilizer management decisions are finalized. The discussion in the paragraphs that follow will concentrate on the importance of the consideration for the environment in making management decisions.

B. The Environmentally Sensitive Landscapes

When environmental impacts are considered, most of the attention is devoted to effective and efficient management of N. There is major concern for the concentration of nitrate–nitrogen (NO_3-N) in the groundwater. Since our groundwater is the source of drinking water for the majority of the population, high concentrations of NO_3-N can have serious implications for human health. Consequently, a standard of 10 ppm nitrogen in the nitrate form has been established. Drinking water with NO_3-N concentrations in excess of this standard is considered to be potentially harmful to the health of infants. [See GROUND WATER.]

Nitrate–nitrogen is mobile in soils and can move through the root zone whenever excess water also moves through this zone. The amount of water held against the force of gravity varies with soil texture. Sandy soils hold less water that is available for plant use than fine textured soils. So, downward movement of NO_3-N is considered to be more of a potential problem where soils are sandy. This downward movement (leaching) is especially important in growing situations when the water table comes close to the soil surface.

Leaching is also a major concern for situations where fractured limestone is covered by a thin cap of soil material. With excessive rainfall, the NO_3-N

moves first through the root zone, then through the fractured limestone rock to the groundwater.

Movement of water through the soil profile is very slow process for fine-textured soils that have a high clay content. Artificial tile drainage is usually installed in these soils to improve water flow through the root zone. For these situations, excessive amounts of $NO_3 - N$ in the root zone are moved through the tile lines to surface impoundments of water such as ponds and lakes. High concentration of $NO_3 - N$ can also be a serious problem in surface waters.

Nitrate–nitrogen will also move downward through fine-textured soils where artificial tile drainage has not been installed. The movement in this environment, however, is much slower than the leaching that occurs in sandy soils.

C. Best Management Practices for Nitrogen Fertilizer Use

There are several management practices that can be applied to N fertilizer application that will substantially reduce the potential for movement of $NO_3 - N$ to the groundwater. The selection of the rate of N to use is probably the single most important decision that affects groundwater quality. In sensitive landscapes, any applied N that is not utilized by the crop has a potential for loss to the groundwater. Rate prediction, however, is not an exact science at the present time. There is not a soil testing procedure for N that is considered to be accurate for crop production on sandy and/or shallow soils. In addition, selection of a realistic yield goal is a major challenge because of the sensitivity of these soils to fluctuations in rainfall received during the growing season.

Irrigation of coarse-textured soils adds some stability to crop production and the selection of a realistic yield goal becomes less difficult. The use of irrigation water, however, adds another management variable. Application of excess water from surplus irrigation can cause leaching as easily as excessive rainfall. For these production systems, scheduling of irrigation water is just as important as effective N management.

The use of split applications of N fertilizer is an effective management practice for reducing the potential for nitrogen loss on irrigated sandy soils. There are several combinations that can be used for the split applications. The ideal combination will vary with crop, soil properties, and length of the growing season.

Regardless of the system used for timing of the N fertilizer, the major portion of the total N applied should be in the root zone at the time of maximum N uptake by the crop. The growth stage at which maximum uptake occurs varies substantially with crop.

For most crop production systems, the source of N fertilizer used has had little, if any, impact on movement of $NO_3 - N$ to the groundwater. The nitrification of ammonium (NH_4^+) to nitrate (NO_3^-) nitrogen in the ammoniacal nitrogen fertilizers (anhydrous ammonia, urea) proceeds rapidly in most soils. Consequently, availability of N to crops from the commonly used N fertilizers should be nearly identical. Results from numerous research trials with a variety of crops have verified that there is very little, if any, effect of N source on crop yield providing the source has been applied properly.

From the fertilizer technology standpoint, there have been research efforts to develop N fertilizers that would release N to the crop slowly throughout the growing season. The early products resulting from these research efforts concentrated on sulfur coated urea that dissolved in soils over various periods of time. These products were evaluated extensively for a number of crops and the yields produced from the use of these materials were usually lower than yields resulting from the use of the more conventional N fertilizers. As a result, there have not been extensive efforts to market these products for the production of agronomic crops.

More recently, there has been an effort to develop gelled fertilizers with the objective of releasing N throughout the growing season. The field evaluation of these products is limited. Consequently, these fertilizer gels have not, as yet, become products commonly sold in the fertilizer industry.

In addition to interest in slow-release N fertilizers, there has also been a substantial effort to develop products that will delay the conversion of $NH_4 - N$ to $NO_3 - N$. These products are collectively referred to as nitrification inhibitors. Several have been developed. One (nitrapyrin) has been marketed on a fairly wide scale with some success. There are other products that will inhibit the nitrification process, but there have been no intensive efforts to market them on a broad scale.

The use of nitrification inhibitors has been beneficial for crop production in special situations where there is a high potential for loss of $NO_3 - N$ from the soil system. Potential for loss is greatest in soils where denitrification or leaching losses are major concerns. These situations are found on a limited number of crop acres and, subsequently, the potential for sales of nitrapyrin is limited.

D. Immobile Nutrients and Environmental Quality

In addition to N, P has the potential to have a negative impact on environmental quality. With P the concern is directed toward the quality of surface waters. High concentrations of P stimulate the growth of algae which, in turn, increases oxygen consumption resulting in a reduction of the fish population.

Very small amounts of P enter surface waters dissolved in rainfall or snow melt that leaves the landscape. Most of the P entering surface waters is attached to soil particles that leave the landscape in soil erosion. Therefore, any conservation practice that reduces soil erosion will reduce the amount of P that enters ponds and lakes.

Fertilizer placement can also have a major impact on the amount of P lost to surface waters. The broadcast application of P fertilizers coupled with incorporation by a tillage implement mixes P with a relatively large volume of soil near the surface of the landscape. When erosion takes place, soil particles at or near the surface are lost and any P attached to those particles is also lost. Another option is to place the phosphate fertilizer in a concentrated band close to the roots of the growing crop but at some distance below the soil surface. Unless erosion is extremely serious, the soil in and around the fertilizer band will not be lost and the amount of P entering the surface water will be reduced substantially.

At the present time, other essential nutrients (potassium, calcium, magnesium, sulfur, zinc, iron, manganese, copper, boron, chloride) are not considered to have a negative impact on environmental quality. The quality of both surface and groundwater can be improved or maintained with the use of best management practices of nitrogen and phosphate fertilizers. These management practices have evolved from the results of a substantial number of research projects. If used, these practices will minimize the loss of NO_3-N to both surface and groundwater and the loss of P from the landscape to surface waters.

IV. Fertilizer Management for Farm Profitability

A sustained profit in any farm enterprise is highly dependent on achieving optimum yield with the most efficient use of inputs. Management decisions for fertilizer use can have a major impact on profitability. Soil properties, climate and weather, intended crop, and availability of equipment will have a major influence on these management decisions. [See Soil Management.]

Fertilizer management practices that are needed to achieve sustained profitability routinely focus on rate selection and placement. Selection of the most appropriate source of a given nutrient may be important in special situations for some crops. The various fertilizer products that are in use today are adequate and effective in meeting nutrient demands. Consequently, there is not a major research effort that is focused on the development of new products.

A. Nutrient Mobility and Profitability

Concerns for both environmental quality and farm profitability have a major influence on management decisions involving the mobile nutrients. The previous section provides a discussion of the relationship of nutrient mobility to environmental quality. Sustained profitability is also affected by the potential for movement of plant nutrients in soils. Some corrective management decisions are needed if one or more of the mobile nutrients (N, S, B) are moved below the root zone because of excessive rainfall and/or irrigation water usage. Split applications of N fertilizers can be used to prevent major losses of this nutrient from the root zone if environmental conditions routinely favor the leaching process. Split applications of N have been especially favorable for optimum production for corn and small grain production when these crops are grown on sandy soils.

Although considered to be mobile, S and B move through the root zone more slowly than NO_3-N. Leaching of these two nutrients can and does occur, but the consequence of the loss is not as dramatic as the loss of N from the root zone. In general, the research that has focused on the management of these two nutrients leads to the conclusion that multiple applications are not necessarily needed for optimum yields. With appropriate consideration for the intended crop, the S and/or B fertilizers needed can be either broadcast and incorporated before planting or applied in a band at planting time. The preferred time of application may vary with crop, but split applications have not generally improved yields.

Because of mobility and associated leaching, deficiencies of N, S, or B may develop on some sandy soils when rainfall or irrigation water application has been excessive. When deficiencies are confirmed, they can frequently be corrected with an in-season application of the appropriate fertilizers. With irrigated sandy soils, for example, the nutrients needed can be injected into the irrigation water. Other methods of application must be used when irrigation water is not available in the cropping system. The method used for this application will be highly dependent on the growth stage of the crop and the soils involved.

Except for specialized crops or cropping situations, the foliar application of these plant nutrients has not corrected the deficiency problem. The foliar fertilization approach may result in an improvement in appearance, but improvements in yields have been minor.

Because P and K are not considered to be mobile in most soils, there is less opportunity to take corrective action if deficiencies of these two nutrients are identified in field situations. Therefore, more emphasis must be placed on selection of the appropriate rate before a crop is planted.

For most crops, suggestions for the use of phosphate and/or potash fertilizer are derived from established response data. These data relate response to soil test levels for P and/or K and define the rate of fertilizer needed for optimum yield. Therefore, the amount of phosphate and potash suggested can be no better than the data base that has been developed. The phosphate and potash suggestions provided to the grower are not intended to produce maximum yield. Maximum profit is not usually achieved at maximum yield. Most suggestions for phosphate and potash use are intended to provide for optimum yield. This is a yield level slightly less than the maximum yield.

Requirements for phosphate and potash fertilizer use are not the same for all crops. The soybean crop, for example, will achieve optimum production at lower soil test levels when compared to corn. Similar differences exist for other crops. The response of a wide variety of crops to soil test level has usually been documented through research. Because of improvements in variety or hybrid, higher levels of production, and the use of improved crop management practices, research is always needed to refine the nature of crop response in a wide range of soil and climatic conditions.

When the nutrient requirements of various crops are considered, major attention is devoted to fertilizer suggestions for nitrogen, phosphate, and potash. Although required and used in smaller amounts, the micronutrients (zinc, iron, manganese, copper, and boron) are just as important. Deficiencies of these micronutrients, when they occur, can cause substantial reductions in crop yields. The additions of small amounts of zinc (Zn) (1 kg ha^{-1}) in a fertilizer program has doubled corn yields in certain situations. Similar examples of major increases in production could be cited for the application of copper (Cu) for small grains growing on organic soils.

The requirement of one micronutrient for one crop does not imply that this micronutrient is needed for all crops grown in a specific region. For example, Zn may be needed in a fertilizer program for corn and edible beans grown on soils in the northern Corn Belt. Soybeans, wheat, and alfalfa do not respond to Zn usage when grown on the same soils. Therefore, the intended crop as well as the soil test level for Zn, must be considered when fertilizer recommendations for Zn are considered.

Except for B, the micronutrients are not considered to be mobile in most soils. Therefore, fertilizers used to supply these nutrients, when needed, should be added to the soil prior to planting. The banded or broadcast applications can be used for this purpose. Because only small amounts of micronutrients are needed, it is possible to supply them in a foliar application. This method of application has worked well for some citrus and other specialized crops. A more extensive use of this practice for other crops has not been demonstrated to be profitable. For example, it is possible to use foliar application of various iron (Fe) fertilizers in an attempt to correct iron chlorosis in soybeans. The success rate of this practice has been limited and other management practices are usually suggested.

The micronutrients can be supplied to a fertilizer program from a number of sources. These sources are compatible with either a liquid or dry fertilizer program. These sources vary substantially in cost. Limited research has been completed to evaluate these various materials. The summary of the available information suggests that all sources of micronutrients have an equal effect on production when they are needed in a fertilizer program.

B. Fertilizer Placement and Profitability

Nutrient mobility characteristics have a major influence on management decisions that pertain to fertilizer placement. The mobile nutrients (N, S, B) move to the plant root with soil water by a process called mass flow. Therefore, the placement of these nutrients is not a major concern. N is used in relatively large amounts by most crops and there are several options for efficient and effective placement. Smaller amounts of S are needed for crop production. Therefore, a banded application for row crops creating a situation of easy accessibility is a more appropriate placement choice. The same reasoning applies to the micronutrient, B, which is absorbed in very small amounts by most crops. Broadcast application of these mobile nutrients has been shown to be highly appropriate for perennial crops.

The nutrients that are not mobile reach plant roots by the process of diffusion. This movement mechanism is slow. Consequently, there is considerable importance attached to placing immobile nutrients in a position that will increase the probability of their coming in close contact with the plant roots. The banded application of the immobile nutrients is one very popular option used for enhancing this probability.

Models have been developed and tested which describe uptake of P or K if certain soil, plant growth, and root growth parameters are known. These models suggest that phosphate and potash fertilizers can be banded with a small portion of soil and supply the P and K needs of growing crops. The volume of soil fertilized with the banded application is dependent to a large extent on soil properties.

The band placement of phosphate and/or potash fertilizers improves the efficiency of use because the contact between soil and fertilizer is reduced. Fixation or tie-up is reduced when this contact is reduced. In calcareous soils, this fixation takes place in the form of various calcium phosphate compounds. Where soils are dominated by clays that trap the potassium ion, the banded application of potash fertilizer reduces potassium fixation.

When there is a reduced potential for fixation, lower rates of phosphate and/or potash fertilizers are needed. The use of lower rates translates to savings in fertilizer costs and, therefore, enhanced profitability.

Fertilizer recommendations from some states are adjusted for placement considerations. Compared to the rates used for broadcast applications, suggested rates are reduced by one-third to one-half if banded applications of phosphate and/or potash are used. The reduction is also adjusted for soil test level. When soil test values for P and/or K are in the low or very low range, there is a major difference between suggested rates for broadcast and banded applications. For soil test values in the medium range, the differences in recommendations for banded and broadcast applications are small.

Fertilizer placement decisions must also take the intended crop into consideration. For most perennial crops, for example, there is little opportunity to use banded applications of phosphate and/or potash fertilizers after establishment. This leaves the broadcast placement as the most reasonable alternative. For annual crops, there is considerable research information which suggests that banded applications are more efficient than broadcast usage. There are some annual crops, however, that do not fit this pattern. With soybeans, for example, several research trials have provided evidence that broadcast applications of phosphate produce higher yields than the banded placement. The explanation for this change in response is not clear. It is obvious that much more research with band applications is needed.

There is not an ideal position for banded fertilizer. When banded applications were first introduced, there was a general recommendation to apply the fertilizer approximately 5 cm to the side of and 5 cm below the seed at planting. This placement could be achieved with crops such as corn but was not reasonable with small grain.

With the equipment available today, the fertilizer band can usually be placed at any desired location. More recent research indicates that distance between seed and fertilizer is not critical. This distance can become too large and the growth stimulating effect of the band is lost.

Some growers have adopted the practice of applying some of the fertilizer directly with the seed. This practice is frequently referred to as a "pop-up" application. This placement, however, can create problems with germination. Emergence can be reduced if high rates are used or if certain fertilizer materials are applied with the seed. Both research and farmer experience have shown that urea, ammonium thiosulfate, and boron fertilizers, when applied in contact with the seed, can cause serious germination damage. To eliminate problems with germination, most growers are advised to keep approximately 3 cm of soil between seed and fertilizer when planting.

C. Precision Fertilizer Placement and Special Problems

The concept of precision in fertilizer placement has not been an important one until recent years. Stimulated by the switch to conservation tillage planting systems, there has been a switch in thinking from broadcasting to banding. As evidence continues to accumulate, it becomes more apparent that successful production systems of this nature will be highly dependent on the banded application of fertilizer. The accumulating research evidence also suggests that it will be important to match fertilizer placement with tillage system.

The use of banded potash has been successful in solving a special problem for those who produce corn in a ridge-till planting system in the northern Corn Belt. Although many soils in the region traditionally have high soil test values for K, K-deficiency symptoms were appearing. The application of potash fertilizer in the center of the existing ridge in the fall before planting seemed to correct the problem. The rate of K_2O needed was in the range of 40–50 kg ha^{-1}. The explanation for the appearance of this problem is not apparent at this time.

The use of banded fertilizer has also helped with production problems of several crops in the southeastern United States. Many soils in the region develop dense clay layers at some distance below the soil surface. These layers severely restrict downward movement of water and root growth. Because of this root restriction, it is difficult for crops to get the needed nutrients for optimum production.

Special tillage equipment has been developed to disrupt this dense soil layer. At the same time, this equipment has been modified to apply banded fertilizer below the layer of dense clay. The practice has proven to be successful. Crop yields have increased and this has improved profitability.

The potential is bright for use of banded fertilizer in the years ahead. Banding fits easily with the emphasis on fertilizer efficiency. There are ample opportunities to fit banding into various crop production enterprises.

Bibliography

Engelstad, O. P. (1985). "Fertilizer Technology and Use," 3rd ed. Soil Science Society of America, Madison, WI.

Follett, R. H., Murphy, L. S., and Donahue, R. L. (1981). "Fertilizers and Soil Amendments." Prentice-Hall, Englewood Cliffs, NJ.

Palgrave, D. A. (1991). "Fluid Fertilizer Science and Technology." Marcel Dekker, New York, NY.

Tisdale, S. L., Nelson, W. L., and Beaton, J. D. (1985). "Soil Fertility and Fertilizers," 4th ed. Macmillan, New York, NY.

Walsh, L. M., and Beaton, J. D. (1973). "Soil Testing and Plant Analysis." Soil Science Society of America. Madison, WI.

Finance

JOHN B. PENSON, JR., PAUL N. ELLINGER, *Texas A&M University*

I. Micro Agricultural Finance
II. Macro Agricultural Finance

Glossary

Agribusinesses Term commonly used when referring to farm input supply firms, food processing firms, fiber manufacturing firms, and other firms in the nation's food and fiber system other than crop and livestock producers

Certainty equivalent value Value an individual would accept for an asset if all risks were removed

Credit scoring Approach used by lenders to quantitatively evaluate the credit worthiness of a borrower

Farm Credit System System of federally chartered, privately owned banks and associations that lend primarily to agricultural producers and their cooperatives

Farmers Home Administration Governmental agency involved in direct lending and loan guarantees to credit-worthy borrowers that may have a difficult time obtaining financing from commercial sources

Financial intermediaries Entity which obtains loanable funds from savers in the economy and then lends these funds to borrowers

Financial leverage index Ratio of returns on total capital to returns on equity capital; this ratio shows the relative returns earned on debt versus equity capital

Food and fiber system Network of input supply firms, crop and livestock producers, food processing firms, fiber manufacturing firms, and related distribution firms associated with the supply of food and fiber products to final demand

General equilibrium That combination of prices and quantities at which buyers and sellers in all markets in the general economy are satisfied

Macro economic policy Typically refers to the monetary actions taken by the Federal Reserve System, the government spending authorized by the U.S. Congress, and the taxation policies approved by the U.S. Congress and implemented by the Internal Revenue Service

Net present value Discounted sum of projected net cash flows for a potential investment

Risk efficient frontier Set of assets that offer the maximum possible expected returns for a given level of risk

Risk premium Difference between a decision maker's expected risky return and value the decision maker would accept if all risks were removed

Times interest earned ratio Ratio of earnings before interest and taxes plus depreciation to total interest payments. A measure of cash flow stress associated with financial leverage, this ratio illustrates the degree to which firms are able to service their debts out of current earnings, or how far earnings could fall before firms would be unable to cover current interest costs

Vertical integration Coordination and integration of successive stages in production, processing, and distribution

The field of agricultural finance encompasses a broad range of interest ranging from "micro" issues associated with firm-level investment and financing decisions made by crop and livestock producers as well as agribusiness firms to "macro" issues associated with the effects that macro economic policy, farm commodity policy, resource policy, and international trade policy have upon the financial structure and performance of the nation's food and fiber system.

I. Micro Agricultural Finance

Topics in micro agricultural finance include concepts of investment and financing decisions under both certainty and uncertainty, including the methods used to evaluate investment projects and alternative approaches to acquiring these resources.

A. Overview of Financial Management

The concepts of financial management in agriculture involve the acquisition and utilization of financial resources by crop and livestock producers, and by agriculturally related businesses. Emphasis in this section is placed on the introductory concepts of theory of investment and financing decisions, the evaluation of new investments, resource acquisition in agriculture, financial analysis in agriculture, and the financial intermediaries involved in delivering debt capital to agriculture. Major micro issues related to agricultural finance are also presented. These issues and concepts are linked throughout the entire food and fiber system: from input supply firms and financial intermediaries to crop and livestock producers, and onto food and fiber manufacturers and distributors.

B. Theory of Investment and Financing Decisions

The fundamental concepts of finance theory apply similarly to farms and ranches as well as other firms in the economy. Crop and livestock producers typically have relatively little market power, often being price takers in both input and product markets. Agribusinesses like input manufacturers have more market power, and often participate in thinner, less-liquid markets.

1. Concepts of Investment and Financing Decisions under Certainty

The major components of financial theory include a decision maker's utility function, productive investment alternatives, and financial markets. A simple model with no taxes, no transaction costs, and no uncertainty of investment decisions is used to outline the theoretical framework. Decisions are made in a one-period context. The decision maker is endowed with income at the beginning of the period and the end of the period. At the beginning of the period the individual determines how much to consume (C_0) and how much to invest to provide for end-of-period consumption (C_1). All individuals prefer more consumption to less (marginal utility of consumption is always positive) and the marginal utility of consumption is decreasing. Utility curves for beginning-of-period and end-of-period consumption

are shown in Fig. 1. Each individual may have different utility curves. The dashed contour lines indicate trade-offs between beginning-of-period consumption and end-of-period consumption. Utility is equal at points along these contour lines, and the lines thus are referred to as indifference curves. The slope of a line tangent to an indifference curve measures the rate of trade-off between C_0 and C_1 and is referred to as the marginal rate of substitution between beginning-of-period consumption and end-of-period consumption. The slope of this line can be represented as $-(1 + r)$, where r is the individual's subjective rate of time preference.

Assume individual decision makers have opportunities to invest in productive assets that allow units not consumed at the beginning of the period to be augmented to more than one unit of future consumption. In the absence of financial markets, an individual decision maker will invest in all productive opportunities that have rates of return higher than the decision maker's subjective rate of time preference (r).

To complete the model, assume financial markets exist and thus, the opportunity to lend and borrow unlimited amounts at a market-determined rate of interest (i). These borrowing and lending activities allow the individual decision maker to reallocate consumption between the beginning and end of the period to attain higher levels of utility and thus improve economic well-being. The presence of financial markets allows the individual decision maker to invest in

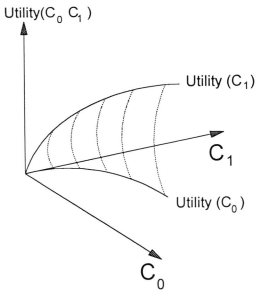

FIGURE 1 Utility functions and indifference curves.

all productive assets that have rates of return that equal or exceed the market rate of interest (i) instead of the subjective rate of time preference.

These concepts are illustrated in Fig. 2. The production possibilities set is represented by P_0P_1 and the set of indifference curves by U_1 and U_2. Given that interest rates are positive, all funds lent at the beginning of the period will receive interest plus principal at the end of the period. The future value of one unit lent at the beginning of the period is increased by a factor of 1 plus the market-determined rate of interest (i). Thus, the slope of the capital market line is $-(1 + i)$.

Suppose the initial endowment is point A. The individual decision maker may move along the capital market line or production possibilities set to achieve the highest possible utility. In this example, the higher return is achieved by moving up the production possibilities set to point B where the rate of return on investments is equal to the market rate of interest. By borrowing at the market rate of interest, a tangency with the subjective rate of time preference (U_2) is achieved at point C. This tangency is at a higher level of utility than that achieved without financing opportunities.

Thus, the process can be depicted as a two-stage process. First, the individual decision maker invests in all production opportunities that have returns that equal or exceed the market rate of interest. Second, the individual decision maker borrows or lends in the financial market until the market rate of interest is equal to the decision maker's subjective rate of time preference. The first step does not use the decision maker's utility function and thus, under certainty con-ditions, the investment condition (stage 1) is considered separate from the financing condition (stage 2). This condition is known as the Fisher Separation theorem.

2. Concepts of Investment and Financing Decisions under Uncertainty

Crop and livestock producers are inherently faced with risk. Commodity price fluctuations, weather variability, spoilage, disease, and changes in government policies interject considerable risk into their decision-making process.

The three theoretical concepts essential in understanding financial models under uncertainty include concave utility functions, certainty equivalents, and risk premiums. The marginal utility of profit declines for concave utility functions. Crop and livestock producers with concave utility functions are considered risk averse. Risk averse decision makers prefer a certain investment to one with an equal but uncertain return. A risk averse decision maker is willing to pay a price for a certain investment that yields the same utility as the expected utility of the risky investment. The completely certain price is considered the certainty equivalent. The difference between the expected value and the certainty equivalent value is the risk premium. The risk premium is the decision maker's required compensation for accepting risky investments.

A risk averse decision maker's preference structure between risk and return can be represented by indifference-curve analysis. Figure 3 shows indifference curves for risk averse decision makers. The direction of preference is represented by the arrow (up

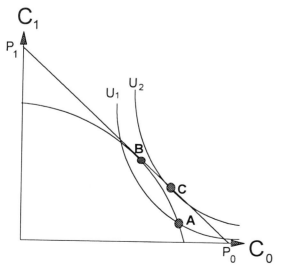

FIGURE 2 Optimal investment and financing decisions.

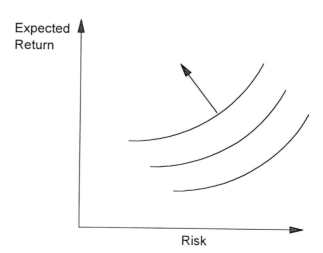

FIGURE 3 Indifference curves and attitudes toward risk.

and to the left). The slope of the indifference curves indicates the marginal rate of substitution between risk and return. In this case, the marginal rate of substitution is the amount of expected return the decision maker requires for an additional unit of risk. Different decision makers will have different degrees of risk aversion and thus, will have different marginal rates of substitution.

3. Investment Decision Techniques under Certainty

In the previous sections a simple one-period model is discussed. These models are extended to incorporate multi-period investment decisions and refined to evaluate alternative projects. The methods are referred to as capital budgeting techniques. These techniques are used to aid investment decisions for all types of agribusiness firms. Refinancing of debt and buy versus lease decisions are also analyzed using these techniques. The techniques can be used to select among independent projects or rank mutually exclusive projects based on specific budget constraints. In general, there are five capital budgeting techniques used to evaluate investment decisions. These include: (1) the payback method, (2) the accounting rate of return method, (3) the net present value method, (4) the internal rate of return method, and (5) the modified internal rate of return method.

The payback and accounting rate of return methods do not account for time value of money and thus, limit their overall usefulness. The payback period is calculated as the number of years it takes to recover the initial cash outlay. The accounting rate of return is the average after-tax profits divided by the initial outlay.

The three other methods each account for the time value of money. The net present value of a project is calculated as the sum of all discounted cash flows of the project. Each cash flow is discounted by factors that convert each cash flow to a net present value. The factors are based on the decision maker's opportunity cost of capital. The internal rate of return of a project is the rate that equates the present value of all inflows and outflows. However, the method assumes that all cash flows can be reinvested at the internal rate of return. The modified internal rate of return is calculated by first finding the net present values of all cash outflows using the decision maker's opportunity cost of capital. Second, the future value of all cash inflows are estimated also using the decision maker's opportunity cost of capital. The modified internal rate of return is the discount rate that equates the present value of the cash outflows with the future values of cash inflows.

The net present value and modified internal rate of return are the preferred methods. Mutually exclusive projects of similar size will be ranked the same with each method. However, when size differences among the projects occur, the net present value method provides a more consistent indicator of how an individual project will affect the overall value of a firm.

4. Adjustments for Risk in Decision Making

Each of the five methods discussed in the previous section assumes certainty of future cash flows. However, considerable uncertainty is present among agribusiness firms. Four general methods have been used to account for risk in the investment decision framework. These include: (1) the maximin decision criterion, (2) the coefficient of variation criterion, (3) the expected present value criterion with adjusted discount rates, and (4) the certainty-equivalent criterion. Each of the methods has drawbacks with the choice of method depending on the frequency the decision maker is confronted by similar investment decisions, the magnitude of the risk involved, and the decision maker's aversion to risk.

The maximin decision criterion uses the maximum (or largest) of the minimum (or smallest) outcomes associated with a decision alternative. This criterion simply selects the decision alternative with the best of the worst outcomes. The method does not account for the probability of any of the outcomes. The coefficient of variation is the ratio of the standard deviation of possible outcomes divided by the expected present value. For the coefficient of variation criterion, the decision maker chooses the decision alternative that has the lowest, nonnegative coefficient of variation. This method does not account for differing degrees of risk aversion.

Another commonly used method is to adjust the discount rate for decision alternatives with different levels of risk. A problem with this method is the data required to estimate the adjusted discount rate. The certainty equivalent criterion involves selecting the decision alternative with the highest certainty equivalent. This criterion incorporates the risk aversion of the decision maker. However, the values that are used to estimate a decision maker's utility function and certainty equivalent are subjective and difficult to estimate quantitatively.

C. Resource Acquisition in Agriculture

The financial barriers to enter production agriculture have increased. Inflation, technological change, and increases in farm size have been the primary causes of the increased capital requirements. The combination of increasing capital requirements and low profit margins restricts crop and livestock producers in their capacity to acquire control of the land, machinery, livestock, and other resources necessary to compete. The increased capital requirements also limit growth. Crop and livestock producers are evaluating and using alternative methods of resource control and management.

Sources of funds used to acquire control of resources can be broadly classified as debt and equity capital. The degree that debt capital is used by a producer is a key issue. Tax deductibility and cost usually favor the use of debt capital over equity capital, while administrative and bankruptcy costs increase as the proportion of debt capital increases. Thus, theoretically each decision maker may have an optimal equilibrium combination of debt and equity.

1. Equity Capital

The primary source of equity capital in production agriculture is through retained earnings or surplus profits kept in the business. Other common sources of equity capital have resulted from gift and inheritances from previous generations and pooling of equity capital through partnerships or corporations.

There are two types of partnerships common in agriculture: general partnerships and limited partnerships. With general partnerships, each partner is explicitly involved in both ownership and management. Furthermore, each partner has unlimited liability for obligations incurred by the business and the liabilities incurred by other partners. Limited partnerships are comprised of limited and general partners. The liability of the limited partners is restricted to their investment in the business.

The corporation is a legal entity held as shares or claims on the net worth and profit stream of the business. While partnerships and sole proprietors dissolve upon death, corporations permit continuity over generations. Two types of corporations are important in agriculture: Subchapter S and Subchapter C. A Subchapter S corporation is limited to 35 stockholders and taxed as a partnership. With the Subchapter S corporation, all profits are allocated to the stockholders for income tax purposes. A Subchapter C corporate stockholder must pay taxes only on the cash dividends received and thus, this entity may offer some income tax incentives for high-tax-bracket stockholders.

Many corporations and partnerships are created for the purpose of pooling family equity capital. However, public and private placement of equity shares in production agriculture are becoming more common in agriculture. An example is life insurance companies who are becoming more active in acquiring equity shares in agricultural operations as well as direct investment in agricultural assets as methods to diversify pension funds.

2. Leasing

An arrangement commonly used in agriculture is the farm lease. The lease basically transfers capital from the lessor to the lessee for an agreed period of time. Leasing is a common method for producers to control farmland. Share leases and cash leases are common with real estate leases. With crop- and livestock-share leases, the lessor and lessee share in the costs and production, whereas the cash lease is simply an agreed cash price paid for the rental of the land.

Machinery and equipment leasing is also becoming common in agriculture. In agriculture, operating and capital leases are used to acquire control of machinery and equipment. Operating leases are short-term contracts ranging from a few hours to a year. Custom hiring is a common operating lease arrangement. Custom hiring involves the owner furnishing the machine, operating expenses, and labor. Capital leases are longer term arrangements. The financial obligations of capital leases are quite similar to debt arrangements.

3. Contract Production

Agriculture has witnessed strong trends toward increasing specialization and coordination at the various stages of the production cycle. The coordination may be with successive stages in production and distribution (vertical) or between two or more units of production within the same economic stage (horizontal). Vertical integration of input suppliers, processors, and distributors is becoming more common in agriculture. An increasing proportion of assets used in the farming sector is being supplied or financed by input suppliers, processors, and distributors. Vertical integration of vegetable and fruit industries has been in existence for a long time. However, livestock industries such as poultry and hogs are also becoming more vertically coordinated. A producer may be able to shift price and yield uncertainties to the contracting firm with vertical coordination. However, future contractual arrangements create additional uncertainties.

4. Debt Capital

Debt capital are funds acquired from financial intermediaries. Costs include interest costs, fees, and closing costs. Interest costs are fully tax deductible and thus, will typically carry a lower cost than equity capital. Debt capital is typically distinguished between operating debt and term debt. Operating debt is used to finance the purchase of operating inputs while term debt is often used to finance depreciable assets and farm real estate. Operating debt is typically repaid during the production cycle while term debt is paid over several years.

D. Financial Analysis of Agricultural Producers

The traditional accounting practices followed by many crop and livestock producers have traditionally been both informal and simplistic. However, the increasing use of debt capital and the formation of more complex organizational structures have increased the need of standardization of financial records for crop and livestock producers.

1. Accounting Practices

In conjunction with the 1987 Agricultural Credit Act, a presidentially appointed commission on agricultural finance emphasized the need for greater standardization of financial reports and analysis of the farm industry. As a result, the Agricultural Division of the American Bankers Association formed a task force of representatives from lending institutions, academic institutions, regulatory agencies, computer software firms, the farm management consulting industry, and the accounting industry. The Farm Financial Standards Task Force (FFSTF) provided guidelines regarding the reporting of financial information for farm businesses.

The four financial statements recommended by the FFSTF include: (1) the balance sheet, (2) the income statement, (3) the statement of cash flows, and (4) the statement of owner equity. These four statements are linked to provide a coordinated information system. The balance sheet is a systematic listing of all items owned by a business (assets) and the levels of debt and equity used to acquire the assets. The income statement is a summary of the revenue and expenditures of the business over a specified period of time. The statement of cash flows is a detailed summary of the cash inflows and outflows over a specified period

of time. The cash inflows and outflows are separated according to operating, financing, and investment activities of the firm. The statement of owner equity reconciles the change of equity from one period to the next.

Each of these statements may be prepared on a historical basis or a pro forma (projected) basis. These financial statements organize the data needed to analyze the risk and performance of the business. The primary areas of analysis include solvency, profitability, liquidity, repayment capacity, and financial efficiency. Solvency measures the level of debt relative to the equity capital or the overall capital of a business. Profitability is the ability of the firm to generate earnings while liquidity relates to the firm's capacity to generate cash to meet financial commitments without loss of value. Repayment capacity measures relate cash generated by the operation to cash obligations of the firm. Financial efficiency measures refer to the utilization of assets within the business. Other financial efficiency measures relate operating and financing expenses to total production.

2. Credit Scoring

Financial statements and financial ratios measure the degree of financial risk faced by a crop or livestock producer. Crop and livestock producers use the measures to monitor financial strength and future growth capabilities while financial intermediaries use the measures to determine credit worthiness of an operation.

More formal methods of credit evaluation are currently being implemented by agricultural lenders. Credit scoring models have been developed through lender's experiences as well as statistical methods. The lender-experience models are formulated by lenders based on historical observations of variables that are related to overall loan performance. Statistical development of a credit scoring model involves the mathematical representation of a group of subjective and objective independent variables into an equation that determines the credit worthiness of a business. The objective variables often include collateral amount, financial ratios, production efficiency measures, and trend values of financial measures. Management ability is a common subjective measure included in credit scoring models. The subjective component often allows the lender more flexibility to adjust the model results in order to compensate for poor objective components. The applications of credit scoring models include determination of credit acceptance, loan pricing based on riskiness of the loan, establishment of loan loss provisions, and loan portfolio monitoring.

The dependence on the model results varies among lenders. In some cases, model results are used as the sole determinant in the decision process, while other lenders use the results in conjunction with other criteria.

The statistical approaches used to determine the variables and their respective coefficients include linear regression, discriminant analysis, and logistic regression. The independent variables include various financial, economic, and subjective variables while the dependent variable is a measure of historical loan performance. In general, results indicate that the independent variables selected and their respective coefficients differ substantially across studies and are very sensitive to the data sample.

E. Providers of Debt Capital

The major sources of debt capital to agriculture include: (1) commercial banks, (2) the Farm Credit System, (3) life insurance companies, (4) Farmers Home Administration (FmHA), (5) farm-related trade and agribusinesses, (6) individuals, and (7) Farmer Mac. Each of these sources play a vital role in providing debt capital to agriculture. However, sources of funds, regulatory constraints, and individual risks faced by each are different.

The amount of farm debt outstanding, excluding operator household debt, at the end of 1992 was $139.7 billion. On December 31, 1992, commercial banks held 37.3% of all farm loans with the Farm Credit System holding 25.3%. This is a significant shift in market shares from 1982 when commercial banks held 22.2% and the Farm Credit System held 34.0%. A large reason for the shift in market shares has been the increased emphasis of commercial banks on farm real estate lending. The market share of farm real estate debt by commercial banks has increased from 7% in 1982 to 25% by year-end 1992. The market share for the Farm Credit System declined from 43 to 33% over the same time period.

Currently, the major issues involving providers of debt capital to agriculture include: (1) the role and performance of the Farm Credit System, (2) consolidation activities of commercial banks, (3) the increased competitive position of nontraditional lenders, (4) the role and viability of Farmer Mac, and (5) the transition of government-sponsored lending.

1. Role and Performance of the Farm Credit System

The Farm Credit System are federally chartered, privately owned service and lending institutions. One objective of the charter is to improve the income and well-being of crop and livestock producers by furnishing competitively priced credit and related services to credit-worthy borrowers through all economic conditions.

The primary source of funds for the Farm Credit System district banks and banks for cooperatives is obtained through the sale of system-wide securities in the national financial markets. The Federal Farm Credit Bank Funding Corporation is responsible for selling the securities. The securities are treated as Governmental Agency Securities and trade at 20 to 50 basis points above U.S. Treasury securities. Equity capital of the various cooperatively controlled banks and associations is obtained by sale of stock to borrowers and through retained earnings. The banks are regulated by the Farm Credit Administration.

During the early 1980s, the Farm Credit System experienced severe financial problems. The System's capital and surplus declined over $6.1 billion in 1985 and 1986. The problem involved loan losses resulting from producers' financial problems as well as lowering net interest margins. The Farm Credit System held a large volume of long-term securities at high interest rates while current market rates on loans were low. As a result, in December of 1987 the U.S. Congress passed the Agricultural Credit Act of 1987. The major provisions included restructuring options of the Farm Credit System, federal financial assistance, greater flexibility in capitalizing the system, and creation of an insurance fund.

Currently, most of the Farm Credit System institutions have restored the soundness of their operations: Restructuring of the System's banks and lending associations is continuing as these institutions seek greater efficiency and risk-bearing capacity in their lending operations. On January 1, 1988, there were 12 districts with a total of 377 associations. On April 1, 1994, there were 8 districts, and 238 associations. The impact the corporate restructuring of the Farm Credit System has on the delivery of debt capital to farm and ranch borrowers has also received considerable interest among policy makers, academicians, credit institutions, and borrowers themselves.

2. Consolidation Activities of Commercial Banks

Considerable consolidation has occurred within the commercial banking industry. Over 3500 mergers and acquisitions of commercial banks have occurred since 1980. The total value of these merger and acquisition activities since 1980 has exceeded $120 billion.

The bank merger and acquisition activity was higher than any other industry over this time period. As a result of changes in federal and state legislation, interstate acquisitions by bank holding companies have been a large part of this acquisition activity. As more states liberalize geographical expansion regulations, interstate banking is expected to increase.

The growth of mergers and acquisitions in the banking industry has been accompanied by a multitude of theories and philosophies debating the rationality and public benefits of this expansion activity. Opponents of bank combinations suggest that undue concentration may inhibit competitive forces and thus, increase monopoly elements in the economy. In addition, opponents in rural areas argue that acquisitions often result in locally disinterested intermediation activities and decisions. Some of the activities suggested by adversaries of bank expansion include siphoning deposits out of rural areas, warehousing out-of-market loans at the subsidiaries, and allocating nonproportional operating expenses to subsidiaries. These adverse activities could result in higher credit costs to borrowers or reduced credit availability to agriculture and other small businesses in local communities. Advocates of bank expansion suggest that combinations will benefit society by reducing inefficiencies in the banking system through resource reallocation. The potential for geographical and product diversification also exists. In addition, local community services may be enhanced by additional services available through larger institutions.

The consequences of the heightened consolidation of the banking industry are essential components in the agricultural economy as well as the national economy. The banking industry comprises almost 25% of the U.S. Finance, Insurance, and Real Estate Services sector of the national income and product accounts while commercial banks hold over $52 billion of agricultural debt outstanding. As a result, estimations of inefficiencies within the banking industry and the evaluation of the changes in competitive forces due to structural shifts within the banking industry are research areas receiving considerable attention among researchers in agricultural finance.

3. Increased Competitive Position of Nontraditional Lenders

Another current issue in agricultural finance relates to the emergence of other nontraditional lenders. Vertical integration is becoming more prevalent in some areas of production agriculture, especially in the livestock sector. The vertically integrated firms are typically much larger and more complex than the traditional family-operated businesses. Furthermore, credit demands for these firms are also different. In many cases the small-community bank and the Farm Credit System have been unable to meet the credit demands of these firms. Therefore, these firms have accessed nontraditional sources of capital through large commercial banks or investment banking firms.

Other nontraditional lending sources are also becoming more competitive. These nontraditional lenders include input supply firms and farm implement dealers. Loans from these firms are typically derived from the purchase of a farm input or product. However, these firms are also expanding into operating lines of credit. The facilitation of sales, convenience to borrowers, and profitability are primary motivations for these firms to offer credit. Compared to the highly regulated banking industry and Farm Credit System, these nontraditional firms face few regulatory hurdles. Opponents of these firms often argue that an unfair playing field exists. The evaluation of the competitiveness and viability of these firms to deliver debt capital to crop and livestock producers is an emerging concern in agricultural finance.

4. The Role and Viability of Farmer Mac

A secondary market for farm real estate mortgages was authorized by the Agricultural Credit Act of 1987. The secondary market operates under the jurisdiction of the Federal Agricultural Mortgage Corporation and is regulated by the Farm Credit Administration. The objectives of the program are: (1) to increase the availability of long-term debt capital to crop and livestock producers at stable interest rates, (2) to provide greater liquidity and lending capacity in extending debt capital to crop and livestock producers, (3) to facilitate investments in agriculture by providing access to fixed rate, long-term lending, and (4) to improve availability of debt capital for rural housing.

The basic operation of the program is that a financial institution (loan originator) completes a loan to a qualified agricultural borrower that meets Farmer Mac's underwriting standards. A certified pooler will purchase part or all of the loan. Servicing may continue with the originator or move to the pooler or a third party. The pooler combines originated loans into pools and issues mortgage-backed securities or pooled-participation certificates for private or public decision makers to purchase. On January 1, 1993, the seven certified poolers were composed of four affiliated with life insurance companies, two security companies, and one Farm Credit Bank.

Farmer Mac is also involved in the secondary loan sales of loans guaranteed by the Farmer's Home Administration. This program is referred to as Farmer Mac II. Under this program Farmer Mac serves as a pooler for the guaranteed portion of loans sold by originating lenders.

Farmer Mac has been very slow to develop. At the end of 1992, only four pools totaling $681 million had been established. The liquidity and competitiveness of other lenders have reduced the loan demand for the product. Increased loan demand is essential for Farmer Mac to become a cost-effective and viable source of long-term debt capital for agriculture.

5. The Transition of Government-Sponsored Lending

As an agency of the United States Department of Agriculture, the FmHA serves as a source of debt capital for rural Americans. The agency, often termed the lender of last resort, is a decentralized network with over 1900 county offices, more than 200 district offices, and 46 state offices. FmHA makes loans to qualified applicants who have experience in farming and ranching, are the owners or operators of a farm or ranch at the time of the loan, and whose livelihoods depend on farming or ranching.

Concerns have surfaced regarding government subsidies which has focused increased interest on reducing FmHA direct lending and increasing its emphasis on loan guarantees. In 1992, FmHA guaranteed loan obligations accounted for $1.6 billion or 67.9% of its total loan program. Loan guarantees transfers the funding and loan administration to private lenders and provides greater flexibility in loan pricing.

II. Macro Agricultural Finance

The second major area of emphasis in agricultural finance reflects an aggregate or "macro" view of the economic performance and financial structure of our nation's farms and ranches and their relationship to other sectors in the general economy. Information on macro agricultural finance developments is of interest to macro economic policy makers, farm commodity policy makers, financial institutions, agribusinesses, and rural development specialists. [*See* MACROECO-NOMICS OF WORLD AGRICULTURE.]

A. Sector Economic Accounting

An important foundation to macro agricultural finance has been the development of a system of economic accounts for agriculture. Most economists are familiar with the national income and product accounts maintained by the U. S. Department of Commerce and the flow of funds accounts and national balance sheet maintained by the Federal Reserve System. Few, however, are likely aware of the role the U. S. Department of Agriculture plays in supplying the sectoral information for agriculture incorporated in these national accounts, or the applications agricultural economists make of these sectoral data. The set of economic accounts for agriculture, developed and maintained largely by the U. S. Department of Agriculture, not only provides input to the national income and product accounts and other aggregate accounts, but also represents a major source of data to descriptive and quantitative behavioral research in agricultural finance.

1. Sector Income Account

The U.S. Department of Agriculture's sector income account dates back to the early 1900s. This account has expanded over the years to provide detailed information on cash receipts from farm marketings of crop and livestock commodities, government payments received by producers, and other sources of farm-related income. This account also provides detailed information on specific categories of cash farm production expenses, capital consumption, and capital expenditures for such durable inputs as tractors and other farm machinery and equipment, trucks, and farm structures. Figure 4 shows the historical trends in nominal and real net farm income (i.e., adjusted for inflation) reported in the sector income account. This figure shows that, while nominal net farm income increased sharply in the 1980s, the purchasing power of net farm income did not. In fact, real net farm income of $4.95 billion in 1983 approached the purchasing power of net farm income during the Great Depression in the early 1930s.

2. Sector Balance Sheet Account

The U. S. Department of Agriculture began to publish a balance sheet for agriculture in the 1940s. This statement presents a measure of wealth of farm businesses as of December 31st each year. The asset coverage in this account includes the value of farmland, farm buildings, livestock on farms, crop inventories, farm machinery, and other farm inputs. This

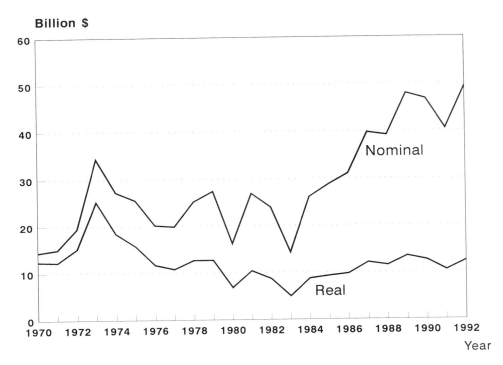

Billion $

FIGURE 4 Nominal and real net farm income.

coverage also includes financial assets held for farm business purposes. The liability side of the balance sheet provides information on year-end real estate and nonreal estate debt owed by producers. The debt-to-asset ratio published with this account represented the major aggregative financial indicator used by analysts for many years.

In addition to these sector accounts published at the national level in its *Economic Indicators for the Farm Sector* series, the U. S. Department of Agriculture also periodically publishes the income and balance sheet accounts on a state basis for those desiring to conduct regional- or state-level analyses. Other related data important to macro agricultural finance researchers contained in this publication series include measures of productivity and efficiency, costs of production for crop and livestock operations, and trends in agricultural resources. Figure 5 illustrates the historical trends in nominal and real net worth of farms and ranches nationwide presented in the sector balance sheet account. The $200 billion loss in nominal net worth during the financial stress period of the mid-1980s had largely been made up by the end of 1992.

3. Other Accounts

The income and balance sheet accounts provided the basis for the development of other accounts such as a sources and uses of funds or cash flow statement for agriculture. This account, developed in the early 1970s, illustrates the financing of farm and ranch operations as well as their expansion. This account permitted the measurement of a variety of analytical ratios designed to monitor the financial performance and financial strength of agriculture. These ratios, which include a financial leverage index and a times interest earned ratio, gained increased attention in the early 1980s as agriculture underwent a severe financial crisis. Among the lessons learned from this experience was the need to rely on more than the debt-to-asset ratio when assessing financial well-being. Today the U. S. Department of Agriculture publishes a wide variety of financial ratios focusing on both flow and stock relationships which enable users of these accounts to stay abreast of financial stress pressures in agriculture.

4. Research Applications

The information contained in the U. S. Department of Agriculture's sector economic accounts not only is vital to current situation analysis, but also represents a major input to research designed to project the effects that a broad range of macro economic, farm commodity, and international trade policies have upon the economic growth and financial performance

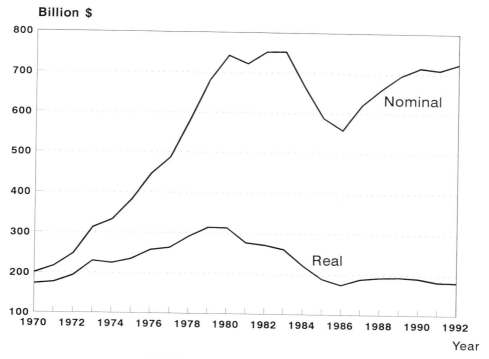

FIGURE 5 Nominal and real net worth.

of agriculture. Researchers dating back to the early 1950s have been developing computer-based models of agricultural activity using, to varying degrees, information contained in these and related accounts published in the *Economic Indicators of the Farm Sector* series by the U. S. Department of Agriculture.

B. Aggregate Investment and Financing Behavior

A second dimension to macro agricultural finance research has to do with understanding and projecting aggregate investment and financing behavior in agriculture. Considerable resources have been committed to modeling these aggregate flows of funds over the post-World War II period in both the public and private sectors.

1. Modeling Farm Investment Behavior

Early studies of aggregate investment behavior in agriculture focused principally on expenditures for farm tractors. Many of these studies made overly simplifying assumptions with respect to the cost of capital and measurement of capital stocks and flows of depreciable assets like farm tractors. More recent research efforts have expanded coverage of the cost of capital to include not only the purchase price of

the capital input and the interest rate on farm loans, but also other arguments included in the implicit rental price of capital (e.g., price of the good, cost of debt capital, cost of equity capital, the ordinary income tax rate, the investment tax credit rate, tax depreciation allowances, and the physical deterioration of the input's productive capacity). This allows researchers to capture the direct and indirect effects of changes in monetary and fiscal policy on the demand for farm tractors and other durable capital inputs.

Farmland has traditionally accounted for over two-thirds of the value of all farm business assets (e.g., farmland represented 74% of total farm asset values at the end of 1992). Relatively few studies have focused on the rate at which real estate is transferred by discontinuing proprietors and to what degree this land remains in agriculture. The capital flow associated with these transfers is a significant use of funds in the sector cash flow statement, and requires the use of considerable debt capital. One determinant of this cash flow has received a great deal of attention: the price of farmland. These studies have used methods ranging from those projecting current farmland values based largely on land values observed in the previous period to studies which have modeled the entire land market. The ability to project farmland prices enables policy makers, lenders, and others to see how specific events might alter the demand for debt capital in agriculture and the financial strength of crop and livestock producers.

2. Modeling Farm Financing Behavior

The use of debt capital relative to internal equity capital has changed dramatically over the years, as economic conditions changed, as financial intermediaries serving agriculture and as capital requirements of crop and livestock producers changed. Focusing on the time period since the end of World War II, we have seen the relative importance of debt capital as a means to finance farm capital expenditures increase from a secondary role to a dominant role. This has allowed agriculture to expand and to adopt emerging technologies more rapidly than it might have otherwise. In a sector which is as highly capitalized (e.g., value of assets per worker) as agriculture, expanded use of financial leverage translates into billions of dollars in farm debt outstanding. At the end of 1992, for example, total farm debt outstanding, according to the sector balance sheet discussed previously, was $140 billion. Total farm debt outstanding reached a peak of nearly $200 billion in the early 1980s, but fell to approximately $140 billion by the beginning of 1993.

A major reason for this decline in farm debt outstanding was the economic shock experienced by both borrowers and lenders during the early 1980s which had its origin in the macro economic policies adopted in Washington. These policies led to rising interest rates and a stronger dollar relative to the currencies of our major agricultural trading partners. This translated into declining net farm incomes and net worth levels, and a high degree of financial stress for those borrowers who expanded their operations during the 1970s with the help of variable rate mortgages. This stress led to rising loan default rates at rural commercial banks and other financial intermediaries serving agriculture. The result has been increased internal and external credit rationing as both borrowers and lenders positioned themselves for the 1990s. Lenders began to place greater emphasis on the cash flows generated by loans as opposed to the collateral value of assets securing the loan. Lenders also increased equity requirements on loans made and shortened the lengths of loans made. Borrowers attempted to lower their exposure to financial risk by retiring loans early, and to ration their use of additional debt capital.

The market shares of the financial intermediaries providing loan funds to producers in the United States have also been the subject of agricultural finance re-search. The focus has been on the roles played by public versus private lenders, the individual roles played by commercial banks, the Farm Credit System, and other lenders, and on alternative approaches to projecting future net flows of loan funds and year-end debt outstanding.

Attempts to model the annual net flows of loan funds in agriculture over a protracted period of time have been both varied and largely unsuccessful. Previous approaches have ranged from determining the total amount of net new money required after applying available internal equity capital to determining the individual market shares of specific financial intermediaries serving agriculture. The growing dichotomy in agriculture (a larger number of large businesses, a larger number of small part-time operations, and a shrinking number of mid-sized farms), the changing structure of financial markets, and the financial crisis experienced in the 1980s have made predicting the relative market shares of specific financial intermediaries extremely difficult.

C. Linkages to Rest of Economy

Previous mention was made of the effects that macro economic policies have upon the financial strength and performance of agriculture and the financial intermediaries who supply producers with loan funds. Researchers focusing on modeling the potential impact of these policies have to decide to what degree they want to endogenize the interface between agriculture and the rest of the economy. This issue can be viewed from two perspectives: (1) the interface between agriculture and the domestic economy and (2) the interface between agriculture and the world economy.

1. Domestic Interface

The interface between agriculture and the domestic economy occurs in the markets in which producers acquire inputs (including loan funds) as well as the markets in which they sell their products.[1] Furthermore, policy actions and other economic shocks occurring outside agriculture can be transmitted to crop and livestock producers in these markets. For example, research has shown that monetary policy directly affects the current operations and growth of agriculture through the cost and availability of loan funds. This represents a direct linkage between the policy

[1]The large integrated firms in the broiler, turkey, egg and hog businesses frequently endogenize many of these relationships within the firm, thereby increasing the efficiency of their operations.

action and the farm borrower. This same monetary policy, however, has an impact on other sectors of the economy as well, and can thus alter the general equilibrium levels of prices in all markets, including those in which producers buy inputs and sell products. This is important because crop and livestock producers are typically price takers in both markets. For example, macro economic policy which alters interest rates in the economy affects not only farm production costs in the form of higher interest payments, but also farm revenue through the effects that changing exchange rates have upon agricultural trade flows. Contractionary monetary policy actions, which raise interest rates and exchange rates, has been shown to depress net farm incomes as well as farmland values, and thereby lower real farm net worth over time. This, in combination with expansionary fiscal policy which also puts upward pressure on interest rates, is precisely what occurred in the early 1980s and led to the financial crisis in agriculture which saw interest expenses rise, exports shrink, incomes fall, investments decline, and net worths plummet.

A variety of approaches have been taken to modeling this interface over time. The first generation of models attempting to capture this interface can be referred to as "stand alone" models because they would: (1) take a multi-year baseline of macro economic activity as input to an agricultural sector model but (2) ignore the potential that events in agriculture over the period would have any impact on the macro economic baseline. For example, an increase in the price of beef in the current year would have *no effect* on the food component of the Consumer Price Index. A second generation of models attempting to capture the interface between agriculture and the general economy are recursive in nature. While events in agriculture are allowed to alter projections of macro economic activity, they do so with a one period lag. Here, an increase in the price of beef in the current year would not show up in the food component of the Consumer Price Index until the *following year*. A third model approach has been to treat the linkages between agriculture and the rest of the economy in a simultaneous fashion. This means an increase in the price of beef in the current year would affect the Consumer Price Index in the *current year*. With the added complexity of the second and third approaches comes additional requirements to develop and maintain larger, more comprehensive models. The choice of approach dictates the extent to which one can address the full effects of a change in policy.

2. International Interface

Mention was made in the previous paragraph of exchange rate effects on agricultural trade flows and the impact this has been shown to have upon farm income. Considerable attention in the literature has been given to modeling international agricultural trade flows, including the effects that changes in foreign currency exchange rates have on net exports of major crops like wheat and corn. The implications for finance are that higher exchange rates depress sales of domestic production overseas, cause stocks to accumulate, and depress U. S. grain prices. This has a negative impact on net income of crop producers, but lowers the costs of production to livestock producers. In addition to exchange rate effects, barriers to trade in the form of tariffs and marketing quotas also affect the growth in profits, net worth, and the liquidity and solvency of farming and ranching operations. The advent of regional trading blocks like that envisioned by the North American Free Trade Agreement (NAFTA) will likely bring additional focus to the financial implications of international agricultural trade.

D. Evaluation of Policy Impacts

An important dimension to macro agricultural finance is the impact that macro economic, farm commodity, international trade, and other policies have upon producers as well as the rest of the food and fiber system. In discussing each of these areas, it is important to distinguish between the general impacts of these policies in addition to their financial implications.

1. Macro-economic Policy Impacts

Macro economic policy makers want to know the likely effects of their actions not only on the general economy, but also on specific sectors in the economy like agriculture. Not all sectors are affected the same when a policy change or economic shock occurs in the economy. Perhaps no other sector exhibits the unique direct and indirect effects from a macro economic shock as agriculture. Of interest here is the fact that a large share of the "cause and effect" is financial in nature. Table I summarizes the short run effects specific combinations of monetary policy are hypothesized to have upon agriculture.

2. Farm Commodity Policy Impacts

Farm commodity policy also has unique effects on agriculture. Low commodity prices have traditionally meant higher deficiency payments paid to producers

TABLE I

Short-Run Effects of Policy Actions on Agriculture

Policy effects on	Expansionary		Contractionary	
	Monetary policy (1)	Fiscal policy (2)	Monetary policy (3)	Fiscal policy (4)
Farm crop prices				
Domestic demand	Raise	Raise	Lower	Lower
Export demand	Raise	Lower	Lower	Raise
Net impact	Raise	Lower[a]	Lower	Raise[a]
Farm livestock prices	Lower	Raise[a]	Raise	Lower[a]
Farm input prices	Raise	Raise	Lower	Lower
Farm interest rates	Lower	Raise	Raise	Lower
Net farm income	Raise	Lower[b]	Lower	Raise[b]
Farmland prices	Raise	Lower[c]	Lower	Raise[c]

[a] Direction of change is not unambiguous, but rather conditional upon the relative market share for export demand and relative price elasticity of export demand. A relatively high market share for exports and/or relatively high price elasticity of export demand is assumed.

[b] Assumes the impact on crop prices and interest payments offsets the impact on livestock prices when calculating net farm income both for crop and livestock producers. Deficiency payments are held constant here.

[c] Assumes the impact on crop prices and interest rates offsets the impact on livestock prices when calculating farm land prices.

participating in federal farm programs. These policies affect sales activity in forwardly and backwardly linked sectors as well as the level of government spending. For example, policies which idle productive resources in agriculture have a dampening effect on tractor sales by equipment manufacturers. This lowers employment and output by these manufacturers and results in less economic activity at local dealerships. These policies also get translated into farmland values, which in turn affect the net worth positions of borrowers from commercial banks and other farm lenders. Adverse trends in agriculture have been shown to influence the stability of lenders closely tied to agriculture, the borrowers and depositors at these financial institutions, the level of local nonfarm business activity, and the tax base from which rural governments are financed.

3. Resource Policy Impacts

Agriculture is a dominant user of our nation's natural resources, such as water, timber, and land. Numerous government agencies such as the Environmental Protection Agency, the U. S. Department of Agriculture, and the U. S. Department of the Interior have supervisory jurisdiction over the use of these resources. In recent years many have become concerned with pollutants in water supplies and carcinogens in our food supply caused by agricultural pro-

duction practices. Resource policy concerns have led some to propose a ban on the use of specific agricultural chemicals in the production of food grains and other crops. Research has shown, however, that the resulting drop in yields per acre would have different financial implications for crop and livestock producers in different regions in the country. Net farm income at the national level was shown in a recent study to increase marginally under these policies. Crop producers, particularly those in the corn belt, would benefit economically from a chemical use ban at the expense of livestock producers who would face higher feed grain and protein prices. The financial performance and position of farm borrowers would vary accordingly, with crop producers in northern regions faring better than crop producers in the more temperate southern regions, and with crop producers in general doing better financially than livestock producers.

4. Trade Policy Impacts

Policies which reduce barriers to trade should benefit highly efficient crop and livestock producers in the United States. Producers of specific crop and livestock products stand to gain from the North American Free Trade Agreement (NAFTA) while others may lose. The successful completion of the Uruguay Round of the General Agreement on Tariff and Trade (GATT) negotiations, which placed heavy emphasis on agriculture, is also seen as important to strong international trade flows. Increased U. S. agricultural exports led to higher net incomes and enhanced debt repayment capacity of producers of the crop or livestock product being traded.

Bibliography

Barry, P. J., Ellinger, P. N., Hopkin, J. A., and Baker, C. B. (1994)."Financial Management in Agriculture," 5th ed. Interstate, Danville, IL.

Copeland, T. T., and Weston, F. J. (1988). "Financial Theory and Corporate Policy," 3rd ed. Addison-Wesley, Reading, MA.

Farm Financial Standards Task Force (1991). "Recommendations of the Farm Financial Standards Task Force—Financial Guidelines for Agricultural Producers, 1991."

Lee, W. F., Boehlje, M. D., Nelson, A. G., and Murray, W. G. (1980). "Agricultural Finance," 7th ed. Iowa State Univ. Press, Ames.

Penson, J. B., Jr. (1988). Evaluating financial trends in agriculture. Agric. Finance Rev. December.

U.S. Department of Agriculture (1993). "Economic Indicators of the Farm Sector: National Financial Summary, 1991." Washington, DC.

U.S. Department of Agriculture (1993). "Economic Indicators of the Farm Sector: State Financial Summary, 1991." Washington, DC.

Floriculture

H. MARC CATHEY, *American Horticultural Society, Alexandria, Virginia*

Glossary

Crop modeling Analysis of the various environmental (light, temperature, gases, and relative humidity) and physical (media, nutrition, and water) factors which regulate growth; it is used to develop mathematical equations for predicting plant growth under a wide array of environmental conditions

Double glazing of greenhouses Two layers of a covering (plastic/glass) with a still area in between the two layers which allows visible light to penetrate into the greenhouse but significantly lowers the re-radiation of heat waves back into the sky

Endogenous growth substances Hormones are naturally occurring chemicals which regulate one or more steps in the growth processes; there are five recognized classes of hormones for plants—cytokinins, ethylene, auxins, gibberellins, and abscisic acid

Ethylene Naturally occurring or made chemical that blocks or promotes the effects of $CH_2{=}CH_2$ on the many processes of plants

Genetic engineering Applied field of science whereby scientific principles are used to discover new methodology and instrumentation to produce new forms of and uses for biological entities

HID High-intensity discharge lamps are marketed under the names of metal halide and high-pressure sodium; they are currently the most efficient and longest burning sources to create visible light from electricity for plant growth

Intellectual properties By the processes of invention and interpretation, an individual or a team proposes and patents plants, processes arts, oral, visual, or written creations of the mind

Micropropagation Utilizes the most advanced technology of producing new plants: Tissues from specific parts of the plant are excised, made sterile, and placed in a sterile vial filled with a sterile medium which has been fortified with sugars, mineral ions, and chemical growth factors; the closed vial is held in a standardized environment where the cells divide, organize, and eventually develop roots, leaves, and stems

Photoperiod Controls the growth and development of a wide range of plants; plants are classified into three major types: (1) Day natural (no response to day length), (2) short day (responses favored by decreasing day length), (3) long day (responses favored by increasing day length)

Phytochrome (plant pigment) The blue photo-reversible pigment, extracted from green plants, which detects the active or inactive forms of the growth controlling substances (germination, elongation, branching, flowering, and many other phenomena)

Phyto-sanitary standards By the process of anticipating the risks or the chances of injury, scientists establish the methods to certify that plants have acceptable limits of pests

Postproduction Practices that deal with the processes and factors which influence the longevity and quality of plants

Thermal blankets Energy-conserving covering placed over plants, between the structure covering and the plants, to block the re-radiation of heat from plants back into the sky

Floriculture is the science and practice of growing, harvesting, storing, designing, marketing, and exporting of foliage and flowering plants as cut or container-grown plants. The plant products of floriculture are used in the care and making of home gardens, market gardens, flower shops, garden centers, supermarkets, and greenhouses. The products of floriculture are used in floral displays/gifts for weddings, funerals, births, and other traditional ceremonies. They provide the plant-raising phase for landscaping parks, estates, and botanical gardens. The plants are also involved in the interior landscaping of public and private spaces, the revival of old heritage cultivars, habitat restoration, and the commercialization of native or collected plants. To grow a great range of plant species successfully, the floriculturist must learn how to ward off pest and stress conditions. This requires careful selection of cultivars, cultural procedures, and adaptations on thousands of species. The floriculturist must be aware of plant geography, climate, and global climate change in creating production facilities and where the plants ultimately will be grown. They must also be proficient in the exact identification of the species involved, and their potential for breeding by traditional or genetic engineering means. Floriculture is an avocation for more people than any other kind of hobby in the world and is represented by numerous general or specialized organizations and societies. It is also the most rapidly developing segment of agriculture, producing $8.145 billion at the farmer cash receipts in 1990.

I. Statistics

Statistics on the cash farm value of floriculture are confused with receipts from landscape, nursery, and arborists sales. The 1990 value of just the floriculture segment was $2.77 billion, up 10% from 1989 and up 23% from 1988. These records are incomplete numbers. They represent only a survey of 28 crops from 28 states. The true size of the industry is unknown, but is projected to be almost $5.0 billion. There are currently 41,000 florist shops nationwide, increasing by 635 shops per year. There are also many other outlets for florist crops and its services. Thus, no one knows its true size and it is often not included in with traditional agriculture. Some states in the United States do not recognize floriculture as bona fide agriculture. We also do not know its total economic impact, particularly associated service industries, such as grounds maintenance, interior landscaping, and seedling plug production. Estimates as high as $45 billion are suggested by some economists.

The entire florist and nursery sector, (F&N) including floral crops, sod, nursery, arbor, and bedding plant, totals over $8.145 billion in farm value. It ranks, collectively, behind corn and soybeans but ahead of wheat, cotton, and tobacco. F&N continued to outpace all other major farm sectors, by 7% over 1989, and contributes 10% of all farm crop cash receipts. It ranked seventh among all commodity groups and in 21 states it ranked in the top five commodities in cash receipts. It thus, along with nursery or arbor crops, is the only sector of agriculture that offers employment, land use, production, and sales in all 50 states and 83,000 local jurisdictions. Floriculture (and the green industries) thus has the greatest potential to expand in the next years and should become the dominant plant sector of American agriculture.

II. Historical Developments

The origin of floriculture as a commercial enterprise arose from the practices developed by private estates and public gardens. The motivation for excellence in crop production was for spectacular display effects at any cost. Fancy greenhouse structures were designed for growing plants which required labor-intensive techniques to bring flowering plants to the desired time of display. Secrets of preparing and growing flowers were hoarded by growers. Our problem, even today, is how to put a science into a research area whose final use becomes an "art" (floral design, interior display, exterior bedding). The additional, often undefined and almost undocumented aspects of environmental participation of floral crops continue to baffle floricultural scientists. One only has to mention the debate over the removal of gift plants from a hospital room to see the conflicting force at play in seeking recognition and a national plan for floricultural science. [See ENVIRONMENTAL HORTICULTURE.]

III. Current Issues of Research

A. Plants

A few crops dominate the current production of floral crops in the United States. The short list of cut flowers includes roses (Fig. 1), carnations, chrysanthemums, gladiolus, orchids, and lilies. The container-grown flowering plants are dominated by poinsettias, chrysanthemums, lilies, hydrangeas, azaleas, african violets, begonias, and geraniums. Potted foliage plants include aglaonema, diffenbachia, peperomia, philodendron, and syngonium. Bedding plants include ageratum, impatiens, petunia, marigold, and zinnia.

FIGURE 1 Response of roses to daylength and supplemental lighting. Upper level: Short (8 hr) days, natural winter days (8 to 11 hr), and ND + 4 hr of incandescent light (100 lux) from 10 PM to 2 AM to provide a long day. Lower level: ND + 16 hr (800–2400) 10,250 lux low pressure sodium, ND, ND + 16 hr (800–2400) 6600 lux high pressure sodium.

Other than the rose, chrysanthemum, petunia, and orchid species, most cultivars are derived from a single species with relatively little genetic improvement. The breeding lines from which these advances were realized had their origin in the hands of commercial breeders and are proprietary. With such crops as petunia, poinsettia, chrysanthemum, and impatiens, it is becoming more difficult to separate the cultivars of one commercial source from another. The advances anticipated from the applications of genetic engineering principles to florist crops are yet to be achieved. The costs of and the priority given to most florist crops have limited published reports to relatively few introductions. The promise of a blue rose based on the blue gene (for example) found in petunia is still not on the market. Unusual forms or flower colors, however, have been rescued by the micropropagation techniques created to support the genetic engineering studies. Most florist crops will ultimately benefit from the advances being made in the rapid detection of new genes for resistance to diseases, insects, stress, and postproduction practices. Scientists

trained to use these new techniques will transfer this technology to florist crops.

B. Production

1. Control of the Environment, Media, Nutrition, and Water

Regulation of florist crops began with the selection of day–night temperatures. The plants were "forced" into flower from already formed sets of flower buds. All that had to be done was to warm the plants to bring them into flower ahead of their traditional time of flowering. Spring and summer flowering bulbs, deciduous and evergreen shrubs, and winter flowering annuals fit into this framework of growing. The discovery of the photoperiodic responses in plants by Garner and Allard in the 1920s and the introduction of energy-efficient and sunlight-simulating artificial light sources (fluorescent to HID, high-intensity discharge) in the 1970s have permitted growers to create controlled environments. Now most crops can be manipulated for year-round propagation and culture. Development of soilless growing media, day/night temperature shifts, and regulated nutrients, water, relative humidity, carbon dioxide, and air flow in greenhouses or growth chambers have helped standardize, monitor, and give consistent crop production (Fig. 2). The research continues to use crop modeling techniques, to learn how producers can capture the maximum of radiation and convert it into a maximum of salable product while conserving resources (CO_2, water, nutrients) (Fig. 3). All operations must focus on the postproduction performance of the marketed floral crops, not solely on speed or volume of production. Complex analysis of the products of photosynthesis and the endogenous growth substances regulating maturation and aging will provide the foundation for future research on florist crops. The flowering of crops such as Achimenes, epiphytic Rhododendrons, and Hoya cannot be controlled by the physical or chemical means currently being practiced. We await the identification and reapplication of flower-inducing compounds. There is a popular press report that Japanese scientists have isolated the chemical product(s) produced by the blue photo-reversible pigment, phytochrome. Regulation of growth, flowering, and stress tolerance will continue to be primary areas of research for scientists working with florist crops.

C. Environment

1. Adaptation to Global Climate Change

Floriculture by tradition has often ignored the natural environment by constructing artificial conditions

DARK   LIGHT

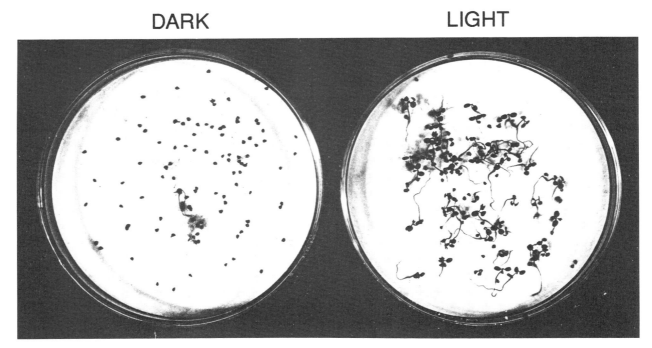

FIGURE 2 Response of impatiens seed to 1 min of red light 24 hr after being held in the dark at 20°C. Left, continuous darkness. Right, 1 min red light promotes germination.

FIGURE 3 Response of Chrysanthemums to increasing concentrations of a chemical growth retardant. Untreated plant on left.

FIGURE 4 Response of petunia to increasing concentration of carbon dioxide and artificial light on growth and flowering. Greenhouse control on right.

to allow for the optimal production of the plants. The primary concern was not the cost of growing the plants, but having an otherwise unavailable and unique flower. All this has changed with the advent of a global floriculture market and airplanes; most flowers can be purchased year-round because they can be grown in other parts of the world. [*See* HORTICULTURAL GREENHOUSE ENGINEERING.]

Floriculture has only recently become concerned with environmental problems. The unavailability of cheap heating/cooling energy sources has forced a reappraisal of production facilities. Growers have installed double glazing on their structures, hung thermal blankets inside to trap the heat, and introduced alternative crops to cut energy requirements. Floriculture continues to become more complex as environmentalists become more concerned about the leaking or releasing of water or air contaminated with fertilizers, pesticides, or gases from the facilities. Research into ways to produce florist plants without fouling the environment will require many creative approaches,

total refitting and redesigning production facilities, and selecting new types of florist crops to be marketed.

The plants of the florist industry have been shown by NASA scientists to function as "clear air machines." They reported that more than 500 chemicals were found in the atmosphere of space capsules that were going to be used for interplanetary travel. They found that traditional florist crops such as chrysanthemum and philodendron could remove some of the toxic compounds from the atmosphere. The full impact of these studies about ways that florist crops can be used in interior or exterior gardening to help improve the environment awaits well-defined research programs.

IV. Quality

Blemish-free florist crops must be marketed without any apparent insect or disease damage. They must also not harbor any eggs or spores that could become

FIGURE 5 Response of petunia to daylength and supplemental lighting. Upper level, short (8 hr) days, natural winter days ND (8 to 11 hr), and ND + 4 hr of incandescent light (100 lux) from 10 PM to 2 AM to provide a long day. Lower level, ND + 16 hr (800–2400) 10,250 lux low pressure sodium, ND, ND + 16 hr (800–2400) 6600 lux high pressure sodium.

noticeable or damaging during the marketing and consumer phases. This has meant that florist crops were subjected to the most massive bombardment of chemicals experienced by any agricultural crops. Many pesticides were used that could not be registered for use on food crops but were considered to be safe on nonconsumable florist crops.

Over the past 20 years, this has changed. Many of the more toxic or questionable chemicals have been banned or withdrawn from the market. Alternative control measures based on botanicals (naturally occurring compounds found in plants) and oils and soaps (physically limiting or disrupting processes by penetrating into the cells of the pest) have become routine control measures again. IPM (integrated pest management) is now used to introduce beneficial insects and microorganisms into a well-defined environment to provide control without the use of persistent pesticides. The scientists researching these crops must combine awareness of the plant's requirements with life cycles, feeding, and breeding requirements of the pests and their predators. [*See* INTEGRATED PEST MANAGEMENT.]

The quality of the plant products must also be defined by how they are conditioned in preparation for shipment to the seller, the care they receive while being sold, and their performance in the hands of the consumer. Scientists have only recently began to relate practices during the production phase to the plant's later performance (Fig. 4). The florist industry currently relies on reducing the nutrient levels in the plants as they mature, and toughening them with reduced light, temperature, and water (Fig. 5). They also add anti-ethylene compounds to the keeping solutions of sugars and preservatives to help prolong the life of the cut flowers. When pathways of senescence can be controlled and new anti-aging genes can be introduced into the plants, the creative research approaches to many florist crops can be realized. There are thousands of cultivars and species hybrids to evaluate—the future for research in this field can be extremely productive.

V. Teams

A. Interdisciplinary Cooperation

Agricultural scientists by tradition have always formed small teams to solve problems of shared concerned. Scientists working on florist crops must become knowledgeable with the culture and performance expectations of several thousand species. Each one has its own special light/temperature/nutrition/ water requirements. Applications of the newer techniques of biotechnology will require the full participation of highly specialized scientists—growers to help make the approaches and findings valid.

VI. Export

Currently 50% of the cut roses, 80% of the carnations and chrysanthemums, and 97% of the gypsophila sold in the United States are imported, primarily from the Andes Mountains of South America. Even with such significant numbers of imported flowers, the U.S. grown florist crops also continue to expand in numbers, variety, and production facilities. There are relatively few countries (the Netherlands, Israel, Germany, Japan, Australia) whose governments maintain significant research and training programs in floriculture. The U.S. land-grant college system continues to be the most important source of trained floricultural scientists. As the world consumption of florist crops continues to expand at 8 to 10% per year, employment in floriculture internationally will continue to be an option for well-trained professionals. Also, the potential markets for the crops of floriculture for export should also become more of an opportunity. Over 130 countries across the world are working out political agreements to have trade between all countries based on the same phyto-sanitary standards, the honoring of intellectual properties, and the most effective ways to provide and fund technology transfer. Floriculture, internationally, has the greatest potential of any sector of agriculture to thrive from the global opportunities for marketing, professional activities, and profitability.

Bibliography

Ball, V. (ed.) (1991). "Ball Red Book," 15th ed. Geo. J. Ball, West Chicago, IL.

Graf, A. B. (1979). "Tropica-Color Cyclopedia of Exotic Plants and Trees from the Tropics and Subtropics," 1st ed. Roehrs, East Rutherford, NJ.

Heriteau, J., with Cathey, M. H. (1990). "The National Arboretum Book of Outstanding Garden Plants." Simon and Schuster, New York, NY.

Johnson, D. C. (1992). Floriculture and environmental horticulture outlook. In "Annual Agricultural Outlook Conference."

Mastalerz, J. W. (1977). "The Greenhouse Environment—The Effect of Environmental Factors on Flower Crops." Wiley, New York.

Larson, R. A. "Introduction to Floriculture," 2nd ed. Academic Press, San Diego, CA.

Sage, L. C. (1992). "Pigment of the Imagination (A History of Phytochrome Research)." Academic Press, San Diego, CA.

Food Biochemistry: Lipids, Carbohydrates, and Nucleic Acids

G. M. SMITH, J. R. WHITAKER, University of California, Davis

I. Overview of Cellular Structure
II. Biological Substances and Their Roles in Food

Glossary

Agar Polysaccharide thickening and stabilizing agent obtained from red algae; it is a mixture of two components, agaropectin and agarose

Alginate Polysaccharide thickening or stabilizing agent obtained from certain brown algae; composed of chains of mannuronic acid and guluronic acid

Amphipathic Describes compounds that contain both polar and non-polar regions

Anomers Cyclic sugars differing in structure only by the stereochemical configuration about the carbon atom originating from the aldehyde or keto group of the straight-chain form of the sugar

Blanching Literally, turning white or losing color, hence a brief heating or cooking of a food that may cause a change in color; the process usually serves to inactivate enzymes that would otherwise lead to deterioration of quality; microorganisms may also be destroyed

Calorie Unit of heat energy describing how much energy can be extracted from foods by the human body; the Calorie is related to the thermodynamic Calorie used in chemistry, which is the amount of heat required to raise the temperature of 1 g of water one Celsius degree; one Calorie = 1000 Calories = 41846 Joules

Carrageenan Polysaccharide from red seaweed composed of β-D-galactopyranose and 3,6-anhydro-galactopyranose, linked by α-1,3 and β-1,4 glycosidic bonds; used as a thickener and stabilizer

Condensation reaction Reaction in which two (or more) molecules join together to form one; usually involves a carbonyl group

Covalent bond Chemical bond in which a pair of electrons is shared by two atoms; to be contrasted with ionic bonds in which two "atoms" (actually, ions) are held together by electrostatic attraction

Dispersion Fine mixture of two physical phases such as solid and liquid (a suspension), oil and water (an emulsion), or liquid and gas (a foam)

Disproportionation Chemical reaction involving two molecules of the same compound, one of which becomes oxidized, and the other reduced

Emulsion Dispersion of two immiscible liquid phases, usually oil in water (o/w) or water in oil (w/o)

Epimers Two sugars that differ only in the configuration about a single carbon atom

Furanose Monosaccharide in which an internal condensation reaction has formed a five-membered ring (four carbon atoms and one oxygen atom)

Hemicellulose Polysaccharide component of plant cell walls (together with cellulose and lignin). Its composition varies from species to species; one class of hemicellulose, the pentosans, is also found in flour (together with starch)

Isoprene 5-carbon repeating structural unit of isoprenes and isoprenoid compounds such as carotenoids

Lignin Highly crosslinked connective tissue found in plants

Neutral lipid Generally refers to triacyl glycerols, the principle component of edible fats and oils

Nucleosides Compounds containing ribose or deoxyribose linked through a β-glycosidic linkage to a purine or pyrimidine base

Nucleophile Compound or ion that possesses a non-bonded pair of electrons in its valence shell and is therefore capable of attacking an electron-poor compound (an electrophile) to form a covalent bond

Oil Lipids that are liquids at room temperature; edible oils must be distinguished from petroleum-based oils, which are generally hydrocarbons

Oligomer (Oligo, meaning *few*) a molecule made of a few repeating units, as opposed to polymers (many units) or monomers (single units)

Optical activity Ability of a compound to rotate the plane of plane polarized light passing through it; the property arises from molecular asymmetry, and thus, is very responsive to small structural differences among similar compounds

Organelle Subcellular structure found in eukaryotic cells, usually composed of or surrounded by a membrane (e.g., mitochondria, chloroplasts, and the Golgi apparatus)

Phytosterols Cholesterol-like compounds found in plants

Polyisoprenoid Compounds containing the repeating structural unit, isoprene

Biochemistry is the study of the structure, properties, and function of biological molecules. Food biochemistry is the study of these same processes and molecules in food and the changes that occur in them during processing, storage, preparation, and consumption.

The first premise of chemistry and biochemistry is that anything the size of an atom or larger is a chemical. All chemicals, including the chemicals of life, are governed by the same rules of chemistry and physics and their structures and functions can be understood by application of these principles. Even the "natural" ingredients in "natural" foods are chemicals, have chemical names, and undergo chemical reactions.[*See* FOOD CHEMISTRY; FOOD COMPOSITION.]

I. Overview of Cellular Structure

All living things (larger than viruses) are composed of individual structural and metabolic units called cells. Many food components are associated with specific structures or parts of the cell. Other components are extracellular. The structure of a cell depends on the kind of organism it represents. Cells can be classified according to various criteria, the most common being whether they do or do not contain a nucleus (eukaryotes and prokaryotes, respectively) and whether they contain a cell wall (bacteria, fungi, and plants) or not (animals). All cells are enclosed in a membrane composed of a double layer ("bilayer") of phospholipids. Many important proteins are attached to the surface of or imbedded in the membrane. Plant, bacterial, and fungi cells are further enclosed in a rigid cell wall

composed of cellulose or crosslinked amino acids and sugars. The exact composition, structure, and thickness of the wall vary from organism to organism. The walls of bacteria are generally covered by an additional, outer membrane composed of a phospholipid bilayer. From the exterior surface of most cells protrude short chains of sugars, called cell-surface determinants, which are recognized by viruses, antibodies, lectins, or other cells. Extracellular structures and compounds also exist (bone, ligament, seed hulls).

The cytoplasm is the aqueous solution that fills the cell. Soluble proteins, carbohydrates, and other metabolites are found in the cytoplasm. Its physical state is unknown, but it is probably very viscous. In the cytoplasm of eukaryotes are membrane systems involved in specific cellular functions, such as transport and protein synthesis. Smaller compartments or structures such as mitochondria (aerobic eukaryotes only) and chloroplasts (green plants and algae only) are suspended in the cytoplasm. These organelles are covered with their own membrane. In eukaryotes, the genetic material DNA and its bound proteins, together called chromatin, are contained in a nucleus. Bacteria have no such organelles or compartments and no nucleus. Some cells have vacuoles that contain protein, starch, or other substances. [*See* PLANT BIOCHEMISTRY; PLANT CYTOSKELETON.]

Especially in higher organisms, cells are organized into tissues (e.g., liver cells, muscle bundles, or phloem), and tissues are organized into organs (e.g., a liver, a heart, or fruit). Some of these tissues or organs serve as food for humans.

II. Biological Substances and Their Roles in Food

A. Lipids

1. Occurrence and Importance in Foods

Lipids are biomolecules that are composed of largely hydrophobic ("disliking water") units. In fact it is solubility, rather than common structural feature, that constitutes the criterion for classifying a compound as a lipid. Lipids are therefore quite structurally diverse, but most fall into a half-dozen or so classes. With the exception of lipid-soluble vitamins and cholesterol, only the most abundant lipids have major importance in food science. These are the acyl lipids: fatty acids, triacyl glycerols, and phospholipids. [*See* FATS AND CHOLESTEROL, ROLE IN HUMAN NUTRITION.]

2. Fatty Acids

Fatty acids (FA's) are simply carboxylic acids of alkanes or alkenes; that is, they have the structure $HOOC-(CH_2)_n-CH_3$ or $HOOC-(CH_2)_m CH=CH(CH_2)_n-CH_3$. Nearly all are linear chains, usually between 4 and about 24 carbon atoms long (18 is most common), and usually of even numbers of carbon atoms. Some FA's are called saturated fatty acids because they are saturated with hydrogen atoms, i.e., have no carbon–carbon double bonds. Others, the mono-unsaturated FA's, have one double bond. Others still, have two or three double bonds (polyunsaturated fatty acids). These fatty acids are common enough to have names (see Table I), but an abbreviated nomenclature exists which employs numbers. The system is i:j(k) where "i" is the number of carbon atoms, "j" is the number of carbon–carbon double bonds, and "k" is the carbon atom at which double bonds begin. The numbering system begins with the carboxylic acid. For example, oleic acid is 18:1(9) (read 18 colon 1...9 or 18 colon 1 Δ 9) because it is 18 carbons long, and contains one double bond which begins at carbon 9. A family of fatty acids of different lengths all having double bonds starting at carbon 9 can be called Δ9 fatty acids. Another system, sometimes used to identify the position of double bonds, counts from the terminal carbon toward the carbon where the double bond begins and expresses this number with the prefix ω (omega). For example, ω3, ω6, and ω9 are the common classes.

Fatty acids, stored as triglycerides, are the most energy-rich storage compounds of animals. Since the

TABLE I

Names and Structures of Some Common Fatty Acids

Common name	Designation	Comments	Structure
Saturated fatty acids			
butyric acid	4:0		$CH_3CH_2CH_2COOH$
caproic acid	6:0		$CH_3CH_2CH_2CH_2CH_2COOH$
caprylic acid	8:0		$CH_3CH_2CH_2CH_2CH_2CH_2CH_2COOH$
capric acid	10:0		$CH_3(CH_2)_8COOH$
lauric acid	12:0		$CH_3(CH_2)_{10}COOH$
myristic acid	14:0		$CH_3(CH_2)_{12}COOH$
palmitic acid	16:0		$CH_3(CH_2)_{14}COOH$
stearic acid	18:0		$CH_3(CH_2)_{16}COOH$
arachidic acid	20:0		$CH_3(CH_2)_{18}COOH$
Monounsaturated fatty acids		Nonconjugated *cis-* double bonds	
myristoleic acid	14:1(9)	Δ9 family	$CH_3(CH_2)_3CH=CH(CH_2)_7COOH$
palmitoleic acid	16:1(9)	Δ9 family	$CH_3(CH_2)_5CH=CH(CH_2)_7COOH$
oleic acid	18:1(9)	Δ9 family, ω9 family	$CH_3(CH_2)_7CH=CH(CH_2)_7COOH$
erucic acid	22:1(13)	ω9 family	$CH_3(CH_2)_7CH=CH(CH_2)_{11}COOH$
Di- and polyunsaturated		Nonconjugated *cis-* double bonds	
linoleic acid	18:2(9,12)	ω6 family	$CH_3(CH_2)_4CH=CHCH_2CH=CH(CH_2)_7COOH$
γ-linoleic acid	18:3(6,9,12)	ω6 family	$CH_3(CH_2)_4CH=CHCH_2CH=CHCH_2CH=CH-(CH_2)_4COOH$
arachidonic acid	20:4(5,8,11,14)	ω6 family	$CH_3(CH_2)_4CH=CHCH_2CH=CHCH_2CH=CHCH_2CH=CH(CH_2)_3COOH$
α-linolenic acid	18:3(9,12,15)	ω3 family	$CH_3CH_2CH=CHCH_2CH=CHCH_2CH=CH(CH_2)_7COOH$
trans fatty acids		Nonconjugated *trans-* double bonds	
elaidic acid	18:1(tr9)	*trans* isomer of oleic acid	$CH_3(CH_2)_7CH=CH(CH_2)_7COOH$
Branched-chain fatty acids			
pristanic acid	2,6,10,14 tetramethyl-pentadecanoic acid		COOH
Odd-carbon chain fatty acids			
margaric acid	17:0		$CH_3(CH_2)_{15}COOH$

liberation of energy involves oxidative reactions, the more reduced a compound is, the more energy it liberates upon oxidation. Accordingly, fats contain about 9 Calories per gram, about twice the energy content of proteins and carbohydrates. Proteins and especially carbohydrates can be converted to fat in the body via conversion to acetyl coenzyme A (coenzyme A is made in the body from the vitamin pantothenic acid. It functions as a carrier of acyl groups such as acetate). The acetate groups are condensed together and reduced, and the long chain so produced is esterified to glycerol to form the actual storage compound, fat. Triglycerides exist in lipid bodies, attached to lipoprotein complexes or in vacuoles of fat cells in adipose tissue. When needed by the body, the acylglycerols are cleaved from glycerol and broken down, two carbons at a time, by formation of acetyl CoA. The two acetate carbon atoms of acetyl CoA are passed to the Krebs Cycle, where they are oxidized to CO_2, which is expired. However, to burn fat, Krebs cycle intermediates must be present to accept the incoming acetate group. Since these intermediates can be made only from sugars and some amino acids, it is necessary to have adequate carbohydrate in the diet or a large supply of liver glycogen (see Carbohydrates) in order to obtain energy from fatty acids.

Fatty acids are the major structural units of edible fats and oils as well as membrane phospholipids, but free fatty acids are not very abundant in foods. They can be produced by alkaline hydrolysis of neutral lipids ("fat"), and the resulting free fatty acids solidify into soap, in a process called saponification. Despite the presence of a hydrophilic carboxyl group, long chain fatty acids dissolve with difficulty in water because of the hydrophobicity of their carbon chain. Since the carbon chain cannot be solvated by water, free fatty acids in water tend to form structures in which their carbon chains associate with one another so that their carboxylic acid ends are at the interface with water. These structures include micelles, spherical structures with the hydrophobic chains on the inside and polar groups on the outside, and complexes of fatty acids with nonpolar substances in which a layer of fatty acids coats the surface with their polar groups toward the outside. Molecules like fatty acids that have both polar and nonpolar character are called amphipathic.

The same concept is important in food science. Emulsions are dispersions of immiscible phases, typically oil in water (O/W) or water in oil (W/O), so that one phase forms droplets suspended in the other (the continuous phase). Emulsions tend to be unstable because of the absence of favorable interactions between the surface of the droplet and the continuous phase. The emulsion breaks when the droplets coalesce to form larger droplets, which present a smaller surface area per unit volume to the continuous phase. Rising or settling of the droplets separates them from the continuous phase and encourages coalescence. Amphipathic molecules can coat the surface of a droplet and interact favorably with both phases, thereby stabilizing the emulsion. In the case of an oil droplet coated by anionic fatty acids, charge–charge repulsion prevents the droplets from approaching one another, and discourages coalescence. Molecules capable of stabilizing emulsions are known as emulsifiers. Polar lipids, including fatty acids, are good examples of emulsifiers.

Fatty acids of chain lengths greater than about 14 have little, if any, flavor or odor. Short chain fatty acids, especially butyric acid, have pungent odors and are detectable at very low levels. Small amounts of butyric acid give a pleasant sweet smell to chocolate and butter, but it is usually considered an off-flavor in other foods. Especially in milk, the hydrolysis of fatty acids from neutral lipids or phospholipids by enzymes such as bacterial lipases produces this off-flavor, which is called hydrolytic rancidity. Oxidative rancidity, the major flavor defect arising from lipids, is caused by the oxidation or peroxidation of unsaturated fatty acids in acyl lipids. [*See* FOOD BIOCHEMISTRY: PIGMENTS, FLAVORS, AROMAS, AND STABILITY.]

3. Acyl Glycerols
a. Fats and Oils Triacyl glycerols (also called triglycerides or neutral lipids) are hydrophobic, uncharged compounds, formed from esterification of the three alcohol groups of glycerol to three fatty acids. The fatty acids are usually not the same, but what governs the fatty acid chain length and the positions to which they are esterified is unknown. A sample of fat or oil, then, contains many different molecules composed of different combinations of fatty acids esterified to different positions of the glycerol. A process called interesterification, in which the different glycerol oxygens exchange their fatty acids, leads to randomization of the fatty acids, which changes some of the properties of the fat and makes studies of the biological phenomenon of nonrandom positioning difficult.

The weak polarity of the ester groups is almost entirely overpowered by the hydrophobicity of the fatty acid chains. Triglycerides do not interact with water and consequently aggregate to present as little surface as possible to the water that surrounds them. The fatty acid side chains interact with one another, and, because of their linear, zig-zag structure, form a crystalline arrangement (see Fig. 1). Triglycerides tend to assume a conformation in which fatty acid chains associate with one another, leaving the third to point in the opposite direction, along the same axis. The molecules resemble a tuning fork, if the fatty acids on C1 and C3 point in the same direction, or like a chair, if an end fatty acid and the center point in the same direction. These chair-shaped or tuning fork-shaped units can pack together into a crystal. Actually, more than one crystalline arrangement is possible. These different crystal forms have different stabilities and therefore, different melting points. A sample of solid fat may therefore have three melting points, which actually correspond to transitions among the different crystal forms, and to a liquid. In tristearin (all three fatty acids are stearic acid), these phase transition temperatures are 54.7°, 64.0°, and 73.3°C. This behavior is typical of edible fats and oils. Of course, the crystal form of a fat or solidified oil depends on the temperature. At room temperature, processing temperature, or consumption temperature, the material may exist in any of the crystalline states or as a liquid. Fat crystals called the β form are large (25–50 μm) and tend to grow during aging,

producing a coarse, grainy texture. β' crystals, found in rearranged (interesterified) lard and hydrogenated cottonseed oils, are small needles of about 1 μm and are capable of trapping microscopic air bubbles upon whipping. The creamy texture of the β' form is advantageous in margarine and products used for frostings, etc. Solid fats are not entirely uniform on a microscopic scale and, at moderate temperature, exist as mixtures of particles and liquid.

Structural features that disturb the regularity of packing decrease the stability of a crystal form and lower its melting point. Branched chains, which occur relatively rarely, decrease the phase transition temperature. *trans*-Unsaturated fatty acids disrupt the packing slightly, because carbon–carbon sp^2 bond angles are different from carbon–carbon sp^3 bond angles. *cis*-Unsaturations cause a major disruption in packing with saturated chains and are very effective in decreasing the phase transition temperature of a triglyceride. The difference between a fat and an oil, which is simply whether the substance is a solid or a liquid at room temperature, is determined largely by the occurrence of double bonds in the fatty acids. Oils are characterized by a greater number of double bonds and fats contain fewer. Vegetable shortening is produced from oil by partial catalytic hydrogenation to give the consistency required for the intended use.

b. Synthetic Fats Because fats are the food components with the highest number of Calories and because of the perception that fats in the diet are associated with hypercholesterolemia and coronary heart disease, development of fat substitutes is an active area of research. Although polysaccharides and proteins are successful at mimicking texture and some other properties of fat, none of these products can be heated to 375°F (190°C) for long periods of time for the purpose of frying. A successful attempt to duplicate the important physical and chemical properties of triglycerides is to attach fatty acids to polyalcohols other than glycerol. Polyacyl sucrose has been used. Digestive enzymes do not recognize this acylated sugar as a triglyceride, so it is metabolically inert, yields no Calories, and does not alter lipid metabolism. This product is not yet available and may never reach the market. It is not clear how the body deals with a particular nonmetabolizable material; though the bulk may be excreted, small amounts may build up in various organs and pose a health hazard. Hence, extensive testing is necessary before nonnutritive "foods" are allowed on the market.

A

B

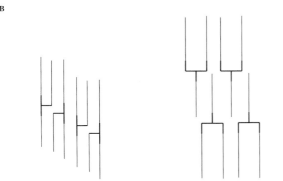

FIGURE 1 Lipid structures. (A) A hypothetical triglyceride containing a saturated fatty acid (myristic acid), a *trans*-monounsaturated fatty acid and a *cis*-di-unsaturated fatty acid, linoleic acid. (B) Crystal forms of triglycerides: chair shape of β crystals, tuning fork of β' crystals.

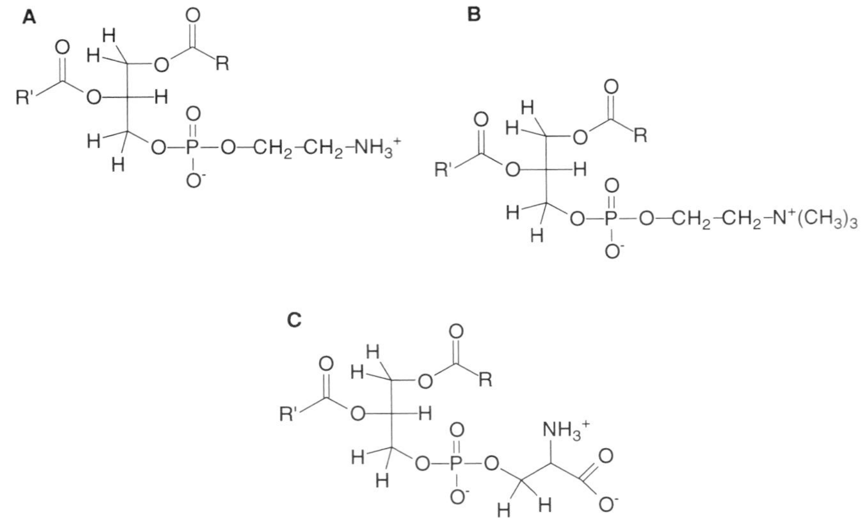

FIGURE 2 Structures of phospholipids. (A) Phosphatidylethanolamine, (B) phosphatidylcholine, and (C) phosphatidylserine.

c. Phospholipids

Polar acyl glycerols, phospholipids and glycolipids, also exist. Phospholipids are the major component of cell membranes and intracellular membrane networks. Glycolipids are a less abundant component. In foods that contain little fat (e.g., grains, fruits), phospholipids and glycolipids can comprise 50% of the total lipid.

Phospholipids are 1,2-diacyl glycerols, esterified on the remaining position of glycerol by phosphoric acid, which is also esterified to a short alcohol. The alcohol is often choline, ethanolamine, or serine. These compounds are called phosphatidyl choline (also known as lecithin), phosphatidyl ethanolamine, and phosphatidyl serine (Fig. 2).

Like the neutral lipids, phospholipids contain fatty acids that are generally not identical. They may be saturated, or unsaturated, short or long; the fatty acids determine the phase transition properties of the phospholipid.

Unlike neutral lipids, phospholipids have a strongly polar end, termed the "polar head group," which associates with water. The fatty acids, or nonpolar "tails," do not. There are several aggregated structures that allow the proper contacts to occur (Fig. 3). Micelles, like those formed by free fatty acids and detergents can occur in which the phospholipids form a sphere with the fatty acids on the inside.

Another structure that allows polar–polar and nonpolar–nonpolar interaction is one in which the phospholipids coat a hydrophobic structure or droplet. An example of this kind of structure is one in which phospholipids act as emulsifiers in O/W emulsions.

Phospholipids can also stabilize W/O emulsions by the same mechanism; the polar head group dissolves in the water droplet and the hydrophobic chains are solvated in the continuous phase.

An example of another emulsion structure involving phospholipids is the milk fat globule, the particles of cream that rise to the top of milk. The globule is a droplet containing the neutral lipids and fat-soluble vitamins of milk. The droplet is surrounded by a lipid monolayer "membrane." There is a double layer of proteins associated with the hydrophilic surface of the membrane that is held by polar interactions.

Cellular and subcellular membranes are composed of phospholipid bilayers in which polar head groups face the inside and outside of the cell, and nonpolar tails face one another. In this structure, the fatty acid side chains pack against one another in an ordered way, but at room temperature have enough energy to maintain a fluid state, or liquid crystalline state. At lower temperatures (determined by the fatty acid composition), the side chains form a gel. Since fluidity of cellular membranes is necessary for many cellular processes, life is not possible at temperatures at which the membrane is a gel. This is one of the reasons that refrigeration inhibits bacterial growth. In food, however, the crystalline, liquid crystalline, and gel states may exist and are important.

Other structures of phospholipids in water include hexagonal phases. These are tubular arrangements constructed of stacked rings of phospholipids. The tubes pack together in a hexagonal arrangement, in some cases with a seventh tube in the center. Two types

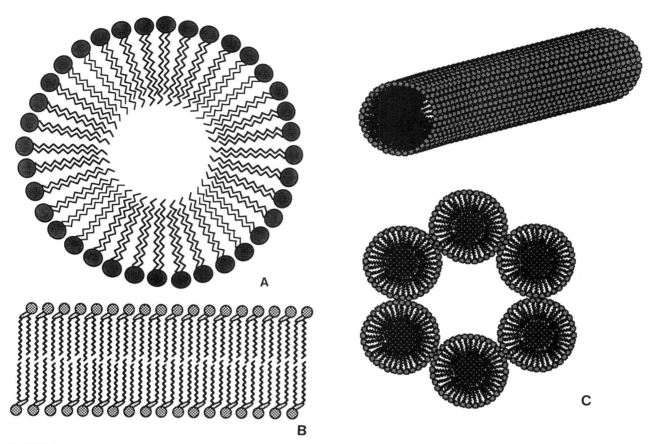

FIGURE 3 Aggregates of polar lipids. The round shaded represent the polar head group; the zig-zag lines represent the fatty acid chains. (A) A cross-section of a phospholipid micelle. Micelles are approximately spherical. The fatty acids are not drawn to the same scale as the diameter of the micelle. (B) A phospholipid bilayer membrane. (C) A cylindrical arrangement of phospholipids that stack in a hexagonal fashion. There may be a seventh cylinder in the center of the hexagon.

of tubes can exist: tubes formed with heads on the outside and tails on the inside are hydrophilic, while those with the nonpolar tails on the outside are hydrophobic.

4. Nonsaponifiable Lipids

Carotenoids are also important food lipids. Carotenoids are branched, unsaturated compounds containing 40 carbon atoms that occur in two main classes, carotenes and xanthophylls. Carotenes are hydrocarbons, whereas xanthophylls contain oxygen atoms, as well (Fig. 4). The importance of carotenoids in food is threefold: they are pigments that provide red and yellow color in foods, they are precursors of flavor and aroma compounds, and they are precursors of provitamin A. Carotenoids are produced only by plants, but are transmitted to animals in their diet. The most dramatic example is perhaps the yellow or orange color of egg yolk, which arises from carotenoids in the feed.

Cholesterol, the quintessential steroid, has the structure shown in Fig. 4. It is found in substantial amounts only in animal products, and may occur as the free alcohol or esterified to a fatty acid. It occurs in membranes, in fat, and in lipoprotein complexes such as the famous high-density and low-density lipoproteins of blood serum. Although buildup of cholesterol deposits in arteries is a serious health problem, the relationship between dietary cholesterol and atherosclerosis remains controversial. Cholesterol derivatives cholic acid and deoxycholic acid are secreted into the digestive tract where they help emulsify and aid in the digestion of ingested lipids.

Although plant lipids are nearly devoid of cholesterol, cholesterol-like compounds, the phytosterols, exist. Since several phytosterols exist and are present in differing ratios in different plants oils, phytosterol composition can be a useful criterion for detecting adulteration of oils with less-expensive oils.

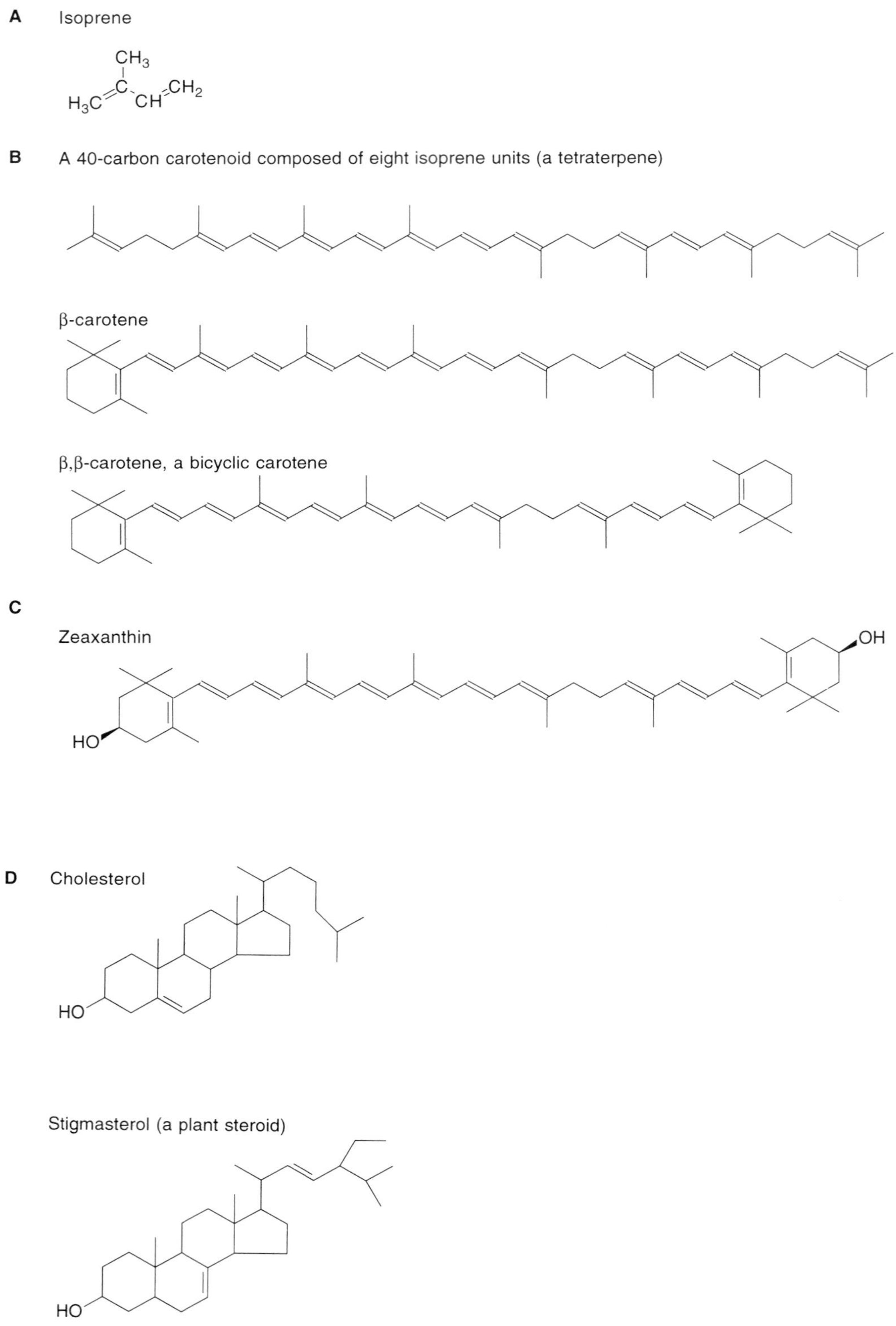

A   Isoprene

B   A 40-carbon carotenoid composed of eight isoprene units (a tetraterpene)

β-carotene

β,β-carotene, a bicyclic carotene

C

Zeaxanthin

D   Cholesterol

Stigmasterol (a plant steroid)

FIGURE 4 Nonsaponifiable lipids. (A) Isoprene, the structural unit of carotenoids. (B) Carotenes, carotenoids that contain only carbon and hydrogen. (C) A xanthophyll, a carotenoid that contains oxygen. (D) Cholesterol and a cholesterol-like steroid of plant origin.

B. Carbohydrates

1. Occurrence and Importance in Foods

Carbohydrates are diverse, abundant, and widely distributed. They are the ultimate source of all food on our planet, which arises from photosynthetic carbon fixation. Digestible carbohydrates provide about 4 Calories per gram to human beings. They also provide important structures in plants and, together with other material, the cell walls of plants, fungi, and bacteria. [*See* CARBOHYDRATES, ROLE IN HUMAN NUTRITION.]

Carbohydrates are categorized as monosaccharides, oligosaccharides, or polysaccharides, the members of the latter categories being constructed from the members of the first.

2. Simple Sugars, Sugar Alcohols, and Oligomers

Although some argument could be made that the two-carbon aldehyde glycolaldehyde is a sugar, it is practical to call the three-carbon compounds glyceraldehyde and dihydroxyacetone the simplest sugars (Fig. 5). As the word "carbohydrates" implies, their empirical formula (e.g., $C_3H_6O_3$ or $(C_1H_2O)_n$) suggests them to be hydrates (H_2O) of carbon. Glyceraldehyde, with an aldehyde group at C1 is an "aldose"; dihydroxyacetone, a ketone, is a "ketose." Glyceraldehyde has another property of note: because of the tetrahedral geometry about the center carbon and the nonequivalence of carbons 1 and 3, it exists in two forms. In standard notation (a Fischer projection), the most oxidized carbon is drawn at the top, the most reduced at the bottom, and the two lateral bonds

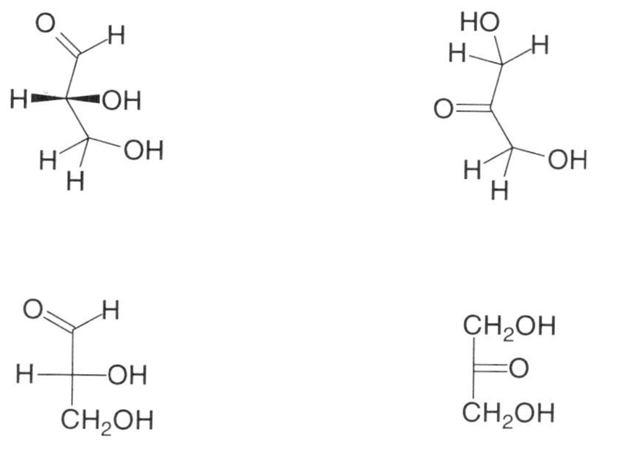

Glyceraldehyde   Dihydroxyacetone

FIGURE 5   The structures of glyceraldehyde and dihydroxyacetone, the "simplest sugars." Two ways of drawing the structure are shown.

are drawn protruding from the paper. The form of glyceraldehyde with the OH group protruding to the right is called the D isomer, the other is the L isomer. These terms relate to the direction that plane polarized light is rotated as it passes through a solution of these optically active compounds; D for dextro, L for levo.

More complex monosaccharides can be drawn by adding additional H–C–OH units to the structure immediately below the carbonyl carbon. If another H–C–OH were drawn in the structure of dihydroxyacetone, it could be drawn in either of two ways. If the newly drawn OH points to the right, the structure is a D sugar, if it points to the left, it is an L sugar, by analogy to the structure of glyceraldehyde (Fig. 6). Many other sugars can be drawn by inserting H–C–OH units into these structures (see Fig. 6). The direction of the OH on the next-to-the-bottom carbon determines whether it is D or L. Most sugars of biological origin are D sugars. Sugars of biological origin occur with structures like these, having three to seven carbon atoms. Those with five carbons (e.g., ribose) and six carbons (e.g., glucose, galactose, fructose) are most common.

Aldehydes and ketones are very reactive groups and are subject to attack by nucleophiles, such as –OH groups. The structure formed when an alcohol R–OH reacts with a carbonyl group is a hemiacetal or a hemiketal (Fig. 7). Accordingly, sugars typically cyclize when one of the OH groups attacks its own carbonyl group to form an intramolecular hemiacetal or hemiketal. Because of the bond angles about carbon and oxygen, the structures involving five-membered ("furanose") and six-membered ("pyranose") rings are stable and most important. For a six-carbon aldose, the important structure is a pyranose formed by attack of the C5-OH group.

One more variation exists: the OH group could attack the carbonyl from either side and the C-OH resulting from the C=O could point up or down (see Fig. 8). The isomer in which the OH at C1 points down is the α isomer, the one in which it points up is the β isomer. These kinds of isomers at the site of condensation are called anomers. The structure formed by the condensation is an (α or β) aldopyranose (Fig. 8). For glucose and galactose in water, there is little of the open chain form, and the α and β forms of the pyranose dominate.

Fructose is a six-carbon ketose that otherwise resembles glucose. Although the -OH group of C6 can attack the keto group to form α and β ketopyranoses, the -OH group of C5 can also attack to form α and β ketofuranoses (Fig. 8). Fructose exists in water as a mixture of the four cyclic forms, α and β ketopyr-

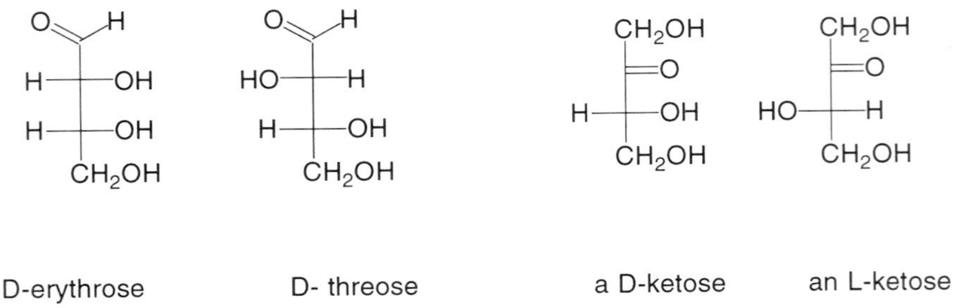

D-erythrose   D- threose   a D-ketose   an L-ketose

FIGURE 6 Structures of isomers of 4-carbon sugars: two D-aldoses and a D- and an L-ketose, derived from drawing additional H-C-OH group beneath the carbonyl carbons of glyceraldehyde and dihydroxyacetone.

anoses and α and β ketofuranoses plus a very small amount of the straight chain form.

Ketones and aldehydes are easily oxidizable groups. For this reason, free ketoses and aldoses are called reducing sugars.

There exist monosaccharides other than the simple H-C-OH structures described above, but most of them are derivatives of these simple monosaccharides. The most common of these variations are deoxysugars, in which an OH group is replaced by a hydrogen atom (e.g., deoxyribose), amino sugars, in which an OH group is replaced by an NH_2 group (e.g., glucosamine), acetylated aminosugars (N-acetylglucosamine), sugar alcohols, in which the aldo or keto C=O group has been replaced by H-C-OH (e.g., glycerol, sorbitol, glucitol), and sugar acids, in which C1 or the bottom carbon or both have been oxidized to an acid (COOH). Phosphorylated sugars, in which an -OH group is replaced by a $-OPO_3^{2-}$ group, are common metabolites. In fact, free monosaccharides are rather rare in biochemistry compared to their phosphorylated derivatives. In sugar-rich foods, the sugars exist either as free monosaccharides or as polymers (see below).

3. Oligosaccharides

Oligosaccharides are chains of two or more monosaccharides linked together by shared oxygen atoms.

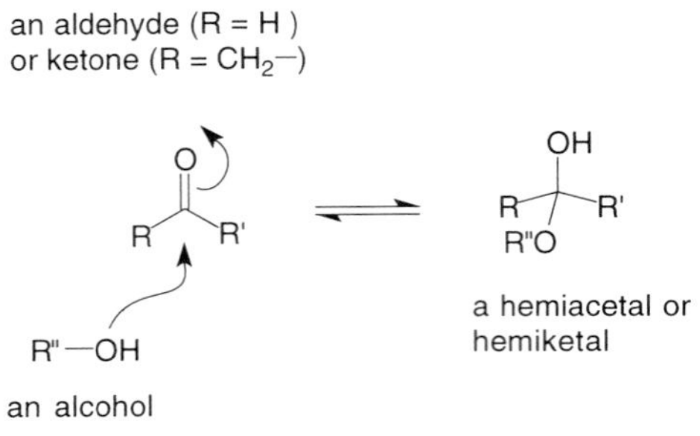

an aldehyde (R = H)
or ketone (R = CH$_2$−)

a hemiacetal or hemiketal

R″—OH

an alcohol

FIGURE 7 Formation of a hemiacetal (or hemiketal) from the attack of an alcohol on an aldehyde (or ketone).

Since any of the hydroxyl oxygen atoms on the sugar can be shared (but not the ring oxygen), attachment can occur in several ways (see Fig. 9). Usually, at least one of the carbon atoms bonded to the shared oxygen is the "anomeric carbon," where ring condensation occurred, and such linkages are called glycosidic bonds. The remainder of the name of the linkage is derived from the numbers of the carbon atoms that share the oxygen and information about the configuration of the anomeric carbon, if it is involved. Lactose is composed of galactose and glucose in a β-1-4 linkage; the C1 of galactose is in the β anomeric configuration and is attached to the oxygen on the C4 of glucose. Note that, unlike the C1 of the galactose moiety, the C1 of the glucose moiety is unattached and can be either α or β (both α and β lactose exist). Lactose is therefore a reducing sugar, and glucose is at the "reducing end." Another disaccharide, sucrose, is composed of fructose as a five-membered ring, and glucose, but the anomeric carbon atoms are both involved in the linkage; sucrose is therefore not a reducing sugar.

Many other di- , tri-, tetra-, etc., saccharides exist; complex sugars containing up to about 10 monomer units are generically called oligosaccharides.

4. Polysaccharides

Strings of monosaccharides of more than about 10 units are called polysaccharides. The structures of the monomer units are similar and the linkages are the same as for oligosaccharides, but the chains are longer. The average length of the chain of a polysaccharide is expressed as its degree of polymerization (DP), the average number of monomer units.

Some polysaccharides are constructed of a single kind of monomer (e.g., glucose), whereas others are composed of several different sugars. Polysaccharides composed only of glucose monomers are called glucans.

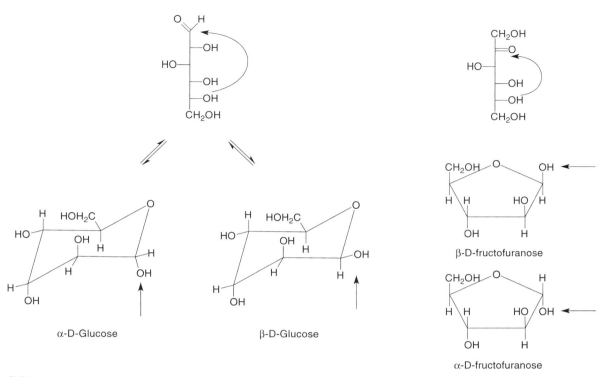

FIGURE 8 Formation of glucopyranoses and fructofuranoses from the open-chain forms of the sugars. The position of the hydroxyl group of the reducing carbon (arrows) determines whether the sugar is the α or β anomer.

Even though the monomer units are the same in all glucans, they can be quite different because the units can be strung together in several different ways. Starch, for instance, the primary storage compound of plants, is composed of amylose, a linear α-D-glucopyranosyl polymer with α-1,4 linkages (and occasional branches with α-1,6 linkages), and amylopectin, a branched α-D-glucopyranosyl polymer with α-1,4 linkages and frequent α-1,6 branches. Starch, which is soluble in warm to hot water and is digestible, is the most abundant polysaccharide in the human diet. Cellulose, the principal component of plant cell walls, has essentially the same structure as amylose except that the linkages are β-1,4 and the chains tend to be longer. However, because mammals lack β glycosidases, enzymes capable of hydrolyzing the β-1,4 linkages of cellulose, this compound is completely undigestible, contributes no Calories or carbon to the human diet, but is nutritionally important as dietary fiber. It is also notably insoluble because of its large chain length. So, although polysaccharides may have superficially similar structures, their properties and roles in food are sufficiently different to be discussed individually.

a. Starch Starch exists as granules of 2–100 μm in various plant cells such as in potato tubers, beans, and grain seeds. The granules contain a ratio of amylose to amylopectin that varies from species to species. A typical ratio is between 20 and 40% amylose. The DP of amylose and the extent of chain branching in amylopectin also vary from species to species. The DP is about 1000–2000 in wheat, but may be as high as 4500 in potato. Amylopectin is composed of short, linear runs of 15–30 residues in α-1,4 linkages, attached at their reducing ends via α-1,6 linkages to other linear runs of 15–30 residues in α-1,4 linkages, and so on. This treelike structure can become very large and can contain up to a million glucosyl units. It is thought that the branches wrap around the strand from which they have branched to form a double helix (see Fig. 10).

Starch granules do not dissolve in cold water, but swell remarkably in heated water to form a thick suspension of swollen granules of dissolved starch. The temperature at which the swelling and dissolution occur, known as the gelatinization temperature, varies with the source of the starch, usually occurring between about 52° and 80°C. When the temperature

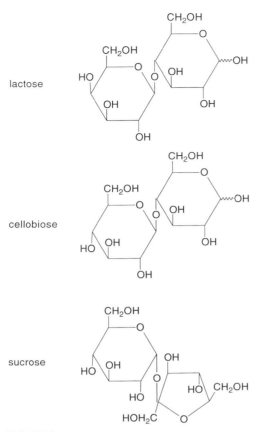

FIGURE 9   Structures of three disaccharides, lactose (milk sugar), cellobiose (a breakdown produce of cellulose), and sucrose ("sugar").

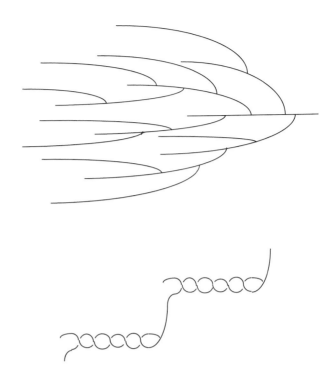

FIGURE 10   Schematic depiction of amylopectin structure. The branches of the treelike structure of amylopectin (above) are probably wound about each other in a double-helical fashion (below).

of gelatinized starch is lowered while stirring, the solution increases in viscosity. If cooling is not accompanied by stirring, a gel is formed. The gel often undergoes a further transformation, called retrogradation, to a microcrystalline state.

These transitions appear to be determined by structural changes in amylose. In starch granules, amylose exists as two strands wound around each other in an extended double helix. In the starch granules of cereals, these double helices are bundled in groups of seven, with six on the outside of the bundle and one in the center (A-type amylose). In potato starch and retrograded starch, the bundles contain six double helices, arranged hexagonally with water in the center (B-type amylose). In legume starch, a combination of both types occurs. The double helices are stabilized by hydrogen bonds (formed when a hydroxyl oxygen and an oxygen atom of a nearby glucose monomer share a hydrogen atom). Water molecules exist between the packed helices. Upon swelling, the structure changes to a thicker, shorter helix, the V-helix.

Although hydrogen bonds also stabilize V-type amylose, the helix must be rather flexible because small molecules can diffuse in and alter its diameter. The internal channel of the helix lacks hydroxyl groups and is hydrophobic, so, in cereal grains, lipids are enclosed in the helix, which stabilizes the structure, but limits swelling. Because these conformational changes are reversible, the structure of the amylose can change with time, and the change can affect starch-containing products. Fresh bread, for instance, contains the V-amylose of gelatinized starch, but stale bread has B-type amylose, which is characteristic of retrograde starch.

Amylopectin can be dissolved in hot water to form a viscous solution. However, it neither gels (except at very high concentration) nor undergoes retrogradation.

Starch and its glucan components have many uses in foods. Starch, amylose, and amylopectin are all used as thickeners and binders in dressings, sauces, gravies, puddings, and mayonnaises. Amylose forms thin, tasteless films, and can be used as a protective coating to retard oxidation or prevent sticking in various foods.

Even though starch is a versatile ingredient, it has been made more versatile by modification. These modifications include the following: (1) Gelatinization, followed by drying starch, makes a product that will take up cold water and form a gel. (2) Limited acid hydrolysis of starch yields shorter chains. Viscosity depends upon molecular asymmetry, and, since shorter chains are less asymmetric, solutions of hydrolyzed starch are less viscous than those of unhydrolyzed starch. (3) Chemically modified products such as hydroxypropyl and carboxymethyl starch are used as thickeners and to form gels. (4) Chemical crosslinking, using any of several bifunctional reagents (adipic anhydride, epichlorohydrin, or phosphorous oxychloride), yields a stronger, more heat-resistant starch that is widely used in foods.

b. Cellulose Cellulose, the β-1,4 polymer of D-glucopyranose, is a large, insoluble polymer, with a DP of 1000 to 14,000, depending on its source. It is the principle component of plant cell walls, and forms an appreciable fraction of the solid portion of wood. Cellulose forms fibers and fiberlike crystals stabilized by intermolecular hydrogen bonds. The strength of this structure contributes to its insolubility and to its strength as a structural material. It does not hydrate well and does not swell readily when moistened. It is used in foods as a filler and as a dietary fiber supplement. It is obtained for the latter purpose from the hull of cereal grains ("bran") or from saw dust. Bran also contains the polysaccharide hemicellulose and lignin. Small particles of microcrystalline cellulose suspended in aqueous media can give a creamy mouth feel and are sometimes used as fat substitutes. Some of its derivatives are even more useful. These include alkyl (often methyl or methylethyl) cellulose, hydroxyalkyl (typically methyl, propyl, or propylmethyl) cellulose, and carboxymethyl cellulose. These are used as thickeners in products like sauces, oil-free salad dressings, milkshakes, and nondairy whipped topping, to form gels, and as coatings for fried foods. Methyl cellulose has the peculiar property of gelling at high temperature and melting upon cooling; it is therefore suitable for use in systems in which running during cooking would be a problem.

c. Pectin Pectin is a polysaccharide formed from 150 to 500 D-galacturonic acid units bonded in α-1,4 linkages. Galacturonic acid is a sugar acid of galactose in which C6 has been oxidized to a COOH group. There are also L-rhamnose units in the main chain (about 10%) and branches containing β-D-galactopyranose and α-L-arabinofuranose. The carboxylic groups of the galacturonic acid often exist as methyl esters. Pectins can differ in degree of esterification, and fall into two groups, low-methoxy pectin (<50% acidic groups esterified) and high methoxypectin (>50% acidic groups esterified), which have different gelling properties. High-methoxy pectin can be de-esterified to produce low-methoxy pectin.

The gelling process is different in the two types of pectin. High-methoxy pectin gels at low pH (2.0–3.5) and in the presence of other dissolved solids (e.g., sucrose). The low pH protonates unesterified carboxylic acid groups and the chains associate by hydrophobic interactions, stabilized by interchain hydrogen bonding. The other solids (sucrose) are thought to aid gellation by decreasing the amount of water available to solvate the pectin, thereby forcing it to seek other interactions. Low-methoxy pectin gels over a wider pH range (2.5–6.5) and at a much lower level of dissolved solids. The gellation requires Ca^{2+} ion, which bridges between anionic groups on different chains.

Pectin is obtained from apple and citrus pulp by extraction at elevated temperature at low pH. Conditions are not sufficiently harsh to hydrolyze the glycosidic or ester bonds. It is used primarily as a thickener in jams and jellies, but, because of its partial hydrophobic character and viscosity production, can act as an emulsifier and stabilizer. A gel formed from pectin and calcium may be sheared to produce an applesauce-textured ingredient or homogenized to produce a "creamy" ingredient for use as fat substitutes. Because gels can contain as little as 1% pectin, the gels contain very few Calories per gram.

d. Agar A gel-forming mixture of polysaccharides called agar is isolated from red algae. Its two main components, agarose and agaropectin, contain the same backbone structure, β-D-galactopyranose and 3,6-anhydro-α-L-galactopyranose (a single oxygen atom is shared by carbons 3 and 6). These units occur with alternating 1-4 and 1-3 linkages. In agarose, a hydroxyl group of about every 10th galactose unit is esterified to sulfuric acid. Agaropectin contains more sulfate esters and contains molecules of pyruvate held as a ketal between the C4-OH and C6-OH groups of the D-galactose residues.

Agar can be dissolved in hot water then gels upon cooling, even at very low concentrations (as low as 0.04%). Gellation is reversible, and agar can be redissolved by heating, but the melting temperature of the gel may be 30° or more above the congealing temperature. This hysteresis makes the gel uniquely heat-stable.

Agar is produced by extraction in hot water, and then washing of the gel that forms upon cooling. It is perhaps most familiar as the solid microbiological medium used in plate, slant, and stab cultures. It is used for gelatinlike confections in Asia and in pastry fillings in Europe and the United States. In addition to its gelling properties, it is an emulsifier and stabilizer and is used in sherbets, ice cream, and yogurt, often together with other stabilizers. It is not digestible and may be considered as dietary fiber.

e. Alginates The cell walls of brown algae contain alginates, linear polymers of β-D-mannuronic acid and α-L-guluronicacid linked by 1-4 glycosidic bonds. The protonated (free acid) form, alginic acid, is not soluble. Sodium and potassium salts, but not calcium salts, are soluble. These properties are exploited in the isolation and purification of alginates and in controlling its gelling properties.

There are three types of sequences in alginates: oligo β-1,4-D-mannuronate, oligo α-1,4-L-guluronate and alternating oligo β-D-mannuronate-α-L-guluronate. Each kind of sequence runs for about 20 residues before changing to another type. The ultimate degree of polymerization is between about 200 and 1000. The ratio of mannuronic to guluronic acids in these chains is generally about 1.5:1, but varies from species to species.

As might be guessed, the gellation mechanism involves crosslinking of chains by Ca^{2+}. The calcium complex involves four guluronate residues, two adjacent residues from the same chain, and two from another, which links the chains. Many such crosslinks can exist between the same two chains, so the association is very strong. Many alginate molecules can line up side by side to produce a large crosslinked network. To obtain a strong, uniform gel, crosslinking must occur slowly, so Ca^{2+} ion is added as insoluble salts, which dissolve slowly as newly solvated calcium ions are taken up by the gel network. The gels so formed are not thermally reversible.

Because alginic acid is insoluble, it cannot be used in acidic foods. Instead, the acid groups can be partially esterified by reaction with propylene oxide. The resulting propylene glycol alginate ester forms a soft, elastic gel in the presence of Ca^{2+}, down to pH 2.

Alginates are used as thickeners in sauces, whipped toppings, yogurt, bakery fillings, and as a stabilizer in ice cream. Alginates have recently been used as gelling agents in the production of fabricated foods, such as fabricated onion rings and cherries.

f. Carrageenan Also isolated from seaweed (red seaweed of the class Rhodophyceae) is the polysaccharide carrageenan. Like agar, carrageenan is composed of β-D-galactopyranose and 3,6-anhydro-galactopyranose, but linked via alternating α-1,3 and β-1,4 glycosidic bonds. Some of the hydroxyl groups are esterified to sulfuric acid. The anhydrogalactose content, and the extent and position of the esterification define three types of carrageenan: κ, ι and λ. κ carrageenan is about 34% anhydrogalactose and is 25% esterified (as galactose-4-sulfate); ι carrageenan is about 30% anhydrogalactose and is 32% esterified (galactose-4-sulfate and anhydrogalactose-2-sulfate); λ carrageenan contains little anhydrogalactose and is 35% esterified (as galactose-2-sulfate and galactose-2,6-disulfate). The degree of polymerization for κ and λ carrageenan is between 1000 and about 4500.

In hot water, carrageenan exists as unstructured monomers. Upon cooling of κ or ι carrageenan, helices and double helices are formed, providing crosslinks that eventually lead to a continuous network, resulting in a thermally reversible gel. Because the attached sulfate group enhances solubility, κ carrageenan, the least esterified, forms an opaque gel (i.e., containing precipitate), while ι carrageenan gels are clear and elastic. Excessive aggregation causes the expulsion of water (synersis) from the gel, which then becomes brittle. The sequence of λ carrageenan and high degree of esterification favor a zig-zag structure rather than a double helix, so λ carrageenan does not gel. It does, however, build viscosity.

As in alginates, cations can play a major role in gelling. κ-Carrageenan binds K^+ and ι-carrageenan binds Ca^{2+}, and both interactions result in strengthened interchain crosslinks. Thus, cation concentration as well as carrageenan concentration can be used to adjust gel strength and gelling temperature.

Because of its appreciable negative charge, carrageenans interact strongly with positive regions of κ-casein on the surface of the casein micelle. The distil ends of carrageenan form crosslinks. Carrageenans are therefore used in dairy products. Carrageenan is also used in combination with locust bean gum, which has regions to which carrageenans bind separated by regions to which they do not. The result is long-range crosslinks without closely packed aggregation. Elasticity is therefore increased and synersis is reduced. Because of the strength and elasticity of gelled carrageenan, it is currently used in low-fat formulations of ground beef products.

g. Other Thickeners and Stabilizers Other carbohydrates that act as thickeners and emulsifiers in-

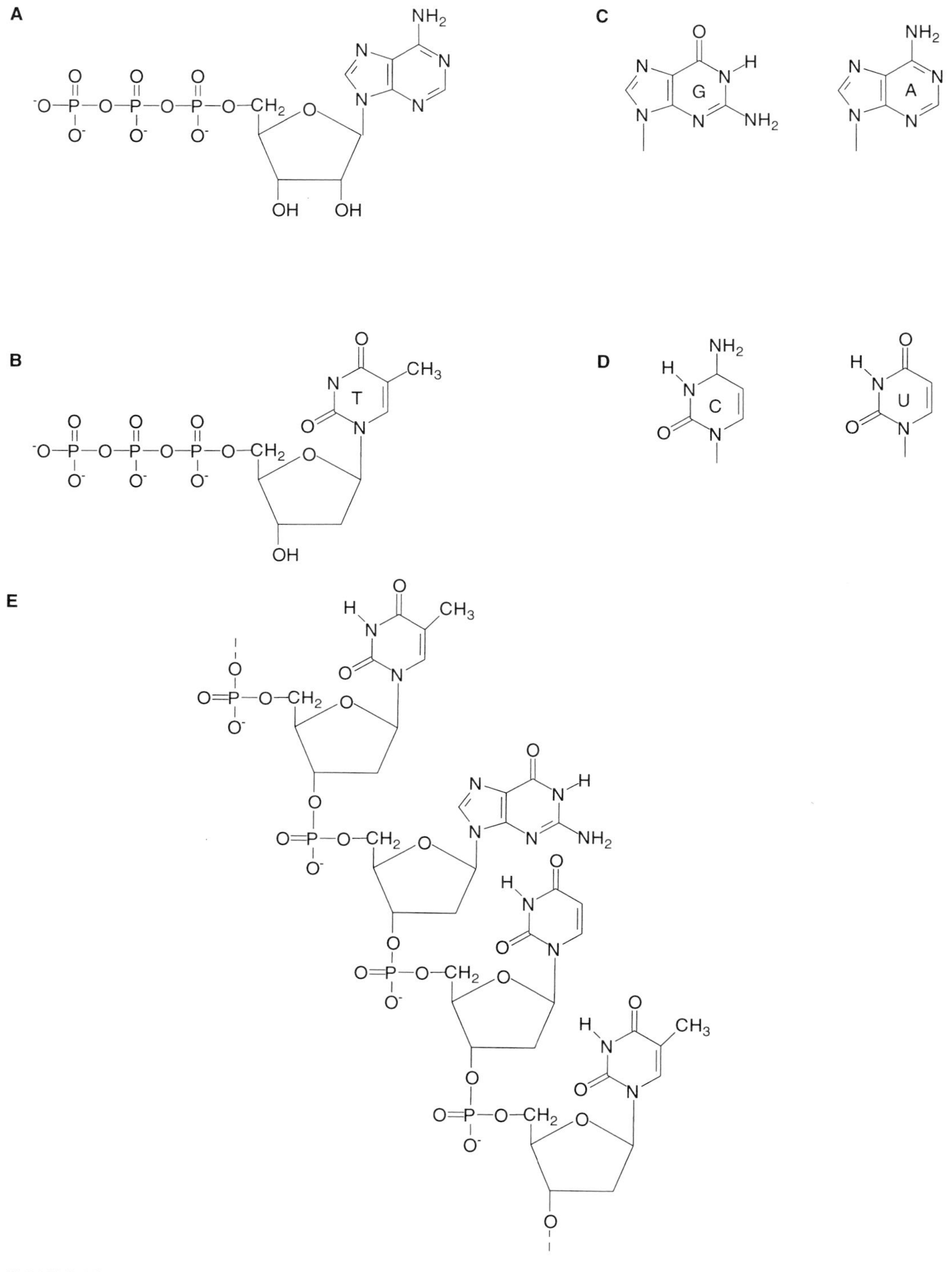

FIGURE 11 Nucleic acid structure. (A) ATP, (B) dTTP, (C) purines, guanosine and adenine, (D) pyrimidines, cytidine and uracil, (E) a small stretch of single-stranded DNA.

clude locust bean gum, xanthan gum, gum arabic, gum tragacanth, and guar gum.

C. Nucleic Acids

The nucleic acids (Fig. 11) include the energy storage compounds ATP, GTP, CTP, and UTP, the genetic material DNA, and RNA, which occurs as mRNA, tRNA, or a structural component in ribosomes. Despite their immense importance to biology, from a nutritional perspective, nucleic acids are not very important because all components of nucleic acids can be made by the body. There are, however, some conditions (e.g., gout) in which nucleic acids are not metabolized properly. Foods rich in nucleic acids, such as organ meats, should be avoided by those suffering from such conditions.

In muscle during onset of rigor mortis, ATP is broken down to several compounds, including IMP.

Other nucleotides are also degraded to similar compounds. These products contribute some of the flavors associated with meat or meat broth. Accordingly, IMP and GMP are now used commercially as "flavor enhancers" to supplement or replace MSG, which has some negative effects in some individuals.

Bibliography

Belitz, H.-D., and Grosch, W. (1987). "Food Chemistry." Springer-Verlag, Berlin.
Fennema, O. R. (ed.) (1976). "Principles of Food Science, Part I." Marcel Dekker, New York.
Rawn, J. D. (1989). "Biochemistry." Neil Patterson, Carolina Biological Supply Co., Burlington, NC.
Whitaker, J. R. (1994). "Principles of Enzymology for the Food Sciences." 2nd edition Marcel Dekker, New York.
Wong, D. W. S. (1989). "Mechanism and Theory in Food Chemistry." Van Nostrand Reinhold, New York.

Food Biochemistry: Pigments, Flavors, Aromas, and Stability

G. M. SMITH, J. R. WHITAKER, *University of California, Davis*

I. Pigments and Colorants
II. Flavor
III. Instability of Food Components

Glossary

Alcohol Organic compound that contains a -C-OH group of atoms of which the carbon atom is participates only in single bonds to hydrogen atoms or to carbon atoms; methyl alcohol (CH_3OH) is the simplest alcohol; while the term ''an alcohol'' refers to any compound having this structural feature, the term ''alcohol'', when otherwise unmodified, refers specifically to ethyl alcohol (CH_3CH_2OH)

Anatto Colorant obtained from the seeds of a tropical bush; the main component is cis-bixin

Anthocyanins Deeply colored compounds found in fruits and flowers

Aspartame Trade name for aspartylphenylalanine methyl ester, an artificial sweetener

Autoxidizable Said of a compund that reacts readily with oxygen or readily donates one or more electrons to other oxidants

Betalain Group of red and red-violet pigments found in red beets

Bixin Major component of annato, a colorant used in foods isolated from the seeds of a tropical bush

Carboxylic acid Organic compounds containing the structural unit -COOH; they are generally weak acids; prominent carboxylic acids in foods include fatty acids, amino acids and di- and tricarboxylic acids such as succinic acid, tartaric acid, and citric acid

Counterion Ion (chemical having a net positive or negative charge) that is associated with another ion because they bear opposite charges

Denatured Having lost some property associated with a compound; good examples are enzymes that have lost activity due to a structural change, perhaps caused by heating or by addition of acid; opposite of ''native''

Disproportionation Chemical reaction in which the same compound becomes both oxidized and reduced; in the simplest cases, such a reaction involves two molecules, one of which becomes oxidized, and the other reduced

Hemochromes Generic reference to colored compounds created when groups other than the natural ligands bind to the iron of heme groups; they are responsible for the color of cured and some cooked meats

Hemoprotein Protein that contains a heme group

Hydroperoxide Compound that contains the structural group -O-OH

Invertase Enzyme that catalyzes the hydrolysis of sucrose to glucose plus fructose

Isoprene 5-Carbon repeating structural unit of isoprenes and isoprenoid compounds called terpenes

Lake Food dye that has been bound to a powdered solid material so that it can be dispersed in an oil-based food product, such as cake icing

Myoglobin Heme protein that carries oxygen to muscle tissue; different states of its heme produce the various colors of raw, cooked, or cured meats

Peroxidation Oxidation reactions involving peroxides or addition of O_2 to a compound to form a peroxide or hydroperoxide

Phosphocreatine Energy-storage compound found in muscle

Phospholipid Polar lipid; composed of one molecule of glycerol esterified to two fatty acids, with a phosphodiester of an alcohol on one of the end carbon atoms

Porphyrin Polycyclic aromatic compound that binds iron ions; iron-porphyrin complexes are called hemes; composed of four pyrrole rings that are cyclized into a larger ring

Saponifiable, saponify Literally, converting to soap; base-catayzed hydrolysis of the ester bond be-

tween glycerol and the fatty acid of a lipid molecule; saponifiable lipids are those that contain ester bonds
Umami Mild flavor characteristic of asian soups and some meats, typified by the flavor of monosodium glutamate (MSG)
Xanthophylls Class of carotenoids that contain oxygen atoms, as opposed to carotenes, which do not

Compounds that give foods their characteristic aromas and colors are important for palatability, for assessment of freshness and quality, and sometimes for nutritional reasons. Changes in flavor, aroma, and color during processing, ageing, or storage may reflect a loss in quality. Some changes, such as ripening of cheese, actually create an improvement in flavor and aroma. The compounds responsible for these properties are discussed below.

I. Pigments and Colorants

There are many different kinds of compounds that contribute to color. Some of them occur naturally in the food, others are produced by heating or processing, and others are added solely or partly to alter the color.

A. Colored Components Occurring in Food

1. Carotenoids

Carotenoids are the most abundant class of colored compounds in plants. Carotenoids are polyisoprenes, being built of isoprene units (Fig. 4, *Food Biochemistry: Lipids, Carbohydrates, and Nucleic Acids*), and fall into two classes: the xanthophylls, which contain oxygen, and the carotenes, which do not. Carotenes, such as α- and β-carotene, are typically orange and are found in most fruits and vegetables. They provide the orange color of carrots, tomatoes, squash, and many other foods. Both classes of carotenoids are nonpolar. They are thus oil-soluble and rarely water-soluble. An exception is bixin, a common food colorant (see below).

β-Carotene is itself significant because it is an immediate precursor of the eye pigment, retinal (vitamin A). Green and yellow vegetables contain the "provitamin" β-carotene, each molecule of which can be converted to two molecules of retinal by oxidative cleavage. Cleavage is usually not efficient, and less than 20% of dietary β-carotene is converted to vitamin A. During processing, cooking, or storage, up to 40% of vitamin A can be lost, chiefly by oxidation,

but also due to isomerization and fragmentation. These changes alter the color of food as well as its nutritional quality. Dietary deficiency in vitamin A leads to night-blindness, which progresses to total blindness. This condition is currently common in famine-stricken regions of the Third World. In addition, toughening of eye tissue and thickening of the skin, especially the palms, may occur.

Although carotenoids are not synthesized by animals, they are transmitted by feed to animal tissue where they accumulate. The yellow-orange pigment of egg yolk is a carotenoid of vegetable origin. In fact, children who consume large amounts of foods rich in carotene (e.g., baby foods such as cooked carrots) may actually accumulate carotene in the skin and take on a jaundiced appearance. This condition, called carotenosis, has no other symptoms.

Xanthophylls, such as zeaxanthin (found in corn, spinach, and green pepper), are typically yellow. Polyisoprenes contain many *trans* double bonds; double bonds tend to be chemically reactive. Oxidation, photolysis, or isomerization (to the *cis* form) of these double bonds leads to loss of the orange or yellow colors.

Carotenoids form part of the photosynthetic ("light-harvesting") apparatus of green plants. They are widely distributed, especially in leaves, where their presence is obscured by chlorophylls, the primary photosynthetic pigments.

2. Anthocyanins

Anthocyanins are orange, red, blue, or purple colors found in fruits and flowers. They are glycosides of compounds called anthocyanidins (Fig. 1). The presence of the sugar and the acidic -OH groups makes them both water-soluble and pH-sensitive. They also decompose in acid by hydrolysis. However, because they possess hydrophobic rings, they associate with one another, forming stacks of pigment in which the molecules are protected from hydrolysis. Different hydrophobic compounds can be present in the same stack.

The red-violet and yellow colors associated with beets are produced by a group of compounds called betalains. The general structure of betalain is shown in Fig. 1. The violet members of this class, called betacyanins, contain an additional aromatic substituent as R or R′. In the yellow betalains, the betaxanthins, the substituent is not aromatic.

3. Chlorophylls

Chlorophylls a and b are the active photosynthetic pigments, and are therefore found in green leaves

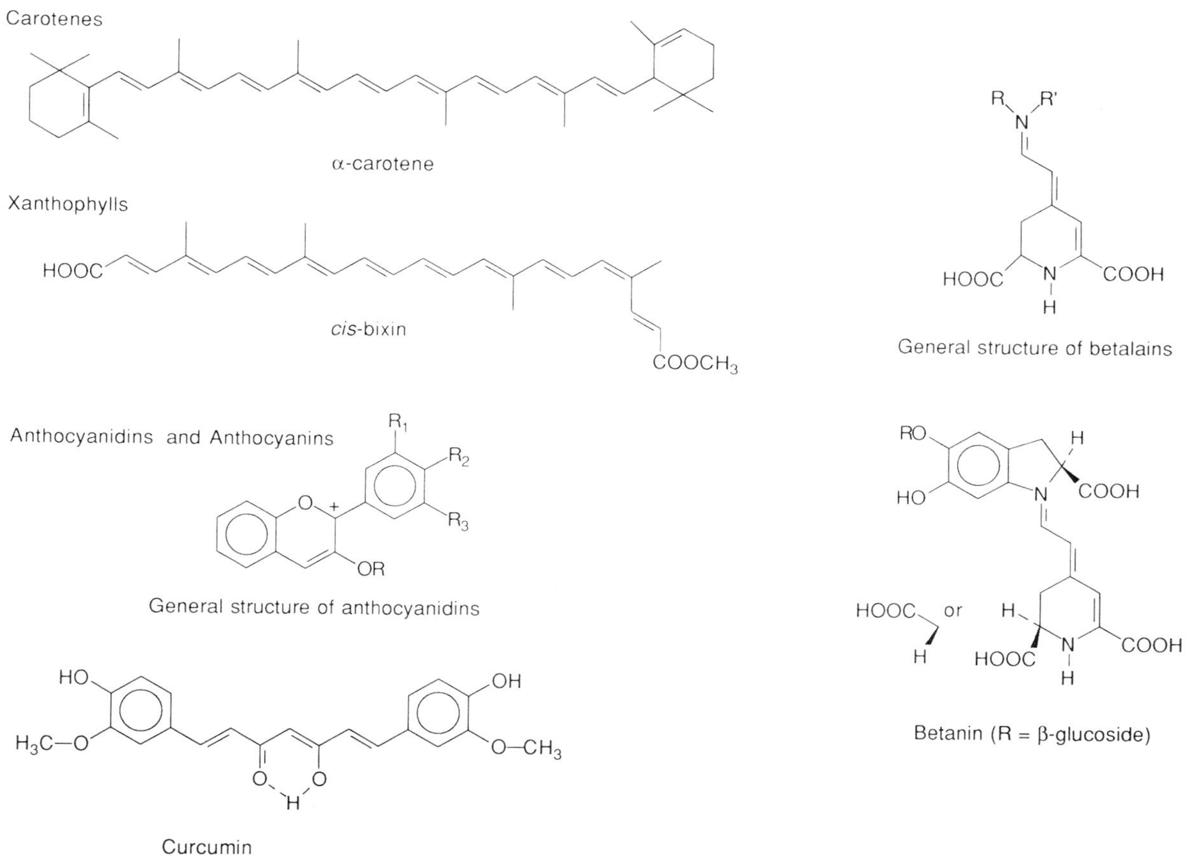

Carotenes

α-carotene

Xanthophylls

cis-bixin

Anthocyanidins and Anthocyanins

General structure of anthocyanidins

Curcumin

General structure of betalains

Betanin (R = β-glucoside)

FIGURE 1 Structures of some important pigments found in foods. Carotenes and xanthophylls are both carotenoids. *cis*-Bixin is one isomer of the colored material in anatto, a common food colorant. Anthocyanidins are derivatives of anthocyanins. Curcumin is the yellow color found in turmeric. Betalains form a family of pigments that differ by the identity of R and R'. Betanin, a red betalain found in beets, occurs in two isomers as indicated.

where they constitute the major green pigment. The color arises from the magnesium complex of the chlorin ring, which is itself associated with protein. The chlorophyll is oil-soluble and is responsible for the green color of extra-virgin olive oil. The copper complex of chlorophyll is green and is used as colorants in candies.

4. Hemoproteins

Myoglobin and hemoglobin are the principal colored compounds in fresh meat; myoglobin predominates in well-drained meat. The globins become denatured upon heating or curing, which causes the change in color of meat upon cooking (see below). The cytochromes, which function as electron carriers in oxidative phosphorylation, may contribute some red color to meat. [*See* Food Biochemistry: Proteins, Enzymes, and Enzyme Inhibitors.]

Muscle types, often characterized as light, intermediate, or dark, are of different color largely because of their differing myoglobin content, although the exact structure of the muscle fibers also differs. Muscles that are used for rapid but not prolonged contraction generally derive their energy more from glycolysis (nonoxidative degradation of sugars to produce lactic acid) than from aerobic metabolism. Muscles that must undergo sustained contraction would build up lactic acid under anaerobic metabolism, which would lead to fatigue and cramping. Therefore, these muscles use the more efficient pathway: conversion of sugars or fatty acids to acetyl coenzyme A, then oxidation of the two carbon atoms to CO_2, generating ATP via electron transport in the mitochondria. Substantial amounts of oxygen are required for this process, hence the need for myoglobin. Heart muscle is quite aerobic and has many mitochondria and much myoglobin. The "flight" muscle (breast and wings) of chickens and turkeys, which rarely fly, apparently finds anaerobic metabolism adequate for short bursts of fluttering flight. Thus, this white meat contains less myoglobin than thigh and "drumstick" muscle, which must be in constant use when the bird stands.

5. Riboflavin

Riboflavin, usually thought of as a vitamin, adds a yellow color to food in which it exists. Care must be taken in adding it to foods, however, because it can act as a pro-oxidant and photosensitizer.

B. Colorants Added to Foods

Caramel is one of the more common colorants. It is produced by heat decomposition of sugars (e.g., corn syrup). It has a characteristic color and flavor. Caramel contains many compounds (polymers) of unknown structure. In addition, there are several different kinds of caramel that differ in the conditions used to produce them (e.g., pH, presence of salts, or amino acids). Because the properties of these caramels are different, they are used in different products.

Other natural colorants added to foods primarily for color include annatto and curcumin. Anatto is an extract of a tropical plant that contains an orange carotenoid called *cis*-bixin. *cis*-Bixin is a polyisoprene chain with carboxylic acid groups at each end, one existing as a methyl ester. Heat treatment during the extraction process converts some of the *cis* isomer to the red *trans*-bixin, which is oil-soluble. Heating the extract in alkali produces the dicarboxylic acid nor-bixin. The acid form of nor-bixin is insoluble in water except at alkaline pH. Curcumin (Fig. 1) is present in the bland spice turmeric, and yields an oil-soluble yellow-orange color often found in Indian dishes.

1. Dyes and Lakes

Most food colorants are compounds that occur naturally, though some of them may actually be produced commercially by chemical synthesis. There are, however, a few man-made food colors approved for use in the United States that do not occur naturally. These compounds, called certified color additives, are compounds that have many conjugated double bonds (i.e., . . . CH=CH—CH=CH—CH=CH . . .). Some of them (e.g., FD&C yellow No. 5 and FD&C red No. 40) contain the group —N=N—, and are accordingly known as azo dyes. These dyes are water-soluble and cannot be dispersed well in oils. However, the dyes can be adsorbed onto particles of alumina hydrate ($Al(OH)_3$) to form insoluble pastes called

lakes. Lakes can be dispersed in fat or oil-based products, such as frostings and fillings.

C. Color Changes Caused by Cooking or Processing

1. Blanching of Vegetables

Vegetables are heated during preparation (cooking) and for sterilization during canning. Before freezing or other storage, they may be "blanched" to inactivate enzymes that would lead to softening, discoloration (e.g., polyphenol oxidase, see below), or other deterioration (e.g., lipoxygenases and peroxidases). The blanching process derives its name from the fact that the characteristic green and yellow colors of fresh vegetables turn pale upon heating. More than one change takes place. The primary green color of plant material is chlorophyll, the hemelike complex of magnesium. Heating, especially at low pH (e.g., in vinegar and lemon juice), causes loss of the magnesium ion, and the resulting compound, pheophytin, is olive green. Another result of heating is the oxidative destruction of carotenoids by lipoxygenase before the enzyme is itself denatured.

2. Nonenzymatic Browning and Sugars

Upon heating in the presence of proteins, amino acids, or other amines, aldoses and ketoses undergo a reaction that produces browning. The phenomenon is actually a series of reactions collectively known as the Maillard reaction (Fig. 2). Amines can condense with amino groups to form imines (also called Schiff bases). Through a shift of the double bond, the sugar can form a second carbonyl group, which can condense with another amine. Continued heating causes further rearrangement, further condensation, and, ultimately, the production of hundreds of new compounds. Many of the compounds are colored, leading to the term Maillard browning, and many of the compounds are flavor and aroma compounds. These compounds are very important to the color, aroma, and flavor developed during baking or roasting. Obvious examples are bread crust, maple syrup, and coffee beans.

3. Browning of Meat

The color of fresh red meat is due mostly to myoglobin. The coordination of the Fe^{2+} ion by four nitrogen atoms of the heme group and one nitrogen atom from a histidine residue of the protein produces a structure that strongly absorbs yellow and some blue light and therefore reflects and transmits red-purple

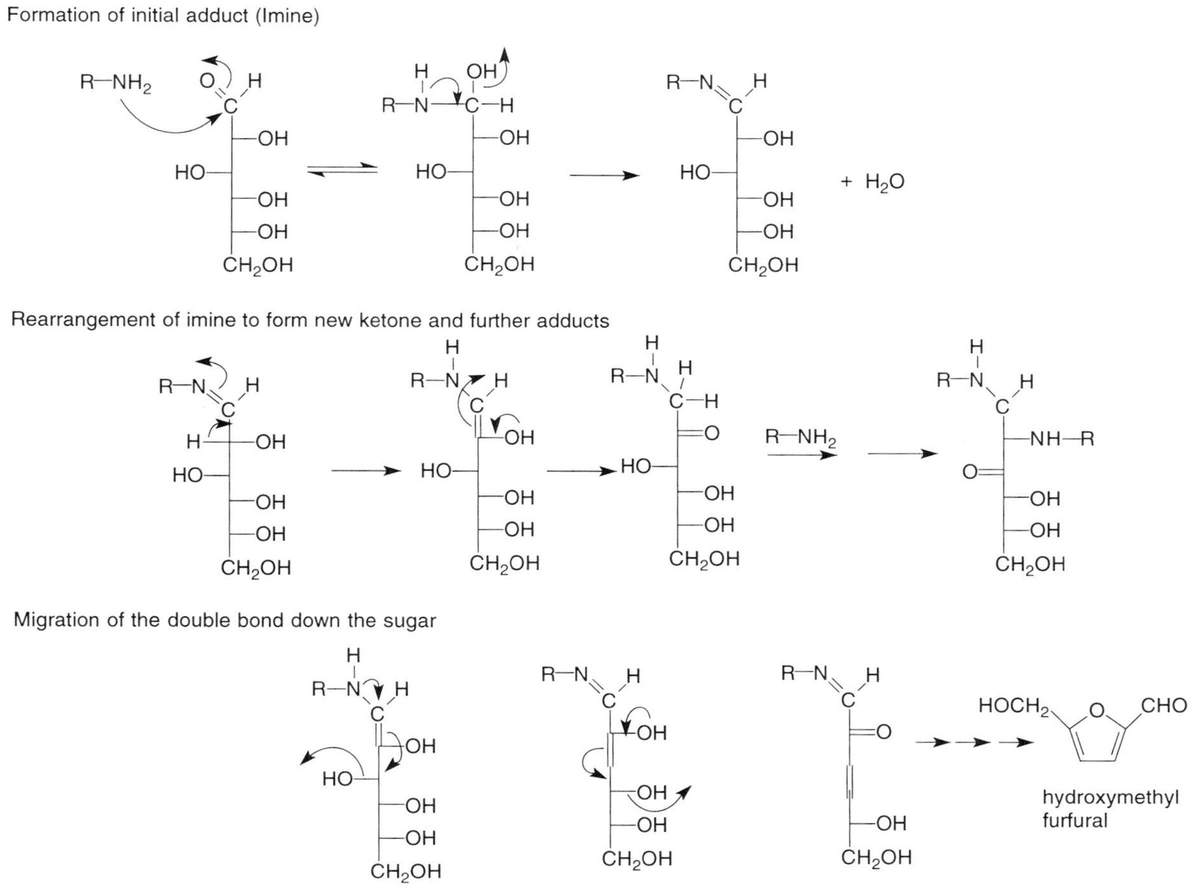

Formation of initial adduct (Imine)

Rearrangement of imine to form new ketone and further adducts

Migration of the double bond down the sugar

FIGURE 2 Important reactions leading to nonenzymatic (Maillard) browning. The reactions involve sugars and amines, such as amino acids or proteins.

light. These molecules bind oxygen as the sixth ligand to the iron ion and the oxygenated species are a brighter red than the deoxy species, corresponding to the difference in color between venous and arterial blood. In cut meat, the globins (mostly myoglobin) are oxygenated. However, the iron ion can be oxidized to Fe^{3+} by the bound oxygen (the presence of other metal ions, especially copper, accelerates this process). The resulting compound, *met*-myoglobin, which has a water atom as the sixth iron ligand, is brownish. The color of raw meat is determined mainly by the ratios of myoglobin to *oxy*-myoglobin to *met*-myoglobin. The shift in this ratio causes meat to turn brown upon storage. Nitrite (NO_2^-) oxidizes myoglobin to *met*-myoglobin, becoming reduced to NO in the process; the NO forms complexes with the iron of myoglobin and *met*-myoglobin that are bright red. Meats cured with nitrites therefore maintain a red color. The denatured forms of the proteins,

which may also be oxidized, contain heme-bound iron, but the two nonheme coordination sites of the iron are occupied by groups other than the normal histidine and water or oxygen. These compounds, called hemochromes, are brown and are responsible in part for the darkening and loss of red color by meat that occurs upon cooking or addition of acid (e.g., lemon juice). Below a pH of about 5, the heme dissociates from the protein and accepts two ligands from the medium. Meats cured with nitrites contain NO coordinated to the heme iron and thus are red even after cooking.

II. Flavor

A. Taste and Aroma

The sensation of the flavor of a food involves the interaction of taste, as perceived by the taste receptors of the tongue, and aroma, as perceived by the olfactory organs. Although texture and mouth-feel play a role in the assessment of "how it tastes," it is the chemical stimulation of taste and odor receptors that is responsible for the flavor of food. As far as taste is concerned, there are chemicals in food that bind to specific receptors of the tongue which produce the sensations known as sweet, sour, salty, and bitter, from which more complex tastes are built. There may be other basic tastes that are less well recognized, such as the "umami" flavor of MSG and Asian soups. The chemicals responsible for stimulating the taste receptors are generally nonvolatile compounds, but some may be volatile, and they may also act as aroma compounds.

Aroma compounds are volatile compounds associated with foods that stimulate the olfactory organs. The variety of aromas seems more complex than that of taste. Aromas may be either pleasant or unpleasant, or the pleasantness may depend on context. Many aroma compounds can be detected at very low concentrations in air. The actual intensity of the aroma depends on the vapor pressure of the compound, which is strongly dependent on concentration, temperature, and the properties of the food in which it is found, such as lipid content, pH, etc. In addition, each compound has its own potency. Some of these factors have been quantitated in combination by determining the lowest concentration of a substance dissolved in neutral water at 20°C that can be detected; this is the odor threshold value (concentration).

In some foods, a single volatile compound, called the character or impact compound, is responsible for the characteristic odor (Table I, Fig. 4). Examples are isopropyl acetate in banana, *trans*-2-*cis*-4-decadienoate esters in pear, and citral in lemon. In other foods, one compound plays a major role, but several compounds are required to create the recognizable characteristic aroma. A good example is the delicious apple, with the character compound ethyl-2-methylbutyrate and supporting aroma from hexanal and *trans*-2-hexenal. The aromas of some foods cannot be duplicated by mixtures of a few compounds. Apricot, for instance contains myrcene, limonene, *p*-cymene, terpinolene, *trans*-2-hexenal, geraniol, linalool, linalool oxide, 2-methylbutyric acid, caproic acid, and several cyclic esters. In a fourth group of foods, exemplified by strawberry, characteristic odors have not been reproduced at all.

Aromas and flavors in foods may be present in the fresh, raw material, or may be developed in numerous ways, through roasting, through fermentations, or by combinations of techniques. Roasted coffee and dried tea leaves are extreme examples of aroma development due to roasting and drying.

B. Sweeteners

Sweetness is the sensation produced when a compound having a "glycophore" (a sweet-carrying group) binds to a sweetness receptor of the tongue. Like enzymes and antibodies, receptors bind only compounds that have the right shape, size, and distribution of charged, polar and nonpolar groups. From years of experimentation, it is known that molecules that bind to the sweet receptors must contain three groups: a hydrogen bond acceptor B, a hydrogen bond donor AH, and a hydrophobic group γ, located at specific distances from one another on the surface of the moelcule. These three structural features must be located such that they interact with complementary groups on the receptor surface. The hydrophobic group need not be large; a single CH group constitutes the entire hydrophobic site on sugars. In synthetic sweeteners, which are many times sweeter that sucrose, the γ group is more hydrophobic, suggesting that the γ group modulates the sweetness.

Sweetness can be quantified in several ways. One method is to determine the lowest concentration of a compound dissolved in water that produces a sweet taste (the recognition threshold). This parameter is expected to correlate with the strength of the binding between the compound and the receptor. Another system for comparing sweetness of different compounds is to determine the relative sweetness of a compound to that of sucrose at the same concentration, or the concentration of the compound that has the same sweetness as a particular concentration of sucrose. However, relative sweetness changes with concentration: a 1.8% solution of glucose is equal in sweetness to a 1% solution of sucrose, but a 13.9% solution is equal to the sweetness of a 10% solution of sucrose. Other parameters, such as temperature, pH, and the presence of other compounds, also affect perceived sweetness.

Some sweeteners have other flavors associated with them. Others have an aftertaste. Sweeteners of the first group can be used in products in which the other taste is complementary to or masked by the tastes and aromas present. Sweeteners with an aftertaste can be used in chewing gum and other candies in which persistence of flavor is considered a positive attribute. Some sweeteners, especially sugars and syrups, lend body or mouth-feel to products. If sugar substitutes are used, other ingredients must be included to maintain the expected texture of the product.

Many compounds are used as sweeteners. They are divided into two groups, nutritive and nonnutritive. Nonnutritive sweeteners are not used by the body to obtain energy (calories) and are therefore employed in diet and other reduced sugar products. These compounds are excreted by the body. Care must be taken in the design and testing of nonnutritive sweeteners to be sure that they are actually excreted and do not build up in tissues to cause damage. Nutritive sweeteners can be degraded by the body to yield calories. These include sugars, sugar alcohols, and sugar syrups, but also some proteins and synthetic peptide compounds, such as Aspartame. Even though proteins, amino acids, and peptides have about the same number of calories per gram as sugar, some, such as Aspartame, are very sweet and can be used at very low levels.

C. Sugars and Sugar Alcohols

Sugars are the paradigm of sweetness. Although the English word "sugar" refers to sucrose (sometimes called saccharose or table sugar) nearly all monosaccharides and oligosaccharides are sweet, although many have other tastes, such as bitter, associated with them. In general, the more monosaccharide units in an oligosaccharide, the less sweet it is. All sugars that are digestible yield 4–5 calories per gram (a rounded teaspoon of granulated sugar weighs about 7 g). [*See* FOOD BIOCHEMISTRY: LIPIDS, CARBOHYDRATES, AND NUCLEIC ACIDS.]

1. Sucrose

Sucrose is the sweet compound against which all other sweeteners are compared. It is produced from cane or sugarbeets, in which it is quite abundant. Sucrose is a nonreducing disaccharide of α-D-glucose and β-D-fructose, i.e., β-D-fructofuranosyl-α-D-glucopyranoside. The "furanosyl" and "pyranoside" portions of the name indicate that the fructose exists as a five-membered ring, the glucose as a six-membered ring, and the monosaccharides are joined through bonds to their reducing carbons. Sucrose is generally regarded as stable, but it (along with other β-fructosides) is more susceptible to hydrolysis than other disaccharides. Hydrolysis, which produces a mixture of α- and β-D-glucopyranose and both pyranose and furanose forms of α- and β-D-fructose, is catalyzed by weak acids and by heating.

In some cases, especially in candies and other sweets, sucrose is intentionally hydrolyzed by the addition of the enzyme invertase, which produces a 50:50 mixture of glucose and fructose known as invert sugar. (The name arises from the fact that plane polarized light that passes through a solution of sucrose is rotated to the right, but in the mixture of glucose and fructose, it is rotated to the left.) Invert surgar is about 95% as sweet as sucrose (at a concentration of 10 g/100 g of solution). Invert sugar is a mixture of reducing sugars, and is therefore more susceptible to nonenzymatic browning reactions than sucrose.

2. Glucose

Glucose, also called dextrose because it is dextrorotatory, is thought of by biochemists as the archtypical monosaccharide. Glucose is a building block of sucrose, starch (an energy and carbon storage material in plants), glycogen (an energy and carbon storage material in mammals), and cellulose, and thus plays a pivotal role in sugar metabolism. It is conveniently produced from starch (obtained from corn, wheat, or potatoes) by acid hydrolysis or by enzymatic hydrolysis using a mixture of α-amylase and glucoamylase. Although glucose syrups are more commonly used in foods, purified glucose is used in pharmaceutical preparations (including intravenous feeding).

3. Fructose

Fructose, also called levulose because it is levorotatory, is the predominant sugar of fruits, although substantial amounts of glucose and sucrose often accompany it. It also contends with glucose for the most abundant sugar in honey. Nonetheless, it is usually prepared from invert sugar by separating it from glucose. It is sweeter than sucrose and is therefore used in reduced-sugar foods. Although it can be interconverted with glucose in the body (via the 6-phosphate derivatives), it appears that it is metabolized somewhat differently than dietary glucose.

4. Liquid Sugars

Starch is not sweet, but it is water-soluble and easily extracted from corn, potatoes, or grain. It can be hydrolyzed enzymatically to the disaccharide maltose, or to glucose. Acid-catalyzed hydrolysis is also common. The high-glucose syrup produced by hydrolysis is sweet and builds viscosity or texture in foods. It is therefore used as a sweetener in many commercial products. Recently, it has become common to convert some of the glucose in corn syrup to fructose using the bacterial enzyme glucose/fructose isomerase. The resulting product, which is similar to invert sugar syrup except that the fructose/glucose ratio can deviate from 1:1, is called high fructose corn sweetener and is used in many products including soft drinks.

Molasses is another sweetener and flavoring that is used as a syrup. It is actually the residual liquid that remains after sucrose has been crystallized from the concentrated extracts of sugar beets or sugar cane. Although molasses from cane and beet processes are different in other components, both contain sucrose as the principal sugar.

Many syrups are used without extensive purification, crystallization, or drying. "Liquid sugar" is easy to handle and dispense. It is also inexpensive because of the savings in energy, equipment, and manpower that would be needed to produce crystalline or dry sugars. Liquid sugars are more expensive to transport, however, because of the weight added by the water content.

5. Lactose

Lactose, milk sugar, is a disaccharide of galactose and glucose (galactopyranosyl glucopyranose). Milk, and consequently, cheese whey, is about 5% lactose; it is a plentiful by-product of the dairy industry. Its importance in dairy products is enormous, because, as the only significant carbohydrate in milk, it acts as the carbon source for the bacteria and molds that cause ripening and development of flavor and texture in cheeses and yogurt. It is not very sweet, not very soluble, and not as digestible as sucrose. It is therefore used as a filler or texture builder in some products in which sweetness is not desirable. It is a reducing sugar and participates in nonenzymatic browning reactions. It is therefore used to enhance browning of crusts, etc.

Lactose tends to form gritty crystals in dairy products, especially concentrated or condensed products; the crystals can become large enough to look like pieces of glass. Additionally, the worldwide occurrence of lactose intolerance is relatively high, especially in Asia, Africa, southern Europe, and the mideast. This condition results from the loss of the enzyme β-galactosidase ("lactase") from the intestinal mucosa of some humans after the age of 4 or 5. Lactose is therefore neither cleaved nor taken up by the intestinal wall, so it passes further down the digestive tract where it provides an osmotic stress in the intestine that leads to diarrhea. Some of the lactose in the intestine is consumed by gut bacteria which produce gas, leading to flatulence. Lactose-hydrolyzed products are available, removing concerns about lactose intolerance,

but hydrolysis tends to increase the sweetness of the food because both products glucose and galactose are sweeter than lactose.

6. Sugar Alcohols

Sugar alcohols, in which the aldehyde or ketone group of the corresponding sugar is reduced to an alcohol, have become popular sweeteners. They are produced by catalytic hydrogenation of the aldose or ketose from which they are derived. This reduction is often carried out on a syrup obtained from the hydrolysis of a polymer of the appropriate material, such as starch (for glucose) or xylan (for xylose). Although the sugar alcohols sorbitol, mannitol, and xylitol can be metabolized by the body and therefore contribute calories to the diet, they are apparently not fermented by the bacteria responsible for tooth decay .

D. Amino Acids, Peptides and Proteins

Compounds other than sugars possess the glycophore triangle and therefore bind the sweetness receptor. Amino acids, for instance, almost by definition, have an AH group (i.e., the α-amino group NH_2), a B group (COO^-), and potentially a γ group (the side chain). But only D-amino acids hold these groups in the right position to interact with the receptor. Since proteins contain only L-amino acids, proteins and natural amino acids are usually not sweet. D-Asparagine, for instance, is sweet, but L-Asparagine, is not. Peptides, however, can assume conformations that allow them to interact with the sweetness receptor. There are more than a dozen di- and tripeptides that have a sweet taste. One of these, L-aspartyl-L-phenylalanyl methyl ester, is about 200 times as sweet as sucrose. In this compound, the side chain β-COO^- and α-NH_2 groups act as the B and AH groups, respectively, while the γ group function is taken on by the methyl ester group. The dipeptide is marketed as "aspartame" under the brand name NutraSweet, and is widely used in soft drinks, diet confections, and even chewable vitamins. For the present, its use it limited mostly by the fact that it cannot be used in cooking because it cyclizes or hydrolyzes upon heating to produce L-amino acids, which are not sweet. Initial concern that hydrolysis by the body would produce methyl alcohol (considered toxic) is now tempered by the realization that many other foods, e.g., apples, contain pectin (polygalacturonate methyl esters) that leads to the production of much more methyl alcohol, without damage to the consumer. Health warnings concerning the use of Aspartame are

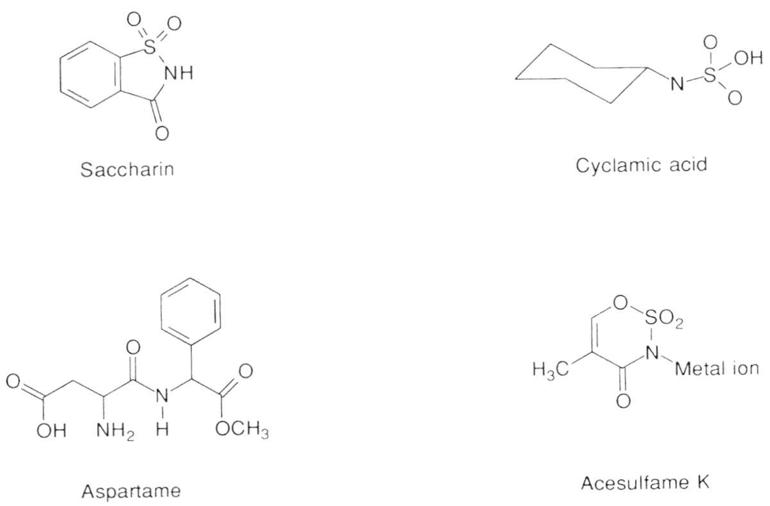

FIGURE 3 Structures of some artificial sweeteners. Saccharine and Aspartame are the most popular in the United States since cyclamates were banned amid controversy.

therefore limited to individuals who have phenylketonuria, a genetic defect in metabolism of phenylalanine.

Despite the general rule that proteins are not sweet, at least a few proteins, monellin (from the berries of a tropical plant, *Dioscoreophyllum cumminsii*), the thaumatins (from the fruit of a west African plant, *Thaumatococcus daniellii*), and miraculin (from the miracle fruit *Synsepalum dulcificum*) are intensely sweet. Thaumatin I, for instance, is 2000 times as sweet as sucrose. These proteins have different structures but have five regions with nearly the same sequence in all three proteins. Whether these sequences confer sweetness is not clear.

E. Nonnutritive Sweeteners

Common nonnutritive sweeteners include cyclamate, saccharin, and acesulfame-K (Fig. 3). All three of these compounds are sulfonamides, meaning that they contain an -SO_2NH- group. An oxygen atom of the sulfonate group functions as the B group, and the NH group functions as the AH group of the glycophore. The γ groups of the compounds are different.

1. Cyclamate

Cyclamate is an amide of sulfonic acid and cyclohexylamine; the cyclohexyl group is much more hydrophobic than any portion of a common sugar, and functions as an effective γ group. Cyclamate is about 40 times as sweet as sucrose. Although cyclamate is

not bitter, the sweetness is not as pleasant as that produced by some sweeteners, and cyclamates are sometimes blended with other compounds. In a still-controversial decision, cyclamates were banned from use in North America where it had been used extensively in soft drinks. It is still used in Europe.

2. Saccharin

In saccharine, the -SO_2NH- group is part of a five-membered ring that is fused to a benzene ring. The benzene ring constitutes the γ group of this sweetener; saccharine is about 450 times as sweet as sucrose. Saccharine is widely used in dietetic products, including soft drinks. It is sold as a liquid (a solution) or as a dry powder, as either the sodium or calcium salt. The calcium salt has wide promotional appeal, because the label can read, "low in sodium, high in calcium." Because it is so sweet and such a small amount constitutes a single serving, sodium or calcium saccharine powder is often dispersed in a soluble carrier, usually glucose, and marketed as a blend of nutritive and nonnutritive sweeteners. Single-serving packages containing 1 g of glucose and enough saccharine to produce the sweetness of a teaspoon (about 6 g) of sucrose contains only 4 calories, versus 28–35 calories for sucrose.

3. Acesulfame-K

The -SO_2NH- group of acesulfame-K forms part of a six-membered ring. The γ group is simply a

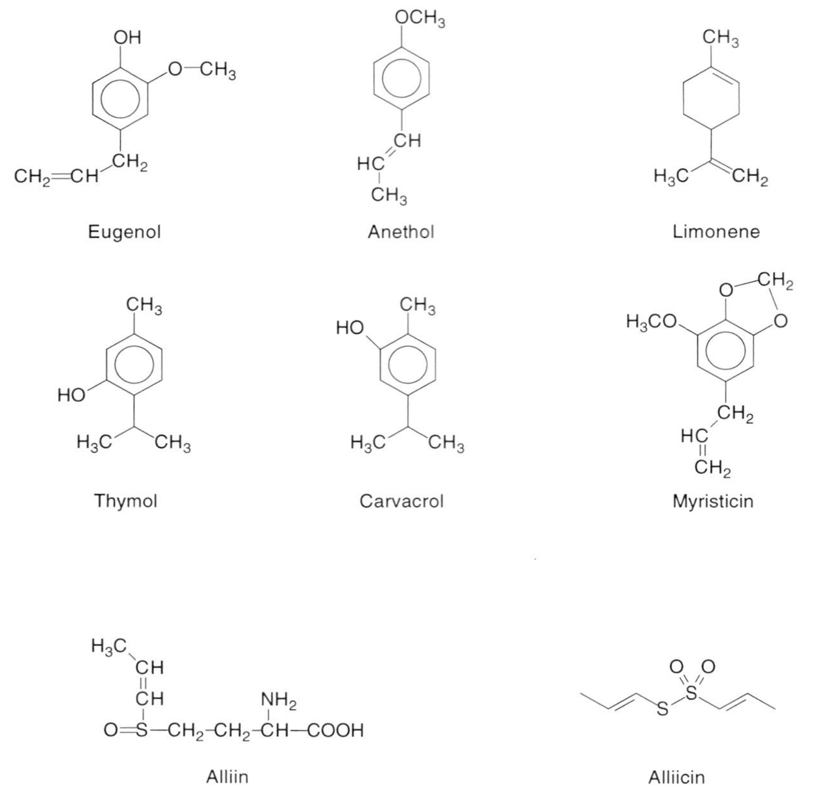

FIGURE 4 Structures of some aroma and flavor compounds referred to in the text or in Table I.

methyl–substituted double bond ($CH_3-C=C-$). Acesulfame-K is about 200 times as sweet as sucrose.

F. Other Flavors

Spices are leaves, fruits, seeds, roots, or bark of plants containing essential oil responsible for their unique flavors and aromas. The aroma compounds are usually either monoterpenes and sesquiterpenes or phenols and phenol ethers. Terpenes are compounds constructed from isoprene. Compounds containing two isoprene units are called monoterpenes; those containing three units are sesquiterpenes. Some important mono- and sesquiterpenes are shown in Figs. 1 and 4.

Phenols are derivatives of phenol (carbolic acid). Some important phenol derivatives are eugenol, carvacrol, thymol, anethole, safrole, and myristicin (see Fig. 4). Spices in which these compounds are important are listed in Table I.

Some flavors are developed during processing or cooking. The Maillard reaction is a condensation between amines (e.g., amino acids) and ketones or alde-hydes (e.g., reducing sugars) followed by various chemical rearrangements. Although the Maillard re-action is usually referred to as a browning reaction, it produces many compounds that have aroma as well as color. A process called the Strecker degradation of amino acids occurs in the presence of ketones or aldehydes and involves the loss of ammonia and CO_2 to yield an aldehyde containing one less carbon than the amino acid:

$$RCH(NH_2)COOH + R'COR''$$
$$\rightarrow RCHO + R'CNH_2R'' + CO_2.$$

One of the results of this reaction is that the variety of aldehydes available to participate in the Maillard reaction is increased, and thus, the number of products of the Maillard reaction is increased. The Maillard and Strecker reactions therefore produce hundreds of aroma compounds, including pyrazines, pyrroles, pyrrolines, pyrrolidines, and oxazoles.

1. Onions and Garlic

The strong, characteristic aromas of garlic, onions, shallots, chives, and leeks arise from compounds that

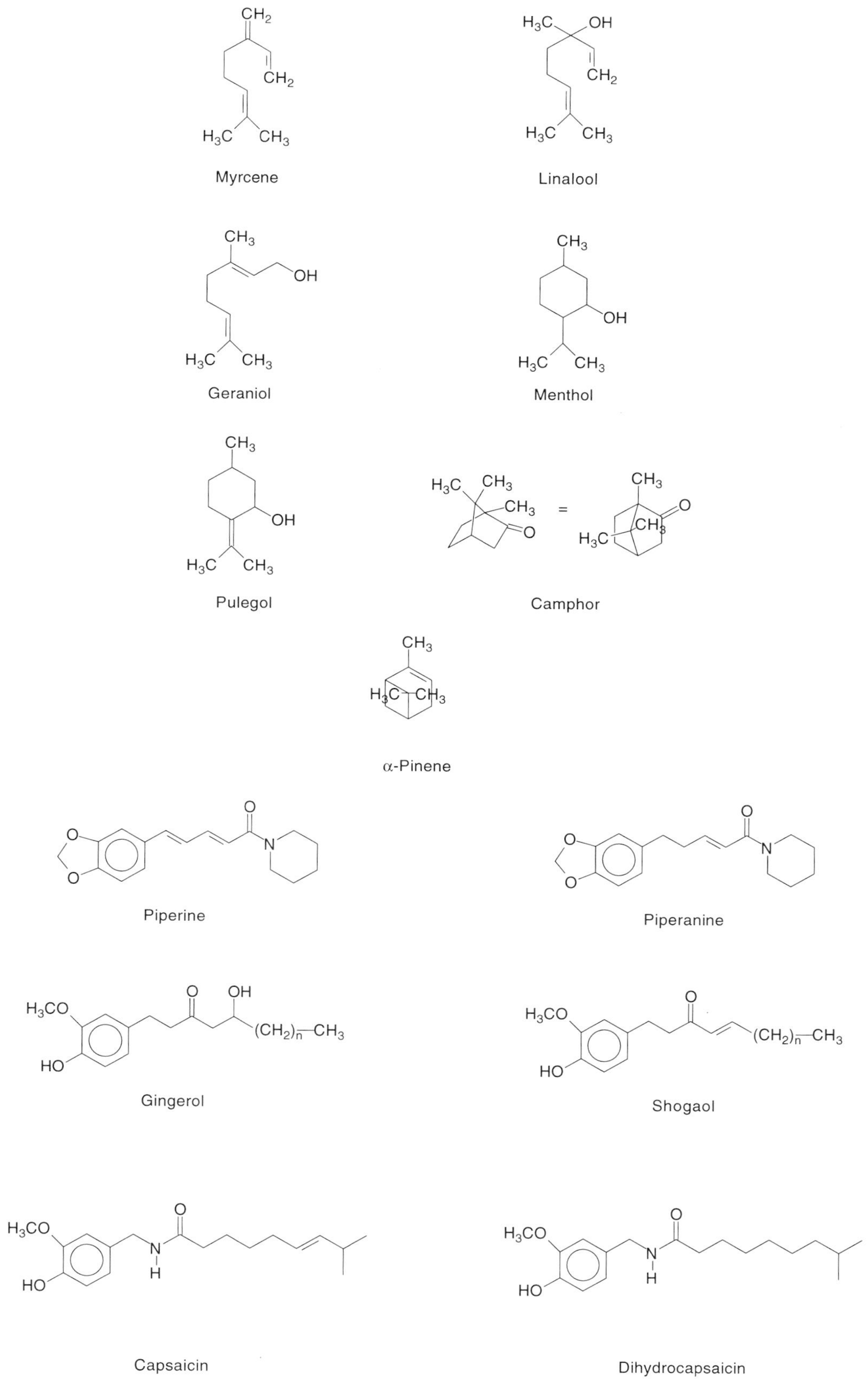

Myrcene

Linalool

Geraniol

Menthol

Pulegol

Camphor

α-Pinene

Piperine

Piperanine

Gingerol

Shogaol

Capsaicin

Dihydrocapsaicin

FIGURE 4 (*continued*)

TABLE I

Some Important Compounds Responsible for Flavor and Aroma of Foods and Spices

	Flavor/aroma compound	Aroma or flavor	Comments
Food			
Almond	Benzaldehyde	a	
Apple	Ethyl-2-methylbutyrate	a	Character impact
	hexanal, *trans*-hexenal	a	"Unripe" note
Apricot	Limonene	a	Very complex
	Cymene	a	
	Geraniol + linalool	a	
	Acetic acid		
	Myrcene	a	
Banana	Isopentyl acetate	a	Character impact
	Eugenol	a	Plus eugenol derivatives
Lemon	Limonene	a	Major component of citrus oils
	Citral (= geranial + neral)	a	Character impact
Meat	Many compounds, (depending on cooking method)	a	Resulting from Maillard reaction and amino acid decomposition
	Amino acids and peptides, lactic acid	f	
	Glutamic acid, IMP	f	Flavor enhancers
Onion	Propyl- and propenyl disulfides	a	Cooked onions
	Alkylthiosulfonates	a	Raw onions
	Propanethial-S-oxide		Lachrymator produced by alliinase in cut onions
Orange	Limonene	a	Major component of citrus oils
	8, 9, 10, 11-carbon aldehydes		
Strawberries	Over 300 compounds	a	
Spices	Aromas compounds of spices are largely components of essential oils		
Allspice	Eugenol, methyleugenol	a	
	β-Caryophyllene	a	
Bay leaf	1,8-Cineole, α-pinene, β-pinene	a	
Caraway	Carvone, limonene	a	
Chili pepper	Capsaicin, and derivatives	f	Hot sensation
Cinnamon	Cinnamaldehyde, eugenol, safrole, linalool, camphor	a	
Cloves	Eugenol, caryophyllene, eugenol acetate	a	
Dill	Carvone, dihydrocarvone, limonene	a	
Garlic	Allicin, diallyldisulfide	a	Character impact, produced from alliin and related compounds by alliinase
Ginger	Zingiberene,	a	
	Shogaol, gingerol, zingerone	f	Hot sensation, nonvolatile
Oregano	Carvacrol, thymol, *p*-cymene	a	
Pepper (black)	α-Pinene, sabinenene	a	In essential oils
	β-Caryophyllene		
	Piperine, piperanine, others	f	Hot sensation, nonvolatile
Rosemary	1,8,-Cineole, camphor, β-pinene, camphene	a	
Sage	1,8,-Cineole, camphor, thujone		
Thyme	Thymol, *p*-cymene, carvacrol, linalool		
Beverages			
Beer	Long-chain alcohols, acetaldehyde, H_2S and organic thiols, phenols, pyrazines	a	
Coffee	Over 600 compounds, including aldehydes, phenols, pyrazines	a	Products of browning reactions developed during roasting
Tea	Linalool, furanlinalool oxides, *t*-2-hexene-1-al, hexanol, *t*-3-octen-2-one, benzaldehyde	a	Plus ~50 identified trace components that determine the exact "flavor"

are not present in the tissue until the tissue is cut or damaged. Derivatives of cysteine, the sulfhydryl amino acid, are precursors of the aroma compounds. The most important derivatives are trans-S-(1-propenyl)cysteine sulfoxide in onion and S-allyl-cysteine sulfoxide (alliin) in garlic, which differ from each other only in the position of a double bond (see Fig. 4). Upon damage of the tissue, the odorless substrate comes into contact with the enzyme alliinase, which catalyzes the loss of pyruvate to yield 1-propenesulfenic acid in onion or 2-propenylsulfenic acid in garlic. In garlic, two molecules of the sulfenic acid condense with one another to form allicin, which can decompose to allylsulfenic acid plus acrolein, which can in turn form other aroma compounds. In onion, the 1-propenylsulfenic acid formed by alliinase rearranges into syn-propanethial S-oxide, a lacrimator. During cooking, propenyl and propyl disulfides are formed to produce the aroma of cooked onions.

G. Other Seasonings

1. Table Salt

The most widely used flavoring is table salt, NaCl. In addition to its role as a flavoring, NaCl is a preservative and an important moisture-controlling compound. NaCl is produced either from the mining of natural deposits or from evaporation of seawater. Commercial table salt contains small amounts of calcium or magnesium carbonate, plus a trace amount of potassium ferrocyanide which are added to prevent lump formation. Small amounts of dextrans are also added for similar purposes. In addition, iodized salt to which 10–100 μg of KI is added per gram of NaCl, is also widely used to ensure adequate iodine intake.

Sodium salts are notably soluble, and most sodium is therefore found dissolved in extracellular and cellular fluids, including blood and lymph. Sodium ion is important in adjusting the osmotic strength of fluids and, together with protons and potassium ion, maintains electric gradients and concentration gradients across cell and organelle membranes.

Sodium salts in food alter the osmotic strength (and water activity) of a material, strongly influencing its water content. Water content determines texture, viscosity, and other rheological properties. NaCl has long been used as a preservative, because low water content or high salinity place an osmotic stress on spoilage microorganisms.

High sodium content in the body results in overhydration and swelling of tissue (edema). High concentration of salt in the blood serum leads to high blood pressure and damage to renal tubules and an increased probability of stroke.

The sodium intake of individuals varies considerably. The sodium content of most fresh food is rather low. The major source of salt in the diet is the addition of table salt to foods during preparation or consumption, which is at the discretion of the consumer. The variability arises due to individual taste. Processed foods, however, may be relatively high in salt. In processed foods, the salt may be added as a flavor, as a preservative, or to maintain water content and distribution (which affects texture and mouth-feel). The production of low-salt (i.e., low-sodium) products often requires addition of other osmotically active compounds to maintain texture.

Since diets are rich in chloride, dietary deficiency and data on the required daily amount are not known. It does not appear that chloride plays an important role in foods other than in providing ionic (and osmotic) strength. Because most of its salts are soluble, chloride acts as the counterion to many cations, including protons (i.e., hydrochloric acid in stomach acid) and sodium in blood and other extracellular fluids. In the human body, chloride is apparently quite important: the single defect causing the disease cystic fibrosis is in trans-membrane chloride transport. This single lesion is presumably responsible, at least indirectly, for all other symptoms of the disease.

2. Acids

Acids are also important flavorings, the most important of which is acetic acid. Vinegar is a 5–15% solution of acetic acid that may contain other substances. Acetic acid is responsible for the sour flavor of pickled vegetables, pickled meats, and condiments, as well as other foods. Some acetic acid is produced chemically from ethyl alcohol or acetaldehyde, then diluted for use in food. In this case, the only flavor associated with the vinegar is that of acetic acid. However, vinegar may be produced by fermentation of wine, apple juice, malt mash, whey, or ethyl alcohol by bacteria of the genus Acetobacter. Vinegars produced by this method contain flavors originating from the fruit or carbohydrate source used in the fermentation, from bacterial by-products, and from the action of bacterial enzymes on other compounds in the fermentation medium. Thus, vinegars from different sources have distinct flavors.

Other acids used in foods as flavors include citric acid (e.g., lemon juice is ~6% citric acid), tartaric acid, and lactic acid. Not unlike acetic acid, these acids are sometimes added to foods as acid components to lower pH, but contribute to flavor, nonetheless. Tartaric acid is used in fruit drinks and candies; citric acid is used in candies, juices, jellies, and canned vegetables. Citric acid is also used in fermented dairy products to improve aroma. Lactic acid is the dominant acid product of fermentations used in dairy products such as yogurt, buttermilk, and ripened cheese, carried out by bacteria of the genus *Lactobacillus*. Other food products, including sauerkraut, spanish olives, and other pickled vegetables also contain lactic acid, either added directly as a flavor or from the fermentations carried out by other lactic acid bacteria.

Fatty acids usually originate from hydrolysis of lipids originating in the food. Because their odor is detectable at low concentration, some (mostly short-chain) fatty acids lend desirable flavor to fermented foods like ripened cheese. However, the same fatty acids occurring in other foods (e.g., butyric and caproic acids in "fresh" milk) are considered off-flavors.

H. Flavor Enhancers

Some compounds, called flavor potentiators, increase or decrease (mask) the intensities of other flavors. The most widely used of these is the flavor enhancer monosodium L-glutamate. A class of enhancers seemingly unrelated to MSG are the 5' purine nucleoside phosphates IMP and GMP, which can be prepared by total hydrolysis of RNA using the enzyme ribonuclease. These three compounds have a mild, unique flavor of their own called umami, but also enhance the perception of other flavors. In fact, GMP reduces the threshold of MSG by 100-fold; IMP reduces the threshold level of MSG by 10-fold. The commercially available 50:50 mixture of IMP and GMP is often mixed with MSG for this reason.

III. Instability of Food Components

Common off-flavors in foods result from oxidative or hydrolytic decomposition of food components, particularly lipids. Some of the decomposition reactions are actually catalyzed by vitamins and minerals in the food. Bacterial spoilage often causes off-flavors and aromas by deposition of metabolic end products on the food. For instance the sweet sulfury aroma of hydrogen sulfide is often found on poultry spoiled by *Salmonella*. Microorganisms may also destroy flavor compounds present in fresh food. Certainly chemical

contamination of food products can also lead to off-flavors. In animal products, especially milk, off-flavors can enter the food via the feed.

A. Deterioration of Proteins and Amines

Flavor development and texture changes such as those that take place during cheese ripening involve decomposition of proteins. Residual chymosin and pepsin from the rennet together with proteases from the bacteria or fungi used for ripening all contribute to decomposition. Small peptides may have bitter or salty tastes, but do not produce major off-flavors. Further decomposition, however, may cause the production of ammonia, especially in soft ripened cheeses like brie and camembert.

Fish contain the characteristic amine trimethylamine oxide. Saltwater fish have unusually high levels of the compound which functions at least in part to regulate internal osmotic pressure. After death of the fish, the TMAO is reduced to trimethylamine (TMA) by bacteria. TMA is volatile and has a strong ammoniacal odor. TMA and similar amines (e.g., triethylamine) are responsible for the "fishy" taste of fish. The total alkylamines produced can exceed the TMAO known to be present, so some must arise from the breakdown of other amines such as choline and amino acids.

Also in fish, microbial enzymes decarboxylate histidine to produce histamine. Although traces of histidine do not alter flavor, histamine which normally participates in the allergic response, can cause anaphylactic shock in some individuals which can be serious.

B. Deterioration of Lipids: Rancidity

Fats are involved in the production of two distinctly different kinds of deterioration, both of which affect food quality. The most common is oxidative rancidity. Double bonds in fatty acids are labile to oxidation; several factors can lead to oxidative degradation of lipids by different mechanisms.

1. Autoxidation

Autoxidation occurs when some component in the lipid, an initiator, removes a hydrogen atom (H·) from a fatty acid, often from the $-CH_2-$ between two double bonds, to make CH·. The uncharged organic species that remains, which has an unpaired, non-bonded electron, is called a free radical. The radical is quite reactive, and attacks a molecule of oxygen to produce a dioxygenated compound, a peroxide radical, that also has an unpaired electron (see Fig.

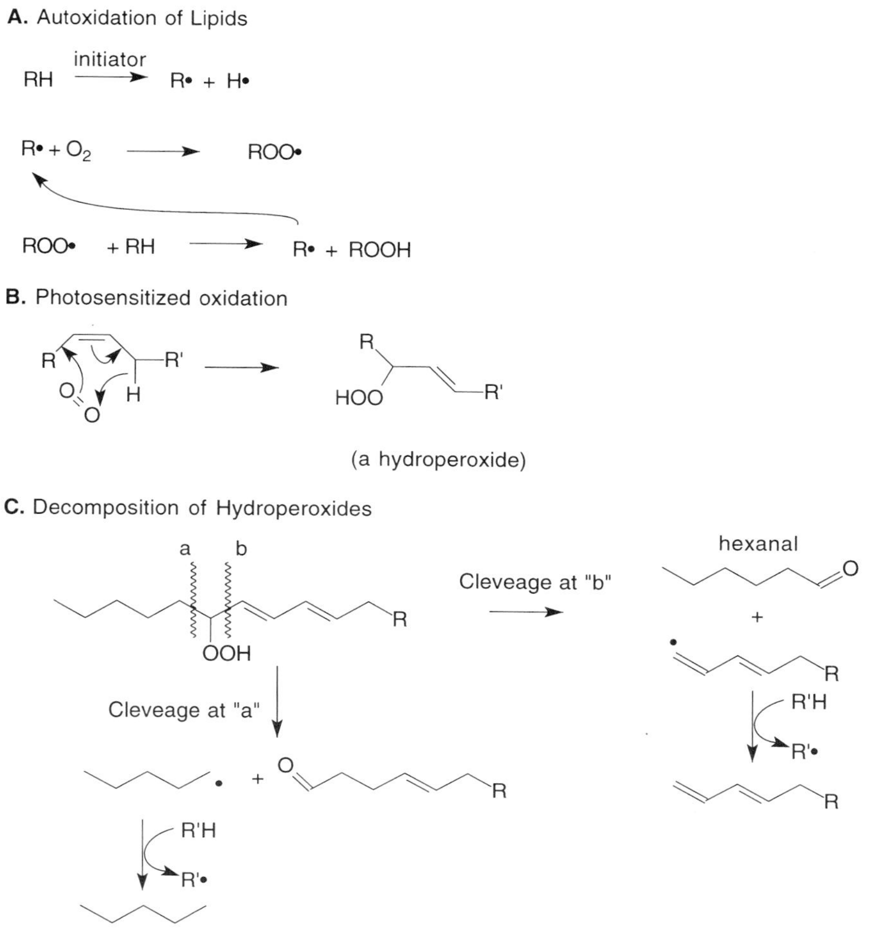

A. Autoxidation of Lipids

B. Photosensitized oxidation

(a hydroperoxide)

C. Decomposition of Hydroperoxides

FIGURE 5 Reactions important in peroxidation of unsaturated fatty acids. (A) Autoxidation that begins with a free radical initiator. Note that one of the products is a free radical, R·, which propagates the chain reaction. (B) The reaction of singlet oxygen produced by photoactivation with an unsaturated fatty acid. (C) The decomposition of a hydroperoxide to several possible products including hexanal.

5). This peroxide radical abstracts a hydrogen atom from another fatty acid, becoming a hydroperoxide and turning the second fatty acid into a free radical. The process continues as a chain reaction which builds up the level of hydroperoxides and continues to replenish the supply of free radicals. The process can terminate when two free radicals or a free radical and a peroxide, or two peroxides meet each other and their unpaired electrons form bonds. These processes can be blocked by the addition of antioxidants, which are generally compounds that trap radicals. Once the hydroperoxides are formed, however, their decomposition causes the cleavage of the fatty acid (Fig. 5).

The most potent of the likely initiators is the hydroxyl radical OH·, but the superoxide radical O_2^-· is also important. Metal ions can be very important in the generation of initiators. For instance, Fe^{3+} in the presence of ascorbic acid or the reduced coenzymes

NADH or $FADH_2$ can generate superoxide radicals. Thiols such as glutathione and cysteine produce superoxide radicals in the presence of Fe^{3+}. Superoxide radicals disproportionate to become oxygen (O_2) and hydrogen peroxide (H_2O_2). Hydrogen peroxide reacts with Fe^{2+} to produce the potent initiator, OH·. Metal ions are not major components of foods, but some ions are usually present due to leaching from equipment or containers. Because of the cyclical interconversion of Fe^{2+} and Fe^{3+} in these reactions, one metal ion can participate many times in the production of the initiator.

2. Photosensitized Oxidation

Oxygen itself can be made very reactive when it interacts with a photosensitizer such as chlorophyll or flavins. This excited state of the oxygen molecule is called singlet oxygen. Singlet oxygen adds to double bonds (see Fig. 5) to produce hydroperoxides as in autoxidation, but the process does not involve free radicals and is not blocked by radical-trapping antioxidants.

3. Enzymatic Peroxidation

Enzymes can carry out peroxidation of fatty acids. Lipoxygenase, an enzyme present in many vegetables and in animal tissue, catalyzes the production of the same hydroperoxides produced by nonenzymatic peroxidation. There are several kinds of lipoxygenase, each characterized by its specificity.

4. Decomposition of Lipid Hydroperoxides

Fatty acid hydroperoxides produced as described above decompose in several ways to give a variety of products. Peroxidation of $\omega 6$ fatty acids produce hexanal from loss of the terminal carbons. From a polyunsaturated fatty acid such as linolenate, hexanal, 2-octenal, 2-heptanal, and a host of other products, including the crosslinking agent malonaldehyde, can be produced. Aldehydes impart flavor at very low concentrations and can cause off-flavors in any food containing fatty acids. In milk, for instance, oxidation of lipids gives an off-flavor described as "cardboard," "painty," or "cucumber." Monitoring of peroxidation products such as hexanal can be a good way to investigate the quality or oxidation history of a product.

5. Antioxidants

There are several food components that have antioxidant activity. In general, these are compounds that have the ability to destroy free radicals. The vitamin E compounds, tocopherols, are good examples. When one of these compounds (AH) is attacked by a free radical (R·), a hydrogen atom is abstracted, but the radical that is formed (A·) is not very reactive. In fact it is most likely to react only with another free radical to form a stable compound, as shown in the sequence below. The antioxidant therefore can remove two free radicals.

$$R· + AH \rightarrow RH + A·$$

$$R· + A· \rightarrow R-A$$

Vitamin E is a tocopherol, a two-ring compound with a 16-carbon branched side chain. As shown in Fig. 6, the aromatic ring is methylated; the 5,6,7-trimethyl derivative, called α-tocopherol, has the highest vitamin A activity. The 5,8-dimethyl- and 7,8-dimethyl- derivatives, called β- and γ-tocopherol,

respectively, have less activity and the 8-methyl derivative, δ-tocopherol, has very little activity. Their vitamin E activity correlates closely to their ability to quench singlet oxygen and is consistent with the vitamin E function as an antioxidant. α-Tocopherol converts singlet oxygen to the less-reactive triplet oxygen catalytically, but also can take up a singlet oxygen to form a hydroperoxide, which decomposes to nonradical products. It is also an efficient free-radical chain-reaction-breaking agent that terminates lipid peroxidation by donating its own hydrogen atoms to make nonradical products. As an antioxidant, vitamin E is important in protecting vitamin A, quinones, hormones, and proteins as well as lipids.

In addition to tocopherols, vitamin C and phenolic compounds are natural anitoxidants. Synthetic antioxidants are also phenols. They are most effective if they are lipids-soluble, since lipids are a major site of oxidative damage. Common synthetic antioxidants are 2,6-di-tert-butyl-p-hydroxytoluene (BHT) and tert-butyl-4-hydroxyanisole (BHA) and tert-butyl-hydroquinone (TBHQ) (Fig. 6).

6. Hydrolytic Rancidity

A second kind of off-flavor associated with fat is hydrolytic rancidity, which arises from enzyme-catalyzed hydrolysis of the fatty acids from the glycerol backbone. Although many fatty acids might be liberated by such a reaction, only butyric and caproic acids are easily detected by the nose. The pungent, sweet odor of butyric acid is a definite off-flavor in many foods. The fact that hydrolysis of lipids in the stomach liberates butyric acid and gives regurgitated stomach fluid a characteristic odor is probably one reason for the distaste with which human beings regard the odor.

The bulk of fatty acids in most foods is sequestered in lipophilic structures, away from water. Neither water, a necessary reactant in a hydrolysis reaction, nor an enzyme (a lipase) can come into direct contact with most of fat. This off-flavor is therefore most readily obtained in lipid dispersions, particularly milk and dairy products, where the necessary participants can meet at the surface of the milk fat globule. Milkfat globules are coated with phospholipids and a double layer of proteins. However, when milk is homogenized to decrease the size of the globules in order to prevent creaming, additional surface becomes exposed. Serum proteins, including lipases, associate with the nascent surface, increasing the density of the globules. If the proteins that bind are lipases, hydrolytic rancidity results. Phospholipids on the sur-

α-Tocopherol ("Vitamin E")

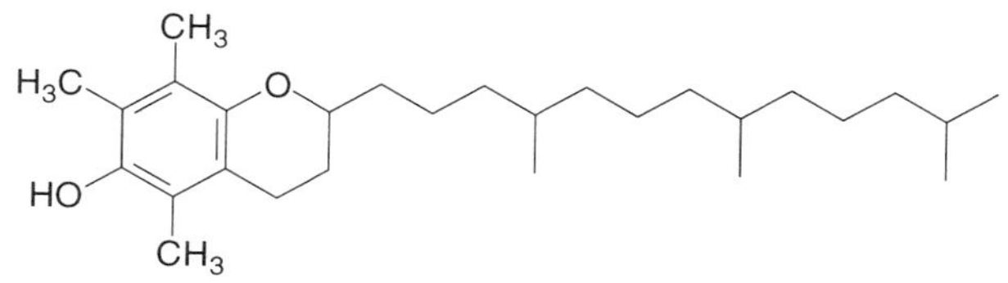

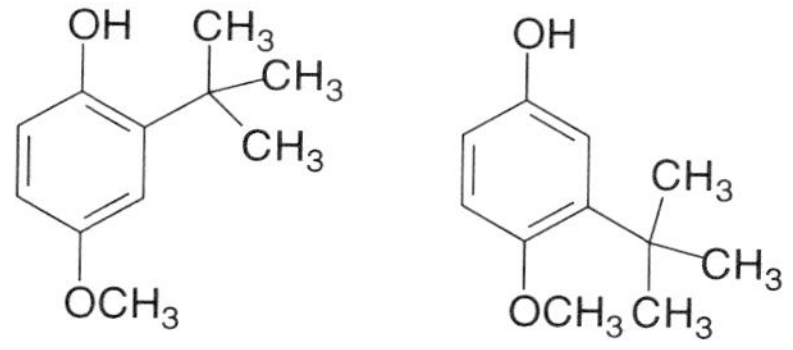

Isomers of butylated hydroxyanisole (BHA) 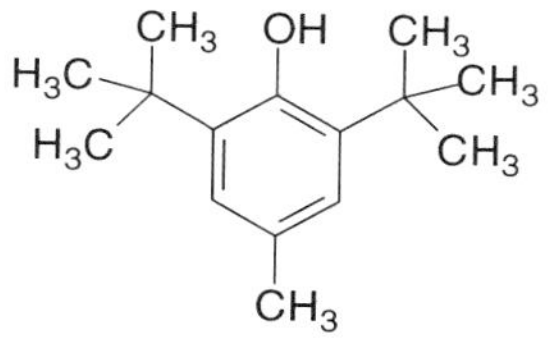   Buthylated hydroxytoluene (BHT)

FIGURE 6 Structures of some common antioxidants.

face of the milk fat globule as well as neutral lipids are targets of the hydrolytic enzymes.

C. Enzymatic Browning

Perhaps the most striking color change in food is that which occurs upon slicing of apples, potatoes, etc. The browning reaction is catalyzed by a copper-containing enzyme called polyphenol oxidase (PPO). This enzyme has many substrates and actually catalyzes two separate reactions. It oxidizes *ortho*-diphenols to *ortho*-quinones. But it also adds an oxygen atom from O_2 in the form of a hydroxyl group to monophenols such as tyrosine, to create *ortho*-diphenols, which are substrates for the oxidation reaction. The *ortho*-quinones condense with nucleophiles and become oxidized to form colored compounds. In bananas, the major phenol is dihydroxyphenethylamine (dopa, a metabolite of aromatic amino acids). It is oxidized by PPO to the quinone form, then cyclizes (see Fig. 7), and is reoxidized to a purple quinone. Many molecules of this purple compound react with one another nonenzymatically to produce the brown pigment melanin. Similar discoloration reactions can occur in many other foods.

Bisulfite ion (HSO_3^-) is often used to prevent these enzymatic browning reactons in various foods. It can be used as sulfur dioxide gas, which takes up a water molecule when it dissolves in water ($SO_2 + H_2O \rightarrow H_2SO_3 \rightarrow H^+ + HSO_3^-$), or as sodium sulfite. Although the sulfite was once thought

to inhibit the process by acting as a reducing agent, the mechanism is more complex. It adds to any quinones to produce a sulfonate and inactivates the enzyme due to reduction of the Cu^{2+} to Cu^+, which dissociates from the enzyme. Sulfites are often used to prevent browning of lettuce and sliced fresh fruit. Sulfur dioxide also has antimicrobial activity and is useful as a preservative. Unfortunately, SO_2 and sulfites aggravate respiratory conditions in some individuals and must be used with care and proper labeling. Ascorbic acid and thiol compounds can be used in place of bisulfite.

D. Contributions of Vitamins and Minerals to Instability of Food Components

Vitamins and bioactive minerals are by nature reactive compounds as evidenced by their roles in metabolism. However, after harvest or slaughter, when biological control mechanisms that require energy tend to fail, the chemical reactivity of vitamins and minerals can produce undesirable changes in food components.

1. Riboflavin

Vitamin B_2, also known as riboflavin, is the precursor of two important cofactors, flavin adenine dinucleotide (FAD) and flavin mononucleotide (FMN). Both contain a flavin ring (isoalloxazine). The flavin ring can exist in three forms, a quinone form, a semiquinone form, and a hydroquinone form, which differ from one another by one electron. Flavins can there-

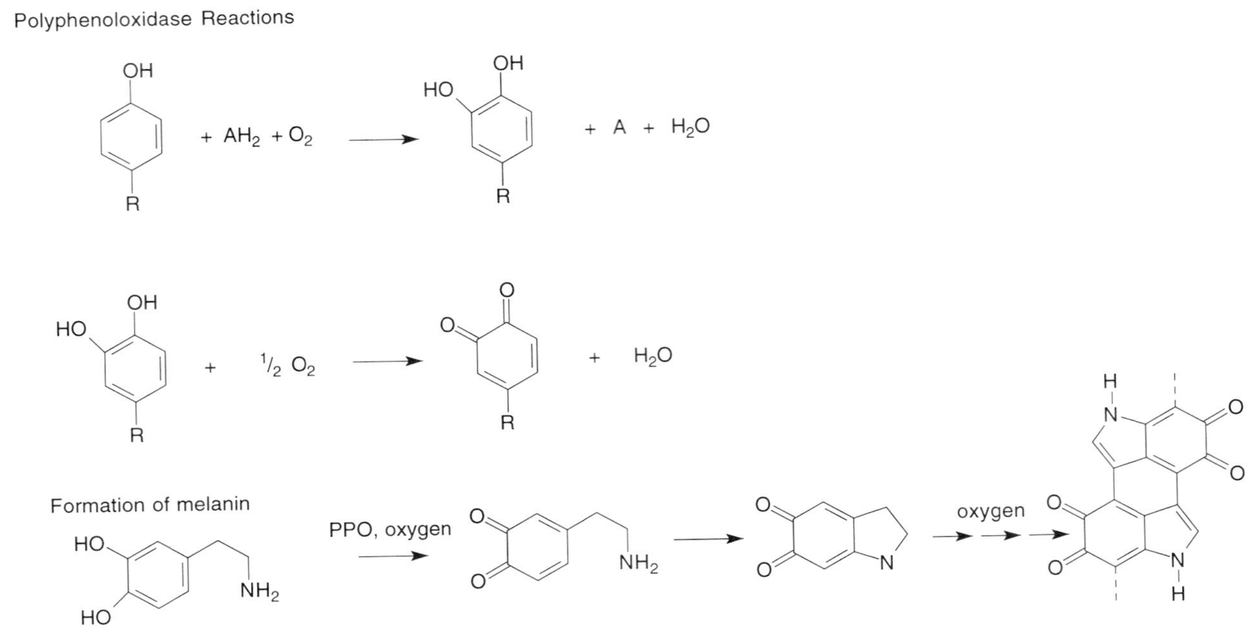

Polyphenoloxidase Reactions

Formation of melanin

FIGURE 7 Polyphenoloxidase leads to the production of brown pigment. In cut or damaged food, e.g., fruit, the process is known as enzymatic browning. The production of melanin, e.g., in skin, is a normal process.

fore undergo one-electron and two-electron (from the quinone to the hydroquinone) oxidation/reduction reactions and are used for mediating between one-electron and two-electron carriers, or in hydride (two electrons plus a proton) transfer reactions. Flavins are pale yellow since they absorb blue and violet light. They also absorb ultraviolet radiation to act as photo-sensitizers and can catalyze photo-oxidation of unsaturated fatty acids and amino acids. Milk, which is rich in riboflavin, is therefore rather unstable in sunlight. Fats become oxidized and the amino acid methionine is converted to methional, which imparts an exceedingly unpleasant flavor called light-activated flavor. Normal amounts of ultraviolet radiation do not deplete milk of flavins.

2. Vitamin C

As a reducing agent, ascorbic acid can function as an antioxidant, both in food and in the body. For example, it protects folic acid reductase from inactivation, thus indirectly aiding one-carbon transfer reactions. Although it is not lipid soluble, ascorbate protects against lipid peroxidation. It does so by reducing the lipid-soluble vitamin E that has become oxidized to a radical during some of its antioxidant functions. It also protects against enzymatic browning (see above). However, in the presence of metal ions, ascorbic acid can act as a pro-oxidant because metal

ion-catalyzed oxidation of ascorbate produces hydrogen peroxide.

In food, vitamin C is lost primarily due to oxidative mechanisms. But, nonoxidative destruction is acid-catalyzed and proceeds appreciably at low pH. Because of the ketone and aldehyde groups on many of the breakdown products of ascorbic acid, discoloration of food can occur by reaction with amino groups (the Maillard reaction).

Mammals, except humans and guinea pigs, make ascorbic acid to the extent of 5–15 g/day per 70 kg body weight and have no dietary requirement. In humans, the amount of dietary vitamin C required to prevent scurvy is only 50–80 mg/day for adults (which have a typical body weight of about 70 kg). This 100-fold discrepancy between what animals produce and that required to prevent scurvy in humans has led to the proposal that to derive maximum benefit, the human diet should contain much higher levels of vitamin C than the minimum required to prevent scurvy. The controversy over optimum dietary levels has subsided without clear resolution.

3. Minerals

Despite the metabolic necessities and resulting dietary requirement for iron, its occurrence in food is problematic. Iron catalyzes the oxidation of lipids and other compounds, decreasing storageability and quality by altering the flavor, color, and vitamin content of the product. Iron can also precipitate in foods or cause turbidity (as in wine). It supports the growth of chemotrophic and photosynthetic bacteria in drinking water. [*See* MINERALS, ROLE IN HUMAN NUTRITION.]

Copper occurs at the active site of several important proteins and enzymes including cytochrome oxidase, uricase, amine oxidases, polyphenol oxidase, and ceruloplasmin. The latter enzyme catalyzes the oxidation of Fe^{2+} to Fe^{3+} so that the iron can be bound by transferrin for transport. The copper–containing enzyme polyphenyl oxidase is responsible for "enzymatic browning" described above. Furthermore, copper is even better than iron, in some cases, at causing oxidative deterioration in foods. Furthermore, copper pipes in hot water systems provide a direct source of copper contamination in foods and water. Copper deficiency is essentially unknown. Zinc is required by more than 154 enzymes that catalyze several types of group reactions. Zinc is therefore critical for proper health.

Bibliography

Belitz, H.-D., and Grosch, W. (1987). "Food Chemistry." Springer-Verlag, Berlin.

Fennema, O. R. (ed.) (1976). "Principles of Food Science, Part I." Marcel Dekker, New York.

Rawn, J. D. (1989). "Biochemistry." Neil Patterson, Carolina Biological Supply Co., Burlington, NC.

Whitaker, J. R. (1994). "Principles of Enzymology for the Food Sciences." 2nd ed. Marcel Dekker, New York.

Wong, D. W. S. (1989). "Mechanism and Theory in Food Chemistry." Van Nostrand Reinhold, New York.

Food Biochemistry: Proteins, Enzymes, and Enzyme Inhibitors

G. M. SMITH, J. R. WHITAKER, *University of California, Davis*

Glossary

Actomyosin Complex of the muscle proteins actin and myosin

Albumins Globular water-soluble proteins found in many biological fluids and food systems; albumen refers specifically to egg white proteins

Calorie Unit of heat energy describing how much energy can be extracted from foods by the human body; the Calorie is related to the thermodynamic calorie used in chemistry, which is the amount of heat required to raise the temperature of 1 g of water one Celsius degree; one Calorie = 1000 calories = 41846 Joules

Casein micelle Particle composed of submicelles linked together by short chains of calcium phosphate. The submicelles are spherical globules composed of proteins called caseins

Chylomicrons Lipoproteins found in blood

Chymosin Enzyme that catalyzes the hydrolysis of κ-casein, which causes the disruption of the casein micelle and formation of a curd

Denaturation Loss of some property associated with a compound; when applied to enzymes, the term refers to loss of enzymatic activity; it may also imply unfolding of the protein or precipitation

Dimer Compound composed of two structural units; if the units are covalently attached (as in dinucleotides, disaccharides, or dipeptides) the units have the same basic structure; may also refer to any grouping of two units; a protein is a dimer if it is composed of two polypeptide chains which may or may not be identical

Disproportionation Chemical reaction in which the same compound becomes both oxidized and reduced. In the simplest cases, such a reaction involves two molecules, one of which becomes oxidized, and the other reduced

Electronegativity In a chemical bond, the ability of one of the atoms to withdraw electrons from the other; the most electronegative element is fluorine, and the second is oxygen

Emulsification Ability to form or stabilize an emulsion

Gliadins Smaller proteins (compared to the glutenins) found in the gluten of wheat flour

Glycosylated Refers to the attachment of a sugar (a monosaccharide or oligosaccharide) to a protein

Hydrophobic Literally, "disliking water", said of nonpolar compounds (e.g., hydrocarbons) or nonpolar regions of larger molecules; opposite of hydrophilic

Inhibitor Relatively specific term that describes a compound that decreases the rate of an enzyme-catalyzed reaction, often without destroying the enzyme (e.g., reversible or competitive inhibitors); compounds that destroy an enzyme are inactivators or irreversible enzyme inhibitors

Isoelectric point Referring to a compound that contains both acidic and basic groups, the pH at which the compound has no net charge (i.e., the numbers of positive and negative charges are equal)

Isomers Molecules having the same chemical formula (i.e., the same proportions of the same atoms) but different structures

Maillard reaction Condensation reaction between an amine and a ketone or aldehyde followed by numerous rearrangements and further condensations that leads to browning and development of flavor and aroma compounds; also referred to as non-enzymatic browning

Methional Oxidation product of the amino acid methionine, responsible for off-flavors

Metmyoglobin Inactive form of myoglobin in which the iron ion has been oxidized from its normal Fe(II) state to Fe(III); Metmyoglobin is brown compared to myoglobin, and is therefore responsible for discoloration of meat during storage

Micelles Spherical aggregations of amphipathic molecules or ions such as detergents and polar lipids that associate, in water, with their nonpolar groups on the inside of the sphere and their polar groups toward the water; the casein micelle is therefore not really a micelle, but the current model of submicelles fits this definition

Myofibril Structural unit of a muscle fiber, composed primarily of the proteins actin and myosin.

Myoglobin The major heme protein in meat; functions as an oxygen-storage molecule in the living animal and contributes the red color to fresh meat; other forms of its heme produce the colors of cooked and cured meats

Myosin One of the principal muscle proteins

Optical activity Ability of a compound to rotate the plane of plane polarized light; property arises from molecular asymmetry, and thus, is very responsive to small structural differences among similar compounds

Porphyrin Polycyclic aromatic compound that binds an iron ion; iron-porphyrin complexes are called hemes; porphyrins are composed of four pyrrole rings that are cyclized into a larger ring

Precipitation Forming a solid after having been dissolved in a liquid

Procollagen Assembled, triple-helical protein which is processed further, then attached to other procollagen molecules to form collagen

Protease, proteinase Enzyme that catalyzes the hydrolysis of the peptide bonds of proteins

Putrefaction Microbial fermentation in which proteins are degraded, often liberating amines and sulfur-containing compounds that have unpleasant odors

Rennet Extract of the stomach of a suckling calf which contains chymosin and other enzymes; used in cheesemaking

Resolution (of rigor) Processes that lead to the tenderization of meat after the onset of rigor mortis

Sarcolemma Membrane that surrounds muscle fibers, which are bundles of myofibrils

Sarcoplasm Cytoplasm of a muscle cell

Stoichiometric Fixed ratio that exists among the number of molecules of reactants and of products in a chemical reaction

Tropocollagen Single polypeptide chain that associates with others to form collagen

Tropomyosin Strand of protein that, together with actin, forms the muscle thin filament

Although proteins are found in nearly all foods, those foods usually considered to be high in protein are meats, fish, poultry, beans, and dairy products (other than butter and cream). The human body itself contains substantial amounts of protein, notably in bone, muscle, and blood. In fact, every cell contains many kinds of proteins, all of which must be synthesized by the body. Food proteins are broken down into their component parts, amino acids, and the amino acids are used by the body to make its own proteins. Some of the amino acids can be synthesized from other molecules in the body, but others, known as essential amino acids, cannot; essential amino acids must be obtained from food. This is one reason that proteins are an essential part of the human diet.

I. Proteins

Like carbohydrates and fats, protein also provides energy. Proteins that can be digested by the human digestive system give about 4–5 Calories (kcal) per gram. A few proteins that either are insoluble (e.g., zein, a protein from corn) or act as protease inhibitors (see below) are not easily digested.

Some proteins, such as collagen, elastin, and acto-myosin are structural proteins which form major structures in the body or food. Other proteins function in transporting oxygen, minerals, or other compounds. These proteins are generally soluble proteins, which means that they are dissolved in cellular water and diffuse or move around within the cell. Other proteins, especially receptors, channels, and trans-membrane pumps, are not water-soluble, but remain associated with or embedded in lipid membranes of the cell. Many proteins, both soluble and membrane-bound, are "enzymes" which catalyze (increase the rate of) chemical reactions in the body or food. Enzymes are of fundamental importance because, by accelerating the appropriate reactions, they carry out and control nearly all cellular processes.

A. Amino Acids

Although any compound that has both an amino (-NH$_2$) group and an acidic group (e.g., -COOH) can be called an "amino acid," the term actually refers exclusively to about 20 compounds that have the structure (RCH(NH$_2$)COOH), where "R" represents one of the chemical structures shown in Table I, called the side chain. In this list, isoleucine, leucine, lysine, methionine, phenylalanine, threonine, tryptophan, and valine are the "essential" amino acids referred to above. In addition, histidine is required by infants. The human diet contains almost no free amino acids (except for the flavor enhancer monosodium glutamate, MSG); amino acids come from the breakdown of proteins and from biosynthesis.

Furthermore, the amino acids occurring in proteins are in the L configuration rather than D. This nomenclature refers to the way in which the NH$_2$, COOH, and R groups are attached to the central (or α) carbon atom which are so named because of their structural relationship to D-glyceraldehyde. [*See* FOOD BIOCHEMISTRY: LIPIDS, CARBOHYDRATES, AND NUCLEIC ACIDS.]

After proteins are synthesized from the 20 or so amino acids in Table I, some chemical changes in some of the side chains may take place. These changes, which are carried out by specific enzymes, include hydroxylation of lysine and proline, phosphorylation of histidine, serine, threonine, or arginine, methylation of lysine, and attachment of sugars, lipids, or vitamin derivatives.

Metal ions can associate with proteins via interactions with amino acid side chains as well. Notable examples are zinc, iron, copper, and calcium. These ions are bound specifically, and sometimes quite tightly, by coordination to carboxylate groups of aspartate and glutamate, imino nitrogens of histidine, the sulfur atom of cysteine, the hydroxy group of tyrosine, or occasionally other polar side chains. Complexes of iron and copper undergo changes in oxidation state (i.e., Fe(II)–Fe(III)–Fe(IV) and Cu(I)–Cu(II)) over a physiologically useful potential range and usually function as carriers of electrons, either in electron transport chains or in enzymes catalyzing oxidation or reduction reactions. Zinc, magnesium, and calcium, on the other hand, do not gain or lose electrons at physiologically accessible potentials, and function mainly in binding of substrates or coenzymes or as "structural" metal ions, which simply strengthen the protein's structure.

Iron, magnesium, and cobalt are bound to some proteins with the aid of another class of organic molecule, tetrapyrroles. Tetrapyrroles are planar or near planar structures composed of four pyrrole rings that have been cyclized to produce a larger ring with the four pyrrole nitrogens at the center (see Fig. 1). These nitrogen atoms provide coordinate bonds to the metal ion. The metal ion in this structure generally has six ligands in approximately octahedral geometry, at least one of which comes from the protein. The remaining position (if one remains) is filled by either a small molecule or by another amino acid side chain from the protein. Hemoglobin and myoglobin contain an iron-coordinating tetrapyrrole called heme, which is red in color. The tetrapyrrole of chlorophyll is a substituted chlorin ring and it complexes Mg^{2+} ion. The chlorophyll/protein complex gives the characteristic green color to leaves of green plants.

TABLE I

Structures of the Common Amino Acids

Amino acid	Abbrev	Side chain structure
Small, neutral		
Gly	Gly, G	-H
Ala	Ala, A	-CH$_3$
Polar		
Serine	Ser, S	-CH$_2$OH
Threonine	Thr, T	-CH$_2$(OH)CH$_3$
Cysteine	Cys, C	-CH$_2$CH$_2$SH
Asparagine	Asn, N	-CH$_2$CONH$_2$
Glutamine	Gln, Q	-CH$_2$CH$_2$CONH$_2$
Methionine	Met, M	-CH$_2$CH$_2$SCH$_3$
Histidine	His, H	(imidazole ring structure)
Anionic		
Aspartate	Asp, D	-CH$_2$COO-
Glutamate	Glu, E	-CH$_2$CH$_2$COO-
Cationic		
Lysine	Lys, K	-CH$_2$CH$_2$CH$_2$CH$_2$NH$_3^+$
Arginine	Arg, R	-CH$_2$NHC(NH$_2$)$_2^+$
Hydrophobic		
Leucine	Leu, L	-CH$_2$CH(CH$_3$)$_2$
Isoleucine	Ile, I	-CH(CH$_3$)CH$_2$CH$_3$
Valine	Val, V	-CH(CH$_3$)$_2$
Aromatic		
Phenylalanine	Phe, F	(benzyl structure)
Tyrosine	Tyr, Y	(hydroxybenzyl structure)
Tryptophan	Trp, W	(indolylmethyl structure)

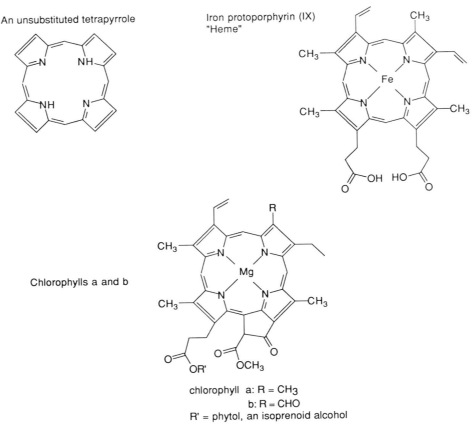

An unsubstituted tetrapyrrole

Iron protoporphyrin (IX) "Heme"

Chlorophylls a and b

chlorophyll a: R = CH3
b: R = CHO
R' = phytol, an isoprenoid alcohol

FIGURE 1 Structures of tetrapyrroles. Shown are a prototypical tetrapyrrole, the heme group of hemoglobin and myoglobin, and chlorophylls a and b.

B. Structure and Physical State of Proteins

1. Globular Soluble Proteins

Organic acids and amines can form bonds to one another called amide bonds. Amino acids are both amines and organic acids, so they can form chains in which each carboxyl group is bonded to the amino group of the next amino acid. These amide bonds are considered to be special bonds, so they are given their own name, peptide bonds. These linear strings of amino acids are called peptides. They may be called dipeptides, tripeptides, etc., if they contain only two or three amino acids; oligo peptides, if they contain any small number of amino acids, or polypeptides, if they contain many amino acids. Proteins are polypeptides. Because of the directionality of the peptide bond, a peptide or protein has an N-terminal end and a C-terminal end. Proteins and peptides are usually written with the N-terminus on the left and, if amino acids are numbered for reference, the numbering always starts at the N-terminus. In speaking of the sequence of a protein or the occurrence of a particular amino acid at a particular location in the sequence, amino acids are commonly referred to as "residues" (e.g., a glycine residue, a lysine residue . . .) for historical reasons.

Polypeptide chains are usually not extended structures, but fold upon themselves, and perhaps with other polypeptides to form globular structures. The exact way in which a protein folds depends on the sequence of amino acids of which it is composed. Hence, the sequence of amino acids determines the shape and therefore, the function and properties of the protein. (The information that determines the sequence of amino acids in proteins is carried by genes, which are strands of DNA. In fact, the traditional definition of a gene is that it is the amount of DNA that codes for one protein chain.) The mechanism of folding and rules that govern the folding of proteins are still under intense investigation, but several aspects are understood. Proteins fold to remove the peptide backbone and hydrophobic ("disliking water") side chains from water (which surrounds them). Soluble globular proteins therefore are said to have a hydrophobic core and a hydrophilic ("liking water") surface, due to the charged and polar side chains, which are generally on the surface. However, proteins that are embedded in membranes, which are hydrophobic, have few exposed charged side chains so that they can interact with lipids instead of water.

There are also some specific interactions that stabilize the structure of proteins. An important interaction, called hydrogen bonding, occurs when a single hydrogen atom becomes shared by two electronegative atoms (O, N, or S), as shown in Fig. 2A. The attraction of the two groups for the same proton holds the two groups together. Although the energy (degree of stabilization) afforded by this bond is low, the stabilization can be substantial if many such interactions occur. Two common structural motifs often found in proteins stabilized by hydrogen bonding are the α-helix and the β-pleated sheet (see Fig. 2). The α-helix is a structure in which the polypeptide chain is coiled like a spring. The coil is stabilized by hydrogen bonds between the C=O oxygen of an amino acid and the N-H proton of the third amino acid away in the sequence. The α-helix is a right-handed helix, meaning that the chain turns clockwise, like the threads on a screw.

The β-sheet also involves interactions between the C=O and the N-H proton, but of different chains or of distant regions of the same chain (Fig. 2C). The two strands of protein engaged in a β-sheet may be parallel or anti-parallel. For both parallel and anti-parallel β-pleated sheet, several chains can be involved to yield a relatively rigid sheet, "woven" of polypeptide chains.

Many other structural patterns are possible for proteins, but, because of the bulk of some of the side chains and the strain that would be placed on bond angles, only a few folding patterns, or conformations, are energetically favored. A hypothetical typical protein might have a few stretches of α-helix and some portions of β structure, with some less well-defined stretches of amino acids connecting them. However, some proteins are mostly helix, having a series of helix-turn-helix structures, while other proteins are mostly β-sheet.

Since β-sheet can occur between different amino acid chains, these interactions can be found in complex proteins made of subunits, each subunit of which is a separate peptide chain. Other interactions, most notably the hydrophobic interaction, are also involved in holding together multi-subunit protein complexes.

Other interactions that are important in stabilizing the folding of proteins include electrostatic interactions between charged amino acid side chains (e.g., -COO$^-$ and -NH$_3^+$). This interaction is known as a salt bridge. Amino acid side chains that are not charged, but polar, can interact weakly with each other.

The strongest of the side chain–side chain interactions is the disulfide bond which can be formed between the sulfur atoms of two cysteine side chains. This is the only covalent bond normally formed between amino acid side chains and can confer considerable stability to a protein, especially if several disulfide bonds exist.

From the preceding discussion, it is clear that proteins have four levels of structure, and the following jargon has arisen. "Primary structure" refers to the amino acid sequence of an amino acid chain (polypeptide). "Secondary structure" refers to specifically identifiable structural motifs, such as α-helix and β-sheet. "Tertiary structure" refers to the overall three-dimensional folding of the protein. "Quaternary structure" refers to the assembly of a protein from subunits (i.e., more than one polypeptide chain). In recent years, another term, "domain," has come into use to describe identifiable structural units within a protein that can be excised in one way or another, and studied separately on their own. Examples of domains are self-contained globular structures that are somehow separable from the remainder of the protein.

2. Examples of Globular Proteins

Some important food proteins exemplary of globular proteins include hemoglobin and myoglobin, the principal color substances of red meat and the enzyme ribulose bisphosphate carboxylase, the principal protein of green plant leaves. Most known enzymes are globular proteins.

3. Structural Proteins of Meat and Bone

Globular proteins are usually water-soluble, with charged and polar side chains on the outside and nonpolar groups on the inside. Other proteins, such as fibrous structural proteins and muscle proteins, fold according to the same rules as globular proteins, but because of their size and the nature of their surfaces, are not soluble. They therefore form relatively solid structures in the body rather than dissolving in its fluids. Meat contains good examples of several kinds

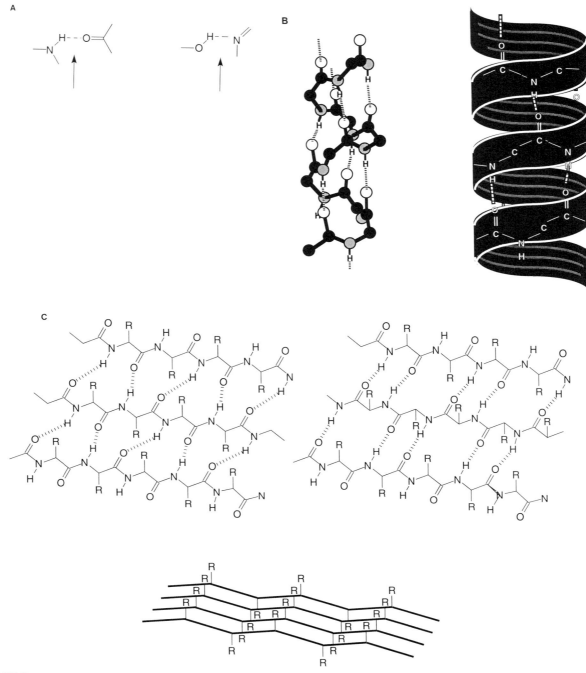

FIGURE 2 Hydrogen bonding and the common folding patterns in proteins stabilized by hydrogen bonding. (A) Hydrogen bonding occurs between a proton bonded to an electronegative atom (usually N or O) and an adjacent atom with a nonbonded electron pair (often N or O). (B) Hydrogen bonding stabilizes the α-helix as shown by the structure and accompanying schematic. (C) Hydrogen bonding stabilizes two kinds of β-sheet: parallel (left) and antiparallel (right). Both forms give the impression of a pleated sheet, as shown below.

of proteins. Besides the soluble proteins hemoglobin and myoglobin, the other major components of meat, the connective tissue proteins collagen and elastin, and the contractile proteins actin and myosin are insoluble, have characteristic structures and are of central importance in foods of animal origin.

a. Muscle Proteins The contractile system of skeletal muscle (i.e., meat) is composed primarily of two groups of protein, actin and myosin, which are arranged into a complex intracellular structure, the myofibril, and surrounded by cellular fluid, the sarcoplasm. Myofibrils are arranged into muscle fibers, each surrounded by a membrane called the sarcolemma. Groups of filaments occur in bundles which are surrounded by connective tissue called endomesium.

The myofibrils are composed of two kinds of filaments, the thick filaments and the thin filaments. The striations of striated muscle actually arise from the arrangement of these filaments. The areas where the thin or thick filaments overlap appear as dark bands, and where only one type of filament exists, appear as light bands across a muscle fiber (see Fig. 3). During muscle contraction, the two types of fiber slide along one another to increase the amount of overlap.

Thin filaments are composed of four strands of protein. Two of the strands are composed of many molecules of a globular protein called actin (M_r 42,000), lined up end to end, resembling a double string of pearls. The two strands of actin wind about each other. Along the outer surface of each strand is a series of helical dimers (M_r 70,000) of a protein called tropomyosin. Bound to each tropomyosin dimer is

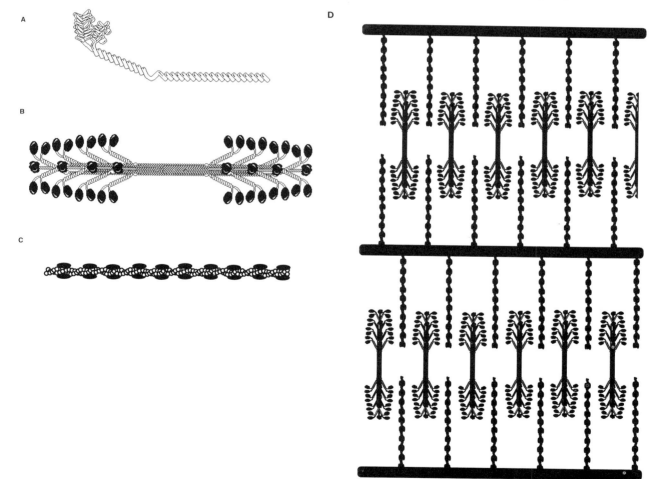

FIGURE 3 Sketch of muscle protein structure. (A) Myosin structure: the head region is at the left, attached to the hinge region. (B) Arrangement of many myosin dimers into a thick filament. (C) Structure of a thin filament: threads of tropomyosin twist around a beadlike arrangement of actin. Troponin complexes dot the surface of the strand. (D) Organization of thin and thick filaments into two sarcomeres, which meet at the z-line. (Drawn by Daniel Santillano after Rawn (1989). Used with permission.)

a complex of three proteins, collectively called troponin, which have molecular weights of 37,000, 24,000 and 18,000. The functional unit of the muscle fiber is called the sarcomere. The ends of the thin filaments interacting with a set of thick filaments in a sarcomere (see below) and the thin filaments interacting with a group of thick filaments of an adjacent sarcomere meet at an area called the Z-disc, which, when viewed from the side, appears as a line called the Z-line. The space between two Z-lines, i.e., thin filaments, overlapping thick and thin filaments, thick filaments, overlapping thick and thin filaments, thin filaments, defines the sarcomere (Fig. 3D).

The thick filaments are composed of a few hundred molecules of myosin, a protein composed of six subunits arranged in clearly identifiable domains. Two identical "heavy chains" are α-helical and wind about each other to form a twisted double strand (Fig. 3A). There are two flexible regions of the heavy chains, the hinge and swivel regions, which occur near the N-termini, where the coiling of the two α-helices around one another is interrupted. Near the N-termini of the heavy chains (M_r 200,000 each) are the "heads" of the chains, which have globular structures, and are attached to two sets of globular light chains, which are themselves composed of a larger ($M_r = 20,000$) and a smaller ($M_r = 16,000$) protein. In the thick filament, helical regions of the heavy chains associate with one another into bunches (Fig. 3B). The heads are arranged at either end of the bunch, leaving only helical regions in the center.

In the region where thick and thin filaments overlap, where muscle contraction takes place, the myosin heads touch the actin/tropomyosin filament. The exact conformation of myosin at the head and swivel regions depends on the presence of other agents, namely ATP (the metabolic energy carrier), ADP, inorganic phosphate (P_i), and Ca^{2+} ion. The head is capable of hydrolyzing ATP to ADP plus P_i, but releases the products very slowly. So, the resting state of myosin contains bound ADP and P_i. When ADP and P_i are released, the swivel region flexes, which pulls the actin along the myosin. When another molecule of ATP binds, the myosin releases the actin fiber, hydrolyzes the ATP, and reverts to the resting conformation, and the process is repeated. By this process the myosin heads crawl along the actin fiber, increasing the amount of actin/myosin overlap and shortening the fiber. This is the contraction process (Fig. 4). The ATPase activity of myosin is stimulated by the binding of Ca^{2+} to troponin, which causes a tightening of the tropomyosin–actin association in the thin filament and alters its interaction with myosin. In living muscle, nerve impulses cause rapid release of Ca^{2+} from the sarcoplasmic reticulum to the filaments, stimulating the ATP hydrolysis and the resulting contraction. An ATP-driven transport system in the sarcoplasmic reticulum pumps the Ca^{2+} back across the membrane, allowing the fibers to relax. Both the myosin head conformational change and removal of Ca^{2+} ion from the fiber are ultimately driven by the hydrolysis of ATP, which may be replenished from the energy storage compound phosphocreatine or from energy metabolism.

After slaughter of an animal, when blood flow ceases, phosphocreatine, ATP, and even ADP are depleted. Since there is no oxygen for oxidative phosphorylation, only glycolysis continues to function, which supplies a small amount of energy but a large amount of lactic acid. The pH falls to a level characteristic of the species and storage temperature (and other factors) called the ultimate pH.

Because of the cessation of energy metabolism, there is neither ATP nor ADP to bind to the myosin, so the conformation is locked in the one producing contraction. The muscle stiffens into a state called rigor mortis. The rate of rigor mortis onset depends on the species (chicken, 2–4 hr; pig, 4–18 hr; beef, 10–24 hr) and postmortem temperature (high temperature hastens onset).

Meat excised during rigor is tough, but the tissue softens upon ageing. Microscopic investigation shows that the Z-disc is disrupted during ageing, causing the myofibrils to separate and become more labile to enzymatic degradation. One of the troponins, troponin T, also becomes hydrolyzed. This postrigor tenderization, called "resolution of rigor," is indeed caused by proteolysis by several endogenous proteases. A Ca^{2+}-activated neutral protease called calcium-activated factor, CAF, can hydrolyze troponin and disrupt the Z-disc. Other proteases, such as cathepsin B, may also play a role. However, Ca^{2+} alone also causes some tenderization by another, unknown mechanism.

Artificial tenderizing processes involve physical destruction of muscle bundles by pounding or partial flaking, or by incubating the meat with proteases. Papain, the highly stable protease from papaya, is perhaps the most widely used, but proteases from fresh pineapple fruit and ginger root can provide the same effect. Marinating the meat in vinegar or lemon juice may also effect some tenderization by destabilizing the muscle fibers and by increasing the activity of cathepsins and lysosomal acid proteases.

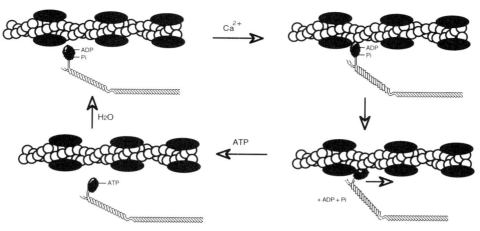

FIGURE 4 Sequence of events leading to muscle contraction. Only one myosin head is shown for clarity. In the resting state, the myosin head binds ADP and phosphate. In the presence of Ca^{2+} ion, which is released by nerve impulses, the hinge region flexes and the myosin head touches the thin filament. When ADP and phosphate are released, the hinge region flexes further and propels the thin filament to the right. When ATP binds, the head releases the thin filament. The head hydrolyzes the ATP and the sequence begins again.

b. Collagen Collagen, the principal protein of bone and skin, contains two unique structural features: the collagen helix and unusual interchain crosslinks. Collagen is made from polypeptide chains called tropocollagen. The amino acid sequence of tropocollagen is quite regular, every third residue being a glycine. Many of the glycine residues are either followed by a proline residue or preceded by a 4-hydroxyproline residue, or both. In addition to the modified amino acid 4-hydroxyproline, collagen also contains 5-hydroxylysine and an aldehyde derivative of lysine, allysine. To the hydroxyl group of many of the hydroxylysine residues of collagen is attached a disaccharide (α-1,2 glucosyl galactose in a β-1 linkage). 4-Hydroxyproline and 5-hydroxylysine are made from specific proline and lysine residues of tropocollagen by the enzymes proline hydroxylase and lysine hydroxylase. Allysine is formed from a lysyl residue of tropocollagen by the enzyme lysyl oxidase. All three of these enzymes require ascorbic acid (vitamin C) as a cosubstrate. The conversion of lysine to the aldehyde amino acid allysine is significant because aldehydes are very reactive and condense with side chains of lysine and hydroxylysine residues or with other allysine residues to form crosslinks that strengthen the collagen structure. Thus, it is clear why people who have vitamin C-deficient diets suffer from weakness of connective tissue, notably in arteries, skin, and gums.

The glycine–proline sequence does not favor the formation of an α-helix. Instead of an α-helix, the pro-α collagen forms a left-handed helix that is not stabilized by C=O to NH hydrogen bonds. Since every third residue is a glycine, one surface of the helix contains only glycine, the smallest amino acid (see Table I). Three molecules of pro-α associate with one another along this surface, gently twisting around each other to form a right-handed superhelix. This superhelix is stabilized by interchain hydrogen bonds and by covalent crosslinks involving allysine. This trimer, called procollagen is trimmed by proteases into the actual structural units of collagen, tropocollagen. In mature collagen, tropocollagen molecules lie side by side in a staggered fashion and are crosslinked to form strong microfibrils.

When collagen is heated (i.e., cooked), the triple helix is disrupted, and the tissue shrinks. Fragments of the collagen are water-soluble and are called gelatin. Food and manufacturing gelatins are made by acid or alkaline hydrolysis of proteins from animal skin and bone. As the gelatin is cooled, it binds water and forms patches of secondary structure, forming a gel. The properties of the gel depend on the protein concentration, size of polypeptides present, and rate of cooling. It is notable that collagen is relatively deficient in the essential amino acids, and gelatin is therefore not a "high-quality" food protein. Collagen and gelatin are digested by a number of proteases.

c. Elastin Another major kind of fibrous protein is elastin, which is found in skin, blood vessels and ligaments. Small amounts of elastin, together with collagen are included with actin and myosin in meat. It is a crosslinked system of monomers of molecular weight 64,000. Elastin contains high proportions of glycine and proline, but little hydroxyproline and no hydroxylysine. Allysine, participates in two kinds of crosslinks. Allysine may be condensed with the amino group of a lysine residue to form a collagen-like cross-link, or it can condense with other allysine side chains to produce desmosine, a multichain cross-link unique to elastin. Because of the high glycine and proline content of elastin, it forms neither α-helix nor β sheet, but an irregular structure called random chain. Together with the high degree of cross-linking, this random chain confers both flexibility and strength. It contains a higher proportion of hydrophobic amino acids than does collagen, and therefore does not swell appreciably upon heating in water. Its digestion involves initial cleavage by the enzyme elastase, which is secreted by the pancreas.

4. Complexes of Proteins with Lipids: Membrane Proteins and Lipoproteins

Whereas some globular proteins ("peripheral membrane proteins") may have a charged surface and interact with the polar head groups of lipid bilayers that form cell and intracellular membranes, other proteins contain very hydrophobic regions and actually are embedded in the membrane. The hydrophobic regions of the protein interact with the fatty acyl chains of the lipids, while polar or charged surfaces protrude into the aqueous medium outside the membrane. Some membrane proteins span the thickness of the membrane and have polar domains on each side of the membrane. [See Food Biochemistry: Lipids, Carbohydrates, and Nucleic Acids.]

Proteins and lipids also form structures other than lipid bilayers with adsorbed and embedded proteins. Lipoproteins are proteins that bind tightly but noncovalently to lipids. The lipids involved in such complexes include phospholipids, neutral lipids (triacylglycerols), and cholesterol and its esters. The ratio of protein content to content of the various lipids varies from protein to protein. Since lipids and proteins have substantially different densities, lipoproteins are conveniently separated by ultracentrifugation and classified by their densities into four categories, chylomicrons, very low density lipoproteins, low density lipoproteins (LDL's), and high density lipoproteins (HDL's). The most popularly known example of lipoproteins are HDL's and LDL's of human blood serum, which are involved in the controversial relationship between cholesterol and atherosclerosis. There are also lipoproteins of substantial importance to foods, such as the (chicken) egg yolk LDL and β-lipovitellin, and the LDL of cows' milk. The milk fat globules of cows' milk contain adsorbed LDL on their surfaces.

5. Caseins: Milk, Cheese, and Yogurt

There are other aggregates of protein that are unusually important in food systems. Prominent examples of these are the caseins of ruminant milk. "Casein" is actually a mixture of proteins, the major components of which are called α-casein, β-casein, and κ-casein. These are not pure proteins, either, but contain minor components of slightly different structure. α-Casein in particular occurs in two main subgroups, α_{s1}-casein and α_{s2}-casein. The subscript "s" stands for "sensitive" (to calcium) and is appended because the α_s-caseins precipitate in the presence of excess Ca^{2+} ions. The three-dimensional structures of caseins are not known, but it is clear that caseins have definite polar and nonpolar regions in their sequence. The caseins do not appear to be typical globular proteins: structural studies indicate that they have very little α-helix or β-structure, and they are unusually susceptible to proteolytic degradation. These observations suggest a loose or flexible structure. [See Dairy Processing and Products.]

Caseins occur in large aggregates called the casein micelle. The current model of the casein micelle depicts the system as being composed of submicelles. The submicelles are composed of a hydrophobic core, with the polar regions containing the many phosphoserine groups of α- and β-caseins on the surface. These polar regions bind calcium ions which in turn bind to phosphate ions that are present in milk serum. The result is that submicelles become attached to one another by binding to opposite ends of a cluster of calcium and phosphate which has the formula $Ca_9(PO_4)_6$. This calcium phosphate cluster is referred to as colloidal calcium phosphate because it is suspended in the milk fluid by virtue of its attachment to the submicelles. The amounts of calcium and phosphate held by the casein micelle far exceed the solubility of several calcium phosphate minerals, which would otherwise form stones, making them unavailable to the calf or consumer and quite unappetizing.

The most polar region of κ-casein, the C-terminal region of which contains the single phosphoserine and the glycosylated threonine, is also on the surface and is believed to stabilize the structure of the submicelles by spacing out the other caseins to prevent electrostatic repulsion between their phosphate groups or excessive crosslinking.

Milk is the only substance consumed by humans that was designed over eons by evolution for the single purpose of nourishing young mammals. It is therefore not surprising that the casein micelle provides large amounts of high-quality, easily digestible protein and readily available calcium and phosphate. These are the major components of bone (which is composed of collagen and a calcium phosphate mineral) and of muscle.

The protease chymosin is the major enzyme in an extract of the stomach of suckling calves (veal) called rennet. This extract, which also contains the protease pepsin, is used in the making of various kinds of cheese. When a small amount of the extract is added to milk, chymosin specifically hydrolyzes κ-casein between phenylalanine 103 and methionine 104. This cleavage removes the protein's hydrophilic C-terminus, which is water soluble and leaves the micelle. The remainder of the κ-casein ("para-κ-casein") is hydrophobic, and either retreats to the interior of the micelle or precipitates, and is no longer able to provide stabilization. The micelle and colloidal calcium phosphate are disrupted, so α_s-casein binds the calcium, precipitates, and forms a curd that contains α_s-, β- and para-κ-casein.

The exact nature of the gelled curd depends on many factors, including the amount of chymosin added, the pH of the milk, the temperature, and the amount of stirring or agitation. Usually there is little agitation after the initial mixing, and the curd is one continuous custardlike gel. The gel is cut with knives, and the liquid (cheese whey) is allowed to separate. The curd, which is soft and moist, contains caseins crosslinked by Ca^{2+} (but in a different way than by the colloidal calcium phosphate), entrapped milkfat globules, lactose, salts, and some nutrients dissolved in the remaining water. Some of the chymosin, pepsin, and other proteases also become entrapped in the curd, and lipid-soluble vitamins remain in the entrapped fat globules. The whey contains lactose, the globular whey proteins, β-lactoglobulin, α-lactalbumin, serum albumin, immunoglobulins, and a few minor proteins and metabolites. Much of the phosphate, but almost none of the calcium, appears in the whey.

The curd may be warmed, cooked, or pressed before being stored for ageing. The proteases entrapped in the curd continue to hydrolyze proteins during ageing, which causes the development of flavor and aroma as well as changes in texture.

In many cheeses, bacteria or molds are added to the mixture during the process. Many of the microorganisms used consume lactose and generate lactic acid, which contributes flavor and aroma and lowers the pH. The pH modulates the solubility of Ca^{2+} ion, and thus alters the curd texture by adjusting the degree of crosslinking. Bacterial and fungal proteases also affect the texture by continued hydrolysis of the caseins. The enzymes of the microorganisms also contribute to the development of characteristic flavors and aromas of ripened cheeses.

The casein micelle can be disrupted in another way. If acid is added to milk to reduce the pH to 4.6, the caseins begin to precipitate. This pH is near the isoelectric point of the caseins, where they have a net neutral charge and are therefore less soluble. Acid, however, increases the solubility of calcium phosphates, so the curd formed by acid coagulation contains relatively little calcium compared to the rennet curd, in which calcium is actually concentrated from the milk.

For some uses, caseins are forced to undergo isoelectric precipitation from defatted milk, washed, then redissolved by neutralization with NaOH. The dried product is sold as sodium caseinate for use as a food ingredient. Acid-precipitated caseins have several nonfood manufacturing uses, such as in plastics and paper sizing.

The curd formed by acid addition depends on temperature and the rate of acid addition, slower addition yielding a smooth, uniform curd. One way to add acid very slowly is by using a starter culture of lactic acid bacteria, which converts some of the lactose to lactic acid. These organisms are therefore capable of clotting milk by themselves, but also may be added to milk to lower the pH and contribute flavor before addition of rennet. Examples of cheeses prepared by acid coagulation are cottage cheese (a soft, unripened low-fat cheese) and cream cheese (a soft, unripened, high-fat cheese). Both cheeses are relatively low in calcium compared to the rennet-coagulated hard cheeses such as cheddar and swiss. However, rennet is often used as a co-coagulator in the preparation of cottage cheese, and since the serving size is much greater than for most cheeses, cottage cheese is a reasonable source of dietary calcium.

In yogurts, no whey is removed and the yogurt has the same composition as the milk from which it was made, except for the changes brought about by the starter culture (i.e., consumption of lactose and production of acid). The cultures also affect flavor and aroma by production of other metabolites. Some starter cultures excrete mucopolysaccharides which improve the texture of the yogurt. Stabilizers and thickeners can also be added for the same purpose, but there is better consumer acceptance of a product labeled "live cultures" than one listing the perceived "artificial" ingredients xanthan gum, carageenan, etc.

As an aside, Asian cultures, which do not include cheese in their diets, nonetheless have a loose analog to cheese: tofu or bean curd. Tofu is prepared by hydrating and grinding soy beans in water, then heating the suspension to extract the soluble proteins and pasteurize the solution. The addition of $CaSO_4$ to this "soy milk" causes precipitation of the proteins to form a curd, in rough analogy to chymosin-induced clotting, which also involves calcium-induced precipitation. The resulting gel is pressed to form a soft or dry curd, depending on its intended use. In some cases, this nondairy "cheese" is inoculated with *Actinomucor elegans,* which leads to a ripened product called *sufu.*

6. Wheat Proteins and Baking of Bread

Another aggregated state of protein of epochal importance to civilization are those proteins of wheat that lead to pliable, elastic dough formation: the gluten proteins. The proteins of wheat are classified according to their solubility: albumins are water-soluble, globulins are water-insoluble but soluble in 10% NaCl, gliadins are soluble in ethanol, and glutenins are soluble in acid or alkali, but water- and ethanol-insoluble. The water-insoluble protein-containing material, called gluten, is about 75–80% protein, 5–10% lipid and 2–15% carbohydrates.

The proteins in gluten are mostly gliadins and glutenins, which are storage proteins for the wheat seed. The structures of the gliadins are well studied. Most of them have molecular weights between 32,000 and 42,000, except for ω-gliadin, which is near 74,000. Disulfide bonds in gliadins are largely intramolecular. At least one of the gliadins, A-gliadin, is known to form long fibrils 70–80 Å in diameter and several thousand angstroms long. The glutenins are less well understood. Their average molecular weights appear to be about 300,000, but may be more than 1 million. They are typically large complexes of about 15 subunits. Hydrophobic interactions are important in the stability of these complexes, but many intermolecular disulfide bonds also exist.

The carbohydrates of gluten are largely pentosans, a mixture of polysaccharides and glycoproteins. The carbohydrate portion is of irregular structure, consisting mostly of a poly β-1-4 xylopyranose backbone with monosaccharide (β-arabinofuranoside) branches at some of the 2- or 3-positions of the xylose. Six to seven percent of the structure is glucose. The glycoproteins contain branched arabinoxylans. These carbohydrates are capable of binding large amounts of water.

It is believed that the gluten complex occurs during mixing by aggregation of the high-molecular-weight glutenins into a spongy grid in which the other components are dispersed. The physical stress of kneading causes reorientation and stretching of the glutenin protein network. The new structures produced are stabilized by reshuffling of disulfide bonds of the glutenins (not gliadins), and noncovalent interactions. Other components of the flour (e.g., starch) are entrapped in the network. During leavening, the network traps gas (e.g., CO_2 given off by the yeast), and, because of its elasticity, the dough swells as it fills with evenly distributed bubbles.

During baking, the proteins denature, starch gelatinizes, and lipids, originating in the gluten, migrate to the starch. Nonpolar lipids, such as shortening, probably play a role in trapping gas bubbles during rising and in early stages of baking. [See Wheat Processing and Utilization.]

C. Functional Properties

Proteins have properties that affect the nature of numerous foods in ways that are only marginally related to nutrition. Proteins form gels and foams and stabilize emulsions.

"Denaturation" means loss of or change in some natural property. For enzymes, the enzymatic activity is usually the important property. Since the structural features leading to enzyme action are sometimes rather fragile, only subtle changes can cause the protein to be denatured. However, in general use, "denatured" usually is synonymous with "unfolded." The globular structure exists to shield hydrophobic substances from water. Heating disrupts the globular structure, exposing the hydrophobic interior to water. Since water cannot solvate hydrophobic areas, the protein precipitates, or the hydrophobic regions of many proteins stick together to exclude water, forming large insoluble complexes. Sometimes denatured proteins renature, but rarely in concentrated solution or after they have aggregated and precipitated. A classic example of a heat-denatured globular protein is the white (largely egg albumen) of a boiled egg. Denatured proteins, because they are unfolded, behave differently in food formulations than native proteins.

Many proteins form gels when heated in water. Gellation is a two-step process; the first step is denaturation. After denaturation, the proteins aggregate to form a crosslinked network. If the aggregation process is fast, the gel is coarse and opaque, and tends to lose water. If aggregation is much slower than denaturation, a viscous intermediate state exists and the resulting gel is finer, more elastic, and more transparent. If the gel formation is reversible, the gel melts upon heating, and ultimately forms a solution of denatured protein, called a progel. Gels formed in this manner (e.g., gelatin) are called thermoset, or reversible gels, and are distinguished from irreversible or thermoplastic gels (e.g., from milk proteins).

Many proteins also stabilize emulsions and foams. Emulsions and foams are examples of dispersions, in which one phase is suspended in another. There are therefore interfaces between the phases; proteins stabilize the dispersions by acting at the interface. When air or another gas is introduced into an aqueous solution of protein (such as during beating of egg white or CO_2 bubbles rising in beer) the gasses form bubbles surrounded by dissolved, surface-denatured proteins. The liquid drains from between the gas spaces, and the thin film eventually breaks. Proteins adsorbed at the gas–water interface prolong the lifetime of the foam by (1) increasing viscosity to retard drainage, (2) preventing thinning of the film between bubbles by electrostatic repulsion, and (3) providing a rigid component to the surface of the aqueous film.

Proteins can act as surfactants to stabilize O/W or W/O emulsions by coating the discontinuous phase and providing a surface that interacts more favorably with the continuous phase. Not all proteins stabilize emulsions equally well. It is not merely total charge or total hydrophobicity of a protein that makes it a good emulsion stabilizer, but the distribution of charged and nonpolar residues. Proteins denature at the oil–water interface because of the uneven solvation effects. Nonpolar residues can interact with the nonpolar phase, and charged or polar residues can interact with the aqueous phase. Proteins that have large areas of charged residues and large areas of nonpolar residues should be more effective stabilizers than proteins with polar residues evenly dispersed in the sequence. Loops and tails of the protein can project into each phase. Certainly factors such as pH, temperature, and salt concentration affect the structures of proteins, both native and denatured, modulating their effectiveness as emulsifiers. [See FOOD BIOCHEMISTRY: LIPIDS, CARBOHYDRATES, AND NUCLEIC ACIDS.]

Foam stabilization and emulsification are examples of protein "functionality," or "functional properties" of proteins, the term "functional" being used in a practical sense rather than a biological sense.

D. Artificial "Fat"

Polysaccharides have been used extensively in recent years to mimic the texture of fat in low-fat and re-duced calorie products. Polysaccharides generally fail in two areas: they do not duplicate the lubricity of fat and cannot be used for frying. Spherical microparticles (0.1 to 3.0 μm) of protein produced by shearing at high temperature give a similar mouth-feel to that of fat when they are suspended in water. Eggwhite and milk proteins are currently used. These suspensions have fewer than 2 calories per gram and can be used to replace most of the fat in some foods, such as baked goods and frozen desserts. The products are not sufficiently heat-stable to permit their use in deep frying.

II. Biologically Active Food Proteins: Enzymes and Inhibitors

A. Enzymes

Enzymes are proteins that catalyze chemical reactions. By accelerating reactions that would otherwise proceed very slowly, enzymes guide and control nearly every process that occurs in tissue. In addition, by "coupling" two reactions, one that requires energy and one that produces energy, enzymes are able to drive the energetically unfavorable processes. Because enzymes are catalysts, i.e., they are not consumed in a chemical reaction, but enhance its rate, they are much more important than might be guessed from their concentration.

Enzymes are classified and named according to the reaction they catalyze. There exists an Enzyme Commission nomenclature in which each enzyme-catalyzed reaction is assigned a number. However, since enzymes found in different organisms or tissues that catalyze the same reaction may have different structures and properties, it is essential to specify the source of an enzyme.

Enzymes catalyze reactions by lowering the "transition state" energy of a reaction, that is, the energy barrier. Enzymes accomplish this reduction in energy by binding the reactants (called "substrates") near one another and in the proper orientation for reaction to occur, and using acidic and basic amino acid side chains to move protons from one position to another. Many enzymes use nonprotein groups such as heme groups, thiamine, lipoic acid, and biotin. Since another article is devoted to food enzymology, only a few aspects will be discussed here.

B. Hydrolases

The enzymes most important to food science are hydrolases and oxidases. Hydrolases break down biopolymers such as starch and protein, and are thus important in digestion, processing, and spoilage. Oxidases generally participate in deterioration of foods and are thus of interest to industry and consumers alike. [*See* FOOD BIOCHEMISTRY: PIGMENTS, FLAVORS, AROMAS, AND STABILITY.]

1. Proteases

Proteases (proteinases or peptidases) hydrolyze peptide bonds of proteins. Exopeptidases cleave the N-terminal (aminopeptidases) or C-terminal (carboxypeptidases) amino acid from a protein or peptide; endopeptidases hydrolyze peptide bonds other than those to the terminal residues. Many proteases are highly specific for certain amino acids in the sequence of a protein, without regard to its occurrence at the terminus or in the interior. For instance, trypsin cleaves almost exclusively at the carbonyl side of peptide bonds involving the basic amino acids lysine or arginine; chymotrypsin has a high specificity for cleavage of the peptide bond in which the aromatic or nonpolar amino acids tyrosine, phenylalanine, tryptophan, and leucine contribute the carbonyl group. Other specific proteases described elsewhere in this chapter are papain, cathepsins, pepsin, chymosin, and fungal proteases used as chymosin substitutes.

2. Glycosidases

Glycosidases are enzymes that catalyze hydrolysis of the glycosidic bonds of polysaccharides. [*See* FOOD BIOCHEMISTRY: LIPIDS, CARBOHYDRATES, AND NUCLEIC ACIDS.] The most important of these is perhaps α-amylase, which hydrolyzes starch. Although mammals do not produce enzymes that hydrolyze cellulose, cellulases obtained from other sources can be used to decompose cellulose to glucose, which can serve as the substrate of various industrial fermentations, such as in the production of alcohol.

3. Lipases

Lipases and phospholipases hydrolyze the fatty acids from neutral lipids and phospholipids, respectively. [*See* FOOD BIOCHEMISTRY: LIPIDS, CARBOHYDRATES, AND NUCLEIC ACIDS.] Lipases hydrolyze neutral lipids (acyl glycerols) to liberate fatty acids and either glycerol or remaining glycerol esters. Some lipases hydrolyze the ester bonds at positions 1 and 3 preferentially, while others hydrolyze esters at all three positions. One peculiarity of the lipase reaction is that the substrate is insoluble, while the enzyme is soluble. The reaction therefore occurs at the interface between water and the fat. In many kinds of food,

such as the fat on a beefsteak, there is relatively little opportunity for water, the enzyme, and fat to come into contact. Emulsions or systems containing emulsified fats or oils provide a much greater opportunity for contact between the substrates (lipid and water) and the lipase. Emulsions are therefore more susceptible to flavor defects and chemical changes due to lipolysis. Phospholipids form structures in which the head group is at the lipid–water interface and are susceptible to phospholipases.

The action of lipases can alter the properties of food decisively, because they convert fat, which is by definition hydrophobic, to glycerol, which is hydrophilic, plus fatty acids, which have detergent properties. Furthermore, short-chain fatty acids, especially butyric, capric, and caproic acids, tend to have pungent or goaty aromas.

C. Inhibitors of Hydrolases: Protease Inhibitors and Amylase Inhibitors

Regulation is very important in living organisms. Regulation results from control of biosynthesis of many compounds, including hormones, enzymes, energy-generating systems, by proteins, peptides, and other compounds that inhibit a variety of enzymes. Organisms produce these compounds not only to control the direction of enzyme reactions, but also to protect the organism from premature activation of endogenous enzymes, such as in the pancreas and blood as well as for protection against external invaders (insects, microorganisms, plants, and animals).

The best-studied naturally occurring enzyme inhibitors are those against proteases and α-amylases. Trypsin inhibitors are probably ubiquitous. Soybeans contain two types of proteinaceous trypsin inhibitors, the Kunitz inhibitor ($M_r = 21,000$) and the Bowman-Birk inhibitors ($M_r = \sim 8000$). Common beans contain about 0.2% Bowman-Birk type inhibitors. The Kunitz inhibitor, specific for trypsin, is relatively easily destroyed by cooking, since it has only two disulfide bonds. However, it requires about 1 hr under boiling conditions to inactivate the Bowman-Birk inhibitors, which have seven disulfide bonds. Most Bowman-Birk type inhibitors combine simultaneously with one trypsin and one chymotrypsin. Thus, they are double-headed inhibitors. Rat feeding studies have shown repeatedly that sustained feeding of beans with active protease inhibitors, or feeding rations that contain added inhibitors leads to enlargement of the pancreas as the system attempts to compensate for

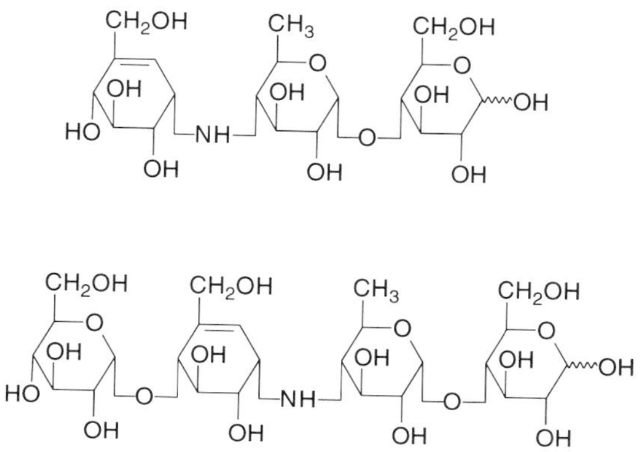

FIGURE 5 The carbohydrates of amylase inhibitors.

chronic loss of trypsin and chymotrypsin. More limited studies indicate this is also true in humans.

There are three types of α-amylase inhibitors. These include the microbial nitrogen-containing carbohydrates with oligobioamine units, the microbial polypeptides such as Paim (pig pancreatic α-amylase inhibitor from microbes; $M_r = 6000$-7420) and Haim (human pancreatic α-amylase inhibitor of microbial origin; $M_r = 8500$) and the large protease inhibitors, found in cereals, legumes, and some other higher plants (molecular weights range from ~8,000 to ~60,000). The protein inhibitors were discovered in 1933; however, most of the research has been done since the 1970s, because of their medical, nutritional, and insect control implications. The primary structures of several of the microbial N-containing carbohydrates (see Fig. 5; these include the oligostatins, amylostatins, and the trestatins) and the polypeptides are known (see Fig. 6), but the complete amino acid sequence for the large protein inhibitors is not yet known. Partial sequence analyses have shown the large protein inhibitors from beans have considerable homology with lectins and arcelins. Up to 5% of the total proteins of some beans are α-amylase inhibitors. It requires up to 1 hr cooking to inactivate them.

The α-amylase inhibitors combine stoichiometrically with susceptible α-amylases to produce an inactive complex. The microbial N-containing carbohydrate and polypeptide inhibitors may be prescribed for persons with diabetes and hyperglycemia to slow down the rate of digestion of starch to glucose, so as to decrease the levels of glucose in the blood following a meal. The protein α-amylase inhibitors also perform in a similar fashion. However, there is much more interest in their potential use to control weevil damage during storage of legume and cereal seeds.

D. Lectins

Lectins form an important class of proteins found in plants, especially legume seeds. These are sugar-binding proteins, and can therefore bind to the surface glycoproteins of various cells. They bind and precipitate red blood cells and are consequently also known as hemagglutinins. Because they bind bacterial cells, they may function as antibodylike molecules. But, some lectins also bind intestinal epithelial cells, preventing absorption of nutrients and inhibiting protein synthesis. Thus, lectins from many sources are quite toxic. Raw beans, for instance, which contain lectins, protease inhibitors, and amylase inhibitors are not nutritional, despite their large protein and starch content, and are actually toxic. Appropriate cooking inactivates the lectins and inhibitors.

Bibliography

Belitz, H.-D., and Grosch, W. (1987). "Food Chemistry." Springer-Verlag, Berlin.

Fennema, O. R. (ed.) (1976). "Principles of Food Science, Part I." Marcel Dekker, New York.

Rawn, J. D. (1989). "Biochemistry." Neil Patterson, Carolina Biological Supply Co., Burlington, N.C.

Whitaker, J. R. (1994). "Principles of Enzymology for the Food Sciences." 2nd edition Marcel Dekker, New York.

Wong, D. W. S. (1989). "Mechanism and Theory in Food Chemistry." Van Nostrand Reinhold, New York.

Paim I ASEPAPACVVMYESWRYTTAANNCADTVSVSVAYQDG

ATGPCATLPPGATVTVGEGYLGEHGHPDHLALOPSS

FIGURE 6 The sequences of a small protease inhibitor.

Food Chemistry

OWEN FENNEMA, *University of Wisconsin*

Glossary

ATP Adenosine triphosphate
Autoxidation Nonenzymic reaction of unsaturated lipids with atmospheric oxygen, involving free-radical reactions and steps of initiation, propagation, and termination
Femtogram 10^{-15} gm
Picogram 10^{-12} gm
Polyunsaturated fatty acids Fatty acids with two or more double bonds

Food chemistry is a major branch of food science dealing with the composition and properties of food and the chemical changes food products undergo during handling, processing, and storage. Attention is given to naturally occurring constituents of food (both desirable and undesirable), to chemical alterations that occur in foods under normal conditions to which they are exposed, and to contaminants.

I. History

Although the origins of food chemistry, in a sense, extend to antiquity, the most significant discoveries began in the late 1700s. We must acknowledge that the early histories of food chemistry and agricultural chemistry are impossible to separate. During the 1700s and early 1800s many world famous chemists made discoveries of fundamental importance to the field of food chemistry, in addition to discoveries for which they are better known. Worthy of mention are Carl Wilhelm Scheele (1742–1786), Antoine Laurent Lavoisier (1743–1794), (Nicolas) Théodore de Saussure (1767–1845), Joseph Louis Gay-Lussac (1778–1850), Louis-Jacques Thenard (1777–1857), Sir Humphry Davy (1778–1829), Jons Jacob Berzelius (1779–1848), Thomas Thomson (1773–1852), Michel Eugene Chevreul (1786–1889), and Justus von Liebig (1803–1873). Findings of importance to food chemistry include isolation of lactic, malic, citric, and tartaric acids from various fruits; establishment of the principle that all plants are capable of being decomposed into a few elements; procedures for quantitatively determining the percentages of carbon, hydrogen, and nitrogen in dry vegetable substances; a procedure for mineral determination by ashing; chemical characterization of vinegar fermentation; and, more generally, the origins of accurate quantitative analysis of organic substances. Von Liebig must also be acknowledged for what is considered to be the first book on food chemistry, *Researches on the Chemistry of Food* (1847).

In the early 1800s, advancements in the field of food chemistry were strongly stimulated by public indignation over the poor quality of foods, as publicized in a book by Frederick Accum (1820) and by an anonymous publication entitled *Death in the Pot* (1831). Accum asserted that, "Indeed, it would be difficult to mention a single article of food which is not to be met with in an adulterated state; and there are some substances which are scarcely ever to be procured genuine." It is no exaggeration to claim that the rapid development of food chemistry in the 1800s, especially the advances in food analysis made in Germany and England, paralleled and were largely caused by the increased prevalence and seriousness of intentional food adulteration.

Food chemistry did not acquire a true identity until the twentieth century. In the United States, inception of this identity can be marked by the activities of Harvey Washington Wiley, chief chemist of the U.S. Department of Agriculture (USDA) during the late 1800s. His campaign against misbranded and adulterated food culminated in passage by Congress of the Pure Food and Drug Act (1906). Intentional adulteration of food in the United States remained a serious problem until about 1920. At that time, regulatory measures and effective methods of detecting adulterants reduced the frequency and seriousness of intentional food adulteration to respectable levels; improvements have continued up to the present time.

In the mid-1900s, chemicals were developed and used extensively to aid in the growth, manufacture, and marketing of foods, and their use increased until about 1980. Since then, public concern about approved food additives has slowed their use. Simultaneously, government agencies have given increased attention to unintentional contamination of foods with pesticides, nitrites, heavy metals, and other by-products of industrialization.

II. Food Analysis

This area of endeavor is broad and rapidly evolving, because most of the techniques are of great value to all facets of the biological and physical sciences. Important to food chemists is an ability to measure the composition of food (significant nutrients, other desirable components such as fiber, naturally occurring toxicants, contaminants, substances developing during processing or storage) and the sensory quality of food (appearance, flavor, texture). This information is necessary to achieve conformity with governmental regulations and company standards.

Methods of food analysis range from simple to sophisticated, including titrimetry, chromatography, spectroscopy, electroanalytical techniques, radioactive tracer techniques, sensory analysis by humans, immunochemical techniques, use of monoclonal antibodies, and DNA amplification fingerprinting. Many of these techniques are similar to those used in the biological and physical sciences. However, techniques of food analysis are sufficiently specific and important to necessitate standardization and publication by various scientific associations, such as the Association of Official Analytical Chemists (AOAC), the American Association of Cereal Chemists (AACC), the American Oil Chemists' Society (AOCS), the American Public Health Association (APHA), the American So-

ciety of Brewing Chemists (ASBC), and other similar organizations.

In the last several decades, improvements bordering on incredible have been accomplished in the accuracy, precision, sensitivity, rapidity, and ease of food analysis. Substance concentration is often determinable at picogram and sometimes femtogram levels when necessary.

III. Food Composition

The major constituents of natural foods are water, carbohydrates, lipids, proteins, and sometimes fiber. Minor constituents of importance include vitamins, minerals, enzymes, pigments, flavors, and undesirable or potentially undesirable compounds. Hundreds of chemicals can be legally added to food, including substances such as sugars, salt, emulsifiers, flavors, spices, nutrients, antioxidants, sequestrants, and antimicrobial agents. The exact list of chemicals sanctioned for use in foods, and the conditions of use, vary with the country. Several extensive compilations of compositions of common foods can be found in the literature. Especially worthy of attention is a series by the USDA (1976). [See Food Composition.]

IV. Major Types of Reactions

Food chemistry is strongly related to organic chemistry, biochemistry, and physiological chemistry, but also has a clear identity of its own. In biochemistry and physiological chemistry, emphasis is on life-sustaining reactions. These reactions are pertinent to food chemists, but the primary focus of food chemists is on reactions, mostly degradative, that affect the appearance, texture, flavor, nutritive value, and wholesomeness of foods.

Chemical changes, some desirable and some not, occur in all foods and food ingredients during processing and storage. Further, these reactions differ depending on whether the food is or is not physiologically active. Desirable chemical reactions that can occur in food include:

1. development or preservation of pleasing colors and flavors. This occurs, for example, during cooking of meat; roasting of coffee beans, nuts, and breakfast cereals; preparation of bakery products; fermentation of cheese and alcoholic beverages; and postharvest ripening of fruits.

2. improvement or preservation of texture. Tenderization occurs, for example, during heating of plant and animal tissues and enzyme treatment of meat. Firming of texture occurs during the development of meat analogs, during gelling and coagulation reactions (eggs, milk, cheese), and during calcium treatment of soft plant tissues.

3. improvement of the functionality of food ingredients. Examples include heat denaturation of whey proteins for subsequent use in bread, chemical modification of starches, alkali processing of soy protein isolates, and glucose–fructose isomerization to achieve greater sweetness per unit weight.

4. inactivation or control of enzymes. Inactivation of endogenous enzymes such as lipases, lipoxygenases, proteases, phenolases, amylases, and ascorbic acid oxidase is almost always necessary if long-term storage of food tissues is desired. If this is not done, enzyme-catalyzed reactions will occur during storage, which will have undesirable effects on the sensory properties and nutritive value of the food. Heat is the most common means of inactivating enzymes in food, but other methods are sometimes used when complete inactivation is not required (e.g., pH adjustment, chemical inhibition, removal of reactants or catalysts).

5. inactivation of antinutritional substances and other approaches to improving nutritional value. Food tissues, especially plants, naturally contain many antinutritional substances (e.g., avidin in eggs, phytates in cereal grains, trypsin inhibitors and hemagglutinins in legumes, thiaminase in fish). Many antinutritional substances are proteins and can be inactivated by moderate heating of moist foods. Other approaches can also be used, including removal or enzymatic hydrolysis of lactose in dairy products intended for lactose-intolerant individuals and removal of phytates from cereal grain by milling. Moderate heating will sometimes improve the bioavailability of nutrients, for example, nicotinic acid in cereals. The addition of vitamins or minerals to certain foods (breakfast cereals, bread, milk) is also common practice.

Undesirable chemical reactions that occur in food include:

1. those causing damage to sensory properties of food (flavor, appearance, texture). Heat sterilization or air drying usually has this effect.

2. those causing damage to the functional properties of food ingredients. Here too, heat is a common offender, causing, for example, a reduction in the water-holding capacity and/or solubility of proteins and a reduction in the activity of desirable enzymes.

3. those causing damage to nutritional properties and/or the development of toxic or potentially toxic constituents. Vitamins C, D, E, A, and folate are especially susceptible to inactivation by oxidation, and vitamins C, folate, B_6, and thiamin are especially susceptible to inactivation by heat. Proteins are remarkably resistant to loss in nutritive value except in the presence of free carbonyls, especially reducing sugars. The nutritive value of lipids is generally well retained during processing and storage of foods, except when oxygen is present or heating is abusive. Carbohydrates are generally more resistant to processing-induced impairment of nutritive value and to the development of undesirable compounds than either proteins or lipids.

Harvested whole fruits and vegetables and post-mortem prerigor animal tissue are physiologically active. The reactions that dominate are similar to those that occur, or can occur, in these same tissues preharvest or preslaughter. A major difference, of course, is that the dominant reactions (Emden–Meyerhof sequence in both postslaughter muscle and postharvest plant tissues and the citric acid cycle in the latter group) are largely catabolic. Ongoing aerobic respiration in harvested plant foods, for example, follows well-known biochemical pathways of converting carbohydrates to CO_2, H_2O, and energy, but the mechanism for synthesis (photosynthesis) of carbohydrates is inoperative. This ability of plant tissue to carry on aerobic respiration postharvest is responsible, in large measure, for their long storage lives (many months for potatoes, apples, pears) relative to animal tissues.

This "living state" of intact plant tissues postharvest also results in additional storage complexities. Some fruits and vegetables, particularly those of tropical or subtropical origin, are susceptible to "chilling injury." These plant tissues have optimum storage temperatures well above 0°C; lengthy storage at temperatures below their optimum storage temperatures results in physiological defects that are quite noticeable to the consumer (e.g., excessive darkening of the skin of bananas; small, dark pits on the surface of green beans; darkening of the flesh of susceptible fruits). For long-term storage of apples and pears it is also necessary to carefully control not only storage temperature, relative humidity, and air velocity, but also CO_2, O_2, and ethylene concentrations of the atmosphere. [See POSTHARVEST PHYSIOLOGY.]

Physiological reactions persist in animal tissue for several hours following slaughter. These reactions cause a marked decline in pH, reductions in the concentrations of ATP and glycogen, and accumulation of lactic acid. The rate and extent of these reactions, although they are short-lived, can have a profound effect on consumer acceptability of the final product. For example, rapid cooling of postslaughter prerigor red muscle (beef, lamb) to temperatures below ~10°C will increase the rate of glycolysis, cause marked contraction of the muscle, poor water holding capacity, and toughness that persists even after normal cooking. This effect is attributed to cold-induced malfunctioning of the membranes of the sarcoplasmic reticulum, an organelle that controls calcium concentration in the fluid surrounding the contractile fibers. The elevated level of calcium triggers muscle contraction, causing the problems mentioned.

Foods devoid of physiological activity (fabricated foods, postrigor animal tissue, processed plant tissue, food ingredients) can undergo numerous types of chemical reactions, both enzymatic and nonenzymatic, virtually all of which are degradative and undesirable. These changes occur during processing and storage and are summarized in Table 1.

Preservation methods used to render foods moderately stable during long-term storage (canning, freezing, dehydration) effectively stop the growth of microorganisms, terminate physiological processes if present, and often slow, but almost never stop, chemical reactions. For example, degradation of chlorophyll, desirable flavors, and some of the more labile vitamins occurs at significant rates in all processed foods during storage. A major objective of food scientists and technologists is to effectively inactivate pathogenic and spoilage microorganisms in foods and to do so with minimal damage to quality attributes. [See FOOD DEHYDRATION; FOOD MICROBIOLOGY;

TABLE I

Classification of Undesirable Changes that Can Occur in Food

Attribute	Undesirable change
Texture	Loss of solubility
	Loss of water-holding capacity
	Toughening
	Softening
Flavor	Development of
	rancidity (hydrolytic or oxidative)
	cooked or caramel flavors
	other off-flavors
Color	Darkening
	Bleaching
	Development of other off-colors
Nutritive value	Loss or degradation of
	vitamins
	minerals
	proteins
	lipids
	carbohydrates

Source: Fennema (1985b).

FOOD PRESERVATIVES; THERMAL PROCESSING: CANNING AND PASTEURIZATION.]

Synthetic reactions are of commercial importance for some components of food including flavors, chemically modified starches, emulsifiers, antioxidants, some colors, sequestrants, nonnutritive sweeteners, and leavening agents.

Shown in Figs. 1–3 are summaries of nonphysiological reactions that food lipids, proteins, and carbohydrates can undergo during processing and storage. A few reactions are sufficiently unique and of such widespread importance in foods that they deserve special attention here.

1. The Maillard Reaction (Nonenzymatic Browning)

This reaction, discovered by Louis-Camille Maillard, a French scientist, in the early 1900s, involves the interaction of amino groups and carbonyls. ε-Amino groups of lysine residues in proteins are the most frequent source of amino groups, and carbonyls are usually supplied by reducing sugars. This reaction results in a brown color (desirable or undesirable de-

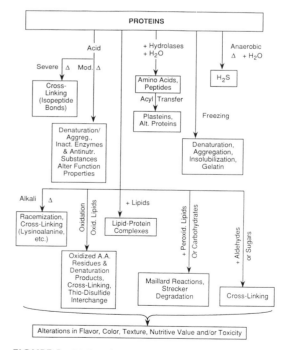

FIGURE 1 Major chemical reactions that proteins can undergo during the processing and handling of foods. [From Fennema, O. (1985b). Chemical changes in food during processing—An overview. *In* "Chemical Changes in Food during Processing" (T. Richardson and J. W. Finley, eds.) AVI, Westport, CT. Courtesy of Van Nostrand Reinhold.]

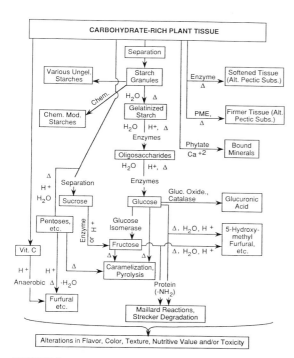

FIGURE 2 Major chemical reactions that carbohydrates can undergo during the processing and handling of foods. PME, Pectinmethylesterase. [From Fennema, O. (1985b). Chemical changes in food during processing—An overview. *In* "Chemical Changes in Food during Processing" (T. Richardson and J. W. Finley, eds.) AVI, Westport, CT. Courtesy of Van Nostrand Reinhold.]

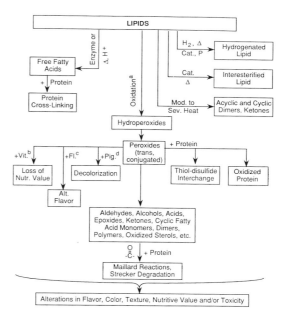

FIGURE 3 Major chemical reactions that lipids can undergo during the processing and handling of foods. [a]Oxidation catalyzed by enzymes, metals, myoglobin, chlorophyll, and/or irradiation. [b]Vit., vitamins A,C,D,E, and folate. [c]Fl., flavor. [d]Pig., carotenoids, chlorophyll, myoglobin, and anthocyanins. [From Fennema, O. (1985b). Chemical changes in food during processing—An overview. *In* "Chemical Changes in Food during Processing" (T. Richardson and J. W. Finley, eds.) AVI, Westport, CT. Courtesy of Van Nostrand Reinhold.]

pending on the product), a reduction in the nutritive value of reacting proteins or amino acids, changes in flavor, and reaction products that are of continuing interest with respect to their wholesomeness. This reaction is commonly observed in bakery products, baked beans, roasted nuts, toasted dry breakfast cereals, cooked meat, and dairy products that are excessively heated.

Maillard reactions typically begin with condensation of a nonionized amino group and a reducing sugar. The first step involves formation of an unstable Schiff base, rapid isomerization into aldosylamines or ketosylamines (depending on the initial reacting carbohydrate), and rearrangement into more stable ketosamines or aldosamines. The second step involves a complex set of reactions that converts the ketosamines or aldosamines into numerous carbonyl and polycarbonyl unsaturated derivatives (such as reductones). These, in turn, react with additional amines, leading to the formation of ammonia, CO_2, and new carbonyl compounds. During the third step, the polyunsaturated compounds undergo both scission and polymerization reactions, giving rise to volatile compounds,

some with desirable flavors, and to brown or black pigments known as melanoidins. The latter compounds are responsible for the Maillard reaction also being called the nonenzymatic browning reaction. Proteins involved in this reaction undergo pronounced reductions in nutritive value, so inhibition of the Maillard reaction is highly desirable in foods that are major sources of protein in the diet.

Development of control measures for the Maillard reaction has received much attention. Successful approaches have included alteration of sample composition (pH, metal ions, water activity, ratios and kinds of carbonyls and amines), use of chemical inhibitors (sulfites, cysteine), and control of storage temperature.

2. Oxidation of Lipids

Oxidation of lipids is a major cause of food degradation and can occur with or without enzyme (lipoxygenase) catalysis. Both mechanisms of oxidation result in off-flavors and loss of some vitamins in a wide range of products. The intermediate products of oxidation—carbonyls—can react with proteins (Maillard reaction), causing a reduction in their nutritive value. Lipids containing polyunsaturated fatty acids are especially susceptible to oxidation. If vegetables are not blanched before freezing or drying, oxidation of lipids will occur, off-flavors will develop, and losses of vitamins susceptible to oxidative degradation (C, folate, A, E) will be great during storage. Blanching will inactivate proteins responsible for enzyme-catalyzed oxidation, but autoxidation will still occur slowly during storage, the most noticeable effects being the gradual degradation of oxidation-sensitive vitamins and the development of off-flavors. Autoxidation (nonenzymatic) is strongly stimulated by the presence of metal catalysts, especially copper and iron. Frozen fish, because they are rich in polyunsaturated fatty acids, are highly susceptible to the development of off-flavors. [*See* FOOD BIOCHEMISTRY: LIPIDS, CARBOHYDRATES, AND NUCLEIC ACIDS.]

A large array of antioxidants, both natural and synthesized, coupled with antioxidant synergists, has been used to inhibit oxidative reactions in foods. Butylated hydroxyanisole (BHA) and butylated hydroxytoluene (BHT) are examples of synthesized antioxidants. Tocopherols and gum guaiac are examples of natural antioxidants. Antioxidant synergists include ascorbic acid (vitamin C) and organic acids such as citric and phosphoric acid (metal chelators).

Other measures to inhibit oxidation can also be used, including removal of oxygen (vacuum packaging), avoidance of exposure to radiant energy, avoidance of contamination with catalysts (copper, iron, myoglobin), and the use of more highly saturated lipids.

3. Protein Denaturation and Aggregation

Protein denaturation is common in foods and involves many kinds of structural changes that are not easily quantified. This characteristic has caused some investigators to recommend that use of the term "protein denaturation" be discontinued. However, better terminology has not been developed, so this term will be used here. Protein denaturation refers to any modification in the secondary, tertiary, or quaternary structure of proteins without disruption of peptide bonds involved in primary structure. Denaturation typically involves partial unfolding of the protein molecule with increased exposure of hydrophobic groups. Partial unfolding is frequently followed by aggregation. Denaturation can alter the native properties of proteins in a variety of ways, including

1. decreased solubility
2. altered water-holding capacity

3. loss of biological properties (e.g., enzymes lose their catalytic activity)
4. increased susceptibility to attack by proteases
5. increased intrinsic viscosity
6. inability to crystallize

Agents of denaturation include heat, cold, mechanical treatments, irradiation, hydrostatic pressure, acids or alkalis, metals, organic compounds, and the presence of interfaces. [*See* FOOD BIOCHEMISTRY: PROTEINS, ENZYMES, AND ENZYME INHIBITORS.]

Protein denaturation and aggregation occur in many proteinaceous foods during processing and storage. These occurrences can have adverse effects on sensory quality (texture, water-holding capacity). Examples during frozen storage include gelation of egg yolk, precipitation of casein in fluid milk, and insolubilization of proteins in fish. Examples during heating include gelation of egg white and other proteins, inactivation of enzymes, and alteration of proteins in meat. Protein denaturation and aggregation also occur during bread making, during texturization of proteins (i.e., in making meat analogs), and during the formation of emulsions when proteins serve as emulsifiers. Protein nutritive value is usually not affected adversely by protein denaturation/aggregation reactions that normally occur in foods.

Not to mention the use of recombinant DNA techniques for foods would be inappropriate because these techniques are already being used on a commercial basis, and greatly expanded use is anticipated. The most likely near-term opportunities appear to be in the areas of microorganisms used in food fermentation, enzymes, flavors, and other food additives.

Control of chemical reactions in food is a major concern of food chemists. Factors governing the kinds and rates of chemical reactions that occur in food are:

1. product factors—chemical properties of individual constituents; pH; water activity; catalysts; oxygen concentration in the food
2. environmental factors—temperature; storage time; composition of the atmosphere; chemical, physical, or biological treatments imposed; exposure to light; contamination; physical abuse

V. Responsibilities of Food Chemists

In industrialized countries of the world, food chemists must assume a special responsibility. In these countries, processed foods constitute well over half of typical diets. Therefore, it is incumbent on food chemists to insure that processed foods are not only wholesome, economical, and of good sensory quality but, most importantly, that they carry their fair share of important nutrients.

Bibliography

Accum, F. (1820). "A Treatise on Adulterations of Food, and Culinary Poisons." Ab'm Small, Philadelphia. Facsimile reprint by Mallinckrodt Chemical Works, St. Louis (1966).

American Association of Official Analytical Chemists (1990). "Official Methods of Analysis." AOAC, Arlington, VA.

Fennema, O. (1985a). "Food Chemistry," 2d Ed. Marcel Dekker, New York.

Fennema, O. (1985b). Chemical changes in food during processing—An overview. *In* "Chemical Changes in Food during Processing" (T. Richardson and J. W. Finley, eds.) AVI, Westport, CT.

Filby, F. A. (1934). "A History of Food Adulteration and Analysis." Allen and Unwin, London.

Gruenwedel, D. W., and Whitaker, J. R. (eds.) (1984). "Food Analysis—Principles and Techniques." Marcel Dekker, New York.

United States Department of Agriculture (1976). "Composition of Foods," Agriculture Handbook 8. Agricultural Research Service, U.S. Department of Agriculture, Washington, D.C.

Food Composition

MARJORIE P. PENFIELD, *The University of Tennessee, Knoxville*

Glossary

Food Materials which when consumed provide nutrients; both liquid and solid materials may be included in this definition

Nutrient Substance which is used by an organism for production of energy, maintenance and production of body tissues, and regulation of life-sustaining processes

Proximate composition Main components of a food including moisture, fat, protein, fiber, carbohydrate, and ash

Food composition can be defined as the chemical compounds contained within the food and the relative proportions of each. Food is the material which when taken into the body provides chemical compounds (nutrients) from which energy is produced, chemical compounds that are used to regulate body processes, and chemical compounds that are used to build, maintain, and repair tissues. Thus, the health and well-being of an individual are influenced by the foods which he or she consumes.

The components of food that are responsible for nutriture of the living organism also are responsible for the nature and quality of the foods we consume. The relative proportions of each component present and the manner in which the components are physically organized determine if the food is an apple, milk, bread, or meat. The composition of the food determines its functional properties or how the food will behave when it is processed, stored, or prepared for consumption.

I. Food Components

For the purpose of illustrating food composition, selected foods representing food groups that serve as a basis for dietary recommendations as well as variation in processing and/or preparation are listed and described in Table I. Food composition data for those foods are listed in Tables II–IV. All components are listed on the basis of a 100-g edible portion of the food. For comparisons with respect to quantities normally consumed, food composition tables sometimes contain information on normal serving sizes. Usual serving size information for the foods in Tables II–IV are included in Table I. Serving size values are given in both customary and metric units to reflect the use of both systems to quantify serving sizes. The differences that are noted when comparing food composition values on the basis of the two systems are illustrated in Fig. 1. On a 100-g basis, Cheddar cheese has the most fat but on a per serving basis beef rib is higher.

Food components generally are divided into two categories, macrocomponents and microcomponents, on the basis of the relative amounts of each present in the food. Macrocomponents are listed in Table II and microcomponents are listed in Tables III–IV.

A. Macrocomponents

The macrocomponents, water, protein, fat, carbohydrates, and fiber, generally are included in lists of components referred to as proximate components. Ash is also one of the proximate components; its constituent parts, the minerals, are microcomponents

TABLE I

Descriptions of Foods Included in Composition Tables and Sources of Information for Data[a]

Food	Description	Amount usually consumed (g)	Miscellaneous composition values (per 100 g food)	Source (date of publication of data) NDB No.
Apple	Raw with skin, 3/lb, 2.75 in. diameter	1 (138)	IDF[b] = 2.03 g; pectin = 1.07; α-Tocopherol = 0.59	AH-8-9 (1981) 09003
Beef, rib	Whole (ribs 6–12), separable lean only, choice, cooked, broiled	3 oz (85)	Cholesterol = 86 mg	AH-8-13 (1985) 13087
Beef, round	Full cut, separable lean only, choice, cooked, broiled	3 oz (85)	Cholesterol = 86 mg	AH-8-13 (1985) 13156
Bread, white, enriched	Commercially prepared, includes soft bread crumbs	1 slice (25)	Calcium values range from 55 to 244 mg. Low-sodium or no-salt added products contain 27 mg sodium. TDF[c] = 2.3 g	AH-8-18 (1991) 18069
Bread, whole wheat	Commercially made	1 slice (28)	Calcium values range from 27 to 256 mg. TDF = 6.9 g	AH-8-18 (1991) 18075
Broccoli, raw		1/2 cup (44)	IDF = 1.4 g; TDF = 2.8 g; α-tocopherol = 0.46 mg; Vitamin A values in Table III are for entire plant, leaves = 16,000, flower clusters = 3000, and stocks = 400 IU	AH-8-11 (1982) 11090
Broccoli, cooked		1/2 cup (78)	TDF = 2.6 g	AH-8-11 (Rev 1989) 11091
Cheese, cheddar	1 cubic inch = 17.2	1 oz (28)	Cholesterol = 105 mg	AH-8-1 (1976) 01009
Chicken, light meat	Broiler or fryer, light meat without skin, cooked, roasted	3 oz (85)	Cholesterol = 85 mg	AH-8-10 (1981) 05041
Cod, Atlantic	Cooked, dry heat	3 oz (85)	Cholesterol = 55 mg	AH-8-16 (1987) 15016
Egg, white	Chicken, raw, fresh, or frozen	1 white (33)		AH-8-01 (1989) 01124
Egg, yolk	Chicken, yolk, raw fresh	1 yolk (17)	Cholesterol = 1281 mg	AH-8-01 (1989) 01125
Ice cream	Vanilla, regular, ≈10% fat, hardened	1 cup (133)	Cholesterol = 45 mg	AH-8-1 (1976) 01061
Milk, whole	3.3% fat, fluid, applies to pasteurized and raw products	1 cup (244)	Cholesterol = 14 mg	AH-8-1 (1976) 01077
Oranges	Raw, all commercial varieties, (38% California naval, 33% California Valencia, 28% Florida)	1 (131)	α-Tocopherol = 0.24 mg	AH-8-9 (1981) 09200
Peanut kernels	Oil-roasted, mixture Spanish and Virginia peanuts, without added salt	1 oz (28.4)	α-Tocopherol = 7.41 mg; TDF = 8.8 g	AH-8-12 (1984) 12181
Pork, loin	Fresh, whole, separable lean only, cooked, broiled	3 oz (85)	Cholesterol = 95 mg	AH-8-10 (1981) 10026
Potato, baked	Baked, flesh only	1 cup (61) 1 potato without refuse = (156)	α-Tocopherol = 0.03 mg	AH-8-11 (1982) 11363
Potato, French fried	French-fried, frozen, restaurant prepared, fried in vegetable oil	10 pieces (50)		AH-8-11 (1982) 11404
Tomatoes, raw	Ripe, red, raw	1 (123)	α-Tocopherol = 0.34 mg; TDF = 1.3 g; Ascorbic acid values in Table III are year-round values, Nov–May ≈.01, June–Oct ≈.026	AH-8-11 (1989) 11529
Yogurt, low-fat	Plain, lowfat, containing 12 g protein per 8-oz serving. Product made with lowfat milk with added nonfat milk solids	0.5 container (113 g)	Lipid content may range (≈0.5-2.0%) with variation in vitamin A and lipid constituents; cholesterol = 6 mg	AH-8-1 (1976) 01117

[a] Values taken from Agricultural Handbook No. 8-. . . , Composition of Foods . . . Raw, Processed, Prepared. United States Department of Agriculture. Specific volume and date of publication for each food are shown in last column.

[b] IDF, insoluble dietary fiber.

[c] TDF, total dietary fiber.

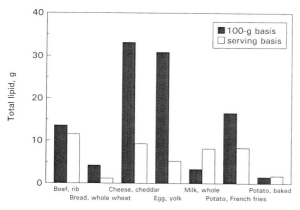

FIGURE 1 Lipid content of selected food shown on a 100-g portion basis and on a usual serving basis. Usual serving sizes are shown in Table I.

of foods. In addition to the proximate components, food energy values, which are dependent on the amounts of fat, carbohydrate, and protein in a food, usually are included in food composition tables. All of these values are listed in Table II. Comparison of the values for the representative foods enables one to see the effects of source of food and processing and preparation techniques on these components. [*See* FOOD CHEMISTRY.]

1. Water

Water is found in all living matter; therefore, it is an important component of food ranging from less than 1% (milk chocolate) to 90% or higher in some fruits. The physical properties of a food are related to its water content. Milk is fluid because it contains 88% water, which serves as a solvent for many components. Fat globules are suspended in the liquid. Most fruits and vegetables contain more water than milk, but are not fluid because their cellular structure, which is composed of carbohydrates, entraps the water. The entrapped water contributes to cellular turgor, which gives the fruit or vegetable a crisp, succulent texture. Loss of water from such products results in a limp, undesirable texture. Snack foods such as peanuts or crackers are crisp or crunchy because they contain little water. Water also affects food quality as a participant in chemical reactions that affect food quality. For example, water is necessary for hydrolysis to occur in fats. In this reaction, fatty acids are split from triglycerides and may result in the development of hydrolytic rancidity, the presence of free fatty acids with undesirable odors. The flavor of the product, therefore, is adversely affected by this reaction.

Additionally, water helps physically bring reactants together.

Water constitutes more than 50% of the weight in a majority of foods listed in Table I. Foods with high levels of water contain small amounts of carbohydrate, lipid, and/or protein, whereas food with low water levels will have higher levels of the other major components. For example, foods in Table I with less than 50% water have high carbohydrate levels (bread), high fat levels (peanuts), or high combined levels of lipid and protein (cheese, egg yolk) or lipid and carbohydrate (French fried potatoes).

2. Proteins

Proteins are composed of carbon, hydrogen, oxygen, and nitrogen. Phosphorous and sulfur are found in some. Protein content varies among foods as shown in Table II. With one exception, the foods of plant origin on the representative list have lower protein contents than those of animal origin. The amount of protein in peanuts is similar to that of the foods of animal origin. [*See* FOOD BIOCHEMISTRY: PROTEINS, ENZYMES, AND ENZYME INHIBITORS.]

Amino acids are small molecules that serve as the building blocks for proteins. Twenty-one different amino acids are found in food proteins, and proteins from different foods vary in the number and sequence of amino acids. Because amino acid content differs, foods vary in nutritional value. Nine amino acids, called indispensable or essential amino acids, are required for humans (Table V). Others are not considered essential because under normal conditions adequate amounts can be synthesized in the body. The nutritional quality or biological value of a protein is dependent on the amounts and proportions of essential amino acids present. Egg and milk proteins are of good quality, whereas cereal proteins are of lesser quality because they are lacking in lysine.

The nature of the proteins, gliadin and glutenin, found in wheat flour facilitates the formation of gluten, the structure responsible for the textural characteristic of yeast bread. Unique proteins make it possible to whip egg whites into a stable foam. Functional properties of a food are attributable to the amino acids present in the protein molecules as well as the amounts present.

Because amino acids affect both nutritional value and functional properties, foods may be analyzed to determine the amounts of each present. Food composition tables frequently include this information. Amino acid composition of several foods is shown in Table V.

TABLE II

Proximate Components and Energy Values of 100 g of Selected Foods[a]

Food	Water (g)	Protein (g)	Total lipid (g)	Carbohydrate (g)	Crude fiber (g)	Ash (g)	Food energy (kcal)
Apple	83.93	0.19	0.36	15.25	0.77	0.26	59
Beef, rib	59.01	26.03	13.55	0.00	0.00	1.14	233
Beef, round	62.29	28.46	8.03	0.00	0.00	1.23	194
Bread, white,	36.7	8.2	3.6	49.5	0.3	1.9	267
Bread, whole wheat	37.7	9.7	4.2	46.1	1.5	2.3	246
Broccoli, raw	90.69	2.98	0.35	5.24	1.11	0.92	28
Broccoli, cooked	90.69	2.98	0.35	5.06	1.11	0.92	28
Cheese, cheddar	36.75	24.90	33.14	1.28	0	3.93	403
Chicken, light meat	64.76	30.91	4.51	0.0	0	1.02	173
Cod, Atlantic	75.92	22.83	0.86	0.0	0	1.49	105
Egg, white	87.81	10.52	0.0	1.03	0	0.64	50
Egg, yolk	48.81	16.76	30.87	1.78	0	1.77	358
Ice cream	60.80	3.61	10.77	23.85	0	0.97	202
Milk, whole	87.99	3.29	3.34	4.66	0	0.72	61
Oranges	86.75	0.94	0.12	11.75	0.43	0.44	47
Peanut kernels	1.99	26.78	49.19	18.48	2.39	3.58	580
Pork, loin	55.50	27.84	15.29	0.0	0	1.36	257
Potato, baked	75.42	1.96	0.10	21.56	0.38	0.97	93
Potato, French fried	37.99	4.03	16.57	39.56	0.75	1.86	315
Tomatoes, raw	93.76	0.85	0.33	4.64	0.65	0.42	21
Yogurt, low-far	85.07	5.25	1.55	7.04	0	1.09	63

[a]Values are taken from Agricultural Handbook No. 8- . . . , Composition of Foods . . . Raw, Processed, Prepared. United States Department of Agriculture. Specific volume and date of publication for each food are shown in Table I.

3. Lipids

Lipid is a general term which is applied to a heterogenous group of organic compounds including fatty acids, glycerides, and phospholipids. Lipids or fats are found in foods of plant and animal origin. Fats, which are added to formulated foods such as baked products or used for processing as for French fried potatoes, may also be of either plant or animal origin. As indicated in Table II foods may be fat-free (egg white), contain very small amounts of fat (fruits and vegetables), or have high fat levels (cheese). Foods such as margarine, butter, and some salad dressing have even higher fat levels than the foods listed in Table II. [See FATS AND CHOLESTEROL, ROLE IN HUMAN NUTRITION; FOOD BIOCHEMISTRY: LIPIDS, CARBOHYDRATES, AND NUCLEIC ACIDS.]

The chemical structures of lipids vary. Of primary interest from a functional standpoint are glycerides, which contain carbon, hydrogen, and oxygen. A glyceride molecule is composed of a molecule of the alcohol glycerol and one, two, or three fatty acids. The terms mono-, di-, and triglycerides are applied to glyceride to denote the number of fatty acids attached to the alcohol. Natural fats are mixtures of triglycerides. Recommendations for selection of a "healthful" diet include statements regarding the consumption of saturated and unsaturated fatty acids. Therefore, food composition tables frequently contain information about the specific fatty acids in a food. A saturated fatty acid contains no double-bonded carbon molecules whereas mono- and poly-unsaturated fatty acids contain one and more than one double-bonded carbon linkages, respectively. Common names for saturated fatty acids include butyric (4:0), palmitic (16:0), and stearic (18:0). Oleic (18:1) is a monounsaturated fatty acid and linoleic (18:2), linolenic (18:3), and arachidonic (20:4) are polyunsaturated fatty acids. Fatty acid data for representative foods are shown in Table VI. Data for these foods illustrate the fact that most of the fatty acids in foods of animal origin (beef and milk) are saturated whereas the fatty acids in peanuts are primarily mono- or polyunsaturated and in baked potato are polyunsaturated. In general, fish differs from other foods of animal origin in that they contain a higher proportion of polyunsaturated fatty acids.

TABLE III

Mineral Content of 100 g of Selected Foods[a]

Food	Calcium (mg)	Iron (mg)	Magnesium (mg)	Phosphorous (mg)	Potassium (mg)	Sodium (mg)	Zinc (mg)	Copper (mg)	Manganese (mg)
Apple	7	0.18	5	7	115	0	0.04	0.041	0.045
Beef, rib	10	2.52	25	202	379	69	6.55	0.094	0.016
Beef, round	5	2.68	28	237	415	64	4.67	0.107	0.016
Bread, white,	108	3.03	24	94	119	538	0.62	0.126	0.383
Bread, whole wheat	72	3.3	86	229	252	527	1.94	0.284	2.324
Broccoli, raw	48	0.88	25	66	325	27	0.40	0.045	0.229
Broccoli, cooked	46	0.84	24	59	292	26	0.38	0.043	0.218
Cheese, cheddar	721	0.68	28	512	98	620	3.11		
Chicken, light meat	15	1.06	27	216	247	77	1.23	0.050	0.017
Cod	14	0.49	42	138	244	78	0.58	0.036	
Egg, white	6	0.03	11	13	143	164	0.01	0.006	0.004
Egg, yolk	137	3.53	9	488	94	43	3.11	0.025	0.069
Ice cream	132	0.09	14	101	193	87	1.06		
Milk, whole	119	0.05	13	93	152	49	0.38		
Oranges	40	0.10	10	14	181	0	0.07	0.045	0.025
Peanut kernels	86	1.92	188	506	703	15	6.62	1.273	1.235
Pork, loin	7	0.93	29	279	418	75	2.92	0.098	0.010
Potato, baked	5	0.35	25	50	391	15	0.29	0.215	0.161
Potato, French fried	19	0.76	34	93	732	216	0.38	0.137	0.192
Tomatoes, raw	5	0.45	11	24	222	9	0.09	0.074	0.105
Yogurt, low-fat	183	0.08	17	144	234	70	0.89		

[a]Values taken from Agricultural Handbook No. 8- . . . , Composition of Foods . . . Raw, Processed, Prepared. United States Department of Agriculture. Specific volume and date of publication for each food are shown in Table I.

The nature (i.e., length of the chain and degree of saturation) of the fatty acids in the glycerides determines the character of the fat. Animal fats, which contain mostly saturated fatty acids, are harder than fats of plant origin, which contain more unsaturated fatty acids. The degree of saturation in vegetable oils may be increased by a process called hydrogenation. Fats that differ in degree of saturation differ in functional performance. For example, saturated fats such as lard or hydrogenated vegetable oil provide more shortening power than unsaturated fats in the production of pastry.

A lipid component of animal origin which is of current concern is cholesterol, which has been implicated in the etiology of heart disease. Cholesterol is found in cell membranes and brain and nerve cells. It is a required component for the synthesis of steroids. Cholesterol is found only in animal foods. Baked or formulated products contain cholesterol only if an animal fat is added. Cholesterol values for foods in Table I are listed under miscellaneous composition values. Values range from 34 mg for a glass (8-oz) of whole milk to 205 mg per egg yolk.

4. Carbohydrates

Carbohydrates, a major component of many foods, are composed of carbon, hydrogen, and oxygen. Food carbohydrates include sugars such as sucrose and glucose as well as complex polymers of sugars including starch, cellulose, hemicellulose, pectins, and gums in plants and glycogen in animals. Starch and glycogen are storage carbohydrates, whereas cellulose, hemicellulose, lignin, and pectins are important structural compounds. Carbohydrate values in Table II were determined by subtracting the percentages for water, protein derived from total nitrogen, total lipid, and ash from 100%. Crude fiber (Table II) and total dietary fiber are both included in this value for carbohydrate.

Carbohydrates function in the plant as a reservoir for storage of energy produced via photosynthesis. Because animals consume plants, the sun serves as a source of energy for all living matter. As illustrated in Table I, foods derived from the muscle tissue of animals (beef, chicken, cod, and pork) contain no carbohydrate. Muscle contains some glycogen, a carbohydrate, but it is metabolized to lactic acid post-

TABLE IV

Vitamin Content of 100 g of Selected Foods[a]

Food	Ascorbic acid (mg)	Thiamin (mg)	Riboflavin (mg)	Niacin (mg)	Pantothenic acid (mg)	Vitamin B-6 (mg)	Folacin (mg)	Vitamin B-12 (mcg)	Vitamin A (IU)
Apple	5.7	0.017	0.014	0.077	0.061	0.048	2.8	0	53
Beef, rib	0	0.094	0.206	3.775	0.379	0.35	8	32.8	
Beef, round	0	0.101	0.229	4.171	0.406	0.50	10	2.98	
Bread, white	0	0.472	0.341	3.969	0.390	0.064	34		0
Bread, whole wheat	0	0.351	0.205	3.837	0.552	0.179	50		
Broccoli, raw	93.2	0.065	0.119	0.638	0.535	0.159	71.0	0	1,542
Broccoli, cooked	74.6	0.055	0.113	0.574	0.508	0.143	50	0	1,388
Cheese, cheddar	0	0.027	0.375	0.080	0.413	0.074	18	0.827	1,059
Chicken, light meat	0	0.065	0.116	12.421	0.972	0.60	4	0.34	29
Cod	1.0	0.088	0.079	2.513		0.283		1.048	46
Egg, white	0	0.006	0.452	0.092	0.119	0.004	3	0.2	
Egg, yolk	0	0.170	0.639	0.015	3.807	0.392	146	3.11	1,945
Ice cream	0.53	0.039	0.247	0.101	0.492	0.046	2	0.470	408
Milk, whole	0.94	0.038	0.162	0.084	0.314	0.042	5	0.357	126
Oranges	53.2	0.087	0.040	0.282	0.250	0.060	30.3	0	205
Peanut kernels	0	0.293	0.101	14.796	2.092	0.398	105.6	0	0
Pork, loin	0.3	0.971	0.421	5.950	0.908	0.46	5	1.08	8
Potato, baked	12.8	0.105	0.021	1.395	0.555	0.301	9.1	0	
Potato, French fried	10.3	0.177	0.028	3.250	0.655	0.236	29.0	0	
Tomatoes, raw	19.1	0.059	0.048	0.628	0.247	0.080	15	0	623
Yogurt, low-fat	0.80	0.044	0.214	0.114	0.591	0.049	11	0.562	66

[a] Values are taken from Agricultural Handbook NO. 8- . . . , Composition of Foods . . . Raw, Processed, Prepared. United States Department of Agriculture. Specific volume and date of publication for each food are shown in Table I.

TABLE V

Amino Acid Composition of Representative Foods[a]

Amino acid	Food (mg/100 g food)					
	Beef, rib	Bread, whole-wheat	Egg white	Milk, whole	Peanut kernels	Potato, baked
Tryptophane[b]	239	140	130	46	324	30
Threonine[b]	880	296	478	149	775	71
Isoleucine[b]	878	376	594	199	1039	80
Leucine[b]	1616	670	887	322	2010	118
Lysine[b]	1669	302	716	261	1035	119
Methionine[b]	507	155	362	83	275	31
Cystine	239	214	273	30	343	25
Phenylalanine[b]	819	463	615	159	1530	87
Tyrosine	674	289	409	159	1285	73
Valine[b]	999	443	670	220	1211	110
Arginine	1350	449	573	119	3604	90
Histidine[b]	667	224	237	89	780	43
Alanine	1338	358	608	113	1182	60
Aspartic acid	1884	536	1071	250	3599	479
Glutamic acid	3147	2957	1398	689	6354	328
Glycine	1531	384	369	70	1848	58
Proline	944	969	409	319	1299	70
Serine	820	463	726	179	1495	85

[a] Values are taken from Agricultural Handbook No. 8- . . . , Composition of Foods . . . Raw, Processed, Prepared. United States Department of Agriculture. Specific volume and date of publication for each food are shown in Table I.
[b] Essential amino acids.

TABLE VI

Fatty Acid Composition of Representative Foods[a]

Fatty acid[b]	Food (g/100 g food)				
	Beef, round	Cod, Atlantic	Milk, whole	Peanut kernels	Potato, baked
Saturated, total	2.90	0.168	2.08	6.851	0.026
4:0			0.11		
6:0			0.06		
8:0			0.04		
10:0	0.00		0.08		0.001
12:0	0.00		0.09		0.003
14:0	0.20	0.012	0.34	0.025	0.001
16:0	1.70	0.117	0.88	5.166	0.016
18:0	0.86	0.038	0.40	1.103	0.004
Monounsaturated, total	3.44	0.124	0.96	24.488	0.002
16:1	0.00	0.021	0.08	0.009	0.001
18:1	3.01	0.078	0.84	23.814	0.001
20:1	0.00	0.019	trace	0.663	
22:1		0.004	trace		
Polyunsaturated, total	0.34	0.292	0.12	15.597	0.043
18:2	0.25	0.006	0.08	15.593	0.032
18:3	0.02	0.001	0.05	0.003	0.010
18:4		0.001	trace		
20:4	0.05	0.028	trace		
20:5		0.004	trace		
22:5		0.130	trace		
22:6		0.154	trace		

[a]Values are taken from Agricultural Handbook No. 8- . . . , Composition of Foods . . . Raw, Processed, Prepared. United States Department of Agriculture. Specific volume and date of publication for each food are shown in Table I.
[b]Fatty acids are designated by chain length : number of double bonds.

mortem; glucose may be present in very small quantities (approximately 0.01%), which is not evident by the method used for determining composition. Milk and eggs contain carbohydrate. The primary carbohydrate in milk is the sugar lactose; glucose is present in small amounts in egg white.

5. Fiber

Table II includes values for the crude fiber contents of the foods of plant origin; foods of animal origin contain no fiber. As noted previously, the value for crude fiber is also included in the value for carbohydrate. Fiber includes those compounds that cannot be hydrolyzed in the human gut and are, therefore, not available for energy. The crude fiber values found in food composition tables are derived by digesting the food with acid and alkali and measuring the residue. This process is more rigorous than is the human digestion process, so these values tend to be underestimates of the fiber in foods. Other methods for fiber determination give high values which, when available, are noted in Table I. Fiber includes cellulose, hemicellulose, lignin, pectin, and gums.

6. Food Energy

Values for food energy are frequently included in food composition tables as is the case in Table II. The values represent physiological energy or the energy which is available after losses for digestive and metabolic functions are subtracted. Caloric values reflect the fat, carbohydrate, and protein content of the food; fat supplies 9 kcal per gram of fat and carbohydrate and protein supply 4 kcal per gram.

B. Microcomponents

In addition to the macrocomponents, food contains many components that are present in relatively small quantities. The microcomponents are important from a nutritional standpoint in that they work with the macrocomponents to maintain bodily functions. Some of them also make major contributions to the nature and quality of food.

1. Ash (Minerals)

The value for ash is a composite measure. The inorganic residue which is obtained by incinerating a sample of food is used as a measure of the total mineral content of the food. Values for ash are included in Table III. The differences between ash values for white bread and whole-wheat bread reflect the loss of mineral-rich components of wheat as it is milled for the production of refined flour. As cheese is produced from milk, minerals become more concentrated as reflected in the ash values for the two foods. [See MINERALS, ROLE IN HUMAN NUTRITION.]

Although more than 20 minerals participate in metabolic processes food composition tables usually include the nine that are listed in Table III. Variation among foods is seen for all of the minerals listed. Each of the minerals listed has specific functions in the human body.

2. Vitamins

Vitamins are important for the nutritional well-being of the human and include a number of organic compounds that occur naturally in food materials. Vitamins also may be added to foods to ensure a uniform supply in a particular food product or to replace those lost during processing. Vitamins are added to foods to make them like foods for which they will substitute. Thus, vitamins A and D are added to margarine, a substitute for butter. Food may be fortified with vitamins to increase levels above inherent amounts. For example, some cereals are fortified with vitamins to make them a good source of the vitamins added.

Vitamins are divided into two groups based on their solubility. Fat-soluble vitamins include A, D, E, and K. Ascorbic acid (vitamin C), thiamin (B_1), riboflavin (B_2), niacin, pantothenic acid, biotin, B_6, B_{12}, and folacin are soluble in water. Levels for the representative foods for vitamin A and all of the water-soluble vitamins except biotin are listed in Table IV.

Vitamin A (retinol) is obtained from animal foods (milk, egg yolk, liver) and carotene, a precursor of retinol, is found in deep yellow and orange fruits and vegetables. Although broccoli is green, it also contains carotene.

Values for α-tocopherol, a form of vitamin E, are listed in Table I for the representative foods. Vitamins D and K are not listed in the composition tables because few foods are sources. Liver and eggs supply vitamin D and it is added to milk. Green leafy vegetables contain vitamin K.

Water-soluble ascorbic acid (vitamin C) is found primarily in fruits and vegetables as shown in Table IV. Heating can destroy this vitamin as illustrated by the fact that cooked broccoli contains less ascorbic acid than does raw broccoli. Small amounts of ascorbic acid are found in animal products.

With the exception of vitamin B_{12} the other water-soluble vitamins are found in many different foods. Amounts vary widely with source as shown in Table IV. Vitamin B_{12} is found in foods from animal sources.

3. Enzymes

Enzymes constitute another class of microcomponents of food. They are proteins that serve as catalysts for essential metabolic reactions. After slaughter or harvest, some enzymes in animal or plant foods continue to function and thus affect the quality of the foods that we eat. For example, apples and bananas turn brown when cut because the enzyme polyphenol oxidase catalyzes the reaction of polyphenolic compounds with oxygen to form quinones. Quinones, which are light in color, polymerize to form the dark compounds that are responsible for the brown color.

Other enzymes effect flavor production. Allinase-type enzymes catalyze reactions resulting in production of volatile sulfur compounds, important contributors to the flavors of onions, garlic, and cabbage.

Lipases catalyze the removal of fatty acids from triglycerides. Accumulation of free fatty acids may result in the development of rancidity. Whole-wheat flour, which contains the lipid portion from the germ of the wheat kernel, may become rancid because of the action of this enzyme. This reaction is important in many foods.

Enzymes occur naturally in foods, but they also may be added to produce a desired characteristic in a product. For example, proteolytic enzymes are used to tenderize meat because they break down the proteins which makes the meat easier to chew. The enzyme lactate is added to milk to facilitate the breakdown of the sugar lactose into its component monosaccharides, glucose and galactose. This treatment is important to individuals who lack the intestinal enzyme to breakdown the lactose. Glucose isomerase is an enzyme used in the conversion of glucose to fructose, an important step in the production of high-fructose corn syrup, the sweetener used in soft drinks. Many other examples of the enzymes found in foods could be given.

4. Pigments

The vast color array of foods is attributable to another class of microcomponents, pigments. Values for these microcomponents are not found in food composition tables, as they for the most part are not important from a nutritional standpoint.

Myoglobin is the pigment responsible for the color of meat. Pork contains less myoglobin that beef and is, therefore, not as red. Changes in the myoglobin molecule are responsible for changes in the color of meat. The pigment binds with oxygen when meat is exposed to air, giving it the bright cherry red that consumers associate with fresh meat. The pink color of cured meats is attributable to a reaction of myoglobin with nitric oxide and subsequent heating of the meat. [See FOOD BIOCHEMISTRY: PIGMENTS, FLAVORS, AROMAS, AND STABILITY.]

Pigments of fruits and vegetables may be divided into two broad groups, water-soluble and fat-soluble pigments. Major water-soluble pigments include the flavonoids (yellows), anthocyanins (reds, purples, and blues), and betalains (red of beets).

Fat-soluble pigments include chlorophyll, which is responsible for the color of green vegetables, and the carotenoids, which are responsible for yellows, oranges, and reds. The orange of carrots, the yellow of corn, and the red of tomatoes may be attributed to β-carotene, cryptoxanthin, and lycopene, respectively. The presence of some of the carotenes is reflected in food composition tables. β-Carotene and other carotenes are precursors for vitamin A and thus their presence is reflected in the vitamin A values for plant materials. Some of the vitamin A value of milk and milk products results from the presence of carotenoids in the fat of milk.

5. Flavor Components

Other components in food contribute to the flavor of food. Some are responsible for the taste of food, perceived when the compound in solution comes in contact with taste receptors in the taste buds on the tongue. Sugars, acids, and salts contribute to sweetness, sourness, and saltiness of foods, respectively. Bitterness, the fourth basic taste, is contributed by compounds such as caffeine, quinine, and naringin, a compound found in grapefruit.

Other compounds contribute to the second component flavor, odor. Many volatile compounds are present in foods in small quantities. The volatility of these components facilitates their association with olfactory receptors that are found in the nasal passage. Minute variations in the amounts and kinds of these compounds in foods contribute to their unique flavors.

6. Food Additives

In addition to the components previously discussed, another class of compounds which are referred to as food additives may be found in foods. Intentional additives are added for specific purposes, whereas unintentional additives are compounds which find their way into the food during processing and/or from the package. Such additives are carefully monitored and acceptable levels are set by the Food and Drug Administration (FDA) and/or the United States Department of Agriculture (USDA).

Additives are used to increase shelf life or keeping quality and to stabilize or improve the color, flavor, texture, and/or nutritive value of a product. Additives are used to assist in the process of preserving food for future use. Some food additives are compounds that naturally occur in the foods, but the level may be increased during production. Other additives are added by the processor. Additives are listed on product labels as required by law. [See FOOD PRESERVATIVES.]

The addition of additives is reflected in some values in the food composition tables. White bread (Tables III and IV) is enriched by adding riboflavin, niacin, thiamin, and iron. The sodium content of a product is increased when salt is added for taste, or sodium bicarbonate is included for leavening. The addition of calcium chloride to maintain firmness in canned tomatoes influences the calcium content.

Table VII includes a listing of several categories of food additives, their functions in very general terms, and examples of additives commonly used in foods. The list does not include all types of or specific additives that are used in foods. Some may serve more than one function in a food.

II. Determinants of Food Composition

Food composition varies within food classes and among food classes. We rely on both plants and animals for nutriture. Obviously, the composition of foods from those two diversely different biological sources will vary, and foods within each group vary. Milk, the function of which is to nourish the young of the species, differs from muscle tissue. Additionally an egg, the source of nutrients for the developing chick, differs from the muscle tissue of the chicken. These differences are evident in the composition values shown in Tables I–IV.

Foods from different parts of the same animal may differ. Fat content of muscles from the loin are higher in fat than are muscles from the leg (round). Beef loin and round (Table II) contain approximately 14 and 8% fat, respectively. Such differences are not as evi-

TABLE VII

Types of Food Additives, Their Functions, and Examples

Type of additive	Functions	Examples
Acidulants	To add flavor, to prevent browning of fruits and vegetables, to prevent microbial growth	Acids: acetic, citric, malic, phosphoric
Antimicrobials (preservatives)	To prevent growth of microorganisms (yeasts, molds, and bacteria)	Acids, benzoates, nitrates, propionates, sorbates, sulfites
Antioxidants	To prevent development of rancidity in fats	Butylated hydroxyanisole (BHA), butylated hydroxytoluene (BHT), propyl gallate, ascorbic acid
Color additives	To impart desirable color to foods	Caramel, carotene, approved color additives (FD&C colors)
Firming agents	To maintain firmness in processed fruits and vegetables	Calcium salts
Flavoring agents	To provide or enhance flavors of foods	Spices, herbs, vanillin, benzaldehyde, hydrolyzed vegetable proteins
Humectants	To keep foods moist	Sorbitol, propylene glycol, glycerol, invert sugar
Nonnutritive sweeteners	To replace sugar in dietetic foods and reduce calorie content of foods	Acesulfame-K, Aspartame, saccharin
Nutrients	To enhance or restore nutritive values	Vitamins, minerals, protein, and amino acids
Sequesterants	To bind metals which will contribute to the prevention of oxidation of fats and maintain clarity in soft drinks	Citrates, phosphate, tartrates, ethylenediaminetetraacetic acid (EDTA)
Surfactants	To act as emulsifiers (contributes to distribution of fat in aqueous mediums such as cake batters and salad dressing) to improve or maintain texture	Lecithin, mono- and diglycerides, propylene glycol
Thickening agents	To control viscosity or consistency of products	Modified starches, carrageenan, gum arabic

dent with respect to plant materials because we usually do not consume as many different parts of a specific plant, i.e., we eat the apple from the apple tree, the root of the carrot plant, and the pods and seeds of the green bean plant. However, one such difference is found among the parts of the broccoli plant. The vitamin A values in Table III represent composites of leaves, flower clusters, and stalks. Vitamin A values of those parts vary as noted in Table I. Nutrient-rich components (the leaves) may be discarded by the consumer in such cases.

Cultivars, or breeds, within a species may vary in composition. Plant geneticists and biotechnologists have the tools available to allow development of cultivars that exhibit increased or decreased levels of selected components. Components may be genetically engineered to improve nutritional value, improve functionality, or improve keeping quality. For example, triticale, a hybrid of wheat and rye, was bred in an attempt to combine the best aspects of each grain into a more desirable one. Of particular interest was the high lysine (an amino acid) content of triticale. These attempts have met with limited success. Although the protein content of triticale is high (average, 13.4%), its functional performance is limited in products that require production of quality gluten, the structural component of bread. Increasing the solids content and eliminating the enzyme polygalacturo-

nase in tomatoes via genetic engineering have reduced processing and transportation costs. There is less water to remove from the tomato and shelf life is longer.

Agricultural practices affect the composition of foods. Factors that may be controlled or altered include light, growing location, water availability, and time of harvest (maturity). Numerous examples of the complex effects of these factors may be found in the literature. Postharvest handling and storage are major influential factors.

Processing of raw materials into food products results in changes in composition. The functions of processing are to create a product which meets consumer expectations and to preserve the food for future use. The effect of preservation on the composition of the food is dependant on the method selected. For example, freezing of a product has minimal effect on its composition. Canning will, however, result in reduction in levels of some of the vitamins in a fruit or vegetable as they are altered by the heat process or lost in the liquid in which the product is canned. Differences in the vitamin levels in raw and cooked broccoli (Table III) reflect the varying effects of heat on vitamins. Drying results in concentration of components of a food as the water is removed. Physical changes in a product also will change composition. Milling grains may result in loss of some nutrients if the products made from the grain are not whole-grain products. Millers are in most cases required by law to add nutrients that were lost to the products. The amounts added are indicated in FDA-defined standards of identity for each product. Such addition of nutrients is called enrichment. The similarities between the levels of thiamin, riboflavin, niacin, and iron contents (Tables III–IV) of white bread which is enriched and whole-wheat bread illustrate the effects of enrichment.

Food manufacturers and consumers affect the composition of manufactured or formulated foods by selection of the formula and the ingredients used for production of the food. This concept is of particular importance in a society where reduction of the calorie and fat contents of products is of paramount concern. The fat content of a baked product may be varied by selection of a fat substitute that exhibits the same functional properties as the fat in the product. The carbohydrate content of a carbonated soft drink can be reduced by use of an alternative, noncarbohydrate sweetener substitute for corn syrup.

The factors that affect the composition of food are numerous. In combination with the heterogenous nature of food this results in a complex food supply that varies in composition.

III. Sources of Food Composition Data

Collection of food consumption data should be and is an on-going process. As food producers and processors take advantage of the development of new and/or improved cultivars and genetic strains, composition data become outdated. In addition, the development of new and more precise analytical techniques for the measurement of food components provides means for obtaining more accurate values. As food processing and preparation methods are changed over time the need for reassessment of currently available data is evident.

Collection of data for food composition tables is a time-consuming and expensive proposition. The length of time required for USDA to publish its series of revised *Handbooks on Food Composition* (Handbook 8) exemplifies this point. The first of the series of 23 was published in 1976 and the last of the proposed issues was released in 1992. The length of time involved in this process is understandable in view of the fact that the earlier edition of *Handbook of Food Composition* (1963) contained data for approximately 2500 items. The new editions contain 4346 items. The number of components included in the list for each

of these foods has also increased, reflecting the ability of scientists to more completely analyze foods. In addition, yearly supplements will result in additional new items and updating of previously published values. The increase in number of items represents an ever-expanding proliferation of new food products and new or altered processing and preparation methods.

Several sources of food composition data are available. Provision of comprehensive food composition table is considered to be a responsibility of USDA. In addition, researchers with expertise in food analysis publish values in the scientific literature. Food companies, upon demand from consumers who want to know what they are eating, also publish nutrient values for their products. Individual medical centers maintain data bases which may be very comprehensive, because they are compilations of data from many sources. International agencies such as FAO also have published tables of food composition data; these tables usually apply to geographic regions.

Computers have had an impact on the availability of food composition data. When storage and use of values were dependent on hand calculations, the number of values included in data bases was limited by ability to easily retrieve the information. Large mainframe computers as well as personnel computers have made it possible to store, retrieve, and use values for many more foods.

IV. Uses of Food Composition Data

Food composition data are important to many. To the consumer, food composition data, as shown on the nutrition labeling of a food product, may be considered in choosing foods to purchase in the supermarket. For example, a high-fat content may dissuade a consumer from purchasing a product for medical reasons, because he or she feels that high-fat diets are not healthful, or because it is not part of a weight reduction plan. For other consumers food composition data may provide guidance for not choosing foods which contain chemicals to which they are allergic. Food and nutrition educators use food composition data as a basis for helping individuals select foods as a part of a healthful diet. For dietitians, nutritionists, and medical personnel accurate assessment of nutrient intake is dependent upon the availability of comprehensive and accurate food composition data. For the epidemiologist, food composition data are essential for understanding disease patterns and the role of food consumption in those patterns. Internationally, food aid agencies must rely on food composition data when making decisions about shipments of food to areas of need. Accurate data are essential to the food manufacturer who must provide nutrition information on the labels of the company's products. Regulatory agencies depend on food consumption data for the formulation and enforcement of laws pertaining to food nomenclature, labeling, and advertising. For food scientists and technologists food composition data are important because the composition of the food affects its performance during processing, storage, and preparation. Changes in each of the components of food may influence the quality of the product and thus influence consumer decisions regarding the product.

V. Summary

Food composition is complex because the materials used for food are biological materials and thus contain the many components necessary to sustain life. Food composition varies as the nature of the organisms from which the food is derived also varies. Knowledge of food composition increases as analytical methods become more sophisticated. Increased knowledge allows scientists to better utilize all components of foods and to improve the quality of the many foods available for the enjoyment and nutriture of the consumer.

Bibliography

Branen, A. L., Davidson, P. M., and Salminen, S. (1990). "Food Additives." Marcel Dekker, New York.

Coultate, T. P. (1989). "Food. The Chemistry of Its Components," 2nd ed. Royal Society of Chemistry, London.

DeMan, J. M. (1990). "Principles of Food Chemistry," 2nd ed. Van Nostrand Reinhold, New York.

Holland, B., Welch, A. A., Urwin, I. D., Buss, D. H., Paul, A. A., and Southgate, D. A. T. (1991). "McCance and Widdowson's The Composition of Foods," 5th revised and extended ed. The Royal Society of Chemistry and Ministry of Agriculture, Fisheries and Food, Cambridge, UK.

Igoe, R. S. (1989). "Dictionary of Food Ingredients," 2nd ed. Van Nostrand Reinhold, New York.

Karmas, E., and Harris, R. S. (1988). "Nutritional Evaluation of Food Processing," 3rd ed. Van Nostrand Reinhold, New York.

Kung, S-D., Bills, D. D., and Quatrano, R. (eds.) (1989) "Biotechnology and Food Quality." Butterworth-Heinemann, Boston.

Pennington, J. A. T. (1989). "Bowes and Church's Food Values of Portions Commonly Used," 15th ed. J. B. Lippincott, Philadelphia, PA.

USDA (1976–1992). "Composition of Foods: . . . ; Raw Processed, Prepared." AH8-1 (1976) "Dairy and Egg Products," AH8-2 (1977) "Spices and Herbs," AH8-3 (1978) "Baby Food," AH8-4 (1979) "Fats and Oils," AH8-5 (1979) "Poultry Products," AH8-6 (1980) "Soups, Sauces, Gravies," AH8-7 (1980) "Sausages and Luncheon Meats," AH8-8 (1982) "Breakfast Cereals," AH8-9 (1982) "Fruits and Fruit Juices," AH8-10 (1983) "Pork Products," AH8-11 (1984) "Vegetables and Vegetable Products," AH8-12 (1984) "Nut and Seed Products," AH8-13 (1990) "Beef Products," AH8-14 (1986) "Beverages," AH8-15 (1987) "Finfish and Shellfish Products," AH8-16 (1986) "Legumes and Legume Products," AH8-17 (1989) "Lamb, Veal and Game Products," AH8-18 (1992) "Baked Products," AH8-19 (1991) "Snacks and Sweets," AH8-20 (1989) "Cereal, Grains and Pasta," AH8-21 (1988) "Fast Foods," Agricultural Handbooks, Human Nutrition Information Services, United State Department of Agriculture, Washington, DC.

USDA (1991). "Nutritive Value of Foods." Home and Garden Bulletin 72, United States Department of Agriculture, Washington, DC.

Food Dehydration

DIGVIR S. JAYAS, *University of Manitoba*

Glossary

Constant rate dehydration process Process during which there is no change in the moisture removal rate during dehydration of foods

Critical moisture content Moisture content of food at an instant during drying when the dehydration process changes from constant rate drying to falling rate drying; it is impossible to predict theoretically for various foods, therefore it is determined experimentally; in certain drying situations it is possible that a constant rate drying period may not exist

Equilibrium moisture content Moisture content of food in equilibrium with the surrounding air that is determined experimentally; if a food material is left undisturbed for an infinitely long time under constant air conditions, the food material will reach equilibrium with the surroundings

Falling rate dehydration process Process during which the moisture removal rate decreases as drying progresses; many foods may exhibit more than one falling rate period

Food dehydration is one of the oldest unit operations used by the food processing industry. Food dehydration is a process of reducing moisture of food to low levels for improved shelf life by adding one or more forms of energy to the food. However, it does not include removal of moisture from food by mechanical pressing or concentration of liquid foods. Most commonly, heat is added to the food by hot air, which also carries the moisture away from the food. The process of food dehydration involves simultaneous transfer of mass and heat within the food and the medium used to transfer energy to the food. In food dehydration methods that supply energy to the food using media other than hot air, air or some other gas may be required to move moisture away from the food.

I. Moisture in Foods

Water is the most abundant material in food, has the most influence on its storability and organoleptic characteristics, and is the most expensive to remove from food. It is a historical observation that food material can be preserved for a longer duration if its moisture content is reduced. A dry food product is less susceptible to spoilage caused by the growth of bacteria, molds, and insects. Dehydration can improve palatability, digestibility, color, flavor, and appearance of a food. Packaging, handling, and transportation of a dry food product are easier and cheaper. The spoilage of food is a direct function of the available water in the food as expressed by the relative humidity of the surrounding atmosphere in equilibrium with food. For a food, equilibrium relative humidity (ERH) can be called water activity (a_w), with the distinction that water activity is used to indicate an intrinsic parameter of the food, whereas the ERH refers to the property of the surrounding atmosphere. The biochemical reactions responsible for deterioration of food, such as lipid oxidation, enzymatic reactions, and development of microorganisms on food, are influenced by a_w or ERH.

The phenomenon of water binding in foods is not yet well understood. Foods are complex systems in which water is present along with solids (e.g., proteins, carbohydrates, fiber, etc.), liquids (e.g., lipids), and gases (e.g., air and other volatiles). Food material can bind water physically or chemically. Physically bound water is adsorbed to surfaces in food such as proteins, carbohydrates, and other hydrophilic colloids, whereas chemically bound water represents a definite proportion by mass of the specific compounds. An example of the latter is the water of hydration in chemical compounds of foods. The water also fills the intercellular space in the solid–liquid matrix of the food and is known as free water. In the dehydration process, free and physically bound water is usually removed and, at times, a portion of the chemically bound water may also be removed. The majority of moisture in liquid foods such as skim milk exists as free water and for dehydration of the liquid foods some preconcentration is usually done. [*See* FOOD CHEMISTRY; FOOD COMPOSITION.]

In food dehydration, when hot air is used to transfer heat to the food, the temperature and relative humidity of the air determine the final moisture content to which a food can be dried. If the food is left in contact with air at constant conditions for an infinitely long time, it will reach equilibrium with the air. The moisture content of the food at equilibrium is known as equilibrium moisture content (EMC). The EMC–ERH relationships of foods thus have practical utility in calculating drying times and energy estimates for removing the moisture from food. A sorption isotherm (Fig. 1) represents the EMC–ERH interactions macroscopically. The typical isotherm for food is sigmoidal in shape. Foods can attain equilibrium either by losing or by gaining moisture depending on whether the vapor pressure of the surroundings is lower or higher than the vapor pressure of the moisture in food. The former process is called

desorption and the latter is called adsorption, thus resulting in desorption and adsorption EMC, respectively. The desorption EMC values are greater than the adsorption EMC values at constant temperature and ERH. The difference between the desorption and the adsorption EMC values for the same ERH is called the hysteresis effect. [*See* FOOD PROCESS ENGINEERING: HEAT AND MASS TRANSFER.]

II. Psychrometric Properties

Dry air and water vapor exert pressure upon each other when they are mixed. These pressures are called partial pressures. The difference in the partial pressure of water vapor in the air and the pressure of the moisture in the food is the driving force for dehydration.

The properties of air and water vapor mixture are called psychrometric properties and can be summarized on a psychrometric chart. The changes in these properties can be used to analyze the dehydration process. The skeleton of the psychrometric chart and the dehydration process on the chart are shown in Fig. 2. Dry bulb temperature is the air temperature indicated by an ordinary thermometer. Humidity ratio or absolute humidity is the ratio of mass of water vapor to the mass of dry air. The ratio of vapor pressure to saturation vapor pressure at the same temperature is called relative humidity. Relative humidity is an indication of the maximum moisture that the moist air can hold at a given temperature. The 100% relative humidity line (saturation line) constitutes the extreme left boundary of the psychrometric chart. Wet bulb

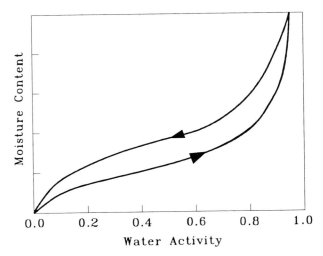

FIGURE 1 A typical sorption isotherm.

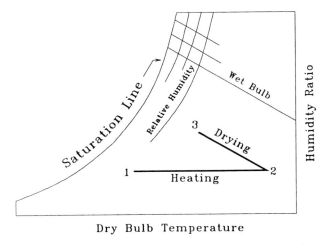

FIGURE 2 Skeleton of the psychrometric chart showing the adiabatic drying process.

temperature is the temperature shown by a thermometer whose sensor is wrapped by a dampened cloth and exposed to the moving air. Air must blow at a speed of 5 m/sec (18 km/hr) over the moistened cloth to obtain a correct wet bulb temperature. Enthalpy is the heat content of the moist air. Enthalpy lines are almost parallel to the wet bulb lines on the psychrometric chart.

III. Dehydration Process

Dehydration methods have evolved around every product's specific requirement. The dehydration process can be classified based on energy source (adiabatic and nonadiabatic processes), process time (batch and continuous processes), and moisture removal rate (constant and falling rate processes).

In adiabatic processes, heat of vaporization is supplied by sensible heat of air in contact with the material to be dried. In nonadiabatic processes, heat of vaporization is supplied by radiant heat or by heat transferred through walls in contact with the material to be dried.

The adiabatic dehydration process is shown in Fig. 2. Point 1 is the ambient air condition; point 2 is the air after being heated to a certain temperature T2; point 3 represents the exit conditions of drying air after it has passed through the dryer. Note that in the drying process air has been cooled while taking up moisture from the product. Often the line between points 2 and 3 is a straight line and is parallel to the wet bulb temperature line.

In a batch dehydration process, the moisture is removed from a certain quantity of food at a time. The dryer is loaded with the wet food and, after drying, the dried product is removed. The next load of food is then loaded in the dryer and the process is repeated until the total quantity of food is dried. The batch-drying chambers are rooms that have controlled heating and ventilation.

In a continuous dehydration process, wet food material is fed continuously into the drying chamber. The food is dried during travel through the drying chamber and dried food is collected at the exit. Generally the process conditions remain steady except during start-up of the dryer or during process upsets. Depending on the direction of flow of both air and food, these types of dryers can be further classified as concurrent, countercurrent, and crossflow dryers. In concurrent dryers, both hot air and food travel in the same direction through the drying chamber; in countercurrent dryers, hot air and food travel in opposite directions; and in crossflow dryers, hot air and food travel perpendicular to each other.

Removal of moisture from wet food as a function of time is shown in Fig. 3. In the dehydration process, moisture moves from the inside of the food to the surface and is then removed by the carrier gas. Thus there are two resistances to moisture removal from food (internal and external). Initially, the food product is wet and moisture moves easily (i.e., low internal resistance) to the surface, thus keeping the surface wet. The vaporization of the moisture is similar to that occurring from an open water surface. The moisture removal rate during this phase of drying is constant and is a function of only the air conditions. As drying continues, the movement of moisture inside the food is slowed down (i.e., internal resistance starts increasing) and the food surface contains dry and wet spots. The moisture is removed at a declining rate from the surface of the food. Eventually, as the evaporation of moisture occurs inside the food material, the removal of moisture is further slowed down.

In a constant rate dehydration process, the rate of moisture removal remains constant with time, and in a falling rate dehydration process, the rate of moisture removal decreases as the drying progresses. The moisture content of food at which the falling rate period starts is known as the critical moisture content.

IV. Types of Dryers

A. Selection of Dryer

Dehydration of food materials is a complex process. Therefore, many different drying systems are used in

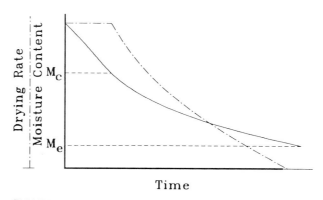

FIGURE 3 The moisture content (solid line) and the moisture removal rate (solid-dot line) for a typical food during dehydration. (M_c = Critical moisture content and M_e = equilibrium moisture content.)

the food industry to dry various foods. The selection and commissioning of dryers is usually by a trial and error process. Dryers can be classified based on the drying processes discussed here or on the type of design used in the drying process. For example, a dryer could be a concurrent tunnel or countercurrent tunnel. Some common types of dryer designs are discussed in the following sections. The analysis of the drying process in any of these dryers can be done by conducting energy and mass balances on the food material and the drying or cooling medium.

B. Sun Dryer

The simplest of the sun dryers consists of an open surface on which wet food product is spread in a thin layer (usually 1–5 cm thick) and is dried by the energy from the sun. The evaporated moisture is removed by the natural movements of atmospheric air. The material being dried may be stirred or turned occasionally or regularly. Spices, fruits, meat, and fish have been dried using sun dryers since time immemorial. The main limitations of the sun dryers are: large area requirement, labor-intensive, inability to control drying process, and potential of food loss and contamination. Numerous attempts have been made around the world to develop simple solar dryers that overcome one or more of these limitations. A schematic of a typical solar dryer is shown in Fig. 4. The dryer consists of an insulated cabinet and a south-facing transparent wall to allow direct radiation of the product spread on a perforated sheet. The air movement through the product is by natural convection. Many simple modifications to this dryer can improve it or yield other types of solar dryers. For example, by adding a small fan at the inlet or outlet, the air movement can be increased by forced convection. A device can be installed to turn the product at regular intervals.

A separate solar collector can be added to increase the temperature of the incoming air or multiple layers of food may be spread in the cabinet or both.

C. Cabinet or Tray Dryer

A cabinet or tray dryer can be considered as a small room with the capabilities of heating and circulating the air. The product is held in trays and is dried in batches. Heat from a drying medium (hot air) to the food product is transferred by a convection mechanism. The convection current passes over the product and not through the product. It is suitable for dehydration of fruits, vegetables, and meat. It is relatively easy to set and control the optimum drying conditions in cabinet dryers. For this reason, various heat-sensitive food materials can be dried in small batches. The heat source is usually steam batteries or steam coils.

The turbo-dryer shown in Fig. 5 can be classified as a cabinet or a tray dryer. Trays in the turbo-dryer are rotating instead of being stationary. The wet material enters the turbo-dryer through a feed chute in the roof of the housing (cabinet) onto the first shelf. The shelves are circular with cut-out center and radial slots. The shelves are rigidly mounted on an inner supporting frame, forming a vertical stack that rotates slowly as a unit. Material flows onto each shelf from the one above, forming a pile. The rotation of the

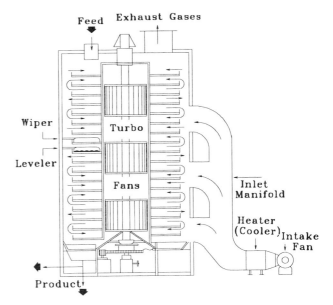

FIGURE 5 Schematic of the turbo-dryer, a type of a cabinet or tray dryer. (Reproduced with permission of the Wyssmont Company Inc., Fort Lee, NJ. Copyright 1993.)

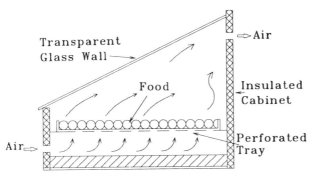

FIGURE 4 Schematic of a typical solar dryer.

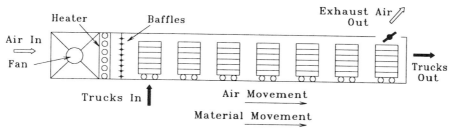

FIGURE 6 Principle of concurrent tunnel dryer. (Reproduced with permission of Elsevier Science Publishers Ltd., New York, NY.)

tray (shelf) assembly carries the freshly formed pile past a stationary blade set to level the pile to fill the tray at a uniform height. At the end of revolution, another stationary blade wipes the tray and material flows onto the shelf below. Dried product is discharged through a chute in the bottom of the housing. Air or other drying medium is supplied to the dryer through a side-mounted vertical manifold with control dampers.

D. Tunnel Dryer

Tunnel dryers consist of a tunnel (drying chamber) that is usually rectangular in shape, although they may have many different configurations. The number of tunnels in a dryer is quite variable and can be as high as 100. Truck loads of the wet material are moved at intervals into one end of the tunnel. The whole string of trucks is periodically advanced through the tunnel, till these are removed at the other end. Air movement, circulation, and heating methods vary in tunnel dryers. Three different arrangements, namely, counterflow, concurrent flow, and a combined flow, are possible. Figure 6 shows a concurrent arrangement. These dryers are simple and versatile in comparison to other types of dryers, and food pieces of any shape and size can be handled. If solid trays are incorporated, fluids can also be dried. In a three-tunnel dryer arrangement wet loads are moved in at intervals in the outer wet tunnels. At the end of wet tunnels the trolleys are loaded alternatively to the central dry tunnel. This, in effect, reduces the residence time in the dry tunnel to half in comparison to residence time in wet tunnels. The dry tunnel is normally operated at a lower temperature than wet tunnels to prevent long time exposure of the product to high temperatures and to save energy.

E. Conveyor Dryer

A conveyor dryer (also called conveyor band dryer or belt dryer) has a single or several perforated wire mesh conveyor belts as the main component (Fig. 7). The wet material is fed evenly at the feed end and is conveyed along the length of the dryer. Hot air is forced through the bed of moving material, and the dried product is continuously discharged at the end of the dryer. The air characteristics such as temperature and relative humidity may be adjusted throughout the passage to satisfy the drying characteristics of the product. The direction of air movement through the permeable bed of the product may be vertically upward or downward. The thickness of the bed of the product is kept between 25 and 250 mm. This thin layer of the product and higher airflow rates result in the uniform drying of the product. In the illustrated dryer (Fig. 7), a portion of the moist air is being recycled.

F. Spray Dryer

Spray dryers are used to dry slurries or liquid foods. A typical spray dryer consists of a cylindrical or a rectangular drying chamber in which the liquid is introduced in the heated airstream in an atomized form (Fig. 8). When hot air is replaced by superheated steam, the process is called superheated steam drying. Application of superheated steam drying to food materials is, however, limited. The atomization may be done by a rotary or a nozzle atomizer. Dried product is separated from the airstream using cyclone separators, settling chambers, or bag filters. The performance of spray dryers thus depends on the uniformity of the atomized droplets. The arrangement of flows of air and product could be concurrent, countercurrent, or mixed flow type. The design of spray dryers ranges from very simple to very complex depending on the fluid. The main differences in the designs are the variations in atomizing devices, in the airflow patterns, in air heating systems, and in separating and collecting systems. Some of the dry food powders may stick to the walls of the drying chamber.

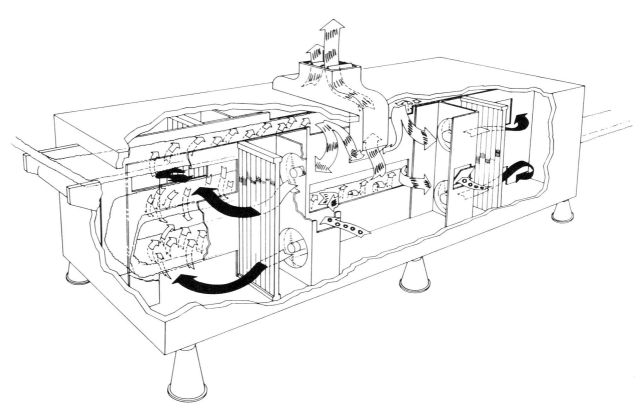

FIGURE 7 Schematic of a typical conveyor dryer. Solid arrow is hot air; partially shaded arrow is moist air after drying; arrow with circles is ambient air; and conveyer belt ends are shown at the top left and bottom right. The conveyer belt has three lengths through the drying chamber. (Courtesy of Food Engineering Corporation, Minneapolis, MN.)

G. Freeze Dryer

In freeze drying water is removed at low temperatures (about −10°C) by sublimation rather than evaporation. Therefore, freeze drying, is done under vacuum (at absolute pressures of about 2 mm Hg) on frozen

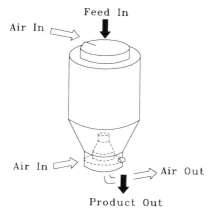

FIGURE 8 Schematic of a typical spray dryer with integrated fluid bed. (Courtesy of Niro, Soeborg, Denmark.)

products. It is applicable to food products that may be damaged by heat in other dryers or that are high-value products. The quality of the product after freeze drying is better than obtained by any other drying method. The structural rigidity of the product is maintained during the sublimation process and products retain better flavor and aroma. Freeze drying, however, is an expensive process because of slow drying rate and the use of vacuum.

H. Drum Dryer

Drum dryers are used to dry slurry, liquid, or pastelike food materials. The material is spread in a thin layer on the surface of a drum by various methods of application (Fig. 9). The material is dried on the outer surface of an internally heated revolving drum. The drums are heated by steam or by direct firing inside the drum. The drums rotate slowly and in the course of about 300 degrees of rotation, the product is dried. The dried product is scraped off the surface using a blade. For heat-sensitive materials, drum dryers may be operated under vacuum (Fig. 9).

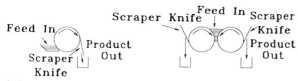

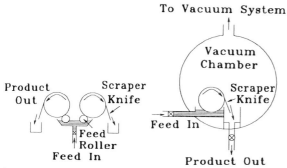

(a) Single Drum Drier **(b) Double Drum Drier**

(c) Twin Drum Drier **(d) Vacuum Drum Drier**

FIGURE 9 Various feeding arrangements for drum dryers. (Reproduced with permission of Elsevier Science Publishers Ltd., New York, NY.)

I. Fluidized Bed Dryer

Fluidized bed, spouted bed, and flash dryers are examples of suspended bed dryers because the food particles being dried are supported and carried by the hot air. These dryers are suitable for drying of heat-sensitive materials. In a fluidized bed dryer, the food material is supported on a perforated metal at the bottom of a drying chamber (Fig. 10). The hot air is forced through the material at high velocities such that the particulate material is fully suspended in the hot air-stream. All particles are completely exposed to drying air, resulting in high rates of heat transfer. This system is more suitable for batch drying but could also be applied to continuous drying of particulate materials. The dryer shown in Fig. 10 is a continuous type. The characteristics of food materials that are suitable for fluidized bed drying are an average particle size between 10 μm and 20 mm, narrow particle size distribution, and regular particle shape.

J. Spouted Bed Dryer

Spouted bed dryers are suitable for food materials that are too coarse to be readily fluidized. A schematic of a spouted bed dryer is shown in Fig. 11. The dryer consists of a cylindrical or rectangular drying chamber fitted with a nozzle in the conical bottom and a cylindrical draft tube in the center. The hot air is introduced at velocities that fluidize and support the food material in the central column. The material moves down in a plug flow in the outer annulus and is picked up by

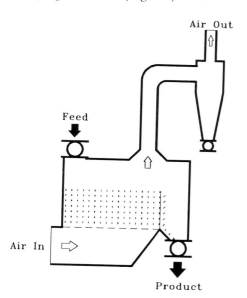

FIGURE 10 An example of a fluid bed dryer. (Courtesy of bēpex corporation, Minneapolis, MN.)

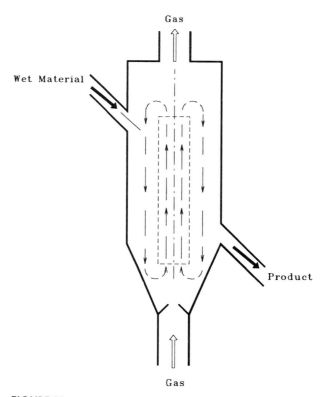

FIGURE 11 A typical spouted bed dryer. [Reprinted from A. S. Mujumdar (ed.). (1987). "Handbook of Industrial Drying," p. 420, by courtesy of Marcel Dekker, New York.]

the incoming air after some reconditioning during downward travel. By adjusting the discharge rate, the material may be recirculated a number of times.

K. Flash Dryer

In a flash dryer, heated, low-pressure drying air or inert gas is injected in the drying chamber such that the solid material is hydrodynamically supported and conveyed through the chamber (Fig. 12). Wet material is metered into the return zone of the drying torus by a feeding unit such as a screw conveyer. The small particles are fluidized by the high-speed steam of the drying gas and are circulated to the top of the dryer into the classification chamber. Classification is initiated by centrifugal force, with large particles returning to the drying chamber for further size reduction and drying.

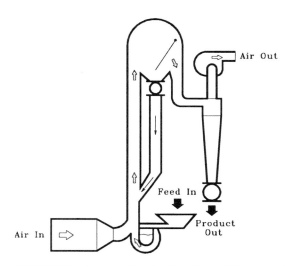

FIGURE 12 An example of a flash dryer. (Courtesy of bepēx corporation, Minneapolis, MN.)

L. Microwave Dryer

In microwave dryers, the energy used for evaporation of water is in the form of microwaves, which are electromagnetic waves of frequency 300 MHz to 300 GHz and wavelength 1 mm to 1m. The microwaves are not heat but are forms of energy that are manifested as heat as a result of interaction with food. Industrial applications of microwave drying of food are limited. Research and development work is being conducted on food applications around the world.

Bibliography

Brennan, J. G., Butters, J. R., Cowell, N. D., and Lilley, A. E. V. (1990). "Food Engineering Operations," 3rd ed. Elsevier Applied Science, New York.

Geankoplis, C. J. (1983). Drying of process materials. *In* "Transport Processes and Unit Operations," pp. 508–571. Allyn & Bacon, Toronto.

Iglesias, H. A., and Chiriffe, J. (1982). "Handbook of Food Isotherms." Academic Press, New York.

Karel, M. (1974). Fundamentals of dehydration processes. *In* "Advances in Preconcentration and Dehydration of Foods" (A. Spicer, ed.), pp. 45–94. Applied Science Publishers, London.

Keey, R. B. (1978). "Introduction to Industrial Drying Operations." Pergamon Press, New York.

Mujumdar, A. S. (ed.). (1987). "Handbook of Industrial Drying." Marcel Dekker, New York.

Mujumdar, A. S. (ed.). (1994). "Handbook of Industrial Drying," 2nd ed. Marcel Dekker, New York.

Shatadal, P., and Jayas, D. S. (1992). Sorption isotherms of foods. *In* "Drying of Solids" (A. S. Mujumdar, ed.), pp. 433–448. International Science Publisher, New York.

Sokhansanj, S., and Jayas, D. S. (1987). Drying of foodstuffs. *In* "Handbook of Industrial Drying" (A. S. Mujumdar, ed.), pp. 517–570. Marcel Dekker, New York.

Van Arsdel, W. B., and Copley, M. J. (1973). "Food Dehydration," Vol. 1. AVI Publishing, Westport, CT.

Van Arsdel, W. B., and Copley, M. J. (1973). "Food Dehydration," Vol. 2. AVI Publishing, Westport, CT.

Food Irradiation

P. M. NAIR, ARUN SHARMA

Food Technology and Enzyme Engineering Division, Bhabha Atomic Research Center

Glossary

Absorbed dose Amount of radiation energy absorbed per unit mass of irradiated matter (the mean or average dose), in practice the minimum absorbed dose (D_{min}) and the maximum absorbed dose (D_{max}) are recorded; D_{av} can only be determined by an extensive dose mapping exercise; However, put simply, $D_{av} = D_{max} + D_{min}/2$. Gray (Gy) is the SI unit of radiation dose, being equal to one joule of energy absorbed per kilogram of matter being irradiated; its relationship to the formerly used unit, the rad, is $1\ Gy = 1\ J\ kg^{-1} = 100\ rad$. A commonly used multiple is kilogray, $1\ kGy = 10^3\ Gy$

Becquerel (Bq) The SI unit of activity, being one radioactive disintegration per second; it has dimensions S^{-1}, and its relationship to the traditional special unit Curie (Ci) is $1\ Bq = 2.7027 \times 10^{-11}\ Ci$

Dose rate Increment of absorbed dose in a particular medium during a given time interval

Dose uniformity Ratio of maximum to minimum absorbed dose in the product, dose uniformity or dose uniformity ratio $U = D_{max}/D_{min}$

Dosimetry Measurement of radiation quantities, specifically absorbed dose and absorbed dose rate

Dwell time Time the product remains in irradiation position in an irradiator

Electron volt (eV) Unit of energy; one electron volt is the kinetic energy acquired by an electron in passing through a potential difference of one volt in a vacuum: $1\ eV = 1.60219 \times 10^{-19}\ J$; $10^6\ eV = 1\ MeV$

Half-life Time taken for the radioactivity of an isotope to reduce to one-half its original value; the half-life of 5.27 years for Cobalt-60 means that after 5.27 years only half of the original isotope remains and after 10.54 years one half of the half or one quarter of the isotope is left; this corresponds to a reduction in activity of a Cobalt-60 source by 12.324%/year or 1.096%/month

Radappertization Application of a dose in the range of 25–45 kGy of ionizing radiation sufficient to eliminate the number and/or activity of viable microorganisms as determined by recognized methods; in the absence of postprocessing contamination, no microbial spoilage or toxicity should become detectable with currently available methods, no matter how long or under what conditions the food is stored

Radicidation Application of a dose of ionizing radiation in the range of 2–8 kGy sufficient to reduce the number of specific viable nonspore-forming pathogenic microorganisms to such a level that none are detectable when the treated food is examined by recognized methods; when the process is used specifically for destroying enteropathogenic and enterotoxigenic organisms belonging to the genus *Salmonella*, it is referred to as *Salmonella* radicidation

Radurization Application to foods of doses of ionizing radiation in the range of 0.4–10 kGy sufficient to enhance keeping quality (usually at refrigerated temperature) by causing a substantial decrease in numbers of viable specific spoilage microorganisms

Food irradiation is the controlled application of the energy of ionizing radiations such as γ rays, X-rays, and accelerated electrons to agricultural commodities, food, and its ingredients, for improving hygiene and safety and increasing storage and distribution life. The technology holds promise because in many cases it has an edge over conventional methods. It could be

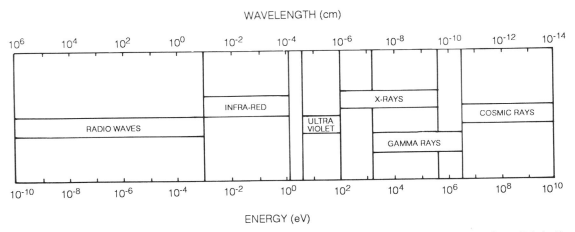

WAVELENGTH (cm)

ENERGY (eV)

FIGURE 1 Electromagnetic spectrum. X-rays up to 5 MeV can be used. Most energetic γ-rays are from Cobalt-60 (1.33 MeV).

applied judiciously where conventional methods are inadequate, uneconomical, or pose potential health risks. It can also be used as a complementary process with many existing procedures. The process helps in keeping chemical burden in food low and increases packaging possibilities. These benefits accrue from the cold nature of the process and high penetrating power of the ionizing radiations.

I. Food Irradiation Technology

A. Ionizing Radiations

Ionizing radiations are packets of electromagnetic energy emanating from the nucleus of decaying radionuclides or generated through machine sources. The process of food irradiation requires use of either γ-rays emitted by radionuclides such as Cobalt-60 and Cesium-137 or high-energy electrons and X-rays generated from machine sources. Both γ-rays and X-rays are part of the electromagnetic spectrum as shown in Fig. 1.

In the case of radionuclides, emission of radiation results in conversion of the isotope into a stable atom. This results in reduction in the number of radioactive atoms over a period of time. The time required by a radionuclide to display half of its original radioactivity is called "half-life."

When γ- or X-rays are absorbed and interact with matter, the photon energy is used to eject an electron from an atom. The ejected electron causes ionization of molecules. The energy of radiation emitted by a radionuclide is fixed; however, in the case of machine sources variable energies can be obtained.

γ-Ray sources provide lower dose rate compared to machine sources. Reactions employed in chemical dosimetry of radiation include oxidation of ferrous salts to ferric and reduction of ceric salts to cerous. Changes in absorption and luminescence of chemicals and plastics have also been used to monitor dose. Of the chemical dose meters the Fricke's dose meter is the most common. It involves radiation-induced oxidation of ferrous ions in a 0.4 M sulfuric acid solution to ferric ions.

B. Radionuclide Sources

Cesium-137 is a fission product. It is obtained from the reprocessing of spent fuel. Since there are only a few reprocessing plants in the world the availability of Cesium-137 is rather limited. On the other hand Cobalt-60 is easily obtained by neutron bombardment of the nonradioactive isotope Cobalt-59 in a nuclear reactor. For use as a radiation source, Cobalt-60 pellets are encapsulated in stainless-steel pencils. This geometry minimizes self-absorption and heat build up. With a half-life of 5.27 years an annual replenishment of 12.3% is needed to maintain source strength. A basic design of a γ-irradiation facility is shown in Fig. 2. Goods to be irradiated are conveyed to the irradiation chamber through a labyrinth, which prevents radiation from reaching the work area and operator room. When the facility is not in operation, Cobalt-60 is stored in a source rack under water at a depth of about 6 m. The water thus absorbs the radiation. The source hoists the rack to the irradiation position after activation of all safety devices. The irradiation chamber is shielded with concrete walls usually about 1.5–1.8 m thick. The goods in aluminum

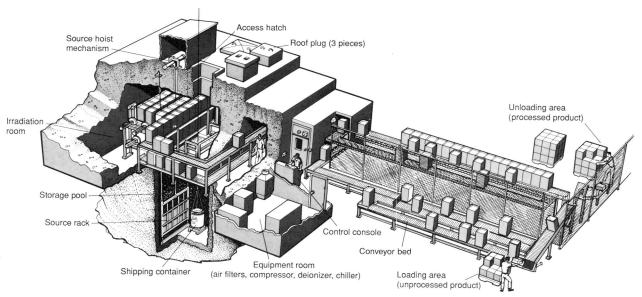

FIGURE 2 An automatic tote box irradiator. [Reproduced with permission from Nordion International, Inc.]

carriers or tote boxes are mechanically positioned around the source rack and are turned around their own axis so that the contents are irradiated on both sides. The absorbed dose is determined by the dwell time of the carrier or tote box in the irradiation position. The dwell time can be preset after taking into consideration the dose rate, which in turn would depend upon the source strength. Absorbed dose is checked by placing dose meters at various positions in a tote box or carrier. The efficiency of source utilization depends upon the utilization of the emitted radiation. Well-designed γ irradiation facilities have an efficiency of about 30%.

C. Machine Sources

Machine sources used in food irradiation include various types of electron accelerators. The electron beam emerging from the accelerator can be either used directly or converted into X-rays. There are two designs available for electron accelerators. One is the DC (direct current) accelerator, and the other is microwave or radiofrequency linear accelerator (linac). In both types, electrons are accelerated close to the speed of light in an evacuated tube. Electrons emitted from an electron source are pushed from the negative end of the tube and attracted by the positive end. The higher the potential difference, higher the speed attained by electrons. A scanning magnet at the end of the accelerator tube deflects the monoenergetic electron beam onto the material being irradiated. In a linac, pulses of electrons produced at the thermionic cathode are

accelerated in an evacuated tube by driving radiofrequency electromagnetic fields along the tube. The linac electrons are monoenergetic but the beam is pulsed. As the electron beam can be directed at the product, efficiency of electron accelerators is about 20% higher than that of γ sources. Energy and current determine the output capacity of an electron accelerator. Because of the lower depth of penetration (5 mm/MeV in water), electron beams cannot be used for the irradiation of thick chunks of food or bulk packages. This difficulty could be overcome by converting electrons into X-rays by fitting a water cooled converter plate to the scanner. The electrons upon striking the metal plate are converted into X-rays. The conversion efficiency depends on the material of the metal plate and energy of striking electrons. A tungsten target can convert 5 MeV electrons with about 20% efficiency and 10 MeV electrons with 30% efficiency depending upon the target thickness. A diagram of an electron accelerator with X-ray converter is given in Fig. 3. The X-rays are as penetrating as γ-rays. Overall conversion efficiency is typically 10% or less, however. In fact use of electrons or X-rays could be carried out in the same facility. A number of aspects are considered during the choice of an irradiator. These include type of product, required throughput and penetration, technical and economic feasibility, and sociopolitical implications.

D. Process Control

During irradiation processing the aim is to expose the material to at least the minimum required dose which

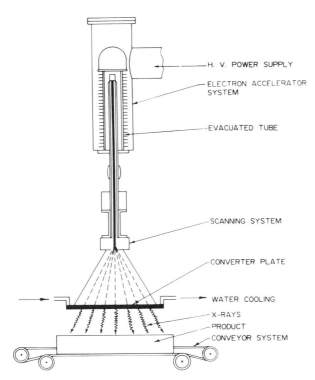

FIGURE 3 An electron accelerator with X-ray converter.

H. V. POWER SUPPLY

ELECTRON ACCELERATOR SYSTEM

EVACUATED TUBE

SCANNING SYSTEM

CONVERTER PLATE

WATER COOLING

X-RAYS

PRODUCT

CONVEYOR SYSTEM

governs the effectiveness of the process. Correct measurement of dose and dose distribution in the product ensures that the radiation treatment is both technically and legally correct. Application of an experimentally established dose for the purpose of irradiation processing of a specific food is important both technologically and economically. The design of a facility should ensure uniform distribution of absorbed dose in the given product. Dose and dose distribution are determined by the product and source parameters. Product parameters are primarily the density of the food itself and the density of the food packages placed in the tote box or carrier. Source parameters vary with the type of irradiation. In the case of radionuclides, the type of isotope, strength, geometry, source pass configuration, irradiation distance of carrier box from the source, conveyor speed, and dwell time are important. For machine sources, the type of radiation, beam energy, beam power, scan width, scan frequency, pulse rate and dead time (in the case of pulsed beam), beam pass configuration and conveyor speed are important. It is essential to determine the dose and dose distribution by dosimetry with dose meters strategically placed in the product box. Dosimetry thus shows the highest dose (D_{max}) and the lowest dose (D_{min}) and the average dose (D_{av}) the product

received. The dose uniformity ratio, D_{max}/D_{min}, depends upon factors including plant design, type and kind of product, and type and energy of radiation. Though lower dose uniformity ratios are desirable, in commercial practice a ratio as high as 3 can be acceptable. The dose uniformity ratio can be improved by reducing the size of package and confining the packages to the center of tote box or carrier, at the expense of efficiency.

II. Effects of Ionizing Radiations

γ-Rays, X-rays, or electrons produce ionizations and excitation in the absorbed material; hence, they are also called ionizing radiations. Ionizing radiations act through two basic processes. The primary processes or events cause the formation of ions, excited molecules, or molecular fragments. The secondary events involve interaction of the products of primary events with the material. While the primary events are independent, the secondary events depend upon variables such as temperature, pressure, and gases. The products of primary and secondary events are called radiolytic products. The chemical change is usually expressed as G value, which is a measure of the number of atoms, molecules or ions produced ($+G$) or destroyed ($-G$) by 100 eV of absorbed energy. The extent of radiation effect depends on the radiation energy absorbed. It increases linearly with dose in the dose range normally used in food irradiation. Dose rate from γ sources is usually below 10 Gy/sec and dose rate effects are not observed at this level. Dose rate from electron accelerators vary between 10^4 and 10^9 Gy/sec. At higher dose rates the radiolytic products tend to react with each other, resulting in a less radiolytic change. In general dose rate effects in food irradiation are rather insignificant.

Water is an important as well as an abundant constituent of most foods and all living cells. Therefore, interaction of radiation with water has a major role to play during irradiation. The radiolytic products of water are hydroxyl radical, hydrated electron, hydrogen atom, hydrogen, hydrogen peroxide, and hydrated proton. While hydroxyl radical, hydrated electron, and hydrogen atom are very reactive transient species, hydrogen and hydrogen peroxide are the only stable products of radiolysis of water. Thus, both reducing and oxidizing powers are generated during radiolysis of water. Presence or absence of oxygen, pH of aqueous systems, and temperature play an important role in radiolysis. Freezing can reduce the extent of radiolytic changes by trapping the reactive intermediates. When a food is irradiated, the molecules of the substrate can be affected by direct absorption of energy or indirectly by interacting with the radiolytic products of water. Thus, under conditions of abundance of water, indirect effects predominate, whereas, direct effects prevail when water content is low. Besides water, food contains macronutrients such as carbohydrates, proteins, lipids, and micronutrients such as vitamins and minerals. Radiosensitivity of constituents of food in dilute pure solutions cannot be extrapolated to their actual sensitivity in foods. In general the effect of radiation is attenuated in foods. None of the studies on irradiated foods has yet led to detection of unique radiolytic products. The compounds produced in irradiated foods are also found in other products occurring naturally, or in foods treated by other methods. In other words the changes in food after irradiation are common, predictable, and not unique.

Radiation sensitivity of living organisms varies inversely with their size and complexity. Thus, the viruses are much more resistant than the higher organisms. Microorganisms are associated with foods as spoilers as well as pathogens. Spoilage microflora in food reduce its shelf life, whereas pathogens pose health risks associated with consumption of contaminated foods in the form of food poisoning and intoxications. Therefore, it becomes important to study the effect of irradiation on food microflora. The sensitivity of an organism to radiation is conveniently expressed in terms of the number of grays (Gy) required to kill 90% of the population present. This is called the D_{10} value, or the dose required to reduce the population of viable cells by a factor of 10. This is also known as decimal reduction dose. From the standpoint of microbiological quality irradiation of food serves a number of objectives. Reduction in the overall contamination level to delay spoilage is one of the objectives. This process is called radurization. A second objective is to destroy pathogens in food. The process is called radicidation. One often can achieve the two combined. The radiation dose is chosen by taking into consideration the expected level of contamination and D_{10} value of the organism(s). A third objective is to obtain a sterile product. This is achieved by the application of the $12D$ concept, as applicable in thermal sterilization ("canning"), and the term radappertization is used for this process. For achieving sterility in any product the aim is to reduce the chances of survival of spores of deadly *Clostridium* to less than 1 out of an initial population of 10^{12} spores. That is a reduction of 12 log cycles. To accomplish this a dose 12 times the D_{10} value is given. D_{10} value varies from organism to organism and is quite high for *Clostridium botulinum* spores (ca. 0.2–0.4 kGy). In food preservation *C. botulinum* remains the organism of utmost concern, especially in low-acid, low-salt, high-moisture foods. The D_{10} value of any microorganism is affected by its environment and food constituents exert a protective effect. Tissue enzymes which show relatively higher radiation resistance may be inactivated by combining irradiation with heat treatment such as blanching. [*See* FOOD MICROBIOLOGY.]

Yeasts and molds are frequent spoilers of foods. Some molds also produce toxic metabolites called mycotoxins which are carcinogenic. The molds occur in both single-celled form as spores and multicellular or multinuclear (coenocytic) vegetative hyphae. The spores of fungi display sensitivity similar to that of vegetative bacteria. However, multicellular or multinuclear hyphae of fungi are more resistant. [*See* FOOD TOXICOLOGY.]

A number of human and animal viral pathogens are associated with food. Viruses require very high doses for inactivation (ca. 60 kGy or more). Fortunately viruses are very sensitive to heat. A temperature of 60–70°C for a short time easily inactivates viruses.

Foods such as cereals, pulses, and spices may be contaminated with eggs or larvae of insect pests. During storage adults emerge and spoil the product. Insects may also be associated with certain fruits. Foods for export that may be contaminated with insect pests are often subject to quarantine regulation. Dividing cells of insects during stages of development are sensitive to radiation; however, adults are quite resistant. Hence, while lower doses are required for causing sexual sterilization, for killing adult insects higher doses are needed. In general, males are more resistant than females. From the practical standpoint only prevention of adult emergence and sterilization of adult insects is needed for stored products as well as for quarantine. Irradiated adults are known to feed at a much lower rate than the normal adults, if at all.

A major advantage of the irradiation process is that it can be applied to prepacked foods as the packaging material does not hinder the treatment. It is therefore essential to ascertain that the material used for packaging food does not release radiolytic products and also retains its functional qualities after exposure to radiation. For the doses normally employed in food irradiation practice, the effects on packaging materials have been found to be generally insignificant. [*See* FOOD PACKAGING.]

III. Safety of Irradiated Food

For the irradiated food to be acceptable, it should meet the criteria of wholesomeness. These criteria include radiological, microbiological and toxicological safety as well as nutritional adequacy.

A. Radiological Safety

The terms irradiated and radioactive are easily confused by the lay public. Irradiated foods are the foods that have been exposed to radiation from a radioactive or a machine source. On the other hand radioactively contaminated foods are foods laced with radioactive atoms or radionuclides (e.g., foods that were contaminated by radioactive "fall-out" from the Chernobyl nuclear reactor explosion). Food irradiation thus has nothing to do with radioactively contaminated foods. The possibility, if any, of induction of radioactive transmutation of elements during the process of irradiation of food has been examined. At the energies employed in food irradiation practice, i.e., 10 MeV for electrons, 5 MeV for X-rays, and 1.33 MeV for Cobalt-60 γ-rays, no induction of radioactivity has been observed.

B. Toxicological Safety

Over the years a huge amount of experimental data has accumulated on this subject. No other food treatment has undergone as much scrutiny at the hands of toxicologists as food irradiation. This has included elaborate multigeneration animal feeding studies. All these studies have precluded the possibility of any radiation-specific toxin or poison in irradiated foods. In the various studies foods exposed to doses up to around 100 kGy did not show any significant *in vitro* or *in vivo* toxic effects attributable to radiation. Experiments have also been carried out with human volunteers. In recent Chinese studies several hundred volunteers were fed irradiated diets for periods of 7–15 weeks. Clinical tests failed to discern any significant differences between the control and test groups. In fact, foods irradiated at dose level up to 10 kGy and foods comprising no more than 0.01% of the daily diet such as spices irradiated up to 30 kGy are considered safe for human consumption and do not need any further toxicological testing.

C. Microbiological Safety

Microbial interactions in food ecosystems have an important bearing on food quality. Microbes differ in their sensitivity toward irradiation. Surviving microflora have a different competitive environment and may behave differently under reduced or eliminated competition. A primary cause of concern has been that certain irradiated foods may favor or support growth of pathogens, in other words, become more susceptible to the proliferation of pathogenic microbes, if present. Both these concerns have been the subject of numerous scientific investigations and the associated risks with irradiated foods have been well assessed.

Nonspore-forming bacterial pathogens in foods are quite sensitive to radiation. These include the pathogens *Salmonella*, *Staphylococcus aureus*, *Shigella*, *Escherichia coli*, *Brucella*, *Vibrio*, and newly discovered human pathogens belonging to genera *Listeria*, *Campylobacter*, *Aeromonas*, and *Yersinia*. Spore-forming pathogens such as *C. botulinum*, *C. perfringens*, and *Bacillus cereus* have higher resistance to radiation. Irradiation with nonsterilizing doses largely eliminates normally competing radiation-sensitive spoilage microflora, thus creating more favorable conditions for germination, growth, and toxin production by the surviving spores. The problem of post-irradiation outgrowth does not apply to dry or frozen foods where the survivors would not be able to multiply. Acid foods, where the growth of pathogenic microbes remains in check, would also be safe. In refrigerated foods the only organism of concern is *C. botulinum* type E which can grow and produce toxins at a temperature as low as 5°C. Therefore, in the case of irradiated seafoods a storage temperature of 3°C has been recommended. *C. botulinum* type E is normally associated with certain seafoods. Fortunately, botuline E toxin is quite sensitive to heat. Since raw irradiated seafoods would normally undergo cooking this risk becomes marginalized. It should be emphasized that any sublethal treatment such as heating, salting, or use of chemical preservatives can bestow selective advantage to the surviving microflora and therefore selective effects are not unique to radiation.

The possibility of mutations arising in the microflora of radiation exposed foods has also been assessed. Available experimental evidence has failed to show such changes in irradiated pathogens. On the contrary, surviving pathogens have shown reduced fitness and virulence or toxin production after exposure to radiation. It is possible that mutants generated, if any, disappear under competition and nonselection. Agents such as heat, ultraviolet radiation, chemical preservatives, and salts also have the mutagenic potential of ionizing radiation; therefore, the question is not unique to ionizing radiations. In this connection it is important to note that efforts to produce toxigenic strains from nontoxigenic strains of bacteria by application of repeated doses of γ radiations have not been successful.

Some food-spoiling molds are known to produce toxins. A well-known example in this category is the aflatoxin producing molds of *Aspergillus flavus–parasiticus* group. There have been reports of increased aflatoxin production by the spores of these fungi that have been exposed to γ radiation under artificial conditions. Experiments designed to assess the risk have clearly shown that irradiation does not enhance the aflatoxin-producing potential of the fungus nor does the food exposed to radiation in any way favor the growth of aflatoxin-producing fungi. There are no indications that any food irradiated and stored under conditions prevailing in practice would be at risk of increased formation of aflatoxin.

D. Nutritional Adequacy

Animal feeding studies have shown that irradiation of foods at any dose level of practical interest under state-of-the-art conditions will not impair the nutritive value of these components. Further, it has been observed that essential amino acids in proteins show no significant reduction even at the sterilizing doses of irradiation. It has been observed in various animal feeding studies that irradiated diets have no effect on the growth and general development of animals. Digestibility, biological value of proteins, and protein efficiency ratio at the doses applicable in food irradiation remain unchanged.

Similarly the observed losses of vitamins exposed in pure solutions are not realistic to actual losses during food irradiation. Vitamin losses may be compounded by the conditions and duration of postirradiation storage and treatment. Vitamin B1 and E, the most radiation-sensitive vitamins, can be protected not only by exclusion of oxygen but also by irradiation at low temperature. Losses of vitamin C also depend upon the nature of the commodity and dose of irradiation. There is a partial conversion of vitamin C to dehydroascorbic acid upon irradiation. However, the dehydro form of ascorbic acid also has the vitamin C activity in man. Normally at the doses applicable in food irradiation, the loss of this vitamin is not very high. The potential nutritional losses in foods treated with irradiation are comparable to losses caused by conventional methods. Conventional methods of heating and drying can be more detrimental to nutritive value of food than irradiation. Cooking also typically results in some nutrient losses.

E. Detection

Because of the small amount of energy involved in food irradiation, usually no significant difference in terms of appearance, smell, or taste can be detected if the process has been carried out properly. It is even difficult to detect any change by simple means. At the same time, sophisticated techniques have been used for detection of irradiated foods primarily for the benefit of regulatory agencies. These include detection systems based on electron spin resonance spectroscopy, chromatography, luminescence, and deoxyribonucleic acid (DNA) diagnostics. The only way for consumers to know if a food has been processed by irradiation is for the product to carry a label that clearly declares the treatment in words, with a symbol, or both.

IV. Practical Application of Food Irradiation

Irradiation has a multipurpose role in the processing and conservation of foods. Depending upon the product and the applied dose at least four functions can be achieved by the application of radiation.

- Destruction of spoilage microbes
- Elimination of pathogens and parasites
- Inhibition of sprouting and delay in senescence
- Eradication of insect pests

On the basis of radiation dose food irradiation applications could be classified into low dose ($\leq$ 1 kGy) medium dose (1–10 kGy), and high dose (10–45 kGy) applications as shown in Table I.

A. Sprout Inhibition in Vegetable Crops

Sprouting is a major cause of economic losses in a number of vegetable crops. It has been established that irradiation is an effective means of keeping these foods for extended periods without sprouting losses. Though effective, chemical sprout inhibitors, such as maleic hydrazide, isopropyl carbamate, and chloroisopropyl carbamate have been found to leave harmful residues on these crops and consequently are banned in many countries. Irradiation is a safe alternative. A dose in the range of 0.05–0.15 kGy is applied after harvesting the crop. The success of irradiation de-

TABLE I

Applications of Ionizing Radiations in Foods

Food	Dose (kGy)	Purpose
A. Low dose (< 1 kGy)		
Potato, onion, yam, garlic, shallot, ginger	0.05–0.15	Inhibition of sprouting
Fruits and vegetables (mango, banana, tomato, mushrooms)	0.2–1	Delay in ripening and maturation
Fruits	0.1–0.7	Disinfestation for quarantine regulations
Cereal grains and grain products, pulses, dried fruits, vegetables, and nuts	0.2–0.7	Disinfestation
Meat	0.3–0.5	Hygienization by destruction of parasites
B. Medium dose (1–10 kGy)		
Fruits, vegetables, sliced bread	1–3	Destruction of bacteria, molds and yeasts and improving shelf life
Meat, poultry, fish	1–5	Improving refrigerated shelf life by reducing microbial load
Meat, poultry, eggs, egg powder, froglegs, frozen sea food, etc.	3–10	Hygienization by destruction of pathogens
Spices, dried vegetables and dry ingredients	3–10	Hygienization and reducing microbial load
C. High dose (10–45 kGy)		
Meat, poultry, seafood	25–45 (minimum dose)	Sterile products for long-term shelf stability at ambient temperature
Sterile hospital diets	25–45 (minimum dose)	For immune compromised patients

pends upon the variety, quality, time elapsed between harvest and treatment, and postirradiation storage of crop.

In the case of potatoes the level of reducing sugars increases with time upon storage at 5°C rendering them unsuitable for processing. Storing potatoes at higher temperatures (10°C) lowers reducing sugar levels, but accelerates sprouting. Storing potatoes at higher temperatures (15°C) after irradiation (0.05–0.15 kGy) can result in potatoes with low sugar content desired by the processing industry. Some varieties of potatoes are prone to show after-cooking darkening after irradiation. Irradiation may cause accelerated rotting in new tubers which can be reduced by allowing 2 weeks of curing of crop after harvesting. Irradiation could also serve as an effective means to control potato tuber moth (*Phthormoea operculella*) infections prevalent in certain potato growing regions. Irradiation at 0.3–0.9 kGy can inhibit sprouting in onion. In general onions should be irradiated within 4 weeks after harvest. A discoloration of the interior of bulb due to the death of meristem has been observed when onions are irradiated after this period and stored. In tropical countries irradiation of agricultural commodities other than yams may be coupled with low temperature (15°C) storage to achieve effectiveness. Inhibition of sprouting by γ irradiation has also been observed in sweet potato, garlic, shallot, carrot, red beet, turnip, ginger, and Jerusalem artichoke. Figure 4(a,b) shows a comparison of stored irradiated and unirradiated potato and onion.

B. Delay in Senescence

Irradiation of climactric fruits in the mature green state to a dose of 0.4 kGy can delay their ripening by 6–8 days. This treatment becomes useful for tropical fruits such as banana, mango, and papaya during their transportation and export. Irradiated fruits undergo normal ripening after the delayed period. Irradiation of peaches with a 3-kGy dose accelerates formation of anthocyanins and carotenoids, enhancing their color and eye appeal.

C. Insect Disinfestation

A very promising application of irradiation is the control of storage pests. Fumigants such as ethylene dibromide, ethylene oxide, methyl bromide, and aluminum phosphide have been or are being banned in various countries due to the health risks associated with their use. Irradiation holds much promise for insect control in cereals, pulses, flours and their products, dried fruits, nuts and vegetables, dried fish, and spices. Most insects found in stored cereal grains can be inactivated by a 0.5-kGy dose. In dehydrated products disinfestation doses do not cause any perceptible change in the material. Another important use of dis-

FIGURE 4 (a) Irradiated (showing no sprouts) and unirradiated (sprouted) potatoes. (b) Irradiated (showing no sprouts) and unirradiated (sprouted) onions.

infestation by irradiation is in the area of quarantine regulation. The dose requirements vary from 0.1 to 0.7 kGy. The lower doses can prevent adult emergence from eggs or larvae and cause sterility in adults. Since many fruits can tolerate these doses, radiation provides an effective replacement for hazardous fumigation methods.

D. Elimination of Meat Parasites

A number of human parasites are present in raw uncooked or undercooked meat. These include *Trichinella spiralis* (Trichina), causing trichinosis; *Taenea solium* (tapeworms), causing cysticercosis; and *Toxoplasma gondii* causing toxoplasmosis. Most of these parasites are transmitted through pork but other meats could also be infected. Low dose irradiation can effectively eliminate these parasites. Irradiation with a dose of 0.3 kGy can inactivate trichina in pork. A dose of 0.4 kGy can eliminate tapeworm cysts. These doses do not affect sensory qualities of treated meat.

E. Extension of Shelf Life of Fruits

Microbial load on fresh fruits and vegetables can be reduced by application of radiation in the dose range of 1–3 kGy. This can improve hygiene and extend shelf life. Many fruits are largely spoiled due to mold growth. Fruits respond differently to radiation depending upon the dose. A dose of 2 kGy coupled with refrigeration can effect a significant reduction in mold damage caused to fruits such as strawberry and apple. Doses up to 3 kGy have been used to control mold damage in orange. A combination of heat (50°C/ min) and radiation has been found to be very effective in the control of molds. The combined treatment has shown promise for citrus, papaya, mango, nectrine, and cherry. Irradiation of ripe tomato extends the normal shelf life at 25°C by about a week.

F. Hygienization of Dry Ingredients

Addition of dry ingredients such as spices and seasonings with high microbial load and pathogens could lead to spoilage of processed products and risk of food poisoning. Instances of Salmonellosis have been attributed to the use of contaminated spices. Most of these dry ingredients are sensitive to heat. Earlier practice of fumigation has recently been banned. Under these conditions irradiation offers a very promising alternative. Hygienization of dry ingredients, herbs, spices, and dehydrated vegetables can be accomplished efficiently with a dose of 5–10 kGy. Dry ingredients retain their sensory and quality attributes much better than the commodities with higher moisture content. A dose of 5 kGy can eliminate mold spores and 10 kGy can achieve commercial sterility in spices. These doses also automatically take care of insect infestation, if any, in spices. A number of countries have allowed commercial irradiation of spices. Irradiation of dehydrated vegetables and food ingredients such as gums and enzymes is also assuming importance.

G. Radiation Processing of Meat and Poultry

There are two major objectives of treatment of meat and poultry with medium dose irradiation. Improvement of keeping quality and shelf life of the refrigerated products by reduction of load and simultaneous destruction of pathogenic microbes. Irradiation offers a very good means of eliminating pathogens such as *Salmonella*, *Vibrio*, *Shigella*, and *Campylobacter* which are common in poultry, froglegs, and seafoods and responsible for a number of outbreaks of food poisoning. In seafoods like shrimp where peeling is done by hand the risk of contamination with the pathogens becomes greater. Salmonella-free poultry products such as eggs, egg powder, egg albumin, and blood plasma can be obtained by application of radiation. Radurization can also lower the energy requirements

during storage. For example, products that normally undergo frozen storage may be stored under refrigerated conditions after radurization.

Dry ingredients such as spices, enzymes, and some foods such as meat, poultry, and some seafood items can tolerate higher doses of radiation in the range of 25–50 kGy. For room temperature storage of meat, poultry, and seafoods the lysosomal enzymes need to be inactivated by the application of mild heat treatment such as blanching prior to packaging and high dose irradiation. It is essential to exclude oxygen by vacuum packing and carry out irradiation at low temperature (−20 to −40°C). At low temperature free radical movement is restricted and therefore flavor-related changes could be prevented. For dry ingredients, however, these precautions may not be essential. Naturally operations like blanching, vacuum packaging, and low temperature during irradiation at very high dose would escalate tremendously the cost of the product. However, these products will have demand in hospitals, space centers, and mountaineering and trekking institutes. Like other conventional sterilization processes usefulness of radiation sterilization is rather limited. All foods are not amenable to radiation preservation. Some foods like milk and milk products and beer are very sensitive and develop off odors even at low doses of irradiation.

Thirty-seven countries have cleared more than 40 items of foods. Recently, it has been estimated that approximately 500,000 tons of agricultural commodities, meat, poultry, seafoods, and food ingredients are being irradiated annually. About 23 countries are using irradiation to reduce postharvest losses and ensure hygienic quality of foods.

V. Regulation of Irradiation Process

Two important documents that have had considerable influence on worldwide developments in the regulation of irradiated foods are Codex General Standard for Irradiated Foods and the Recommended International Code of Practice for the Operation of Irradiation Facilities used for the treatment of foods. These model regulations provide valuable guidelines for governments wishing to harmonize their national legislations relating to the practical application. The main purpose of these regulations is to establish and organize appropriate measures for the three successive stages in the control of irradiation of foods:

1. Approval of irradiation plants. The radiation treatment of foods is to be carried out in facilities

licensed and registered for this purpose by a competent national authority. It should take into consideration data pertaining to seismicity of plant site, source of radiation, its loading and replenishment in the case of radioisotopes, radiation levels, and shielding, safety systems, operating, and emergency procedures.

2. Control of food irradiation process. This ensures that irradiation processing is carried out by qualified persons and in accordance with the general requirements of the Codex Standard and International Code of Practice. Plant managers and operators should keep adequate records including quantitative dosimetry. The facility and records should be open to inspection by national and international regulatory authorities.

3. Control of trade in irradiated foods. This control is designed to prevent entry of foods not treated by appropriate procedures in unapproved facilities. International trade in irradiated foods would be facilitated if there exists a harmonized and standardized system to control irradiation dosimetry, inspection, and safety procedures which should form the basis of certification and ensuring that the food to be imported has been irradiated in an authorized facility and all regulations have been complied with. The regulations require that irradiated food be labeled with a logo shown in Fig. 5 along with the statement "Treated with irradiation" in addition to information required by other food regulations.

Though the irradiation process offers distinct advantages, it cannot replace the acceptable norms of food processing regarding good manufacturing practices. The process can neither be utilized to mask serious microbiological contamination or spoilage of food nor can it be used to detoxify any preformed toxin. The process itself is relatively capital intensive and nonlabor intensive, but comparable economically to other capital-intensive food processes.

VI. Consumer Response and Acceptance

The ultimate success of irradiated foods depends upon their appreciation and acceptance by the consumer at large. A new product or process sometimes can meet initial resistance. In the past many beneficial technologies such as milk pasteurization have been initially resisted for a variety of reasons including lack of knowledge, selfish motives, and politics. It is, therefore, to be expected that irradiated foods may meet initial consumer resistance.

Though irradiation can provide wholesome food free of health risks, its benefits have not yet reached

Treated with radiation

FIGURE 5 The logo of food irradiation.

the public at large due mainly to lack of education on the subject and, thus far, nonavailability of free choice of irradiated foods. It is believed that through education and product introductions consumers can be enlightened on the subject. In countries where consumer organizations have been involved in the introduction of irradiated foods, a positive stand has been taken. In instances where irradiated foods have been test-marketed, consumers have indeed shown an obvious preference for them when all other factors were kept equal. Countries that contemplate commercialization of food irradiation should strive for full consumer participation by effective public information and education by the government as well as industry.

Bibliography

Diehl, J. F. (1990). "Safety Of Irradiated Foods." Marcel Dekker, New York.
Farkas, J. (1988). "Irradiation Of Dry Food Ingredients." CRC Press, Boca Raton, FL.
Josephson, E. S., and Peterson, M. S. (eds.) (1983). "Preservation Of Food By Ionizing Radiation," 3 Vols. CRC Press, Boca Raton, FL.
Urban, W. M. (1986). "Food Irradiation." Academic Press, New York.
World Health Organization and Food and Agricultural Organization of the United Nation (1988). "Food Irradiation: A Technique for Preserving and Improving the Safety of Food." WHO, Geneva.
ICGFI (1988). Guideline for Preparing Regulations for the Control of Food Irradiation Facilities (International Consultative Group on Food Irradiation, Document No. 1).
International Atomic Energy Agency (1982). "Training Manual on Food Irradiation Technology and Techniques," Technical Report Series 114, 2nd ed., Vienna.

Food Marketing Systems

TIMOTHY M. HAMMONDS, *Food Marketing Institute, Washington, DC*

Glossary

Broker Independent business serving as manufacturer's agent selling products to local retailers or wholesalers, and providing the necessary support services needed by those buyers

Food bank Charitable nonprofit institution collecting safe and nutritious products that might otherwise have been discarded from supermarkets, food warehouses, or food manufacturers; these products are sorted, checked for quality and safety, and then donated to local individuals or institutions

Private label Line of products controlled by a retailer or wholesaler for exclusive distribution in its own stores

Supermarket Self-service retail store stocking meat, produce, and grocery items doing at least $2 million dollars in annual sales

Universal product code (UPC) Twelve-digit computer-readable code used to identify individual items sold in supermarkets

Wholesaler Direct buyer purchasing merchandise from manufacturers, storing it in distribution centers, and re-selling the items to retail store operators; shipment to stores is generally provided although in some cases retailers may pick up the goods themselves

The U.S. Food Marketing System is a network of over 500,000 firms that store, transport, process, wholesale, and retail our food and fiber products from the time it leaves the farm gate until it reaches the final consumer. These products include categories as diverse as processed groceries, seafood, beverages, flowers, plants, seeds, clothing, pet food, textiles, tobacco, and leather footwear. Marketing beyond the farm gate accounts for 9.2% of our gross national product. While much of our output is consumed in America, the United States is the world's largest exporter of agricultural products.

I. Introduction

With the fall of the Berlin Wall, pictures of Soviet grocery stores (one could not call them supermarkets) with empty shelves and long lines of customers became the metaphor for the failure of communism. This was a fitting symbol, for the power of a nation rests on its ability to provide for the well-being of its citizens, and food is one essential component for providing that well-being.

The failure of the Soviet system was not due to a shortage of production. Indeed there were adequate food supplies available, even though there was ample room for improvement here as well. The failure was to provide an adequate food distribution system. Food production was concentrated in areas of low population; there were inadequate storage facilities which produced high levels of spoilage along with extensive rodent and insect damage; there was not an adequate transportation system for moving products quickly without contamination; and there were no modern grocery stores to sell the products in forms so familiar in the developed countries. In addition to all of this, there was no mechanism for translating consumer wants and preferences into the continuous feedback to producers and processors that constantly fine tune product offerings in the West.

Not only do modern food production and distribution systems contribute directly to the well-being of customers by supplying healthy and nutritious products at good values, the efficiency of these systems contributes indirectly by releasing human and capital resources to be used productively in other sectors of their economies. America in the 1990s feeds its citizens and serves a large and growing export market with less than 2% of its people living on farms. Efficient food distribution systems are essential for developed countries capable of remaining competitive in the global economy.

Because efficient food distribution systems allow a society to employ resources in other income-generating activities, wealth increases for the society as a whole. Because food expenditures are relatively fixed compared to other ways that consumers spend their money, increasing wealth further lowers the proportion of income that is spent on food. This phenomenon was first given scientific prominence in 1857 by a Prussian mining engineer by the name of Ernst Engel who published a study of family expenditure patterns for different income levels. He wrote that "the poorer a family is, the greater the proportion of total expenditures (income) which it must use to procure food." This pattern has been verified time and time again and the relationship is so strong that it has now become known as a basic law of economics. The modern statement of Engel's law is that as consumer incomes increase, the proportion of income spent for food decreases.

As consumers make their food expenditures, they find that grocery stores and restaurants are the most visible components of the food distribution system. However, these stores are only the tip of the vast production and logistics system that operates largely unseen by the average shopper to deliver a constant supply of food products throughout the country. This system is constantly evolving to meet changing consumer tastes and preferences; to respond to the ever-changing consumer demographic and ethnic mix; and to take advantage of the latest in new technologies which lower production costs, develop new products, improve packaging, and protect the environment.

This vast system is subject to government regulations that are designed primarily to protect the safety and wholesomeness of products as well as providing income protection for producers of certain supported commodities. However, the system is coordinated primarily by the free-market system. That is, constant experimentation is either rewarded or ignored by consumers and the system is constantly altered by the feedback that shoppers provide in deciding how to spend their dollars. These consumer decisions are not purely about price. Quality, safety, nutrition, convenience, cleanliness, taste, and environmental concerns all play important roles.

One important feature of the food distribution is the speed with which consumers can impact the system. Purchases of durable goods such as automobiles, appliances, or clothing are made very infrequently and are often so costly that consumers cannot afford a great deal of experimentation. Shoppers for food products make their choices felt on at least a weekly basis. In addition, the individual products are low enough in cost to allow constant experimentation and to allow expressions of social or environmental concerns to be made at a reasonable cost. This system is therefore one of the most accurate and responsive mirrors of consumer lifestyles to be found anywhere in our economy.

II. Size and Functions of the Food Distribution Sector

The total distribution system for the nation's food and fiber is one of the largest sectors in our economy. In 1990, this system employed over 17% of the workforce and contributed over 16% of the nation's gross domestic product.

Of the approximately $462 billion dollars spent in 1991 for food that originated on American farms, the marketing portion represented over $360 billion, or 78% while the farm value of the products represented just over $101 billion, or 22%. The marketing component of food expenditures is, therefore, triple the farm value of the basic commodities. This large marketing component has developed because Americans today demand their food in ever more convenient forms that minimize preparation time, increase shelf life, and are available on the go at fast food restaurants.

The farm value of food products varies widely among types of food. For animal products such as eggs, the farm value averages about 60% of the retail price. For highly processed foods such as potato chips, the farm share is only about 16%. The more highly processed the food, the lower the farm value as a share of the total expenditure. However, this lower share as a percentage of the total does not mean lower income for producers of these processed products. By presenting the food in a more convenient form, the market is expanded resulting in greater sales and higher total farm income than if all food had to be sold at roadside stands in its raw form.

Food spending by consumers accounted for 11.5% of total disposable income in 1991. This percentage has declined steadily over the years because incomes in America have risen faster than food expenditures. In 1960, this share would have been almost 18% of income. Over the last 30 years, Americans have shifted their food expenditures increasingly toward food away from home with fast food restaurants showing the fastest growth rates. In 1960, the share of income spent for food away from home was 3.5% growing to 4.3% by 1991. The food at home share, by contrast, declined over this same period from 14.0% in 1960 to 7.2% in 1991.

One measure of the efficiency of this system is a comparison of the share of income spent for food in the United States versus other countries. Because different types of food are consumed from country to country, an exact comparison is impossible. However, we can estimate expenditures closely enough for relative comparisons using the percentage of personal consumption expenditures for food consumed at home. This number for the United States is well under 10% (see above) the lowest of any major developed country. In contrast, the number is 11.6% for the United Kingdom, 14.8% for Australia, 18.8% for Italy, 21.6% for Spain, and 52.8% for the Philippines.

Because our food production and distribution system is so efficient, Americans enjoy an extremely high standard of living, with a much higher percentage of their incomes available for items other than food, than any other major developed country in the world. The distribution system has, as its primary components Food Manufacturers, Food Wholesalers and Brokers, Food Retailers, Food Service Outlets, an Import–Export Sector, and various Government and Private Food Assistance Programs.

III. Food Manufacturers

Approximately one out of every 20 U.S. manufacturing companies is a food manufacturer or processor, and the food and beverage industry is our second largest manufacturing sector (following transportation equipment). In general, the terms food manufacturer and food processor are used interchangeably. This sector generally buys commodities from farmers or their agents, processes the raw products, and sells their output to food wholesalers or directly to retailers. The government recognizes 49 separate food processing industries with the largest in terms of numbers of firms being meat processors, bakery product producers, grain millers, dairy processors, and beverage producers. As a further indication of the size of this sector, food processors are the nation's largest advertisers spending almost $12 billion in direct consumer advertising in 1990. In addition, this sector is the nation's largest users of packaging materials.

Food manufacturers process and package commodities into forms more convenient for consumers to store and use. This might involve something as simple as grading eggs for size and consistency, or as complex as producing corn flakes from grain. As consumers change their lifestyles, less and less time is available for shopping and meal preparation. The result is an increasing demand for convenience foods, microwaveable products, and even whole ready-to-eat packaged meals. At the same time, not everyone eats their food in highly processed or packaged form. In addition to convenience foods, the incredible diversity of lifestyles and preferences in America require a continuing supply of basic food products and ingredients. These can readily be seen in supermarket fresh fruit and vegetable (produce) sections, meat counters, and dairy departments.

IV. Food Wholesalers and Food Brokers

Large, integrated retailers have sufficient resources to buy directly from suppliers and to warehouse and transport their own products. However, many retailers are far too small to perform these functions on their own. Almost half of the grocery stores in America today are run by family-owned independent operators, not chains. Many of these are one-store companies. These smaller operators rely on wholesalers for support. Sales of products directly to the final user or consumer are called retail sales. Sales to businesses that will in turn resell the product to the final user are called wholesale sales.

Food wholesalers pool the buying power of their many individual customers to give small operators the volume purchasing clout of much larger companies. They negotiate with suppliers and manufacturers for products, warehouse the goods until time for shipment to the stores, and provide transportation to move the products. Many wholesalers also provide financial, technical, and computer support services to companies who could not afford them on their own. In addition, they may prepare advertising programs to be used by local grocers, produce product labels for the shelves, help with employee training, and maintain inventory control systems. As a result, small, family grocery retailers have remained highly competitive in the United States while they play a much smaller role in many other countries lacking our extensive wholesaler support structure.

Wholesalers are structured in two primary types of organizations: cooperatives and voluntaries. Cooperatives are owned by the retailers they serve, and their business customers sit on the Board of Directors of the wholesaler. Cooperative customers, therefore, have an ownership interest in the wholesaler and are called members. Generally, only the member-owners are eligible to buy from the cooperative wholesalers. Voluntary wholesalers are generally public companies, owned by stockholders, selling goods to any business customer without membership requirements. These wholesalers take ownership of the goods they buy from producers and manufacturers, and carry the risk of price changes before the goods are sold to the retailers who market them directly to the public. [See COOPERATIVES.]

Manufacturers and their agents also sell many products directly to retail stores without passing them through a chain or wholesaler warehouse. These tend to be products requiring specialized knowledge and handling, or those products that must be fresh daily. Bread and dairy products are good examples of products often sold by processors directly to retailers, and delivered directly to stores several times each week, sometimes daily. Many manufacturers or processors will be large enough to have their own sales forces. However, smaller manufacturers who cannot support their own salesmen will typically make use of food brokers.

Food brokers are independent businesses serving as manufacturers' agents selling products to local retailers or wholesalers, and providing the necessary support services needed by those buyers. Brokers generally do not take ownership of the goods they represent and generally do not have their own warehouses. Instead, they arrange for shipment of products directly to the stores or to warehouses owned by the wholesalers or retailers. Generally brokers represent several manufacturers in a given market area.

Wholesale sales of food and kindred products reached $431 billion in 1990. Of these sales, cooperative and voluntary wholesalers accounted for $239 billion, brokers serving as agents for manufacturers accounted for $109 billion, and manufacturer direct sales representatives accounted for $83 billion.

Inventory costs can represent up to 80% of the total costs of a food retailer. The rest is accounted for by expenses such as employee wages and benefits, rent, utilities, and supplies. As a result, companies are making every effort to cut down on the extra stock that might be carried on the shelves or in back rooms. Wholesalers and chain warehouses are therefore developing the grocery industry equivalent to just-in-time delivery. This concept was pioneered by Japanese manufacturing facilities and involves using computerized sales data to deliver products to the store just before it is needed to stock the shelves rather than piling it up in the back room. This frees up space to be used for new sales departments and frees up capital resources to be invested in the business. In the process, retailers and wholesalers are becoming more closely linked than ever before.

V. Food Retailers

Food and grocery products are sold through a wide array of retail stores including supermarkets, convenience stores, specialty shops, and other retailers such as drug stores and department stores that also stock some grocery products. However, the dominant retail outlet continues to be the supermarket. Grocery stores are familiar to everyone in America and are found in every community. They sell a wide array of products primarily intended for consumption at home although the assortment of ready-to-eat products is growing rapidly to meet today's busy lifestyle needs.

These grocery stores range in size from small convenience stores to huge markets over 200,000 square feet in size and selling well over $1 million dollars in products every week. Suburban stores cater primarily to shoppers who come by automobile and tend to carry extensive offerings of nonfood as well as food products. Inner-city stores tend to be small with limited selections of goods because of the expense of land and the difficulty of finding sites large enough to accommodate a modern supermarket. One supermarket that opened in 1992 in inner-city Newark, New Jersey, required over 10 years to assemble over 60 individually owned parcels of land into one site of suitable size.

Larger stores stock a full range of fresh and processed food products but also offer an extensive range of specialty departments and nonfood sections. One distinguishing feature of the grocery store is self-service. Although there are full-service specialty stores where clerks select the products, and there are service departments within the supermarket, customer self-service for the majority of products is a defining characteristic of the modern grocery store. A supermarket, by definition, is a full-line self-service grocery store stocking meat, produce, and packaged grocery products, and doing over $2 million per year in sales volume. Food retail operations below this annual dollar volume are known simply as "other grocery stores." Convenience stores are small grocery stores selling a very limited variety of goods with their sales typically concentrated in cigarettes, magazines, bread, milk, and other beverages. Many convenience stores also offer gasoline although gasoline sales volume has been excluded from the sales volumes reported below.

In 1990, all grocery store sales reached $368.5 billion with $271.7 billion (73.7%) in supermarkets, $69.9 billion (19.0%) in other grocery stores, and $26.9 billion (7.3%) in convenience stores. Supermarkets are of two general types. Chains are those businesses with 11 or more stores under the same ownership, and independents are those with 10 or fewer retail stores. By ownership, 49.2% of all grocery stores in 1990 were independents (with 41.1% of the sales volume), 12.2% were chains (with 51.6% of the sales), and 38.6% were convenience stores (with 7.3% of sales).

Specialized food stores, those with limited lines of goods, added another $24 billion to retail food sales with meat and seafood markets accounting for $7 billion, baked goods stores $6 billion, produce stores $3.1 billion, and candy and nut stores $4.7 billion.

As more and more families in America are made up of households where all adults work outside the home, time for shopping is scarce. As a result, supermarkets have added a wide variety of departments and services under one roof to make one-stop shopping a reality. It is common today for supermarkets to offer, in addition to the basic food products, services as varied as video rental, floral sales, ready-to-eat carry-out foods such as hot pizza, health and beauty care items, and pharmacy prescription departments.

It is also common for retailers to offer private label products to consumers. These are lines of products controlled by the retailer for exclusive distribution in its own stores. Large chains can develop their own private label products while independent operators typically take advantage of the private labels offered by their wholesalers. These products often carry the name of the store on the label and are, therefore, often called store brands or own-label products. In 1991, nearly $26 billion in private label products were sold.

Private label items are used to offer the consumer a value alternative to nationally branded items. These can be priced attractively for the consumer because they do not carry the large advertising and research budgets typically carried by manufacturer brands. The industry worked hard throughout the 1980s to upgrade these products and now most provide attractive packaging and quality levels very competitive with the national brands. In 1992, private label products accounted for almost one in five (18.2%) of all grocery items sold in supermarkets by item count and 13.7% of all grocery products by dollar share.

Grocery stores as a group are one of the largest employers in the nation providing 2.9 million jobs to Americans. An estimated 134,000 self-employed and unpaid family workers also work in grocery stores as part of their family businesses. Most workers are young with one-quarter of the jobs (25.1%) held by people between 16 and 20 years of age. By comparison, this age group holds only 7.3% of the jobs throughout the U.S. economy. This sector therefore provides the first job for a tremendous number of Americans who need entry-level experience in the job market.

Because grocery stores are open long hours, often around the clock, and because shopper traffic tends to concentrate in a few peak shopping hours, many part-time jobs are available. The average grocery store worker is employed for fewer than 30 hr per week. This makes the sector particularly attractive for young workers with school responsibilities. Although there are highly skilled professions in the grocery store such as meatcutters and bakers, many of the jobs can be learned in a short period of time and are available to entry-level employees. However, employers prefer high school graduates for long-term employees. Because stores continue to add service departments in tune with today's lifestyles, employment in grocery stores is expected to increase over 20% over the next 10 years.

VI. The Modern Supermarket

The supermarket concept was "invented" in 1930 to replace the small store where clerks used the shopper's grocery list to select the products behind their counters and prepare the customer's order. The idea was born during the great depression as a means of providing groceries at a cost low enough to help shoppers stretch their budgets. The concept was to move to the outskirts of town where land was cheaper, slash operating costs by asking shoppers to pick their own products from the shelves, provide free parking, assemble all of the essentials in one place to make one-stop shopping a time saver, and take only a low profit margin on each item relying on high volume to generate income.

The supermarket was truly an American invention. By 1958 the concept had grown so rapidly that *Life Magazine* featured it as "an American institution." International visitors came from all over the world to see this wonderful new innovation and to learn how to take the concept to their own countries. Queen Elizabeth II toured a supermarket as part of her American visit in 1957 as did Russia's Nikita Khruschev in 1959 and Boris Yeltsin in 1989. Even though supermarkets have spread throughout all of the developed countries, international visitors still tour American grocery stores to see the latest innovations and trends.

Supermarkets come in a wide variety of sizes to fit the local neighborhoods. Sizes range from 8000 square feet to over 180,000 square feet with the average in 1991 at 42,000 square feet. However, with this wide range of sizes, it makes more sense to talk about size by type of store. By type (format) there are:

- *Conventional Supermarkets*. the original format offering between 10,000 and 20,000 items in meat, produce, and grocery; doing at least $2 million in annual sales; and averaging about 29,000 square feet for those recently built.
- *Superstores*. Larger versions of the conventional stores with at least 30,000 square feet of space; carrying approximately 30,000 items; offering a variety of service departments such as delicatessens, bakeries, and seafood departments; and averaging about 43,500 square feet for those recently built.
- *Combination Stores*. Superstores with pharmacy counters and expanded general merchandise and health and beauty care sections; carrying about 35,000 items; and averaging about 49,000 square feet for those recently built.
- *Warehouse Stores*. Low margin supermarkets with reduced variety, lower service levels (consumers typically bag their own groceries), spartan decor, and attractive pricing; and averaging about 48,000 square feet for those recently built. The number of items carried will be more typical of conventional supermarkets averaging between 10,000 and 20,000 items.
- *Hypermarkets*. Very large supermarkets with an extensive general merchandise section added. There are too few of these to talk meaningfully about averages, but they are at least 100,000 square feet in size, often reaching more than 200,000 square feet.

With the importance of one-stop shopping, supermarkets continue to bring more and more lines of business under one roof. It is typical today to find departments such as bakeries, delicatessens, service seafood, greeting cards, pharmacies, video rentals, floral departments, household goods, automotive supplies, toys, clothing, sit-down cafeterias or restaurants, banking services, postal services, film processing, and catering to mention only a few of the most common. To keep track of consumer preferences in such large stores, supermarkets typically use computerized scanners.

Scanners at the front end checkout counters read the symbol of light and dark lines on the packages known as the Universal Product Code. This symbol contains five digits that identify the product manufacturer and five digits that identify the specific item within that manufacturer's line. A leading digit identifies the type of product (dry grocery versus beauty care for example) and a trailing digit is used by the computer to check whether the code has been read properly. A total of 12 digits are, therefore, contained in the standard code. The price is not contained in the coded symbol; it is assigned by the retailer and entered into the store's computer memory. Once the UPC symbol has been used to identify the item, the computer looks up the proper price for the product, displays it on a screen, and prints it on the shopper's receipt along with the name of the item.

The five manufacturer digits are assigned by the Uniform Product Code Council located in Dayton, Ohio. The five product digits are then assigned by the manufacturer and communicated to the retailer. This system not only moves shoppers through the checkout line more quickly, it also tracks purchase preferences so that the grocer can stock more of the popular items and fewer of the slow movers. This system puts the shopper in the driver's seat in determining which products succeed and which fail.

The dominant marketing philosophy in the supermarket industry is to hold profit margins low and rely on the high volume generated for profits. There are two key profit measures that give a picture of the industry: return on sales (net profit), and return on assets.

Return on sales measures the portion of the consumer's food dollar which remains after the grocer restocks the inventory purchased and pays all expenses including taxes. In 1992, this return was 0.77%, that is, just under 8/10ths of one penny out of each consumer's dollar. Over the last 20 years this net profit percentage has consistently been in the 0.5

to 1.2% range, among the lowest for any industry group.

This low level of profit on each dollar spent translates into a reasonable total return because of high transaction volumes. The broader measure of total returns that can be used to compare this industry with others is return on total assets. This is a measure of the net profits generated by the industry as a percentage of all assets employed in operating the businesses. In 1992, this measure was 3.3%, about average for all industries. Successful strategies must then maintain a strong consumer focus to continue to generate the volumes necessary for adequate total returns. If the customer count falls for an individual store, not only do the low margins per transaction make it difficult to stay in business, but the spoilage of perishables that stay too long on the shelves increases operating expenses dramatically. The very financial structure of the industry guarantees that only those stores doing an excellent job for their local customers will survive.

VII. Food Service Outlets

Food service operators sell products fully prepared and intended for on-premise or immediate consumption. These operations can include schools, airplanes, fast food outlets, bars, hotels, and restaurants.

Separate food service outlets sold $227.3 billion dollars of products in 1990. The largest sectors included fast food outlets at $72.7 billion, restaurants at $65.4 billion, hotels and motels at $12.2 billion, hospitals and extended care facilities at $11.9 billion, and elementary and secondary schools at $11.5 billion.

In the restaurant and fast food sector, a growing trend is the purchase of food from carryout counters, drive-through windows, or home delivery for consumption off-premise. In 1990, almost half, 46%, of restaurant and fast food outlet meals were eaten off-premise. Of those off-premise meals, 60.8% were carried out by the consumer, 31.0% were purchased at drive-through windows, and 8.2% were obtained through home delivery. With today's hurried lifestyles, this carry-out trend continues to grow as two-career couples find eating at a restaurant expensive and time consuming.

In addition to these separate food service outlets, many supermarkets and convenience stores have also added products intended for immediate consumption such as salad bars, deli sandwiches, and frozen yogurt. This trend continues to grow blurring the lines between fast food outlets and supermarkets.

VIII. Exports and Imports

Although America's food industry is primarily a domestic market, the United States is the world's largest exporter and importer of food and food products. The industry exported 5.4% of its 1991 production. This was the first year since 1978 that America achieved a trade balance surplus in foods and beverages exporting $19.6 billion in commodities and importing $19 billion.

Japan, Canada, South Korea, Mexico, and the Netherlands are the major markets for food and kindred products. The top import markets are Canada, Australia, Brazil, France, and Mexico. The United States generally exports basic commodities such as feeds, meat, poultry, and fish. Imports are more heavily weighted toward higher value and processed products such as confections, baked goods, alcoholic beverages, and gourmet fruit and vegetables.

Import and export figures alone are not the whole story of America's international involvement in food and food products. Many of our largest food processors and manufacturers sell substantial dollar volumes through their foreign plants or under licensing agreements with foreign plants to produce their brands. U.S. investment in overseas subsidiaries and joint ventures has increased over 25% in just the last 4 years to almost $16 billion in 1990. As a result, nearly $3.5 billion in foreign income flowed into America in 1990. As a result of foreign food industry investments here, $1 billion in income flowed from the United States to overseas companies.

Most U.S. international investment in food processing has been made in Europe accounting for approximately 53% of the total. Canada ranks second at 14% while Mexico's share is the fastest growing now in third place at 6%. The North America Free Trade Agreement between America, Canada, and Mexico holds great promise for expanding this international trade in the near future. [See TARIFFS AND TRADE.]

IX. Government and Private Food Assistance Programs

Food assistance for needy families and individuals has been in existence for more than 50 years at the Federal level, and for almost all of our history at the local level. Modern programs are designed to improve the nutritional status, and therefore the health, of low-income people while at the same time improving farm income through the distribution of surplus foods.

Domestic food programs at the Federal level are administered through the Food and Nutrition Service of the U.S. Department of Agriculture (USDA) in cooperation with State and local governments. In total, the USDA spent over $30 billion dollars spread over 13 different food assistance programs for Americans in 1991. The largest and best known form of aid is the Food Stamp program. This program, tested in 1961, implemented in 1964, and extended nationwide in 1974, provides stamps or coupons that can be spent like money at local stores to buy food.

Eligibility is determined by income levels, asset limits, and work requirements. The income limits are set using the federal poverty guidelines and revised each year. Benefits are issued monthly based on household size and income and are intended to reflect the USDA's Thrifty Food Plan, a market basket of foods that provide a low-cost, nutritious diet. In 1991, funding for this program was $19.6 billion with participation of approximately 26 million people. Over half of the recipients were children and more than 80% of the aid went to families with children.

The Special Supplemental Food Program for Women, Infants, and Children (WIC) serves almost one-third of all children born in America. This program is designed to improve the nutrition and health of pregnant women and infants up to the age of 5 years. In addition to food, the program also provides nutrition education and access to health services.

The National School Lunch Program serves more than 24 million children in over 92,000 schools. This program provides free or reduced-price lunches depending on need. Other companion programs include the School Breakfast Program, the Summer Food Service Program, the Special Milk Program, and the Nutrition Education and training Program.

In addition to Federal programs, the food industry participates in a number of private food assistance programs aimed at the local communities. One of the most innovative of these of the Food Bank program. The largest food bank network is known as Second Harvest.

Food Banks are charitable, nonprofit institutions that collect products which might otherwise have been discarded from supermarkets, food warehouses, and food manufacturers. These are quality products usually with some minimal damage such as torn labels that make them difficult to sell in retail stores. The Food Banks then sort these products, check them for quality and safety, and donate them to local individuals or institutions. This voluntary network saves millions of dollars of nutritious products that would otherwise find their way into landfills. It is one of the great success stories of this industry.

X. Future Trends

Although the media often depicts the food distribution sector as "stable," it is a constantly changing, evolving sector. New products alone appear and disappear at a dizzying pace. Throughout the grocery industry, over 12,000 new products are introduced each year by grocery manufacturers. Some of these are regional or local products in limited distribution. Many, however, are national market introductions.

Some of these new products were developed to take advantage of a new technology such as microwave cooking. Others were developed to take advantage of ethnic trends such as salsa products which passed ketchup in national sales volume in 1992. Still others were developed to respond to social or health concerns such as recyclable containers or soybean meat substitutes. Whatever the reason, the consumer is given an opportunity each week to try an impressive array of new offerings. Success or failure is determined by consumers themselves.

How consumers spend their dollars on food and grocery products provides constant and immediate feedback to producers and retailers. The food distribution system will, therefore, continue to evolve keeping pace with basic trends in American life. We can look at these trends as guideposts along this path.

A. Demographics

Demographics refer to the composition of our population. Such factors as the distribution of age groups across the population, ethnic mix, and household formation are important.

One of the strongest demographic trends in America over the last three decades has been the increasing proportion of working women. The proportion of adult women working outside the home rose from about 38% in 1960 to just under 60% in 1990. As we see more single-parent households and households where both adults work outside the home, time for shopping and meal preparation becomes scarce. Convenience foods become very important and the microwave oven continues to become a major cooking appliance. Carry-out foods also play an increasing role as families seek the ultimate in ease of meal preparation.

Even basic commodities are purchased in different forms to add convenience. Consumers, for example, buy their beef in a form easy to use such as hamburger, and buy fewer roasts which take longer to prepare and cook.

Time as a scarce commodity also encourages one-stop shopping. Supermarkets have responded to this need by building larger and larger stores to bring more goods and services under one roof.

Another strong trend is the slowing of the birth rate. The U.S. population was growing at a rate of 10% yearly in the 1980s, dropping off to about 7% in the decade of the 1990s, with projections of only 5% in the decade to follow the turn of the century. As this happens, more and more of our population growth comes from immigration. Immigration accounted for 16% of the U.S. population growth in the 1960s, 27% in the 1980s, and 33% by the year 2000. Asian-Americans are America's fastest growing ethnic group followed by Hispanics.

The growing ethnic influence broadens America's taste for new foods and styles of cooking adding to our already rich cultural diversity. Hispanic and Asian cooking and products, particularly new fruits, vegetables, and spices, spread outside their ethnic origins to mainstream America. Add to these two rapidly growing cultures the cooking patterns of countless other ethnic groups arriving in America from all over the world, and you have an incredibly exciting and vibrant food industry.

Another consequence of a lower birth rate is an aging population. By 2030, the number of elderly in the United States will be double its level in 1990. Almost 65 million people (almost 21% of the population) will then be over the age of 64 and over 10% of the population will be over 74. This will change not only the types of food that people buy but how it is marketed as well.

The older age groups spend more per capita on food because they can generally afford to eat whatever they want at this stage in their lives. Studies have shown that older shoppers eat more than average amounts of fresh fruits and vegetables, cereals, bakery products, poultry, and pork. They tend to consume less than average amounts of red meat, milk, soft drinks, and snacks. They also tend to be increasingly health conscious and to often enjoy shopping as a social activity.

B. Lifestyles

Just as our basic demographics change, so do our basic lifestyles. Two of the strongest trends are an increasing interest in health and nutrition, and an active interest in the environment.

Two reports have been seminal in galvanizing an already growing interest in food and health: *The Surgeon General's Report on Nutrition and Health* published by the U.S. Department of health and Human Services in 1988, and *Diet and Health—Implications for Reducing Chronic Disease Risk,* published by the National Research Council in 1989. These two reports not only established a scientific link between improving diets and reducing the risk of disease, they also gave clear recommendations for specific dietary changes.

Americans have taken these recommendations to heart and are changing their dietary patterns as a result. The most direct consequence has been an increase in the consumption of fresh products, particularly fresh fruits and vegetables. We have also seen a dramatic increase in concern over the fat content of foods of all types because of its link with coronary disease. Low fat, low cholesterol, low calorie foods have become very popular with consumers.

Along with this interest in healthful foods has come a demand for more useful nutrition information on packages. New guidelines for manufacturers were finalized by the Food and Drug Administration and the U.S. Department of Agriculture with standard nutrition information panels to be required on virtually all packaged food products by the mid 1990s. Prior to this, providing nutrition information on packages has been voluntary with only about half of the products making it available.

Interest in the environment is another strong trend making itself felt in the food industry. By volume, 30% of all landfill waste is packaging, much of it from food products. This makes the industry a very important part of the solution to environmental issues. [*See* FOOD PACKAGING.]

Of the 180 million tons of garbage generated in the United States yearly, 73% is deposited into landfills (13% is recycled and 14% is incinerated). One-half of the existing 6000 landfills are expected to close by 1995 either because they are full or because of fear of contamination of local water tables. This pressure on space available for disposal will keep the reduction of solid waste high on the public policy agenda.

People have already changed their habits in response to environmental concerns. A national research consumer panel found that in 1990 only 16.1% of consumers separated newspapers for curbside recycling. By 1992, that number had reached 77.5%. In 1990, 45.2% reported taking aluminum cans to a recycling center, in 1992, 75.3% do so. This same panel reported that in 1990, 3.3% of their communities required mandatory plastic recycling while this had risen to 15.0% by 1992.

The food industry has responded to these concerns in a number of ways. Perhaps the most visible is an ongoing program to reduce excess packaging. Grocery manufacturers have moved to more concentrated detergents sold in smaller packages, developed more refillable dispensers for products like liquid soap, and reduced unnecessary double wrapping on many products. In addition, supermarkets are now salvaging cardboard boxes removed in the back room to make the cardboard available for recycling. Many other changes in packaging and business practices can be expected as we learn more about effective ways to reduce solid waste and protect the environment.

The profile of this industry is one of constant change. Constant monitoring of local consumer purchase patterns means that food marketing systems and products will continue to evolve in tune with modern shoppers.

Bibliography

Food Marketing Institute. (1992 and annually). "Facts About Store Development." Washington, DC.

Food Marketing Institute. (1992 and annually). "Trends"—Consumer Attitudes & The Supermarket." Washington, DC.

Gallo, A. E., et al. U.S. Department of Agriculture, Commodity Economics Division, Economic Research Service (1992 and annually). "Food Marketing Review." Washington, DC.

Manchester, A. C. U.S. Department of Agriculture, Commodity Economics Division, Economic Research Service (1991). "The Food Marketing Revolution, 1950–90." Washington, DC.

Maclean Hunter Media (April 1992 issue and annually). "Progressive Grocer Magazine's Annual Report of the Grocery Industry" (M. Sansolo, ed.). Stamford, CT.

Food Microbiology

RANDALL K. PHEBUS, *Kansas State University*

Glossary

Bacterial growth Increase in bacterial numbers over time depicted by lag, log, stationary, and death phases of a traditional growth curve

Enterobacteriaceae Relatively homogeneous group of gram-negative nonsporulating bacteria that are facultatively anaerobic and normal inhabitants of the intestines of animals

Foodborne disease outbreak Two or more persons having similar illness after ingestion of a specific food at a particular time and place

Food fermentations Use of specific groups of microorganisms to alter various foods through the metabolism of carbohydrates, usually with production of acids, alcohol, and/or carbon dioxide

Food irradiation Process used to reduce microbial levels, particularly pathogens, in foods, employing nonionizing radiation from cobalt 60, electron beams, or X-rays; other applications include inhibition of sprouting and maturation, and insect disinfestation

Pathogen Biological agent that can produce disease in a susceptible host

Quality control Use of strategies, programs, analyses, and personnel during processing to assure that food products are safe, wholesome, aesthetic, and consistent at all times

Sanitation Science of effecting healthful and hygienic conditions depicted by strategies to control filth and pests within processing facilities, in conjunction with procedures to clean and sanitize the environment for microbial reductions

Shelf life Time that a food product can be stored or displayed without demonstrating signs of deterioration

Starter cultures Specific microorganisms intentionally inoculated into specific foods to cause predictable reactions due to their metabolic activities; lactic acid bacteria are among the most popular of these and are used in many fermentation processes

Food microbiology may be broadly defined as a science focusing on the roles and activities of microscopic organisms in food production, food processing, spoilage, and foodborne disease. Food microbiology is a diverse area of study that plays a critical role in all aspects of food—from on-farm production of raw commodities, to conversion of these commodities into food during processing, to distribution and retail marketing, and finally to personal consumption. Food microbiology is of concern at the farm level since this is the initial source of specific microorganisms that contaminate many products. Examples at this production point include the microbial evaluation of raw milk, screening of poultry flocks for salmonellae, and testing corn for aflatoxins produced by certain species of the mold *Aspergillus*. Significant research is focusing on preventing herd or flock contamination and detecting animals harboring human infectious agents before these animals enter processing facilities. Microbiological issues are key during the processing of raw commodities into food products. Bacteria, yeasts, and molds are utilized to produce some foods such as bread, wine, cheese, and fermented meats. In other processing environments, these organisms can cause rapid product spoilage and can lead to unsafe foods.

Reduction or elimination of these microbial types is paramount in the food processing industry. A major charge to the food microbiologist is the development of sensitive, accurate, reliable, and rapid techniques for detecting, enumerating, and identifying specific groups of microorganisms from complex food matrices. Ultimately, food microbiology is a science that strives to provide an abundance of quality foods to all humans, keeping food safety as the primary concern.

I. Introduction

The roots of microbiology as a science are strongly intertwined with early discoveries involving the causes of spoilage of various foods. Antonie van Leeuwenhoek of the Netherlands was the first to describe microorganisms as "animalcules" in 1683 using a crude form of microscope. van Leeuwenhoek's discoveries endowed him the title "Father of Microbiology" in history. Hints of microbiological theory preceded van Leeuwenhoek's observations. In the mid-1600s, a monk named Kircher attributed the decay of bodies and some foods to invisible agents. Robert Hooke also described fruiting structures of molds using magnifying lenses in 1664. During this era, the theory of spontaneous generation was controversial in the scientific community. This theory hypothesized the emergence of living organisms from nonliving matter and was supported by the microscopic observations of multitudes of bacteria in putrefying foods that were initially unspoiled. Opponents of this thought said that these spoilage flora contaminated the product because of their presence in the air surrounding it. Offering support for this hypothesis were individuals such as Abe Lazzaro Spallanzani, an Italian priest, who heated sealed containers of gravy to destroy microorganisms and prevent spoilage. Proponents of spontaneous generation were relentless in their beliefs and argued in favor of their ideas even until the early 20th century. They said that treatments such as those of Spallanzani destroyed a "vital" attribute of air needed for life. Louis Pasteur provided the decisive evidence against this theory in the mid-1800s with his work on filtering air through cotton to remove bacteria followed by his development of the Pasteur flask, a swan-necked flask that effectively trapped bacteria before they could reach heat-sterilized infusions. These infusions remained unspoiled, thereby proving that actual bacteria in the air and not a "vital" element of air led to product deterioration.

The heating methods for various foods that were used to disprove the hypothesis of the spontaneous generation of life were the forerunners of canning as a means of food preservation. In 1795, the French government offered an award to anyone who developed an effective method of preserving foods. Nicholas Appert captured this prize in 1810 by boiling foods and then sealing them hermetically to maintain sterility; his feat earned him 12,000 francs. Pasteur continued to play a pivotal role during the infancy of food microbiology. He was the first person to demonstrate the role of bacteria in milk spoilage in 1837. He continued to investigate such spoilage phenomena over the next three decades and proved in 1857 that alcoholic fermentations arose by the action of yeasts on sugars. Around 1860, Pasteur heated wine and beer to kill undesirable microorganisms, a process that became known as pasteurization. The newly found knowledge of sterilization practices, the development of better microscopes, and the application of better microbial growth media perpetuated the rapid development of food microbiology to its role in the production of food today. [See THERMAL PROCESSING: CANNING AND PASTEURIZATION.]

With the knowledge that we have currently, it is interesting to look back at the early history of human manipulations of foods. Since humans began producing foods (approximately 10,000 years ago), problems of spoilage and disease undoubtedly existed. Although these early people had no understanding of microbiology, they did develop methods to help preserve foods. Fermentations were used to produce beer by 7000 B.C. and sea salt was used to preserve foods approximately 3000 B.C. Other preservation methods documented in history included the use of oils, smoking, drying, and snow packing. People realized that these practices preserved foods for longer periods while also providing products that were unique and often more flavorful.

II. Sources and Types of Microorganisms in Foods

The food supply is not, nor will it be in the future, free from microorganisms. Therefore, we must understand and deal with the likelihood of foodborne diseases and food spoilage. Only a few special types of foods, such as some medically oriented products, can be considered sterile. Canned foods that have undergone retort processes are "commercially" sterile. This term means that some heat-resistant spores of certain bacteria may have survived the heating process and could initiate growth given proper conditions. However, with continued package integrity and maintenance of proper storage conditions of these commercially sterile foods, several years of storage are possible. The majority of our foods are perishable; food microbiologists strive to develop methods to increase the shelf life and safety of foods.

Microorganisms are ubiquitous in nature; everywhere that food is grown, processed, sold, and prepared there are potential sources of microbial contamination. The types or groups of microorganisms most prevalent in a particular food vary depending on its growth, storage, and processing environment. Generally, raw food commodities are contaminated with a diverse population of microflora. Processing usually involves various steps that reduce microbial levels including canning, pasteurization, blanching, freezing, and acidification. A more homogeneous bacterial population normally results since organisms that are more resistant to the specific processes (i.e., thermal tolerant) survive and perpetuate. In the case of refrigerated foods, psychrotrophic bacteria, those that can grow at refrigeration temperatures, become dominant. Fermented foods would likely demonstrate high populations of lactic acid tolerant microorganisms.

The term "microorganism" signifies a living entity that is smaller than 0.1 mm in diameter and cannot be seen without magnification. Several types of foodborne organisms fit into this category of living creatures. Bacteria, molds, yeasts, and protozoa are the most familiar members of the group; however, other microbial groups such as nematodes, cestodes, and trematodes do cause food-related problems. Viruses are usually considered microorganisms although they are not free living and require a living host to multiply and cause disease. Microorganisms are often described and classified based on such characteristics as their growth requirements, optimal growth temperatures, and tolerance to certain environmental conditions.

Sources of microorganisms in foods are numerous. Many raw agricultural products can be contaminated with soil during growth and harvest. Water and soil often contain similar microbial species because of their close relationship during rain and runoff. Both can cause food contamination while in the field. Contaminated drinking water may be a route for certain pathogens to infect live animals and later be carried into the processing environment. Some of the most common genera of bacteria found in soils include *Acinetobacter*,

Bacillus, *Pseudomonas*, *Corynebacterium*, and *Clostridium*. In addition to these bacteria, *Aeromonas*, *Alteromonas*, and *Vibrio* are frequent contaminants of water and contain species that are associated with human disease. Many fungi are present in the environment and can cause food spoilage, usually when conditions limit growth of bacteria. A few of the most significant soil-associated molds are *Aspergillus*, *Fusarium*, *Mucor*, *Penicillium*, and *Rhizopus*. Protozoa can be important disease-causing entities in certain foods; *Cryptosporidium parvum*, *Entamoeba histolytica* and *Giardia lamblia* are examples associated with soil and water.

Air is an important source of microbial contamination, especially in the processing environment. A vast abundance of bacteria can be carried on dust particles and vapor droplets into food products. Gram-positive bacteria tend to be encountered most often; *Bacillus*, *Clostridium*, and *Micrococcus* species are very common. Air is also a transporter of high levels of mold spores that can spoil foods. Food processors invest significant amounts of time and resources in ensuring that air within processing facilities is of high microbiological quality.

Hide removal from livestock and feather removal from poultry are critical points during slaughter to reduce bacterial contamination of meat products. Hides and feathers contain an array of bacteria, often pathogenic, that are derived from feces, dust, and feed. These bacteria can potentially contaminate the dressed meat and be carried further into processing and fabrication of carcasses. Animal feeds often contain bacteria that can ultimately be found in food products. Poultry feeds have been implicated as sources of salmonellae. Animals contain very high levels of bacteria in their intestinal tracts which, during slaughter and evisceration, can contaminate carcasses. This major source of pathogenic bacteria such as toxigenic *Escherichia coli*, *Campylobacter jejuni*, *Salmonella*, and *Yersinia enterocolitica* must be held to an absolute minimum to ensure food safety. One protozoan, *Toxoplasma gondii*, is often associated with animal intestinal tracts and can contaminate foods.

During processing of foods, microbial contamination can occur at numerous points. Worker hygiene is a key aspect of producing quality products. Workers can carry many types of microorganisms on their hands, clothes, and processing utensils. This is also a potential source of foodborne viruses, which are currently becoming of more concern to food microbiologists. Worker education and supervision are important features of quality control programs. Equipment can readily spread bacteria during food processing. It is essential that sanitation programs are adequate and that thorough cleaning of all equipment takes place as needed. Finally, ingredients used in production of many products are potential sources of bacteria. All ingredients must be screened carefully; specific microbiological tolerances must be determined.

III. Characteristics of Foods That Affect Microbial Growth

Growth of microorganisms is greatly affected by many characteristics of their environment. Several of the factors influencing microbial growth and/or survival are inherent in the tissues of specific food products and are called intrinsic parameters. Others are characteristics of the storage environment and are called extrinsic parameters. Note that manipulation of only one of these parameters is hardly ever sufficient for controlling product spoilage, and combinations of parameters are far superior for purposes of food preservation. This is sometimes referred to as "hurdle technology;" the more hurdles an organism is required to overcome, the longer the quality of the food will be maintained.

A. Intrinsic Parameters

Moisture availability is a key factor in the growth of microorganisms and is defined in terms of water activity (a_w) of various substrates. The a_w of foods is the ratio of the vapor pressure of the food to the vapor pressure of pure water at the same temperature (pure water having an a_w of 1.00). Addition of solutes such as salt or sugar to foods decreases moisture availability or a_w. Microorganisms vary in their requirements for water. Generally, bacteria require more available moisture than fungi. Most spoilage bacteria are restricted at an a_w of 0.91, yeasts at 0.88, and molds at 0.80. These values are not strict thresholds, however, and certain xerophilic and halophilic organisms can multiply at lower levels. The most important pathogenic bacterium capable of growing in these dryer conditions is *Staphylococcus aureus,* which produces a disease-causing toxin. *Listeria monocytogenes* has also been demonstrated to survive in relatively high salt concentrations. The lowering of the a_w of a food reduces the rate of bacterial spoilage by extending the lag phase of cellular growth and decreasing the final numbers of bacteria attained. Since the typical a_w of most fresh foods is approximately 0.99, microorgan-

isms are readily supplied adequate moisture for rapid proliferation; therefore measures must be taken if shelf life extension is desired. Other parameters are usually focused on to slow deterioration. [*See* FOOD DEHYDRATION.]

The pH of foods is often manipulated for preservation and safety purposes. The development of acidity is the basis for the effectiveness of fermentation reactions in food preservation. Other products are directly acidulated or are naturally acidic, restricting bacterial growth. Bacteria flourish at pH close to neutral (i.e., pH 7.0). However, many can grow at or tolerate significantly lower and higher values. Lactic acid bacteria are used as starter cultures for their acid-producing abilities in many fermentations. Some members of this group, however, are spoilage organisms predominant in foods such as beer, wine, and vacuum-packaged meats. They can grow at pH values ranging from 3 to 10.5. Most of the commonly encountered pathogenic bacteria are restricted at pH ≤ 4.0. As with water activity, bacteria are the least tolerant to pH extremes (both low and high). Yeasts are more tolerant to low pH and can grow at pH values as low as 1.5. Molds are extremely resistant to adverse pH environments and grow over a pH range of 0 to 11. The pH of specific foods influences the type of spoilage that normally occurs. Fruits generally have a pH from 3.0 to 4.5 and undergo fungal spoilage. The majority of fresh vegetables, meats, fish, and dairy products range in pH from 5.0 to 7.0 and readily spoil by bacteria.

The oxidation–reduction potential (Eh) of a food system is influential in selecting the types of microorganisms present. In definition, Eh is a measure of the ease with which the substrate becomes oxidized or reduced and can be measured in millivolts. Positive Eh values indicate oxidized conditions whereas negative values indicate reduced conditions. Aerobic bacteria, yeasts, and molds favor positive Eh values and anaerobic bacteria require negative values. A large group of bacteria called facultative anaerobes and many yeasts can grow in either situation.

Microorganisms, like all other living organisms, require nutrients to grow. There are vast differences in the requirements for specific nutrients for specific microorganisms. However, all need water, energy, vitamins, minerals, and nitrogen to multiply. Foods differ in levels of these nutritional factors and in the chemical form in which they are presented, thereby selecting for specific groups of microorganisms. For example, only a few types of bacteria can adequately break starches into sugars for energy requirements.

Lack of specific vitamins in foods restricts growth to those organisms that have the ability to synthesize these vitamins. Molds have the least nutritional requirements, followed by yeasts and bacteria.

Many types of foods contain naturally occurring compounds and systems that retard bacterial growth. Several spices and their essential oils have demonstrated antibacterial and antifungal effects in numerous foods. These agents vary a great deal in their effectiveness against specific organisms or groups, and research data concerning their effects are often confusing. The concentrations applied, the media tested, the analytical approaches used, and the microorganisms evaluated contribute to these variances. Several spices, essential oils, and vegetable extracts display antimicrobial properties. Milk contains several components that have antibacterial properties. These include casein (predominant milk protein), lactoferrin, lactoperoxidase, lactotransferrin, lysozyme, and free fatty acids, all of which have been shown to inhibit both gram-positive and gram-negative bacteria. Eggs contain lysozyme, conalbumin (binds iron), and enzyme inhibitors that effectively restrict the growth of some bacteria.

Natural coverings of numerous food products offer inherent resistance to invasion by microorganisms. Just as our skin integrity is a formidable barrier that prevents infectious agents from entering our bodies, peels, skins, membranes, and shells protect certain foods. Rapid spoilage often occurs in products such as fruits, vegetables, nuts, and eggs once this initial barrier is disturbed.

B. Extrinsic Parameters

Of all factors affecting the stability of food products, storage temperature is the crucial element for the majority of products. Microorganisms can grow over a wide range of temperatures depending on the specific organisms. Some organisms can multiply at temperatures close to 0°C; however, foods stored at refrigerated temperatures (4–5°C) have significantly longer shelf lives. Most important pathogens in foods grow best in a range of 16–38°C. In food preparation, the "40–140" rule should be followed to help ensure food safety. This rule states that foods should be held below 40°F (4.4°C) or above 140°F (60°C) to preclude the growth of pathogenic bacteria, although this rule is not entirely foolproof. *Listeria monocytogenes, Y. enterocolitica,* and a few other pathogens can grow slowly below 40°F. Freezing of foods is very effective in preventing microbial spoilage; however, it is not a

process that will kill significant numbers of bacteria. Most organisms can resume growth once the product has been thawed.

The gas composition of the food's storage atmosphere has significant effects on rate and type of microbial growth. Modified and controlled atmosphere storage and packaging (MAP and CAP) are often used to increase the shelf life of foods. In these processes, air inside a package or storage area is altered by removal and/or replacement with higher levels of other gases. Carbon dioxide and nitrogen are most often utilized in MAP in various ratios. Aerobic bacteria, the most prevalent organisms in the spoilage of fresh products, are restricted and microbial populations tend to become more facultatively anaerobic. In general, these organisms grow more slowly and produce less offensive by-products, leading to longer storage capabilities. Vacuum packaging is a form of MAP that is extremely popular, especially in processed meats, and often leads to microbial dominance by lactobacilli. [*See* FOOD PACKAGING.]

Relative humidity affects the microbial spoilage rate of certain foods, especially for those products employing low water activity as a means of preservation. Packaging materials are very important in these types of products to prevent moisture gain. The type of product, in conjunction with relative humidity, must be considered when selecting packaging conditions. If humidity within the package or storage area is too low, some products will lose moisture, resulting in quality loss.

IV. Microbiological Food Spoilage

Food deterioration is inevitable, although we can completely sterilize foods using appropriate processing conditions such as extreme heat or high levels of ionizing radiation. Deterioration is defined as a reduction in product quality and can be depicted by nutrient loss, undesirable organoleptic changes, decreased safety, and decreased aesthetic attributes. These problems can arise from physical, chemical, and biological factors. Not all food spoilage issues are a result of microbiological agents. Enzymes, oxidation products, food component interactions, physical contaminants, and other nonbiological occurrences often cause food spoilage as demonstrated by lipids becoming rancid, light causing oxidation flavors in milk, and sugars and proteins causing browning. Biological agents do cause a tremendous amount of food spoilage. Insects, worms, and rodents are significant contributors to this category of spoilage. Microorganisms are first envisioned when one thinks about spoilage. An estimated 40% or more of the world's food supply is lost annually due to spoilage. Spoilage of foods is a natural occurrence and occurs at different rates depending on the type of food, the storage conditions, the types and numbers of microorganisms present, the type of packaging, and the presence of antimicrobial substances. For microbial spoilage to occur, five components must exist:

1. source of microorganisms
2. substrate to support microbial growth
3. available moisture
4. enough time to reach levels of organisms to cause spoilage
5. temperature conducive to microbial growth

Effective preservation practices must eliminate or manipulate some or all of these factors in foods. The fact that bacteria multiply in logarithmic fashion demonstrates the extreme importance of producing a food product that is initially of high microbiological quality. A product such as ground beef may spoil in 5 days if it initially contains 1,000 bacteria per gram, whereas spoilage would likely occur in approximately 3 days when initial levels of bacteria are 10,000 per gram. Storage temperature is equally important because of its effects on microbial generation times (time required for a bacterium to reproduce itself). Generally, generation times approximately double for every 18°F decrease in storage temperature.

Each category of food has its own broad group of microorganisms that tends to dominate and cause spoilage. Vegetables are very good substrates for yeasts, molds, and bacteria. They are normally high in moisture and contain proteins, carbohydrates, and other nutrients needed for microbial growth. Furthermore, the pH of most vegetables (pH 5.0–7.0) allows rapid bacterial growth by predominantly aerobic and facultatively anaerobic genera. Two classes of microorganisms are associated with vegetable spoilage. Saprophytic organisms invade vegetable tissues as a result of senescence (ripening), insect damage, or other types of loss in tissue integrity. Others are true parasites of plants and can invade healthy tissue and grow at the expense of the host. Soft rots, wilts, cankers, spots, specks, and blights are all forms of microbial spoilage of fresh vegetables. *Erwinia* and *Pseudomonas* species often cause soft rots as a result of their secretion of pectinases, enzymes that destroy tissue pectin. Other members of the Enterobacteriaceae group such as *Proteus, Serratia,* and *Escherichia*

can lead to rots and wilts. Certain fungal genera are agents of vegetable spoilage including *Botrytis, Geotrichum, Rhizopus, Phytophtora,* and several others.

Like vegetables, fruits contain almost all the nutrients needed for most microbial growth. However, unlike vegetables, bacteria are not ordinarily etiological agents of spoilage because the pH of most fruits ranges from 2.3 for lemons to approximately 5.0 for bananas, too low for bacterial growth. Yeasts and molds are by far the most obtrusive agents in fruit spoilage. In addition to the molds mentioned for vegetable spoilage, researchers have reported that approximately 30% of all fruit decay is caused by the blue-green molds *Penicillium italicum, P. expansum,* and *P. digitatum.* For fruits and vegetables, the most important factors to reduce spoilage are to have products with low initial microbial numbers, to store and handle the products where further growth and contamination is reduced, and to handle the commodities in a gentle manner to prevent damage to tissues.

Dairy products undergo rapid deterioration unless proper storage and processing conditions are utilized. Milk is contaminated by bacteria as it passes through the teat canal during milking of cattle and on subsequent handling. Since much of this contamination comes from an animal environment, pathogenic bacteria are a great concern in such products. The use of pasteurization greatly reduces the risk of illness from milk and other dairy products; however, some raw (unpasteurized) milk and dairy products are still used today and pose a significant health hazard. Pasteurization of milk does not provide a sterile product but is designed to eliminate pathogenic bacteria. Spoilage flora still remain and cause product deterioration on extended storage. Pasteurized and refrigerated milk spoils fairly rapidly. Raw milk contains an abundance of bacteria and, since milk is held at cooler temperatures, these tend to be dominated by psychrotrophic genera. *Lactococcus, Micrococcus, Streptococcus, Pseudomonas, Proteus, Bacillus,* and several other species are often encountered. A condition called ropiness is occasionally seen in raw milk held at cool temperatures for several days because of the production of a type of slime by *Alcaligenes viscolactis.* Other bacteria including strains of *Lactobacillus, Micrococcus, Streptococcus,* and *Escherichia* can also produce a ropiness. The production of lipases, enzymes that attack fats, by several bacteria leads to increased levels of short-chained fatty acids such as butyric acid, giving off-flavors and odors. *Pseudomonas fragi, P. fluorescens,* and *Achromobacter* species are frequent culprits for these problems. Pasteurization temperatures destroy many bacteria and thermotolerant genera of bacteria take charge in spoilage. *Bacillus*, *Lactobacillus*, *Lactococcus*, and *Streptococcus* species are most often encountered. Other dairy products such as butter, cheese, and yogurt also spoil but normally by microorganisms different than those found fluid milk. Butter can become putrid because of organisms such as *Pseudomonas putrefaciens* or rancid because of lipase production by *Pseudomonas* species, *Serratia marcescens*, and *Achromobacter lipidis*. Several types of fungi may attack butter, rendering it spoiled. Cottage cheese can spoil by bacteria including *Pseudomonas*, *Alcaligenes*, *Proteus*, and others that tend to cause a slimy curd, or by certain fungi such as *Geotrichum candidum* and *Penicillium* species. Other cheeses such as cheddar and colby may undergo gaseous spoilage by the sporeformers *Bacillus* and *Clostridium* which produce carbon dioxide. Gas production can also occur because of the growth of coliforms and yeasts in these types of cheeses. [*See* DAIRY PROCESSING AND PRODUCTS.]

Meats and seafood are notorious for their rapid spoilage characteristics because of the abundance of nutritional factors they supply for microbial growth and their relatively neutral pH. Unspoiled meats normally contain an abundance of bacteria representative of the natural environment of the animal or of microorganisms encountered in the processing environment. Spoilage flora, however, tend to be more homogeneous in nature, certain few species predominate depending on the type of meat, the type of storage, the antimicrobial treatments received, and the type of packaging. For red meats, animal slaughter is followed by cooling of the carcasses. If proper internal cooling is not achieved, species of Enterobacteriaceae and *Clostridium perfringens* can lead to spoilage. Properly cooled meats normally spoil because of surface bacteria. Fresh aerobically stored or packaged meats usually spoil because of growth of gram-negative pseudomonads. Other genera such as *Acinetobacter*, *Moraxella*, *Aeromonas*, and *Psychrobacter* are prominent in fresh meats. Fresh meat bacterial spoilage is characterized by the production of by-products, largely the diamines cadaverine and putrescine, from protein breakdown. Ammonia, hydrogen sulfide, and indole are other odorous compounds produced. Off-odors are generally evident when spoilage flora reach approximately 10^7 per gram; slime production occurs 10^8 per gram. When carcasses are aged in coolers for extended periods, mold can begin to grow on surfaces. *Mucor*, *Thamnidium*,, and *Cladosporium* are common fungal agents. [*See* MEAT PROCESSING.]

Vacuum packaging of meats drastically alters the spoilage flora leading to domination by lactobacilli and *Brochothrix thermosphacta*, although other flora including *Serratia*, *Shewanella*, *Leuconostoc*, and *Yersinia* can dominate in some instances. Spoilage usually becomes evident at microbial levels of 10^6 per gram. Processed meats such as bologna, sausage, and frankfurters usually spoil by bacteria and yeasts with characteristic greening, slime production, or souring. A majority of these types of spoilage are a result of lactobacillal and enterococcal growth. Cured meats undergo processes such as salting and smoking that restrict bacterial growth. Therefore, molds tend to be the major spoilage organisms for products such as bacon and cured hams. Bacteria can, however, cause problems in such products leading to souring and gas production. Hams are pumped with curing solutions that can carry bacteria into the interior of the meat. Sours can be caused by species of *Clostridium*, *Acinetobacter*, *Lactobacillus*, *Streptococcus*, and others, whereas gassiness is usually caused by clostridia species.

Poultry is mostly spoiled by pseudomonads; genera such as *Corynebacterium*, *Flavobacterium*, *Acinetobacter*, and certain yeasts also play more minor roles. Fresh fish spoils predominantly as a result of *Pseudomonas*, *Moraxella*, *Achromobacter*, and *Acinetobacter* contamination. The ratio of these particular bacterial populations is largely influenced by the microbiological species present in the waters from which the fish are harvested. [*See* POULTRY PROCESSING AND PRODUCTS.]

Many other types or categories of foods have differing etiologic agents of spoilage. Jay (1992) provides extensive coverage of spoilage phenomena of most food groups.

V. Foodborne Illness

There is uncertainty about the actual number of food-related incidences of illness in the United States. This is even more true throughout the world, because in many instances sanitation problems, lack of inspection, and improper handling of foods occur at high frequency. In the United States, the Food and Drug Administration has estimated the annual incidence of foodborne disease to be between 25 and 81 million cases, costing as much as 8.4 billion dollars. It is believed that as many as half of all diarrheal incidences in the United States can be attributed to consumption of contaminated foods. All these figures are merely estimates by the Centers for Disease Control and Prevention in Atlanta, Georgia, or by other scientific groups, since many of the illnesses go unreported because the brief and relatively mild symptoms resemble the flu or a stomach virus, and no professional medical attention is sought.

Figures seem to estimate that foodborne diseases are on the increase. Many reasons can be hypothesized for these increases. Probably the primary contributing factors are our heightened awareness of the problem, improved methodologies for isolation and identification of disease agents, and better reporting and epidemiological strategies. The evolution of different and more resistant strains of pathogens also seems to be occurring. This has been documented with incidences involving *Salmonella* and other pathogens. The population and its eating habits have undergone a tremendous metamorphosis during the last few decades. Individuals tend to live longer today than they did 10 years ago and, with this increased longevity, comes decreased immunity. Diseases such as AIDS and other illnesses that result in poorly functioning immune systems render individuals much more susceptible to foodborne disease organisms. Infectious doses of pathogens for this segment of the population are substantially lower than infectious doses for healthy individuals. A vast majority of foodborne disease outbreaks occur because of improper handling and preparation at the point of consumption. Most of the time, this is a result of improper cooking or storage of foods or is caused by cross-contamination after proper preparation. As life-styles change, more people are regularly eating at restaurants, which have a history of causing larger illness outbreaks because of the numbers of people eating from the same prepared dish. Another likely factor is the trend for "natural" foods that contain no preservatives or that are produced through the use of organic farming methods. No preservatives means no antimicrobial additives, and bacteria may be able to perpetuate at a higher rate. Organic farming uses no chemical pesticides or fertilizers and relies on natural methods such as manure or sludge fertilization, both of which have a natural propensity to harbor organisms that are pathogenic to humans.

Microbial foodborne poisoning is a result of ingesting a food containing a preformed chemical toxin produced during prior microbial growth in the product or of ingesting the live microorganisms contained in the food, with subsequent growth within the body. These types of food poisoning are called intoxications and infections, respectively. A brief discussion of some of the more common microorganisms involved in human disease will be provided. However, the author suggests reference to Jay (1992) and Jones (1992) for more detailed presentations.

A. Foodborne Intoxications

Foodborne intoxications result from ingestion of exotoxins formed in foods by growth and metabolism of specific types of microorganisms. Exotoxins refer to toxins that are excreted by particular organisms into their environment without requiring the rupture of the cell itself. Most of these toxins are proteins produced by gram-positive bacteria. One of the most frequent of all foodborne illnesses is *S. aureus* food poisoning. This facultatively anaerobic bacterium is common in the environment and is often found on human hair and skin or in the nasal passage. Introduction of this bacterium into foods occurs easily by infected food handlers during preparation. Most outbreaks occur during the period from June to December when picnics, church and club socials, and other warm-weather group events are held. Delis, school cafeterias, and restaurants are frequently implicated in outbreaks. *Staphylococcus aureus* and other strains produce heat-stable enterotoxins (seven distinct types have been observed) that react with the intestinal lining, causing violent gastroenteric symptoms including a very rapid onset (usually within 4 hr; ranges from 1 to 6 hr), nausea, sweating, headache, vomiting, severe stomach cramping, and prostration. A drop in body temperature can occur. Symptoms can persist for up to 72 hr, but death is a rare occurrence. Estimations in the United States suggest over 1.5 million cases occur annually. Foods most likely to be contaminated are those of animal origin or those extensively handled by humans. Meats and meat salads, cream-filled pastries, lunch meats, poultry and egg products, and potato salads are most often implicated in disease outbreaks. Note that cooking is not a means of ensuring food safety regarding staphylococcal food poisoning. If the organism has been afforded the opportunity to grow and produce toxin prior to heating, high temperatures will kill all live staphylococci but the toxin will not be destroyed. Analysis of suspected foods may reveal no *Staphylococcus* bacteria, and only methods designed to detect the toxin itself are applicable. Proper holding temperatures for both raw and cooked product, accompanied by good personal and kitchen hygiene, are the most effective ways to prevent this kind of poisoning.

Botulism invokes a sense of fear in almost all knowledgeable people. This is the most severe of all food poisonings and is caused by the gram-positive, anaerobic, sporeforming bacterium *Clostridium botulinum.* The disease was first recognized as long ago as 1793 in Germany; however, other diseases documented over 1000 years ago were likely to be botulism. This microbe produces the most toxic biological substance known; 1 oz pure toxin is capable of killing 200 million people. These neurotoxins are polypeptides produced within the *C. botulinum* cell and released by autolysis of the cells. Eight toxin types can be encountered; toxins A, B, and E are most important in foods. Many of today's food preservation principles are established to ensure against the growth and toxin formation of *C. botulinum,* including the addition of nitrate to meats, the time and temperature combinations mandated for canning, and the acidification of some foods. Generally stated, toxin production does not occur under pH conditions less than 4.6; however, certain conditions such as the growth of mold in tomato juice have been demonstrated to allow toxin production at lower pH values. Substantially more botulism cases occurred in the past because of the popularity of home canning. Today there are usually fewer than 50 reported cases annually in the United States. Concern in the food industry arises in products that are vacuum packaged, salted and/or smoked (e.g., smoked fish), packaged using modified atmospheres, and previously heated followed by packaging in air-tight containers. These processes often eliminate competing microflora and, with anaerobic or semi-anaerobic conditions, can allow clostridial growth. After ingestion of foods containing the botulism toxin, symptoms will occur in 10–72 hr and are manifested as nausea, vomiting, dizziness, and headache initially. The severity of symptoms proceeds to dryness of mouth and throat, constipation, muscle paralysis, double vision, and respiratory failure (ultimately death if untreated). A mortality rate from 30 to 65% is not unusual. Foods, especially those processed, containing high moisture contents and stored under anaerobic conditions should be of concern to producers and consumers. Luckily, thorough cooking does destroy the toxin. Refrigeration of foods is not a complete safeguard against *C. botulinum* since some strains can grow at 3.3°C. Infant botulism is a condition that occurs when an infant ingests spores of *C. botulinum* that germinate in the intestinal tract and produce toxin. This can be a severe disease leading to infant death. Products such as honey and syrup should not be given to infants under 1 yr of age since these products often contain these environmental spores.

Several molds produce toxins (mycotoxins) that are of importance in food products. Of most concern are the aflatoxins produced by *Aspergillus flavus, A. parasiticus,* and *A. nominus;* these are considered probable human carcinogens. Aflatoxins demonstrate extreme toxicity in laboratory animals; liver cancer is a common outcome of chronic ingestion. Aflatoxin is highly regulated in the United States. Action levels are set at 0.5 ppb in milk and 20 ppb in other human foods. Feed for animals is also regulated. Other mycotoxins include fumonisins (*Fusarium moniliforme*), zearalenone (*Fusarium* species), trichothecenes (*Fusarium, Trichoderma,* and others), ochratoxins (*Aspergillus* and others), citrinin (*Penicillium citrinum* and *P. virdicatum*), and patulin (*Penicillium* and *Aspergillus* species).

B. Foodborne Infections

Many of the most familiar types of food poisoning are termed infections and require the actual ingestion of live organisms. Depending on the specific pathogen and the susceptibility of the individual, the infectious dose required to initiate illness can be as few as 10 organisms to more than 1 million. Many of these infectious agents are gram-negative bacteria that produce illness by producing endotoxins that are released on cell lysis. The endotoxin acts as an exogenous pyrogen that ultimately causes fever in the infected host. Only a brief coverage of these infectious bacteria will be attempted. Readers are again referred to Jay (1992) and Jones (1992) for excellent detailed discussions of particular organisms.

Listeria monocytogenes is a gram-positive rod-shaped bacterium of great concern in foods because of its possible disease manifestations in certain population segments. The majority of individuals would only exhibit flu-like symptoms with *L. monocytogenes* infection; however, severe conditions such as meningitis, abortion, and stillbirth can occur. Cheeses and other dairy products have commonly been implicated, especially unpasteurized products, as have various meat products and raw vegetables. At present in the United States, there is a zero tolerance for this organism in cooked products. An important characteristic of this pathogen is its ability to grow at refrigeration temperatures. Proper cooking will destroy *L. monocytogenes* and is the critical factor for safety assurance. It would be wise for women to abstain from eating raw vegetables, soft-type cheeses, and uncooked processed meats during pregnancy.

Salmonella is a common cause of foodborne illness; estimates exceed 2 million annual cases at a cost of approximately 1.5 million dollars in the United States. Over 2000 pathogenic serotypes of this gram-negative bacterium exist. Symptoms are typified by general gastroenteritis within 12–24 hr of ingestion. The infective dose varies (1–10 million cells); however, the very young and elderly or immunosuppressed persons are much more susceptible, contributing to as many as 2000 deaths annually. The organism is associated with almost all animal products, but meats and poultry are of most concern. However, many other products including apple cider, chocolate, and melons have been implicated in illness.

Concern for two very important gram-negative bacteria has continued to increase in recent years. *Campylobacter jejuni* is now considered to be the most common cause of gastroenteritis requiring medical treatment, with an estimated annual incidence of over 4 million and a cost of up to 1 billion dollars. Poultry, meat, and raw milk products are the usual culprits of infection. Symptoms of gastroenteritis occur in 2–5 days. Severe diarrhea, often containing blood, is characteristic of the disease. A common occurrence is the infection of school children taking field trips to local dairy farms and consuming unpasteurized milk. *Escherichia coli* is of great concern at present. Media attention focused on disease outbreaks occurring in 1992 and 1993 from undercooked contaminated meats has forced the Food Safety and Inspection Service of the Department of Agriculture to re-evaluate the entire meat inspection system. This uproar was brought about by a specific strain, *E. coli* 0157:H7, which produces a cytotoxin that leads to hemorrhagic colitis or, more severely, hemolytic uremic syndrome and thrombocytopenic purpurea. Foods of animal origin are most suspect for the 0157:H7 strain; however, apple cider and contaminated water have also caused outbreaks. Ground meat products are implicated with the highest frequency; proper cooking (to 157°F internally) is the major safety measure. Many other strains of *E. coli* have been associated with disease and are classified as enteropathogenic, enterotoxigenic, enteroinvasive, or enterohemorrhagic. In countries with poor sanitation programs, *E. coli*-produced diarrhea is a major cause of mortality.

This discussion has in no way covered all bacteria of concern in food products. Other prominent agents of foodborne illness include *Bacillus cereus*, *C. perfringens*, *Shigella*, *Aeromonas hydrophila*, *Vibrio cholerae*, *V. parahaemolyticus*, and *Y. enterocolitica*. Other bacteria such as *Plesiomonas shigelloides*, *Citrobacter*, *Entero-*bacter, *Providencia*, and pathogenic streptococci may prove to be more common causes of foodborne disease than previously believed. We cannot forget viruses, which have only recently been receiving their deserved attention as foodborne problems. Hepatitis A, Norwalk virus, polio virus, and enteroviruses are among those associated with foods and often originate from infected food preparers or foods from contaminated environments (such as oysters). Other forms of foodborne disease such as histamine poisoning and illness from certain fish toxins are sometimes encountered.

VI. Food Preservation and Processing

Practically every form of food undergoes some type of preservation practice, if nothing more than simple washing or refrigeration. Certain preservation principles are ancient and include drying, salting, fermentations, and snow-packing. Many of these ancient technologies remain in practice, although in most cases conditions are highly optimized to better ensure proper results. Consumers have grown to expect foods to be available throughout the year, to have reasonably long shelf lives, and to be pathogen free. In many foods and beverages, chemical preservatives are added to prevent or delay bacterial or fungal growth. Most of these substances are considered by law as food additives and are highly regulated under the Food Additives Amendment (1958) to the Food, Drug, and Cosmetic Act of 1938. Salt, nitrite, sulfite, and numerous organic acids find common use as antimicrobial agents; however, many other compounds are also used (see discussion by Branen *et al.*, 1990). These chemicals, along with chemicals used for other functional purposes, are continually scrutinized for their effects on human health and on their effectiveness in specific food-dictated situations against certain organisms. Generally, antimicrobials are either cidal to specific organisms or extend the lag phase of growth. [*See* FOOD PRESERVATIVES.]

Packaging is a critical element in food preservation. Many products are packaged to eliminate certain bacterial groups such as aerobes. Aseptic packaging is a revolutionary method of processing that heats product, usually liquid or pureed, to high temperatures and subsequently cools it and fills it into presterilized containers. This is only one of several techniques utilizing heat to destroy bacteria. Retorting is the term for commercial canning that eliminates all vegetative bacterial cells, providing a commercially sterile product. These processes are defined in terms of D value, which is the time required at a specific temperature to destroy 90% of bacteria present. For canning processes for low acid foods (pH > 4.6), a 12-D process is mandated to ensure that the minimum heat process will reduce the probability of survival of *C. botulinum* spores to 1 in 10^{-12}. Pasteurization is a process used for many products that is designed to eliminate pathogenic organisms while reducing levels of spoilage flora. Milk is the most commonly pasteurized product; heating is to 63°C for 30 min or to 72°C for 15 sec (high temperature, short time, HTST). Several other products are pasteurized, including juices, some meats, egg products, wines, and beer.

Numerous other methods of preservation are utilized. Some of these are becoming much more sophisticated. For example, genetic engineering of products has allowed them to resist disease, stay firmer during processing and storage, or resist molding in the field or in storage. Biocontrol of spoilage is gaining popularity. The use of competitive exclusion in poultry-growing operations to out-compete pathogenic organisms is an example. Also, fermentations are a form of biocontrol since the use of specific cultures and their metabolites restricts many spoilage and pathogenic species. Furthermore, many organisms such as lactic acid-producing cultures produce natural antimicrobials such as bacteriocins that have specific antagonistic properties. Food irradiation has been a controversial topic for some 40 years; however, vast amounts of research data indicating its safety are leading to the irradiation of more products to control spoilage and pathogens. Irradiation is approved for numerous products in 37 countries. Just recently, the process was approved for fresh poultry products in the United States. [*See* FOOD IRRADIATION.]

VII. Other Important Aspects and the Future

This brief overview of the very integrated and complex science of food microbiology is not meant to be all inclusive. Fermentations and biotechnology in the food industry are themselves exciting and innovative disciplines, as are the closely related topics of processing plant sanitation and quality control. The government is becoming increasingly involved in food safety; programs such as Hazard Analysis and Critical

Control Points (HACCP) will undoubtedly continue to improve the safety of American foods and imported foods. A critical issue, especially for ensuring the safety of meat products, is the continued development of improved methodologies for the isolation of specific pathogens of concern. During the past decade, technologies such as enzyme-linked immunosorbent assay (ELISA) tests and DNA probing have revolutionized microbiological detection of pathogens from foods. However, an abundance of work remains to develop methodologies such as those needed for HACCP programs that provide definitive answers specifically, accurately, economically, and in a short time. In food microbiology, it seems that when one problem is answered, another surfaces. This is constantly occurring with so-called "emerging" pathogens such as *E. coli* 0157:H7, only realized as a pathogen since 1982, and with the development of new processing technologies such as the *sous vide* process in Europe. Without doubt, the roles of food microbiologists will continue to expand. [*See* PLANT BIOTECHNOLOGY: FOOD SAFETY AND ENVIRONMENTAL ISSUES.]

Acknowledgment

This material is based on work supported by the Cooperative State Research Service, U.S. Department of Agriculture, under agreement No. 89-34187-4511. Contribution No. 94-285-B Kansas Agricultural Experiment Station, Manhattan, Kansas 66506.

Bibliography

Branen, L. A., Davidson, P. M., and Salminen, S. (1990). "Food Additives." Marcel Dekker, New York.

Concon, J. M. (1988). "Food Toxicology-Contaminants and Additives." Marcel Dekker, New York.

Fung, D. Y. C., and Matthews, R. F. (1991). "Instrumental Methods for Quality Assurance in Foods." Marcel Dekker, New York.

Jay, J. M. (1992). "Modern Food Microbiology," 4th Ed. Chapman & Hall, New York.

Jones, J. M. (1992). "Food Safety." Eagan Press, St. Paul, MN.

Pierson, M. D., and Stern, N. J. (1986). "Foodborne Microorganisms and Their Toxins: Developing Methodology." Marcel Dekker, New York.

Vanderzant, C., and Splittstoesser, D. (1992). "Compendium of Methods for the Microbiological Examination of Foods." American Public Health Association, Washington, D.C.

Food Packaging

AARON L. BRODY, *Rubbright●Brody, Inc.*

Glossary

Blow molding Process of extruding a thermoplastic into a tubular shape followed by injection of pressurized air to expand the still hot plastic tube to conform to the shape of an external mold which is in the form of a bottle or jar

Cartons Three-dimensional package structures usually manufactured from paperboard; sometimes used to describe three-dimensional package structures made from corrugated fiberboard

Corrugated fiberboard Three layers of paper consisting of two outer flat liner sheets connected by fluted internal medium sheet at the peaks of the flutes; provides a structure with impact and vertical stacking strength

Extrusion Process of melting thermoplastic materials and forcing them by pressure through a die to form film, sheeting, or a three-dimensional package such as a bottle

Flexographic printing Printing process in which ink in a solvent base is placed on top of elevations in rubber or rubberlike materials on cylinders; the ink is transferred from the peaks to the substrate as the cylinder rotates

Form/fill/seal Packaging machines which begin with roll stock flexible packaging materials which unwind and are drawn around a device which forms them into a tube; simultaneously, a seal is made along the longitudinal edge and product is introduced into the tube and transverse seals are made at the ends to complete the package

Hot filling Food preservation process in which high-acid (i.e., pH <4.6) food is heated to temperatures of up to 95°C to destroy most microorganisms, and is filled into heat-resistant packages where the hot fluid food destroys most microorganisms on the package interior; cooling of the sealed package leads to condensation of the steam and creation of a partial vacuum

Injection molding Plastic-forming process in which hot fluid thermoplastic material is forced by pressure into matched metal molds which are cooled to set the plastic after it has been fully injected

Kraft paper Paper manufactured from virgin pulp derived directly from trees by sulfate process; usually a strong paper as implied by the name Kraft, the German word for strong

Orientation Process of stretching thermoplastic film or sheet to align the polymer molecules thus enhancing the tensile strength and impact resistance of the resulting material; uniaxial orientation is stretching in one direction only and biaxial involves stretching in two directions to further improve physical properties; orientation is also applied to improve the physical properties of plastic bottles

Pearlized Films such as oriented polypropylene whose continuity has been interrupted by voids or cavities thus imparting a pearllike appearance as well as other properties

Rotogravure printing Printing process in which ink in a solvent base is drawn into recesses in a cylinder and released from these tiny cavities onto the substrate to be printed as the cylinder rotates

Shrink film bundling Enclosing a product or package in a thermoplastic film and applying heat to the film to shrink the film tightly to the contents

Stretch film bundling Wrapping a product or group of packages with a plastic film capable of stretching during the wrapping and adhering to itself so that it ties the contents together in much the same manner as a rubber band

Tentering Transverse stretching of plastic film to impart cross-directional orientation to toughen the film, making it more resistant to tearing and slightly improving its barrier properties

Thermoforming Process of forming plastic cups, tubs, and trays by heating thermoplastics to their softening point and then forcing them into open molds by vacuum or pressure or both and then cooling the mold to set the plastic

Food packaging has a primary function of protecting the contents against physical damage, losses of volatile constituents, and biological deterioration, and secondarily to facilitate distribution of the product from the source to the consumer. It should also identify and assist in the marketing of the product. Food packaging must perform these functions at minimum total system cost because the package itself usually has relatively little intrinsic value to the consumer.

I. Introduction

Packaging assists product preservation by reducing infestation, contamination, and recontamination, and thus spoilage; resists pilferage and tampering; makes economical use of distribution space; and conserves labor in both distribution and marketing. Packaging fosters effective marketing of the food through our current dominant self-service retailing channels. [*See* FOOD MARKETING SYSTEMS.]

The term packaging deals not only with the materials in contact with the product which serve as the "primary" barrier but also with secondary and unitizing distribution packages, structure, equipment and staffing to marry the package to the food, end-use, total costs, and the ultimate disposal of the spent material.

The food's physical and chemical characteristics determine the protection required to slow or prevent its quality loss and/or deterioration. The distribution system influences the product's quality and therefore imposes requirements for its protection. To be effective in its distribution function, the food package also must be attractive, convenient, and identifiable to the consumer. Total systems economics including materials, labor, and damage loss together must be low. Equipment for integrating the package material and the food must be available, efficient, and in total, economic. Now, food packagers must consider overtly the disposal of the food package after use by the consumer.

To comprehend the protection function, the deteriorative mechanisms must be comprehended. Food deteriorates by means of biochemical, enzymatic, microbiological, and physical mechanisms. The biochemical vector is the result of interactions of inherent food chemicals because of their proximity and reactivity with each other, and is usually only by temperature reduction and/or by oxygen or water vapor access reduction. Enzymatic changes are biochemical actions catalyzed by naturally occurring enzymes, and are difficult to alter by packaging. Microbiological deteriorations, i.e., from yeasts, molds, and bacteria, are the most common food spoilage vectors due to naturally present entities, and can, in extreme circumstances, be of public health concern. Thus, microbiological control is a packaging function, in part. [*See* FOOD MICROBIOLOGY.]

Physical changes are usually due to gain or loss of water and damage arising from impact, stress, etc. Elevated water activity in dry food increases the rate of internal biochemical reactions and so water must be kept from such foods. In foods with high water contents such as fresh leafy vegetables, water loss radically changes the physical characteristics; excess gain of moisture can lead to favorable conditions for microbiological growth. In a physical sense, one key function of food packaging is to ensure against gain or loss of water. Many biochemical activities are increased by oxygen in the air, and so air exclusion is yet another packaging function.

Most deteriorative reactions are accelerated by increasing temperatures, a variable not usually directly mediated by packaging. [*See* FOOD PRESERVATIVES.]

II. Packaging Requirements of Specific Foods

Fresh food products include meats such as beef, pork, and poultry; vegetables, and fruits that are unprocessed or limited to trimming and cleaning. Fresh or minimally processed foods should be consumed rapidly after harvest, catch, or kill, and thus should be handled in a manner to retard quality loss and spoilage which is relatively rapid at ambient temperature, and slowed by temperature reduction.

Commercially, fresh meats and fish are chilled rapidly to below 50°F (10°C) before or after packaging or both. Most fresh vegetables and fruits, except for those injured by chilling, are reduced in temperature to below 40°F (4.4°C) by exposure to cold air, water, or ice.

Minimally processed foods include those which have been altered in a minor way to facilitate their distribution or use and to help retard quality losses, but which are still subject to rapid quality loss if not carefully handled. Most dairy products for example must be refrigerated after the mild heat of thermal pasteurization; salt and nitrite cured meats also must be kept cold after processing to ensure against microbial growth, because neither product segment is sterile or necessarily free of enzymatic activity.

Processed foods are those which have received intensive thermodynamic action intended to achieve long-term shelf life without microbiological deterioration at room temperature, and include almost all canned, frozen, and dried foods.

III. Fresh Foods

A. Meat

Fresh meats include beef, lamb, veal, pork, poultry, and fish, all of which are highly susceptible to microbiological, enzymatic, and physical deteriorative changes.

1. Beef and Pork

The main objectives of red meat preservation are to retard microbiological spoilage, enzymatic changes, and weight loss through evaporation, and to deliver red color at consumer level.

In distribution, after cutting, beef and much pork are usually packaged under reduced oxygen/temperature conditions in high oxygen/water vapor-barrier flexible materials to retard moisture loss and microbiological growth. Fresh meats are distributed to retail at temperatures below 50°F (10°C) to retard microbiological growth. The natural color of meat pigment is purple while the bright red color of the freshly cut meat is an oxygenated oxymyoglobin. At retail level, exposure to oxygen from air restores the consumer-desired bright red oxymyoglobin color. Oxygen-

permeable flexible packaging such as plasticized polyvinyl chloride (PVC) film overwraps employed at retail permits oxygen into the package to generate the bright red color while retarding the loss of moisture.

2. Poultry

Poultry is susceptible to microbiological deterioration and is also a substrate for the growth of potentially pathogenic *Salmonella* microorganisms. It is therefore essential that temperature be reduced as rapidly as possible after slaughter. Packaging at plant level in the United States is in bulk low-density polyethylene or plasticized PVC films which retard moisture loss. The poultry is then often further master packed in polyolefin film bags as secondary packaging. Sometimes vacuum is drawn and/or carbon dioxide is added to further retard microbiological and oxidative enzymatic spoilage.

3. Fish

Fish, which is usually contaminated with microorganisms, is packaged to retard water loss but not microbial growth. Package material for frozen fish, a common distribution method, generally is low moisture permeability to permit long-term distribution without freezer burn, i.e., surface desiccation. Polyethylene-coated paperboard cartons and moisture barrier flexible films such as polyethylene usually are employed to package frozen fish.

IV. Fresh Fruit and Vegetables

The major deteriorative vector for fresh fruit and vegetables is enzymatic. Nevertheless, fresh produce suffers from the presence of microorganisms on the surface. Physical damage to the produce can provide channels through which the microorganisms can enter to initiate microbiological spoilage which is increased by the normal enzymatic activity of the tissues. [*See* POSTHARVEST PHYSIOLOGY.]

Fresh produce packaging is often in bulk in a variety of traditional wood crates and corrugated fiberboard cases waxed to protect both the fiberboard and the produce from moisture gain. Bulk produce is often repackaged at retail level in gas-permeable flexible materials such as PVC. Increasingly, cut produce is factory packaged in polyolefin film to generate internal modified atmosphere to extend chilled shelf life.

V. Minimally Processed Food

Minimally processed food products are subject to microbiological spoilage and so still require refrigeration in distribution.

A. Cured Meats

Ham, bacon, frankfurter, etc., are cured with salt and nitrite to reduce their water activity and to suppress microbiological growth even under refrigeration. Cured meats have refrigerated shelf lives measured in weeks in an absence of oxygen. Most cured meats are packaged under reduced oxygen on thermoform/vacuum/gas flush/seal equipment, usually using high oxygen-barrier nylon-based package materials, and distributed under refrigeration. Some nitrite cured meats are packaged in gas-barrier film under nitrogen after oxygen removal to avoid the pressure of vacuum packaging. The reduced oxygen which is maintained by the gas-barrier packaging also reduces deteriorative oxidative reactions such as lipid rancidity.

B. Dairy Products

Heat pasteurization destroys disease microorganisms in dairy products, but not necessarily all of the microorganisms that could cause spoilage, and so pasteurized dairy products are almost always distributed under refrigeration unless they undergo further processing such as conversion to cured cheese. [See DAIRY PROCESSING AND PRODUCTS.]

Extrusion blow-molded high-density polyethylene bottles or polyethylene-coated paperboard gable top cartons are usually used for packaging and distributing pasteurized fluid milk in the United States. In Canada, flexible pouches made from medium density polyethylene are used for fluid milk packaging.

In aseptic packaging, the milk is thermally sterilized in heat exchangers and packaged under sterile conditions in high gas/water vapor-barrier paperboard/aluminum foil/plastic laminations or all plastic gas/water vapor package materials which are sterilized by chemical means independently. The two components meet in a sterile environment where the package is filled with the product and hermetically sealed to produce a packaged sterile milk which may be distributed at ambient temperature without microbiological deterioration.

Cheeses are microbiologically fermented milk products which are subject to further microbiological deterioration if not packaged and distributed properly. Cheese products are maintained under refrigeration in hermetically closed flexible gas/moisture-barrier plastic, or polystyrene or polypropylene cups or tubs or trays. Much cured cheese is packaged under nitrogen or nitrogen/carbon dioxide to help retard oxidative spoilage.

Ice cream is usually milk fat plus sugar and is not subject to microbiological deterioration because the below-freezing-point distribution and use temperatures are too low for microbiological growth. Ice cream packaging is generally minimal: polyethylene extrusion-coated paperboard cartons, polyethylene-coated paper (for novelties), molded polystyrene or high-density polyethylene tubs or, for bulk, spiral wound composite polyethylene-coated paperboard tubs or cartons.

VI. Fully Processed Foods

Processed foods are those treated and packaged so that their ambient temperature shelf lives can be indefinite from a microbiological standpoint, although biochemical changes can limit high-quality retention periods.

A. Canned Foods

Canning extends shelf life by imparting thermal energy to destroy microorganisms and enzymes. Sterility is maintained by hermetic sealing in gas- and moisture-impermeable packaging such as metal cans or glass jars that preclude recontamination. The resulting food is fully cooked as a result of the thermal exposure. [See THERMAL PROCESSING: CANNING AND PASTEURIZATION.]

Whether a metal can or glass jar is used as the package, air that can cause oxidative damage and internal pressurization is removed. Air removal, however, leads to an internal anaerobic condition which can permit the growth of pathogenic *Clostridia* microorganisms if they survive the heat process or enter by recontamination. The package is hermetically sealed and then heated, sometimes under pressures of up to one atmosphere. The package must be able to withstand up to about 212°F (100°C) temperature for high-acid products (<pH 4.6) and up to 260°F (127°C) for low-acid products (>pH 4.6) which must receive added heat to destroy heat-resistant pathogenic microbial spores such as *Clostridia*. The thermal process is calculated on the basis of the time required for the most difficult-to-heat element of the packaged food to achieve a time–temperature integral that will destroy *Clostridia* spores. After reaching that temperature, the package must be cooled rapidly to retard further cooking and consequent deterioration. To achieve this heating cycle, the package is often subjected to pressure and pressure differentials as well as temperature which it must withstand.

Packages for canned foods must exclude air, withstand heat and pressure, and maintain their hermetic seals during processing and distribution.

Attempts have been made to thermally sterilize in gas-barrier flexible plastic or plastic composite pouches or trays: the flexible retort pouch, for example, has a higher surface-to-volume ratio of aluminum foil lamination than a rigid metal can and employs a fusion heat seal rather than the mechanical closure of the can or jar. Semi-rigid retort trays fabricated from gas-barrier plastic have higher surface-to-volume ratios than cylindrical cans and are generally heat-seal closed. Plastic cans intended for heat sterilization and subsequent microwave reheating by consumers have bodies constructed from multi-layer high oxygen-barrier plastic plus double-seam easy-open rigid aluminum closures.

B. Frozen Foods

Freezing reduces the product temperature sufficiently that microbiological, enzymatic, and biochemical activities are essentially arrested. Whether the product is frozen inside or outside of the package, most freezing processes use high-velocity cold air or liquid nitrogen to remove the heat from the bulk unpackaged product or from packaged product.

Individually quick frozen (IQF) product (i.e., product frozen outside the package) is packaged after freezing in polyethylene-coated paperboard cartons, or polyethylene film or polyethylene-coated paper pouches. Frozen foods are susceptible to freezer burn damage due to internal water loss from the ice. Many prepared foods are packaged in microwavable packaging such as crystallized polyester trays or polyester-coated paperboard trays.

C. Dry Foods

Removing water from food products markedly reduces water activity and its subsequent biochemical activity, and thus also significantly reduces the potential for microbiological growth. [*See* Food Dehydration.]

Dry products include those directly dried from liquid form such as instant coffee, tea, and milk or engineered mixes of dried components. In the former, the liquid is spray, drum, or air-dried, or even freeze-dried, i.e., sublimation lyophilized, to remove water. Moisture can change physical and biological properties. Engineered dry products include beverage mixes such as blends of dry sugars, citric acid, color, flavor, etc.; and soup mixes which include dehydrated meat stock plus noodles, vegetables, meats, etc., which become a heterogeneous liquid on rehydration with hot water. Such products must be packaged in very moisture-resistant structures to ensure against water vapor entry which can damage the contents.

Products containing relatively high fat such as bakery or some soup mixes also must be packaged so that the fat does not interact with the packaging materials and ultimately become oxidized from exposure to air. Flavoring mixes that contain seasonings and volatile flavoring components can unfavorably interact with interior polyolefin packaging materials to scalp or remove flavor from the product if improperly packaged. Packages for dry products must be hermetically sealed; for example, provide a total barrier against access by water vapor, and, for products susceptible to oxidation, also exclude oxygen after removal of air from the interior of the package.

D. Lipid Products

Fats and oils may be classified as those with and those without water. Cooking oils such as corn or canola oil and hydrogenated vegetable shortenings contain no water and so are stable at ambient temperatures if properly treated otherwise to preclude rancidity.

Unsaturated lipids are susceptible to oxidative rancidity or the breaking of fatty acid chains at double-bond sites to form hydroperoxides and ultimately short chain and usually odorous aldehydes and ketones. Oils are more subject to oxidative rancidity than fats, but both are usually sparged with and packaged under nitrogen to reduce oxygen. Hydrogenated vegetable shortenings generally whipped with nitrogen are packaged under nitrogen in spiral wound composite paperboard cans to ensure against oxidative rancidity. Edible liquid oils are packaged in injection blow-molded polyester bottles and extrusion blow-molded PVC bottles usually under nitrogen.

Margarine and butter and analogous bread spread products consist of fat plus water and water-soluble ingredients which contribute flavor and color to the product. Often, these products are distributed at refrigerated temperatures to assist in quality retention. Fat-resistant packaging such as polyethylene-coated paperboard, aluminum foil/paper laminations and parchment paper wraps, and polypropylene tubs are used to package butter, margarine, and similar bread spreads.

E. Cereal Products

Dry breakfast cereals generally are sufficiently low in water content to be susceptible to water vapor absorption and so require good moisture- as well as fat-barrier packaging. Further, packaging should retain the product flavors. Breakfast cereals are usually packaged in coextruded polyolefin films fabricated into pouches or bags inserted into or contained within printed paperboard carton outer shells. Sweetened cereals are packaged in aluminum foil or gas-barrier plastic films or laminations to retard water vapor and flavor transmission.

Soft bakery goods such as breads, cakes, and muffins are highly aerated structures and are subject to dehydration and staling or internal starch hardening. In moist environments, baked goods are often subject to microbiological deterioration as a result of surface growth of mold and other microorganisms. To retard water loss, good moisture barriers such as coextruded polyethylene film bags or polyethylene extrusion-coated paperboard cartons are used for packaging.

Hard baked goods such as cookies and crackers generally have low water but high fat contents. Water, however, can be absorbed, so that the products can lose their desirable texture properties and become subject to oxidative or even hydrolytic rancidity. Package structures for cookies and crackers include fat- and moisture-resistant coextruded polyolefin film pouches within paperboard carton shells and thermoformed polystyrene trays overwrapped with polyethylene or oriented polypropylene film. Soft chewy cookies are packaged in high moisture-barrier laminations containing aluminum foil to improve the barrier.

F. Salty Snacks

Snacks include dry cereal or potato products such as potato and corn chips, and pretzels, and include roasted nuts, all of which have low water and high fat contents. Snack food packaging problems are often compounded by the presence of flavorings such as salt, a catalyst for lipid oxidation. Snacks are usually packaged in flexible pouches made from oriented polypropylene or polyester to provide low moisture transmission and now sometimes metallized for enhanced barrier. Snack food producers depend on rapid and controlled product distribution to minimize fat oxidation. Some salty snacks are packaged under nitrogen both in pouches and in rigid containers such as spiral wound paperboard composite cans to extend shelf life. Generally, light which catalyzes fat oxidation, harms snack products, and so opaque packaging is often employed.

G. Candy

Chocolate, a mixture of fat and nonfat components such as sugar, is subject to slow flavor change. Ingredients such as nuts and caramel are susceptible to water content variation. Chocolates, which are generally shelf stable at ambient temperatures, are packaged in fat-resistant papers and moisture/fat barriers such as pearlized polypropylene film.

Hard sugar candies are flavored amorphous sugars which are very hygroscopic because of their extremely low moisture contents. Sugar candies are packaged in low-moisture-transmission packaging such as unmounted aluminum foil or oriented polypropylene film.

H. Beverages

Beverages may be classified as still, carbonated, alcoholic, or nonalcoholic. The largest quantity of packaging in the United States is for beer and soft drinks, both of which contain dissolved carbon dioxide which generates internal package pressure. Thus, the package must be capable of withstanding the internal pressure of carbon dioxide especially due to temperature increases in distribution. Aluminum cans and glass and polyester plastic bottles are the most commonly used packages for beer and carbonated beverages.

Beer is more sensitive than other carbonated beverages to oxygen, loss of carbon dioxide, external off-flavors, and light. Most American beer is thermally pasteurized after closure. Thus, the internal pressure within the package can build up to over 100 psi at 145°F (63°C), a usual pasteurization temperature. Beer and other carbonated beverages are generally packaged at very high speeds, often in excess of 2000 units per minute, which means that the packages must be free of defects and dimensionally uniform.

Still beverages include water which requires very low odor packages, and fruit juice and drinks which usually require low oxygen packaging to reduce oxidative flavor and color deteriorations and hot filling to reduce the microbiological population. Hot filling at temperatures of about 190°F (90°C) can generate reduced oxygen and reduced pressure which the package must withstand.

VII. Packaging Materials and Processes

Many different package materials and converting processes are needed to produce a broad range of packaging to accommodate the wide variety of food packaging applications: paper, metal, glass, and plastic, in cans, bottles, pouches, trays, cups, etc.

A. Paper

Paper consists primarily of cellulose fibers most often derived from wood. The packaging properties of paper, i.e., its strength, and mechanical properties, depend on the selection of the fiber sources, their treatment, and the incorporation of fillers and binding materials at the paper mill. Whatever physicochemical properties paper and paperboard possess, such as minimum permeability to vapor and gases, fat resistance, etc., are derived from mill impregnation with additives or plastic, surface coating, and/or laminating. Materials used to enhance paper barrier include plastic coatings with polyethylene and blended resins such as urea formaldehyde. Most packaging papers offer little more than protection from light and mechanical damage.

Paper may be converted into flexible packaging or as base structural material for construction of semi-rigid containers. Flexible packaging applications include multi-wall bags, pouches, and overwraps. Some of the important types of paper used for bag purposes include virgin Kraft or sulfate paper, greaseproof papers, and glassines. Glassines are made of Kraft paper fibers, highly supercalendered to deliver smooth surfaces capable of accepting coating and print, and to be fat resistant.

Semi-rigid paperboard containers are constructed from paperboard which is paper greater than 0.010 in. (0.254 mm) in gauge (caliper) and include folding cartons, corrugated fiberboard cases, and spiral wound composite cans. Many paperboard cartons require the use of inner liners or overwraps, made usually from coextruded plastic or aluminum foil laminations.

B. Folding Paperboard Cartons

Paperboard folding cartons are intended to protect food products from impact and crushing. Certain dense or easily flowing dry products such as rice or pasta can be retained in position by the paperboard carton structure. Generally, folding paperboard cartons by themselves are used to contain less than 3 lbs. of food. Paperboard for packaging food not in contact with the food contents may be made from recycled paper and paperboard. Such structures have an interior virgin flexible material liner that prevents direct contact between the product and the recycled paperboard of the carton and thus avoids potential food contamination.

Carton liners such as coextruded polyolefin film pouches help prevent loose product sifting and moisture migration. Polyethylene extrusion coatings cover the interior or exterior of paperboard folding cartons if they are used to contain liquids as with heat-sealable gable top milk and juice and juice drink cartons. Plastic extrusion coatings can be used with paperboard cartons when higher levels of water/moisture protection are required.

C. Composite Paperboard Cans

Composite paperboard cans usually are either spiral or convolute wound paperboard or paperboard aluminum foil-laminated bodies with seamed metal, mechanically affixed paperboard, or heat-sealed flexible closures. The can usually has a printed paper label covering the entire body. Composite paperboard cans using aluminum foil interior are used for packaging refrigerated biscuit and cookie doughs, some salty snackfoods, juice concentrates, and hygroscopic dry powders. Convolute wound cans are used for cocoa powder, roasted and ground coffee pouches, and candy.

D. Distribution Cases

Most food products in the United States are distributed in corrugated fiberboard cases engineered to meet governmental regulation specifications. Corrugated fiberboard is the most widely used material for tertiary or distribution packaging. Printed, cut, and fabricated into boxes or trays, corrugated fiberboard forms the distribution protection entity.

Polyethylene shrink film wrapping of corrugated fibreboard trays is less common in the United States than in other countries. Equipment erects trays, fills the trays with primary packages such as cans, jars, or cartons, wraps the grouping in polyolefin shrink film, and heat shrinks the combination. Shrink film wrapping keeps primary and secondary packaging materials clean and dry.

VIII. Metal Cans

Most cans are aluminum for beer and carbonated beverages, with two- and three-piece steel cans usually used for food and still beverage packaging.

A. Two-Piece Cans

Almost all aluminum and some steel cans are two piece, i.e., a cylindrical body with a mechanically seamed closure.

Two-piece can manufacturing starts with a coil of metal fed into a cupping press, which forms the sheet into shallow cups which are fed into an ironing press, where successive rings draw the can body side wall. Interior coatings to protect both metals with the coatings are applied by a spray gun. After application, the cans are baked to remove the solvent and cure the coating.

B. Three-Piece Cans

Most steel cans, whether or not tin-plated, are three-piece, i.e., a body and two ends. For welded side-seam cans, sheets of steel are coated, baked to cure the coatings, and slit into body blanks. The cut blanks are fed into the bodymaker and the blank is formed into a cylinder with the edges overlapped at the side seam and tack welded. The cylinder is then passed between electrodes which weld the edges together. Side-seam coating coverage is achieved by applying an epoxy material to both sides of the hot side seam after welding. Residual heat from the weld fuses and cures the stripe coating.

At a flanger, the top and bottom edges are curled outward to form the "flange." Roll or die-necking now reduce the can body diameter at the end to reduce end material use. When the flanged or necked and flanged three-piece can bodies leave the flanger after top coat spraying, they go to a double seamer, where one end is applied.

C. Protective Coatings

Interior can coatings limit interactions between cans and their food contents. Exterior can coatings may be used to provide protection against the environment, or as decoration. Coatings are applied to the steel blanks in the flat before fabrication. Because of the metal deformation with surface coating disruptions which occur in draw and ironing operations, such containers must be coated internally after fabrication.

Among the internal coatings for food containers are oleoresinous, vinyl, acrylic, phenolic, and epoxy-phenolic materials. Two basic methods are used for the application of protective coatings to metal containers: roller coating and spraying. Roller coating is used if physical contact is possible, i.e., for sheet and coil. Spraying techniques are used if physical contact is not possible, i.e., two-piece cans. Coatings are heated in a forced convection oven after application for solvent removal, oxidation, and/or polymerization.

More recently, polyester and polypropylene films have been laminated to base steel sheet to impart protection to the metal of two-piece drawn cans.

D. Environmental Aspects

More than two-thirds of aluminum cans in the United States are returned from the field for recycling into cans. Not only does recycling save on the mass of materials, it also saves energy.

Because of the vast quantities of scrap steel available from automobiles and appliances, recycling of steel cans has been growing at a relatively modest rate. Nevertheless, up to 30% of steel cans are now returned from the waste stream into useful applications.

IX. Glass Packaging

Glass is silica sand, combined with sodium carbonate and calcium carbonate, with stabilizers such as aluminum oxide. Glass is recyclable, and so cullet from crushed glass is a part of almost every raw material batch.

Glass is virtually chemically inert and impermeable. Coatings protect the original high strength of glass containers and retard strength deterioration. In hot end treatments in glass fabrication, newly formed hot bottles and jars are subjected to an atmosphere of vaporized metallic compounds which react with the glass surface by chemical bonding, resulting in a coating which provides permanency to the "cold end" treatment.

Another protective coating applied after the cooling section of the bottle or jar annealing lehr, usually at a bottle temperature about 300°F (149°C), is a polyethylene emulsion. The purpose of the second coating is to impart lubricity to the container surface to reduce abrasion and other strength-reducing surface damage from bottle-to-bottle or bottle-to-guide rail contact during normal handling.

The mixture of materials for glass container manufacture is prepared in unit batches. Mixing is critical since complete homogeneity of the batch is necessary to produce quality glass. Cullet which must be of the same color and basic composition as the glass to be melted is added to the batch. The cullet must also be free of contamination such as metal bottle caps, tramp metal, etc.

Press and blow operations are used to produce wide-mouth containers and in recent years, narrow neck containers including beer bottles. The difference between the press and blow operation and the blow and blow operations is that the parison is pressed to shape by a plunger that fills the complete void in the parison replacing the settle, blow, and counterblow operations. The rapid transfer of heat and the mechanics of blowing the glass create both thermal and mechanically stresses in the newly formed bottle. To relieve the stresses, the newly formed bottles undergo heat annealing processes.

X. Plastic Packaging

Most plastic packaging materials are thermoplastic, i.e., reversibly fluid at high temperatures and solid at ambient temperatures. Plastic materials may be modified by copolymerization, blend additives, alloying, and/or surface treatment.

A. Low-Density Polyethylene (LDPE)

Slightly cloudy, with high tensile-strength and good moisture-barrier properties but high gas permeability, LDPE film is employed for shrink and stretch bundling and pallet wrapping, as drum and case liners for bulk foods, and to package bread, fresh vegetables, and fruit, and stable food products. LDPE may also be extrusion blow molded into soft-sided or squeeze bottles. More LDPE plastic resin is used than any other for food packaging.

LDPE density for film ranges from <0.90 to approximately 0.93 g/cm^3. To make film, the resin is melted in a heated hollow barrel and converted to film by extruding through a circular or slot die. Tubular film material is collapsed and slit into film ranging in gauge from less than 0.25 to above 0.75 mm. Because of its extensibility, LDPE film is usually printed on central impression-drum flexographic presses, but modern presses permit rotogravure printing.

B. Linear Low-Density Polyethylene (LLDPE)

Films from LLDPE resins have 75% higher tensile and 50% higher elongation-to-break strengths than films from LDPE resins and a higher but broader heat-seal initiation temperature. Impact and puncture resistance are also improved but moisture and gas permeation properties are similar to those of LDPE films.

Linear low-density polyethylene films are used in many of the same packaging applications as LDPE with thinner gauges.

C. High-Density Polyethylene (HDPE)

High-density polyethylene resins range in density from 0.93 to 0.96 g/cm^3. HDPE films are more translucent and stiffer that LDPE films, with moisture and gas permeabilities slightly higher than those of LDPE. Softening and melting points are high, and they are not easily sealed on flexible packaging equipment.

High-density polyethylene film is produced by blown-film extrusion methods.

The most important packaging use for HDPE, however, is for extrusion blow molding of milk, water, etc., bottles.

High-density polyethylene coextrusions with ethylene vinyl acetate copolymer or ionomer to deliver heat-seal properties are widely used as liners in paperboard food cartons.

D. Polypropylene (PP)

Polypropylene film may be produced as unoriented (CPP) or oriented (OPP) films. Because of poor cold-temperature resistance and a very narrow, short, heat-seal temperature range, CPP film is not widely used for packaging. In film form, the material is a good heat sealant for packages that have high temperature requirements. Coextrusions of PP/PE and CPP are used to separate sliced cheese produced by extruding directly on film. CPP film is used as a transparent bag material, as twist wrap for candy, and in other applications.

Oriented polypropylene film (OPP), a widely used food package material, may be classified into heat-set and nonheat-set, blown and tentered, coextruded, and coated. Orientation improves the heat resistance and other physical properties. Biaxially oriented heat-set oriented polypropylene film (BOPP) is used to wrap soft and dry bakery products, as lamination plies for potato and corn chip pouches, and for packaging pastas and for numerous other pouch and wrapping applications. Nonheat-set OPP is often used as a transparent shrink-film overwrap for printed paperboard cartons of candy, serving as a moisture barrier and a means to enhance esthetic appeal.

Oriented polypropylene film may be manufactured by blown or slot-die extrusion processes. In the slot-die or tenter-frame process, polypropylene film is extruded through a flat die and stretched in the machine direction. Gripped along its edges, the film is stretched laterally during longitudinal motion to impart transverse directional orientation. To impart heat-seal and other desirable properties, the film may be coated with acrylic or PVDC resin or extruded with another polyolefin. In the blown film orientation process, the resin is extruded through a circular die and reblown to produce a biaxially oriented, heat-set film.

Almost all OPP producers today have expanded the core of the film, creating a foam structure with lower density, greater opacity, and a stiffer more paperlike feel, often designated pearlized polypropylene. Vacuum metallization of either transparent or opaque film enhances water-vapor-barrier properties.

Oriented polypropylene film has excellent water-vapor- but poor gas-barrier properties, excellent clarity, and good heat-seal properties in its many packaging applications.

E. Polyvinyl Chloride (PVC)

Highly plasticized PVC film is transparent and soft, with very high gas permeation, but low water-vapor transmission rates. PVC film is generally produced by blown-film extrusion, although casting and calendering are employed for heavier gauges.

The main packaging applications of PVC film are as an air-permeable, but moisture-impermeable, wrap for fresh red meat, poultry, and vegetables. Transparency combined with the ability to transmit air to maintain red meat color or to avoid respiratory anaerobiosis in fresh produce offer advantages in these uses.

F. Polyester (PET)

Polyethylene terephthalate polyester film possesses fairly food gas- and water vapor-barrier properties which can be enhanced by PVDC coating, very high tensile and impact strengths, and temperature resistance. Applications include as an exterior web in laminations to protect aluminum foil, coated with PVDC to function as the sealing web for vacuum/gas flush packaging of cured meat, cheese, or fresh pasta.

Polyester is manufactured by extrusion through a slot die and biaxially orientation by stretching first in a longitudinal and then in a transverse direction.

Polyester film is the prime substrate for vacuum metallizing and silica coating, processes that enhance moisture and gas properties. Vacuum-metallized polyester film is used for large pouch packaging wine and bulk tomato and fruit products, and for packaging snack foods.

G. Nylon

Nylons are thermoplastic polyamide materials which are fairly good oxygen barriers in film or sheet form. Nylon films are usually tough and thermoformable, but only fair moisture barriers.

Nylon films are usually used in lamination or coated form to ensure heat sealability and improve barrier properties. The major uses are as thermoforming webs for vacuum/gas flush packaging of processed meats and cheeses. Other uses include pouches for fresh red meat, boil-in-bag frozen foods, bag-in-box for wine, and the external layer for aluminum foil in cookie and vacuum coffee pouches.

H. Polyvinylidene Chloride (PVDC)

Polyvinylidene chloride (PVDC) is often known by its saran designation. As either a solvent or emulsion coating, PVDC imparts high oxygen, fat, aroma, and water-vapor resistance to film substrates such as oriented polypropylene, polyester, and nylon.

Among the major commercial resins and films, PVDC has the best total moisture and oxygen, aroma-, and fat-barrier properties. Unlike other high-gas-barrier materials, PVDC is almost insensitive to water and moisture.

By itself, PVDC film is used to wrap cheese and sometimes for vertical form/fill/seal chub packaging of sausage and ground meat. Mostly, however, PVDC is used as the high barrier component of laminations not containing aluminum foil. It is infrequently used alone in commercial packaging because of difficulty of heat sealing.

I. Polystyrene

Polystyrene packaging film is clear and stiff, and, because of high permeability to moisture and gas, it is suited for packaging fresh produce. Packaging applications are limited to folding-carton windows for appearance, and overwraps for tomato trays and lettuce wrapping, for gas permeation.

Foaming polystyrene resin by blending with gas delivers a low-density opaque sheet useful for beverage bottle and plastic can labels to substitute for paper, and as materials for thermoforming into trays for meat. Polystyrene sheet is a clear easily thermoformable material.

J. Coextruded Films

In coextrusion, two or more resin melts are extruded simultaneously and in parallel through the same die. Coextrusion permits intimate layering of precise quantities of functional materials. Incompatible plastic materials are bonded within the coextrusions with thermoplastic adhesive layers also coextruded. Coextruded films may be made by extrusion blowing or slot casting.

Among the relatively simple coextrusions, polypropylenes are coextruded with copolymer heat-seal layers and LDPE's are coextruded to impart toughness. HDPE, LDPE, and EVA resins may be coextruded to produce stiff, heat-sealable films for use as liners in cereal, cookie, and cracker cartons. Coextruded films of EVA and pigmented LLDPE are employed for packaging of frozen vegetables and fruits. In such applications, one layer imparts toughness, opacity, or stiffness, and the other heat sealability.

XI. Flexible Packaging

Flexible packaging is composed of both mono- and multilayer structures, with multilayer further subdivided into laminated, coated, and coextruded, or combinations of these.

Mono- and/or multilayer films may be adhesive or extrusion-bonded in the laminating processes. In extrusion lamination, a thermoplastic such as polyethylene is extruded as a bond between the two flat materials which are assembled between nip rolls.

Flexible materials are printed in roll form by rotogravure or flexographic or now web offset printing. The detail produced by rotogravure and web offset printing is finer than that produced by flexography. Rotogravure is usually used for long production runs and high-resolution reproduction, while flexography is usually used for shorter runs and bolder design. Both flexography and rotogravure are extensively used to print flexible package materials in the United States. Printed or extruded coatings applied on or off press protect the print surfaces.

Bag material is either small monolayer or large multiwall with paper as a substrate. Pouches are small and fabricated from laminations. Bags usually contain a heat-sealed or adhesive-bonded seam running the length of the unit and a cross-seam bonded in the same fashion.

Preformed bags are opened by the food packager, filled with food product, and closed by adhesive bonding, heat-sealing, metal clipping, or sewing.

Heavier gauge flexible materials, usually with nylon, are thermoformed in line into trays to vacuum or gas flush package cured meats or cheeses.

Large quantities of flexible packaging materials are employed on horizontal flow wrap form/fill/seal machines for unit packaging for candies, cookies, and crackers.

In horizontal form/fill/seal operations with face-to-face heat seals, the resulting pouches, usually aluminum foil laminations, are high moisture and oxygen barriers and used for packaging sensitive dry foods such as condiments and soup and beverage mixes.

Most flexible packaging material is used in vertical form/fill/seal applications to package loose, flowable products such as potato and corn chips, nuts, and roasted and ground coffee. Vertical form/fill/seal machines usually use moisture-barrier flexible materials.

In other applications, flexible materials are used to bundle multiples of cans, bottles, cartons, or cases and to bind the cases or bags on pallets.

XII. Rigid Containers

Most rigid plastic is used in bottles and jars fabricated by injection, injection blow, or extrusion blow processes.

Injection molding is used to fabricate closures, specialty packages, and polyester bottle preforms. In conventional injection molding, the plastic resin is melted in an extruder which forces a measured quantity or shot into a chilled mold. The pressure of the extruder forces uniform plastic distribution throughout the mold. Cooling the mold solidifies the plastic.

Cups and tubs for dairy products, specialty frozen food applications, and returnable distribution cases for carbonated-beverage and milk bottles are injection-molded from HDPE. High- and medium-density polyethylenes are injection-molded as snap-on reclosure covers for metal and paperboard composite can closures. Many bottle and jar closures are injection molded from polypropylene. High impact or rubber-modified polystyrene is injection molded for refrigerated dairy product and specialty food cup packaging.

Insert injection molding is used to manufacture snap-on closures for dairy product cups and tubs for yogurt and ice cream. In insert injection molding, a die-cut paperboard or flat plastic material is placed in the mold. The plastic is extruded around the insert to form a precision skeletal structure and hold the sheet in place.

Injection molding is used to prepare polyester preforms for blow molding into bottles (e.g., carbonated beverages) and jars (e.g., peanut butter). Resins such as polyester with narrow melt temperature ranges require sequential fabrication steps. A tube-shaped parison is injected at melt temperature and, after forming, precisely reheated for stretching or blowing into a bottle or jar.

Thermoforming includes the extrusion of sheet thicker than 0.25 mm, followed by forming the reheated sheet in an open-face mold by pressure or vacuum, or both. Sheet less than 0.25 mm gauge may be thermoformed in-line and filled with contents such as processed meats, cheeses, and pastas prior to sealing.

Thermoformable sheet may be mono- or multilayer with the latter produced by lamination or mainly by coextrusion. Multilayer sheets are employed to incorporate high oxygen-barrier materials between structural or high moisture-barrier plastics. Both ethylene vinyl alcohol copolymers and PVDC are used as high gas-barrier core layers, with polystyrene or polypropylene as the structural layers.

In steam-chest expansion, polystyrene resin in which gas is already present is molded with steam injection. The steam increases the temperature close to the melting point and expands within the structure to create beads with food cushioning and insulating properties. Expanded polystyrene is used for insulation in frozen food packaging and for hot cups such as used for dry soups.

Thermoforming is a common commercial method to convert sheet into packages. The sheet is heated to its softening point and is forced by air pressure into an open-top chilled mold where it solidifies. Conventional thermoforming of polystyrene and PVC is a widely used technique for producing tubs for dairy products and for cups and trays.

Thermoforming may be integrated with filling and sealing on thermoform/fill/seal machines operated by food packagers themselves. The base web is gripped and moved through heating and forming operations. The open-top units are filled and a second web of flexible material is sealed to the flange of the base after which the packages are severed.

Retortable multilayer barrier plastic cans and trays for low-acid foods may be hermetically sealed and thermally sterilized up to 260°F (125°C). Such high gas/moisture-barrier cans or trays are fabricated from five-layer coextrusions of PVDC or EVOH as the gas barrier with polypropylene as the structural and water vapor layer. Counterpressure and temperature during retorting must be carefully controlled to avoid can and seal closure distortion.

In conventional blow molding, a single extruder forces the plastic through a circular die to form a tubular parison to be delivered into the open mold. A tube is inserted through the neck opening and pressurized air is blown in to expand the plastic to the chilled walls of the mold.

Extrusion blow molding produces narrow-neck bottles from high- and low-density polyethylene. Incorporating EVOH as a high oxygen barrier with polypropylene permits coextruded bottles used for packaging tomato catsup, barbecue sauce, mayonnaise, pickle relish, and other foods.

Materials with a very narrow melt temperature range are formed into bottles by injection stretch blow molding. A test-tube shape is first formed by injection. This preform is transferred to the blow-molding machine and heated. The heated parison is transferred to a blow mold where it is stretched and blown to shape.

PET carbonated-beverage bottles are usually produced by injection stretch blow molding. Multilayer injection stretch blow molding has been commercialized for both narrow neck bottles and wide-mouth jars. The basic form may also be fabricated by injecting multiple layers such as polypropylene and EVOH plus adhesive or tie layers and blowing the parison. High oxygen-barrier cans with plastic bodies have been introduced. Cans containing polypropylene and EVOH in their structures are retorted after filling to resist retort temperatures up to 260°F (125°C).

Recognition of hot filling foods into plastic packaging, followed by sealing and cooling, has led to a need for high oxygen-barrier plastic containers capable of resisting temperatures up to 200°F (85°–90°C). Plastics with distortion temperatures above 212°F (100°C), e.g., polypropylene, may be filled with hot liquid without thermal distortion. On the other hand, polyester requires heat stabilization in which the container is molded and secured in the mold while at elevated temperature. Thus, the crystalline structure of the polyester is altered to resist moderately elevated temperatures. This technique is employed to produce PET bottles for hot filling products such as juices and juice drinks.

Bibliography

Anonymous (1980). "A Processor's Guide to Establishment, Registration and Process Filing for Acidified and Low Acid Canned Foods." FDA, HHS Publication 80-2126, U.S. Department of Health and Human Services.

Anonymous (1991). "Food Packaging Technology International 1991," Issue 4. Cornhill Publications Limited, London.

Aseptic Processing and Packaging of Foods (1985). IUFOST Symposium, Tylosand, Sweden.

Bakker, M. (ed.) (1986). "The Wiley Encyclopedia of Packaging Technology." Wiley, New York.

Benning, C. J. (1983). "Plastic Films for Packaging," Technomic, Lancaster, PA.

Briston, J. H., and Katan, L. L. (1983). "Plastics Films," 2nd. ed. Longman Scientific & Technical in association with The Plastics and Rubber Institute, Essex, England.

Broderick, H. M. (1982). "Beer Packaging." Master Brewers Association of America, Madison, WI.

Brody, A. L., and Shepherd, L. M. (1987). "Modified/Controlled Atmosphere Packaging: An Emergent Food Marketing Revolution," Schotland Business Research, Princeton, NJ.

Brody, A. L. (ed.) (1989). "Controlled/Modified Atmosphere/Vacuum Packaging of Foods." Food & Nutrition Press, Trumbull, CT.

Brody, A. L. (1987). Proceedings, International Conference on Controlled/Modified Atmosphere/Vacuum Packaging—CAP '87. Schotland Business Research, Princeton, NJ.

Brody, A. L. (1988). Proceedings, International Conference on Microwaveable Foods—Microready Foods, '88. Schotland Business Research, Princeton, NJ.

Brody, A. L. (1989). Proceedings, International Conference on Microwaveable Foods—Microready Foods, '89. Schotland Business Research, Princeton, NJ.

Gray, J. I., Harte, B. R., and Miltz, J. (eds.) (1987). "Food Product-Package Compatibility." Michigan State Univ. School of Packaging Seminar Proceedings, Technomic, Lancaster, PA.

Griffin, R., and Sacharow, S. (1982). "Food Packaging," 2nd ed. Avi, Westport, CT.

Griffin, R. C., Sacharow, S., and Brody, A. L. (1985). "Principles of Package Development," 2nd, ed. Avi, Westport, CT.

Hanlon, J. F. (1984). "Handbook of Package Engineering," 2nd ed. McGraw-Hill, New York.

Hotchkiss, J. (ed.) (1988). "Food and Packaging Interactions." ACS Symposium Series 365, American Chemical Society, Washington, DC.

Hsu, D. S. (1979). "Ultra High Temperature Processing and Aseptic Packaging of Dairy Products." Damana Tech., New York.

Jenkins, W. A., and Harrington, J. P. (1991). "Packaging Foods with Plastics," Technomic, Lancaster, PA.

Kadoya, T. (1990). "Food Packaging," Academic Press, San Diego, CA.

Lopez, A. (ed.) (1987). "A Complete Course in Canning—Book I. Basic Information of Canning. The Canning Trade, Baltimore, MD.

Lopez, A. (ed.) (1987). "A Complete Course in Canning—Book III. Packaging; Aseptic Processing; Ingredients." The Canning Trade, Baltimore, MD.

Lopez, A., (ed.) (1987). "A Complete Course in Canning—Book II. Processing Procedures for Canned Food Products." The Canning Trade, Baltimore, MD.

Osborn, K. R., and Jenkins, W. A. (1992). "Plastic Films—Technology and Packaging Applications." Technomic Lancaster, PA.

Paine, F. A., and Paine, H. Y. (1983). "A Handbook of Food Packaging," Leonard Hill, London.

Paine, F. A., and Paine, H. Y. (1983). "Principles of Food Packaging." Leonard Hill, London.

Paine, F. A. (ed.) (1987). "Modern Processing, Packaging and Distribution Systems for Food." Van Nostrand Reinhold, New York.

Reuter, H. (ed.) (1989). "Aseptic Packaging of Food." Technomic, Lancaster, PA.

Risch, S. J., and Hotchkiss, J. H. (eds.) (1991). "Food Packaging and Interaction, II." American Chemical Society Symposium Series 473, ACS, Washington, DC.

Robertson, G. L. (1993). "Food Packaging—Principles and Practice." Marcel Dekker, New York.

Sacharow, S., and Brody, A. L. (1987). "Packaging: An Introduction." Harcourt Brace Jovanovich, Duluth, MN.

Selke, S. E. M. (1990). "Packaging and the Environment—Alternatives, Trends and Solutions." Technomic, Lancaster, PA.

Swalm, C. M. (ed.) (1974). "Chemistry of Food Packaging." ACS Adv. Chem. Ser. 135, American Chemical Society, Washington, DC.

Food Preservatives

P. MICHAEL DAVIDSON, *University of Idaho*

I. Antibrowning Agents
II. Antioxidants
III. Antimicrobials

Glossary

Bactericidal/fungicidal Death of a bacterial or fungal population as demonstrated by the inability of cells to recover and multiply in a nutrient environment in the absence of an inhibitor

Bacteriostatic/fungistatic Inhibition of the most resistant cells of a bacterial/fungal population as indicated by a level or decreasing growth curve, often reversible

Food additives Chemical compounds added to foods directly or indirectly through production, processing, storage, or packaging that have an effect on the characteristics of the food. Food additives are generally added to maintain or improve nutritional value, maintain freshness, assist in processing or preparation, or improve sensory characteristics

Foodborne pathogens Microorganisms capable of causing food poisoning in humans. Food poisoning may result when microorganisms grow and produce toxins in the food. This is called an "intoxication." Bacteria such as *Clostridium botulinum* and *Staphylococcus aureus* cause intoxications. Food poisoning may also be caused by consumption of a food poisoning microorganism and subsequent growth of the microorganism in the gastrointestinal tract. This type of food poisoning is called an "infection." Examples of bacteria causing infections are *Campylobacter jejuni*, *Escherichia coli*, *Listeria monocytogenes*, *Salmonella*, and *Yersinia enterocolitica*

Food spoilage microorganisms Microorganisms which utilize nutrients in a food and produce off-flavors, off-odors, or undesirable color and texture changes. Various species of bacteria, molds, and yeasts are all capable of causing food spoilage

Generally recognized as safe (GRAS) Food additives which are judged to be safe for human consumption by experts qualified to evaluate toxicological safety. Bases for safety judgments come from (1) toxicological studies or (2) experience with safe use in foods; however, only those food additives in use prior to January 1, 1958, may be considered GRAS using the latter basis

Food preservatives are a class of direct food additive which maintain the appearance, palatability, and wholesomeness of various foods. The purpose of food preservatives is to prevent the degradation of products by oxygen or microorganisms. To protect a food from the effects of oxygen, an antibrowning agent or antioxidant may be used. These agents prevent or delay undesirable enzymatic browning or autoxidation reactions in food products. To protect a food from spoilage or pathogenic microorganisms, a food antimicrobial is used.

Neither class of food preservative is capable of concealing spoilage in a product. Rather, the purpose of these compounds is to extend the shelf-life of food. The food remains wholesome during its extended shelf-life. Neither class of compound will preserve a food indefinitely. Depending upon storage conditions, the food product will spoil or become hazardous. The benefits of food preservatives to food processors, those marketing food products, and consumers include extended shelf-life and reduction of potential health hazards. Food preservatives are regulated by agencies which deal with food products such as the Food and Drug Administration (FDA) and Department of Agriculture (USDA) in the United States.

I. Antibrowning Agents

A. Enzymatic Browning

Enzymatic browning occurs when certain fruits and vegetables are cut, peeled, or bruised. Fruits and vegetables such as apples, bananas, mushrooms, peaches, pears, and potatoes contain copper-containing enzymes known as phenolases (*also called*: polyphenol oxidase, tyrosinase, catecholase). When the tissue is cut or bruised, naturally occurring phenolic substrates react with the enzyme. In the presence of oxygen, phenolases catalyze the hydroxylation of monophenols to *o*-diphenols and subsequently oxidize *o*-diphenols to orthoquinones (Fig. 1). Orthoquinones are further oxidized and polymerized to form a brown and/or black pigment called melanin. Phenolic substrates for the reaction include tyrosine, caffeic acid, chlorogenic acid, and protocatechuic acid.

While enzymatic browning or blackening is desirable in some products such as black tea, cocoa, and cider, it is generally undesirable. Control of enzymatic browning in processed foods can be achieved by inactivating phenolases, chelating copper, or excluding oxygen. Physical processes, such as blanching with steam or hot water at temperatures above 70–75°C, may be used to inactivate the enzyme. However, blanching is used only for fruits and vegetables to be canned or frozen as it causes undesirable softening in fresh products. Storage under vacuum or immersion in salt brine, sugar syrup, or even water may be used to inhibit enzymatic browning by excluding oxygen. Chemical agents can also function to control browning by direct inactivation of the enzyme, by reduction of the pH to inactivate the enzyme, or through chelation of copper.

B. Antibrowning Agents

Citric acid (Fig. 2) and its calcium, potassium, and sodium salts inactivate phenolases by acting as acidulants to reduce pH. The pH must be reduced and maintained at 3.0 or less to inactivate the enzyme. In addition, citric acid chelates copper which is required by the enzyme as a prosthetic group. Citrates are considered multiple purpose GRAS food additives by FDA.

Sulfur dioxide and sulfite salts (Table I) cause irreversible inactivation of phenolases. The bisulfite ion (HSO_3^-) is the primary component which inactivates the enzyme. Sulfites, primarily as salts, are added to processed fruits and vegetables through sprays or dips. In addition to inhibiting enzymatic browning, sulfites are added to certain dehydrated fruits and vegetables to inhibit nonenzymatic browning during storage. The FDA considers sulfur dioxide and sulfite salts as GRAS for use as antibrowning agents and antimicrobials. However, sulfites are prohibited on fruits and vegetables to be consumed fresh. The reason for this action is that some consumers, especially asthmatics, have shown serious adverse reactions to bisulfites. Because they degrade thiamine (vitamin B_1), sulfites are not allowed in foods considered to be important sources of the vitamin in the human diet.

Ascorbic acid (Fig. 2) acts as a reducing agent by transferring hydrogen atoms back to quinones to produce dihydroxyphenylalanine (DOPA). It is also an oxygen scavenger. Ascorbic acid plus citric acid, in conjunction with vacuum packaging in gas-impermeable plastic film, controls enzymatic browning during storage of fruits and vegetables to be

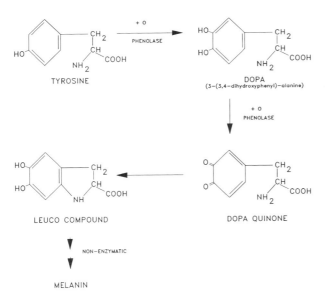

FIGURE 1 Selected steps in enzymatic browning. [Modified with permission from Schwimmer, S. (1981). "Source Book of Food Enzymology." AVI, Westport, CT.]

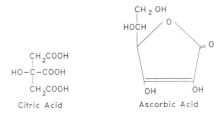

FIGURE 2 Structures of ascorbic acid and citric acid.

TABLE I
Sulfur Dioxide and Sulfite Salts Used in Foods

Name	Formula
Sulfur dioxide	SO_2
Sodium bisulfite	$NaHSO_3$
Sodium sulfite	Na_2SO_3
Sodium metabisulfite	$Na_2S_2O_5$

consumed fresh. The compound may be used to control browning in apples, peaches, apricots, potatoes, mushrooms, olives, and cauliflower. Ascorbic acid and its calcium and sodium salts are GRAS for use as food preservatives without limitation for the amount used.

II. Antioxidants

A. Autoxidation

Oxidation of lipids in edible oils and fat-containing foods leads to off-flavors and odors resulting in reduced shelf-life and spoilage. Lipid oxidation may also lead to loss of nutritional quality through degradation of essential fatty acids (linoleic and arachidonic acids), vitamin A and vitamin E. Autoxidation, or oxidative rancidity, is caused by a reaction between unsaturated fatty acids and oxygen and proceeds in three steps: initiation, propagation, and termination (Fig. 3). In the initiation step, free radicals are formed by metal catalysis, exposure to light, hydroperoxide decomposition, or by singlet oxygen ($^1O_2$). A free radical is formed when a hydrogen atom is removed from a double bond or a carbon at a position adjacent (α) to a double bond. The free radical can then react with oxygen to form a peroxy radical (ROO$^\cdot$). Peroxy radicals can react with other unsaturated fatty acids removing hydrogen atoms and forming hydroperoxides (ROOH) and new free radicals (R$^\cdot$). The new free radicals react with oxygen to form peroxy radicals and the cycle is repeated. Free radical formation is accompanied by shifts in the position of double bonds and results in several isomeric hydroperoxides. Hydroperoxides are relatively unstable and will decompose to more free radicals, alcohols, aldehydes, acids, ketones, hydrocarbons, epoxides, dimers, and polymers. The decomposition products of the hydroperoxides cause the off-flavors associated with oxidative rancidity. [*See* FOOD BIOCHEMISTRY: LIPIDS, CARBOHYDRATES, AND NUCLEIC ACIDS.]

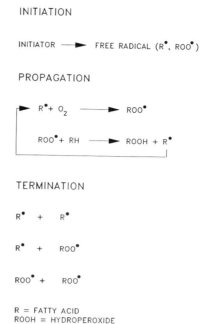

FIGURE 3 Steps in autoxidation. [Reprinted with permission from Nawar, W. W. (1985). Lipids. "Food Chemistry" *In* (O. R. Fennema, ed.), 2nd ed., p. 177. Copyright © 1985 reprinted with permission by courtesy of Marcel Dekker, Inc., New York, NY.]

Unsaturated fatty acids are more susceptible to autoxidation than saturated fatty acids. Fatty acids most susceptible to autoxidation, in decreasing order of susceptibility, are: arachidonic (5,8,11,14-eicosatetraenoic acid), linolenic (9,12,15-octadecatrienoic acid), linoleic (9,12-octadecadienoic acid), and oleic (9-octadecenoic acid). Free fatty acids are more susceptible to oxidation than those in acyl glycerols (e.g., triglycerides). The rate of autoxidation is influenced by oxygen concentration, temperature, surface area, water activity, presence of pro-oxidants (heavy metals), and radiant energy.

Antioxidants delay onset or slow the rate of autoxidation by inhibiting the formation of free radicals (initiation) or interrupting propagation. Initiation is inhibited through decomposition of peroxides, metal chelation, or singlet oxygen inhibition (free radical acceptors). The antioxidant is able to terminate free radical propagation by reacting with peroxy radicals which prevents the peroxy radical from reacting with another unsaturated fatty acid. Therefore, the production of a new free radical is stopped and the autoxidation reaction is delayed.

Multiple antioxidants or antioxidants used in combination with metal chelators often demonstrate synergism. This occurs when two compounds together show greater activity than the sum of the activities of the compounds alone. Mixed free radical acceptors show synergism when one is more effective than the other. This allows the more active free radical acceptor to donate a hydrogen to the fatty acid free radical. The less active free radical acceptor then donates a hydrogen to the more active of the pair causing regeneration of the more active species. Metal complexing agents act as synergists. Metals such as copper and iron are pro-oxidants, i.e., they increase the rate of oxidation through hydroperoxide decomposition, formation of free radicals, and activation of singlet oxygen. Metal chelators reduce pro-oxidation.

The effectiveness of antioxidants is dependent upon their oil solubility, volatility, and stability during processing. They must be oil soluble to have access to the free radicals. They must not be highly volatile or they may be lost in processing and they must be stable to the heat used in processing. The choice of antioxidant depends upon its ease of incorporation, carry-through, pH sensitivity, production of discoloration or off-flavors, availability, and cost.

B. Antioxidants/Synergists

Tocopherols (Fig. 4), which exhibit vitamin E activity, are the primary naturally occurring antioxidants in vegetable oils. They are fat soluble due to their long alkyl chains. Antioxidant effectiveness of the various forms of tocopherols in decreasing order of activity is: δ-tocopherol, γ-tocopherol, β-tocopherol and α-tocopherol. The vitamin E activity of tocopherols is inverse to the antioxidant effectiveness with α-tocopherol having the greatest activity. Tocopherols are free radical acceptors and become oxidized to quinones. They are somewhat heat sensitive and may be

lost during processing. Tocopherols are used in bacon, baked goods, butterfat, lard, margarine, rapeseed oil, safflower oil, and sunflower seed oil. These compounds are considered GRAS for use in foods as antioxidants without limitation to the concentration used.

Phenolic antioxidants are synthetic compounds. Butylated hydroxyanisole (BHA; MW = 180.0; Fig. 5) is the most common synthetic antioxidant and exists as the 2- and 3-isomers of tertiary-butyl-4-hydroxyanisole, with the 3-isomer predominating. Butylated hydroxytoluene (BHT; MW = 220.36; Fig. 5) is also known as 2,6-ditertiary-butyl-p-cresol. Tertiary butylhydroquinone (TBHQ; Fig. 5) and propyl gallate (PG; n-propyl ester of 3,4,5-tri-hydroxy-benzoic acid; Fig. 5) have molecular weights of 166.22 and 212.0, respectively. Solubilities of these compounds are shown in Table II. Phenolic compounds are good electron donors and therefore good antioxidants. Monohydric (BHA and BHT) and polyhydric (TBHQ, PG) phenolic antioxidants are relatively stable due to resonance delocalization and lack of positions suitable for attack by molecular oxygen. Hydroquinones (e.g., TBHQ) form stable semiquinone

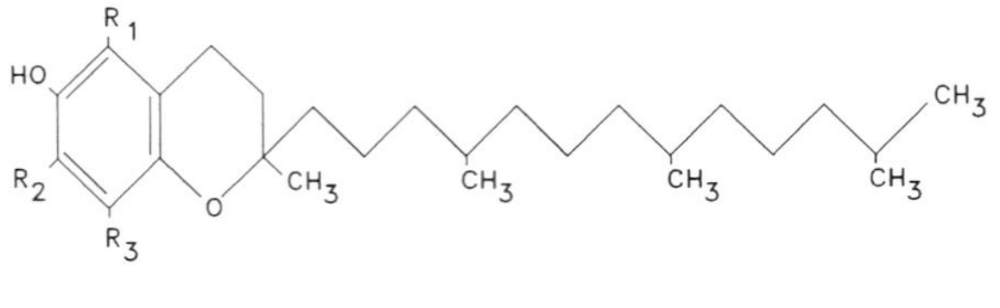

	R$_1$	R$_2$	R$_3$
Alpha–tocopherol	CH$_3$	CH$_3$	CH$_3$
Beta–tocopherol	CH$_3$	H	CH$_3$
Gamma–tocopherol	H	CH$_3$	CH$_3$
Delta–tocopherol	H	H	CH$_3$

FIGURE 4 Structures of tocopherols.

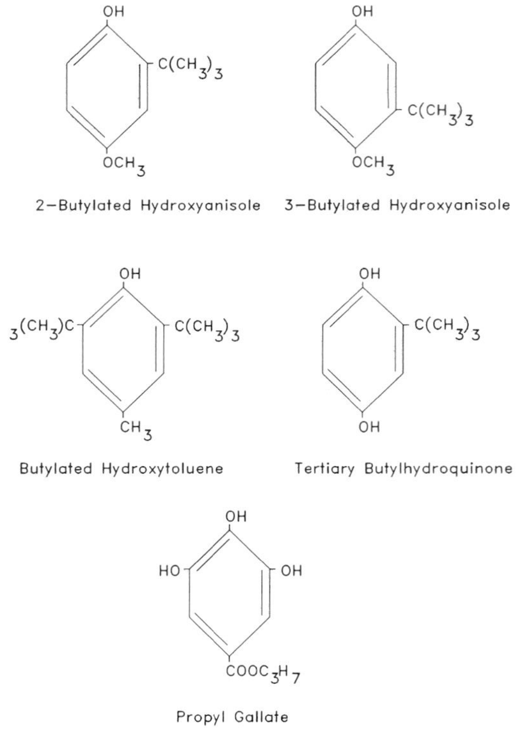

FIGURE 5 Structures of phenolic antioxidants.

TABLE II
Solubility of the Phenolic Antioxidants in Various Solvents

Solvent	Temp (°C)	Solubility (g/100 g)			
		BHA	BHT	TBHQ	PG
Water	25	Insol[a]	Insol	<1	<1
	95	—	—	5	—
Ethanol	25	>50	25	60	>60
Propylene glycol	25	70	—	30	55
Coconut oil	25	40	—	—	—
Corn oil	25	40	30	10	Insol
Cottonseed oil	25	30	—	10	1
Peanut oil	25	40	30	—	<1
Soybean oil	25	50	30	10	2[b]
Lard	50	50	—	5	1
Tallow	25	—	40	—	—
Safflower oil	25	—	—	5	—

[a] Insol, insoluble.
[b] At 85°C.

resonance hybrids (Fig. 6). Monohydric phenolics are sterically hindered which further reduces initiation following hydrogen donation and have radical intermediates with moderate resonance delocalization. In the United States, BHA, BHT, and PG are GRAS for use in food at a maximum concentration of 0.02% based on the weight of oil or fat content of the food. In addition to approval in the United States, phenolic antioxidants are approved for use in foods in at least 60 other countries. Butylated hydroxyanisole, BHT, and TBHQ are also permitted for use as direct food additives for specific food uses. For TBHQ, regulations permit use alone at 0.01% in animal or poultry fat or 0.02% in nonanimal fats or oils with BHA or BHT (based on weight of fat or oil). Phenolic antioxidants can be used to delay oxidation of lipids in vegetable oils and animal fats (tallow, lard). These compounds are used in meats, such as beef, poultry, and pork sausage, to prevent odor and flavor changes and in confections, nuts, gum bases, food flavors, citrus oils, fried foods, baked goods, and dehydrated potatoes to prevent oxidation. Phenolic antioxidants

may be applied directly to breakfast cereals or used in the packaging of these products.

Ascorbic acid (Fig. 2) and its sodium and calcium salts act as oxygen scavengers by removing oxygen from solution. The compounds also act as reducing agents by transferring hydrogen to oxygen making it unavailable for further reactions. Ascorbates are also synergists with other antioxidants by acting as metal chelators. The ascorbates are GRAS for use in foods in the United States. Ascorbates may be used in beer, citrus oils, fats and oils, food flavors, fruit drinks, nuts, peanut butter, potato chips and soft drinks to delay oxidative rancidity. Ascorbyl palmitate (6-O-palmitoyl-L-ascorbic acid) is a fat soluble ester of ascorbic acid which is also GRAS. It may be used as a synergist with tocopherols and is used primarily in vegetable oils.

Citric acid (Fig. 2) and its sodium, potassium, and calcium salts are metal chelating agents that act as synergists with antioxidants. Salts of ethylenediamine tetraacetic acid (EDTA) are metal chelators and act as synergists in emulsion (fat/water) type products such as salad dressings, mayonnaise, and margarine.

Natural antioxidants exist in many foods and include spices, herbs, tannins, flavonoids, wood smoke compounds, and nonenzymatic browning products. Ground rosemary and rosemary extracts are used in some countries as antioxidants in lard, potato chips, and vegetable oils.

III. Antimicrobials

Microorganisms, including bacteria, molds, and yeasts, are capable of reproducing in food products. Viruses and protozoa are also found in foods but are generally only carried by the food product. One of the primary objectives of food processing is to destroy or inhibit the growth of foodborne microorganisms which cause spoilage or food poisoning. There are a number of methods which have been developed to preserve foods from the effects of microorganisms.

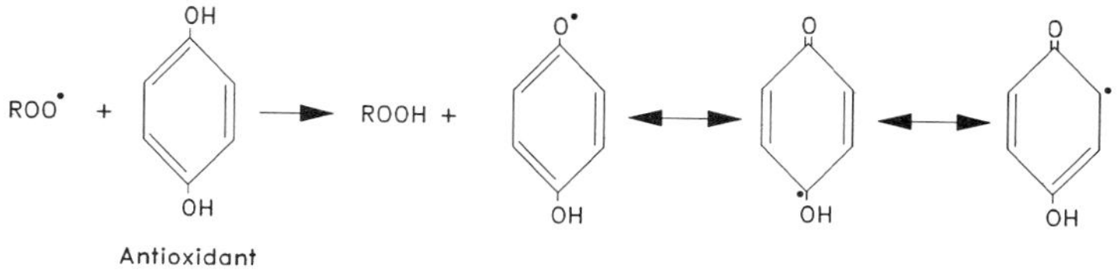

FIGURE 6 Resonance forms of a hydroquinone antioxidant.

Physical methods are designed to kill or delay growth of microorganisms in foods and include heat (e.g., pasteurization, canning), freezing, refrigeration, reduced water activity (use of humectants or drying), irradiation, modified atmosphere packaging, and pH reduction. [*See* FOOD MICROBIOLOGY.]

Food antimicrobials are used in foods as a barrier to the growth of food spoilage and pathogenic microorganisms. These compounds are generally only bacteriostatic or fungistatic and not bactericidal or fungicidal. Food antimicrobials are most often used with other preservation techniques such as refrigeration, modified atmosphere packaging, pH reduction, reduced water activity, or fermentation.

The most universally important factor influencing the effectiveness of food antimicrobials is pH. Many food antimicrobials are weak organic acids and are most effective in their undissociated form. This is most likely because they are able to penetrate the cytoplasmic membrane of a microorganism more effectively in this form. Therefore, the pK_a value (pH at which 50% of the acid is undissociated) of these compounds is important in selecting a particular compound for an application. The lower the pH of a food product, the greater will be the proportion of organic acid in the undissociated form and the greater will be the antimicrobial activity. The initial number of microorganisms in and storage conditions of a food product also greatly influence the effectiveness of an antimicrobial.

A. Acetic Acid/Acetates

Acetic acid (Fig. 7) is the primary component of vinegar. The acid and its sodium, potassium, and calcium salts, sodium and calcium diacetate, and dehydroacetic acid (methylacetopyronone; $C_8H_8O_4$) are some of the oldest food antimicrobials. Because the pK_a of acetic acid is 4.75, it is more effective as an antimicrobial at low pH. Acetic acid is inhibitory to a wide variety of bacteria, molds and yeasts. Only *Acetobacter* species (microorganisms involved in vinegar produc-

tion) and lactic acid bacteria are tolerant to the effects of acetates. Species of both gram-positive and gram-negative bacteria are sensitive to acetates. Bacteria inhibited by acetic acid under a variety of conditions of pH, temperature, and acid concentrations include *Bacillus* species, *Clostridium* species, *Listeria monocytogenes*, *Salmonella*, *Staphylococcus aureus*, *Escherichia coli*, *Campylobacter jejuni*, and *Pseudomonas*. Molds and yeasts, which generally tolerate lower pH than bacteria, are relatively more resistant to acetic acid. Yeasts and molds sensitive to acetic acid include *Aspergillus*, *Penicillium*, *Rhizopus*, and some strains of *Saccharomyces*.

In experimental applications, acetic acid has been shown to be effective as an antimicrobial for incorporation into meat products, as a spray sanitizer on meat carcasses, and in scald water for poultry. Sodium diacetate is effective against molds in cheese spread and against rope-forming bacteria (*Bacillus* species) in bread. It is useful in the baking industry because it has little effect on the yeast used in baking. Dehydroacetic acid has a high pK_a of 5.27 and therefore retains activity at higher pH. It is inhibitory to bacteria at 0.1–0.4% and fungi at 0.005–0.1%.

Acetic acid, acetates, and diacetates are all GRAS with food-dependent concentration limits of 0.15–0.8% for acetic acid (up to 3.0% may be used in sauces and gravies and 9.0% in condiments), 0.007–0.6% for sodium acetate, 0.0001–0.2% for calcium acetate, and 0.05–0.4% for sodium diacetate. Acetates may be used in baked goods, breakfast cereals, candy, cheeses, condiments and relishes, dairy product analogues, fats and oils, fillings, gelatin, gravies, jams and jellies, meat products, pudding, sauces, snack foods, soup mixes, sweet sauces, syrups, and toppings. Dehydroacetic acid is approved only for cut or peeled squash so that the concentration remaining does not exceed 65 ppm (mg/kg).

B. Benzoic Acid/Benzoates

Benzoic acid (Fig. 8) is found naturally in spices and foods including cloves, cinnamon, cranberries,

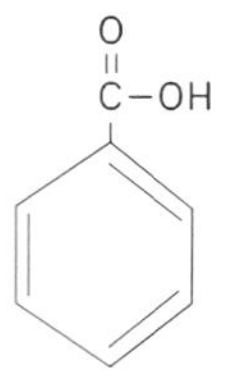

CH₃COOH   CH₃CH₂COOH

Acetic Acid   Propionic Acid

CH₃CHOH COOH   HOOC CH=CH COOH

Lactic Acid   Fumaric Acid

FIGURE 7 Structures of antimicrobial organic acids.

FIGURE 8 Structure of benzoic acid.

plums, and prunes. Benzoic acid and its sodium salt are the most prevalent forms of the antimicrobial, although the potassium and calcium salts are also approved for use. The sodium salt is much more soluble in water (66.0 g/100 ml at 20°C) than the acid (0.27 g/100 ml at 18°C) and is therefore preferred for food use.

Sodium benzoate and benzoic acid are most effective against molds and yeasts and inhibit most species at undissociated acid concentrations of 0.05–0.1%. The compounds are effective against some foodborne pathogens and spore-forming bacteria at 0.1–0.2%; however, most spoilage bacteria require much higher concentrations. The effectiveness of a particular concentration of the acid is dependent upon the pH at which it is applied. The pK_a of benzoic acid is 4.2; therefore, the compound is most effective at pH 2.5–4.0 and has little activity above pH 4.5.

Sodium benzoate and benzoic acid are used in a wide variety of foods including carbonated beverages, cider, fruit salads, jams, jellies, margarine, olives, pastry fillings, pickles, pie fillings, preserves, relishes, salad dressings, soy sauce, still beverages, and syrups. Benzoates are listed as GRAS antimicrobials by the FDA and may be used to a maximum of 0.1% in foods. In many countries of the world, the compounds are allowed in foods at concentrations of 0.15–0.25%.

C. Lactic Acid/Lactates

Lactic acid (Fig. 7) is produced naturally during fermentation of foods by lactic acid bacteria. While it acts as a preservative in these products, its primary use as a food additive is as a pH control agent and flavoring. In addition to lactic acid, the sodium, potassium, and calcium salts of the acid may be used in foods. The pK_a of lactic acid is 3.79 which requires that it be used in foods with a low pH. The antimicrobial activity of lactic acid is dependent upon the type of food to which it is applied and the target microorganism. Against some bacteria, such as B. coagulans, S. aureus and Yersinia enterocolitica, lactic acid is very inhibitory, while against others, the compound has little activity. Lactic acid has much less activity against yeasts and molds. Lactic acid sprays (1–1.25%) and dips have been proposed for use to control spoilage bacteria on meat cuts and carcasses and poultry. Sodium lactate (2.5–5.0%) inhibits C. botulinum, C. sporogenes, L. monocytogenes, and spoilage bacteria in various meat products. Lactic acid is GRAS for use as an antimicrobial in any food product without limitation

upon the concentration used except that it may not be used in infant formulas or infant foods.

D. Propionic Acid/Propionates

Up to 1% propionic acid (Fig. 7) is produced naturally in swiss cheese by Propionibacterium freudenreichii ssp. shermani. The acid (pK_a = 4.87) and its sodium, potassium, and calcium salts have been used primarily to control the growth of molds and bacteria in foods. The compound inhibits B. mesentericus (subtilis) strains which cause rope formation in bread as well as mycotoxin-producing molds. Propionates may be added directly to bread dough because they have no effect on the activity of baker's yeast. Propionic acid and propionates are GRAS for use as antimicrobials in baked goods and cheeses. There is no limit to the concentration of propionates allowed in foods but amounts used are generally less than 0.4%.

E. Sorbic Acid/Sorbates

Sorbic acid (Fig. 9) was first isolated in 1859 by A. W. von Hoffman from berries of the mountain ash tree (rowanberries). The acid is slightly soluble in water (0.16 g/100 ml at 20°C) while the potassium salt is highly soluble (58.2 g/100 ml at 20°C). The compound is also available as sodium and calcium salts. As with other organic acids, the antimicrobial effectiveness of sorbates (pK_a = 4.75) increases as the pH decreases and is essentially nonexistent above pH 6.0–6.5.

Sorbates are highly effective against a variety of yeasts and molds involved in spoilage, including those molds which produce mycotoxins. The compounds are also effective against some bacteria involved in spoilage (e.g., Pseudomonas) and certain foodborne pathogens including Salmonella, C. botulinum, S. aureus and Vibrio parahaemolyticus. Lactic acid bacteria are relatively resistant to sorbates which means the compounds can be used in products fermented by these microorganisms.

Sorbic acid and its salts are GRAS for use as antimicrobials in foods. The compound may be used in baked goods, beverages, cheese, fermented products, fruit products, jams and jellies, margarine, meat and poultry products, salads and salad dressings, syrups,

$$CH_3CH=CH-CH=CH-COOH$$

FIGURE 9 Structure of sorbic acid.

and wine. Concentrations used are dependent upon the product but are generally 0.05–0.3%.

F. Miscellaneous Organic Acids

Many organic acids and their esters have been studied for potential as antimicrobials but most have little or no activity. Their use in foods is as acidulants or flavoring agents rather than preservatives. Fumaric acid (Fig. 7) has been shown to be an effective antimicrobial in wines. Esters of fumaric acid were shown to inhibit *C. botulinum* in canned bacon and mold on bread. Citric acid (Fig. 2) inhibits microorganisms primarily through its ability to chelate metals. Experimental work with citric acid has demonstrated that it is inhibitory toward thermophilic and mesophilic spore-forming bacteria, including *C. botulinum* (types A and B), *C. sporogenes*, *L. monocytogenes*, *S. typhimurium*, *P. fluorescens*, *S. aureus*, and the molds *A. parasiticus* and *A. versicolor*. Inhibition by citric acid occurs only at low pH and/or high concentrations of the compound. In combination studies with benzoic acid, sorbic acid, ascorbic acid, EDTA (chelator), or glucono-δ-lactone, citric acid has been used successfully as an antimicrobial. Citric acid is a multiple purpose GRAS food additive. In experimental work, caprylic acid was shown to inhibit some molds and bacteria. Adipic, malic, succinic, and tartaric acids have no antimicrobial action except that due to decreasing pH.

G. Nitrites

Sodium ($NaNO_2$) and potassium (KNO_2) nitrite have a specialized use in cured meat products. The function of nitrites in these products is to form and stabilize cured meat color, function as an antioxidant and antimicrobial, and contribute to cured meat flavor. At one time, sodium and potassium nitrate ($NaNO_3$, KNO_3) were used extensively in cured meat production; however, their use was extensively curtailed by regulatory agencies when it was discovered that nitrate was converted to nitrite and that the latter was the only effective antimicrobial agent.

The primary use of nitrites as antimicrobials is to inhibit growth and toxin production of *C. botulinum* in cured meats. It also inhibits other *Clostridium* species and, at high concentrations, *S. aureus*. Nitrite has little or no effect on lactic acid bacteria or *Salmonella*. Nitrite functions against spores by inhibiting their outgrowth. The antimicrobial activity exhibited by nitrite in cured meats is possible only in concert with other components of the curing mix including salt, ascorbate or erythorbate, polyphosphates, and reduced pH. Nitrite is most effective at acidic pH, under anaerobic conditions, and at low temperature and is influenced by salt and nitrite concentrations.

Meat products that may contain nitrite include bacon, bologna, corned beef, frankfurters, luncheon meats, ham, fermented sausages, shelf-stable canned cured meats, and perishable canned cured meat. The concentration used in these products is specified by governmental regulations but is generally limited to 156 ppm for most products and 100–120 ppm in bacon. Sodium erythorbate or isoascorbate is required in products containing nitrites as a cure accelerator and as an inhibitor to the formation of nitrosamines. Nitrosamines are carcinogenic compounds formed by reactions of nitrite with secondary or tertiary amines. In some European countries, sodium nitrite is allowed for controlling spoilage of cheeses by *C. tyrobutyricum* and *C. butyricum*. [*See* MEAT PROCESSING.]

H. Sulfites

The use of sulfur dioxide and its salts dates back to ancient Rome when these compounds were used to treat wines. Sulfur dioxide is a colorless, nonflammable gas with a strong, penetrating odor. Sulfur dioxide, sodium sulfite, sodium bisulfite, and sodium metabisulfite (Table I) and their potassium salts set up a pH-dependent equilibrium mixture in water (Fig. 10). The pK_a values for sulfur dioxide are 1.76 and 7.20.

Effectiveness of sulfites as antimicrobials is dependent upon pH, concentration, type of microorganism, duration of contact, and binding of the compounds. Undissociated sulfurous acid (or sulfur dioxide in wa-

$$SO_2 + H_2O \longleftrightarrow [H_2SO_3]$$

Sulfur   Sulfurous
Dioxide   Acid

$$[H_2SO_3] \longleftrightarrow HSO_3^- + H^+$$

Bisulfite
Ion

$$HSO_3^- + H^+ \longleftrightarrow SO_3^{2-} + 2H^+$$

Sulfite
Ion

FIGURE 10 Equilibrium forms of sulfur dioxide in water.

ter) is the active form of the compound. Therefore, the compound is most effective when the pH is less than 4. Neither bisulfite ion (HSO_3^-) nor sulfite ion (SO_3^{-2}) is as effective. Sulfites form addition compounds (sulfonates) with aldehydes and ketones which are also less active than free sulfites. The primary mechanism by which the compound inhibits microorganisms involves inhibition of cellular enzymes.

Sulfites are active against certain types of bacteria, yeasts, and molds. The target microorganisms for sulfites are those associated with fruits and vegetables and include acetic acid producing bacteria, malolactic bacteria, fermentation and spoilage yeasts, and molds on fruits. Oxidative yeasts are generally more sensitive than fermentative yeasts. Against target fungi, the concentration of sulfites required for inhibition is relatively low. Concentration ranges (mg/liter) for inhibition of some yeasts are *Saccharomyces*, 0.1–20.2; *Zygosaccharomyces*, 7.2–8.7; *Pichia*, 0.2; *Hansenula*, 0.6; and *Candida*, 0.4–0.6. Sulfur dioxide at 1–10 mg/liter is capable of inhibiting lactic acid bacteria in fruit products.

Sulfites are used to control the growth of spoilage microorganisms in soft fruits, dehydrated fruits, fruit juices, wines, fresh shrimp, acid pickles, and during extraction of starches. It is added to expressed grape juices for making wines to inhibit molds, bacteria, and undesirable yeasts. The concentration used in wines is generally 50–100 mg/liter. Sulfur dioxide is maintained at 50–75 mg/liter in wine after fermentation to prevent changes by microorganisms during aging. In some countries (e.g., United Kingdom), sulfites are allowed for use in fresh meat products to stabilize color and inhibit bacterial spoilage. The compounds delay growth of molds, yeast, and bacteria (including *Salmonella*) during storage. Approval of sulfites for meats is rare as most world regulatory agencies believe that their use leads to consumer deception because the compounds mask color changes.

Sulfur dioxide and its salts are GRAS in fruit juices and concentrates, dehydrated fruits and vegetables, and wine in the United States. Common use levels are 0.01–0.2%. The maximum amount of sulfite in wine is set at 350 mg/liter. Sulfites are not used in food products which are sources of thiamine (vitamin B_1) or on raw fruits and vegetables to be consumed fresh (see above).

I. *Para*-Hydroxybenzoic Acid Esters (Parabens)

In most countries, methyl (Fig. 11), propyl (Fig. 11), and heptyl esters of *p*-hydroxybenzoic acid (parabens)

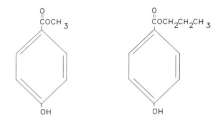

Methyl Paraben   Propyl Paraben

FIGURE 11   Structures of methyl and propyl parabens.

are allowed for direct addition to foods as antimicrobials. The ethyl and butyl esters are allowed in some countries. As might be expected, water solubility is inversely related to alkyl chain length. Parabens are stable in air and are resistant to cold and heat, including steam sterilization.

Esterification of the carboxyl group of benzoic acid allows the molecule to remain undissociated up to pH 8.5 versus the 50% dissociation of benzoic acid at pH 4.2. While the pH optimum for antimicrobial activity of benzoic acid is below 4.5, the parabens are effective at pH 3 to 8.

Parabens are effective against a wide variety of gram-negative and gram-positive foodborne bacteria. As the alkyl chain length of the parabens increases, inhibitory activity generally increases. Increasing activity with decreasing polarity is more evident against gram-positive than gram-negative bacteria. Fungi are much more susceptible to parabens than bacteria. As with bacteria, inhibition of fungi increases as the alkyl chain length of the parabens increases.

In the United States, the methyl and propyl esters of *p*-hydroxybenzoic acid are GRAS at a maximum concentration of 0.1% each. When used in combination, the total may not exceed 0.1%. To take advantage of their respective solubility and increased activity, methyl and propyl parabens are normally used in a combination of 2–3:1 (methyl:propyl). The *n*-heptyl ester is approved for use in fermented malt beverages (beers) at a maximum of 12 mg/liter and in certain noncarbonated soft drinks and fruit-based beverages at a maximum of 20 mg/liter. Many other countries permit the use of the methyl and propyl esters, and some, including Japan, allow use of the butyl ester. Parabens have been suggested for use in a variety of foods including baked goods, beverages, fruit products, jams and jellies, fermented foods, syrups, and fillings.

J. Sodium Chloride

Sodium chloride (NaCl) or common salt is probably the oldest known food preservative. While its primary use at the present is as a flavoring agent, salt continues to be useful in combination with other preservation methods to inhibit microorganisms. Sodium chloride indirectly inhibits microorganisms by lowering the water activity of solutions. In addition, sodium chloride also may act by limiting oxygen solubility and interfering with enzyme function.

A wide variety of tolerances to sodium chloride exist among microorganisms. Spoilage bacteria, such as *Achromobacter*, *Flavobacterium*, and *Pseudomonas*, grow in the presence of 1.5–5.0% salt. Lactic acid bacteria and spore-forming bacteria tolerate salt solutions of 4–15%. In general, pathogenic foodborne bacteria are inhibited by a water activity of 0.92 or less (equivalent to a sodium chloride solution of 13.5%, w/v) with the exception of *S. aureus*. The minimum water activity for growth of *S. aureus* is 0.83–0.86. Toxin production by the bacterium is reduced by sodium chloride concentrations of 4–10%. Another relatively salt tolerant foodborne pathogen is *L. monocytogenes* which is capable of survival in saturated salt solutions at lower temperatures. Fungi are more tolerant of low water activity than bacteria. Most spoilage fungi are inhibited by water activities of 0.80–0.88, but some xerophilic molds and osmophilic yeasts are capable of growth to 0.60–0.61. It must be noted that the type of solute has an effect on growth of microorganisms at low water activities. In many cases, microorganisms are capable of growth at lower water activities in the presence of sugars than sodium chloride. Inhibition by sodium chloride is influenced by pH, temperature, and the presence of other preservatives. As acidity increases or pH decreases, tolerance to sodium chloride decreases. Generally, as the temperature decreases, microorganisms grow more slowly in the presence of sodium chloride. In some instances, tolerance to, but not necessarily growth in, sodium chloride may actually increase at lower temperatures. Some fungi have shown increased resistance to heat in the presence of 3–16% salt.

K. Dimethyl Dicarbonate (DMDC)

Dimethyl dicarbonate (Fig. 12) is a colorless liquid which is slightly soluble in water (3.6%). The compound is very reactive with a number of substances including water, ethanol, alkyl and aromatic amines, and sulfhydryl groups. In water, DMDC hydrolyzes to form methanol and carbon dioxide. Hydrolysis

$$H_3C-O-\overset{\overset{\displaystyle O}{\|}}{C}-O-\overset{\overset{\displaystyle O}{\|}}{C}-O-CH_3$$

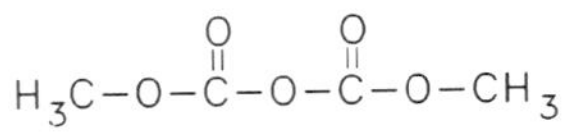

FIGURE 12 Structure of dimethyl dicarbonate.

increases with increasing temperature and decreasing pH.

The primary target microorganisms for DMDC are yeasts. In alcohol-free beverages, fungicidal concentrations range from 30 to 250 mg/liter for species of *Saccharomyces*, *Zygosaccharomyces*, *Rhodotorula*, *Candida*, *Pichia*, *Torulopsis*, *Torula*, *Endomyces*, *Kloeckera*, and *Hansenula* (28°C, pH 2.8–4.7). The compound has also been shown to be bactericidal at 30–400 mg/liter to a number of species including *A. pasteurianus*, *E. coli*, *P. aeruginosa*, *S. aureus*, several *Lactobacillus* species, and *Pediococcus cerevisiae*. Molds are generally more resistant to DMDC than yeasts or bacteria. Concentration ranges for lethality against molds are 50–1000 mg/liter. In wine containing 10% ethanol, 50 mg/liter DMDC is lethal to most yeasts. The antimicrobial activity of DMDC is dependent upon temperature, pH, and chemical composition of the product. The most effective pH range for DMDC is 3–4. Ethanol in the product increases effectiveness of DMDC, while proteins decrease effectiveness. The mechanism by which DMDC acts is most likely related to inactivation of enzymes of the microorganism.

In 1988 the FDA approved DMDC for use in wine at a maximum of 200 mg/liter as an antimicrobial. Ethylmethyl carbonate, a reaction product of ethanol hydrolysis with DMDC, must not exceed 2 mg/liter in the treated wine.

L. Biologically Derived Compounds

Food antimicrobials produced by microorganisms are sometimes termed "biologically derived" compounds. Nisin and natamycin are two compounds produced by microorganisms that are approved by most regulatory agencies for use in foods. In addition, there are a number of other antimicrobials produced by microorganisms which have been evaluated for their potential in foods. Most of these compounds are produced by lactic acid bacteria.

1. Nisin

Nisin is a bacteriocin produced by some strains of *Lactococcus lactis* ssp. *lactis* (formerly *S. lactis*). A bacteriocin is generally classified as protein which exerts a bactericidal mode of action on susceptible bacteria. Nisin was isolated, characterized, and named by

A. T. R. Mattick and A. Hirsch in 1947. The compound contains 34 amino acids and has a molecular weight of around 3500 D; however, it usually occurs as a dimer with a molecular weight of 7000.

The solubility of nisin is dependent upon pH. At pH 2.5, the solubility is 12%, at pH 5.0, 4.0% and it is insoluble at neutral and alkaline pH. In dilute hydrochloric acid at pH 2.5, nisin is stable to boiling with no marked loss of activity. At pH 7.0, inactivation occurs even at room temperature. In the dry form, nisin is very stable but it is gradually inactivated in foods. Nisin is inactivated by some, but not all, proteases.

Nisin inhibits the growth of gram-positive bacteria but does not generally inhibit gram-negative bacteria, yeasts, or molds. Vegetative bacteria inhibited by nisin include *L. lactis* ssp. *cremoris*, *Corynebacterium*, *Lactobacillus*, *Listeria*, *Micrococcus*, *Mycobacterium*, *S. aureus*, and *Streptococcus*. Nisin is sporicidal to species of *Bacillus* and *Clostridium*, including *C. botulinum*.

A few microorganisms are resistant to the effects of nisin. One possible cause for resistance of microorganisms is production of the enzyme nisinase. Nisinase is produced by *L. plantarum*, *S. thermophilus*, some other lactic acid bacteria, and certain *Bacillus* species.

Nisin-producing starter cultures were first used in foods as a preservative to prevent "blowing" of swiss-type cheese caused by *C. tyrobutyricum* and *C. butyricum*. Nisin has been recommended for use in canned vegetable products to prevent the outgrowth of *C. botulinum* when less severe sterilization conditions are desired or required. It also could be used to control heat-resistant thermophilic spore-formers, such as *B. stearothermophilus* and *C. thermosaccharolyticum*, which are capable of spoilage of canned foods stored at elevated temperatures (e.g., in warm climates) and *C. pasteurianum* and *Bacillus* species which may spoil high-acid canned foods. Studies have demonstrated variable to poor success in research applications of nisin to meat products. Reasons for reduced activity in meats may be due to binding of nisin by meat particles, uneven distribution, poor solubility, or interference by phospholipids.

Nisin is permitted for use as an antimicrobial in approximately 47 countries. Food products for which it is approved include: cheeses, processed cheeses, canned vegetables and fruits, confectionery creams, milk, milk products, cooked meats, custard, ice, bakery products, and mayonnaise. It is approved in the United States only for use in pasteurized cheese spreads and pasteurized process cheese spread to in-

hibit the growth of *C. botulinum* at a maximum of 250 ppm.

2. Natamycin

Natamycin was first isolated in 1955 from a culture of *Streptomyces natalensis*, a microorganism found in soil from Natal, South Africa. The generic name "natamycin," which is approved by the World Health Organization, is synonymous with "pimaricin," a name used in earlier literature.

Natamycin is a polyene macrolide antibiotic, meaning it possesses a macrocyclic ring of carbon atoms closed by lactonization (Fig. 13). Natamycin has low solubility in water and polar organic solvents and is practically insoluble in nonpolar solvents. At room temperature, 30–100 mg of natamycin is soluble in 1 liter of water. The stability and/or antimycotic activity of natamycin are affected by pH, light, oxidants, and heavy metals. While pH has no apparent effect on antifungal activity, it does influence stability of the compound. Natamycin retains greatest activity at pH 5–7, the pH range of most food products. Under normal storage conditions, temperature has little effect on natamycin activity. Irradiation due to sunlight and contact with certain oxidants (e.g., organic peroxides and sulfhydryl groups) and heavy metals all adversely effect stability of natamycin solutions or suspensions.

Natamycin is active against nearly all molds and yeasts, but has no apparent effect on bacteria or viruses. Most molds are inhibited by concentrations of natamycin from 0.5 to 6.0 mg/liter while some species require 10–25 mg/liter for inhibition. Most yeasts are inhibited by natamycin concentrations from 1.0 to 5.0 mg/liter.

Natamycin is approved by the FDA under the trade name Delvocid for use on any cheese for which antimycotics are allowed. The low solubility of natamycin makes it suitable for use as a surface treatment on cheeses because it remains at the surface.

3. Other Bacteriocins Produced by Lactic Acid Bacteria

While nisin is the only bacteriocin produced by lactic acid bacteria approved for use in foods by regulatory agencies, a number of other compounds may have potential for use as antimicrobials in foods in the future. *Pediococcus pentosaceus* produces a bacteriocin, designated pediocin A, which inhibits species of *Bacillus*, *Clostridium*, *Lactobacillus*, *Leuconostoc*, *L. monocytogenes*, *S. aureus*, and *Streptococcus*. There is no effect of pediocin A on yeasts or gram-negative bacteria.

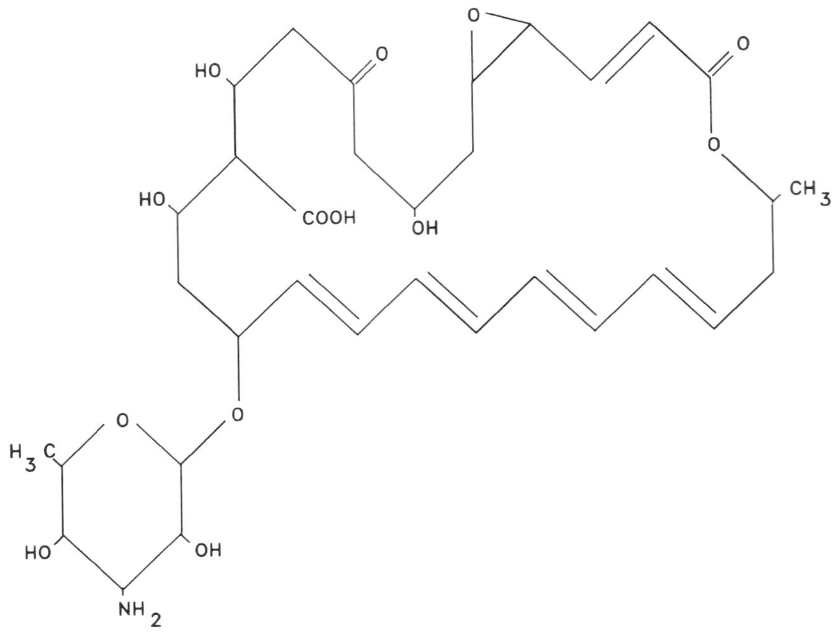

FIGURE 13 Structure of natamycin.

Pediocin PA-1, a bacteriocin produced by *P. acidilactici* PAC 1.0, inhibits *B. cereus, Leuconostoc mesenteroides, L. monocytogenes, S. aureus,* and *S. faecalis.* A bacteriocin produced by *P. acidilactici* H and named pediocin AcH has antimicrobial activity against *L. monocytogenes* but has little effect on growth of *C. botulinum* spores. Sakacin A, produced by *L. sake* 706, is inhibitory to *L. monocytogenes.* These compounds and others produced by species of *Lactococcus, Lactobacillus, Leuconostoc, Carnobacterium, Bifidobacterium,* and *Propionibacterium* have potential use when produced by starter cultures in fermented foods or as purified compounds added to foods. More research on application of purified bacteriocins to foods is necessary prior to their widespread acceptance by regulatory agencies or the food industry.

M. Naturally Occurring Compounds and Systems

Many food products contain naturally occurring compounds which have antimicrobial activity (Table III). In the natural state, these compounds may play a role in extending the shelf-life of a food product. In addition, a number of these naturally occurring compounds have been studied for their potential as direct food antimicrobials.

Several enzyme systems and proteins have been shown to possess antimicrobial activity. In bovine milk, lactoperoxidase combines with hydrogen peroxide to oxidize thiocyanate resulting in several products including hypothiocyanate, cyanosulfurous acid, and cyanosulfuric acid. This system, called the lactoperoxidase system (LPS), is active against hydrogen peroxide-producing microorganisms such as *Lactococcus, Lactobacillus,* and *Streptococcus* as well as a number of gram-negative bacteria including *Pseudomonas.* Bovine milk contains sufficient lactoperoxidase (15–30 mg/liter) and thiocyanate (1–10 mg/liter) to activate the system. Only hydrogen peroxide is deficient. Hydrogen peroxide may be added to the milk directly or produced through the growth of *Lactobacillus* in the milk. The LPS system has been suggested for use as a preservative for raw milk, infant formula, and liquid whole eggs. [*See* FOOD BIOCHEMISTRY: PROTEINS, ENZYMES, AND ENZYME INHIBITORS.]

Conalbumin and lactoferrin are proteins which bind iron in eggs and milk, respectively. These proteins are capable of inhibiting the growth of microorganisms which require iron. Gram-positive bacteria, including species of *Bacillus* and *Micrococcus,* are the most sensitive but others including *L. monocytogenes* and the gram-negative *E. coli* have also been shown to be inhibited. Avidin is a protein present in eggs which binds biotin. Microorganisms which have a requirement for biotin may be inhibited by avidin.

Lysozyme (*N*-acetylhexosaminidase) is an enzyme present in eggs, milk, and other biological secretions.

TABLE III

Sources of Naturally Occurring Antimicrobials in Foods and Related Products

Antimicrobial component	Food/product	Remarks
Lactoperoxidase	Bovine milk	Reacts with thiocyanate and hydrogen peroxide to form inhibitory components
Lactoferrin	Milk	Binds iron
Conalbumin	Eggs	Binds iron
Avidin	Eggs	Binds biotin
Lysozyme	Milk/eggs/biological secretions	Lyses peptidoglycan of bacterial cell walls
Eugenol	Cloves	—
Cinnamic aldehyde	Cinnamon	—
Thymol	Oregano/thyme	—
Terpenes	Sage/rosemary	—
Allicin/thiopropanal-S-oxide	Onions/garlic	Through the enzyme allinase
Humulones/lupulones	Hops	—
Oleuropein	Olives	Phenolic glycoside
Caffeine/theophylline/theobromine	Coffee/cocoa beans/tea	—
Phenol/cresol/formaldehyde	Woodsmoke/smoked foods	—

It catalyzes hydrolysis of the β-1,4 linkages between N-acetylmuramic acid and N-acetylglucosamine of the peptidoglycan of bacterial cell walls. Lysozyme is most active against gram-positive bacteria including *C. botulinum*, *C. thermosaccharolyticum*, *C. tyrobutyricum*, *B. stearothermophilus*, and *L. monocytogenes*. It is less effective against gram-negative bacteria, but their susceptibility can be increased if the cells are starved or injured, with a chelator (e.g., EDTA) or with polymyxin B. Lysozyme is one of the few naturally occurring antimicrobials approved by regulatory agencies for use in foods. In Europe, lysozyme is used to prevent gas formation in cheese by *C. tyrobutyricum*. Lysozyme is used to a great extent in Japan to preserve seafood, vegetables, pasta, and salads. The enzyme also has potential for use as an antimicrobial in meat products.

Spices and their essential oils have varying degrees of antimicrobial activity. The earliest report on use of spices as preservatives was in Egypt around 1550 B.C. The strongest antimicrobial activity among spices has been shown with cloves, cinnamon, oregano, and thyme. The major antimicrobial fraction of these spices is in their essential oils. The spice and its corresponding essential oil are: cloves, eugenol (2-methoxy-4-allyl-phenol); cinnamon, cinnamic aldehyde; oregano and thyme, thymol (Fig. 14). These compounds have inhibitory activity against a number of bacterial species, molds and yeasts. Sage and rosemary also have antimicrobial activity against a number of gram-positive and gram-negative bacteria. The inhibitory effect of these spices is attributed to their terpene fraction. Many other spices which have been tested show limited or no activity.

Plants and plant extracts have a number of antimicrobial compounds. Probably the most well characterized antimicrobial system is that found in the juice and vapors of onions (*Allium cepa*) and garlic (*A. sativum*). The antimicrobial component of garlic is allicin (diallyl thiosulfinate) which is formed by the action of the enzyme, allinase, on the substrate alliin (*S*-(2-propenyl)-L-cysteine sulfoxide). The reaction only occurs when cells of the garlic are disrupted, releasing the enzyme to act on the substrate. A similar reaction occurs in onion except the substrate is *S*-(1-propenyl)-L-cysteine sulfoxide and one of the major products is thiopropanal-*S*-oxide. The products which appear to be responsible for antimicrobial activity are also responsible for flavor of onions and garlic. Microorgan-

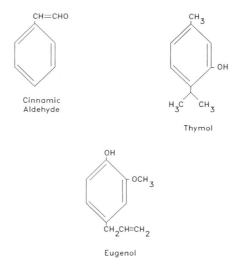

FIGURE 14 Structures of antimicrobial compounds in spices.

isms which are inhibited by onion and garlic include the bacteria *B. cereus, C. botulinum* type A, *E. coli, S. typhimurium,* and *S. aureus,* the molds *A. flavus, A. parasiticus,* and the yeasts *C. albicans, Cryptococcus, Rhodotorula, Torulopsis,* and *Trichosporon.* In addition to onions and garlic, extracts of snap beans, beets, brussel sprouts, cabbage, carrots, cauliflower, horseradish, peas, peppers, potatoes, radishes, rhubarb, spinach, sweet potatoes, and tomatoes have limited activity against certain microorganisms. Phenolic acids (protocatechuic, vanillic, gallic, syringic, ellagic), hydroxycinnamic acids (caffeic, chlorogenic, *p*-coumaric, ferulic), and tannins, found naturally in a number of fruits and vegetables, are inhibitory to certain gram-positive bacteria, yeasts, and molds. Humulones and lupulones are major constituents of hop resin from the flowers of the hop vine (*Lupulus humulus*). This resin, used in the brewing industry for imparting a desirable bitter flavor to beer, has antimicrobial activity against gram-positive bacteria at 1–100 ppm. Smoking of foods not only imparts desirable flavor to foods such as meats, cheeses, fish, and poultry, it also has a preservative effect. Compounds in wood smoke responsible for antimicrobial activity include phenol, cresol (methyl phenol), and formaldehyde.

N. Miscellaneous Compounds

Certain fatty acid esters, including glyceryl esters of fatty acids and sucrose fatty acid esters, have been found to exhibit antimicrobial activity in foods. One of the most effective of the fatty acid esters is glyceryl monolaurate (Fig. 15). Some polyphosphate compounds (Table IV) have demonstrated antimicrobial activity in foods. The normal functions of polyphosphates includes stabilizing emulsions, improving ten-

$$H_2C-O-\overset{\overset{\displaystyle O}{\|}}{C}-(CH_2)_{10}-CH_3$$
$$|$$
$$CHOH$$
$$|$$
$$CH_2OH$$

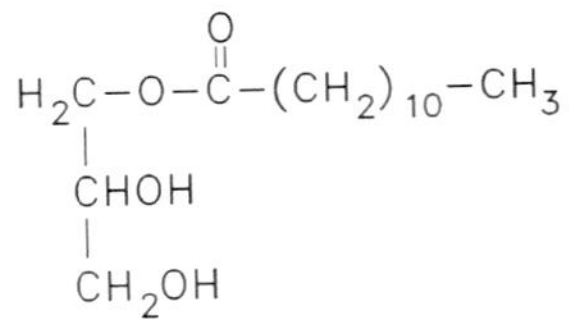

FIGURE 15 Structure of monolaurin.

TABLE IV

Phosphate Derivatives with Antimicrobial Activity

Name	Abbreviation	Formula
Sodium acid pyrophosphate	SAPP	$Na_2H_2P_2O_7$
Tetrasodium pyrophosphate	TSPP	$Na_4P_2O_7$
Sodium tripolyphosphate	STPP	$Na_5P_3O_{10}$
Sodium tetrapolyphosphate		$(NaPO_3)_{4-10}$
Sodium hexametaphosphate	SHMP	$(NaPO_3)_{10-15}$

derness, retaining color, and improving flavor in meat products, dispersing proteins and buffering in dairy products, and mineral supplementation. Generally, gram-positive bacteria, including *C. botulinum* and *S. aureus,* are susceptible to the polyphosphates.

Certain gases have antimicrobial activity, especially carbon dioxide (CO_2). Carbon dioxide is most active against molds and gram-negative psychrotrophic bacteria. Carbon dioxide has been used in mixtures with nitrogen and oxygen in gas-impermeable films to produce modified atmosphere packaged products. The concentration of carbon dioxide in these mixtures varies with the product being stored.

Bibliography

Anonymous (1992). "Code of Federal Regulations—Food and Drugs-21-Parts 170 to 199." Office of the Federal Register, National Archives and Records Administration, Washington, DC.

Block, S. S. (1991). "Disinfection, Sterilization and Preservation," 4th ed. Lea and Febiger, Philadelphia, PA.

Branen, A. L., Davidson, P. M., and Salminen, S. (ed.) (1990). "Food Additives." Marcel Dekker, New York.

Davidson, P. M., and Branen, A. L. (ed.) (1993). "Antimicrobials in Foods," 2nd ed. Marcel Dekker, New York.

Fennema, O. (ed.) (1985). "Food Chemistry," 2nd ed. Marcel Dekker, New York.

Furia, T. E. (ed.) (1972). "Handbook of Food Additives," 2nd ed. CRC Press, Cleveland, OH.

Russell, N. J., and Gould, G. W. (ed.) (1991). "Food Preservatives." Blackie and Son Ltd., Glasgow.

Jay, J. M. (1992). "Modern Food Microbiology," 4th ed. Van Nostrand Reinhold, New York.

Schwimmer, S. (1981). "Source Book of Food Enzymology." AVI, Westport, CT.

Food Process Engineering: Heat and Mass Transfer

A. K. DATTA, *Cornell University*

I. Heat Transfer
II. Phase Change Heat Transfer during Freezing
III. Phase Change Heat Transfer during Evaporation
IV. Mass Transfer
V. Future Directions in Food Process Engineering

Glossary

Angle of respose of solids Angle made by a material with respect to the horizontal when piled; the coefficient of friction between granular materials is equal to the tangent of the angle of internal friction of the material; it is generally assumed that the angle of friction and the angle of repose are approximately equal

Colligative properties Depend on number but not on the nature of molecules in a system; they play an important role in a number of separation processes and purification processes in food manufacture, and water activity, including boiling point elevation, freezing point depression, and osmotic pressure

Flow models Many fluid foods do not follow Newton's law of viscosity in which the shearing stress is directly proportional to the shearing rate (velocity gradient); among the flow models for foods that show non-Newtonian behavior, the power law is widely used: the shearing stress is assumed to be proportional to the shearing rate raised to a power

Jenike's flow function Flowability of powders; it is an important property in designing bins and hoppers

Reaction kinetics A number of chemical changes take place when foods are either stored at a constant temperature or subjected to a thermal process in which a range of temperatures is used and it is important to model the changes so that the extent of chemical changes can be calculated; in foods, most

chemical and physical changes can be described by either zero-order or first-order kinetics

Reynolds number Dimensionless number whose magnitude defines laminar and turbulent flows; it is also used in the calculation of friction losses in pipes

Sanitary standards Sanitary and microbiological considerations play important roles in the design of transportation and storage systems of foods; they include the use of stainless-steel and other approved materials of construction, the use of sanitary fittings, the design of pipe lines to eliminate stagnation zones and to facilitate drainage of the foods, the control of temperature and humidity of storage, and, often, minimal contact with oxygen to minimize degradation reactions

Transport properties In the context of food, transport processes typically refer to the transport of momentum (fluid flow), transport of thermal energy (heat transfer), and transport of species (mass transfer); transport properties describe rates of these transport processes (examples are viscosity for fluid flow, thermal conductivity for heat transfer, and mass diffusivity for mass transfer processes)

Unit operations Combination of one or more of physical transport processes combined with biological and chemical changes during that process

While thermodynamics tells us that energy is transferred from a body at higher temperature to a body at lower temperature, heat transfer deals with the rate of this energy transfer process. The subject of mass transfer deals with movement of one material component (species) inside another. [*See* FOOD PROCESS ENGINEERING: STORAGE AND TRANSPORT OF FLUID FOODS IN PLANTS; FOOD PROCESS ENGINEERING: THERMODYNAMIC AND TRANSPORT PROPERTIES.]

I. Heat Transfer

A. Thermodynamics, Rates of Heat Transfer, and the Heat Equation

1. Thermodynamics and the Conservation of Energy

While thermodynamics tells us that energy is transferred from a body at higher temperature to a body at lower temperature, heat transfer deals with the rate of this energy transfer process. The first law of thermodynamics is a statement of conservation of energy and is shown schematically in Fig. 1.

2. Rates of Heat Transfer

Energy is transferred by three common *modes* of conduction, convection, and radiation. In conduction heat transfer, as the temperature of a location increases the molecules in that area vibrate to a greater extent and bump into neighboring molecules. This contact between molecules imparts some of the vibrational motion of the first molecule to the second molecule which then begins to vibrate more. This trend continues throughout the material, spreading heat energy by the introduction of increased vibrational motion. The rate of transport of thermal energy (heat transfer) q_x is related to the temperature gradient as (Fourier's law):

$$\frac{q_x}{A} = -k\frac{dT}{dx}, \tag{1}$$

where x is the direction of heat transfer, A is area perpendicular to this direction, T is temperature, and k is thermal conductivity (a property that measures the ease of energy transfer by conduction).

Convective heat transfer results due to bulk motion of the material and the energy it carries with it. Thus, this mode of heat transfer is true only in liquids and gases. While forced convection is due to an external force, such as a fan, free convection is driven by a density difference in the fluid. Often, convective heat transfer between a surface and a fluid flowing over it is of importance. When fluid at temperature T_2 is

flowing over a surface of area A at temperature T_1, the rate of heat transfer from the surface to the fluid is given by

$$q_{1-2} = hA(T_1 - T_2). \tag{2}$$

In radiative heat transfer, energy is emitted by all matter that exists at finite temperatures above absolute zero. Unlike conduction and convection, radiation does not require a medium. The rate of energy emitted from a surface of area A and at absolute temperature T is

$$\frac{q}{A} = \varepsilon\sigma T^4, \tag{3}$$

where ε is emissivity, a property of the material surface and σ is a universal constant.

3. The Energy Equation

A material is treated as a continuum for heat transfer purposes. To successfully apply equations of conduction and convection when temperature T continually varies inside the material, differential equations of heat (energy) transfer are needed. The energy equation is derived by combining the fundamental thermodynamic principle of conservation of energy (Fig. 1) and the Fourier's law of heat conduction (Eq. (1)):

$$\underbrace{\frac{\partial T}{\partial t}}_{\text{Storage}} + \underbrace{u\frac{\partial T}{\partial x}}_{\substack{\text{Bulk}\\\text{Flow}}} = \underbrace{\frac{k}{\rho c_p}\frac{\partial^2 T}{\partial x^2}}_{\substack{\text{Diffusive}\\\text{Movement}}} + \underbrace{\frac{Q}{\rho c_p}}_{\text{Generation}}. \tag{4}$$

The first term in the above energy equation represents the storage of energy. Increase in storage with time leads to higher temperature and vice versa. The second term represents the energy carried due to the bulk motion (convection) with velocity u. The first term on the right-hand side of Eq. (4) represents the energy transferred due to diffusion. The second term on the right represents the source or sink of energy. All the problems in energy transfer are solutions to this equation or some other form of it.

B. Thermally Induced Changes during Processing

Thermally induced changes in foods are often treated as first-order reactions described by

$$-\frac{dc}{dt} = k_1 c, \tag{5}$$

where k_1 is the reaction rate constant at temperature

Storage = In - Out + Generation

FIGURE 1 The thermodynamic law of energy conservation.

T. When the temperature of the food varies with time, the reaction rates also vary with time. The integrated effect of the temperature variation with time on nutrient or bacterial concentration is obtained by integrating the above equation as

$$\ln \frac{c_i}{c} = \int_0^t k_1 dt, \tag{6}$$

where c and c_i are final and initial concentration, respectively. In the food literature, the above equation is used in a different but equivalent form. Instead of referring to a final concentration, an equivalent heating time F_0 is used that gives the same final concentration c for a constant processing temperature of T_R. Thus,

$$F_0 = \frac{\ln \frac{c_i}{c}}{k_{T_R}} = \frac{\int_0^t k_1 dt}{k_{T_R}}$$
$$= \int_0^t \exp(E_a / R(1/T_R - 1/T)) dt \tag{7}$$

using Eq. (34) in the article on "Thermodynamic and Transport Properties." When process temperature T is close to T_R, the above expression can be approximated as

$$F_0 = \int_0^t t_p 10^{\frac{T - 121}{z}} dt, \tag{8}$$

where a standard value of $T_R = 121°C$ is used and z is related to the activation energy E_a by Eq. (35) in the article on "Thermodynamic and Transport Properties." In thermal processing of foods, the primary purpose is to determine the processing time t_p for a given temperature history when F_0 is mandated from health standpoint.

C. Uniformity of Heating and Quality of Thermally Processed Foods

1. Uniformity of Heating as Related to Quality

A finite-shaped food material will have a spatial temperature distribution when being heated or cooled. Therefore, in a food material, $T(t)$ will be different for every location in it. Thus, F_0 calculated at every location will be different, providing a distribution of sterilization and other thermally related quality factors. Conceptually, processes with less spread in F_0 values are preferred since they signify more uniformity of heating that leads to better quality since overprocessing is minimized.

In conventional heating (as opposed to microwave heating) all of the material tries to reach the surface temperature, and therefore uniformity of heating increases with time. By contrast, in microwave heating, heat is generated constantly but at varying rates throughout the material. This causes the uniformity of microwave heating to decrease with time. Thus, the ability of microwaves to provide better quality is not universally true and depends on the particular heating situation, material properties, and duration of heating. The faster and more uniform heating of microwaves can provide better quality (less thermal degradation) for many practical processing situations.

2. Slowest Heating Point, Zone, Element, and Average Values

The spatial variation in the heating effect can be lumped into an average value. While this is useful for nutrient retention, from a bacterial inactivation point of view, the locations in food material that consistently stay colder than other locations are of prime concern. The *slowest heating point* or *cold point* is of particular importance for designing a sterilization process due to the fact that bacteria at these points would undergo least inactivation. Therefore, a thermal process is designed based on temperature variation of the food at the coldest point, since all other locations in the food material are sterilized more than the coldest point. Thus, for sterilization, it is the least value of F_0 that we are interested in. In heating of fluids, there is often no one slowest heating point, instead there is a slowest heating zone in which slowest heating points stay during the course of heating.

Conceptually, another important quantity is a slowest heating food element, which by definition is a material element in the food that heats the slowest. In solids, where the food does not move physically, this is same as the slowest heating point. However, in fluid foods, where the material (fluid) element moves during heating, the F_0 for the slowest heating element is generally higher than the time–temperature history at the slowest heating location as shown in Fig. 2 for natural convection heating. This results from all physical fluid elements staying only some time in the slowest heating zone and staying in a warmer zone at other times. Although for practical purposes, sterilization process cannot be designed based on this slowest heating element, it shows that for fluid sterilization, use of slowest point (or zone) can further underestimate the sterilization value and provide more conservative (safer) estimates of the extent of sterilization.

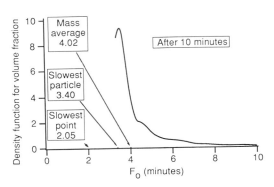

FIGURE 2 Spatial variation in sterilization showing average, slowest element, and slowest point sterilization in a liquid during natural convection heating.

D. Thermal Processing and Heating of Conductive Heated Foods

1. Transient and Spatial Temperatures in Solid Food Materials

In conventional heating of food, temperatures change toward the boundary temperature asymptotically as shown in Fig. 3. The farther the location from the boundary, more is the lag in temperature rise. In contrast, in high rate of microwave heating time–temperature relationships at all points within a material is often linear (Fig. 4). Such linear time–temperature profile results from diffusion being insignificant, as can be seen in Eq. (4) when convection and diffusion terms are dropped and generation rate Q is constant at any location. With continuous and high rate of heat generation, temperatures reach boiling temperature of water in a short time.

Typical spatial variation of temperatures in conventional and microwave heating, respectively, is shown in Figs. 5 and 6, respectively. Although microwaves generally heat more near the surface and less inside, evaporative heat loss and convective heat loss to the

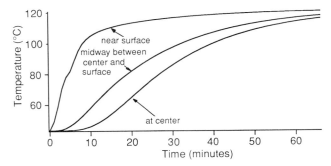

FIGURE 3 Transient temperatures at three locations in a solid food material in a cylindrical-shaped can.

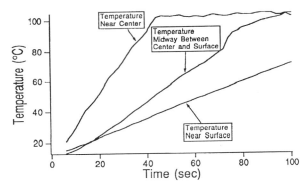

FIGURE 4 Transient temperatures at three locations in a spherically shaped potato under microwave heating.

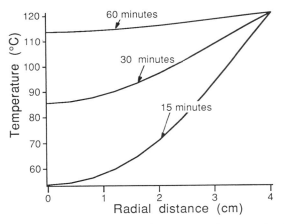

FIGURE 5 Spatial variation of temperatures in conventional heating of cylindrically shaped food material.

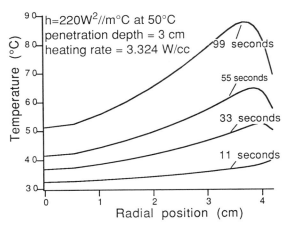

FIGURE 6 Spatial variation of temperatures in microwave heating of a cylindrical-shaped food material (without any focusing effect).

colder surrounding air keeps the surface temperature lower than slightly interior locations.

2. Thermal Processing of Solids

For conduction heating of solid food, we are interested in temperatures at the geometrical center of the can since this is the slowest heating point in the can. The temperature variation in a conduction heated product at any location in an arbitrary shaped solid can be obtained by solving the Energy Eq. (4) and making suitable approximations of the solution as

$$\frac{T - T_m}{T_0 - T_m} = j\, 10^{-t/f}, \tag{9}$$

where T_m is the boundary (retort) temperature for heating, T is temperature at the slowest heating point at time t, and f and j values characterize the shape, size, thermal property of the food material, and the heat transfer coefficient at the surface. This equation can be combined with Eq. (6) for first order kinetics for bacterial destruction to obtain

$$\frac{1}{f/\left(F_0\, 10^{\frac{121 - T_m}{z}}\right)}$$
$$= -\int_{T_m + j(T_0 - T_m)}^{T} \frac{10^{\frac{T - T_m}{z}}}{2.303(T - T_m)}\, dT. \tag{10}$$

Here F_0 defined in Eq. (8) and T are the final temperature of the food at the end of processing. Since F_0 values at lower temperatures are relatively insignificant, we only need to start from 44°C (80°F) below T_m to get all the significant lethalities, which means the integral above can be approximated as

$$\frac{1}{f/\left(F_0 10^{\frac{121 - T_m}{z}}\right)}$$
$$= -\int_{T_m - 44}^{T} \frac{10^{(T - T_m)/z}}{2.303(T - T_m)}\, dT, \tag{11}$$

which is the well-known Ball's formula for sterilization. According to this expression, lethality calculations for the heating process in this formula do not depend on initial temperature or the j value. Further modifications of this formula are done to include lethality during the cooling process of the food following heating. More details on how the industry sets the processing time based on this formula are provided in the article on thermal processing.

E. Thermal Processing in Continuous Heating of Liquids

1. Flow and Temperature Profiles for Conventional and Microwave Heating

The three major types of continuous processing equipment are tubular, plate, and direct contact heat exchangers. For illustration, consider a simple tubular heat exchanger under steam or hot water heating from the surface. The fully developed laminar velocity profile in this exchanger is parabolic as shown in Fig. 7. The temperature profile keeps changing along the total length of the tube as the interior fluid warms up, but the centerline always stays the coldest. At this time, continuous microwave liquid heating apparatus is not available for industrial use.

For laminar flow, since liquid follows the streamline and it has highest velocity and lowest temperature at the centerline, the sterilization is lowest at that location. The cold point is therefore at the centerline. For a given sterilization at the cold point, reduction in tube diameter leads to more uniform heating and less destruction of thermally vulnerable quantities, like the vitamins. A smaller tube diameter is preferable from this standpoint; however, blockage by food clumps or fouling would limit the smallest usable size.

Due to the high apparent viscosity of many non-Newtonian liquid foods, flow is often laminar. The temperature profiles are also modified due to the non-Newtonian nature but stay qualitatively similar to those for Newtonian fluids. Use of microwaves for continuous heating has been demonstrated and ohmic (direct resistance) heating has also been developed where the food is made part of an electric circuit, through which current flows and heat is generated in the food material.

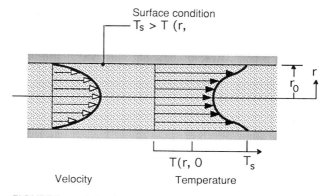

FIGURE 7 Radial velocity and temperature profiles in a tube with specified surface temperature.

2. Effect of Presence of Particulates

Continuous sterilization of liquid only products is currently being extended to liquids with large particulates. Such a system, however, is considerably more complex. The temperature of the solid particles flowing with the liquid is a function of the residence time of the particles in the sterilizer as well as the convective heat transfer coefficient between the liquid and the surface of the particle, information on both of which is currently limited. The temperatures of the moving particles cannot be experimentally monitored either. Studies are continuing to accurately predict temperatures inside the particles to calculate the process time that meets the desired sterility (F_0).

F. Thermal Processing in Agitated Batch (In-Container) Heating of Liquids

1. Flow and Temperature Profiles

Mechanical agitation is frequently used to enhance heat transfer by increasing the surface heat transfer coefficient between the container surface and the liquid in it. Processing time can be markedly shortened due to this uniform and faster heating, generally resulting in improvement of quality. Details of types of agitation are included in the article on thermal processing.

The temperature distribution inside axially rotating cans under direct flame heating and in a steam retort was shown to be quite uniform. Temperature measurements in an end-over-end rotating can also showed uniformity. Heat transfer was much higher in end-over-end agitated cans, as compared to axial rotation and the presence of a minimally sized headspace in end-over-end rotation markedly increased the heat transfer.

The center of the can is generally assumed to be the cold point for agitated heating, temperatures inside being very uniform except near the wall. Presence of particulates inside the container further complicates the heating patterns. The additional critical parameter due to the presence of particles is the convective surface heat transfer coefficient between the fluid and the particles, information on which is currently lacking.

G. Thermal Processing in Nonagitated Batch (In-Container) Heating of Liquids

1. Flow and Temperature Profiles

Nonagitating or still retorts are used when agitations are to be avoided to keep the product or package integrity or for economical reasons in small produc-

tion volumes. Due to slow movement of the liquid from natural convection, heating times required for sterilization are somewhat long. Natural convection heating of pure liquid has been studied in detail experimentally and theoretically. Figure 8 provides the flow patterns inside a can during natural convection heating. The warmer liquid near the wall is lighter and it moves up. The core liquid, being colder, is heavier and moves downward creating a recirculating flow. Temperature values along the axis show that due to deposition of hot liquid, the top stays consistently at a higher temperature. However, at the very bottom, since the bottom wall was heated, the temperature is higher again. The slowest heated zone stayed somewhere in between and typically within the bottom 15% of can height. For non-Newtonian (pseudoplastic) liquid, the recirculation pattern, radial and axial profile, and location of the slowest heating points were found to be qualitatively similar to that of Newtonian liquid discussed above. Presence of particulates reduces natural convection in viscous liquid such as silicone, but has very little effect on convection in thin liquid such as water. Smaller particles cause greater reduction in the convective flow.

Unagitated heating of liquid in microwave leads to similar flow patterns as explained above for conventional heating, since the microwaves heat more near the wall. However, dielectric properties also play a major role in microwave heating. A comparison of average temperatures of oil and water heated in a

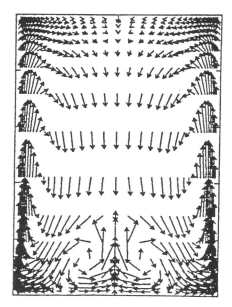

FIGURE 8 Flow pattern in a cylindrical can during natural convection heating.

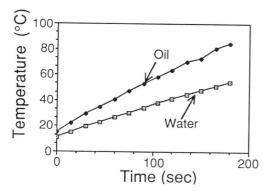

FIGURE 9 Transient mixed mean temperature of water and oil heated in a microwave oven.

microwave oven is shown in Fig. 9. Though oil absorbs significantly less microwave energy, due to the combined effect of a vastly different dielectric constant and a much lower specific heat, temperature rise is actually faster in oil.

II. Phase Change Heat Transfer during Freezing

By lowering the temperature of food, activity of microorganisms and enzyme systems is reduced. This prevents deterioration of the food product. During freezing, the sensible heat is first removed during chilling and then the latent heat is removed during freezing. The latent heat of freezing of water is a substantial portion of the total heat removed on freezing. Food products contain relatively large amounts of water in which various solutes are present. When referring to freezing of foods, it is the solution in the food that is of interest.

A. Freezing Process in Pure Liquids, Solutions, and Tissue Systems

1. Freezing Process in Pure Liquids
In freezing of a pure liquid, four distinct processes can be present: undercooling, nucleation, crystal growth, and maturation.

a. Undercooling (Also Called Supercooling)
Ice does not always form at 0°C. The temperature at which crystallization is initiated is not known a priori.

b. Nucleation
For any kind of crystal to grow, a stable seed which can act as a foundation is required.

These seeds are termed nuclei. Pure water may not freeze until around −40°C. At this temperature, homogeneous nucleation takes place—nuclei spontaneously generate, and the water freezes. However, homogeneous nucleation is not the most common nucleation mechanism for ice. Usually, extraneous (heterogeneous) nuclei are present and they help in the formation of ice. Heterogeneous nucleation takes place at temperatures much higher than −40°C.

c. Crystal growth
Crystal growth is possible once nucleation has taken place. As long as a stable ice crystal is present, further growth is possible. The rate of this growth is controlled in part by the rate of heat removal from the system. Rapid freezing tends to form small ice crystals, whereas slow freezing tends to produce large ice crystals.

d. Maturation
During storage, even at constant temperatures, a process occurs in which smaller ice crystals decrease in size, while larger ice crystals grow in size. With time, the number of ice crystals decreases and their average size increases—in part reversing the initial effects produced by rapid freezing. This increase in crystal size during storage can be important, and, as in the case of ice cream, may reduce the quality of the product.

B. Freezing Process in Solutions

Dissolved solutes in water in food materials depress its freezing point below that of pure water. This new freezing point can be calculated using Eq. (14) in Food Process Engineering: Thermodynamic and Transport Properties, discussed in colligative properties of foods. For a given amount of solution, as its temperature is lowered and freezing takes place, it is the pure water in the solution that freezes, mostly rejecting the solute. Thus, the unfrozen solution gets concentrated and its freezing point lowers further. This process is shown in Fig. 10. The concentration process continues until an eutectic point is reached where all of the solution freezes. In the commercial process of freeze concentration, freezing of a solution is used to concentrate solutions (by taking out the ice) that offer much less thermal degradation due to low temperatures involved. [*see* FOOD PROCESS ENGINEERING: THERMODYNAMIC AND TRANSPORT PROPERTIES.]

C. Freezing Process in Tissue Systems

The process of freezing in plant tissues is considerably more complicated than the freezing of a solution,

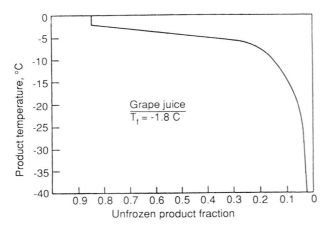

FIGURE 10 Concentration of a solution as temperature is lowered below freezing. Reproduced with permission from Heldman and Singh, 1975.

primarily due to the presence of cellular structure. As cooling proceeds, the intracellular as well as the extracellular fluid reaches the freezing temperature. The cell has been considered devoid of nucleating agents and thus it is normally assumed that ice forms in the extracellular fluid at first, thus concentrating the solution. The cell contents remain unfrozen and supercooled, presumably because the plasma membrane blocks the growth of ice crystals into the cytoplasm. The cell walls are generally considered freely permeable to water. Thus, water flows out of the cell due to osmosis and freezes in the extracellular space. This is one of the arguments given against slow freezing process that often leads to inferior quality of frozen foods.

D. Thawing

Thawing is not exactly the reverse of freezing process. Thermal conductivity of unfrozen food and biological materials is lower than their frozen forms. Thus, temperature during thawing process changes more slowly than freezing. Early work reported that only a portion of the water that flows out of the cell is reabsorbed upon thawing. The extent of rehydration of the cell would depend on the condition of the cell (i.e., whether the cell membrane was punctured or it lost its semipermeable nature).

Uniform heating characteristics of microwave heating can accelerate the thawing of food materials considerably. However, one problem in microwave thawing is the selective overheating of areas or runaway heating. Small fractions of an otherwise frozen food material always stay unfrozen as a concentrated

solution of constituents, such as sugar and salt. The dielectric loss (or energy absorption) is much higher for water in the liquid state as compared to the frozen state. The unfrozen pockets in the food material therefore will absorb larger amounts of energy and may be at boiling temperature while other areas may remain frozen. Ohmic or resistive heating is also being investigated for uniform and rapid thawing of food materials.

E. Estimation of Freezing Time

Some simple analytical solutions for estimating freezing time known as Plank's solution are used for most food freezing applications, although these solutions are true only for a pure liquid such as water. The Plank's solution assumes that initially all material is at freezing temperature but not frozen, there is only one freezing point, the latent heat is constant and is equal to the latent heat of water multiplied by the water fraction of the food, and all thermal properties are constant. Under these conditions, freezing time for a thin slab of thickness $2a$ is given by

$$t_F = \frac{\lambda \rho}{T_m - T_o} \left[\frac{a}{2h} + \frac{a^2}{8k} \right]. \qquad (12)$$

Similar expressions for freezing time are available for other geometries and slabs that are multidimensional.

The three basic assumptions made in Plank's equation, namely sharp freezing point, constant thermal conductivity, and negligible sensible heat (time to cool to freezing temperature and time to cool below freezing temperature), are not true in practice and may lead to serious inaccuracies. Empirical correction factors based on data or computational results are used to correct for the inaccuracies in Plank's equation resulting from the approximations. Other mathematical techniques can be used to calculate freezing time that are far more general and have very few limitations, as compared to Plank's equations or its modified forms. For example, Eq. (4) can be rewritten without convection or source term as

$$\frac{\partial (c_{p_a} T)}{\partial t} = \frac{k}{\rho} \frac{\partial^2 T}{\partial x^2}, \qquad (13)$$

where c_{p_a} is the apparent specific heat defined by Eq. (43) in the article on "Thermodynamic and Transport Properties," and is available experimentally for many materials. Equation (13) can be easily solved numerically to obtain a precise estimate of freezing time.

F. Storage of Frozen Foods

Storage conditions influence the quality of frozen food as much as the freezing process itself. Several chemical changes occurring during frozen storage include lipid oxidation, enzymatic browning, flavor deterioration, protein insolubilization, degradation of chlorophyll and pigments, and degradation of vitamins. Physical changes include increase in size of larger crystals and decrease in size of smaller crystals. Small, unavoidable, regular fluctuations due to periodic operations of refrigerating machines ($\approx$ 1–2°C) have negligible effect. Large fluctuations ($\approx$ 10°C) due to removal of frozen foods from cold storage to transport, and to transfer from vessels to trucks to retail cabinets, have a definite detrimental effect.

III. Phase Change Heat Transfer during Evaporation

In food processing, most often evaporation is the process of removal of water from an aqueous solution. Examples are concentrations of aqueous solutions of beet sugar, cane sugar, fruit juices, whey, milk, and maple syrup. Liquors vary widely in characteristics. Many physical and chemical changes take place in a food during evaporation. These changes are often undesirable. As evaporation proceeds and the solution becomes concentrated, its viscosity can increase tremendously and the heat transfer coefficient drops sharply. Adequate circulation and/or turbulence must be present to keep the coefficient from becoming too low. Continued boiling of a solution after it is saturated causes crystals to form. These crystals must be removed or the tubes may clog. Some solutions deposit scale on the heating surfaces causing the rate of heat transfer to decrease. During evaporation, the boiling point of the solution may also rise considerably as the solids content increases, so that the boiling temperature of a concentrated solution is much higher than that of water at the same pressure as stated under colligative properties of food. Thermal degradation of vitamins and other thermally sensitive components (such as browning) can occur in foods. Special designs are adopted to reduce the exposure to higher temperature and longer heating times.

The heat required for evaporation is generally provided by the condensation of vapor on one side of a metal surface with the evaporating liquid on the other side. The amount of steam required for evaporation depends on the feed liquid rate, its initial concentra-tion, its final (evaporated) concentration, and a number of operating parameters. Detailed calculations are performed to obtain the energy consumption by performing conservation of mass and energy around the evaporator.

The type of evaporating equipment is classified based on the configuration of the heat transfer surface and on the means employed to provide agitation or circulation of the liquid. Evaporators useful for food applications include: long tube vertical evaporators for condensed milk, falling film evaporators for fruit juices, agitated (wiped) film evaporator for gelatin and fruit juices containing pulp, and heat–pump cycle evaporators for fruit juices and milk.

IV. Mass Transfer

A. Thermodynamics, Modes of Mass Transfer, and the Species Conservation Equation

The subject of mass transfer deals with movement of one material component (species) inside another. It is different from fluid flow where bulk motion of all components taken together is of interest. The mass transfer concepts can be studied in almost an identical manner as heat transfer. Mass of a species moves from a location at higher concentration to a location at lower concentration in an analogous manner as energy moves from higher temperature to lower temperature. In both heat and mass transfer processes, the initial and the final equilibrium states determine the rates and extent of transfer. Thus, it is important to understand the final equilibrium states for various mass transfer situations. Transfer of mass between two phases requires the study of interphase equilibrium which has been discussed in the article on "Thermodynamic and Transport Properties."

B. Modes of Moisture Transfer

1. Molecular Diffusion

Unlike the three modes of heat transfer (conductive, convective, and radiative) there can be several modes of mass transfer such as molecular diffusion, capillary flow, electrophoretic migration, etc. In a material with two or more components whose concentrations vary within the material, there is a tendency for mass to move. Molecular mass diffusion is transport of one component from a region of higher concentration to a region of lower concentration. Flux is related to the concentration gradient by the Fick's law that is analogous to the Fourier's law of heat transfer (Eq. (1)).

$$J_{A,z} = (-D_{AB})\left(\frac{dc_A}{dz}\right). \tag{14}$$

Here $J_{A,z}$ is the molar flux of component A in the z direction per unit area perpendicular to that direction, D_{AB} is the diffusivity of species A in B, and c_A is concentration of A as a function of position z.

2. Capillary Flow

Solid food materials are often capillary porous. Capillarity of these materials is due to small pore sizes, and the liquid(generally water) is held at different degrees of tightness which must be overcome for the water to move or mass transfer to occur. Movement of liquid in an unsaturated capillary porous solid can be described by Darcy's law for an unsaturated solid as

$$q = -k\frac{\partial h}{\partial s}, \tag{15}$$

where q is the flux of water, k is hydraulic conductivity, h is hydraulic head, and s is distance. In an unsaturated solid, retention of water by the solid is due to capillary and other attractive forces between the water and the solid, and therefore h is negative. If c is the volume fraction of water in the solid, this equation can be rewritten as

$$q = -k\frac{\partial h}{\partial c}\frac{\partial c}{\partial s} = -\frac{k}{\left(\frac{\partial c}{\partial h}\right)}\frac{\partial c}{\partial s} = -D\frac{\partial c}{\partial s}, \tag{16}$$

where

$$D = \frac{k}{\left(\frac{\partial c}{\partial h}\right)}. \tag{17}$$

Here D is defined as diffusivity. The term $\partial c/\partial h$ is termed differential capacity. The diffusivity D depends on the material properties $h(c)$ and $k(c)$, and is therefore material specific. For foods, $D(c)$ can be measured directly. $D(c)$ reduces as the volume fraction of water c (a measure of water content).

It is important to note that although the term "diffusivity" is used to describe the capillary flow, the process is not the same as molecular diffusion. It so happens that the capillary flow equation can be cast in a form similar to the molecular diffusion (Eq. (14)). In reality, since diffusive, capillary, and other effects are difficult to separate, an effective diffusivity value

D_{eff} is defined as below that includes a number of modes of mass transfer:

C. Classification of Food Materials Based on Water Transport

1. Hygroscopic vs Nonhygroscopic Materials

In hygroscopic materials there is a level of moisture saturation below which the internal vapor pressure will be a function of saturation and temperature (expressed by the equilibrium moisture isotherms) and above which the vapor pressure will be a function of temperature only (expressed by Clapeyron's equation), and thus independent of the material moisture level at all times. According to van Brakel, in nonhygroscopic media, the pore space is filled with liquid if the medium is completely saturated, and filled with air if it is completely dry. The amount of physically bound water is negligible. The medium does not shrink during heating. Examples of nonhygroscopic capillary-porus media are sand, crushed minerals, polymer particles, and some ceramics. In hygroscopic media, there is a large amount of physically bound liquid and shrinkage often occurs during heating; most food materials can be treated as hygroscopic materials.

2. Capillary Porous vs. Porous Materials

The distinction here is based on the presence and size of pores. A porous material is sometimes defined as one that has pore diameters greater than or equal to 10^{-7} m and a capillary-porous material as one having pore diameter less than 10^{-7} m. Most food materials can be treated as capillary-porous materials that are also adsorptive, in which the capillary suction force and adsorption is the mechanism of water retention. Thus, most food materials are hygroscopic capillary-porous media.

In capillary-porous or porous materials (these are structured materials), transport of water is a more complex phenomenon. In addition to molecular diffusion, water transport can be due to vapor diffusion, surface diffusion, Knudsen diffusion, capillary flow, and purely hydrodynamic flow. As mentioned earlier, all of these effects are lumped into an effective diffusivity value. In liquid solutions and gels which are nonporous, transport of water is considered by only the relatively simple phenomenon of molecular diffusion.

D. The Species Mass Conservation Equation

Like heat transfer, for analysis of mass transfer, the material is treated as a continuum and differential equations of mass transfer are developed to apply them at every point in the material. In an analogous way, this is done by combining mass conservation for a species with the rate law described by Eq. (14) above. The final equation for mass transfer is

$$\underbrace{\frac{\partial C_A}{\partial t}}_{\text{Storage}} + \underbrace{u \frac{\partial C_A}{\partial x}}_{\substack{\text{Bulk} \\ \text{Flow}}} = \underbrace{D_{\text{eff}} \frac{\partial^2 C_A}{\partial x^2}}_{\substack{\text{Diffusive} \\ \text{Movement}}} + \underbrace{r_A}_{\text{Generation}}, \quad (18)$$

which looks almost identical to the energy transfer equation since the mass transfer process was also assumed to be diffusionlike (Eq. (14)). The meaning associated with individual terms is similar to those described under energy transfer. The mass generation term comes from generation or depletion of mass in chemical reactions or biological processes, such as the increase in microbial mass in a fermentor. At the same time, there is utilization of resources like O_2 in the fermentor in order to sustain growth.

E. Mass Transfer through Membranes

In a membrane separation process the membrane acts as a semipermeable barrier and separation occurs by the membrane controlling the rate of movement of various molecules between the two liquid phases. The membrane barrier prevents hydrodynamic flow and bulk mixing of the two liquids. Membrane processes are less energy consuming since they do not involve phase change as in evaporation. The two most useful membrane processes in the food industry are ultrafiltration and reverse osmosis. Ultrafiltration is used to separate relatively high-molecular-weight solutes such as proteins, polymers, and colloidal materials. In reverse osmosis, an applied pressure causes the solvent to flow in the direction opposite to what would be due to osmosis, (i.e., from concentrated to dilute solutions). Reverse osmosis is used to separate low-molecular-weight solutes such as sugar. Diffusive flux of a solute through a membrane can be written as

$$N_s = \frac{D_s K_s}{L_m} (c_1 - c_2), \quad (19)$$

where N_s is the flux of solute through the membrane, L_m is the membrane thickness, K_s comes from equilibrium relationship between solute in solution and solute in the membrane, and $c_1 - c_2$ is the concentration difference between the two surfaces of the membrane.

F. Moisture Transfer in Drying Processes

Drying of solids is studied as a diffusive moisture transfer process, although several different modes of moisture transfer process (such as pressure driven bulk flow) can be involved. For convenience, drying processes in solids are often divided into two periods—constant rate period and falling rate period. Constant rate drying period occurs intially when there is lots of liquid in the solid. Water is unbound, typically held in larger capillaries, and has little resistance in moving to the surface and maintaining a continuous film of water. The rate of evaporation under the given air condition is independent of the solid and is essentially the same as the rate from a free liquid surface, hence the name constant rate drying. This period continues only as long as migration of water from interior to the evaporating surface can keep up with the rate of evaporation. [*See* FOOD DEHYDRATION.]

As the water content reduces, the rate of water migration to the surface can no longer keep up with the rate of evaporation. At this point there is insufficient water on the surface to maintain a continuous film of water. Drying becomes limited by the rate at which water can migrate to the surface. The amount of available water, and therefore the rate of water migration to the surface, drops continually, making the drying rate fall. The plane of evaporation slowly recedes from the surface. Heat for the evaporation is transferred through the solid to the zone of vaporization. Vaporized water moves through the solid into the air stream. The amount of moisture removed during the falling rate period is relatively small but the time required may be long.

G. Moisture Transfer in Drying of Slab Shaped Solids

The best way to estimate the time of drying for a given batch of material is based on actual experimental data obtained under conditions where the feed material, relative exposed surface area, gas velocity, temperature, and humidity are essentially the same as in the final drier. The time of drying can also be found from theoretical analysis for various situations. The moisture movement inside the solid is modeled as an effective diffusion process and outside the solid (in the air) as a convective process. Rate of moisture movement within the material is sufficient to keep the surface saturated, while that of removal of water vapor is controlled by the rate of heat transfer to evaporating surface, which supplies the latent heat of evaporation for the liquid. Under these conditions, the constant drying time is given by

$$t_{\substack{\text{constant} \\ \text{rate}}} = \frac{(w_1 - w_c)\lambda_w M_s}{hA(T - T_w)}, \tag{20}$$

where w_1 is the initial moisture content, w_c is the moisture content at the end of constant rate drying, λ_w is the latent heat of evaporation of water, M_s is mass of dry solids, h is heat transfer coefficient, A is surface area of food, T is air temperature, and T_w is wet bulb temperature.

For the falling rate of drying, simplified solution of the species Eq. (18) provides the following estimate of drying time for a slab as

$$t_{\substack{\text{falling} \\ \text{rate}}} = \frac{4\delta^2}{\pi^2 D} \ln \left(\frac{8}{\pi^2} \frac{(w_c - w_e)}{(w - w_e)} \right), \tag{21}$$

where δ is half thickness of the slab, D is moisture diffusivity in the food, and w_e is the equilibrium moisture content for the conditions of drying air. The total drying time needed is the sum:

$$t_{\text{total}} = t_{\substack{\text{constant} \\ \text{rate}}} + t_{\substack{\text{falling} \\ \text{rate}}}. \tag{22}$$

The time for constant rate drying is often much smaller than the time for falling rate of drying.

H. Moisture Transfer in Drying of Liquids in Spray Form

Spray drying is performed by atomizing a concentrated liquid in the path of flowing hot air or gases. The basic processes are quite similar to drying of slab. Initially the spray drop has lots of water and evaporation from the drop is very much like that from a surface of pure water, a situation similar to initial constant rate drying of a slab. The droplet loses moisture at a constant rate per unit surface area and changes size as it falls. Droplet temperature stays constant at the wet bulb temperature during this process. This constant rate of drying continues until the droplet is quite concentrated and the surface no longer stays wet. The time for this constant rate of drying is calculated based on the change in the droplet size:

$$t_c = \frac{\lambda(\rho_0 d_0^2 - \rho_1 d_1^2)}{8k_a(T_a - T_w)}, \tag{23}$$

where λ is the latent heat of evaporation, ρ_0 and d_0 are the density and diameter at the start of the process, ρ_1 and d_1 are the density at the end of constant rate,

k_a is the thermal conductivity of air, T_a is air temperature, and T_w is the wet bulb temperature of the air.

At the end of constant rate period, droplet size remains constant and moisture movement is limited by diffusion to the surface of the droplet from inside. The rate of moisture removal decreases in this falling rate of drying. Droplet temperature no longer remains constant. Drying time can be calculated based on the final moisture content as

$$t_F = \frac{\lambda M_s}{hA\Delta T_{\text{ave}}} (w_c - w_e), \tag{24}$$

where M_s is the mass of solids in a drop, A is surface area, h is the heat transfer coefficient, ΔT_{ave} is the average temperature during the falling rate period, and w_c and w_e are moisture contents at the start and end, respectively, of falling rate period.

I. Moisture Transfer in a Freeze-Drying Process

In the freeze-drying process the original material is composed of a frozen core of material. Under vacuum this ice sublimes to the gaseous phase bypassing the liquid phase (Fig. 11). As the ice sublimes, the plane of sublimation, which starts at the outside surface, recedes and a porous shell of material already dried remains. Since the process is completed at a lower temperature, it is used for highly heat-sensitive mate-

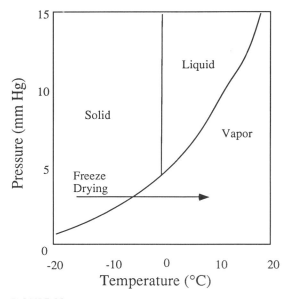

FIGURE 11 Sublimation of water from solid to vapor phase in a freeze-drying process.

rials. It produces the highest quality of dried material with less loss of aroma and flavor. Its slow and elaborate process makes it very expensive.

Heat by conduction, convection, and/or radiation from the gas phase reaches the outer surface. The latent heat of sublimation of 2838 kJ/kg ice is usually conducted inward through the layer of dried material. The vaporized water is transferred through the layer of dried material. Hence, heat and mass transfer are occurring simultaneously. The maximum temperatures reached in the dried and the frozen food must be low enough to keep degradation to a minimum. Thus, it is often the heat transfer process that limits the rate of drying. Based on the heat transfer as the rate limiting step, drying time can be calculated as

$$t = \frac{L^2}{8kV_s} \frac{\Delta H_s}{M_A} \frac{1}{T_e - T_f}. \quad (25)$$

Here L is the thickness of the frozen slab, ΔH_s is the enthalpy of sublimation, k is the thermal conductivity of the dried core, V_s is the volume of solid occupied by a unit kg of water initially, M_A is molecular weight of water, T_e is air temperature, and T_f is the temperature of the frozen core. The model satisfactorily predicted the drying times for removal of 65–90% of the total initial water. However, during removal of the last 10–35% of the water, the drying rate slowed markedly and the actual time was considerably greater than predicted for this period.

J. Use of Microwave Heat in Drying

Toward the later part of a drying process, often the difficulty is to transfer the heat to the inside wet material through an outer dried core. Since microwaves would be selectively absorbed (resulting in heating) in areas of higher moisture and very little of it would be absorbed in areas that are already dry, they are ideally suited for this purpose. This happens because the water molecules are selectively more responsive to microwaves. Thus, microwaves can be used for regular drying as well as freeze-drying. However, large-scale commercial applications of microwave to drying has not yet occurred.

V. Future Directions in Food Process Engineering

A large number of industrial and academic researchers are currently working on many of these topics on food process engineering. There is particularly strong activity in areas such as glass transition, rheology, thermal properties, extrusion, aseptic processing of particulates, microwave processing, controlled atmosphere storage, and frying. Continued research in these areas will revolutionize our knowledge of food processes in the coming years.

Bibliography

Ball, C. O., and Olson, F. C. W. (1957). "Sterilization in Food Technology." McGraw-Hill, New York.

Bruin, S., and Luyben, K. Ch. A. M. (1980). Drying of food materials: A review of recent developments.

Buffler (1992). "Microwave Cooking and Processing." Van Nostrand Reinhold, New York.

Casimir, D. J. (1975). Flame sterilization. *CSIRO Food Res. Q.* **35,** 34–39.

Charm, S. E. (1971). "The Fundamentals of Food Engineering," 2nd ed. AVI, Westport, CT.

Cheryan, M. (1992). Concentration of liquid foods by reverse osmosis. *In* "Handbook of Food Engineering" (D. R. Heldman and D. B. Lund, eds.), pp. 393–436. Marcel Dekker, New York.

Datta, A. K. (1989). Integrated thermokinetic modeling of processed liquid food quality. *In* "Engineering and Food" (W. E. L. Spiess and H. Schubert, eds.) Vol. 1), pp. 838–847. Elsevier, England.

Datta, A. K., and Hu, W. (1992). Quality optimization of dielectric heating processes. *Food Technol.* **46**(12), 53–56.

Datta, A. K., and Teixeira, A. (1988). Numerically predicted transient temperature and velocity profiles during natural convection heating of canned liquid foods. *J. Food Sci.* **53**(1), 191–195.

deAlwis, A. A. P., and Fryer, P. J. (1990). The use of direct resistance heating in the food industry. *J. Food Eng.* **11,** 3–27.

Enami, Y., and Ikeda, T. (1982). System for and method of sterilization of food material. UK Patent Application GB2 098 040.

Hallstrom, B., Skolderbrand, C., and Tragardh, C. (1988). "Heat Transfer and Food Products." Elsevier, England.

Heldman, D. R., and Lund, D. B. (1992). "Handbook of Food Engineering." Marcel Dekker, New York.

Heldman, D. R., and Singh, R. P. (1975). "Food Process Engineering." AVI, Westport, CT.

Hotani, S., and Mihori, T. (1983). Some thermal engineering aspects of the rotation method in sterilization. *In* "Heat Sterilization of Food" T. Motohiro and K. Hayakawa, eds.). Koseisha-Koseikaku Co., Ltd., Tokyo.

Kerkhof, P. J. A. M., and Thijssen, H. A. C. (1977). Quantitative study of the effects of process variables on aroma retention during the drying of liquid foods. *AIChE Symp. Ser.* **163**(73), 33–46.

Lopez, A. (1981). "A Complete Course in Canning. Book 1—Basic Information on Canning." The Canning Trade, Baltimore, MD.

Mazur, P. (1984). Freezing of living cells: Mechanisms and implications. *Am. J. Physiol.* **247,** C125–C142.

Merson, R. L., Leonard, S. J., Majia, E., and Heil, J. (1981). Temperature distributions and liquid side heat transfer coefficients in model liquid foods in cans undergoing flame sterilization heating. *J. Food Processing Eng.* **4,** 85.

Metaxas, A. C., and Meridith, R. J. (1983). "Industrial Microwave Heating." Peter Peregrinus Ltd.

Okos, M. R., Narsimhan, G., Singh, R. K., and Weitnauer, A. C. (1992). Food dehydration. *In* "Handbook of Food Engineering" (D. R. Heldman and D. B. Lund, eds.), pp. 437–562. Marcel Dekker, New York.

Pham, Q. T. (1985). A fast, unconditionally stable finite-difference scheme for heat conduction with phase change. *Int. J. Heat Mass Transfer* **28**(11), 2079–2084.

Rao, M. A., and Anantheswaran, R. C. (1988). Convective heat transfer to fluid foods in cans. *Adv. Food Res.* **32,** 39–84.

Rao, M. A., and Rizvi, S. S. H. (1986). "Engineering Properties of Foods." Marcel Dekker, New York.

Sastry, S. K., and Zuritz, C. A. (1987). A review of particle behavior in tube flow: Applications to aseptic processing. *J. Food Process Eng.* **10,** 27–52.

Skelland, A. H. P. (1967). "Non-Newtonian Fluid Flow and Heat Transfer." Wiley, New York.

Toledo, R. T. (1991). "Fundamentals of Food Process Engineering," 2nd ed. Van Nostrand Reinhold, New York.

Food Process Engineering: Storage and Transport of Fluid Foods in Plants

M. A. RAO, *Cornell University*

Glossary

Angle of repose of solids Angle made by a material with respect to the horizontal when piled; the coefficient of friction between granular materials is equal to the tangent of the angle of internal friction of the material; it is generally assumed that the angle of friction and the angle of repose are approximately equal

Flow models Many fluid foods do not follow Newton's law of viscosity in which the shearing stress is directly proportional to the shearing rate (velocity gradient); among the flow models for foods that show non-Newtonian behavior, the power law is widely used: the shearing stress is assumed to be proportional to the shearing rate raised to a power

Jenike's flow function Flowability of powders; it is an important property in designing bins and hoppers

Reynolds number Dimensionless number whose magnitude defines laminar and turbulent flows; it is also used in the calculation of friction losses in pipes

Sanitary standards Sanitary and microbiological considerations play important roles in the design of transportation and storage systems of foods; they include the use of stainless-steel and other approved materials of construction, the use of sanitary fittings, the design of pipe lines to eliminate stagnation zones and to facilitate drainage of the foods, the control of temperature and humidity of storage, and, often, minimal contact with oxygen to minimize degradation reactions

Foods are fragile materials of biological origin. The design of transportation and storage systems of foods requires special considerations that include the use of approved materials of construction, sanitary fittings, the elimination of stagnation zones, the control of temperature and humidity of storage, and, often, minimal contact with oxygen to minimize degradation reactions. Many foods exhibit shear rate effects and do not follow Newton's law of viscosity. The power law model is used to describe the rheological behavior of many non-Newtonian foods. The flow of powders is based on principles that are different from those for flow of liquids. Jenike's flow function characterizes the flowability of powders. [*See* FOOD PROCESS ENGINEERING: HEAT AND MASS TRANSFER; FOOD PROCESS ENGINEERING: THERMODYNAMIC AND TRANSPORT PROPERTIES.]

I. Storage of Fluid Foods in Plants

The transportation and storage of food products are two very important operations in the food processing industry. Because of the biological and fragile nature of foods, and the ever-present threat of attack by insects and microorganisms, the design of transportation and storage systems poses special challenges and problems. Therefore, sanitary and microbiological considerations play important roles and the design considerations include the use of stainless-steel and other approved materials of construction, the use of sanitary fittings, the design of pipe lines to eliminate stagnation zones and to facilitate drainage of the foods, the control of temperature and humidity of storage, and, often, minimal contact with oxygen to minimize degradation reactions. Foods are stored either for relatively short periods of times in food processing plants when used as ingredients for processed foods or for extended periods in warehouses where they are held as part of the distribution sector. In this article, the emphasis will be on in-plant storage although some of the principles also are applicable to storage of foods on a large-scale in warehouses. [*See* FOOD MICROBIOLOGY.]

Design of liquid ingredient storage tanks depends to some extent on the product to be stored. For foods, such as dairy products, that pose high microbiological risk, 3-A standards (discussed later) need to be consulted with regard to considerations not only for the design of storage tanks but also with respect to the design of the components of the associated transfer systems. For storage of liquid foods, density of the foods is a property that must be known in order to estimate the volume of storage tanks. The density and viscosity (or apparent viscosity) are important properties in the drainage of liquid food storage tanks and in the transportation of liquid foods. The densities of many liquid foods can be calculated from empirical equations compiled from the literature. Because many foods are non-Newtonian fluids, their rheological behavior and properties play an important role in the transportation of liquid foods.

A. Sanitary Standards

Because of microbiological considerations, ordinary pipe and fittings cannot be used for transporting liquid foods in food processing facilities; instead, well-constructed stainless-steel fittings should be used. Foods such as liquid sugars, syrups, and honey are generally not affected by bacteria, but they can support mold and yeast growth; therefore, the piping used should be of stainless steel. Transportation systems for liquid foods, such as dairy and egg products, sensitive to microbial spoilage must be designed according 3-A and E-3-A standards, respectively. According to Imholte, some of the considerations include: (1) self-draining installation of pipe systems without sags where a product could accumulate, (2) for clean in place (CIP) systems, sanitary weld fittings with standard take-apart fittings must be provided at pumps, valves, tanks, and other points of connection, and (3) pipe lines must be rigidly supported. For liquid sugars and syrups, piping systems must be generously oversized; a 3-in. diameter pipe was suggested as the minimum size. For oil handling systems, mild steel pipe may be used. Finally, to avoid contaminating food and to prevent damage to mechanical parts, pipe line strainers and magnets must be used on the suction side of pumps.

B. 3-A Standards

Whereas the sizes of storage tanks are calculated from simple arithmetic expressions, the sanitary aspects of storage of milk and egg products are very important and must be based on 3-A standards for storage tanks for milk and milk products (Number 01-00) and for egg products (Number E-0100). Because the movement of fluid foods in processing plants requires pumps, piping, and other auxiliary equipment, one must be aware of the 3-A standards for the various equipment also. The 3-A Sanitary Standards refers to the development by the original three parties: International Association of Milk Dealers (now the Milk Industry Foundation), the Dairy and Ice Cream Machinery Supply Association (now the Dairy and Food Industries Supply Association - DFISA), and the people associated with city, state, and Federal enforcement. While the title has been retained, it now refers to three different groups: (1) the International Association of Milk, Food, and Environmental Sanitarians, (2) USPHS/FDA, and (3) The Dairy Industry Committee (DIC) which represents a group of eight trade associations.

The 3-A Sanitary Standards set forth several criteria: (1) the material used in the construction of a piece of dairy equipment, (2) the fabrication and design of such material, and (3) its construction, including such things as the finish of the material, which are considered essential from a sanitary standpoint in the use, performance, and maintenance of such equipment. The E-3-A Sanitary Standards set forth the criteria for egg processing equipment. Each standard was developed through the joint collaboration of: (1) manufacturers of the equipment, (2) users of the equipment, (3) the International Association of Milk, Food, and Environmental Sanitarians' (IAMFES) Committee on Sanitary Procedure, (4) Poultry and Egg Institute of America, and (5) representatives of the U.S. Public Service/FDA, U.S. Department of Agriculture. The first rough equivalent of a 3-A Sanitary Standard was developed in 1929 and applied to sanitary fittings used in milk plants. A list of published 3-A Standards and of E-3-A Standards can be found in Handbook of Food Engineering. Because new Standards are needed from time to time, it must be ensured that one has an up to date list of standards by contacting either IAMFES or the *Journal of Food Protection* (502 E. Lincoln Way, Ames, IA 50010).

Labrie suggested that in addition to the 3-A Standards, the requirements according to Pasteurized Milk Ordinance and the FDA's Current Good Manufacturing Practices be also considered. Labrie also suggested several pointers to help provide a clean operating production line: (1) think small when it comes to wet process areas, (2) formation of a project team consisting of the Project Engineer, State Health Inspector, and personnel from plant production, maintenance, and sanitation, and representatives of the equipment manufacturer and the installation contractor, (3) processor participation in equipment design, and (4) essential communication, flow sheets, and sanitary details of installation drawings be used.

II. Rheology and Flow of Fluid Foods

A. Rheological Properties of Fluid and Semisolid Foods

Knowledge of the rheological properties of fluid foods is essential for the proper design and operation of unit operations, as well as for the understanding of the pertinent transport processes in the operations. Several foods, such as milk, syrups, filtered dilute juices, and vegetable oils, are Newtonian fluids. For these foods, knowledge of the viscosity function and its dependence upon temperature and concentration is sufficient for engineering design. The applicable methods can be found in standard texts on unit operations.

However, a large number of fluid foods are non-Newtonian in nature. Non-Newtonian fluid (NNF) foods exhibit flow behavior that is dependent upon shear rate at a constant temperature (Fig. 1). Few NNF foods exhibit time-dependent flow behavior; in these cases, one frequently encounters time-dependent shear-thinning (thixotropic) behavior, as opposed to time-dependent shear-thickening (rheopectic) behavior. In most cases, the time span over which this behavior is encountered is relatively short. Further, because of various mechanical operations in a

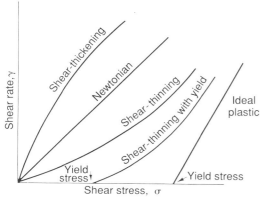

FIGURE 1 Classification of flow behavior of fluid and semisolid foods.

processing line, the time-dependent behavior will not persist for long. One can, to be conservative, design equipment on the basis of the higher magnitudes of rheological parameters for time-dependent fluids.

1. Flow Models

Several flow models have been employed to describe the flow behavior of NNF foods. We consider here only those models that have been employed in studies related to food unit operations. A substantial number of NNF foods are shear-thinning (pseudoplastic) in nature. The power-law model (Eq. (1)) has been employed extensively to relate the shear rate $\dot{\gamma}$ and the shear stress σ of these fluids:

$$\sigma = K\dot{\gamma}^n. \tag{1}$$

Typical magnitudes of the consistency index K (Pa.s^n) and the flow behavior index n (dimensionless) of food products are given in Table I; extensive compilations of power law parameters can be found in the review article by Holdsworth and other reviews. Because of the wide variability in test samples, one encounters a wide range of magnitudes for a specific food. Therefore, the data given in Table I must be used with considerable caution; if possible, the original reference must be consulted.

Some NNF foods possess a yield stress that must be exceeded for flow to occur. One can argue that, given enough time, all materials flow, and question the physical significance of yield stress. Nevertheless, models containing yield stress have been employed in several studies; in these instances, the yield stress can be considered to be important over the relatively short time spans of interest. Yield stress of a fluid food is a desirable property in coating a solid food and in keeping small pieces of spices or vegetables suspended. For the most part, magnitudes of yield stress of foods have been estimated by extrapolation of the shear rate–shear stress data. A few studies have attempted direct measurement of yield stress using the technique of rupturing a food with a vane.

The Herschel-Bulkley model (Eq. (2)), with a yield term added to the power-law model, and the Bingham Plastic model (Eq. (3)) have been employed in some studies on food unit operations:

$$\sigma - \sigma_{0H} = K_H\dot{\gamma}^{n_H} \tag{2}$$

$$\sigma - \sigma_B = \eta'\dot{\gamma}, \tag{3}$$

where the terms K_H and n_H are similar to the power law parameters K and n, σ_{0H} and σ_B represent the yield stress, and η' is the plastic viscosity. It appears

TABLE I

Power Law Parameters of Some Fluid Foods

Product	% Solids	Temp (°C)	Flow behavior index (dimensionless)	Consistency index (Pa.s^n)	Yield stress (Pa)
Chocolate					
Chocolate milk			0.26–0.42	0.39	5.8
Cocoa butter		40	1.0	0.041	
Dairy products					
Skim milk concn.		5–60	0.72–0.92	0.02–4.28	
Whole egg		61	1.0	0.67	
Egg white		62	1.0	0.45	
Egg white, fresh		2	0.56	0.19	
Egg yolk	42.6	5–60	0.87–0.89	0.17–0.77	
Fruit products					
Apple sauce	16°Brix	25	0.25	31–45	
Apricot puree			0.18–0.20	17.8–18.6	
Banana puree		25	0.35–0.62	6.4–27	21–28
Blackcurrant juice	35–64.5	5–60	1.0	2.4–500	
Guava puree	10.3	23.4	0.49	4.36	
Mango pulp	16–30°Brix	30–70	0.28–0.30	2.8–10.3	
Orange juice	65	−19–30	0.7–0.8	0.68–24.5	
Peach puree		25	0.41–0.83	0.6–4.5	8.5–14
Pear puree	18–43	32–82	0.45–0.49	2.3–35.5	
Tomato concentrates			0.18–0.26	70–100	
Tomato ketchup		25	0.38–0.61	2.0–9.4	15–24
Meats					
Raw meat batter		15	0.16–0.72	14–639	
Minced chicken		23	0.088	911	
Miscellaneous products					
Mayonnaise		25	0.54–0.59	4.2–4.7	
Mustard		25	0.21–0.56	3.4–37.0	

Source: Holdsworth, S. D. (1993). Rheological models used for the prediction of the flow properties of food products: A literature review. *Trans. Inst. Chem. Eng.* **71**, (C), 139–179.

that many foods follow shear-thinning with yield behavior, so that the Herschel-Bulkley model would be widely applicable.

2. Effect of Temperature on Flow Behavior

The effect of temperature on the flow behavior must be known when an NNF food is subjected to different temperatures, as in pasteurization and aseptic processing, and other unit operations. The Arrhenius relationship can be used to describe the effect of temperature on rheological parameters. Equation (4) describes the effect of temperature on the apparent viscosity η_a at a specified shear rate:

$$\eta_a = \eta_\infty \exp (E_a/RT), \qquad (4)$$

where η_∞ is a constant, E_a is the activation energy of flow, R is the gas constant, and T is the absolute temperature. For many foods, magnitudes of the activation energy depend on the range of temperatures employed. Therefore, caution should be exercised in

using literature values. The magnitudes of activation energy of most fluid foods are in the range 10 to 20 kJ/mol; the notable exceptions are concentrated fruit juices whose magnitudes of E_a are higher (40 to 80 kJ/mol) and they depend on both their sugar content and temperature range of the viscosity data. Expressions similar to Eq. (4) have been employed for the plastic viscosity of the Bingham Plastic model and the consistency index of the power-law model (Eq. (5)) in the design of continuous sterilizers.

$$K = K_\infty \exp (E_a/RT). \qquad (5)$$

3. Effect of Concentration and Temperature

Also of interest in evaporation and other unit operations is that in the case of some pseudoplastic foods, the effect of temperature and concentration C on apparent viscosity can be described by a single equation:

$$\eta_a = a \exp (E_a/RT)C^b, \qquad (6)$$

where a and b are constants.

B. Isothermal Flow in Tubes

Isothermal or near isothermal flow occurs in circular tubes (pipes) during the conveying of foods between different locations of a plant, in the holding tubes of pasteurizers (aseptic processing units), and in filling operation.

1. Flow Regimes

Because NNF foods are highly viscous, laminar flow will be encountered more often than turbulent flow. Several arguments can be offered for this hypothesis. For NNF foods such as soups, purees, sauces, and concentrates, very high pumping pressures would be required to obtain fully turbulent flow in tubes. These pumping pressures would not be economical for typical production rates encountered in practice. Also, the transition Reynolds numbers are higher for pseudoplastic fluids than for Newtonian fluids. It should be noted that rheological models, such as those described by Eqs. (1–3), are determined when flow is laminar, fully developed, and when there is no slip at the wall. Therefore, the equations to be presented are valid when the flow conditions meet the last two criteria also.

2. Velocity Profiles and Volumetric Flow Rates

Equations describing velocity profiles can be used, among other applications, to study the effect of different rheological models on the distribution of velocities and to understand the concept of residence-time distribution across the cross-section of a pipe or a channel. Volumetric flow rate–pressure drop equations can be used to estimate the pressure drop in a given system for a specific volumetric flow rate, and vice versa.

The velocity profile of a fluid flowing in a tube can be derived from the relationship

$$v = \int_r^R \left(-\frac{dv}{dr}\right) dr, \tag{7}$$

where v is the velocity in the axial direction, r is the radial coordinate, and R is the radius of the tube (Fig. 2). From a simple force balance for tube flow, one can obtain

$$\sigma_{rz} = \sigma_w \frac{r}{R} = -\frac{r \, dp}{2 \, dz}, \tag{8}$$

where σ_{rz} is the shear stress at any radius r, σ_w is the magnitude of the shear stress at the wall ($r = R$), p is the pressure, and z is the axial coordinate. Utilizing Eqs. (7) and (8) and noting that in the rheological

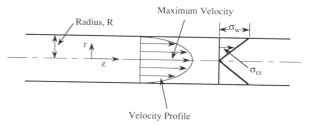

FIGURE 2 Radial and axial coordinates, and velocity and stress profiles for flow in tubes.

equations described by Eqs. (1–3), $\sigma = \sigma_{rz}$ and $\dot{\gamma} = -(dv/dr)$, one can derive equations describing the velocity profiles for laminar flow in a tube.

The volumetric flow rate Q is given by the equation

$$Q = \int_0^R 2\pi r v \, dr = \pi \int_0^R v(r) \, d(r)^2. \tag{9}$$

Integrating by parts the second part of Eq. (9), using the boundary condition $v = 0$ at $r = R$, and using Eq. (8), one can obtain the general equation for the volumetric flow of a fluid in a tube:

$$Q = \left(\frac{\pi R^3}{\sigma_w^3}\right) \int_0^{\sigma_w} \sigma_{rz}^2 \left(-\frac{dv}{dr}\right) d\sigma_{rz}. \tag{10}$$

One can substitute for the shear rate appropriate expressions from different rheological models and derive equations relating Q and pressure drop Δp.

In the case of fluids obeying the power-law model, the pressure drop per unit length $\Delta p/L$ is related to Q and R by the relationship

$$\frac{\Delta p}{L} \propto \frac{Q^n}{R^{3n+1}}. \tag{11}$$

From this relationship, we see that for Newtonian foods ($n = 1$) the pressure gradient is proportional to the R^{-4} power. Therefore, a small increase in the radius of the tube will result in a major reduction in the magnitude of the pressure gradient. In contrast, for a highly pseudoplastic fluid (e.g., $n = 0.2$), increasing the pipe radius does not have such a profound effect on the pressure gradient.

Also of interest is the relationship between the maximum velocity and the average velocity for the design of the length of a holding tube:

$$\frac{v_m}{\bar{v}} = \frac{3n + 1}{n + 1}. \tag{12}$$

For Newtonian fluids in laminar flow, one can de-duce from Eq. (12), the popular relationship that maximum velocity equals twice the average velocity.

In the case of the Herschel-Bulkley and Bingham Plastic models, there is a zone surrounding the center line that moves as a plug. This is because at the center line of the tube the shear stress is zero. The volumetric flow equations for these two models can also be expressed in terms of the radius of the plug r_p and the radius of the tube R instead of the yield stress σ_0 and the wall shear stress σ_w, respectively. We note here that the expressions for the volumetric flow rate can also be obtained by employing the left-hand side of Eq. (9) along with the appropriate expressions for the velocity profiles.

C. Mechanical Energy Balance Equation

The energy required to pump a liquid food through a pipeline can be calculated from the mechanical energy balance (MEB) equation. The MEB equation can be used to analyze pipe flow systems. For the steady-state flow of an incompressible fluid, the mechanical energy balance can be written as follows:

$$gZ_1 + P_1/\rho + (v_1^2/\alpha) - W$$
$$= gZ_2 + P_2/\rho + (v_2^2/\alpha) + E_f, \quad (13)$$

where, Z is the height above a reference point, P is the pressure, v is the fluid velocity, W is the work output per unit mass, E_f is the energy loss per unit mass, α is the kinetic energy correction factor, and the subscripts 1 and 2 refer to two points in the pipe system. The velocities at the entrance and exit of the system can be calculated from the respective diameters of the tanks or pipes and the volumetric flow rate of the food. The energy loss term E_f consists of losses due to friction in pipe and that due to friction in valves and fittings:

$$E_f = \frac{2fv^2L}{D} + \sum_1^N \frac{k_f v^2}{2}, \quad (14)$$

where, f is the friction factor, v is the velocity, L is the length of straight pipe of diameter D, k_f is the friction coefficient for a fitting, and N is the number of valves or fittings. It is emphasized that k_f is unique to a particular fitting and that different values of v, k_f, and f may be required when the system contains pipes of different diameters. Further, losses due to special equipment, such as heat exchangers, must be added to E_f.

1. Calculation of Friction Losses for Power-Law Fluids

For flow in pipes, one can utilize the capillary diagram of $(32Q/\pi D^3)$ vs $(D\Delta P/4L)$ to estimate the pres-

sure drop for a known flow rate. Because the shear rate is not uniform across the cross-section of the tube, the power law parameters K and n may not be applicable over the range of shear rates prevailing in the tube. Also, as in the case of Newtonian fluids, one would like to use a Reynolds number–friction factor chart to estimate the pressure drop.

The Fanning friction factor f is defined by the equation:

$$f = \frac{(D\Delta p/4L)}{(\rho \, \bar{v}^2/2)}, \quad (15)$$

where $\bar{v}$ is the average velocity in the tube. For laminar flow of a Newtonian fluid in a pipe, the friction factor f and Reynolds number Re are related by the expression

$$f = (16/\text{Re}). \quad (16)$$

For an NNF food, one can use the apparent viscosity η_{ap} (from the capillary diagram) in the Reynolds number:

$$\eta_{ap} = K'\left(\frac{8\bar{v}}{D}\right)^{n-1}, \quad (17)$$

where n and K' are the slope and intercept, respectively, of a plot of log $(32Q/\pi D^3)$ vs log $(D\Delta P/4L)$. Here it was assumed that the slope of the shear rate-shear stress is equal to that of a plot of log $(32Q/\pi D^3)$ vs log $(D\Delta P/4L)$. Incorporating the equation for η_{ap} in place of the Newtonian viscosity in the definition of the Reynolds number, one obtains the so-called generalized Reynolds number, Re':

$$\text{Re}' = \frac{D^n \bar{v}^{(2-n)}\rho}{8^{n-1}K}\left(\frac{4n}{3n+1}\right)^n. \quad (18)$$

For an NNF food, the Fanning friction factor when the flow is laminar can be calculated from Eq. (19), employing Re' in the place of Re:

$$f = (16/\text{Re}'). \quad (19)$$

We note that for turbulent flow, f is also a function of the flow behavior index, n.

In the absence of a capillary diagram, the parameter K' can be calculated if data are available in the form of shear rate $\dot{\gamma}$ and shear stress σ. If a power-type relationship exists between the pseudo shear rate ($8\bar{v}/D$) and σ_w, one can assume that the power-law model (Eq. (1)) will also be valid over the relevant ranges of shear rate and shear stress. Also, in most cases the slopes n and n' will be equal so that:

$$K' = K\left(\frac{3n+1}{4n}\right)^n. \quad (20)$$

2. Other Losses

Kinetic energy losses in the MEB equation can be calculated easily provided that the kinetic energy correction factor α can be determined. In turbulent flow, $\alpha = 2$. Graphical and analytical methods are available to calculate a in laminar flow. Losses due to fittings can be estimated using equations available in the literature that were derived from experimental data. For these data and other information on pipeline design and pump selection, the text of Steffe and other texts on the subject should be consulted. Another important consideration in the selection of pumps for some foods is to minimize contact between food and air so that oxygen-induced change is minimized.

III. Storage and Flow of Solid Foods

Both transportation and storage of solid foods are important operations in a food processing plant. A number of topics have been very well covered in other handbooks. For example, conveying of bulk solids, storage and weighing of solids in bulk, packaging and handling of solid and liquid products, and transportation of solids were well covered in the sixth edition of *Perry's Chemical Engineers' Handbook*. The storage and conveying of grains are well covered in *American Society of Agricultural Engineers' (ASAE) Standards*. The storage requirements and properties of perishable products, and the space, weight, and density data for commodities stored in refrigerated warehouses can be found in the *Applications Handbook of the American Society of Heating, Refrigerating, and Air-Conditioning Engineers (ASHRAE)*. The transportation and storage of grains and of fruits and vegetables were covered in a number of texts listed in the Bibliography. Therefore, these topics will not be covered here. In this section, the basic principles of solids storage applicable to food processing plants are discussed. [*See* GRAIN, FEED, AND CROP STORAGE.]

A. Solid Storage Bins

Bins for storage can be various shapes and sizes, but many storage tanks are circular in cross-section with storage capacities ranging from several thousand pounds to over a million bushels. For small and intermediate size bins, stainless steel is the material of choice when frequent wet cleaning is necessary and when the bins can be used for a variety of purposes. This is true for use bins and/or holding bins that are used to hold a product for a short period of time.

For bulk storage of solids, the bins can be built from mild steel and should not be located in wet manufacturing areas. These bins are of welded construction, with continuously welded butt seams and corner welds ground to have a $\frac{3}{16}$- to $\frac{1}{4}$-in. radius. The interior areas of the bins should be free from any horizontal ledges where the product may accumulate. Either the discharge hoppers must be properly sloped (as discussed later) or suitable mechanical unloading devices must be provided for complete product discharge.

Use/holding bins must also be constructed in a manner similar to bulk bins with proper interior and exterior finish, except that the material of construction is stainless steel. Square or rectangular bins must have corner radii of about $\frac{1}{2}$ in. for small bins and 1 to $1\frac{1}{2}$ in. for larger bins. For both use and storage bins, access doors measuring a minimum of 18 in. must be provided. These doors must be fabricated with quick-release fasteners that do not require tools for opening. Mild steel surfaces must be painted with food-grade epoxy enamel.

B. Design of Storage Tanks

The volume of storage tanks can be calculated from either the volume or the mass of the solid or liquid food that needs to be stored. When the mass is known, it can be converted to volume by dividing by the density of the food. The equation relating the volume (V) on one hand and the diameter (D) and height (h) on the other for cylindrical tanks is: $V = h(\pi/4) D^2$ and it can be employed to calculate either the height or the diameter, from knowledge of the other. The densities and bulk densities of several food powders are given in Table II; similar data on grains can be found in the text of Mohsenin.

TABLE II

Densities and Bulk Densities of Some Food Powders

Food	Solid density, ρ_s (kg/m^3)	Bulk density, ρ_b (kg/m^3)
Wheat flour	1450–1490	550–650
Rye flour	1450	450–700
Corn flour	1540	500–700
Corn starch	1620	550
Potato starch	1650	650
Rice, polished	1370–1390	700–800
Cocoa powder, 10% fat	1450	350–400
Cocoa powder, 22% fat	1420	400–550
Sucrose	1600	850–1050
Instant dried whole milk	1300–1450	450–550
Instant dried skim milk	1200–1400	250–550
Roast ground coffee	—	310–400
Instant coffee powder	—	200–430

Source: Rao, M. A. (1992). Transport and storage of food products. *In* "Handbook of Food Engineering" (D. R. Heldman and D. B. Lund, eds.), pp. 199–246. Marcel Dekker, New York.

C. Basic Concepts of Solid Friction

The ratio of friction force, F, and the force normal to the surface of contact, W, is given by the relationship

$$f = F/W, \qquad (21)$$

where f is the coefficient of friction. The commonly accepted concepts of friction are: (1) The friction force can be defined as the force acting in a plane containing the contact points that resists relative motion of the contact surfaces. (2) The friction force can be divided into two main components: (a) a force required to deform and sometimes shear the asperities of the contacting surface, and (b) a force required to overcome adhesion or cohesion of surfaces. (3) The friction force is directly proportional to the actual contact area. (4) The friction force depends on the sliding velocity of the contacting surfaces. (5) The friction force depends on the nature of materials in contact. (6) The friction force is not dependent on the surface roughness except in the case of very fine and very rough surfaces.

Friction phenomenon can be considered to be the sum of shearing force, S, and plowing force, P:

$$F = S + P. \qquad (22)$$

The above equation can be expanded to

$$F = (Ws/p_m) + Ap_d, \qquad (23)$$

where, s is the shearing stress of the softer material. From Eqs. (21) and (23) it can be concluded that the coefficient of static friction f_s is virtually independent of the area of contact. When the plowing term in the above equation is negligible, the coefficient of friction may be expressed in terms of the mechanical properties of the softer material:

$$f = \frac{s}{p_m} = \left(\frac{\text{shear strength}}{\text{yield pressure of softer materials}} \right). \qquad (24)$$

A number of factors affect friction; these include sliding velocity, water film, and surface roughness. In general, at low velocities, the coefficient of friction increases with velocity and at high velocities, friction either remains constant or decreases. Under certain conditions, increase in moisture may cause an increase in friction due to increase in adhesion. For many materials, however, addition of moisture results in lubrication, i. e., reduction in friction. There are considerable data on the coefficient of friction of agricultural materials such as chopped grass, corn silage, chopped alfalfa, shelled corn, and other grains and they can be found in the text of Mohsenin and in ASAE Standards.

1. Rolling Resistance of Materials

In applications such as the gravity conveying of fruits and vegetables, the rolling resistance or the maximum angle of stability in rolling of foods with rounded shapes may be useful information. For the case of a cylindrical or a spherical object of radius, r, and weight, W, rolling over a horizontal surface with a force F, the coefficient of rolling resistance, c, can be defined as

$$c = Fr/W. \qquad (25)$$

From the above equation, the rolling resistance, F, is directly proportional to the weight of the object and the coefficient of rolling resistance, and inversely proportional to the radius, r, of the rolling object. Coefficients of friction for apples and tomatoes are given in Table III.

2. Angle of Repose of Granular Materials

The coefficient of friction between granular materials is equal to the tangent of the angle of internal friction of the material. The angle of repose is the angle made by a material, with respect to the horizontal when piled. While it is generally assumed that the angle of friction and the angle of repose are approximately equal, for some materials, such as sorghum, magnitudes of the two angles can be different. There are two angles of repose, i.e., a static angle of repose taken up by a granular solid that is about to slide upon itself, and a dynamic angle of repose that

TABLE III

Coefficient of Rolling Resistance and Maximum Stability Angle (Degrees) of Apples and Tomatoes

Surface	Coefficient of friction		Rolling resistance (degrees)	
	Static (f_s)	Kinetic (f_k)	Static	Kinetic
Apples (six different varieties)				
Plywood	0.32–0.44	0.24–0.33	12–18	2.5–4.5
Galvanized steel	0.38–0.46	0.28–0.36	13–18	2.5–4.0
Rigid foam	0.34–0.44	0.28–0.38	13–18	2.5–4.0
Soft foam	0.72–0.93	0.55–0.75	11–16	4.0–5.0
Canvas	0.36–0.44	0.25–0.36	12–16	4.0–5.0
Tomatoes (four different varieties)				
Sheet aluminum	0.33–0.52	0.28–0.40	7–11	3.6–4.8
Plywood	0.41–0.60	0.41–0.56	9–14	3.6–4.8
Rigid foam	0.44–0.56	0.48–0.56	11–13	4.2–4.8
Soft foam	0.77–0.83	0.68–0.79	11–13	4.8–4.8
Canvas	0.48–0.75	0.49–0.67	13–14	4.8–7.0

Source: Mohsenin, N. N. (1986). "Physical Properties of Plant and Animal Materials." Gordon and Breach, New York.

arises in all cases where the bulk of the material is in motion, such as during discharging of solids from bins and hoppers.

Magnitudes of angle of repose increase with moisture content. Mohsenin credited Fowler and Wyatt with developing an equation for calculating the angle of repose of wheat, sand, canary seed, and other solids:

$$\tan \Phi_r = an^2 + b\left(\frac{M}{D_{av}}\right) + cs_g + d, \qquad (26)$$

where, Φ_r is the angle of repose, n is the shape factor based on the specific surface, M is the percentage moisture content, D_{av} is the average screen particle diameter, s_g is the specific gravity, and a, b, c, d are constants. The magnitudes of the coefficients were determined to be: $a = 0.4621$, $b = 0.0342$, $c = -0.0898$, and $d = 0.0978$, with a magnitude of the correlation coefficient, $R = 0.97$. These coefficients can be used to calculate magnitudes of the angle of repose of various solids.

3. Angle of Internal Friction

The angle of internal friction is needed for calculating the lateral pressure on a wall of a storage bin or in the design of gravity flow bins and hoppers. For example, the Rankine equation is used to calculate at a point the lateral pressure against the wall, σ_3:

$$\sigma_3 = w \, \gamma \, \tan^2 (45 - \Phi_i/2), \qquad (27)$$

where γ is the distance below the top of the wall, w is the density of the material, and Φ_i is the angle of internal friction. In the design of deep bins, one needs the ratio, k, of the lateral pressure σ_3 to the vertical pressure σ_1. This quantity also can be calculated using the angle of internal friction:

$$k = \frac{1 - \sin\Phi_i}{1 + \sin\Phi_i}. \qquad (28)$$

The horizontal pressure against the wall can be estimated from knowledge of the magnitude of k and the vertical pressure. Several factors affect the lateral pressure in bins, as indicated by Janssen's equation:

$$\sigma_3 = \frac{\rho R}{f_s}[1 - \exp(-kf_sh/R)], \qquad (29)$$

where, R is the hydraulic radius (ratio of area of cross-section to circumference), ρ is the density of the material, f_s is the static friction of the material against the wall, and h is the depth of material.

D. Flow of Powders and Granular Solids

Although there are some similarities in the storage of food grains and food powders, and many properties are common to both, it appears that their flow properties have been studied along separate paths. Further, it is clear that the major impetus to the study of the flow properties of all granular materials was the pioneering study of Jenike at the University of Utah, during the decade of 1960 and listed in the bibliography. In addition, the studies by Peleg and Schubert should be consulted. It should also be recognized that the mechanisms of liquid and solid flow are substantially different. The two major differences are: (1) in liquid flow, the flow rate is proportional to the square root of the liquid head above the outlet. In granular solids, the flow rate is independent, or nearly independent, of the head when the solid bed height is at least 2.5 times the outlet diameter, and (2) particulate solid materials can support considerable shear stresses or form stable structures that will prevent flow despite the existence of a head.

1. Factors Affecting Flow of Powders

The flow of a granular solid is affected by several forces: gravitational forces, friction, cohesion (interparticle attraction), and adhesion (particle-wall attraction). The formation of a stable solid arch above the aperture is also possible. Gravity is the natural driving force of unaided flow that can also cause considerable compaction of the bed. Consequently, the bed, due to enhanced cohesive forces, will have measurable mechanical properties such as tensile strength and compressive breaking strength. Therefore, flow takes place due to solid failure.

Noncohesive or "free-flowing" powders are those in which interparticle forces are negligible and the major obstruction to flow is internal friction. The condition for flow to occur is

$$\tau > \mu\sigma, \qquad (30)$$

where, τ is the shear stress, μ is the coefficient of friction, and σ is the normal stress. We note here that σ is the symbol used for normal stress in the literature on food powders; it must not be confused with the shear stress of liquid foods.

Interparticle forces can develop under special conditions, such as due to moisture absorption, elevated temperature, or static pressure, and they can reduce the flowability, stop it altogether, or form stable bridges (agglomeration). The latter phenomenon is usually referred to as a caking problem characterized by the formation of soft lumps to total solidification. Unlike noncohesive powders, the shear yield stress versus normal stress data for cohesive powders are characterized by: (1) a family of yield loci curves, i.e., at each consolidation level there is a different curve, and (2) the curves do not pass through the origin. At zero normal stress, the compacted powder has nonzero shear strength, called cohesion, whose magnitude depends on the properties of the powder and the consolidation conditions. The yield loci intercepts with the normal stress axis indicate the tensile strength. The tensile strength (T) provides a direct indication of the interparticle forces and its magnitude depends on the consolidation stress. For many powders, the yield loci can be described by the Warren Spring equation:

$$\left(\frac{\tau}{C}\right)^n = \frac{\sigma + T}{T}, \tag{31}$$

where, C is cohesion. From an energy balance of a compacted powder being sheared, one can show that cohesion is proportional to the tensile strength.

The angle of repose is a simple technical test in which the angle the powder forms with the horizontal is determined. Irrespective of the method of measurement of the angle of repose, it can be assumed that a small angle indicates a free flowing granular solid. One rule of thumb is that powders with an angle of repose less than 40° are free flowing, while those exhibiting angles of 50° or more are likely to cause flow problems. Magnitudes of angles of repose determined by different techniques will differ from each other and cannot be compared with each other. Because irregular cone angles are formed in the case of cohesive powders, the measurement of the angle becomes difficult.

2. Flowability of Powders

In 1970, Jenike established fundamental methods for determining flowability characteristics of powders. The experimental yield loci are obtained by plotting the normal stress versus the shear stress at a particular powder porosity. The normal and shear stresses are obtained in a Jenike shear cell. The stress condition of each point on the yield locus may be described by Mohr stress circles. The yield loci curves of many food materials can be approximated by a straight line, although it is expected to be slightly concave for all granular materials. Two Mohr stress semicircles that characterize two important properties are shown in Fig. 3. The larger semicircle characterizes

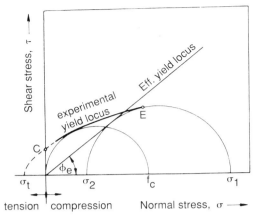

FIGURE 3 Illustration of two Mohr semicircles that define the major consolidation stress (σ_1) and the unconfined yield stress (f_c). (From Schubert, H. (1987). *J. Food Eng.* **6**, 1–32; 83–102.)

the stress conditions during steady-state flow, since it is passing through the point of consolidation conditions at which point steady-state flow, is reached and no changes in stress or volume take place. σ_1 is the major consolidation stress. The smaller semicircle is drawn tangential to the yield locus and passing through the origin; this gives f_c, the unconfined yield stress.

The unconfined yield stress (f_c) and the major consolidation stress (σ_1) are important parameters in design problems. The former is a measure of the solid's strength at a free surface, while the latter is related to the pressure applied to the solid if it were compressed in a cylinder with frictionless rigid wall. The angle of internal friction of the solid is the slope of the yield locus, and it varies from point to point due to the curvature of the yield locus. The flow function, ff_c, is defined as

$$ff_c = \left(\frac{\sigma_1}{f_c}\right). \tag{32}$$

The flow function, ff_c, characterizes the flowability of powders; it is an important property in designing bins and hoppers. Table IV contains a classification

TABLE IV

Flowability of Powders According to Jenike's Flow Function, $ff_c = \sigma_1/f_c$

$ff_c < 2$	Very cohesive, nonflowing	
		Cohesive powders
$2 < ff_c < 4$	Cohesive powders	
$4 < ff_c < 10$	Easy-flowing	
		Noncohesive powders
$10 < ff_c$	Free-flowing powders	

of powders according to their flowability based on the magnitude of the flow function, ff_c. While the flow function, ff_c, is a useful guide to the flowability of powders, a complete description of the flowability of particulate solids can be obtained only by measuring the yield loci at different magnitudes of porosities.

Cohesion, C, of powders described earlier is not as good an index of flowability as the flow function, ff_c. The tensile strength, σ_1, also defined earlier, may be used to interpolate the yield locus in the region in which the Mohr circle is plotted to determine f_c accurately. This is of particular importance in the dispensing of slightly cohesive instant food powders in vending machines.

The tangent to the major stress circle passing through the origin, is called the effective yield locus. The ratio of the two principal stresses σ_1 and σ_2, and the effective angle of friction Φ_e are related by the general equation describing the steady-state flow of powders:

$$\frac{\sigma_1}{\sigma_2} = \frac{1 + \sin\Phi_e}{1 - \sin\Phi_e}.$$ (33)

3. Design of Bins and Hoppers

Jenike's theory and the associated measurements are applied to the design of bins and hoppers. For foods with limited shelf life, mass flow bins, in which the entire bulk powder is in motion during discharge, are preferable to plug flow or funnel flow bins, in which a portion of the powder at the sides of the bin is stationary; in the latter, the food remains in the "dead" regions in which it can remain for long periods of time.

By using a procedure suggested by Jenike, the critical cone angle Θ_c, which is a function of the effective friction angle Φ_e and the friction angle Φ_w between bulk material and the wall may be taken from diagrams in the nomograph by Jenike that contain values of Θ_c as a function of Θ, Φ_e, and Φ_w.

Mass flow occurs when the cone angle $\Theta \leq \Theta_c$. For the particulate solids to flow without the formation of a stable arch, the outlet must have a minimum diameter, d_c. A stable arch is possible only for $\sigma_1' < f_c$; where, σ_1' is the major principal stress acting at the abutment of an arch and its magnitude may be calculated from:

$$\sigma_1' = \frac{\sigma_1}{ff} = \frac{\sigma_1}{f(\Theta,\Phi_e,\Phi_w)}.$$ (34)

The flow factor, ff, as a function of Θ, Φ_e, and Φ_w may be taken from the monograph of Jenike. The critical diameter d_c can be calculated by first assuming the condition $\sigma_1' = f_c$ which allows calculation of the critical stress σ_{1c}' which acts at the abutment of an arch:

$$d_c = \frac{\sigma_{1c}' H(\Theta)}{\rho_B g},$$ (35)

where, ρ_B is bulk density, g is acceleration due to gravity, $H(\Theta)$ is a function of the geometry of the hopper given in diagrams by Jenike. When $d > d_c$, the formation of a stable arch that in turn would prevent the discharge of a powder can be avoided.

Bibliography

ASHRAE (1981). "Fundamentals." ASHRAE, Atlanta, Georgia.

Charm, S. E. (1971). "The Fundamentals of Food Engineering," 2nd ed. AVI, Westport, CT.

Christensen, C. M. (1953). "Storage of Cereal Grains and Their Products," American Association of Cereal Chemists, St. Paul, MN.

Hahn, R. H., and Rosentreter, E. E. (1987). "Standards 1987." American Society of Agricultural Engineers, St. Joseph, MI.

Holdsworth, S. D. (1993). Rheological models used for the prediction of the flow properties of food products: A literature review. Trans. Instit. Chem. Eng. 71(C), 139–179.

IAMFES (1988). International Association of Milk, Food, and Environmental Sanitarians. Ames, Iowa.

Imholte, T. J. (1984). "Engineering for Food Safety and Sanitation: A Guide to the Sanitary Design of Food Plants and Food Plant Equipment." Technical Institute for Food Safety, Crystal, MN.

Jenike, A. W. (1970). Storage and Flow of Solids. Bulletin No. 123 of the Utah Engineering Experiment Station, 4th printing (revised), University of Utah, Salt Lake City.

Kokini, J. L. (1992). Rheological properties of foods. In "Handbook of Food Engineering" (D. R. Heldman and D. B. Lund, eds.) pp. 1–38. Marcel Dekker, New York.

Labrie, J. (1987). Correct the Equipment Design—Don't Fix It on the Job or How You Can Provide a Clean Operating Production Line. FPEI Workshop on Engineering for Sanitation, ASAE, St. Joseph, MI.

Lutz, J. M., and Hardenburg, R. E. (1968). "The Commercial Storage of Fruits, Vegetables, and Florist and Nursery Stocks." Agriculture Handbook No. 66, USDA, U.S. Government Printing Office, Washington, DC.

Mohsenin, N. N. (1986). "Physical Properties of Plant and Animal Materials." Gordon and Breach Science Publishers, New York.

Peleg, M. (1977). Flowability of food powders and methods for its evaluation. J. Food Process Eng. 1, 303–328.

Perry, R. H., and Green, D. (1984). "Perry's Chemical Engineers' Handbook." McGraw-Hill, New York.

Rao, M. A. (1992). Transport and storage of food products. *In* "Handbook of Food Engineering" (D. R. Heldman and D. B. Lund, eds.), pp. 199–246. Marcel Dekker, New York.

Rao, M. A., and Rizvi, S. S. H. (1986). "Engineering Properties of Foods." Marcel Dekker, New York.

Ryall, A. L., and Lipton, W. J. (1979). "Handling, Transportation and Storage of Fruits and Vegetables," Vol. 1, 2nd ed. AVI, Westport, CT.

Ryall, A. L., and Lipton, W. J. (1984). "Handling, Transportation and Storage of Fruits and Vegetables," Vol. 2, 2nd ed. AVI, Westport, CT.

Schubert, H. (1987). Food particle technology. Part I. Properties of particles and particulate food systems. *J. Food Eng.* **6,** 1–32.

Schubert, H. (1987). Food particle technology. Part II. Some specific cases. *J. Food Eng.* **6,** 83–102.

Steffe, J. F. (1992). "Rheological Methods in Food Process Engineering." Freeman Press, East Lansing, MI.

Food Process Engineering: Thermodynamic and Transport Properties

M. A. RAO, A. K. DATTA, *Cornell University*

Glossary

Colligative properties Depend on number but not on the nature of molecules in a system; they play an important role in a number of separation processes and purification processes in food manufacture, and water activity, including boiling point elevation, freezing point depression, and osmotic pressure

Reaction kinetics A number of chemical changes take place when foods are either stored at a constant temperature or subjected to a thermal process in which a range of temperatures is used and it is important to model the changes so that the extent of chemical changes can be calculated; in foods, most chemical and physical changes can be described by either zero-order or first-order kinetics

Transport properties In the context of food, transport processes typically refer to the transport of momentum (fluid flow), transport of thermal energy (heat transfer), and transport of species (mass transfer); transport properties describe rates of these transport processes (examples are viscosity for fluid flow, thermal conductivity for heat transfer, and mass diffusivity for mass transfer processes)

Unit operations Combination of one or more of physical transport processes combined with biological and chemical changes during that process

Food process engineering deals with the application of scientific and engineering principles in the manufacture, storage, and transportation of foods. For convenience, food manufacture is divided into unit operations. Knowledge of colligative and thermodynamic properties of foods is useful in food preservation operations and in extending shelf life of foods. [*See* FOOD PROCESS ENGINEERING: HEAT AND MASS TRANSFER; FOOD PROCESS ENGINEERING: STORAGE AND TRANSPORT OF FLUID FOODS IN PLANTS.]

I. Food Unit Operations and Transport Phenomena

According to Connor, the food processing industries are among the largest of the 20 industry groups in the manufacturing sector. In 1985, the latest year for which economic data were available, the food processing industries shipped products worth $302 billion, and they generated $104 billion in value added. Food process engineering deals with the application of scientific and engineering principles in the manufacture, storage, and transportation of foods. Foods are complex mixtures made up of several components, such as carbohydrates and proteins, with water being an important, if not the principal, component. Because foods are susceptible to attacks by microorganisms that can result in either spoilage or the production of fatal toxins, knowledge regarding harmful microorganisms and sanitary design are important areas of food process engineering. Some food processing operations, such as thermal processing, are designed to increase the shelf lives of foods, but they also alter the physical and chemical composition of foods. Thus, the kinetics of inactivation of microorganisms and of the changes in color, texture, enzymes, and vitamins are essential for the proper design of food processing operations. Other operations, such as mixing and fluid flow, achieve a desired objective other than extension of shelf life. Food process engineering is made up of several areas of knowledge and study, such as physical, thermal, chemical, and thermodynamic properties of foods, and processing unit operations and processes. Some of the important unit operations and the data needed for proper design and operation are listed in Table I. In this article, the transport and thermodynamic properties of foods are discussed. A number of texts and reference volumes have been published that contain much valuable information on these properties, and some of these are listed in the Bibliography; these should be consulted for additional information. [*See* THERMAL PROCESSING: CANNING AND PASTEURIZATION.]

II. Colligative and Equilibrium Properties of Foods

Colligative properties play an important role in a number of separation processes and water activity; they depend on number but not on the nature of molecules in a system. The colligative properties of ideal solutions are independent of the chemical nature of the solute. Typical colligative properties include boiling point elevation, freezing point depression, and osmotic pressure. The thermodynamic basis of colligative properties is discussed in brief.

A. Chemical Potential and Activity Coefficient

The Gibbs's free energy, G, for a closed system is defined as

$$G = H - TS = E + PV - TS, \qquad (1)$$

where, H is enthalpy, S is entropy, E is internal energy, T is absolute temperature, P is the pressure, and V is the volume. In a multicomponent system in which chemical species may be gained or lost, G is a function of $T, P,$ and the number of moles of a species i, n_i. The partial molar Gibbs's free energy $\bar{G}_i$ of a species i, or the chemical potential (μ_i) is defined as

$$\mu i = \bar{G}_i = \left(\frac{\partial G}{\partial n_i}\right)_{T,p,n_j}. \qquad (2)$$

Therefore, chemical potential is the change in free energy of a system due to an infinitesimal change in number of moles of a constituent i when temperature, pressure, and mole quantities of other constituents are held constant. It indicates the driving force in the

transfer of a component; the transfer occurs from a system with high μ_i to a system with a lower μ_i. At equilibrium, μ_i is equal for all systems and states. Specifically, when a solution and its vapor are in equilibrium, the chemical potential in the liquid (L) and the vapor (V) phases are equal:

$$\mu_{iL} = \mu_{iV}. \qquad (3)$$

The chemical potential of a gas can be expressed in terms of measurable functions and in terms of its value at its standard state, μ_i°:

$$\mu_i = \mu_i^\circ + RT \ln P_i. \qquad (4)$$

A new function, fugacity, is introduced such that for real gases at all pressures:

$$\mu_i = \mu_i^\circ + RT \ln f_i. \qquad (5)$$

It is also specified that

$$\lim_{P \to 0} \frac{f_i}{P} = 1. \qquad (6)$$

For a pure material in a solution, we can define the fugacity coefficient as (ϕ_i):

$$\phi_i = \frac{f_i}{P}. \qquad (7)$$

By definition, the activity coefficient, γ_i, of a constituent i is

$$\gamma_i = \frac{f_i}{x_i f_i^\circ}, \qquad (8)$$

where, f_i is the fugacity of component i in solution and f_i° is the fugacity at a standard state; for a pure component, the right-hand side reduces to the activity, a_i:

$$a_i = \frac{f_i}{f_i^\circ}. \qquad (9)$$

B. Water Activity of Food

From the above, the water activity at a constant temperature can be shown to be

$$a_w = \left(\frac{f_w}{f_w^0}\right)_T. \qquad (10)$$

Assuming that the vapor pressure correction factor for the solution and water to be the same, the ratio (f_w/f_w^0) may be replaced by (P_w/P_w°), so that

TABLE I

Major Unit Operations in Food Process Engineering[a]

Unit operation	Typical application in food industry
Absorption	Absorption of gases, typically carbon dioxide, by liquids, such as water, fruit juices, and soft drinks; scientific information, such as solubilities, is needed to control amount of a gas in a liquid food.
Adsorption	Adsorption of moisture, known as adsorption isotherms, by solid foods, especially dehydrated foods; this information is useful in assessing storage stability of foods. Adsorption of flavors during storage is also important.
Blanching	Mild heat treatment process prior to other operations. Blanching prior to freezing is done primarily to inactivate enzymes that change color, flavor, etc. Blanching prior to canning removes tissue gases, softens to facilitate packing, changes enzyme activity, etc.
Crystallization	Can occur spontaneously or be induced deliberately. It is important in sugars, salts, fats, ice, proteins, polysaccharides, and organic acids. Scientific information is needed for either efficient removal of a component or development and control of product texture.
Dehydration	Historically, dehydration has been a major method of food preservation. A variety of dehydrated foods are produced using different drying methods, such as air drying, solar drying, and freeze drying. The latter method is used to produce high-quality products, such as instant coffee.
Distillation	Distillation of weak solutions to obtain concentrated products such as flavors and spirits is used in the food industry. Scientific information is needed on physical and thermodynamic properties of the multicomponent systems.
Drum Drying	Popular methods to dry liquid food. A heated cylindrical drum rotates about a horizontal axis. A thin layer of product adheres to the drum surface and dries. The dried product is removed by scraping with a knife.
Evaporation	Evaporation of water from milk and fruit juices is widely used. Removal of water to sufficiently low levels can inhibit growth of microorganisms and, hence, extend the shelf life of foods. Scientific information is needed for efficient operation of evaporators and to retain desired nutrients, colors, and flavors of foods.
Extraction	Extraction of solutes, such as sugar, coffee, caffeine, and edible oils, using solvents, often water, is widely used. The use of supercritical carbon dioxide as a solvent is an important development. Although solid–liquid extraction is the predominant operation, liquid–liquid extraction also can be practiced. Information is needed for efficient removal of selected solutes, such as solid–liquid and liquid–liquid equilibrium data, and performance of extractors.
Extrusion	Extrusion of low-moisture cereal doughs and proteinaceous foods into foods of desirable structure is widely used; scientific information is needed on the rheological properties of melts, heat transfer during extrusion, performance and control of extruders, and for controlling textural product characteristics.
Freeze concentration	When dilute food solutions are frozen, more of the pure water in the solution changes to ice as freezing progresses (see heat transfer during freezing). This leaves the rest of the solution concentrated. If the ice can be removed from the system, a concentrated solution is obtained without much thermal degradation of the food that might accompany a concentration process using evaporation. Freeze concentration is used for fruit juices, milk, etc.
Fouling and cleaning	Fouling of food processing equipment reduces the efficiency of operation of heat exchangers, evaporators, and other equipment, and contaminates foods with undesirable deposits; it is undesirable beyond minimal levels. Therefore, the cleaning of food processing equipment is also important.
Heat transmission	Foods are heated to induce desirable textural changes, as in baking and roasting, and to inactivate harmful microorganisms, as in canning, also known as thermal processing. Operations such as infrared heating of foods, blanching of fruits and vegetables, aseptic processing of fluid and semisolid foods, and microwave heating and thawing are important operations in which heat is used. Scientific information is needed on rates of heat transmission, thermal properties of foods, flow properties of fluid and semisolid foods, destruction of microorganisms, inactivation of enzymes, and retention of nutrients, color, and texture.
Freezing	A variety of partially processed foods are frozen for availability over a long period of time. Frozen foods are kept frozen through the distribution channels until consumption. Scientific information needed includes freezing rates and times.
Packaging	Plays an important role in the preservation and distribution of processed foods. Some packages, such as cans and retortable pouches, are employed in both the processing and distribution segments. One aim of packaging is to keep a food from being exposed to moisture, oxygen, microorganisms, insects, and light. Another aim is to provide a desired atmosphere of oxygen and carbon dioxide to foods, especially fruits and vegetables; in controlled atmosphere packaging, the desired atmosphere is achieved by active means, usually by supplying nitrogen, oxygen, and carbon dioxide into a chamber, and controlling their concentrations. In modified atmosphere packaging, the gaseous atmosphere is achieved by passive means of balancing the respiration rate of produce and the diffusion characteristics of the packaging material.
Pasteurization	Heating process that kills part but not all of the vegetative microorganisms present in food and consequently it is used for foods which are to be further handled and stored under conditions that minimize bacterial growth. It is a milder form of thermal treatment as compared to sterilization.

continues

continued

Unit operation	Typical application in food industry
Refrigeration	Low and freezing temperatures are used to extend shelf lives of foods. However, refrigeration is generally considered to be a domain of mechanical engineering.
Sterilization	Defined as complete destruction of all viable microorganisms. Since this is impossible to achieve, sterilization is often really "commercial sterilization" where chances of survival of a pathogenic microorganism are extremely small (but nonzero).
Supercritical Extraction	When a gas or liquid is heated and compressed to conditions above its critical point, it becomes a supercritical fluid. Supercritical fluids have a unique combination of solvent and transport properties that make them unique for purifying fine chemicals, foods, and pharmaceuticals. In the food industry, supercritical carbon dioxide has found uses in decaffeination of coffee, extraction of edible oils, extraction of spices, removal of cholesterol from butter and beef, etc.

[a]A unit operation in the food industry is a combination of one or more of the physical transport processes discussed earlier together with biological and chemical changes during that process. For example, drying may involve heat transfer to evaporate the moisture, moisture diffusion inside the solid, viscoelastic deformations of the solid due to heat and the loss of moisture, color changes due to chemical reactions, and so on. Above is a list of the major unit operations that are being used in food industry. Description of other unit operations can be found in chemical engineering texts.

$$a_w = \left(\frac{P_w}{P_w^o}\right)_T.\tag{11}$$

Leung reviewed the thermodynamic basis of water activity and typical magnitudes of water activity (Table II) of foods.

C. Freezing Point Depression

Another important relationship can be derived for an ideal gas. The partial derivative of μ_i with respect to pressure can be written as

$$\left(\frac{\partial \mu_i}{\partial P}\right)_T = RTd(\ln P_i).\tag{12}$$

The above equation after integration and replacing pressure with fugacity becomes

$$\mu_i - \mu_i^o = RT \ln a_i.\tag{13}$$

The freezing point of a solution is depressed on the addition of a solute. Because at equilibrium, the chemical potential of the liquid (μ_L) and solid (μ_s) phases are equal, from Eq. (13) an equation for freezing point depression can be derived:

$$-\ln X_1 = \frac{\Delta H_f (T_o - T)}{RTT_o},\tag{14}$$

where, X_1 is the mole fraction of the solvent, T is the freezing point of the solution, T_o is the freezing point of the solvent, ΔH_f is the heat of fusion, and R is the gas constant.

D. Boiling Point Elevation

The addition of a nonvolatile solute causes elevation in the boiling point, ΔT_b, of the solution that can be

calculated from an expression derived from Eq. (13) assuming equilibrium to exist between the liquid and vapor phases, i.e., $\mu_L = \mu_V$:

$$\Delta T_b = \frac{RT_b^2 Mm}{1000 \Delta H_V},\tag{15}$$

where T_b is the original boiling point, M is the molecular weight of the solvent, ΔH_V is the heat of vaporization, and m is the molality of the solute; for water the expression reduces to $0.51m$.

E. Crystallization

The solubility concentration of a solute in a solvent is defined when the chemical potential of the solute in solution is identical to the chemical potential of a pure crystal of infinite size. At a given temperature, this concentration is the maximum amount of solute allowed in a solution. Solubilities vary with type of solute, type of solvent, and temperature. In general, most substances, such as sugars, exhibit increasing solubility with temperature; however, some salts exhibit a negative solubility curve. The driving force in crystallization is the difference in chemical potential between the solution phase (μ_{liquid}) and the crystalline solid (μ_{solid}). For crystallization, Eq. (13) can be written as:

$$\mu_{solid} - \mu_{liquid} = RT \ln\left(\frac{a}{a_{eq}}\right),\tag{16}$$

where a_{eq} is the activity of the equilibrium solid condition. Because activity data of important food solutions are not available, as an approximation, the activities are replaced by concentrations:

TABLE II

Magnitudes of Water Activity of Some Foods

Food	Water activity (a_w)
Cereal products	
Breakfast cereal (corn flakes)	0.09
Cake mix	0.30
Crackers	0.30
Rice	0.56
Whole wheat	0.68
Whole flour	0.68
Pancake batter	0.87
Cakes	0.72–0.94
Pumpkin pie	0.95
Biscuit dough	0.90–0.94
Bread	0.95–0.97
Dairy products	
Nonfat dry milk	0.14–0.28
Milk powder	0.75
Parmesan cheese	0.75–0.76
Sweet condensed milk	0.83–0.89
Whey cheese	0.88–0.91
Roquefort cheese	0.91
Cheese spreads	0.93–0.97
Cheddar cheese	0.95–0.98
Process cheese	0.97–0.98
Evaporated milk	0.97
Fruit and vegetable products	
Raisins	0.54–0.82
Concentrated orange juice	0.80–0.92
Orange marmalade	0.75
Cherry jam	0.79
Grape jelly	0.80–0.85
Preserves	0.84
Dates	0.85
Maple syrup	0.83–0.86
Tomato paste (28% solids)	0.97
Apple puree	0.97
Fruit cocktail	0.98
Canned vegetable soup	0.98
Meat products	
Fermented sausage	0.65
Cooked bacon	0.64
Dried sausage	0.70–0.74
Hard salami	0.79–0.91
Intermediate moisture dog food	0.75–0.87
Pepperoni	0.90
Raw ham	0.80–0.96
Dried beef	0.80–0.94
Salami	0.90–0.96
Luncheon meats	0.96–0.97
Cooked ham	0.97
Fresh meat	0.98–0.99
Confectionery products	
Plain chocolate	0.31
Chocolate candy	0.69
Milk chocolate	0.60
Corn syrup	0.60
Cake icing	0.76–0.84
Frosting	0.82
Fudge sauce	0.83–0.97
Chocolate syrup	0.91

continues

continued

Food	Water activity (a_w)
Other products	
Dry soup mix	0.21
Potato flakes	0.30
Cocoa	0.40
Dried egg	0.40
Cashew	0.75
Sunflower seed	0.75
Almond	0.79
Soy sauce	0.81
Peanut	0.84
Margarine	0.88
Nondairy whipped topping	0.93–0.97
Vanilla pudding	0.97–0.99

Source: Leung, H. K. (1986). Water activity and other colligative properties of foods. *In* "Physical and Chemical Properties of Food" (M. R. Okos, ed.), pp. 138–185. American Society of Agricultural Engineers, St. Joseph, MI.

$$\mu_{\text{solid}} - \mu_{\text{liquid}} = RT \ln\left(\frac{C}{C_s}\right), \qquad (17)$$

where C is concentration, and C_s is solubility concentration. Defining the supersaturation, S, as the ratio: $\left(\frac{C}{C_s}\right)$, at low levels of supersaturation ($S<1.1$) a good approximation is

$$\mu_{\text{solid}} - \mu_{\text{liquid}} = RT(S-1). \qquad (18)$$

F. Osmotic Pressure

When a solution and a pure solvent are separated by a membrane permeable to the solvent (A) and not to the solute (B), the solvent will move toward the solution. At equilibrium the chemical potential of the solvent on both sides of the membrane is the same, but an osmotic pressure (II) would develop. For ideal dilute solutions, the osmotic pressure can be calculated from:

$$\Pi = C_B RT, \qquad (19)$$

where C_B is the molar concentration of the solute. For nonideal solutions, an osmotic coefficient (ϕ) is defined:

$$\phi = \frac{-m_A \ln a_A}{\nu m_B} \qquad (20)$$

where ν is the number of moles of ions formed from one mole of electrolyte, and m_A and m_B are the molal concentrations of solvent and solute, respectively. The equation for osmotic pressure of non ideal solutions is

$$P = \frac{RT\phi\nu m_B}{m_A V_A}. \qquad (21)$$

G. Vapor–Liquid Equilibrium Relations

If the vapor is an ideal gas, the liquid-phase activity coefficient of a component i in a binary system is

$$\gamma i = \frac{\gamma_i P}{x_i P_i^{\circ}}, \qquad (22)$$

where P is the total pressure and P_i° is the vapor pressure of component i. In addition, from definition, it can be shown that the relative volatility of component with respect to component j (α_{ij}) is

$$\alpha_{ij} = \frac{\gamma_i P_i^{\circ}}{\gamma_j P_j^{\circ}}. \qquad (23)$$

If component i is in trace amounts, i.e., infinitely diluted, and the mole fraction of component j is approximately equal to one, the magnitude of the activity coefficient γ_j is equal to one. Therefore, the equation for relative volatility at infinite dilution becomes

$$\alpha_{ij}^{\infty} = \frac{\gamma_i P_i^{\circ}}{P_j^{\circ}}. \qquad (24)$$

This relationship is useful in the recovery and concentration of trace amounts, typically a few parts per million, of aroma and other volatiles.

H. Equilibrium Between Gas and Liquid

Equilibrium between a gas dissolved in the liquid phase in contact with the same gas in the vapor phase is related by the well known Henry's law for dilute concentrations (Fig. 1).

$$P_A = H' c_A, \qquad (25)$$

where P_A is partial pressure of A in gas phase at equilibrium, c_A is concentration of A in liquid phase at equilibrium, and H' is Henry's constant obtained from experimental measurements. An example would be the relationship between the concentration of oxygen in water and the concentration of oxygen in air that is in contact with the water.

I. Equilibrium Between Gas and Solid

Moisture in a solid in contact with air for a long time becomes in equilibrium with the moisture in air, and

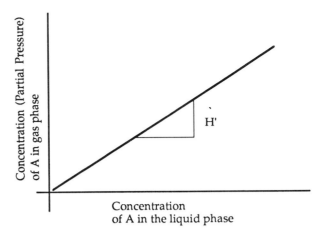

FIGURE 1 Henry's law for equilibrium between a gas and a liquid phase.

the solid stops to gain or lose moisture any longer. This is an example of equilibrium between a gas phase and a solid phase. The relationship between the moisture content of a particular material and its equilibrium relative humidity at the particular temperature can be expressed with an equilibrium moisture curve as in Fig. 2. These curves are often called isotherms because the values plotted for each curve usually correspond to a specific temperature. A number of equations have been developed to describe the isotherms as shown in Fig. 2. An example is the empirical Henderson equation:

$$1 - RH = \exp(-cM^n), \qquad (26)$$

where RH = relative humidity (in fraction), M is equilibrium moisture content(%), and c and n are constants for a material. Such curves are available from experimental measurements for a large number of food materials.

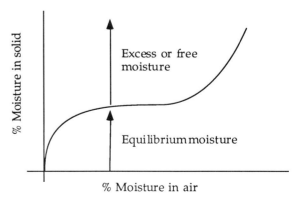

FIGURE 2 Isotherms showing equilibrium between a solid and a gas phase.

III. Reaction Kinetics and Models

A number of chemical changes take place when foods are either stored at a constant temperature or subjected to a thermal process in which a range of temperatures is used. It is important to model the changes so that the extent of chemical changes can be calculated. Because of the complex chemical composition of foods, it has not been possible to quantify all the changes taking place as a result of heating and to relate, in a quantitative manner, the chemical changes to physical changes such as softening. Some of the chemical changes, such as loss of vitamins, themselves are the end result of a thermally induced change.

A. Order of Reactions

For a simple reversible reaction:

$$\begin{array}{c} \xrightarrow{K_f} \\ A \quad B \\ \xleftarrow{} \\ K_r \end{array} \tag{27}$$

where A is the reactant, B is the product, K_f is the forward reaction rate constant, and K_r is the reverse reaction rate constant. The rate of reaction in the forward direction at a constant temperature is given by

$$-\frac{dA}{dt} = KA^n = \frac{dB}{dt}, \tag{28}$$

where n is the reaction order, t is time, dA/dt is the rate of change of A with time, and dB/dt is the rate of change of B.

In foods, most chemical and physical changes can be described by either zero-order or first-order kinetics. For a zero-order reaction

$$-\frac{dA}{dt} = K_0. \tag{29}$$

After integration and denoting the initial composition as A_o,

$$A = A_o - K_o t, \tag{30}$$

where K_o is the zero-order reaction rate constant. For a first-order reaction

$$-\frac{dA}{dt} = K_1 A, \tag{31}$$

where K_1 is the first-order reaction rate constant. After integration, one can obtain

$$A = A_o \exp(-K_1 t). \tag{32}$$

The D-value has been used extensively to characterize microbial death kinetics. The D-value is the time in minutes for a one log cycle change of a quantity, such as microbial population, at a constant temperature. The D-value and K_1 are related by the equation

$$K_1 = \frac{2.303}{D}. \tag{33}$$

B. Effect of Temperature on Rate Constant

In addition to describing the change in a quantity as a function of time at a fixed temperature, one must be able to describe the effect of temperature on the quantity. The reaction rate constant can be related to temperature according to the Arrhenius relationship:

$$K = K_r \left[\exp(-E_a/R) \left(\frac{1}{T} - \frac{1}{T_r} \right) \right], \tag{34}$$

where K is the reaction rate constant (e.g., K_o or K_1), K_r is the reaction rate constant at a reference temperature, E_a is the activation energy (J/mol), T (°K) is the temperature of the system, and T_r (°K) is the reference temperature.

The z-value is used in microbiology to characterize the influence of temperature on the D-value and it is the temperature change that results in a 10-fold change (one log cycle) in the D-value. The z-value and E_a are related by the equation

$$E_a = \frac{2.303 R T T_r}{z}. \tag{35}$$

In addition to the z-value and E_a, the Q_{10} value is used as a measure of the temperature coefficient of chemical and biological reactions and is defined as the change in the reaction rate constant for a change of 10°C:

$$Q_{10} = \frac{K(T°C + 10°C)}{K(T°C)}. \tag{36}$$

For many chemical reactions, the Q_{10} value is about 2.5–4. The relationship between Q_{10} and z-value is

$$z = \frac{18}{\log Q_{10}}. \tag{37}$$

Because of their toxin forming ability, spores of

Clostridium botulinum have received considerable attention; their commonly accepted *D*-value at 121.1°C (250°F) and *z*-value are 0.21 min and 10°C, respectively. Kinetic parameters for inactivation of microorganisms, activation and inactivation of enzymes and coenzymes, and loss of reactivity of amino acids were tabulated by Norwig and Thompson, and of nutrients and organoleptic changes in foods by Villota and Hawkes. The magnitudes of reaction rate constants at specific temperatures and of activation energies of a number of chemical reactions and death of microorganisms are given in Table III.

IV. Thermodynamic Properties Related to Internal Heat Generation

A. Dielectric Heating and Properties

Source term in the heat equation is important in applications such as microwave heating and resistive heating. For microwave heating, heat generation represents conversion of electromagnetic energy. Microwaves are electromagnetic waves and therefore are composed of an electrical and a magnetic field. Their wavelength range is 0.3–30 cm with a corresponding frequency range of 100–1 GHz. A dielectric is an electrically insulating material. Some dielectric materials like water contain permanent dipoles due to asymmetric charge distribution of unlike charge partners in a molecule that tend to reorient under the influence of a changing electric field, thus causing orientation polarization. The rotation of the dipoles in an alternating field to reorient themselves produces heat due to friction. The polarization in a material can also be induced by the electric field by displacing electrons around the nuclei (electronic polarization) or relative displacement of atomic nuclei because of the unequal distribution of charge in molecule formation (atomic polarization). Another source of polarization is the charge build-up in interfaces of components in heterogeneous systems, termed interfacial or space charge distribution. Water, the major constituent of most food products, is the source for microwave interactions with food materials through orientation polarization due to its dipolar nature. The other major source of interactions of microwaves with food materials is the dissolved salts in ionic solutions that act as conductive charge carriers in an electromagnetic field.

For microwave heating, heat generation per unit volume of material *Q* at any location is related to

the electrical field intensity *E* at that location by the Maxwell's equations of electromagnetic waves to be

$$Q = 2\pi f \varepsilon_0 \varepsilon'' E^2, \qquad (38)$$

where the magnetic losses in the food have been ignored. The electric field (and therefore Q) varies with position inside the food, giving rise to non-uniformity in microwave heating. The frequency *f* of the microwaves is 2450 MHz for most domestic ovens and 915 MHz for some industrial ovens. The symbol ε_0 is called the dielectric constant of free space and ε'' is the loss factor for the dielectric (food) being heated. At a given frequency, the dielectric loss factor is a function of composition of the food material and its temperature. Such temperature and composition dependence of the dielectric loss have been widely studied for various food materials.

B. Ohmic (Resistive) Heating and Properties

Ohmic heating is like resistive heating; therefore, its applicability depends on the electrical conductivity of the product. Food formulations with a moderate percentage of free water with dissolved ionic salts are reasonably good conductors and can be heated by the process. Most pumpable foods with water content exceeding 30% conduct electricity well enough for ohmic heating. Covalent, nonionized fluids such as fats, oils, alcohols, and sugar syrups, and nonmetallic solids such as bone, cellulose, and crystalline structures including ice cannot be directly ohmic heated.

Conductivity of most electrolytic solutions (e.g., soups, yogurt, meats, milk, fruit juices) increases strongly with temperature. This effect is often explained by increase in ionic mobility when viscosity decreases. In order to design equipment based on ohmic heating, reliable conductivity data are required. Several advantages of ohmic heating include reduced maintenance (no moving parts except the feed pump), reduced fouling (no hot heat transfer surfaces), increased uniformity of heating, and more efficient use of electrical energy.

C. Respirative Heating in Fresh Foods

In fresh produce, respiration continues during storage. Heat generated by such respiration is an internal heat generation and is often significant. Data on respirative heat generation can be seen in ASHRAE Handbook.

TABLE III

Magnitudes of Apparent First-Order Reaction Rate Constants and Activation Energy for Microbial Death, Inactivation of Enzymes, and Loss of Vitamins

Item	Food or system	Temp. range (°C)	Ref. temp (°C)	Reaction rate (min^{-1})	Activation energy (kJ/mol)
Inactivation of microorganisms					
Bacillus sterothermophilus	Aqueous suspension	100–121	115	0.102	388
	Milk	120–160	150	3.2	346
Bacillus subtilis spores	Aqueous suspension	100–110	100	0.20	367
Clostridium botulinum	Corn puree, pH 6.9	110–116	116	0.283	174
	Distilled water	104–127	121	45.1	334
	Pasteurized milk, 1.5% fat	104–113	113	9.59	351
	Formulated seafood, pH 5.9	100–113	100	0.0601	367
	Macaroni creole, pH 5.0	110–118	110	2.11	313
	Spanish rice, pH 6.0	110–118	110	1.21	313
	Beets	104–116	110	2.11	147
	Carrots	104–116	107	0.936	174
	Corn	104–116	110	1.50	170
Clostridium botulinum, 213-B	Snap beans	104–113	110	2.28	169
	Spinach	107–110	110	1.56	160
Clostridium botulinum, type A spores (A16037)	Tomato juice, pH 4.2	104–116	104	0.384	296
Clostridium perfringens, strain 8798	Beef gravy	99–116	104	0.334	384
Clostridium thermosacchrolyticum (S9) – acid form of spores	McIlvaine buffer	99–121	121	0.012	318
Escherichia coli	Milk, 10% solids	52–58	58	1.64	462
	Cottage cheese, pH 4.6	52–58	52	0.197	312
	Chocolate milk	52–80	57	0.886	375
Lactobacillus plantarum	Tomato juice, pH 4.5		70	0.209	187
Putrefactive anaerobe 3679	Beet puree, pH 6.9	110–127	119	0.555	305
	Corn puree, pH 6.5	110–127	119	0.631	322
	Pea puree, pH 7.0	110–141	119	0.555	305
Saccharomyces cerevisiae	Heated skim milk	55–60	60	7.0	544
	During spray drying skim milk	70–84	70	51	75
Salmonella senftenberg 775W	Chicken a la king	54–66	60	0.24	329
	Liquid egg, pH 5.45–5.55	56–61	60	0.242	165
	Milk chocolate	70–90	70	0.00523	132
Salmonella typhimurium	Egg albumin, pH 9.2	55–59	59	15.4	509
	Milk solution, 10% solids	51–57	57	1.64	528
Staphylococcus aureus 161-C	Cheddar cheese whey	58–62	60	1.73	295
	Skim milk	58–62	60	1.77	659
	Whole milk, pH 6.65	58–62	60	3.07	385
Streptococcus lactis	Cottage cheese	50–55	50	0.12	285
Inactivation of enzymes					
Chlorophyllase	Cut spinach	84–96	84	6.4×10^{-4}	251
Peroxidase	Corn-on-cob	70–100	100	8.9	75
	Green beans	104–177	104	8.5×10^{-4}	76
Loss of vitamins					
Vitamin C	Peas	110–132	121	2.296×10^{-3}	165
Thiamine (B$_1$)	Carrots	109–149	121	1.467×10^{-2}	119
Folic acid	Apple juice, pH 3.4	100–140	121	4.399×10^{-3}	83
Vitamin A	Yellow corn	60–80	80	1.35×10^{-3}	86

continues

continued

Item	Food or system	Temp. range (°C)	Ref. temp (°C)	Reaction rate (min^{-1})	Activation energy (kJ/mol)
Pigment losses					
Chlorophyll a	Spinach puree	116–126	121	0.174	114
Chlorophyll b	Spinach puree	116–126	121	0.0818	103
Anthocyanins	Concord grape pigments	85–95	90	3.60×10^{-3}	79
Anthocyanins	Raspberry juice, New Burg	78–108	88	2.874×10^{-3}	101
Betanine	Beet puree	102–116	110	0.0122	36
Textural changes					
Firmness loss	Peas during canning	99–127	121	0.2503	78
Firmness loss	Carrots during canning	90–120	121	0.492	114
Firmness loss	Shrimp during canning	115–140	121	0.0395	103

Sources: Norwig, J., and Thompson, D. R. (1986). Microbial population, enzyme and protein changes during processing. *In* "Physical and Chemical Properties of Food" (M. R. Okos, ed.), pp. 202–265. American Society of Agricultural Engineers, St. Joseph, MI: Villota, R., and Hawkes, J. G. (1986). Kinetics of nutrients and organoleptic changes in foods during processing. *In* "Physical and Chemical Properties of Food" (M. R. Okos, ed.), pp. 266–366. American Society of Agricultural Engineers, St. Joseph, MI.

V. Thermal Transport Properties of Food Materials

Thermal conductivity, density, and specific heat mentioned above are all important thermal properties of materials. Thermal properties of numerous food materials have been studied. Some useful references are Rao and Rizvi (1986), Okos (1986), and Singh (1993). For thermal conductivity, it is useful to think of a food material as a composite of its ingredients air, water, and ice that have distinctly different thermal conductivity values. Figure 3 shows the approximate magnitudes of thermal conductivity of different food materials in relation to air, water, and ice. Some dried porous foods are processed at below atmospheric pressures for freeze-drying applications, showing very small values of thermal conductivity. As an example of the range of thermal conductivities a single food can have, the thermal conductivities (W/mK) of apple at different processed forms are freeze-dried, 0.043; slices, 0.42; juice 0.56; and frozen, 1.5.

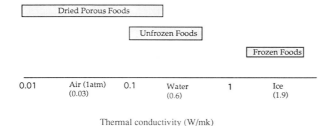

FIGURE 3 Approximate ranges of thermal conductivities of different types of foods.

VI. Mass Transport Properties of Food Materials

Unlike the three modes of heat transfer (conductive, convective, and radiative) there can be several modes of mass transfer such as molecular diffusion, capillary flow, electrophoretic migration, etc. In reality, since diffusive, capillary, and other effects are difficult to separate, an effective diffusivity value D_{eff} is defined as below that includes a number of modes of mass transfer:

$$J_{A,z} = (-D_{eff, AB})\left(\frac{dc_A}{dz}\right), \qquad (39)$$

where $J_{A,z}$ is the total flux resulting from diffusion, capillary flow, and other similar mechanisms. Sometimes internal evaporation develops pressures above atmospheric inside the material. This pressure-driven flow which is conceptually different from diffusive or capillary flow may also be included in D_{eff} simply because its separate effect cannot be easily measured or calculated.

It can be shown that the diffusion coefficient defined in Eq. (39) is one half of the mean-square displacement per unit time. Thus, diffusion coefficient is a measure of mobility. Consequently, diffusion coefficient can be expected to be larger for gases than liquids or solids due to increased molecular mobility of the gases. Likewise, it is higher for liquids than solids. For example, the diffusivities of gases, liquids, and solids as tabulated in the work of Saravacos are of the order of 10^{-5}, 10^{-9}, 10^{-11} m^2/sec, respectively. Most values available for the diffusion coefficient in food materials are experimental and there is great need for determining further diffusivity data for various food systems.

The diffusion coefficient depends on the pressure, temperature, and composition of the system. Since diffusion is related to the mobility of the molecule, it increases with temperature. Also, since the absolute size of a molecule determines how easily it diffuses or moves through matter, it generally decreases with the size of the molecule. For liquids, how easily a molecule travels would also depend on the viscosity of the medium. Thus, diffusion coefficient in liquids decreases with increase in viscosity. When gases diffuse in a porous solid, they cannot move through the small pores easily without being bounced from the walls. Thus, its extent of diffusion also depends on the nature of the pores (porosity and tortuosity) and this particular mode of diffusion is known as Knudsen diffusion.

This fact that diffusivity is a strong function of concentrations is utilized in the selective diffusion concept proposed by Kerkhof and Thijssen. The transport of both water and volatile aroma components in a drying food is governed by molecular diffusion. The diffusion coefficients of water and of aroma decrease strongly with decreasing water concentration. The decrease of the diffusion coefficient of aroma is, however, much stronger than that of water. As water is moved from the surface of the drying food, water concentration gradients develop. Some time after the onset of the drying process, the interfacial water concentration drops to a low enough value such that the diffusion coefficients of the aroma compounds become much lower than those of water and virtually no more aroma is lost by diffusion. Experimental and theoretical work has confirmed the relevance of the selective diffusion concept to spray drying, slab drying, and other drying processes.

The diffusive transport of gases and moisture through uniform materials such as packaging films is often described in terms of a permeability value. The gas or water vapor is first dissolved in the film surface and subsequently diffuses through the film in the direction of lower concentration of gas. The permeability and diffusivity values can be related by the use of solubility S of the gas in the film:

$$J_{A,z} = (-D_{\text{eff, }AB}) \left(\frac{dc_A}{dz}\right)$$
$$= -D_{\text{eff, }AB}S \left(\frac{dp_A}{dz}\right) = -P_{AB}\left(\frac{dp_A}{dz}\right), \quad (40)$$

where S is the ratio of concentration c_A of diffusing

component A in the solid phase divided by the partial pressure p_A of component A in the gas phase that is in equilibrium with the same in the solid phase. Thus, permeability is related to diffusivity as

$$P_{AB} = D_{\text{eff, }AB}S. \quad (41)$$

Typical permeabilities of food packaging films are available in Saravacos (1986).

VII. Effect of Phase Transition on Thermodynamic and Transport Properties

A. Gelation and Melting

Phase transitions take place in food during processing and storage that in turn affect the color, and physical and textural properties of foods. The term transition refers to a change in state due to a change in temperature or pressure. Because a number of food components are high-molecular-weight polymers, the phase transitions occurring during processing may be studied using a polymer science approach. Two common transitions are from a liquid state to a solid state (gelation) and from a solid state to a liquid state (melting). The gelation and melting temperatures either can be nearly equal in magnitudes, i.e., the gelation is reversible, or they differ by a significant magnitude, i.e., the gelation is irreversible. The difference in gelation and melting temperatures is called hysteresis. The creation of edible gels is an important goal in the production of processed foods. Edible gels are created from polysaccharides and proteins; in particular, starch gels play important roles in the diets of people from Africa to America. Therefore, gelation of food polymers is important.

B. Glass Transition

In addition to gelation and melting, the glass transition region is also important. This is because many polymers do not crystallize at low temperatures but reach a glassy state. At higher temperatures, the polymers form viscous liquids. The transition from the viscous state to the glassy state is known as the glass–rubber transition. In contrast to gelation and melting that are first-order transitions, at very slow rates of heating or cooling, the glass–rubber transition shows second-order transition characteristics. Typically, the modulus of elasticity and the viscosity decrease by large factors in a short range of temperature.

Glass transition is also denoted by (1) the change in slope of volume expansion, (2) a discontinuity in the thermal expansion coefficient, and (3) a discontinuity in the heat capacity. The glass transition region may be interpreted as the onset of long-range coordinated molecular motion. Glass transition has been shown to be an important phenomenon in foods, such as in the collapse of freeze-dried products, agglomeration of food powders, plasticization of starch by water, and crystallization of sugars. There are several methods for experimentally observing glass transition in polymers. These methods can be grouped under dilatometry studies, thermal methods, mechanical methods, dielectric and magnetic methods, and melt viscosity. For food systems, the thermal method, differential scanning calorimetry, has been used extensively. Magnitudes of the glass transition of a number of low-molecular-weight carbohydrates were compiled by Levine and Slade in 1992.

Flow can be interpreted as a form of molecular motion and that it requires a critical amount of free volume. One relationship between melt viscosity (η) at any temperature, T, in relation to the viscosity at the glass transition temperature (T_g) and free volume is the William-Landel-Ferry (WLF) equation that can be derived employing the free volume at the glass transition temperature.

$$\log_{10}\left(\frac{\eta}{\eta_{T_g}}\right) = \frac{-C_1(T - T_g)}{C_2 + (T - T_g)}. \tag{42}$$

For many polymers, the values of $C_1 = 17.44$ and $C_2 = 51.6$ may be used. However, the magnitudes of C_1 and C_2 vary from polymer to polymer. The WLF equation with the above values of constants was found to be applicable to molten glucose, undercooled melts of fructose and glucose, amorphous glucose–water mixtures, supersaturated sucrose solutions, amorphous sucrose and lactose powders at low moisture, and concentrated solutions of mixed sugars.

C. Freezing

Since water is often the major constituent in foods to be frozen, many of the property changes during freezing follow those of water. Thus, it is instructive to study how water properties change during freezing. The specific heat of water decreases at and below freezing as shown in Fig. 4. Often an apparent specific heat is defined as

$$c_{p_{apparent}} = \frac{\Delta H}{\Delta T}, \tag{43}$$

that includes the effect of latent heat and is used to

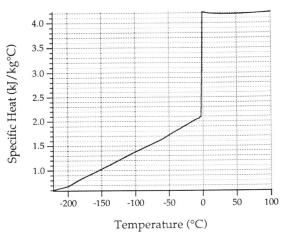

FIGURE 4 Specific heat of water showing decrease due to freezing.

describe phase change processes. In the above equation, ΔH is change in enthalpy due to change in temperature ΔT. For beef, experimentally determined enthalpy and apparent specific heat calculated from this enthalpy are shown in Fig. 5.

Density variation of pure water during freezing is shown in Fig. 6. The specific volume (inverse of density) increases by about 8% during freezing. The difference in density between unfrozen and frozen states of food is directly related to fraction of water frozen and can be calculated from the knowledge of fraction water frozen.

Ice has considerably higher thermal conductivity than water, as shown in Fig. 7. Thus, thermal conduc-

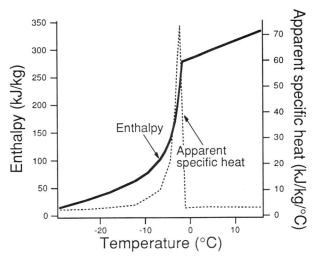

FIGURE 5 Enthalpy and apparent specific heat of beef during the freezing process.

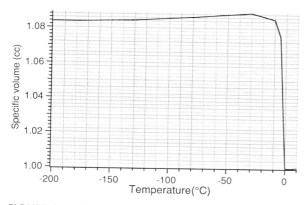

FIGURE 6 Volumetric expansion or change in density due to freezing of water.

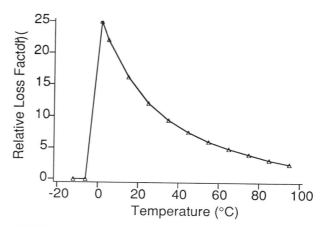

FIGURE 8 Change in the dielectric constant of water during freezing.

tivity of foods increases significantly when they are frozen.

Dielectric loss (a measure of absorption of microwaves) lowers drastically during freezing, as shown in Fig. 8. Food materials follow a similar trend between frozen and unfrozen states. This has significant implications in microwave thawing of frozen foods. [*see* FOOD PROCESS ENGINEERING: HEAT AND MASS TRANSFER.]

Bibliography

ASHRAE (1981). "Fundamentals." ASHRAE, Atlanta, Georgia.

Bengtsson, N., and Risman, P. (1971). Dielectric properties of foods at 3 GHz as determined by a cavity perturbation technique. Measurement of food materials. *J. Micro. Power* **6**(2), 107–123.

Choi, Y., and Okos, M. R. (1986). Thermal properties of liquid foods—Review. *In* "Physical and Chemical Properties of Food" (M. R. Okos, ed.), pp. 35–77. American Society of Agricultural Engineers, St. Joseph, MI.

Connor, J. M. (1988). "Food Processing, An Industrial Powerhouse in Transition." Lexington Foods, D. C. Heath and Co., Lexington, MA.

Datta, A. K. (1991). Error estimates for approximate kinetic parameters used in food literature. *J. Food Eng.* **18**, 181–199.

Heldman, D. R., and Lund, D. B. (1992). "Handbook of Food Engineering." Marcel Dekker, New York.

Leung, H. K. (1986). Water activity and other colligative properties of foods. *In* "Physical and Chemical Properties of Food" (M. R. Okos, ed.), pp. 138–185. American Society of Agricultural Engineers, St. Joseph, MI.

Levine, H., and Slade, L. (1992). Glass transitions in foods. *In* "Physical Chemistry of Foods" (H. G. Schwartzberg and R. W. Hartel, eds.), pp. 83–222. Marcel Dekker, New York.

Moore, W. J. (1972). "Physical Chemistry." Prentice-Hall, Englewood Cliffs, NJ.

Norwig, J., and Thompson, D. R. (1986). Microbial population, enzyme and protein changes during processing. *In* "Physical and Chemical Properties of Food" (M. R. Okos, ed.), pp. 202–265. American Society of Agricultural Engineers, St. Joseph, MI.

Okos, M. R. (1986). "Physical and Chemical Properties of Food." ASAE, St. Joseph, MI.

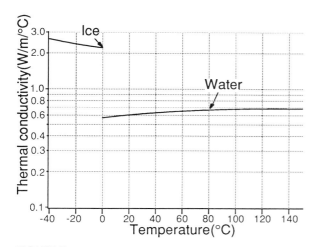

FIGURE 7 Change in conductivity of water during freezing.

Perry, R. H., and Green, D. (1984). "Perry's Chemical Engineers' Handbook." McGraw-Hill, New York.

Rao, M. A., and Rizvi, S. S. H. (1986). "Engineering Properties of Foods." Marcel Dekker, New York.

Roos, Y. H. (1992). Phase transitions and transformations in food systems. *In* "Handbook of Food Engineering" (D. R. Heldman and D. B. Lund, eds.), pp. 145–198. Marcel Dekker, New York.

Saravacos, G. D. (1986). Mass transfer properties of foods. *In* "Engineering Properties of Foods" (M. A. Rao and S. S. H. Rizvi, eds.). Marcel Dekker, New York.

Singh, R. P. (1994). "Food Properties Database." CRC Press, Boca Raton, FL.

Singh, R. P., and Heldman, D. R. (1986). Quality changes in frozen foods. *In* "Physical and Chemical Properties of Food" (M. R. Okos, ed.), pp. 186–201. American Society of Agricultural Engineers, St. Joseph, MI.

Villota, R., and Hawkes, J. G. (1986). Kinetics of nutrients and organoleptic changes in foods during processing. *In* "Physical and Chemical Properties of Food" (M. R. Okos, ed.), pp. 266–366. American Society of Agricultural Engineers, St. Joseph, MI.

Villota, R., and Hawkes, J. G. (1992). Reaction kinetics in food systems. *In* "Handbook of Food Engineering" (D. R. Heldman and D. B. Lund, eds.), pp. 39–144. Marcel Dekker, New York.

Food Toxicology

STEVE L. TAYLOR, *University of Nebraska*

Glossary

Hazard The capacity of a chemical substance to produce injury under the circumstances of exposure; since all chemicals are toxic, the dose and duration of exposure and other factors are critical determinants of a chemical's injurious potential

Risk The probability of harm associated with a certain degree of exposure to a chemical substance; food toxicology involves the assessment and management of risks associated with foodborne chemicals, both natural and human-made

Safety The practical certainty that injury will not result from the use of or exposure to a substance under specified conditions of quantity used or degree of exposure and manner of use or exposure; safety is the reciprocal of risk, that is, the probability that no harm will occur under specified conditions; absolute safety can never be proven because it is impossible to prove a negative

Toxicity The inherent capacity of a chemical substance to produce injury; the central axiom of toxicology is that all chemicals are toxic; the dose and duration of exposure determine the likelihood of injury or harm

Food toxicology can best be defined as the science that establishes the basis for judgments about the safety of foodborne chemicals. Toxicology can simply be defined as the science of poisons, but the central axiom of toxicology is the dictum of Paracelsus, set forth in the 1500s: "Everything is poison. Only the dose makes a thing not a poison." Thus, the food toxicologist is charged with assessing the potential hazards posed by all the chemicals in food, whether they are natural or synthetic, inherent, adventitious, or added. The food toxicologist gathers information on the toxicity of foodborne chemicals and their mechanisms of action and, based on that information, predicts the hazards that these foodborne chemicals might pose to the human population. Food toxicology is a multidisciplinary field drawing from chemistry, biochemistry, food science and technology, nutrition, physiology, pharmacology, and pharmacognosy.

I. Dose–Response Concept: Toxicity vs. Hazard

A. Comparative Toxicity of Foodborne Chemicals

All chemicals found in foods, whether natural or synthetic, inherent, adventitious, or added, are potentially toxic. The vast majority of foodborne chemicals is not hazardous because the amounts of each foodborne chemical in the typical diet are not sufficient to cause injury. However, remember that all chemicals are inherently toxic and will be hazardous if the dose and duration of exposure are sufficient to produce injury.

Many foodborne substances are justifiably viewed as safe and desirable because the benefits of their consumption far outweigh the remote risks of harm posed by the inherent toxicity of these chemicals. Water and vitamin A are examples of such beneficial substances. Nonetheless, it is possible to ingest sufficient amounts of either water or vitamin A, albeit in very abnormal diets, to elicit adverse reactions. Case reports exist of intoxications caused by excessive intakes of water and vitamin A. There are no safe chemicals in foods, only safe doses of chemicals.

Foodborne chemicals vary greatly in toxicity. Some foodborne chemicals, including water and vitamin A, exist in foods at concentrations that pose virtually no risk except under bizarre circumstances. Other foodborne chemicals are extremely toxic. An outstanding example is botulinum toxin, a neurotoxin produced when the bacterium *Clostridium botulinum* grows in foods. Botulinum toxin is the cause of botulism, a very serious foodborne illness sometimes associated with improperly canned foods. Botulinum toxin is an extremely potent neurotoxin; 1 g is an amount sufficient to kill 10 million people. For good reason, today's commercial canning regulations are dictated by the necessity to destroy *C. botulinum*. [*See* THERMAL PROCESSING: CANNING AND PASTEURIZATION.]

Although all foodborne chemicals are toxic, the degree of risk posed by exposure to any specific chemical is determined by the dose, duration, and frequency of exposure. Higher doses of chemicals are more likely to result in toxic manifestations than lower doses of that chemical. Often, threshold doses exist below which toxic manifestations are not encountered. Above this threshold dose, the toxic effects increase with increasing dose.

With longer term exposures, the duration and frequency of exposure are also key determinants of the potential hazard posed by exposure to a foodborne chemical. If the chemical is poorly eliminated, repeated exposures may be uneventful until a toxic threshold dose is reached *in vivo*. If the chemical is detoxified or excreted, then toxic manifestations are encountered only when the dose of the toxic agent is able to reach a hazardous level *in vivo* due to frequent exposures to amounts that are high enough to overwhelm the metabolic or excretory processes. With some toxicants, repeated exposure leads to incremental injury with some irreversible consequences that accumulate until a toxic manifestation is apparent.

Foodborne chemicals can cause a wide spectrum of toxic manifestations. The term "poison" is usually reserved for substances that can cause death, for example, botulinum toxin. To cause death, a toxin must interfere with a biochemical process that is essential for life. Other foodborne chemicals cause less serious manifestations ranging from cancer to diarrhea.

The manifestations of foodborne toxicants can be acute (immediate) or chronic (delayed). The exposure to hazardous doses of foodborne chemicals can also be acute (single exposure) or chronic (repeated expo-

sures). The neurotoxic effects of botulinum toxin are acute effects that follow acute exposures. Occasionally, acute exposures can result in chronic effects, especially if the toxicant cannot be easily eliminated from the body. Lead and mercury are examples of poorly eliminated toxicants than can cause chronic effects after an acute exposure, although exposure to these heavy metals is most frequently chronic. Cancer caused by foodborne carcinogens is an example of a chronic manifestation that most commonly results from chronic exposure.

The toxic effects of foodborne chemicals can be reversible or irreversible. The acute effects of foodborne toxicants are usually reversible. For example, staphylococcal enterotoxin produced in foods by the growth of toxigenic strains of the bacterium *Staphylococcus aureus* causes immediate vomiting, but the duration of the illness typically is only a few hours. Reversibility is sometimes much slower, as in botulism, in which the neurotoxic effects can last several weeks. The reversibility of the toxic effects of foodborne chemicals can also be a function of exposure dose. The effects of ethanol are readily reversible except at high doses, when irreversible liver damage and other effects can occur.

Toxicants can also be differentiated on the basis of the site of the toxic manifestation. Some foodborne toxicants are very site specific. Botulinum toxin targets the nervous system. Aflatoxin, a mycotoxin produced by several species of mold, is a carcinogen that primarily affects the liver. Most foodborne toxicants are systemic toxicants since they affect target organs beyond the gastrointestinal tract. However, a few foodborne toxicants, such as staphyloccal enterotoxin, chiefly cause localized effects directly in the primary organ of insult, the gastrointestinal tract.

Foodborne chemicals are typically ingested as mixtures in extraordinarily complex diets. Thus, it is not surprising that exposure to one chemical might affect the toxicity of a second chemical. Two foodborne chemicals may exert additive effects of toxicity if the two chemicals share a common manifestation. Since all organophosphate pesticides target acetylcholinesterase, an enzyme essential for nerve transmission, two organophosphate pesticides could have additive toxic effects. Synergistic effects can also be encountered, in which the combined effect of two chemicals is greater (often much greater) than the sum of the effects of either chemical given alone. For example, the naturally occurring cyclopropenoid fatty acids found in cottonseed oil can dramatically enhance the carcinogenicity of aflatoxin. Antagonistic effects are also possible and take several forms. In functional antagonism, two chemicals produce opposite effects on the same physiological function. For example, caffeine stimulates the central nervous system whereas ethanol at high doses depresses it, but ethanol at low doses is stimulatory. In chemical antagonism, a reaction between two chemicals produces a less toxic product. For example, the toxicity of mercury can be mitigated by selenium because of a binding between the two chemicals. In dispositional antagonism, the disposition (absorption, metabolism, distribution, or excretion) of a chemical is altered so less of the toxic chemical reaches the critical receptor site. For example, fiber lessens the absorption of many foodborne toxicants by trapping them in the gastrointestinal tract. In receptor antagonism, the interaction of a toxicant with its receptor is blocked by another chemical. This is a common mechanism of action for pharmaceuticals.

The comparative toxicities of several foodborne chemicals are provided in Table I. In this instance, the lethalities of these chemicals in laboratory animals are compared; LD_{50} is the dose (expressed as mg chemical per kg body weight of the animal) that will kill 50% of a group of animals. These numbers would be different if comparisons were made on the basis of other manifestations or were done for humans.

B. Toxicological Assessment Methods

The toxicity of foodborne chemicals is typically determined in laboratory animals and various *in vitro* assays. The toxicity of many food additives, agricultural chemicals, and industrial chemicals has been established in this manner, because their toxic properties are of commercial and regulatory concern. Less fre-

quently, the toxicity of naturally occurring chemicals in foods is evaluated in this manner.

For substances already present in the food supply, epidemiological approaches involving the evaluation of an exposed group of consumers, can be used to determine if ingestion of these substances is linked to specific adverse reactions. Epidemiological studies, although occasionally very useful, face serious limitations such as the identification of a unique at-risk population (these studies involve the comparison of a group exposed to the substance to another group that is not; with foodborne chemicals, identification of an unexposed group can be difficult) and the clear establishment of a cause-and-effect relationship. For example, many factors, dietary and otherwise, can contribute to cancer, so clearly establishing a relationship between ingestion of a specific foodborne chemical and the initiation of cancer in humans is difficult.

Animal bioassays are typically used to evaluate the toxicity of food additives, agricultural chemicals, and industrial chemicals. Animal bioassays also have serious limitations. Clearly, possibly important biochemical and physiological differences exist between humans and laboratory animals such as rats and mice. However, it would be unconscionable to use humans for such experiments, so little choice exists. In these experiments, small groups of laboratory animals are typically exposed to high levels of the chemical in question. Then, extrapolation is used to assess potential adverse effects in humans exposed to lower doses.

A decision-tree approach has been devised for the toxicological assessment of foodborne chemicals (Table II). The first step involves a definition of the test substance. Obviously, it is important to identify any impurities that might have some impact on the toxicity of the test substance. An assessment of the extent of exposure to the substance is also needed in the initial stage of the evaluation. The choice of dose

TABLE I

Comparative Lethalities of Several Foodborne Chemicals

Chemical	LD_{50} (mg/kg)
Ethanol	10,000
Sodium chloride	4,000
Ferrous sulfate (nutrient additive)	1,500
DDT (pesticide)	100
Tetrodotoxin (natural seafood toxicant)	0.10
Dioxin (TCDD, environmental contaminant)	0.001
Botulinum toxin (natural bacterial toxicant)	0.00001

TABLE II

Decision Tree Approach to Toxicological Evaluation of Foodborne Chemicals[a]

Stage 1	Definition of test material
	Exposure assessment
	Acute toxicity
Stage 2	Genetic toxicology
	Metabolism and toxicokinetics
Stage 3	Subchronic toxicity and reproductive toxicology
Stage 4	Chronic toxicity

[a] Progression from one stage to the next stage is dependent on obtaining negative results or inconsistent indications of toxicity in the previous stage.

levels should be based, in part, on the realistic levels of human exposure, although common practice involves the use of test doses that are higher than typical human exposures to compensate for the use of small numbers of animals in each test group and the shorter duration of the exposure (in comparison with the 70-yr or greater potential for human exposure). If the food-borne substance is already in use or present in food, then various methods such as dietary surveys are used to estimate exposure. If the substance is not in use, assumptions must be made to estimate potential exposure. Attempts are made to identify exposure levels for individual consumers or groups who, as a result of dietary practices, are likely to be exposed to high amounts of the particular substance.

Following these preliminary steps, a progressive series of toxicological tests is conducted in laboratory animals or *in vitro* assays. In the decision-tree approach, decisions may be made to eliminate the latter, and more expensive, tests if evidence of toxicity is profound in the earlier stages. Also, the chronic toxicity testing can be eliminated if earlier tests show a profound lack of toxicity and the metabolic studies indicate that the substance is metabolized to normal physiological substances and does not interfere with normal metabolism.

For substances that do not require chronic toxicity or carcinogenicity tests, the usual approach involves the establishment of a "no-observed-adverse-effect" level (NOAEL) by direct inspection of the dose–response relationship in animals, especially during 30-day or 90-day subchronic toxicity tests. Since animal data cannot be directly extrapolated to humans, the concept of the acceptable daily intake (ADI) was devised. The ADI is obtained by dividing the NOAEL by 100. The 100-fold safety factor includes a factor of 10 for individual variation within the human species and a factor of 10 for variation among species, for example, rats and humans. If the data are solid and the toxic effects are of little concern, a smaller safety factor can be applied.

The centerpiece of food toxicology today is the carcinogenicity study in two species, usually rats and mice, lasting for 2 yr or more. The test substance is fed at several dose levels, usually including the maximum tolerated dose—the highest dose estimated from subchronic studies that will not elicit overt signs of toxicity with extended administration. An undosed control group is included for comparison. For food toxicology studies, the oral route of administration is really the only relevant exposure. Fifty animals of each sex are typically included in each dosage group.

An extensive histopathological examination of more than 30 organs and tissues, plus gross lesions and blood samples, is conducted at intervals throughout the study and at the end of the study. Particular attention is paid to evidence of tumors. Data on tumor incidence obtained at high doses in laboratory animals must then be extrapolated to predict the risk in humans exposed to much lower doses of the chemical. Since no one knows the shape of the dose–response relationship at low doses, this quantitative risk assessment process is fraught with assumptions and uncertainty. Thus, the estimates of the risk of cancer in humans posed by foodborne chemicals are always subject to debate and uncertainty. However, the chronic toxicity test in laboratory animals is the best existing test to assess the carcinogenicity of foodborne chemicals. Although short-term, *in vitro* tests have been developed and are used effectively for genetic toxicity evaluations, these tests are not reliable substitutes for animal carcinogenicity tests.

C. Risk Management Concepts

Despite the imperfections of toxicological assessment methods, these methods must be employed in the assessment of potential human health hazards. Although estimates of human risk are imperfect as a result, the risk estimates can be (but frequently are not) used successfully in a comparative fashion. For example, the risks of two alternative foodborne chemicals could be compared to determine which one poses the greatest risk. Risks may be ranked. The elimination of risk is impossible. Inevitably, we are forced to trade one risk for another. For example, pesticides pose some risk to human health even when exposures are limited to trace residues. Elimination of pesticides would not eliminate risk, but would trade the risk associated with pesticides for any risks that might be associated with foods not treated with pesticides. Although these "natural" risks have not been carefully evaluated, increased risks of insect-produced toxins, mold and mycotoxins, and poisonous weeds might be anticipated.

Certainly, the logical approach would be to evaluate the various risks and to select the least risky practice or chemical. Unfortunately, this type of risk management is not mandated by the food laws of most countries.

D. Food Laws and Regulations

Food laws and regulations are intended to control the risks posed by foodborne toxins in the diet. The primary agency involved in regulating the safety of the food supply in the United States, is the Food and Drug Administration (FDA). The FDA enforces the 1958 Food, Drug, and Cosmetic Act, which prohibits the sale of foods containing poisonous or deleterious substances in amounts that would render the food injurious to health.

The U.S. food laws require premarket approval of any new food additive; the premarket approval process typically requires a thorough toxicological assessment of the new additive and careful scrutiny of this data by the FDA. New additives cannot be approved if carcinogenic effects are observed, or if other significant adverse reactions are encountered in the toxicological assessment process. New food additives usually are approved for use in certain foods at specified levels. The 1958 Food, Drug, and Cosmetic Act defined some commonly used food ingredients as Generally Recognized as Safe (GRAS). GRAS food ingredients, such as sugar and salt, can be used in most foods at any level consistent with Good Manufacturing Practice (GMP).

The FDA also establishes tolerance limits for pesticide residues on foods. The Environmental Protection Agency (EPA) is the federal office that approves pesticides for use on agricultural crops. The FDA establishes tolerance limits that are well below levels that elicit carcinogenic or other adverse reactions in experimental animals.

Under U.S. food laws, naturally occurring toxins in foods are regulated more leniently than food additives, or other substances, that are intentionally added to foods. Naturally occurring chemicals are widespread in food. Since all chemicals are toxic under certain conditions, any naturally occurring chemical could be identified as a natural toxin. In reality, most naturally occurring toxins pose only trivial or slight risks, and, in many cases, would be extremely expensive or impossible to eliminate. However, the hazards posed by natural toxins in foods may outweigh the hazards posed by pesticide residues or food additives. The lack of regulatory standards for naturally occurring toxins creates an illogical focus of attention toward trivial risks posed by most pesticide residues and food additives.

On an international basis, most developed countries have food laws and regulations intended to control the risks posed by foodborne toxins. Less developed countries often lack these types of laws and regulations. There are many differences in the food laws and regulations of between countries. However, like the United States, international food laws and regula-tions primarily focus on the safety of intentionally added ingredients as opposed to naturally occurring chemicals.

II. Categories of Foodborne Toxicants

A. Naturally Occurring Toxicants

Although unrecognized by many consumers, naturally occurring chemicals in foods present the greatest risk of any of the chemicals in foods. Certainly, microbiological pathogens cause more illness than any of the categories of foodborne chemicals. It could be argued that nutritional imbalances—including, for example, cholesterol and coronary heart disease and caloric intake and obesity and/or cancer and heart disease—also cause more human morbidity and mortality. The diseases involved with nutritional imbalances are multifactorial, and the contribution of foods to the overall incidence is not precisely known. Although cholesterol, saturated fats, and the like are chemicals, these illnesses can be conceptually distinguished from chemical intoxications. [See FOOD MICROBIOLOGY.]

The hazards posed by naturally occurring chemicals in foods can have several natural sources (Table III). Naturally occurring constituents of unusual "foods" can present hazards, on occasion, to normal consumers ingesting normal amounts of the "food." Exam-

TABLE III

Categories of Hazardous Situations Involving Naturally Occurring Toxicants in Foods

1	Natural constituents of unusual "foods" among normal consumers ingesting normal amounts of the "food"
	Examples: Poisonous mushrooms, e.g., amanitin in toadstools; poisonous plants, e.g., pyrrolizidine alkaloids in *Senecio*
2	Natural contaminants of normal foods among normal consumers ingesting normal amounts of the food
	Examples: Mycotoxins such as aflatoxin contaminating grains and oilseeds; algal toxins such as saxitoxin contaminating seafoods
3	Natural constituents of normal foods among normal consumers ingesting abnormal amounts of the food
	Example: Cyanogenic glycosides in lima beans
4	Natural constituents of normal foods among normal consumers ingesting normal amounts of the food when prepared in an abnormal manner
	Example: Lectins in kidney beans
5	Natural constituents of normal foods among "abnormal" consumers ingesting normal amounts of the food
	Example: Food allergies; lactose intolerance

ples include poisonous mushrooms and poisonous plants. Of course, these materials should not be eaten but, when mistakes occur, intoxications are very likely.

Natural contaminants of normal foods can also present a hazard to normal consumers ingesting normal amounts of the foods. Certain bacteria growing on foods produce toxins; botulinum toxin and staphylococcal enterotoxin are examples. Molds can produce a variety of chemicals while growing on foods. The more highly toxic of these mold-produced chemicals are called mycotoxins. The aflatoxins produced by *Aspergillus flavus* and *A. parasiticus* are good examples. The aflatoxins are potent carcinogens. Microscopic algae (dinoflagellates) that proliferate in the ocean can sometimes produce highly toxic substances that affect the safety of fish and shellfish that have fed on these algae. Examples include paralytic shellfish poisoning occurring from clams, mussels, and so on when shellfish feeding areas are contaminated with dinoflagellates that produce saxitoxin and related neurotoxins, and ciguatera poisoning associated with reef fishes that have ingested toxic dinoflagellates. Insects also are likely to produce toxic chemicals, but this possibility has received little scientific attention.

Some naturally occurring chemicals do not occur in amounts that would create a hazard except when excessive quantities of foods containing these toxicants are consumed. For example, lima beans contain cyanogenic glycosides that release HCN on contact with stomach acid. However, insufficient cyanide becomes available unless a consumer ingests several pounds of lima beans; this has never been reported to occur. Cyanide is an acute toxicant so there is little risk of chronic toxicity.

Natural constituents of normal foods can also present a hazard when these foods are not processed or prepared correctly. Normal processing or preparation conditions frequently remove or inactivate toxicants. For example, the lectins in kidney beans are heat labile and are typically inactivated by cooking. Consumers have experienced intestinal bleeding and diarrhea from ingestion of undercooked kidney beans.

B. Environmental/Industrial Contaminants

A wide variety of chemicals are made or used by humans for industrial or other commercial purposes. These chemicals can be released into the environment intentionally or inadvertently. After environmental release, such chemicals can enter the food chains. Although many examples of releases exist, the hazards created by such situations have been remarkably few in number. Mercury dumped into water can contaminate seafoods, and has caused at least one major outbreak of human illness. Polychlorinated and polybrominated biphenyls (PCBs, PBBs) present substantial hazards when inadvertent environmental release occurs. PBBs were accidentally incorporated into dairy feed in Michigan several decades ago, leading to contaminated milk, dairy products, and meat. PCBs from a leaking electrical transformer were inadvertently incorporated into chicken feed, leading to contaminated eggs and meat. Fish from the Great Lakes, especially Lake Michigan, may contain elevated levels of PCBs, a condition that has led to a ban on commercial fishing in some areas. Accidental and sometimes massive oil spills in near-shore areas may cause concerns about petroleum-based carcinogens in fish and shellfish.

C. Agricultural Residues

Agricultural residues can include insecticides, herbicides, fungicides, veterinary drugs including antibiotics, and other animal feed additives including growth promoters. Considerable public concern surrounds the presence of these residues in foods, especially if the chemicals are proven carcinogens. However, detectable residues of the pesticides rarely occur when these materials are used responsibly according to manufacturer's directions. Very few documented cases of pesticide intoxications from foodborne residues have occurred, all of which involved irresponsible use. The aldicarb intoxications occurring from ingestion of treated watermelons several years ago are an example. It is illegal to use aldicarb on watermelons because this crop tends to accumulate significant amounts of this insecticide. Concerns also exist over imported foods that may occasionally contain residues of pesticides now banned in the United States. Although continued toxicity testing of pesticides and vigilance regarding pesticide use are warranted, this particular foodborne disease hazard has been vastly overstated.

The use of animal drugs and growth promoters can also occasionally lead to the presence of worrisome residues in foods of animal origin. Again, responsible use of these products eliminates the possibility of hazardous residue levels in consumer foods. However, illegal residues have been identified on occasion, raising concerns about the degree of responsible use and control. Several of these substances, sulfamethazine and diethylstilbestrol, are putative carcinogens. Another concern is the development of antibiotic-resistant bacteria as a result of excessive use of antibiotics in animal production.

D. Food Additives

Food additives are those chemicals intentionally added to foods to achieve desired technical benefits. Food additives fall into numerous functional categories based on technical attributes, including nutrients, antioxidants, antimicrobial agents, emulsifiers, thickeners, fat substitutes, colorants, sweeteners, flavors, and leavening agents. Some additives fall into a category known as "GRAS"—Generally Recognized as Safe—based on a long history of safe use. Examples of GRAS food ingredients include sugar and salt. GRAS substances have not necessarily been subjected to a complete toxicological assessment, although many in common use have been examined thoroughly. Other food additives are subjected to an intensive toxicological assessment before approval for use as regulated food additives. Aspartame is an excellent example of an approved food additive that was subjected to a thorough toxicological assessment before approval. [See FOOD PRESERVATIVES.]

Food additives are generally safe when used responsibly. Consumer questions have focused around the weak carcinogenic properties of common food additives such as saccharin, cyclamate (banned in the United States but allowed elsewhere), FD & C Red No. 2 (a red food color banned in the United States but allowed in Canada), and FD & C Red No. 40 (a red food color banned in Canada but allowed in the United States). The evidence of the carcinogenicity of these (and other) food additives is often inconclusive. Many naturally occurring chemicals in foods are stronger carcinogens than these particular food additives. Although concern over foodborne carcinogens is legitimate, food additives are unlikely to play a role in human cancer when reasonable quantities are consumed.

Some food additives can pose acute risks to health if used improperly or if excessive amounts are consumed. For example, niacin, one of the B vitamins, may elicit facial flushing and a red rash when excessive amounts are ingested. Sorbitol, an alternative sweetener used in dietetic products, can cause diarrhea if large amounts are ingested, especially by young children.

A few food additives can cause illness in certain sensitive individuals in the population. Sulfites, common antimicrobial and antibrowning agents, elicit asthmatic reactions in a small subset of the asthmatic population. Papain, a meat-tenderizing enzyme, causes allergic reactions in a few individuals. Many individuals believe that they are sensitive to sugar, aspartame, monosodium glutamate, or some other food additives, but cause-and-effect relationships have not been clearly established.

III. Pathogenesis of Foodborne Toxicants

A. Mechanisms of Action

Many mechanisms of action exist for the toxic effects of foodborne chemicals. The most toxic chemicals in foods are those that (1) retain their toxicity through storage, processing, and preparation; (2) survive digestion, cross the intestinal barrier, and reach target organs; (3) overwhelm defense mechanisms; and (4) interfere with a crucial biochemical or physiological process. Several foodborne toxicants are actually bioactivated in the human body; the mycotoxin aflatoxin is a good example.

Most foodborne toxicants must be absorbed from the intestinal tract to cause illness. However, a few toxicants act directly on the gastrointestinal tract. Copper, for example, causes emesis very quickly after ingestion by interacting with irritant receptors in the gut. Staphyloccal enterotoxins produced by *Staphylococcus aureus* have a similar effect.

Many different organ systems can be impacted by foodborne toxicants (Table IV). Only the brain,

TABLE IV

Tissue Sites of Action of Foodborne Toxicants

Site	Toxicant
Gastrointestinal tract	Staphylococcal enterotoxin, copper
Liver	Aflatoxin (mycotoxin), ethanol
Kidney	Ochratoxin (mycotoxin), mercury
Blood components	Nitrite
Lung	Paraquat (herbicide)
Nervous system	Saxitoxin (natural toxicant), botulinum toxin
Skin	Histamine (natural toxicant)
Heart	Erucic acid (natural toxicant)
Skeletal system	Lead
Brain	Mercury

which is protected by the blood–brain barrier, is resistant to the toxic effects of most foodborne toxicants. As noted in Table IV, the toxic effects of foodborne chemicals tend to be organ specific. In some instances, multiple organs are affected. For example, lead can adversely affect the bones, kidneys, and nervous system although few foods ever contain hazardous levels of lead.

The mechanisms of action are also quite varied. For example, aflatoxin is bioactivated in the liver to an epoxide form that is reactive with DNA. The reaction of aflatoxin with DNA causes a mutagenic event that can ultimately lead to cancer. Saxitoxin, a naturally occurring toxicant occasionally found in shellfish, acts as a neurotoxin that blocks the sodium channels of nerve cells, preventing nerve transmission which can result in respiratory paralysis and death occurring within hours of the ingestion of the toxic shellfish.

B. Defense Mechanisms

Many foodborne chemicals would present great hazards if the human body did not possess some very significant defense mechanisms. The primary defense mechanism against toxic chemicals is the enzymatic detoxification of these chemicals, that is, the conversion of the highly toxic chemicals to less toxic chemicals by the action of enzymes. The liver is a key organ site of this enzymatic activity, although other organ systems including the kidneys, lungs, and intestines are also quite important. In many cases, the toxic chemicals are converted to chemicals that are more easily excreted in the urine. Urinary excretion is a key physiological detoxification process. Many potential foodborne toxicants are detoxified very quickly following absorption. Aflatoxin, for example, can be bioactivated enzymatically in the liver but other enzymatic processes lead to the detoxification of aflatoxin and the excretion of aflatoxin metabolites. Some foodborne toxicants are resistant to detoxification. The heavy metals, such as lead and mercury, are examples. These heavy metals are excreted very slowly from the body and tend to accumulate and reach toxic threshold levels over time. The liver and other tissues possess proteins that bind to such heavy metals, protecting the body from some toxic effects of heavy metals. However, this detoxification mechanism can be overwhelmed.

Other detoxification mechanisms also exist. Protein toxicants such as staphylococcal enterotoxin can trigger immunological defense mechanisms. Toxicants can also be stored in body depots to prevent them from reaching their target organs. For example, fat-soluble toxicants can be stored in body fat. However, these stored toxicants can be released later, especially during fasting or starvation.

These defense mechanisms protect the body by diminishing the toxicity of foodborne and other toxicants. The capacity of these defense mechanisms is considerable.

IV. Special Categories of Foodborne Intoxications

Several categories of foodborne illness affect only certain individuals in the population. These individualistic adverse reactions to foods include food allergies, metabolic food disorders, and idiosyncratic reactions.

A. Food Allergies

Food allergies involve an abnormal immunological response to a chemical (usually a protein) in foods. Several different mechanisms are known to exist: IgE-mediated or immediate hypersensitivity reactions and cell-mediated or delayed hypersensitivity reactions.

In IgE-mediated food allergies, symptoms involving the gastrointestinal tract, skin, and respiratory system develop within a few minutes of ingestion of the offending foods. The most common foods involved in IgE-mediated food allergies include cows' milk, eggs, peanuts, tree nuts, soybeans, crustacea, molluscs, fish, and wheat. However, any food with protein has the potential to cause an allergic reaction. Approximately 4–6% of all infants suffer from food allergies, whereas less than 1% of adults are afflicted.

The prevalence of cell-mediated hypersensitivity reactions to foods remains uncertain. However, one well-documented illness of this type is worthy of mention. Celiac disease, also known as celiac sprue and gluten-sensitive enteropathy, afflicts one in every 3000 people in the United States. The ingestion of the gluten or protein fractions of wheat, rye, barley, and sometimes oats elicits a cytotoxic response in the immune cells of the gut. Basically, the gut ceases to function properly, leading to a malabsorption syndrome characterized by body wasting, diarrhea, anemia, and bone pain.

B. Metabolic Food Disorders

Metabolic food disorders are disease states caused by exposure to a foodborne chemical that is toxic to certain individuals who exhibit some genetic defect in their ability to metabolize that chemical. Lactose intolerance is the best example. Lactose intolerance results from a deficiency of the enzyme β-galactosidase in the small intestine. Without β-galactosidase, lactose or milk sugar cannot be properly metabolized into its constituent monosaccharides, which would then be absorbed. The unabsorbed lactose enters the colon where bacteria ferment the lactose to CO_2, H_2, and H_2O. The result is abdominal cramping, flatulence, and frothy diarrhea. The prevalence of lactose intolerance varies with ethnic groups ranging from 6–12% of Caucasians to 60–90% of Asians, Africans, and some Jewish groups. Lactose intolerance worsens with advancing age as enzyme levels in the intestine diminish.

C. Idiosyncratic Reactions

Idiosyncratic reactions are illnesses of uncertain pathogenesis that may occur in certain individuals following the ingestion of specific foods or food ingredients. Sulfite-induced asthma is the best example. Sulfites used as food additives can cause asthma in perhaps 1–2% of asthmatics. However, the mechanism involved in this response is not known, so it is classified as an idiosyncratic reaction. Although the cause-and-effect relationship between sulfites and asthma is well established, this is not the case with many of the purported food idiosyncrasies.

Bibliography

Cliver, D. O. (1990). "Foodborne Diseases." Academic Press, San Diego.

Hall, R. L., and Taylor, S. L. (1989). Food toxicology and safety evaluation: Changing perspectives and a challenge for the future. *Food Technol.* **43(9),** 270–274, 276, 278–279.

Taylor, S. L., and Scanlan, R. A. (1989). "Food Toxicology: A Perspective on the Relative Risks." Marcel Dekker, New York.

Forages

DONALD M. BALL, *Auburn University*

CARL S. HOVELAND, *University of Georgia*

GARRY D. LACEFIELD, *University of Kentucky*

Glossary

Digestibility The balance of feed ingested less that matter lost in the feces, usually expressed as a percentage

Forage quality Characteristics that make forage valuable to animals as a source of nutrients; the combination of chemical, biochemical, physical, and organoleptic characteristics of forage that determines its potential to produce animal meat, milk, wool, or work

Legume inoculation Addition of effective *Rhizobia* bacteria to legume seed prior to planting for the purpose of promoting nitrogen fixation

Seedling vigor The relative hardiness and growth rate of a seedling plant

Stocking rate The number of animal units per unit of land area over a specific time period

Forage refers to the edible parts of plants, other than separated grain, that can provide feed for grazing animals or that can be harvested for feeding such animals. Thus, the term includes forage that is grazed or browsed, hay, silage, and green chop. Because of the numerous plant species that are considered forages, and the diversity of situations involving these species and their interactions with grazing animals, forages are a complex and fascinating topic.

I. Introduction

A. Importance and Uses

The United States has over 32 million hectares of perennial pastures and over 8 million hectares of annual pastures, plus many more millions of acres devoted to hay and silage production. Most of this is located in the eastern part of the United States and includes over 50 forage species. More acreage of nonforested agricultural land is devoted to the production of livestock forage than to all other crops combined.

A major percentage of the feed units for beef (83%) and dairy (61%) cattle come from forages. In addition, forages supply an estimated 91, 72, 15, and 99% of the nutrients consumed by sheep and goats, horses, swine, and ruminant wildlife respectively. [*See* ANIMAL NUTRITION, NONRUMINANT; ANIMAL NUTRITION, PRINCIPLES; ANIMAL NUTRITION, RUMINANT; FEEDS AND FEEDING.]

Forage crops also provide a substantial amount of the pollen and nectar bees collect, they offer food and cover for many types of wildlife, and some farmers make a substantial portion of their income producing forage crop seed. In addition, forage crops play a critical role in soil conservation, preserving and protecting soil and water resources while beautifying the landscape.

B. Contrast with other Agricultural Production

Much of the land devoted to forage production is not suitable for production of other crops because of a high potential for erosion, and poor soil conditions such as excess or inadequate moisture, acidity, or low fertility. Thus, the production of forage for grazing or hay allows production of animal products from land that otherwise might not profitably produce any product except trees.

With most crops, the goal is to harvest a portion of the plant (i.e., grain, fruit, or tubers) so the remainder of the crop can be returned to the soil. Generally, the harvest is made at the end of the growing season. In the case of forage crops, most of the above-ground portion of the plants may be removed by grazing or hay production, so the photosynthetic capability of the plants is reduced during the growing season.

Forage/livestock production is complex because producers must meet the needs of both livestock and plants. In pasture situations, this may require moving animals or adjusting stocking rates. The decisions made affect animal performance, plant growth, and pasture persistence. In hay production, management practices may also have mixed effects. For example, lengthening harvest intervals may have a positive effect on yield and persistence while reducing forage quality. Thus, the management imposed on forages may be a compromise that does not perfectly achieve all desired goals.

II. Factors Affecting Selection and Use

Adaptation to soil and environmental conditions is of critical importance to a forage crop. In particular, temperatures and the amount and distribution of rainfall have a profound effect on plant survival and growth. Usually climatic extremes, rather than average conditions, determine adaptation.

The vast majority of nonirrigated forage crops grown in the United States is in approximately the eastern half of the nation or in the Pacific Northwest, where annual rainfall ranges from 25 to 60 in. However, even in areas in which total rainfall is substantial, periodic droughts may occur, particularly when temperatures are high and/or the soil has poor water-holding capacity.

Temperature also plays an important role in plant survival. High temperatures and disease-enhancing humidity hurt forage production of temperate species in the South. On the other hand, severe cold in the upper portions of the United States may result in winterkill of many species that are tolerant of climatic conditions in the South.

The result is that pasture hectarage in the lower South is dominated by tropical (in south Florida) or subtropical warm season perennial species, whereas cool season perennials are grown almost exclusively in the upper portions of the nation. In a transition zone in the mid- to upper South, it may be possible to use warm season or cool season perennials. Cool season annuals are commonly used to extend the grazing season in the South, and warm season annuals are used throughout the humid portions of the United States.

To some degree, the effects of climate can be overcome by soil type and/or site. Heavier soils or moist sites can allow temperate forages to be grown further south than would otherwise be the case. Similarly, a site in which trees or topography provide some protection from cold may allow winter survival of a warm season species further north than usual.

III. Overview of Forage Species

The many plants used as forage crops in the humid area of the United States can be classified as (1) grasses or legumes, (2) annuals or perennials, and (3) warm season or cool season plants.

Grasses are herbaceous (not woody), have parallel leaf veins and fibrous root systems, and bear seed on an elongated seed stalk. **Legumes** are dicots (produce two seed leaves), produce seed in a pod, have branched leaf venation, usually have a taproot, and generally have the ability to fix atmospheric nitrogen in nodules on their roots.

Annuals are plants that reproduce by seed, germinate, grow, reproduce, and die in one growing season. **Perennials** can live for more than 1 yr, recovering from tubers, rhizomes, or stolons in succeeding years.

Warm season plants begin growth in the spring or early summer and make most of their growth during the warmest months of the year. **Cool season plants** begin growth in autumn or early spring and make most of their growth during the coolest months of the year, except for the coldest periods in winter. Forage species differ greatly in total yield, seasonal production, and nutritive quality.

The major factor affecting adaptation of the different forage species is temperature (Fig. 1). Forage crops differ substantially in their adaptation to climate, soil conditions, and grazing (Tables I, II).

IV. Fertilization and Liming

As for other crops, the primary nutrient elements essential to growth are nitrogen, phosphorus, and potassium. The secondary nutrients sulfur, calcium, and

FIGURE 1 Mean annual air temperatures.

magnesium are needed by plants in much lower quantities and are less likely to limit growth at naturally occurring levels. Trace elements, including zinc, boron, manganese, iron, and molybdenum, are needed only in extremely small amounts and usually are present in ample quantities in the soil. [See SOIL FERTILITY.]

Nitrogen is needed by plants in the largest amounts and, since it leaches readily, should usually be applied several times per year to forage grasses. Properly inoculated forage legumes fix nitrogen from the atmosphere and, thus, do not require applications of nitrogen fertilizer.

Phosphorus is important in photosynthesis, root growth, and seedling development. Phosphorus does not leach; thus, the requirement for a year's growth can be met in a single application.

Potassium affects stand persistence, particularly in areas where winterkill is a possibility. It also affects root growth and, in some species, susceptibility to diseases. Potassium can leach, although not as readily as nitrogen, and may need to be supplied in two applications on sandy soils in high rainfall areas.

If needed, calcium and magnesium can be supplied by applications of calcitic and dolomitic limestone, respectively. Sulfur fertilizer needs vary widely depending on soil type and proximity to industries where sulfur emissions occur. It usually is not necessary to apply trace elements to forage crops, with the exception of boron, which is recommended at low rates for alfalfa and for clover seed production.

Soil pH, or the degree of acidity or alkalinity, is of critical importance for forages. Soil pH is measured on a logarithmic scale of 0 to 14 with 7 being neutral and acidity and alkalinity being below and above 7, respectively. Most forage crops are best suited to the range between 5.8 and 6.5. Most legumes are not well suited to highly acid soil conditions. [See SOIL, ACID.]

When a soil test indicates that the soil is too acid, applications of lime are recommended. Lime is a fine granular or powdery substance obtained by heating limestone or shell deposits; it has a high calcium and sometimes a high magnesium content and is effective in neutralizing soil acidity. The amount of lime recommended will depend on the degree of acidity and

TABLE I

Adaptation Characteristics of Forage Grasses in Humid Regions of the United States

Name	Type	Climate zone adaptation	Adaptation to environment[a]			
			Soil acidity	Drought	Poor drainage	Severe grazing
Warm season perennial grasses						
Bahiagrass	Creeping	A, B	G	G	G	G
Bermudagrass	Creeping	A, B, C	G	G	P	G
Big bluestem	Bunch	C, D, E, F,	P	G	M	P
Dallisgrass	Bunch	B, C	M	G	G	M
Johnsongrass	Creeping	B, C	M	G	G	P
Switchgrass	Bunch	C, D, E, F	P	G	M	P
Warm season annual grasses						
Corn	Tall bunch	A, B, C, D, E, F, G	M	P	P	P
Pearl millet	Bunch	A, B, C, D	G	G	P	M
Sorghum	Tall bunch	A, B, C, D, E, F	P	G	P	P
Sorghum × sudangrass	Bunch	A, B, C, D, E, F	P	G	P	M
Cool season perennial grasses						
Kentucky bluegrass	Creeping	D, E, F, G	M	P	M	G
Orchardgrass	Bunch	D, E, F	M	M	P	M
Reed canarygrass	Bunch	D, E, F, G	G	G	G	M
Smooth bromegrass	Bunch	E, F, G	M	G	P	M
Tall fescue	Bunch	C, D, E	G	M	G	G
Timothy	Bunch	D, E, F, G	G	P	M	M
Cool season annual grasses						
Annual ryegrass	Bunch	A, B, C	G	P	G	G
Oats	Bunch	A, B	M	M	M	M
Rye	Bunch	A, B, C, D	G	M	M	M
Wheat	Bunch	A, B, C, D	P	M	P	M

[a] G, Good; M, moderate; P, poor.

TABLE II

Adaptation Characteristics of Forage Legumes in Humid Regions of the United States

Name	Type	Climate zone adaptation	Adaptation to environment[a]			
			Soil acidity	Drought	Poor drainage	Severe grazing
Warm season perennial legumes						
Perennial peanut	Creeping	A, B	G	G	P	M
Sericea lespedeza	Erect	B, C, D	G	G	M	P
Warm season annual legumes						
Annual lespedeza	Erect	C, D, E	G	M	M	G
Cool season perennial legumes						
Alfalfa	Erect	B, C, D, E, F, G	P	G	P	P
Birdsfoot trefoil	Semi-erect	D, E, F, G	M	G	G	M
Red clover	Erect	B, C, D, E, F, G	M	M–G	M	M
White clover	Creeping	B, C, D, E, F, G	M	P	G	G
Cool season annual legumes						
Arrowleaf clover	Erect	B, C	P–M	M	P	M
Crimson clover	Erect	B, C	M	M	P	M
Hairy vetch	Viny	B, C, D	G	M	P	M
Rose clover	Erect	B	M	M	P	M
Subterranean clover	Prostrate	B	M	M	P	G

[a] G, Good; M, moderate; P, poor.

on soil buffering capacity. More lime is required to adjust the pH a given amount in a clay soil than in a sandy soil. Lime moves slowly in the soil, so it should be mixed with the soil when new forage plantings are established. Otherwise, it must be applied to the soil surface.

The adverse effects of acidity can also be neutralized by making applications of gypsum (calcium sulfate-$CaSO_4 \cdot 2H_2O$). Gypsum moves through the soil readily and, thus, can be used in areas where the soil cannot be tilled for the purpose of mixing an additive into the soil. Gypsum is not readily available in many agricultural production areas, its consistency often makes spreading a problem, and hauling/spreading costs may be high.

Taking soil samples on a regular basis and following the recommendations based on nutrient analysis is a key forage management practice. Perennial pastures should normally be sampled once every 2–3 yr, whereas hay fields and annual pastures should be sampled annually. [See SOIL TESTING FOR PLANT GROWTH AND SOIL FERTILITY.]

The main source of error in soil analysis is the sampling process. Thus, sampling should be done with great care. Most laboratories recommend that 15–20 subsamples be taken from a given field. For annuals and new pastures, the soil should be sampled to plow depth. In perennial sods, a 5- to 10-cm sampling depth is usually recommended.

V. Seed

As with other crops, some knowledge of seed is needed if forage crop establishment and production is to be successful. Failure to understand essential points regarding seed often results in forage stand failures. Basic considerations such as seeding dates, rates, depth, and appropriate mixtures are critical in stand establishment.

A. Legume Inoculation

Most legumes have a unique symbiotic relationship with bacteria of the genus *Rhizobium* to fix nitrogen from the atmosphere. This allows legumes to provide enough nitrogen for their own growth as well as part or all of that needed for plants growing in association with them or planted after them. Since nitrogen fertilizer is costly, this characteristic is of great economic importance. [See NITROGEN CYCLING.]

The amount of nitrogen fixed by forage legumes varies greatly. Some factors that affect the process are species of legume, percentage of legume stand, temperature, rainfall, and strain(s) and populations of *Rhizobium* bacteria persent. However, the amount of nitrogen fixed is generally in the range of 60–120 kg/ha for annuals and 112–224 kg/ha for perenials.

The practice of "inoculating" legume seed with *Rhizobium* bacteria just prior to planting began early in the 20th century and has become a standard practice. Legume inoculants specifically selected for effectiveness with various legume species are readily available commercially and are relatively inexpensive.

B. Seed Quality

The factors that affect the ability of seed to produce a healthy, vigorous stand are collectively referred to by the term "seed quality." Seed labeling laws are in effect that require certain information pertaining to seed quality to be listed on a tag that is attached to bags of seed.

Some terms that normally are listed on seed labels (percentage of weight basis) are (1) germination—seed that are capable of germinating almost immediately; (2) pure seed—seed that are of the forage variety and species indicated; (3) other crop seed—seed of other crops present; (4) weed seed—weed seed present; (5) inert matter—matter other than seed; (6) hard seed—seed that will not germinate immediately because of a hard seed coat; and (7) total germination—the total seed capable of germinating, obtained by adding germination and hard seed.

C. Other Seed-Related Concerns

Seed is sold on a weight, rather than a volume, basis. "Test weight" refers to the normal weight of a bushel of seed of a particular species. When test weight is low, the quality of seed is presumed to be low. Carrying over seed from one year to the next is likely to lower germination and seedling vigor.

VI. Physiology of Forage Crops

Although most crop plants are grown for their fruit or seed, leaves (the photosynthetic area) of forage plants are frequently being removed. This places great stress on forage plants, making it critical to understand their physiology and how to properly manage them for long life and productivity.

A. Light

Cool season grasses such as tall fescue or ryegrass and all legumes fix energy into 3-carbon units and are called **C3 plants.** Warm season grasses such as bermudagrass, corn, or switchgrass fix energy into 4-carbon units and are called **C4 plants.** The C4 pathway in photosynthesis is more efficient because C4 plants can utilize more sunlight and waste less energy, thus having potential for much higher forage yields. Nitrogen fertilization and irrigation can often increase photosynthesis.

As the amount of leaf tissue increases in a pasture or hayfield, photosynthesis increases up to a point and then levels off or declines because of shading within the canopy and leaf aging. The shading problem is greater with clovers because of their horizontally displayed leaves, compared with many grasses with more vertical leaves that allow light to penetrate deeper into the crop canopy.

Warm season grasses such as corn, pearl millet, or sorghum–sudangrass, with leaves set at an acute angle on tall stems, have a high photosynthetic potential and produce large forage yields over a short growing season. In managing a pasture, forage removal should be frequent enough to prevent the high death losses that occur from shading and aging.

B. Temperature

At optimum temperatures, the maximum growth rate of warm season grasses such as bermudagrass and switchgrass is much greater than that of cool season grasses such as tall fescue and orchardgrass. The optimum temperature for warm season grasses is 30–35°C, whereas the optimum for cool season grasses is about 15–27°C. Optimum temperatures for clovers are 20–24°C, 26°C for alfalfa, and about 30°C for tropical legumes.

The temperature range over which forage is produced at near peak levels is much greater for cool season than in warm season grasses. Growth of warm season grasses falls off rapidly at temperatures below 21°C, with virtually no production at 10°C. However, in the warm season they are dominant species in some temperate pastures or ranges and may offer great productivity. The rather narrow temperature range of warm season grasses means that the productive season gets progressively shorter as they are grown farther north, where cool nights during spring and autumn limit growth.

Warm season grasses differ greatly in cold tolerance. Some cultivars of bermudagrass are easily winterkilled, so they are restricted to the Gulf Coast area of the United States, whereas relatively cold-hardy cultivars can be grown much farther north. Some warm season grasses such as big bluestem, indiangrass, and switchgrass are cold hardy and can be grown in the northern United States.

In colder areas, it is important for perennial forage cultivars to become dormant in winter so they will not grow during short warm periods in winter and, thus, waste carbohydrates needed for survival and early spring production. For this reason, winter-dormant cultivars are grown in cold climate areas, since nondormant types will be winterkilled because of carbohydrate depletion resulting from winter green-up. When winter-dormant cultivars are grown in areas with warm winters, they are unproductive, whereas cool season forage cultivars of Mediterranean origin are less dormant and make considerable winter growth.

C. Water

Water shortage is the major factor limiting plant growth, even when soil fertility and temperature are favorable. Water use efficiency differs among forage species. The C4 species (warm season grasses) are generally more efficient than C3 plants in dry matter production per unit of water. This feature is even more impressive, because the major production of C4 species occurs during summer under high temperatures with high evapotranspiration rates.

Flooding and poor soil drainage reduce growth mainly by restricting oxygen supply to the roots. Thus, forage species in a dormant state are much more tolerant of flooding than when they are actively growing. Oxygen requirements increase with temperature; thus, plants often die with poor drainage during warm weather. Also, some forage disease problems such as *Phytophthora* root rot in alfalfa increase. [*See* SOIL DRAINAGE.]

D. Carbohydrate Reserves

Excess carbohydrates from photosynthesis not needed for respiration and growth are stored in various plant organs. These include roots in alfalfa, red clover, and birdsfoot trefoil; rhizomes in bermudagrass, bahiagrass, reed canarygrass, and switchgrass; stolons in white clover; and stem bases in tall fescue, orchardgrass, and big bluestem. These storage carbohydrates supply respiration needs during winter or summer dormancy, allow regrowth after dormancy, and contribute to winter hardiness. [*See* DORMANCY.]

Good management of forage species can favor adequate carbohydrate reserves. In the southern United States, close continuous grazing of cool season perennial grasses during summer will reduce leaf area for photosynthesis and will deplete carbohydrates, so regrowth will be slow and stands will be weakened. Reduced grazing pressure during hot weather in summer will improve autumn growth and will maintain vigorous stands.

Warm season perennial grasses with erect growth habit such as Johnsongrass, switchgrass, or big bluestem can be damaged by continuous close grazing and should be rotationally stocked to recharge carbohydrate storage organs. In contrast, bermudagrass, bahiagrass, and Kentucky bluegrass maintain leaf area close to the ground and can be grazed closely without adverse effects. Alfalfa, sericea lespedeza, and birdsfoot trefoil are especially sensitive to frequent close defoliation. In the northern United States, root carbohydrates in alfalfa must be maintained by rotational stocking or cutting at the proper time to provide adequate energy for plants to survive the winter and remain productive.

VII. Establishment

A. Conventional Tillage

Establishment of a good stand is a first and very important step in developing a successful forage program. Several factors that are of vital importance in the establishment and maintenance of good forage stands include:

1. matching crops to soils in which they will grow well by taking into consideration factors such as drainage or moisture requirements, rooting depth, and ability to hold nutrients.
2. matching plants to the intended use (example: a plant that is not tolerant of grazing should not be planted in an area that is to be closely and continuously grazed).
3. selection of high quality seed of an adapted variety.
4. supplying proper nutrients to obtain good plant growth.
5. preparing an adequate seedbed.

6. inoculation of legume seed.
7. using proven seeding methods that insure good seed–soil contact and placement of the seed at the proper depth.
8. seeding at the right time with the correct amount of seed (Table III).
9. control of pests.
10. grazing new stands in accordance with crop requirements to allow good production and persistence.

Because weather has a great influence on establishment, the steps just outlined do not guarantee success. However, if followed, they greatly increase the probability of obtaining thick, vigorous forage stands. Once such stands are obtained, the forage must be marketed directly or through livestock products. Perennial plants must be managed to keep stands for several years if top profits are to be realized. Such management can reduce or at least minimize the re-establishment costs that can occur.

B. Sodseeding

Sodseeding is a general term used to describe the practice of establishing forage crops into perennial, usually grass-dominated, hay and/or pasture fields without destroying the existing sod (Table IV). Other terms used to describe this practice include renovation, overseeding, interseeding, frost seeding, honeycomb freeze seeding, no-till seeding, and minimum-till seeding, as well as tread-in, trampling, and walk-on seeding. Applications of this practice have been used with success throughout the United States for many years.

1. Sodseeding Principles

Since much forage land is prone to soil erosion, sodseeding offers advantages over tillage for forage establishment. Likewise, sodseeding can conserve time, labor, fuel, and soil moisture relative to conventional tillage and establishment techniques.

2. Benefits of Multiple Species Pastures and Hay Fields

Research and farmer experiences have shown that establishing legumes into grass-dominant sods can result in several benefits including (1) increased yield, (2) improved quality, (3) nitrogen fixation, (4) improved summer production of cool season grass-dominant fields, and (5) improved winter/

TABLE III

Usual Recommended Time of Planting, Seeding Rates, and Seeding Depths for Tilled Seedbed Plantings of Forage Crops

Forage crop	Time of planting	Seeding Rate[a] (lb/A)	Seeding depth[a] (in)
Alfalfa	Late summer, autumn; also spring in zones C and D	15–20	$\frac{1}{4}$–$\frac{1}{2}$
Alyceclover	Spring, early summer	15–20	$\frac{1}{4}$–$\frac{1}{2}$
Bahiagrass	Spring, summer; also autumn in zone A	15–20	$\frac{1}{4}$–$\frac{1}{2}$
Barley[b]	Autumn	90–120	1–2
Bermudagrass, common	Spring, summer	5–10 (hulled)	0–$\frac{1}{2}$
Bermudagrass, hybrid	Early spring	20 or more bu. sprigs	1–3
Big bluestem[c]	Spring	6–10 (PLS)[d]	$\frac{1}{4}$–$\frac{1}{2}$
Birdsfoot trefoil	Late summer, autumn	4–6	0–$\frac{1}{4}$
Black medic	Autumn	10–12	0–$\frac{1}{4}$
Bluegrass, Kentucky	Autumn	10–15	0–$\frac{1}{4}$
Caley pea (singletary pea)	Autumn	50–55	$\frac{1}{2}$–1
Clover, arrowleaf	Autumn	5–10	0–$\frac{1}{2}$
Clover, ball	Autumn	2–3	0–$\frac{1}{4}$
Clover, berseem	Autumn	20–25	$\frac{1}{4}$–$\frac{1}{2}$
Clover, crimson	Autumn	20–30	$\frac{1}{4}$–$\frac{1}{2}$
Clover, red	Autumn; early spring in zones C and D	12–15	$\frac{1}{4}$–$\frac{1}{2}$
Clover, subterranean	Autumn	10–20	$\frac{1}{4}$–$\frac{1}{2}$
Clover, white and ladino	Autumn; early spring in zones C and D	2–3	0–$\frac{1}{4}$
Cowpea	Late spring, early summer	100–120	1–3
Dallisgrass[c]	Spring	10–15 (PLS)[d]	$\frac{1}{4}$–$\frac{1}{2}$
Fescue, tall	Fall; early spring in zones C and D	20–25	$\frac{1}{4}$–$\frac{1}{2}$
Indiangrass[c]	Spring	6–10 (PLS)[d]	$\frac{1}{4}$–$\frac{1}{2}$
Johnsongrass	Late spring, early summer	20–30	$\frac{1}{2}$–1
Lespedeza, annual	Early spring	25–35	$\frac{1}{4}$–$\frac{1}{2}$
Lespedeza, sericea	Spring	20–30	$\frac{1}{4}$–$\frac{1}{2}$
Millet, browntop	Mid-spring, early summer	25–30	$\frac{1}{2}$–1
Millet, pearl	Mid-spring, early summer	25–30	$\frac{1}{2}$–$1\frac{1}{2}$
Oats[b]	Autumn	90–120	1–2
Orchardgrass	Autumn	15–20	$\frac{1}{4}$–$\frac{1}{2}$
Reed canarygrass	Autumn	5–8	$\frac{1}{4}$–$\frac{1}{2}$
Rye[b]	Autumn	90–120	1–2
Ryegrass	Autumn	20–30	0–$\frac{1}{2}$
Sorghum, forage	Late spring, early summer	15–20	1–2
Sorghum sudan hybrids	Late spring, early summer	30–55	1–2
Sudangrass	Late spring, early summer	30–40	$\frac{1}{2}$–1
Switchgrass[c]	Spring	5–6 (PLS)[d]	$\frac{1}{4}$–$\frac{1}{2}$
Timothy	Late summer, early autumn	6–8	$\frac{1}{4}$–$\frac{1}{2}$
Triticale[b]	Autumn	90–120	1–2
Vetch, common	Autumn	30–40	1–2
Vetch, hairy	Autumn	20–25	1–2
Wheat[b]	Autumn	90–120	1–2

Source: Ball *et al.* (1991).

[a] These are general guidelines for broadcast plantings. Drill plantings may require less seed. Specific recommendations for a given area may vary and some crops are adapted only in certain regions. Seeding rates may vary considerably from these when these crops are planted for seed.

[b] The small grains usually have approximately the following lb/bushel: barley, 48; oats, 32; rye, 56; wheat, 60; triticale, 48.

[c] Germination rate is often low.

[d] PLS, Pure live seed.

spring production of warm season grass-dominant fields.

Sodseeding requires all the principles of conventional seeding except seedbed preparation. In addition, sodseeding requires two additional principles that are of critical importance to success: (1) reduction of existing vegetation before seeding and (2) control of competition from existing or volunteer vegetation after seeding and until the newly seeded legumes are established.

TABLE IV

Summary of No-Tillage Forage Systems

Sod or crop stubble to be planted	Species planted	Planting date
Cool season perennial grasses		
Tall fescue, orchardgrass, Kentucky bluegrass, timothy	Alfalfa, red clover, birdsfoot trefoil, white clover	Autumn/late winter for trefoil; Autumn or winter for clovers; late winter for alfalfa
Warm season perennial grasses		
Bermudagrass and bahiagrass	Small grains; ryegrass; arrowleaf, berseem, crimson, and subterranean clovers; vetch	Early frost
Dallisgrass	White and red clovers, caley peas	
Small grain stubble		
Rye, wheat, oats	Pearl millet, sorghum–sudangrass	Late spring
	Alfalfa, red clover	Late summer, early autumn

Source: Ball *et al.* (1991).

C. Overseeding Winter Annuals

A common practice in the lower South is to sodseed or overseed cool season grasses and/or legumes into dormant perennial warm season grass sods, especially bahiagrass or bermudagrass.

Potential benefits derived from establishing other forage species into perennial grass pastures and hayfields include improved yield and seasonal distribution, improved quality and animal performance, and greater nitrogen fixation. Sodseeding offers much potential for producers who are willing to exercise a higher level of management.

VIII. Forage Quality and Animal Performance

The unique and valuable characteristic of ruminant animals (cattle, sheep, goats, deer, buffalo, llamas), with their four-compartmented stomachs, allows them to digest large amounts of forage with a high fiber content. Ruminant animals, as well as horses (which have a functional caecum and colon in which microbes digest fiber), can utilize materials that cannot be efficiently utilized by monogastric animals.

The constituents of forage grasses and legumes can be divided into two main categories: (1) those present as cell contents or the nonstructural part of the plant tissue (protein, sugar, and starch) and (2) those that make up the structural components of the cell wall (cellulose, hemicellulose, and lignin).

Cell contents are almost completely disgested by animals with a rumen or functional caecum, whereas digestibility of the cell walls varies with many factors such as plant species, age, and temperature. In addi-

tion, minerals, vitamins, and antiquality factors such as tannins, nitrates, alkaloids, cyanoglycosides, estrogens, and mycotoxins influence animal performance, depending on the plant species and environmental conditions.

Digestible proteins are located in the cell contents. Relatively indigestible proteins are found within the cytoplasm, whereas cell walls contain protein that is unavailable to the animal during digestion. Thus, the term "crude protein" based on the total nitrogen in a forage indicates that some of these proteins are unavailable for animal utilization. Young, leafy grasses and legumes are normally high in protein and usually meet the protein needs of grazing animals.

Cellulose and hemicellulose are structural carbohydrates that may be digested by bacterial action in the rumen, but this ability is sharply reduced as lignin content increases. Lignin, indigestible in ruminant animals, is low in legumes such as white clover and birdsfoot trefoil or in annual ryegrass but high in warm season perennial grasses, especially as they mature.

Highly lignified forages remain in the rumen for long periods of time because of their slow rate of digestion, thus decreasing dry matter intake. Animal performance is markedly reduced by the low digestibility of lignified forages because of a reduction in forage consumption. **Digestible energy** is generally the most limiting nutritive factor affecting forage intake and animal performance.

Three major factors affect forage quality: plant, species, climate, and stage of maturity. Cool season grasses are generally more digestible than warm season grasses. Legumes are generally of high quality, and digestibility falls less rapidly with maturity than in warm season perennial grasses. Legumes also generally contain higher levels of protein than grasses.

Digestibility of warm season and cool season perennial species is highest in spring, falling to a low level in mid- to late summer and increasing in autumn. High summer temperature lowers digestibility by increasing lignification. Drought stress has little effect on forage quality as long as the plants remain alive. Moderate stress may actually increase digestibility.

Excess rainfall has no effect on digestibility but may reduce dry matter intake because of increased moisture content. Excess rainfall may reduce protein content of grasses because of leaching nitrogen from the soil.

Maturity has a greater effect on nutritive value than does any other factor. As plants mature and become more lignified, digestible energy and protein content decline. Accordingly, animal performance declines as well.

Nutrient requirements of ruminant animals differ greatly, depending on class of livestock, weight, and desired daily production. Lactating dairy cows require high quality forages for optimum production and are generally fed corn and alfalfa silage. If they are grazed, only high quality pasture grasses and/or legumes should be used. Growing animals such as steers or lambs also have high requirements that can be met with cool season annual or perennial grasses, but preferably with legumes. Warm season grasses lack the quality for high gains and are usually unsatisfactory for profitable grazing of beef steers and lambs.

Most **growing** pastures of warm or cool season perennial grasses will adequately supply the needs of a dry pregnant beef cow. However, after killing frosts, the quality of warm season perennial grasses declines rapidly and protein supplementation will be needed. After calving, nutrient requirements of beef cows increase substantially for rebreeding and providing milk for calves. Until a calf is about 3 mo old, it is mostly dependent on its mother for food.

A controlled breeding season is essential in matching animal nutrient requirements to available pasture and reducing supplemental feeding. This is best done by having the calving season occur prior to the beginning of winter or spring pasture production.

Replacement heifers require special nutritional consideration so they can be bred to calve as 2-yr-olds. Ideally, high-quality cool season annual or perennial grass pasture can meet the nutrient needs of this class of animal. If grass hay is fed, it will generally need to be supplemented with protein and minerals.

A wide variety of pasture grasses is used for horses, often supplemented with grain. Sorghum-sudangrass and other forages in the *Sorghum* genus should not be used for horses because these forages may cause cystitis. Endophyte-infected tall fescue (tall fescue internally infected with the toxin-producing fungus *Acremonium coenophialum*) should not be used as pasture for pregnant mares, especially during the last 3 mo of gestation, since this can result in prolonged gestation, difficult foaling, and loss of the foal.

IX. Pasture Production and Utilization

High pasture leaf production over an extended period of time depends on a number of factors, including (1) effective light interception and high photosynthetic efficiency, (2) high sustained growth rate, (3) low rate of leaf aging and decomposition of leaves, and (4) maintenance of a vigorous tiller or shoot population for regrowth. To manage a pasture well, it is necessary to periodically graze off most of the leaves to improve light penetration, which stimulates growth of new leaves. Adequate light is needed to maintain a good supply of basal buds to develop new shoots.

The productivity and amount of each species in pastures can be rapidly and substantially altered by grazing animals. The effects may be harmful or beneficial, depending on the plants. Grazing animals defoliate, trample, and excrete dung and urine on a pasture, all of which impact on pasture plants. [*See* RANGELAND GRAZING.]

Defoliation is the most important influence of grazing animals on a pasture. Grazing reduces leaf area, thus affecting plant food storage, shoot development, leaf and root growth, light intensity, soil temperature, and moisture. With tall-growing forage species, continued **overgrazing** generally results in weakened plants with reduced root systems, lower forage yield, greater soil erosion and water runoff, and more weeds. Continuous close grazing will favor low-growing species in a mixture.

Undergrazing also has undesirable effects on a pasture. Wasted forage and reduced nutritive quality are most obvious, but other effects occur as well. Undergrazing grass–clover pastures decreases clover stands since the taller growing grasses shade lower growing legumes.

Some general principles on species responses to grazing include the following. (1) Rotational stocking with a rest period or continuous stocking at a higher stubble is required for species such as alfalfa, sericea lespedeza, Johnsongrass, big bluestem, and switchgrass. (2) Semi-erect species such as tall fescue, having food storage and buds near the ground, are fairly tolerant of close grazing except under stress conditions. (3) Prostrate species such as bahiagrass, bermudagrass, Kentucky bluegrass, and white clover are extremely tolerant of close grazing.

Stocking rate and its relationship to available forage are the most important management factors influencing the output of animal product from a pasture, persistence and productivity of a forage species, and financial return. At a low stocking rate, available forage and productivity per animal tend to be high, but output per unit area is low. When pasture quality declines with accumulation of stems and dead forage, dry matter intake by animals decreases and animal output declines.

As stocking rate is increased on a pasture, less forage is available per animal. Individual animal output decreases as animals compete for forage and have less opportunity to select green leaves. However, animal output per unit area increases with stocking rate until individual animal gains are depressed to the point that the additional animals carried do not compensate for the loss.

At high stocking rates, plants are weakened and forage growth is depressed. Pastures must have sufficient leafy green forage available to allow the animals to satisfy their appetites quickly and graze selectively. This will require 1200–1500 kg/ha of dry forage or a plant height of 8–15 cm under continuous stocking.

Several **grazing methods** are employed to adjust the varying available forage over the grazing season to the animal requirements. The advent of low-cost high-voltage electric fence has made it feasible to utilize these grazing methods to reduce pasture waste, conserve surplus forage as hay or silage, maintain stands of desirable forage species, and sometimes improve stocking rate.

(1) **Continuous stocking** is maintaining animals on a single pasture unit during the grazing season. (2) **Rotational stocking** is subdividing the pasture into (usually) 4 to 12 paddocks with animals concentrated on one paddock for a few days and then shifted to another, allowing a rest period between grazings. (3) **Creep grazing** allows young animals to pass through a fence opening (creep) to a special small pasture of higher quality forage than the lower quality forage where their mothers are maintained. (4) **Strip grazing** has movable electric fence ahead of and sometimes behind the animals to ration daily forage. (5) **Deferred grazing** or **stockpiling** is delaying grazing during part of the grazing season, usually autumn, to provide forage during winter or a dry season when growth is greatly reduced. (6) **Limit grazing** is maintaining livestock on lower quality pasture but allowing them access to a high quality cool season annual pasture for a few hours every day or every few days.

A grazing method is a tool that allows a producer to efficiently and profitably harvest the forage with livestock and maintain the pasture in a productive state. Each grazing method involves variable stocking rates which may be achieved by altering animal numbers per area or altering the size of the land area to a fixed number of animals by harvesting surplus forage for hay.

X. Hay

Hay is one of the most versatile of stored forages because (1) it can be kept for long periods of time with little loss of nutrients if protected from weather; (2) a large number of crops can be successfully used for hay production; (3) it can be produced and fed in small or large amounts; (4) it can be harvested, stored, and fed by hand or the production and feeding can be completedly mechanized; and (5) it can supply most nutrients needed by many classes of livestock. Hay is, therefore, the most commonly used stored feed on most farms.

A. Production

Many factors should be considered in hay production including species and variety used (Table V), soils and fertility, plant maturity when harvested (Table VI), harvesting and handling conditions, and storage. The objective of any hay production program should be to harvest an adequate supply of sufficient quality to meet animal needs at the lowest cost in conjunction with good soil conservation.

B. Storage

Hay is made in several types of packages including small round bales, small rectangular bales, large round bales, and stacks. Big package equipment is now available for making a variety of sizes of large round bales.

Small rectangular bales must be protected from weather damage. Covered storage is necessary to preserve both quality and quantity. Large package systems can tolerate more weather damage but considerable losses will occur when high quality hay is left outside unprotected. These losses can be acceptable

TABLE V

Approximate Hay Yield, Crude Protein, and Total Digestible Nutrient (TDN) Content of Various Hay Crops

Type of hay crop	Annual or perennial	Usual hay yield (tons/A)[a]	Approximate usual nutrient level[b]	
			Crude protein (%)	TDN (%)
Cool season				
Alfalfa (early bloom)	P	3–6	17–22	57–62
Arrowleaf clover	A	2–3	14–17	56–61
Birdsfoot trefoil	P	1–3	16–20	57–62
Oats	A	1–4	8–10	55–60
Orchardgrass	P	2–5	12–15	55–60
Red clover	P	2–4	14–16	57–62
Rye	A	1–4	8–10	50–55
Ryegrass	A	1–4	10–16	56–62
Soybean	A	2–3	15–18	54–58
Tall fescue	P	2–4	10–15	55–60
Warm season				
Annual lespedeza	A	1–2	14–17	52–58
Bahiagrass	P	3–5	9–11	50–56
Coastal bermudagrass (4 wk)	P	5–8	10–14	52–58
Common bermudagrass	P	2–6	9–11	50–56
Dallisgrass	P	2–4	9–12	50–56
Johnsongrass	P	2–5	10–14	50–60
Pearl millet	A	2–6	8–12	50–58
Sericea lespedeza	P	1–3	14–17	50–55
Sudangrass	A	2–6	9–12	55–60

Source: Ball *et al.* (1991).

[a] Assuming the crop is grown in an area to which it is adapted using recommended production and harvesting practices.

[b] Dry matter basis, assuming recommended production and harvesting practices and no excessive water damage. Forage quality is affected by many factors.

TABLE VI

Recommended Stages at Which to Harvest Various Hay Crops

Plant species	Time of harvest
Alfalfa	Bud stage for first cutting, one-tenth bloom for second and later cuttings; for spring seedings, allow the first cutting to reach mid- to full-bloom
Orchardgrass, timothy, or tall fescue	Boot to early head stage for first cut; aftermath cuts at 4- to 6-wk intervals
Red, arrowleaf, or crimson clovers	Early bloom
Sericea lespedeza	Height of 15–18 in
Oats, barley, or wheat	Boot to early head stage
Soybean	Mid- to full-bloom and before bottom leaves begin to fall
Annual lespedeza	Early bloom and before bottom leaves begin to fall
Ladino clover or white clover	Cut at correct stage for companion grass
Hybrid bermudagrass	15- to 18-in height for first cutting; mow every 4 to 5 wk or when 15 in high
Birdsfoot trefoil	Cut at correct stage for companion grass
Sudangrass, sorghum–sudan hybrids, pearl millet	Height of 30–40 in

Source: Burns *et al.* (1982).

when lower quality hay is considered; however, with high quality hay, protected storage is advised. Large packages stored outside usually show the greatest loss from bottom spoilage.

C. Feeding

The primary objective of any hay feeding program should be to provide ample quantities of high quality hay to meet, as much as possible, the animal's needs. High quality hay is early cut, green, leafy, pleasant smelling, and free of foreign material and toxic factors. Such hay, when chemically analyzed, will usually reveal high protein and low fiber content.

Since many factors affect hay quality, most livestock producers usually have on hand a hay supply with wide quality variation. Most farms also have a variety of animals with different nutritional needs.

Hay can be most efficiently fed when lots are separated according to quality and animals are separated and fed according to needs. This allows the matching of hay quality to livestock needs so that the highest quality hay is fed to livestock that has the highest nutrient requirements. Best quality hay should be fed to young calves, yearlings, bred heifers, and lactating cows, leaving the lower quality hay for the mature, dry pregnant cows whose nutrient requirements are much lower.

1. Hay Losses during Feeding

The major objective for all feeding systems should be to keep losses to a practical minimum level, thus permitting animals to utilize the majority of hay offered at feeding. Feeding losses include trampling, leaf shatter, chemical and physical deterioration, fecal contamination, overconsumption, and refusal. These losses are associated with feeding method, intervals between feedings, amounts fed at one time, weather conditions, and number of animals being fed.

Hay feeding losses may range from less than 2% under well-controlled feeding methods to over 60% when no attempts are made to reduce loss. Feeding losses of 3–6% are acceptable for most conservative feeding programs, although the lower losses are usually associated with systems of feeding requiring high labor inputs and daily feeding.

Several key points can be made relative to how to minimize losses during hay feeding:

1. Match hay quality to animal's needs.
2. When feeding outside, feed bales on a well-drained site.
3. Restrict animal access to bales with racks or panels and length of feeding period.
4. Restrict animal access to small round bales left in the field by using temporary fence.
5. Force clean up of hay by animals that have low nutrient requirements before feeding more hay.
6. Reseed area of sod killed as a result of feeding.

XI. Silage

Silage is defined as plant material that has undergone fermentation in a silo. A silo is any storage structure in which green, moist forage is preserved.

Harvesting, preserving, and feeding forage crops as silage is a practice used throughout the United States. Silage represents a convenient and economical source of feed for the dairy industry and is increasingly used in beef backgrounding and finishing programs. [See GRAIN, FEED, AND CROP STORAGE.]

Silage has many advantages, including (1) less field and harvest losses than occur with hay, (2) choice of many crops that can be used for silage, (3) mechanization of harvesting the standing crop to feeding, (4) less likelihood of weather damage during the harvesting process, (5) when properly ensiled, storage for long periods with only small losses of nutrients, and (6) flexible use in many livestock feeding programs.

Some disadvantages of silage include (1) bulkiness in handling and storage; (2) requirement for additional equipment and structures for harvesting, storing, and feeding; (3) excessive losses if not stored properly; (4) low marketability if not used on the farm; and (5) requirement of feeding soon after removal from the silo to minimize spoilage.

1. Crops for Silage

High-energy crops (corn, grain sorghum, small grains) are used extensively for silage. Other forage crops (alfalfa, forage sorghum, legume–grass mixtures, and various grasses) are also used, but require wilting to reduce moisture content for proper ensiling. Corn ranks as the best silage crop because it ensiles well, is high in energy, and results in good animal performance.

2. The Ensiling Process

The overall goal of the ensiling process is to utilize the oxygen and lower the pH so the forage material can be pickled or preserved. To accomplish this, two groups of bacteria are essential. The first group are oxygen-using (aerobic) bacteria that give off carbon dioxide and heat. If the silage is packed well and chopped fine, these bacteria will utilize all the oxygen in 4–6 hr. The heat given off in the process will raise the temperature to 27–38°C.

The second group of bacteria (anaerobic) take over the work in the absence of oxygen to produce acetic acid. After the second or third day, lactic acid bacteria become active. Production of lactic acid occurs for 16–18 days, until the pH drops to between 3.5 and 4.2. At this low pH (high acid) the silage is preserved and essentially all bacterial activity stops. At this point, the silage is stable and will keep for long periods of time, provided oxygen does not enter the silo.

3. Silos

In addition to preserving the silage, a silo must protect the silage from damage by air, water, rodents, birds, and animals during storage. The main function of a silo is keeping oxygen out; the microbes produce acid that preserves the silage. Silos are divided into two basic types—upright and horizontal. Upright silos include conventional (concrete stave) and oxygen limiting. Horizontal silos include trench (below ground), bunker (above ground with sides), and stacks (above ground without sides).

Equipment is now available that permits silage to be harvested, packed into plastic bags, and ensiled. Length of the plastic (silo) can vary to meet individual needs. In addition, plastic bags can be used for non-chopped forage. Forages can be cut, wilted, and harvested in large round bales at high moisture content, placed in individual plastic bags, tied, and sealed.

4. Factors Affecting Silage Quality

Type of crop stored, stage of maturity, moisture content, and length of chop affect the quality of silage. Regardless of the crop grown for silage, the stage of maturity when harvested has the greatest effect on quality. As silage plants age or mature, quality declines, resulting in lower animal performance.

5. Moisture Content

Depending on the crop ensiled and the type of silo used, silage can be made over a wide moisture range. When using stacks, trenches, or bunkers, the moisture content of the silage should be 65–70% to obtain adequate packing. Moisture content can be determined using a moisture meter or by drying and weighing samples.

6. Length of Chop

Excluding air is the first, and a critically important, phase of the ensiling process. To insure that this phase

is short, it is important to exclude air by fine chopping (approximately .6–1.3 cm for most forages) and packing adequately.

7. Silage Preservatives and Additives

Several materials have been investigated for their merits in improving silage. Careful consideration should be given to selecting silage additives. No additive can substitute for basic silage-making principles such as harvesting at the proper stage of maturity, storing at the proper moisture content, chopping finely, packing well, and covering adequately. Silage can be no better as a feed than the forage put into the silo.

8. Feeding Silage

Silage is ready to be fed 3–4 wk after it is stored. Silage can supply some or all of the needs of various classes of livestock. Feeding can be mechanized for convenience and efficiency.

XII. Other Benefits of Forage Crops

Perennial grasses minimize soil erosion losses; thus, pastures and hay fields are largely protected. Forages can also be used in rotation with row crops, in waterways, on terraces, and in strip cropping to reduce erosion relative to total or continuous tillage situations.

An especially important result of using forages to reduce erosion is improvement of water quality. In most parts of the nation, the primary contaminant of surface water is soil particulate matter. In addition to reducing particulate matter in runoff, thick sods of forages tend to serve as filters that remove contaminants before they can seep into groundwater. For this reason, forage crops are commonly used to provide vegetative cover in areas where unwanted effluents are discarded.

Improvement of soil tilth due to the addition of organic matter and the activity of earthworms, soil insects, and microorganisms are among the benefits of forages. In addition, the formation of root channels allows the roots of subsequent crops to penetrate more deeply. Also, in the case of legumes, residual nitrogen benefits subsequent crops.

Grassland agriculture requires low energy inputs compared with other agricultural production systems. This includes low tillage requirements and, thus, low fuel usage, less fertilizer requirement, and low usage of agricultural pesticides. Added to this is the fact that forage crops, like all plants, consume carbon dioxide and simultanously release oxygen. However, the high leaf area of most forage canopies results in higher efficiency than with most other crops.

Forage crops are also highly beneficial to many types of game and nongame wildlife, which use them for food and/or cover. For example, deer and wild turkey consume the leaves of many forages; birds of all types eat the seed; and rabbits, rats, mice, and many other animals adopt forage stands as their homes.

A final benefit of forages is beauty and recreation. In addition to photography, hunting, hiking, and camping—which often involve forage lands—many people find peace and satisfaction in viewing a pastoral scene. The production of forage crops is a highly environmentally friendly type of agricultural production.

Bibliography

Ball, D. M., Hoveland, C. S., and Lacefield, G. D. (1991). "Southern Forages." Potash and Phosphate Institute and Foundation for Agronomic Research, Atlanta.

Burns, J. D., Evans, J. K., and Lacefield, G. D. (1982). Quality hay production. In "Southern Regional Beef Cow Calf Handbook."

Climate and Man. USDA Yearbook of Agriculture. (1941). U.S. Government Printing Office, Washington, D.C.

Heath, M. E., Barnes, R. F., and Metcalfe, D. S. (1985). "Forages." Iowa State Press, Ames.

Hodgson, J. (1990). "Grazing Management." Longman Scientific and Technical, John Wiley & Sons, New York.

Langer, R. H. M. (1990). "Pastures, Their Ecology and Management." Oxford University Press, New York.

Pearson, C. J., and Ison, R. L. (1987). "Agronomy of Grassland Systems." Cambridge University Press, New York.

Forest Ecology

RICHARD F. FISHER, *Texas A&M University*

Glossary

Climax Endpoint of a successional sequence, or sere; a community that has reached a steady state under a particular set of environmental conditions

Community Association of interacting populations, usually defined by the nature of their interaction or the place in which they live

Diversity Number of species in a local area (α diversity) or a region (γ diversity). Also, a measure of the variety of species in a community that takes into account the relative abundance of each species

Habitat Place where an animal or plant normally lives, usually characterized by a dominant vegetational or physical characteristic

Niche Ecological role of a species in the community, often conceived as a multidimensional space

Nutrient Cycle Path of an element through the ecosystem, including its assimilation by organisms and its regeneration in a reusable inorganic form

Sere Series of stages of community changes in a particular area leading to a stable state

Succession Replacement of populations in a habitat through a regular progression to a stable state

Forest ecology is that branch of science concerned with the distribution, abundance, and productivity of organisms within a forest setting, and their interactions with one another and with their physical environment. It is a subfield in the discipline of ecology which has been defined as "the study of the structure and function of nature" or "scientific natural history." Ecology is a rather young discipline, and it has only just begun to develop a body of generally accepted theories, principles, and laws. An understanding of forest ecology and the forest ecosystem forms the basis for modern forest land management.

I. Forests and Humans

A. Human Forest Interactions

Mankind developed in the forest. *Homo sapiens* evolved from a tree-dwelling primate ancestor, and for the first million years or so *Homo sapiens* were almost totally dependent upon the forest for food, shelter, and safety. Over subsequent millennia, humans have gradually moved from being controlled by the forest environment to controlling the forest environment. Along the way we have never fully escaped our reliance upon the forest. The rise and fall of civilizations and empires, the dominance of nations, and the economic and military power of societies have been directly dependent to the availability of forests and forest products for most of human history.

At first, humans simply used up local wood supplies and moved on to conquer new lands and new wood supplies. Gradually in Asia, Europe, and eventually North America the need to assure a continual wood supply became apparent and forestry was born. Forestry is generally defined as a profession embracing the science, business, and act of creating, conserving, and managing forests for the continuous production of goods and services.

B. Development of Forest Ecology

Just as forestry developed as a result of the need to ensure an adequate supply of certain goods and services from the forest, forest ecology developed as a practical means of dealing with the complex problems of forest management. Forest ecology provides the necessary means for recognizing, understanding, classifying, and mapping the natural variation in forests. It is the essential biophysical basis for successful forest management.

Because forests are complex, and because they vary both from place to place and through time, they are difficult to manage. However, trees, soils, and forests have vital attributes that are knowable, predictable, and manageable. Forest ecology has developed as that branch of basic ecological science that reduces the complexity and variability in forests by elucidating and understanding it. This knowledge can then be applied through cultural practices to managing the forest. [See SILVICULTURE.]

II. The Forest as a Functional System

A. The Ecosystem Concept

The first forest ecologists specialized in the autecology or relationship to elements of the physical environment, of important timber species. However, gradually ecosystem ecology has come to dominate the fields of both forest ecology and natural resources management. Today the ecosystem concept is the central concept of ecology and of the biologically rational management of natural resources.

An ecosystem is a unit that includes all of the organisms, i.e., the community, in a given area interacting with the physical environment so that a flow of energy leads to a clearly defined trophic structure, biotic diversity, and material cycles, i.e., exchange of materials between living and nonliving parts within the system.

Conceptually an ecosystem has five major attributes. Ecosystems have structure; they are made up of biotic and abiotic components—plants, animals, atmosphere, soil, etc. Each ecosystem has a more or less unique set of these components or a specific structure.

Function is an attribute of each ecosystem. There is a constant exchange of matter and energy between system components, between the physical environment and the organismal community as well as within the community.

Complexity, resulting from the high level of integration within the system, is an attribute of ecosystems, as is interdependency. The abiotic and biotic components of ecosystems are so interconnected that a change in any one will result in a subsequent change in almost all the others.

Temporal change is also a characteristic attribute of ecosystems. These living systems are not static and unchanging; although, the time period over which they change may make them seem so. The great importance of the ecosystem concept for natural resource management lies in its recognition of complexity, interaction, functional processes, and temporal change as basic attributes of a dynamic living system. [See AGROFORESTRY.]

B. The Flow of Energy in Forest Ecosystems

Forest ecosystems are major sinks or stores of energy (Table I). The majority of this energy is tied up in the complex carbohydrate and other carbon compounds contained in living and dead organic matter. Even though these systems are major sinks of energy, energy continuously flows through the system. Green plants capture the energy of the sun and through the process of photosynthesis convert that energy into sugars. The energy captured in this way is then used to produce flowers, fruits, leaves, woody tissue, and a myriad of secondary compounds. Some of these compounds, such as cinnamon, camphor, and turpentine, are familiar to us but most are not. Since ecosystems must obey the laws of thermodynamics, some energy is consumed during the production of these secondary compounds. [See PHOTOSYNTHESIS.]

Any and all of the compounds created by green plants can be consumed by animals. These consumers generate the energy for life from the breakdown of complex carbon based compounds. They also manufacture another large set of unique organic compounds, and they store a large amount of energy in their own proteins, fats, oils, etc. A second and third, etc., layer of consumers, carnivores, obtain their en-

TABLE I

Total Worldwide Biomass Storage, Including Forest Floor and Soil Organic Matter, in Various Forest Types

Forest type	Billion tons
Boreal coniferous	325
Temperate coniferous	141
Temperate deciduous	101
Tropical deciduous	122
Tropical rain	424

TABLE II

Number of Organisms, Biomass, and Energy Flow in a Temperate Forest Ecosystem in Summer

Trophic level	Number/0.1 ha	kg/0.1 ha	kcal/m^2/yr^1
2° Carnivores	2	0.005	1
1° Carnivores	120,000	1	1,000
Herbivores	150,000	3	5,000
Producers	200^a	30,000	13,000

^{a} Producers are large, with 1 tree covering much area.

ergy by consuming animals (Table II). These individuals also store energy in their body mass. Again the laws of thermodynamics are obeyed and energy is lost from the system as each conversion takes place.

The large microbial community that exists in all forest ecosystems derives its energy largely by consuming dead plant and animal matter. These organisms also produce a large number of energy-rich organic compounds, and they cause the release of a large amount of energy from the system.

Some of the compounds produced by plants, animals, and microbes are recalcitrant, that is they are difficult to break down. Thus, forest ecosystems build up a surplus of stored energy and stored carbon (Table III). Meanwhile energy is constantly flowing through the system—in through the plants and out through the plants, animals, and microbes. As forest ecosystems mature, the flow of energy changes and the storage of energy tends to increase to a maximum and then remain constant.

In young ecosystems, early successional stages, the inflow of energy is large and the outflow is small. This leads to a rapid increase in the amount of stored energy and stored carbon. By middle age the outflow of energy has increased, but so has the inflow and the rate at which energy is stored may still be great. As the ecosystem approaches maturity, or stability, the rate of inflow and outflow of energy will become

TABLE III

Average Net Aboveground Productivity in Various Forest Types

Forest type	Net aboveground productivity (t ha^{-1} yr^{-1})
Boreal coniferous	5.9
Temperate coniferous	10.6
Temperate deciduous	12.5
Temperate rain	14.2
Tropical deciduous	20.6
Tropical rain	25.8

equal and the system will be said to have reached climax, in an energetic sense.

C. The Cycling of Nutrients in Forest Ecosystems

A unique characteristic of most forest ecosystems is the development of a distinct forest floor resulting from the periodic return through litterfall of leaves, branches, bark, fruit, and sometimes entire trees. This litterfall contains a large proportion of the nutrients extracted annually by the trees from the soil. The dead vegetation on the floor, in turn, decomposes, liberating minerals for reuse by the growing stand. Other nutrients may be brought in from the atmosphere or made available by biological fixation or weathering of parent rock, while some nutrients are lost through crop harvests, burning, and removal in surface- or groundwater. Thus, it is through a dynamic and rather complex system of geological, chemical, and biological cycling that ecosystem nutrient supplies are replenished and maintained, thereby ensuring continued productivity of the site.

The geochemical cycle involves the transfer of mineral elements into or out of the ecosystem. This cycle includes imports from such sources as dust and precipitation (Table IV), weathering of parent rock (Table V), biological fixation of atmosphere nitrogen, and fertilization; outputs include leaching and erosional losses in drainage water (Table VI), volatile losses from fire and denitrification, and removal in harvests (Table VII). The amounts of nutrients gained or lost annually by an ecosystem are influenced by such factors as soil properties, climatic conditions, type of vegetation, and location of ecosystem in relation to the sea and industrial areas.

Biological cycling involves the transfer of nutrients between the forest floor soil and the associated plant and animal communities. In forest ecosystems it may also include the internal transfer of nutrients among organs within the tree. The major steps within closed cycles, therefore, include: (1) uptake, (2) retention, (3) restitution, and (4) internal transfers (Table VIII).

Nutrient absorption by trees is influenced by type and age of the forest cover and by the soil and climatic conditions of the community. The annual uptake by most forest species is in the same order as that of many agricultural corps, but because a major portion of the absorbed nutrients are returned to the forest floor, or translocated within the tree, relatively small amounts are retained each year in an annual creation of biomass.

TABLE IV

Input of Nutrients in Precipitation in Kilograms per Hectare per Year

Location	Quantity of precipitation (mm/yr)	Quantity of nutrients (kg/ha/yr)				
		N	P	K	Ca	Mg
Wisconsin	—	13.1	0.3–0.4	1.0–4.0	2.0–7.0	0.5–1.1
Great Britain	1717	8.7	0.3	2.8	6.7	6.1
Washington	1360	2.7	trace	0.8	2.8	—
Belguim	—	6.0	—	2.9	9.1	2.3
Puerto Rico	3760	—	—	18.2	21.8	4.9
New Hampshire	1322	6.5	0.1	0.9	2.2	0.6
Germany	624	20.0	0.1	4.6	19	—
Nigeria	1850	14.0	0.4	17.5	12.7	11.3
USSR	204	5.6	0.5	7.7	15.4	2.5
Mississippi	1270	13.3	0.3	4.0	5.0	1.0
Sweden	420–648	1.4–5.2	—	0.6–3.7	2.6–13.9	0.6–2.6
Rio Negro, Brazil	2000	5.6	0.2	—	0.8	2.0
North Carolina	1169	3.5	0.3	0.9	3.4	0.7

TABLE V

Estimated Cation Inputs to Temperate Forest Ecosystems from Weathering of Parent Rock

Location	K	Ca	Mg	Na
		kg/ha/yr		
Brookhaven Forest (Long Island, NY)	11.1	24.3	8.3	6.7
Hubbard Brook Forest (NH)	7.1	21.2	3.5	5.8
Cedar River Forest (WA)	15.2	17.4	—	—

TABLE VI

Precipitation Inputs and Losses to Groundwater or Stream Flow from Three Watersheds

	N	P	K	Ca	Mg	Na
			kg/ha/yr			
Oregon (Douglas-fir)						
Input	0.9	0.3	0.1	2.3	1.3	2.3
Output	0.4	0.5	2.2	50.3	12.4	25.7
New Hampshire (Northern hardwood)						
Input	7.2	—	0.7	2.7	0.6	—
Output	2.3	—	2.0	11.4	3.2	—
New York (oak–pine)						
Input	—	—	2.4	3.3	2.1	17.0
Output	—	—	3.9	9.6	7.3	23.2
Florida (splash pine)						
Input	13.0	0.07	2.5	0.3	—	—
Output	1.5	0.03	1.5	0.03	—	—

A major portion of the nutrients taken up annually into the aboveground components of trees is returned to the soil in litterfall and canopy wash (Table IX). The percentage restitution varies somewhat with species, site, and stand age. For example, a higher percentage of the absorbed nutrients appears to be returned to the soil in vigorously growing stands than in nutrient-deficient stands, and hardwood stands generally return more nutrients than conifers, but the reasons for the wide variations in retentions and returns are not clear. In any case, it is clear that trees and forests are very conservative with respect to nutrients. There is a strong tendency for nutrients to be accumulated in forest ecosystems as they evolve and mature.

Although litterfall is the major pathway of nutrient flow from standing biomass to the soil, considerable amounts of nitrogen, phosphorus, calcium, and magnesium are leached from the tree canopy and returned to the soil in throughfall and stemflow.

TABLE VII

Nutrients Removed in Conventional Bole-wood Harvest

Species	N	P	K	Ca	Mg
			kg/ha		
Northern hardwood (45–50 yr)	120	12	60	241	24
Douglas-fir (36 yr)	125	19	96	117	—
Slash and longleaf pine (40–50 yr)	50	5	20	80	17
Oak (47 yr)	151	11	118	173	23
Beech (37 yr)	128	16	94	79	28
Spruce-fir (various ages)	79	11	47	150	14
Loblolly pine (16 yr)	115	15	89	112	29

TABLE VIII

Annual Uptake, Retention, and Restitution of Some Nutrients in Forest Ecosystems

Forest Cover	N			P			K		
	Uptake	Retention	Return	Uptake	Retention	Return	Uptake	Retention	Return
					kg/ha/yr				
Scots pine (mature)	45	10	35	4	1	3	6	2	4
European beech (mature)	50	10	40	12	2	10	14	4	10
Lablolly pine (20 years)	42	5	37	2	—	—	25	—	—
Scots pine (100 years)	34	12	22	3	1	2	7	2	5
Douglas-fir (37 years)	39	24	15	7	6	1	29	14	15
Norway spruce (100 years)	61	21	40	5	2	3	12	7	5
Red oak–European ash (140 years)	123	44	79	9	4	5	75	21	45
European beech (115–125 years)									
Dioritic soil	—	—	—	9	6	3	8	4	4
Granitic soil	—	—	—	6	3	3	5	2	3

Transfers of nutrients within the tree is an important part of nutrient cycling in forest ecosystems. Such transfer is sometimes referred to as biochemical cycling (Table X). The amount of biochemical cycling varies from element to element and over the age of the tree. There also tends to be greater recycling on poor sites than on rich ones.

In spite of large variations in the amounts of geochemical and biological cycling among ecosystems, there can be little doubt that these cyclic transfers of nutrients play a major role in the continued productivity of forest soils. A good understanding of these dynamic processes is crucial to the development of effective forest management programs.

D. Evolution and Adaptation in Forest Ecosystems

The functions in forest ecosystems are usually considered as general ecological phenomena. The character of these functional relationships, however, depends on the character (morphological, physiological, and behavioral) of individual organisms. Adaptations or evolution in these character traits are what allows a particular organism to survive in a particular ecosystem.

Biological evolution is the change in genetic makeup, genotype, of a population or species over time. Success in reproduction, establishment, growth, etc., is associated with variations in genotype. Those individuals better adapted to their physical and biotic environment will contribute more offspring to the next generation. Such genotypes are said to have greater fitness. As the environment changes over time, different genotypes will prove to be best adapted or fittest in the ecosystem. The process by which such genetic change occurs is called natural selection.

Within a population of organisms the genotype of individuals is varied. Some grow faster in height or

TABLE IX

Average Litterfall and Nutrient Return by Forest Type and Region

Forest region	Number of sites	Litterfall	N	K	Ca	Mg	P
					kg/ha/yr		
Boreal coniferous	3	322	2.9	1.1	3.8	0.3	0.7
Boreal deciduous	1	2645	20.2	9.8	35.5	9.7	5.2
Temperate coniferous	13	4377	36.6	26.1	37.3	5.6	4.4
Temperate deciduous	14	5399	61.4	41.6	67.7	11.0	4.0
Mediterranean	1	3842	34.5	44.0	95.0	9.0	4.7
All stands	32	4373	43.3	27.9	47.3	7.4	3.7

TABLE X

Percentage of Annual Nutrient Requirement Met by
Biochemical Cycling

Species	Nutrient		
	%N	%P	%K
Slash pine (5 yr old)	15	3	28
Slash pine (34 yr old)	11	30	100
Aspen	63	33	19
Sugar maple	94	35	19

diameter than others. There is often similar variation in drought tolerance, resistance to insect or disease attack, cold hardiness, etc. Some species are genetically very diverse or heterogeneous and occupy a wide variety of environments, e.g., Scots pine, while other species are genetically homogeneous and occupy a narrow range of environments, e.g., red pine.

When consistent selection pressure is applied, species populations adapt to form ecotypes. For example, there is a considerable variation in the cold tolerance of Douglas-fir between populations growing on the long growing season, mild winter Pacific Slope and in the short growing season, cold winter Rocky Mountains. Similarly, there is wide variation in drought tolerance between loblolly pine populations growing in the per humid Atlantic coastal plain and in the Lost Pines region of central Texas. Such differences have developed over long periods of time and consistent natural selection pressure.

The speed with which selection pressure, either natural or induced, can alter the genetic makeup of a population is rather slow, particularly outside the humid tropics. Thus, if environmental conditions change rapidly, a population may not be able to adapt fast enough or far enough to accommodate the new environment. The rapidity of global change predicted by some global climate models would seriously test the ability of many tree species populations to adapt to their new environment. [*See* FOREST TREE, GENETIC IMPROVEMENT.]

III. The Abiotic Forest Environment

The physical or abiotic environment provides the basic necessities for autotrophic life: energy and the nutrients and water necessary to capture it and convert it into mass. In autecology this abiotic segment of the ecosystem is generally considered as a series of environmental factors: solar radiation, water, temperature, wind or air, soil, and fire.

A. Solar Radiation

The sun is the major source of energy for life, and photoautotrophs, green plants, are the dominant primary producers in earthly ecosystems. Both the length of the period of solar radiation, photoperiod, and the radiation's intensity are very important to plants.

Most organisms require a sense of time, a clock and/or a calendar. Seasonal variation in photoperiod provides the best such timepiece. Although light is usually only one of several factors that in combination schedule the events in a plant's life, outside the tropics it is by far the most important one.

Trees are said to be short-day or long-day plants. That is, they can flower only if there are fewer or greater than some critical number of hours of light. Obviously such an adaptation restricts the latitudinal distribution of a species. The mount of height or biomass growth a species is able to accomplish is also photoperiod dependent. Tropical and some temperate species may grow well with a short photoperiod, e.g., redwood, most nontropical species require long photoperiods (>16 hr) for good growth, and grow best with 24 hr photoperiods. However, most temperate species require shorter photoperiods to trigger the dormancy reactions necessary to allow them to become cold hardy or frost tolerant.

Thus, for temperate species, change in day length is essential. The shift from short to long days triggers flowering, long days promote more rapid growth, and the shift from long to short days triggers the dormancy necessary to withstand low winter temperatures.

The intensity of radiation also has a dramatic effect on growth. At low light intensities, photosynthesis may not exceed the respiration necessary to maintain life. In such cases there will be little or no growth. At high light intensities the plant may not be able to capture all of the energy that is provided to it. The point at which photosynthesis equals respiration is called the compensation point, while the point at which further increases in light intensity produces no further increase in photosynthesis is called the saturation point. Species with low compensation points are said to be shade tolerant, while those with high compensation points are shade intolerant (Table XI). This concept is often used to infer a species' tolerance to

TABLE XI
Compensation Points for Seedlings of a Variety of Tree Species

Species	Compensation point—% of full sunlight
Ponderosa pine	31
Eastern larch	18
Douglas-fir	13
Lodgepole pine	14
Red oak	14
Englemann spruce	11
Eastern white pine	11
Eastern hemlock	8
Beech	8
Sugar maple	3

competition, although this is an oversimplification of a complex ecological process.

Shade intolerant species generally have higher saturation points than do shade tolerant species. Intolerant species usually are capable of more rapid growth than tolerant ones; although, the latter usually are capable of ultimately reaching greater size.

B. Water

Liquid water is the second most important prerequisite for life on earth. The amount of water available during the growing season controls not only the type of natural vegetation present in an area, but also the vegetations density, its rate of growth and vigor, and its ultimate size. [See WATER RESOURCES.]

Vegetation is influenced by effective precipitation not just total annual precipitation. Both temperature regime and periodicity of precipitation are nearly as important in determining the amount of available water as is total precipitation. For example, the boundary between forest and grassland occurs at a total precipitation amount four times less in the northern prairies of Alberta as in the southern great plains of Texas due to the large differences in average annual and growing season temperatures. Mediterranean climates with their cool wet season and warm dry season have very different vegetation types than do continental climates with similar total precipitation and average temperature but cold moist winters and hot moist summers. [See METEOROLOGY.]

Just as precipitation has considerable influence on the forest, the forest has a profound effect on the fate of precipitation that falls on it. The foliage and branches of trees initially receive most of the precipitation; only a small proportion, called throughfall, goes directly to the forest floor. Some of the precipitation, termed interception, is held by the foliage and evaporates or sublimes back into the atmosphere. Another portion, determined by the architecture of the tree and the season of the year, either drips to the forest floor or runs down the branches and trunk to the ground. This latter portion is termed stem flow.

In dense stands of trees almost no water will reach the soil during light showers. During medium and heavy periods of precipitation a large proportion of the total precipitation will reach the soil, but it does so over a longer period of time and with the transference of much less kinetic energy to the soil surface than in an open field. Overland flow or runoff and the erosion it can cause are consequently rare in closed forest ecosystems. Instead precipitation infiltrates into the soil and reaches streams as base flow rather evenly over a long period of time. [See SOIL-WATER RELATIONSHIPS.]

C. Temperature

Temperature affects the distribution of vegetation types almost as much as does water. Plants are quite sensitive to critically low temperatures, rapid decrease in temperature, and diurnal variation in temperature as well as average daily temperature. This produces a latitudinal distribution of forest vegetation from the poles to the equator that is parallelled by an altitudinal distribution at the equator.

In addition to the effects of "killing frosts," this distribution is driven by the fact that some species require a minimum amount of chilling before they will flower, while others require a minimum amount of heat before they can successfully fruit.

Forests have a large effect on the ambient temperatures and diurnal variation within them. The forest canopy absorbs or reflects most of the sun's energy that reaches it. There is little direct heating of the forest floor by the sun, except during the leafless period in deciduous forests. Much of the energy reaching the canopy is consumed in latent heat of vaporization during evapotranspiration of water, and, since heat rises, little of the heat present in the canopy is transmitted downward into the environment beneath the canopy. Thus, the ambient daytime temperature inside a closed forest ecosystem can be reduced by as much as 3–5°C.

During the night energy is lost by reradiation to deep space. The forest canopy loses a considerable amount of energy in this way, but energy reradiation from the forest floor is low because the cold sky is occluded by the canopy. Consequently, ambient night time temperatures in a closed forest ecosystem may be increased by as much as 2–4°C. Since the daily maximum is lower and the daily minimum is higher in the forest, the mean temperature is very nearly that measured nearby in the open.

D. Wind and Air Quality

At a physiological level, wind is important for mixing the air and equalizing the concentration of CO_2, O_2, water vapor, etc. In the absence of air movement, the air near a leaf may become saturated with water reducing transpiration or depleted of CO_2 reducing photosynthesis.

At an intermediate scale, wind is important in determining the morphology of trees. Open grown trees are exposed to very different wind stresses than are individual trees in a closed stand, and open grown specimens of most species develop quite different crown shapes and stem and branch forms than does the same species grown in stands.

Near upper latitudinal or altitudinal tree line, wind often causes flag-shaped crowns and low trailing growth forms by killing the buds on the windward side or exposed upper surface of the tree. Such wind training and dwarfing sometimes produce large areas of krummholz tree growth at altitudinal tree line and along wind-swept coastlines.

On a regional scale, wind causes blowdowns in which many, if not all, of the trees in a stand are windthrown or broken over. Such events are usually associated with strong cyclonic winds (hurricanes) or tornadoes. The periodicity of these blowdowns determines the maximum size and age of trees in some forest types. These catastrophic events may also maintain large areas in a mosaic of early successional stages.

The quality of the air is as important to the forest as is the force with which it moved. Chemicals that fall out or are washed out of the atmosphere can be a valuable source of nutrients (see Table III). Some of these same chemicals, e.g., N and S, can also be important forms of acidic deposition. When a large amount of acidic materials is deposited from the air onto poorly buffered forest ecosystems, nutrient ions (e.g., Ca, K, Mg), can be stripped from the soil. This can lead to growth decline or dieback. The waters that enter streams and lakes from such forests may be acidified by Al and H ions leading to the decline of plant and animal life in those ecosystems. [*See* Air Pollution: Plant Growth and Productivity.]

Strong oxidants (e.g., ozone), are sometimes present in the air in high concentrations. This phenomenon is usually caused by some form of industrial activity. The tolerance of trees to these airborne oxidants varies widely both between and within species, but in parts of the world the composition of forest ecosystems is dramatically affected by such pollutants.

E. Soil

Soil is the least renewable physical component of the ecosystem. Soil is the naturally occurring, unconsolidated, mineral and organic material in which plants grow. It is a mixture of minerals, organic material (humus), air, and water. An ideal soil is about 50% solids, mineral and organic material, and 50% pore volume. Organic matter can vary from 0 to over 90%, but amounts of 3–8% are most common. Under optimum conditions for plant growth, about half of the pore space is filled with water, leaving the remainder of the pores filled with air. This mixture of minerals and organic matter, water, and air provides the environment for root growth. [*See* Soil Chemistry.]

Soils are very important in determining the kinds of plants that can be grown in an area and how well those plants will grow. Much can be understood about a soil by observing four properties—color, texture, structure, and depth. Each of these easily observable properties is closely correlated to one or more difficult to determine properties that actually control plant growth; therefore, we can infer the ability of a soil to support plants from these four properties. [*See* Soil Fertility.]

Soil color has little direct effect on plant growth but it is an indicator of soil properties that do affect plant development. The overall color of the soil is an indicator of organic matter content, drainage, and aeration. Some soil colors and characteristics associated with them are:

Black. High in organic matter, may be poorly drained. Soil color becomes darker as organic matter increases from 0 to about 8%. At 8% or above, soil is essentially black in color.
Brown. Good organic matter content and well drained.
Red and yellow. Low in organic matter, well drained. The color is due to varying amounts of oxidized iron.
Gray. Low in organic matter and poorly drained. Gray color is due to excess water and poor aeration. [*See* Soil Genesis, Morphology, and Classification.]

Organic matter coats soil particles and masks their natural color. The natural color of soil particles is determined by their mineralogy. Since the abundance of many plant nutrients is also related to mineralogy, the unmasked color of soil particles becomes a key to potential nutrient availability. For example, quartz is a common translucent mineral that contains no plant nutrients, while feldspars, which are opaque white to pink or green minerals, are high in plant nutrients. In general the greater the diversity of colors among soil particles, the higher and more balanced is the potential nutrient supplying power of the soil.

Soil organic matter is important for promoting good soil structure. It is also the major supplier of N and P in the soil, and it helps to retain other plant nutrients in the soil. Soil organic matter is derived from plant and animal remains as they decompose. Although organic material may reside in the soil for several years, it will ultimately be itself decomposed. Thus, the soil requires a constant addition of organic material in order to maintain its organic matter content. Roots and soil organisms that die each year are a major source of organic material for the soil, but a large portion of the material required to maintain organic matter levels must come from aboveground plant production. [*See* SOIL MICROBIOLOGY.]

Soil texture is determined by the relative percentage of sand-, silt-, and clay-sized particles that make up the mineral fraction of the soil. Of course, soils may contain coarse fragments such as gravel or even boulders, but these are not used to determine the basic texture of the soil. Texture is a property that affects soil productivity by influencing water and air movement, ease of tillage, root growth, and nutrient retention.

One of the most important soil properties affected by soil texture is the ability to hold water against the force of gravity. Water is held in a film around soil particles. The attraction between water and clay-sized particles in particular is so strong that even plant roots have difficulty extracting water from the inner portion of the film. However, the outer portion of the water film is readily extracted by plants. When a soil is holding the maximum amount of water it can retain against the force of gravity, it is said to be at its field capacity. When the water films have been reduced by evaporation or root absorption to the point that plants wilt, the moisture level is said to be at the permanent wilting percentage (point). Water is still present (perhaps up to 25% of the soil's weight) but the plants cannot pull it away from the soil particles fast enough to prevent wilting. The moisture content between field capacity and the permanent wilting percentage is the plant-available water (Fig. 1).

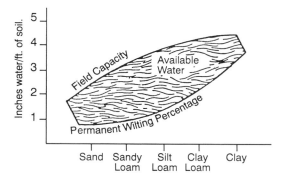

FIGURE 1 Plant available water as affected by soil texture.

Soil structure is determined by the degree to which the soil's primary particles, sand, clay, etc., are bound together to form aggregates. Some of the forces that cause aggregation are cohesive. Silt- and/or clay-sized particles may cling together due to their own electrostatic forces. But most aggregates are held together by adhesive forces, that is, the particles adhere to one another because of organic, colloidal, or metal oxide coatings. The most common adhesive agent is organic matter.

As organic matter coatings build up in a sandy soil, the structure proceeds from single grain through crumb and granular stages to a weak blocky state. During this process many of the large pores in the soil are filled with coatings, and small pores are produced. This has the effect of increasing the soil's water holding capacity. As organic matter is added to a clay soil, the structure changes from massive to a coarse blocky and finally to a fine blocky state. As this occurs, the fracture plains between the blocks produce more and more large pores. This increases both the water and oxygen supplying power of the soil. So we see that as structure develops, the ability of a soil to support plant growth improves no matter what the soil's texture.

The fourth easily observable soil property that serves as a key to a site's ability to support plant growth is depth. This might more properly be called volume. It is important to plants, particularly perennials, how much soil is available for their roots to exploit. An organic rich silt loam soil may hold abundant water and nutrients, but if there are only a few inches of it over solid rock, trees will not prosper. Likewise if a large proportion of the soils volume is made of large coarse fragments the water storage capacity may be quite small. Young soils of glacial till or colluvial origin may contain between 50 and 80% course fragments. Such dilution of moisture storage capacity dramatically affects both forest type and tree growth, particularly in areas with a strong dry season.

Soil acidity, commonly measured in terms of pH, is an easily measured soil property. It has a considerable effect on the distribution of species due to its effect on the solubility or availability of ions held within the soil exchange complex. When soils are near neutral, pH 7, the availability of N, P, and K is at a maximum, but Fe and Mn availability is low. As the soil becomes more acid, Fe availability increases, but P availability decreases. Also at low pH Al, which can be toxic to roots, increases in concentration in soil solution. Tree ranges and vigor are thus indirectly related to soil acidity, and different species prosper on soils of differing acidity. [*See* SOIL, ACID.]

Soil has a profound effect on the distribution of tree species, but trees, in their turn, have a profound effect on soil. Through their protection of the soil from the erosive energy of rainfall, their cycling and conservation of nutrients, their modification of temperature and moisture regimes, and their production of the raw material from which soil organic matter is derived, trees determine the nature of the soil beneath them just as much as the soil determines the nature of the forest. Thus, soil is both an abiotic and biotic component of the ecosystem. It is the least renewable abiotic component, but to a degree it is a resilient, living component as well.

F. Fire

Except in the wettest, hottest, and coldest environments, fire has played a major role in essentially all terrestrial ecosystems. Natural fires set by lightening occur, at least occasionally, almost everywhere on earth, and prior to intentional fire control efforts by humans, such fires often burned vast areas.

Fire was perhaps the first major tool used by humans to alter their environment. It is still used in agriculture, wildlife management, and forestry as a major ecosystem management tool. Fire causes catastrophic change in the ecosystem, but it seldom causes an irreversible change or completely devastates the productive capacity of a locality.

Fire can convert forest to wasteland. There are classic examples of this from the upper midwest of the United States, the Amazon basin, and recently Kalimantan (Indonesia). Such devastating fires are rare in the absence of human activity. When large areas of forests are felled and little wood is removed, or when areas are protected from fire for a protracted period,

extremely large fuel loads build up in the ecosystem. If areas with such fuel loads do burn, extremely high temperatures may be reached during the fire. This usually results not only in the complete combustion of the forest floor, but also in the volatilization of carbon from the soil. Subsequent rainfall may then easily erode away the surface soil, exposing underlying rock or recalcitrant subsoil and permanently altering the substrate for plant growth.

Fire is generally not an anathema to the vast majority of forest ecosystems. In fact, it is essential for the maintenance of many forest types. Fire also has an important role in forest succession. Fire is important in nutrient cycling in systems where large amounts of organic residue tend to accumulate; it is important in disease control, and often essential for the successful establishment of a variety of species, e.g., jack pine, longleaf pine, aspen, etc.

IV. The Biotic Forest Environment

Organisms do not exist in isolation. They have evolved in response not only to the physical, abiotic, environment, but also in response to interactions with the biotic components, other organisms, in their environment. In severe environments abiotic factors are usually the dominant influence on adaptation and evolution, but in more benign environments, biotic factors have great influence.

A. Abundance and Dynamics of Species Populations

Organisms are commonly members of a population. Such membership provides protection from the rigors of the abiotic environment, interchange of genetic information necessary for adaptation to occur, increases in reproduction, and advantage in interspecific competition.

Tree population biology can be divided into three phases. The initial phase is sometimes called seed rain and is composed of the processes of natality and dispersion. Trees have a fecundity (potential maximum number of propagules per female per year or generation) that is genetically determined. They also have an environmentally determined or actual fecundity (number of propagules produced per female per year or generation). Potential fecundity may vary widely between individuals in a species, and actual fecundity varies widely between environments and years or seasons.

Seed rain is a function of the distance from the parent plant, wind speed and direction, abundance of dispersal organisms, landscape scale habitat mosaic, or any other factor that influences dispersal. In the wet tropical forest, animal vectors are extremely important for seed dispersal, while elsewhere wind becomes the dominant dispersal agent. Once propagules are dispersed they enter the seed bank, the community of viable but ungerminated seeds in the soil. The seed bank may contain few seeds or as many as 2000–3000 per square meter.

The second phase is establishment. Each cohort of propagules has a characteristic survivorship curve in any particular environment. There is generally heavy juvenile mortality due to either abiotic or biotic conditions. Tree populations have survivorship and age-class distributions that vary greatly between species and the developmental state of the ecosystem.

Shade intolerant, or pioneer, species have narrow age and size class distributions, i.e., are even-aged, that pass up and out of the community in the course of succession. Shade tolerant, or climax, species have a "reverse-J-shaped" age and size distribution with many small or young individuals and few old or large ones. This distribution remains stable over long time periods in the absence of catastrophic disturbances.

Trees compete for scarce resources in their environment; consequently, both the size and nature of tree populations are determined by density-dependent factors. Both inter- and intraspecific competition are important in the population dynamics of forest trees. Species tolerant of low light intensity, low moisture availability, or low soil fertility will out-compete species intolerant of shade, drought, and infertility. Individuals of the same species must also compete for scarce resources. This leads to density-dependent mortality, so as forests develop, the number of individuals decreases, the size of those remaining increases, and the species composition changes, all in response to competition.

B. Structure and Function of Communities

Forests are communities of organisms dominated by trees. In even-aged forests the trees making up the stands are nearly all the same age and size, while in uneven-aged forests, dominant, codominant, intermediate, and suppressed trees are present. These trees usually differ in age as well as in size.

In all forests many plants other than trees are present: lianas, shrubs, herbs, epiphytes, and thallophytes (lichens, mosses, and liverworts). These plants, to-gether with the trees, constitute the primary producers of the community. The abundance and diversity of plant species in a forest community is a function of the severity of the environment and the developmental stage of the community. Abundance and diversity are far greater in the wet tropical forest with its favorable environment than in the dry thorn forest or the cold boreal forest. As forests develop they may pass through a stage where their dense canopy reduces the light reaching the forest floor to an extent that few plants can persist in the understory. This stage may range from several years to several decades in length, but it is usually short in comparison to the forest's life span.

Animals are also an important part of the forest community. Animals avoid undue competition by evolving different adaptations, tolerances, requirements, and behaviors. Each species evolves so as to exist in a more or less unique ecological niche. A niche is a space defined by habitat, geographical area, and functional role. For example, three warbler species, all of whom are insectivores with the same functional role, can coexist in a boreal forest if one feeds in the outer crown of the trees, one feeds in the inner crown, and one feeds on the understory. Likewise, a sparrow species that feeds on seeds could also exist in the same forest community.

Forest communities that are vegetationally simple, one species of tree and little understory, provide few niches; therefore, they have little animal diversity. Forest communities, such as tropical rain forests, that have high vegetative diversity, provide many niches; therefore, they have high animal diversity.

Animals are an essential part of all forest communities. They are valuable pollinators and seed dispersal agents in many forests, e.g., without squirrels to bury acorns, oak regeneration is greatly reduced. They are important in nutrient cycling, and they are essential in the natural control of pest outbreaks.

Microorganisms are also a vital part of all forest communities. Some perform unique functions such as the conversion of atmospheric nitrogen into a form of nitrogen usable by plants, while others are parasites or pathogens that help to maintain the dynamic equilibrium between species and age classes of a single species within the community. Most importantly microorganisms are the major detritus feeders in all ecosystems. They consume large quantities of organic material and in the process release valuable nutrient ions into the soil where they can be reused by the trees and other primary producers. Without the microbial community the forest would smother in its own waste.

C. Succession

Change is the most fundamental characteristic of ecosystems, and temporal change or development in ecosystem structure and function can easily be observed. It is called ecological succession or simply succession, and is both the sequence of plant, animal, and microbial communities that successively occupy an area over time and the process of change by which the biotic communities succeed each other and by which the physical environment is altered over time.

Succession is usually broken down into primary succession, which occurs in environments that lack organic matter and have not as yet been altered by living organisms, and secondary succession, which occurs in environments that have been modified by living organisms but in which some form of disturbance has removed the previous community. Obviously at this stage in the development of the earth, secondary succession predominates.

Forest succession generally begins after fire, blowdown, forest harvesting, or the abandonment of land from other uses. In the early stages physical conditions are demanding and the site is usually colonized by robust pioneer species. These may be grasses, herbs, shrubs, or trees, but they must be capable of growing in full sunlight, withstanding wide swings in temperature and moisture availability, and tolerating infertile soil conditions. Over time the presence of the pioneers modifies the environment. They provide shade, reduce the amplitude of temperature and moisture availability, increase soil organic matter content and nutrient availability, and provide homes for animals, some of which begin to introduce the seeds of new plant species into the community.

Gradually shade tolerant species begin to occur in the forest. These species, although they may be slower growing than the intolerant pioneer species, have long life spans and reproduce effectively in their own shade. They gradually begin to dominate the area and the community changes toward climax. Climax communities are relatively stable and prolonged stages of community development.

Climax communities are characteristic of the climate in which they occur and the substrates on which they occur. In any climatic zone one climax community will occur on moist well drained soils, while quite different climax communities will occur on excessively wet and dry sites. There may be a tendency for wet sites and dry sites to move toward being moist well drained sites; however, such change occurs over geologic time and is of minor importance on a human time scale.

As the composition of the plant community changes during succession, so does the composition of the animal community. Some animals, e.g., rabbit, towhee, quail, grasshopper, prefer the earliest stages of succession. Others, e.g., deer, red cockaded woodpecker, junco, prefer early to middle successional stage, while still others, e.g., spotted owl, veery, marten, prefer late successional stages. Abundance and diversity also change during succession. White-tailed deer occur in all stages of forest succession, but they are much more numerous in early stages than at climax. In some cases diversity is greatest at climax, but commonly diversity is lower in both early and late succession and reaches a maximum in middle successional stages where pioneer and climax species overlap. The structure and function of the microbial community also change during succession, but this change is more difficult to observe than the changes in plant and animal communities.

The essence of silvicultural forest management is the control of succession. Different tree species grow during different stages of succession. Because some species grow faster, are more pest resistant, provide unique wildlife habitat, or produce wood with more desirable properties than others, foresters often wish to control succession. They do this by means of cutting, fire, herbicide, or other cultural practices so as to maintain an area in a particular stage of succession for a prolonged time.

One of the most common forest practices is to use clear felling and/or fire to maintain an area in a very early successional stage. This is done because pioneer species are fast growing and tend to occur in monospecific stands that are easy to manage and utilize. However, some forests are managed so as to maintain them in a climax community for the production of wood of unique quality or the maintenance of wildlife habitat. In this case, management is necessary to minimize the occurrence of catastrophic fire, insect or disease outbreak, blowdown, or other events that would naturally restart secondary succession on the area.

V. Applications of Forest Ecology to Natural Resources Management

The principles of forest ecology have been applied, either knowingly or unknowingly, to human use of the forest for millennia. Whether our appreciation of natural phenomena comes from practical experience or intense study, mankind tends to apply any such appreciation to the control of the environment in which it exists.

A. Classification and Mapping of Forest Ecosystems

In Roman times sites were classified on the basis of the most productive ecosystem they could support, and owners were taxed on that basis. This classification was based on gross features and, to an extent, those features were controlled by past management practices.

The first classification systems constructed to neutralize the effects of prior management practices were not developed until the late 19th century and were based on understory vegetation. These ecosystem classification schemes were valuable for understanding community dynamics and for management of forests in northern Europe, but they proved to be of limited value elsewhere.

Subsequently, classification schemes based on potential, or climax, overstory, and present understory vegetation were developed in Europe and North America. These habitat type systems have proved to be useful for understanding community dynamics and are widely used in western North America. Their application to management has been less successful.

In eastern North America classifications based on soil characteristics are in common usage. These systems may or may not contain an environmental or vegetative parameter. Complex systems containing environmental, soil, and vegetative parameters are in use in Europe. To a considerable degree, the nature of the classification system used depends upon the scale at which management is conducted. In eastern North America and Europe where management may be carried out on a scale of tens of acres, soil-based systems are powerful and are employed. In western North America where management is carried out on a scale of hundreds or even thousands of acres, vegetatively based classifications may be more useful.

B. Models for Management

Ecological models may be helpful in making management decisions. They have to date, however, proved to be more useful for increasing our understanding of ecosystem structure and function than for providing management direction.

Vital attribute models based on such parameters as tolerance to shade, drought, nutrient deficiency, and fire are valuable both for increasing our understanding of successional progression and for the development of management strategies in a variety of forest types. These models have also been useful for providing an insight into forest ecosystem responses to global change.

As forest management in particular and natural resource management in general become more and more dependent on mathematical models, it becomes increasingly important that management models have an ecological component if not core. Steps toward more clearly functional ecological models are necessary if economic aspects are not to dominate natural resources management.

C. Sustainability

The basic problem when considering sustainability is determining just what is to be sustained. It is rather simple to develop a strategy that will sustain the production of fiber from a forest at a variety of levels. Some of these levels will not sustain the biological diversity of the forest, while others will not sustain the employment level in the local wood using industry or the regional or national consumption of wood fiber-based products. Clearly no management scheme can be expected to sustain an optimal level of biological diversity, employment, and production simultaneously.

The answer to this conundrum may lie in a diversity of management strategies at a landscape scale. It may also require a reduction in the expected standard of living, not only for forest resource-based communities, but for all. It may be that by admixing areas in which biological diversity and productivity of fiber, recreational opportunity, etc., are maximized, we can approach an optimum level of all outputs. Such an optimum would need to be couched in terms of both quality of environment and quality of life. Likely our expectations of the revenue realized from the sale and manufacture of fiber-based products and our expected consumption of such products would both need to be scaled downward.

Bibliography

Kimmins, J. P. (1987). "Forest Ecology." Macmillan, New York.
Spurr, S. H., and Barnes, B. V. (1980). "Forest Ecology." Wiley, New York.
Waring, R. H., and Schlesinger, W. H. (1985). "Forest Ecosystems—Concepts and Management." Academic Press, Orlando, FL.

Forest Tree, Genetic Improvement

J. P. VAN BUIJTENEN, *Texas Agricultural Experiment Station Texas A&M University*

Glossary

Breeding Applied science of systematic genetic improvement of a species or population. Measures for producing genetically better trees vary from leaving the best trees for seed when stands are harvested (mass selection) to intensive hybridization and induction of polyploidy; genetics is the cornerstone of a breeding program, but the principles of other biological and physical sciences are also applied

Clone Group of plants derived from a single individual (ortet) by asexual reproduction. All members (ramets) of a clone have the same genotype and consequently tend to be uniform

Fibril angle Angle between the cellulose molecules in the cell wall and the length axis of the wood fibers; fibers with a small fibril angle are stronger

Provenance Original geographic source of seed, cuttings, or scions. Other closely related terms are geographic race and seed source

Roguing Systematic removal of undesired individuals from a population to prevent their reproduction

Seed orchard Plantation consisting of clones or seedlings from selected trees, isolated to reduce pollination from outside sources, and cultured for early and abundant production of seed for reforestation; forest seed orchards are often established while genetic evaluation of the material is under way; when results of these tests are known, the undesirable individuals are rogued

Site index Measure of the productivity of a forest site; the index is equal to the average height of the dominant and co-dominant trees at a standard age, usually 25 or 50 years

Somaclonal variation Variation that often results when tissue culture is used as a means of asexual propagation; this is particularly common if the tissue passes through a callus stage

Genetic improvement of forest trees is concerned with the improvement of growth, quality, pest resistance, and stress resistance of forest trees and the maintenance of a broad genetic base. This is achieved by means of selective breeding, hybridization, clonal propagation, the induction of somaclonal variation, and molecular genetic methods. In practice it needs to be combined with improved forest management practices to achieve the best results. Other areas of concern include gene conservation and the maintenance of genetic diversity.

I. The Seed Orchard Approach to Forest Tree Improvement

A. Definition

The seed orchard approach is particularly suitable when large quantities of seed are needed to support extensive planting programs. In a newly established program the seed orchard approach consists of mass selection of outstanding trees in natural stands or plantations, the establishment of grafted or seedling seed orchards, establishing progeny tests from the original selections, roguing the orchards to the best clones or families, and finally making new selections within the best families to regenerate a breeding population.

Because the need for improved seed is urgent, seed orchards are usually established immediately even though the genetic value of the selections remains unproven. The genetic worth of a selection can only be determined by progeny testing because desirable qualities of a tree result from both genetic and environmental factors. There are a number of genetically undesirable trees included in the orchards, a price paid in order to have seed available 15 to 20 years sooner than if the progeny testing is done before the orchards are established. Later as progeny tests results become known these undesirable parents are removed (rogued) from the orchards.

B. Tree Selection

1. Characteristics Desired in Trees

Not all organizations emphasize the same qualities in their selection program because these are determined largely by the products they manufacture. What is true for Douglas-fir (*Pseudotsuga menziesii* Franco) may not apply to eucalypts and traits desired by Christmas tree growers may cause serious problems for timber producers. Even so, many characteristics are desirable for many species and users.

Usually one tries to improve several characteristics at the same time. They may include fast growth rate, good pruning ability, straight stem, horizontal branches, small branch diameter, small crown diameter, disease resistance, insect resistance, drought-hardiness, cold-hardiness, and wood properties appropriate for the desired end use.

Since wood production is the usual objective of growing trees, wood properties are special because they strongly affect the end product. Because requirements differ by product there is no such thing as "good wood" per se. One has to ask "good for what." Only then can one define the wood qualities desired in a given species for a given product. The single most important wood property is wood specific gravity. It is normally defined as the oven dry weight in grams divided by the green volume in cubic centimeters. It affects a wide range of properties of almost all wood products. Sometimes specific gravity is defined as wood density expressed in lbs/ft^3 or kg/m^3.

Desirable traits for urban trees differ a great deal from those for forest trees. Most important are resistance to the harsh urban environment, air pollution, drought, soil compaction, and high salt concentrations. For street and yard trees, small to medium mature size, good color and appearance and dense foliage are also important. For park and shade trees, large mature size and spreading crown with attractive and dense foliage are desirable.

Windbreaks also pose some special requirements such as drought resistance, dense low crowns, and tolerance to strong prevailing winds. In the developing world, other traits such as the value of the wood for firewood, the quality of the foliage as fodder, and the nutritional value of the fruit can be of great importance. For agroforestry attributes such as small or open crowns and deep root systems are very beneficial. [*See* CULTIVAR DEVELOPMENT.]

2. Tree Grading Systems

Although there are many tree grading systems in use, most are similar. They can be roughly divided into two groups, comparison or check tree systems and individual tree systems. In the comparison tree system the superior tree candidate is graded against a number (5 to 10) of the very best trees in the immediate environment. These comparison trees serve as a measure of the quality of the environment. The comparison tree systems work best in plantations, not as well in even-aged natural stands, and not at all in uneven-aged stands or mixed species forests.

Individual tree selection systems can be as simple as phenotypic mass selection or as sophisticated as a multiple regression system. If a good data base (a thousand trees or more) is available, the latter system can be extremely useful. To develop such a system one needs measurements of the trees to be selected such as height, diameter, straightness, crown characteristics and wood specific gravity. In addition, measurements are needed of factors influencing these traits such as age, site index, and crown radius (a measure of competition). By means of a multiple regression analysis one can develop a prediction equation and score trees on the basis of the amount by which they exceed their predicted value.

Low intensity selection of a large number of trees followed by open pollinated progeny testing is a viable option if a check tree or regression system is not applicable.

3. Maintaining a Broad Genetic Base

The rotation age of forest trees is long compared to the life span of agricultural crops. It may be as short as 4 years in South America and over 200 years in boreal North America. The breeding cycle varies similarly and may be one-quarter to one-half of the rotation age. As a consequence forest trees are highly exposed to pests, pathogens, and environmental extremes and it takes a long time to develop resistant strains. The best way to safeguard against the disasters that have occurred occasionally in narrow based agricultural crops is the maintenance of a large breeding population (200 to 1000 parents) and a range of genotypes in the trees used for reforestation. The trees included in the production orchard can be a selected portion of the total breeding population.

C. Seed Orchards

There are two major types of orchards: vegetatively propagated orchards by either grafts or rooted cuttings and seedling seed orchards. Both types of orchards have their advantages and disadvantages and the best approach depends on the species involved, the objective of the orchards, and the local circumstances. [See ORCHARD MANAGEMENT SYSTEMS.]

Occasionally attempts are made to combine the genetic testing and the production of seed in one plantation to reduce cost. There are serious drawbacks to this procedure because the two functions are incompatible. Progeny tests should be established at relatively close spacing on the type of site one expects to grow the seedlings commercially. On the other hand, seed orchards require wide spacing, fertilization, irrigation, and control of pests for optimum seed production. Under these circumstances growth, form, incidence of diseases, and insects would be seriously altered making a satisfactory evaluation of the genetic worth of the progenies difficult. The procedure works best when only small quantities of seed are needed or the species is an early and prolific seed producer. In this case the plantation can be originated as a genetic test and then thinned to the best trees of the best families when sufficient genetic information is available.

1. Establishing the Seed Orchard

In planning a seed orchard two major decisions need to be made initially: its size and its location. The size is primarily a function of the projected seed needs, and the expected seed production per tree. This of course varies greatly from species to species. Initial spacing depends very much on the type of orchard and the species. In a seedling seed orchard of an early flowering species the initial spacing could be 10 × 10 ft. or closer, while in grafted orchards initial spacings of 30 × 30 ft. are common. Too close a spacing causes problems because it will be necessary to remove trees for flower production purposes, before

genetic information is available to help in deciding which trees should be removed. Full sunlight is mandatory for seed production.

2. Seed Orchard Management

Seed orchard management is usually divided into two phases: the growth phase and the production phase. During the growth phase the emphasis is placed on establishing healthy, fast-growing plants, which quickly produce a large crown surface on which seed is produced. Irrigation, fertilization, insect and disease control, and control of competing vegetation are principal concerns during this period.

When the trees have obtained sufficient size, the emphasis is shifted to seed production phase management. During this phase the objective is to induce abundant flower production, obtain a high seed set, and carry the highest possible proportion of the seed to harvest. This requires a somewhat different fertilization regime, withholding water at critical periods of time, and protecting the flower and seed crop from insects and diseases.

3. Seed Collection

Depending on the species and circumstances, seed collection is done either manually or mechanically. Manual seed collection requires some kind of scaffolding or lift equipment when the trees get larger. Both the equipment and the labor can be quite expensive. In some species a tree shaker can be used to shake either the cones or the seed out of the crowns. Either they are picked up from the ground by hand or a polypropylene tarp is laid on the orchard floor prior to shaking which is used to collect the seed mechanically.

D. Genetic Testing

Genetic testing must be done for several different reasons. Some of the most common objectives are: (1) to evaluate families for the purpose of roguing seed orchards; (2) to establish plantings from which to make advanced generation selections; (3) to determine heritabilities and genetic correlations useful in improving breeding procedures; and (4) to monitor actual progress made. The genetic improvement in first-generation orchards is obtained in two steps. Step one is the mass selection that is practiced in the original forests. Step two is the progeny testing, followed by roguing of the seed orchards. The step in which one will get the greatest advance depends on how much of the variation is environmental and how much genetic. If most of the variation is genetic there is little additional gain from progeny testing. If most of the variation is environmental one can make substantial gains from progeny testing and roguing. This is the situation for many characteristics of forest trees particularly those related to volume.

Advanced generation selection is another major objective of progeny testing. In this step, progeny test plantations are screened on the basis of characters desired and selections are made on the basis of periodic measurements and data collected on specific individuals or families within the test. Selections made in progeny test plantations are then grafted into scion banks. These scion banks provide seed for further testing and scions for use in seed orchard establishment.

E. Advanced Generation Breeding

1. Selection Methods

Index selection is the best technology currently available. Each tree is given a score based on its family and individual performance. Traits can be combined first using a multiple trait selection index composed of economic weights and genetic parameters. In its simplest form each trait is given a weight indicating its relative economic importance. The index is then simply the sum of the weighted traits. A more elaborate version of weights are derived by means of a multiple regression method maximizing the genetic gain based on known economic weights and the genotypic and phenotypic variances and covariances among the traits. Each family is then given an index value based on its performance in relation to the plantation average. In addition, each tree is given an index value based on its performance in relation to the plot average. The final score is the sum of both indexes. As a result, the best individuals from the best families are selected.

2. Breeding Groups

The purpose of breeding groups (sublines) is to avoid inbreeding in the seed harvested from production orchards. This is accomplished by subdividing the total number of trees in the breeding program into smaller groups. Controlled crosses are done within the breeding groups. The breeding groups themselves will therefore become inbred at a rate that can be carefully controlled by the mating design. Trees within a breeding group are usually selected for the same traits and belong to the same geographic seed source.

The orchard needs to be designed in such a way that members of the same breeding group are isolated from each other to the same degree as ramets from the same clone to maximize crosses among unrelated parents. A minimum of nine breeding groups is needed to accomplish this although a greater number is desirable. More than one selection from a breeding group can be used in an orchard by assigning different selections from the same breeding group to different seed orchard blocks.

II. Natural Variation

Since most forest tree species have no previous history of domestication, natural variation is still extremely important. This includes geographic variation, elevational races, stand to stand variation, and variation among individuals within stands. There are two ways to study natural variation. One can study it as it occurs in nature, in which case one is dealing with both a genetic and environmental component which cannot be readily separated, or one can make genetic tests in one or more common locations of seeds collected from different geographic areas to determine the genetic differences among the various seed sources and how they respond to being planted in different environments. In many species geographic variation is both one of the most useful and most dangerous sources of genetic variation available on a short term basis. By planting the right seed source at a given location a dramatic improvement in growth can often be obtained instantaneously, while planting the wrong seed source guarantees disaster. Provenance variation is different for each species and is important for both native and introduced species.

The genetic tests referred to as provenance tests are experiments designed to determine the geographic variation patterns, formulate rules to guide the movement of seed, and, if sampling is intense enough, pinpoint areas that produce the best seed for use in a given region. In a typical provenance test seeds are collected from several average trees in 10 to 150 natural stands scattered throughout the species range, kept separate by stand (but usually not by parent), and the offspring are tested in replicated experiments planted at several different locations. Provenance testing has been a major means of tree improvement particularly in the northeastern United States, some parts of the west, and those areas of the tropics dealing with subtropical pines from Central America and the Caribbean. In general seed can be moved safely from a dry area to more mesic areas and from southern origins to more northern areas (in the northern hemisphere). The fastest growing provenances are usually found in the most favorable environments, and can be moved to other areas, but tend to require better sites and better care to maintain their superiority. In mountainous areas the local elevational race is generally best and elevational changes should not exceed 500 feet above or 1000 feet below the original source.

A. Stand to Stand Variation

Differences among stands within the same physiographic region are another source of variation useful in breeding programs. The amount of stand to stand differences as compared with geographic seed source differences varies from species to species. For example, in eastern and western white pine (*Pinus strobus* L., *P. monticola* Dougl.) stand to stand differences in rust resistance are negligible because most of genetic differences are associated with families. Growth rate in jack pine (*P. banksiana* Lamb.), however, differs considerably from stand to stand while within-stand differences are less.

B. Individual Tree Variation

In many forest tree species individual tree variation is the most important source of variation for practical breeding programs. With few exceptions, such as red pine (*P. resinosa* Ait.), trees within a stand vary in almost every characteristic studied. Although both the variation and heritability depend on the trait, the species, and the environment some general patterns occur (see Table I). To determine breeding objectives

information about inheritance patterns need to be combined with the economic value of each trait, depending on the species concerned and the local circumstances. For example, breeding for resistance to fusiform rust in loblolly pine (*P. taeda* L.) is very profitable in Georgia where the disease is extremely serious, but is at best marginal in Arkansas where fusiform rust causes only minor losses.

III. Use of Exotics

Exotics are defined as trees not native to the area where they are planted. Exotics have been successfully introduced into a forest economy where rather special conditions existed in regard to the native species. The native species, for instance, may not have the desired wood qualities, may not be suitable for plantation management, may not have the genetic variability necessary for successful breeding, or may be of poor quality or vigor.

A. Donor and Recipient Regions

Although there obviously have to be some similarities between the climates of the donor and the recipient region there are no absolute guidelines to follow. There are however some obvious pitfalls one should try to avoid: (1) Do not move a species or provenance from a uniform climate where both moisture and temperature are distributed evenly over the seasons to a geographic region that is subject to rather wide climatic variations. (2) Do not move trees from a Mediterranean climate to a continental climate.

TABLE I

Inheritance Patterns of Traits of Potential Economic Value in Forest Trees

Trait	Heritability	Number of genes controlling trait	Range of phenotypic values	Genetic gain obtainable per generation
Height	Low–medium	Large	Medium	Modest
Diameter	Low	Large	Large	Modest
Volume	Low	Large	Large	Modest
Wood specific gravity	High	Large	Medium	Modest
Straightness	Medium	Large	Variable	Variable
Disease resistance	High	Few–many	High	High
Insect resistance	Low	Few–many	Medium	Low
Presence of specific monoterpenes in resin	High	One–few	High	High
Presence of specific phenolic compounds in needles	High	One–few	High	High
Resin content of wood	Medium	Medium	High	High

Source: Adapted from van Buijtenen, J. P. (1984). Genetic improvement of forest trees through selection and breeding. *In* "Forestry Handbook." (K. F. Wenger, ed.), pp. 457–488. Wiley & Sons, N.Y.

TABLE II
Successful and Unsuccessful Interregional Tree Exchanges

Recipient region	Donor regions	
	Successful[a]	Unsuccessful[a]
United States (northeastern)	China (west)	Japan (Hokkaido)
	Europe (north)	Mexico
	India (north)	Scandinavia
	Japan (Honshu)	Siberia
	Mediterranean basin mts.	USA (SE and SW)
		USA Pacific Coast
	Rocky Mountains	Canada Pacific Coast
British Isles	Europe (north and west)	Asia (north)
	Japan (mountains of Honshu)	China
	Mediterranean basin	Himalayan Mts.
	USA Pacific Coast	Japan (lowlands)
	Canada Pacific Coast	Mexico
Australia	United States (California)	China (west)
	United States (SE)	
South Africa	United States (California)	United States (NE)
	United States (SE)	
	Australia	
South America	United States (SE)	
	Australia	

Source: Adapted from Wright, J. W. (1962). Genetics of forest tree improvement. FAO Forestry and Forest Products Studies No. 16. FAO. Rome. 399 pp.
[a] These results are somewhat species specific.

(3) Do not move trees between elevational extremes. A change in elevation, however, can be compensated for to some extent by a change in latitude. (4) Do not move trees that are adapted to an alkaline soil to an acid soil and vice versa. Table II gives some examples of successful and unsuccessful combinations of donor and recipient regions.

Some of the species most widely used as exotics are the eucalypts, Monterey pine (*P. radiata* D. Don), slash pine (*P. elliottii* Engelm var. *elliottii*), loblolly pine, Caribbean pine (*P. caribaea* Morelet), and Douglas-fir.

IV. Hybridization

Hybrids have usually been made for the following reasons: to obtain hybrid vigor, to introduce pest resistance from one of the parents, to introduce cold-hardiness from one of the parents, or to improve wood quality. Hybridization must be combined with selection of individuals within each species for cross-compatibility and genetic control of the trait to be improved. This selection can increase consistency of seed yield and performance of hybrids.

Hybrid vigor would be expected in cross-pollinated forest trees which includes the majority of forest species in the northern hemisphere. It has indeed been found, but it has been uncommon and unpredictable. It is also highly dependent on the environment in which the trees are grown. The hybrid *Populus tremula* Mich x *P. tremuloides* L., for example, shows hybrid vigor when grown in Sweden, but is intermediate between its parents when grown in Wisconsin. Further examples of successful hybrids in the United States include hybrid larch *Larix leptolepis* (Sieb. and Zucc.) Gord. x *L. decidua* Mill, various hybrid poplars, and the hybrid between *P. attenuata* Lemm. and *P. radiata* D. Don. The most intensive use of hybrids has been for amenity plantings. Their use in forestry applications has been rather limited. Examples are the use of hybrid poplar in the Pacific Northwest and eucalypts in South America and Africa. Disease resistance can be predictably introduced by hybridization. Following are a number of examples: (1) One species is more resistant to a disease than a closely related one. Interspecific hybridization may be useful here. For example, *Platanus occidentalis* L. x *P. orientalis* L. is widely planted in cities because of greater resistance to anthracnose disease. (2) One geographic race of a species is more resistant to a particular disease than another, in such a case interracial hybridization could be very profitable. For example, crossing East Texas loblolly pine, which is resistant to fusiform rust, with Florida loblolly pine, which is highly susceptible to fusiform rust. (3) Several diseases have been introduced into North America from the Eurasian continent. Since Eurasia and North America have been separated by the Atlantic Ocean for about 200 million years, the North American species have no, or limited, resistance to these pathogens. Asiatic species do, however, and are the best source of resistance. Classical examples of exotic diseases are white pine blister rust, chestnut blight, and Dutch elm disease. The hybrid *P. wallichiana* A. B. Jacks. x *P. strobus* L. for example is resistant to blister rust. (4) Cold resistance can be introduced by hybridizing a southern and a northern race of the same species or two related species differing in geographic range. The hybrid between *P. rigida* Mill. and *P. taeda* L., so successful in Korea, is a good example. This hybrid also looks promising at the northern edge of the loblolly pine range in the eastern United States.

Improvement of wood quality through hybridization is rare. One of the few examples is the hybrid between *L. decidua* Mill. and *L. leptolepis*. It has a higher wood specific gravity than either parent.

The reason for the limited application of hybridization in forest trees is the high cost of producing hybrids on a large scale. This can be overcome in cases where labor cost is low, such as, e.g., in Korea or by the availability of vegetative propagation methods such as in the poplars. If *in vitro* propagation techniques become available at a competitive cost, we might see a much greater application of hybridization in forest trees.

V. Clonal Forestry

Clonal forestry is the most intensive application of genetic improvement methods to forestry operations. It consists of the mass propagation of a few highly selected genotypes by vegetative means and deploying these trees on an operational scale. Poplars are extremely easy to propagate vegetatively and poplar hybrids have been vegetatively propagated and planted for half a century or more. They have been used very extensively in northern Europe and China. This has been the main method of propagation of *Cryptomeria japonica* (Japanese redwood) for hundreds of years and is now a major method used with eucalypts. [*See* PLANT PROPAGATION.]

Monterey pine is being propagated vegetatively in New Zealand, using a very sophisticated process. They begin by selecting the very best individual crosses. Seeds from these crosses are cultured in tissue culture and a limited number of propagules are established from individual embryos. These clones then are further propagated in the nursery by conventional rooted cuttings. The climate in New Zealand is so favorable, and Monterey pine roots so easily, that cuttings can be rooted directly in the nursery bed. These plants are then used for reforestation purposes. In this case the vegetative propagation is used to mass propagate individual outstanding full-sib families. Eventually, when the multiplication rate is no longer limiting, it should be possible to extend this to individual clones.

Norway spruce (*Picea abies* (L.) Karst) is propagated vegetatively from rooted cuttings both in northern Europe and Canada. Recently it has become feasible to propagate Norway spruce via somatic embryogenesis although this is not being applied yet on an operational scale.

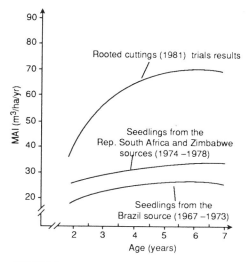

FIGURE 1 The mean annual increment (m³/ha/yr) of *Eucalyptus* plantations of three types. [From Ikemore, Yara Kiemi, Martins, Francisco C., and Zobel, Bruce. 1986. "The Impact of Accelerated Breeding on Wood Properties" 18th IUFRO World Congress. pp. 359–365.]

The biggest success story is the work that has been done in Brazil and Africa with eucalypts. Using a combination of selective breeding and vegetative propagation it has been possible to raise the yields from about 25 cubic meters per hectare per year to 70 cubic meters per hectare per year (see Fig. 1). There are some risks in doing this and the best strategy for deploying genetically improved clones is still a matter of some controversy. Clonal forestry can be the most extreme form of monoculture, carrying the maximum risk of destruction of these forest stands by pests and environmental extremes. This risk can be reduced by deploying multiple clones either in blocks or in mixture. This is an exciting area in forestry and one can expect to see many innovations in the near future.

VI. Breeding for Wood Properties

Since wood is usually the ultimate product there is an outstanding opportunity to improve the quality of the wood through breeding particularly since most wood properties are very strongly inherited. [*See* WOOD PROPERTIES.]

A. What Is Good Quality?

This is a difficult question to answer. Some of the pioneers in forest tree improvement asked managers of forest products industries what properties they desired in wood, and were unable to obtain helpful answers to that question. It was not until the 1970s that breeders learned to ask the right questions. There is a very wide range of products made out of wood and it is therefore necessary to define wood quality in terms of the final product. Wood that is good for furniture is not necessarily good for the manufacture of paper bags, and wood that makes paper bags may be useless for tissue paper.

Another difficulty breeding for wood is the long time horizon a tree breeder faces. In the southern United States there is about a 50-year interval between the time a particular seed orchard is started and the time the trees resulting from this orchard will be harvested. This time interval is considerably less in the tropics, but can be considerably longer in subalpine and boreal climates such as parts of Canada, Sweden, and Finland. During such long periods of time the demands of the market can change a great deal, as well as the technology used in the manufacture of the final product. A lot of products on the market now, such as flake board and oriented strand board, did not exist 25 years ago. Neither did new pulping methods such as thermomechanical and chemithermomechanical pulping. In most circumstances it is therefore prudent to develop a general purpose tree that has wood that is useable for a wide range of products rather than a very specialized end use.

B. What Are the Most Important Wood Properties?

The single most important wood property is wood specific gravity (wood density). It affects virtually all products that can be made from wood from the strength of timber, to the ease of machining wood for furniture, to the quality of pulp and paper. The uniformity within the growth ring is also quite important. Some species such as poplars, spruces, and white pines have a rather uniform wood with a limited contrast in density within the growth rings, while other species such as Douglas-fir, larch, the southern pines and tropical pines have a large contrast in the specific gravity of the earlywood and the latewood. It is this contrast that gives rise to the conspicuous growth rings in these species.

Other traits of importance are fiber length, fiber diameter, fiber wall thickness, fibril angle, chemical composition, compression wood, heartwood, and heat of combustion. Table III indicates how these

TABLE III
Tree Traits Affecting Wood Product Quality[a]

Trait	Effect on product quality
Stem straightness	Better lumber recovery both in grade and quantity
	Higher pulp yield/cord of wood
Good natural pruning	Fewer knots resulting in higher lumber quality (except specialty uses) and fewer rejects in the pulping process
Small branch size	Smaller knots, less reaction wood
Horizontal branch angle	Smaller knots, less reaction wood
High wood specific gravity	Higher pulp yield; higher tear factor; lower tensile strength; lower burst factor
High summerwood percentage (in conifers)	Higher pulp yield; higher tear factor; lower tensile strength; lower burst factor
Long cells (fibers and tracheids)	Higher tensile strength; higher burst factor; higher tear factor; poorer sheet formation
Thick cell walls	Higher tear factor; lower tensile strength; lower burst factor
Low fibril angle	Higher fiber strength
Higher fiber strength	Higher tear factor; higher tensile strength; higher burst factor
Spiral grain	Warped lumber

[a] See van Buijtenen, J. P. (1969). Relationships between wood properties and pulp and paper properties Proceedings. Second World Consultation on Forest Tree Breeding. Washington, DC, August 7–16. FO-FTB-69 4 5. 10 pp.

wood properties influence some of the important wood product properties.

Since wood specific gravity is so important it deserves a little further discussion. It is a very complex trait. Several components contribute to it such as the proportion of earlywood and latewood, the fiber wall thickness in both the earlywood and latewood, the lumen diameters, and the presence of extractives in the wood, as well as the specific gravity of the cell wall material itself. Wood of high specific gravity is generally stronger. It takes more energy to machine it, chip it, or make it into groundwood. On the other hand it produces a higher yield of pulp, with greater tearing strength but lower bursting and tensile strengths. By refining or beating the pulp longer, however, it is often possible to obtain a better combination of tear factor and bursting strength with a high

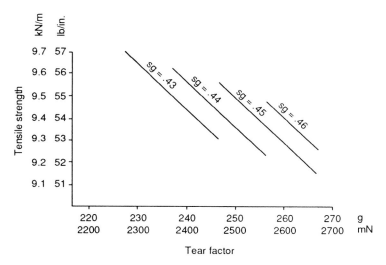

FIGURE 2   Relation between tensile strength and tear factor for wood of constant specific gravity. As wood specific gravity increases a better combination of high tensile strength and high tear factor can be obtained. [From van Buijtenen, J. P. (1986). "Quality Impacts on Pulp and Paper Products." Paper presented at FPRS Marketing and Management Conference, Ft. Worth, Texas, March 18–20, 1986.]

specific gravity wood. This is important for certain grades of paper such as a multi-wall sack paper (see Fig. 2).

Wood specific gravity is generally inherited very strongly. For conifers heritabilities ranging from 0.22 to 0.84 have been reported. This makes it very easy to manipulate genetically. Although it would be easy to breed for wood specific gravity per se, this is not the usual approach. Normally the use of index selection is the preferred method where wood specific gravity is one of half a dozen or so traits that are being improved simultaneously.

In hardwoods most of the work has been done with poplars and eucalypts. Specific gravity in these genera appears to be inherited as strongly as in conifers. In some of the clonal forestry programs dramatic progress has been made in improving wood specific gravity. Other wood properties are also strongly inherited. Their improvement is not as often adopted as an objective in tree breeding programs, because they do not have as strong an effect on the end product as wood specific gravity and they generally are much more expensive to manipulate. This is particularly true for individual fiber properties.

VII. Biotechnology and Forest Tree Improvement

Biotechnology is likely to benefit genetic improvement of trees more than that of crop species because of the extremely long generation times of trees. While corn breeders can complete at least three generations per year, tree breeders require from 15 to 25 years to complete one generation. To accelerate the breeding cycle two complementary approaches are practiced. One is to shorten the period to flower induction or bypass it altogether. The other is to shorten the period needed to test and evaluate the trees. Considerable progress has been made in inducing flowering by application of gibberellins in conifers and by growing trees in oversized greenhouses or with special treatments. Early testing methods have been effective in eliminating undesirable trees at an early age.

Genetic engineering techniques would make it possible to bypass the sexual process altogether and introduce foreign genes directly into the genome. This would be particularly useful for traits which are controlled by a limited number of genes, which seems to be the case in many forms of resistance breeding. Marker aided selection would be particularly useful to shorten the selection phase. This could be especially helpful for selecting genes or gene complexes that are expressed in the later part of the forest rotation. If genetic linkage can be established between the marker and such a gene it could be selected for at the embryo stage if necessary. It would also be possible to use these markers to move blocks of genes from one species to another by hybridizing the species followed by backcrosses. It has already been shown in some crops that the number of backcross generations needed to successfully do this can be reduced from six or seven to two or three generations. *In vitro* propagation techniques are essential to make genetic engineering techniques practical. Since most of the transformation is done in tissue culture with single cells, techniques need to be available to regenerate whole plants from single cells. Unfortunately most forest trees are rather recalcitrant in this respect and, although intensive studies are under way, operational success has not yet been achieved.

Other techniques such as somaclonal variation, *in vitro* selection, and protoplast fusion have long range potential for forest trees, but their adoption in applied tree breeding programs is still a decade or more away.

VIII. Effect of Forest Tree Improvement on Forest Operations

Analogous to the experience in agriculture the use of genetically improved material and the application of more intensive silvicultural practices are closely intertwined. One cannot be fully effective without the other. One of the most visible changes has been the large increase in forest nurseries operated by major industries. Thirty years ago most of the forest nurseries were operated by state and federal agencies. There has also been a noticeable increase in the efficiency of seed use, largely driven by the cost and scarcity of the best genetic materials. The number of seedlings obtained from a pound of seed has increased by at least 25% in the last 15 or 20 years. Another innovation, largely pioneered by the major industries, is the planting of trees in single family blocks. This opens up the possibility of matching specific families to specific sites, in much the same way foresters match specific species to specific sites. This in turn has made it necessary to intensify the forest inventory systems to be able to track these individual families, thus building the data base necessary to do a good job of matching families and sites, since the genetic tests performed by the breeding programs give only a limited amount of site specific information.

Clonal forestry takes this concept one step further. Not only is it now possible to match an individual clone to a specific site, but it is even possible to match an individual clone with a specific product. This is particularly true in tropical countries where rotation ages are short. The type of work done in Brazil can be carried out in a time span short enough to keep up with changing market demands and although it may not be possible to breed for specific products in the long run, it is fairly easy to select specific clones out of a large population that are particularly well suited for individual products now of major importance.

There are some environmental concerns about these approaches, and it is not clear how these concerns will be resolved in the future. It is likely that the multiple use concept will become obsolete and will be replaced by a more specific use concept such as in agriculture. The primary use for some forests could be wilderness, others could be for protection of environmentally sensitive areas, such as steep mountain sites, while others could be devoted to the intensive culture of domesticated trees and production of desirable wood at a low cost. [*See* FOREST ECOLOGY; SILVICULTURE.]

Bibliography

Wright, J. W. (1976). "Introduction to Forest Genetics." Academic Press, New York.

Zobel, B., and Talbert, J. (1984). "Applied Forest Tree Improvement." Wiley, New York.

Zobel, B. J., and van Buijtenen, J. P. (1989) "Wood Variation, Its Causes and Control." Springer-Verlag, Berlin.

Fungicides

NANCY N. RAGSDALE, *USDA-National Agricultural Pesticide Impact Assessment Program*

I. Overview of Fungi That Cause Plant Diseases
II. Surface Protectants
III. Systemic Organic Compounds
IV. Nonfungitoxic Compounds
V. Fungal Resistance to Fungicides
VI. Environmental Concerns
VII. Human Health Concerns
VIII. Future Directions

Glossary

Electron transport system Multienzyme system that transfers electrons produced during respiration through a series of oxidative steps to ultimately react with molecular oxygen releasing energy, a large portion of which is conserved in physiologically utilizable phosphate-bond energy

Enzyme Protein produced by functional cells that catalyzes specific biochemical reactions

Membrane Selectively permeable boundary inside the wall and around organelles within the cell composed of proteins, lipids, and carbohydrates in various ratios depending on the type of membrane; membranes may have functional and barrier properties and are involved in many cellular processes including transport of chemicals, energy conversion (e.g., oxidative phosphorylation), and biosynthesis

Metabolism Sum of biochemical processes in living organisms that provides energy, builds functional matter and structural components, and breaks down macromolecules into simpler substances for specific uses

Metabolite Any product of metabolism

Oxidative phosphorylation Chemical reaction that is coupled to the electron transport system capturing the energy released from that system in the formation of adenosine triphosphate (ATP); this energy is subsequently available for cellular processes

Fungicides are antifungal chemicals used primarily to control fungi that cause diseases. The term "fungicide" usually applies to compounds that reduce the incidence of plant diseases, and that is the context in which the subject matter is discussed in this article. Fungicides may be grouped by chemical class or by fungicidal mode of action, which is the toxic mechanism by which a given compound affects fungi. Fungicides may be applied to soil prior to planting, seeds, established plants, and harvested products to prevent diseases. Certain fungicides may be applied to plants to eradicate infections. Postharvest uses serve to reduce infections that impact storage, shipment, and shelf life. Fungicides, in conjunction with nonchemical pest control methods, are necessary for farmers to prevent yield losses and for consumers to assure the availability, at reasonable prices, of varied agricultural products that are free from microbial contamination.

I. Overview of Fungi That Cause Plant Diseases

Fungi belong to the kingdom Mycetae. They are small, usually microscopic, lack chlorophyll, and have cell walls that contain chitin, cellulose, or both. Most fungi have a vegetative body made up of filaments (mycelia or hyphae). They are eukaryotic, which means that their hereditary information is carried in a defined nucleus located within the cellular structure. Fungi reproduce primarily by sexual or asexual spore production. Classification of the fungi is mainly based on morphological characteristics. There has been discussion if the organisms in one class, the Oomycetes, are true fungi or whether they should be in an entirely different kingdom. For the purposes of this chapter, the Oomycetes, which cause diseases such as downy mildew and potato late blight, will be regarded as fungi.

There are about 100,000 known fungal species. Approximately 50 cause diseases in humans, 50 in animals, and 8000 in plants. Disease-causing fungi are frequently referred to as pathogens or pathogenic fungi. As many as 50 different fungi can cause disease in one plant species. The fact that fungi are quite small, making individual organisms difficult to see without a microscope, is probably the reason they were named for the disease symptoms they cause. Thus, we have rusts, smuts, powdery and downy mildews, blasts, rots, scab, and so on.

Infection by fungi interferes with the normal physiological function of the host plant and can cause great reduction in yield and product quality. Some fungi produce toxins in plants, making the affected plant material dangerous for human and animal consumption. These fungal-produced toxins, know as mycotoxins, may cause cancer and be nerve and organ (e.g., kidney and liver) poisons. In addition, many plants, in response to contact with a fungus, form antifungal compounds called phytoalexins. These phytoalexins may be toxic to humans and animals.

The incidence of plant disease is dependent on the presence of specific factors, referred to as the disease triangle. A susceptible host, pathogenic organism, and suitable environment must be present for disease to occur. Host plants can vary in susceptibility (be disease tolerant), and the pathogen may not be present when the host is most susceptible or when the climatic conditions are suitable. Climatic conditions (moisture in the atmosphere, in soil, and on plant surfaces in addition to optimum temperatures for infection and disease development) may explain why some geographic regions are much more likely to experience crop loss due to fungal infections. Generally, if host and pathogen are present, the amount and distribution of moisture over a given period of time can be closely correlated with the occurrence of many diseases. Fungicides are used together with nonchemical disease controls to reduce damage from fungal infections. However, proper use of fungicides is dependent on understanding the interaction of the disease triangle components and the progress of disease development (epidemiology). This article discusses fungicides that are currently in use and those that may be available in the near future. Current regulatory requirements for maintaining registered uses of these chemicals could impact their future use and availability. [*See* PLANT PATHOLOGY.]

II. Surface Protectants

All the fungicides discussed in this section must be applied to agricultural commodities prior to fungal infection. Because they are not absorbed or translocated by the plant, they serve only for prophylactic use. Generally, they are reasonably effective in controlling a broad spectrum of disease, and their multiple effects on pathogens has led to their classification as broad spectrum, multisite, surface protectants (Table I).

A. Inorganic Fungicides

Sulfur, one of the oldest fungicides, is still widely used. While sulfur is used to control pests other than fungi, this discussion will focus on its use as a fungicide. A primary reason for the continued use of sulfur is its low cost. Disadvantages include the limited spectrum of diseases controlled, phytotoxic effects to some plant species, and the large quantities required. Elemental sulfur is primarily used to control powdery mildews, but also shows some efficacy in preventing certain rusts, fruit rots, and leaf blights. A lime–sulfur spray may also be used for these diseases. Although there are various theories on the toxic action of sulfur, the strongest scientific evidence supports its effects on the fungal electron transport system at a site between cytochromes b and c. Electrons normally utilized in oxygen reduction are used in sulfur reduction instead. As a result, sites of energy conservation are bypassed. Although the primary mechanism of toxicity is attributed to this interference with energy production, reactions with other cellular components, such as proteins, may contribute to the overall effect.

The only other inorganic fungicides to play a major role in disease control are copper-containing compounds. By adding lime to copper sulfate, the phytotoxicity of copper sulfate is reduced and copper serves as the fungitoxic moiety in this preparation known as Bordeaux mixture. Actually, there are various Bordeaux mixtures resulting from a variety of ratios of lime to copper sulfate to water. Bordeaux mixtures are used to control downy mildews, leaf spots, anthracnoses, cankers, and blights. Other copper fungicides (fixed coppers) have been developed in efforts to avoid the phytotoxic effects of Bordeaux mixtures; however, these compounds are generally less effective fungicides. The cupric ion is the fungitoxic component of Bordeaux mixtures and other inorganic copper fungicides. Little biochemical specificity exists for the cupric ion, and its success as a fungicide relies on greater exposure of fungal rather than plant cells. Cupric ions probably bind to groups on the cell surface inhibiting enzymatic processes and causing membrane damage, which results in leakage of metabolites.

TABLE I

Surface Protectant Fungicides

Class	Example	Target site	Primary uses
Inorganic	Sulfur	Electron transport	Powdery mildew of fruit
	Bordeaux mixture fixed copper	Membranes, many enzymes	Downy mildew of fruits and vegetables
Organic			
Dialkyldithiocarbamate	Thiram	Many enzymes	Soil-borne and foliar diseases of many crops
Ethylenebisdithacarbamate	Maneb	Thiol groups	Many diseases of fruits and vegetables
Quinone	Dichlone	Electron transport, thiol groups	Seed treatment; many diseases of fruits and vegetables
Phthalimide	Captan	Thiol groups	Seed treatment; many diseases of fruits and vegetables
Isophthalonitrile	Chlorothalonil	Thiol groups	Many diseases of wide crop variety
Triazine	Anilazine	Thiol groups	Turf and vegetable diseases
Cationic surfactants	Dodine	Membranes and enzymes	Fruit tree diseases
Organotin	Triphenyltin	Oxidative phosphorylation	Pecan diseases
Nitrobenzene	Quintozene	Hydrophobic regions	Soil-borne diseases of many crops

B. Organic Surface Protectants

Since the dithiocarbamates were introduced for use almost a half century ago, they have remained an extremely widely used and important group of fungicides. The dithiocarbamates are divided into two classes, the dialkyldithiocarbamates and the mono-alkyldithiocarbamates. The dialkyldithiocarbamates are derived from secondary amines. They include thiram, ziram, and ferbam. These compounds are used to control soil-borne and foliar diseases on a wide variety of commodities. In biological systems, these compounds undergo many reactions, making a precise determination of their primary mode of action extremely difficult. They inhibit a variety of enzymes.

The monoalkyldithiocarbamates are derived from primary amines. Zineb, maneb (Fig. 1), and manco-

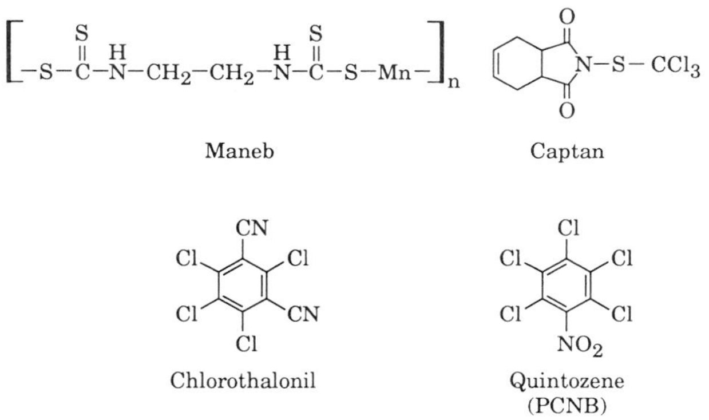

FIGURE 1 Examples of surface protectant fungicides.

zeb are the prominent members of this class. Because they are derivatives of ethylenediamine, they are referred to as the ethylenebisdithiocarbamates (EBDC). These fungicides control a wide variety of diseases including leaf spots, rots, and blights of vegetables, fruits, flowers, turf, trees, and shrubs. The fungitoxicity of the EBDCs has been attributed primarily to the capacity of these compounds to generate isothiocyanate, which inactivates sulfhydryl (thiol) groups of enzymes and metabolites in cells. However, additional sites of action analogous to those of the dialkyldithiocarbamates cannot be overlooked.

Quinones are present naturally in many plants and are considered part of the plant's natural defense system. Dichlone is a synthetic quinone developed as a seed treatment and also used for a variety of diseases that occur on fruits and vegetables. Two mechanisms appear to be involved in fungitoxic action: (1) binding to thiol and amino groups and (2) interference with electron transport.

Captan (Fig. 1), the best-known of the phthalimide fungicides, was introduced in the early 1950s. It is used as a seed protectant for many crops; as a spray to control a variety of diseases on fruits, vegetables, ornamentals, and turf; and as a postharvest dip for certain fruits and vegetables. The interaction of captan with fungal cells leads to a rapid decomposition of the fungicide. The predominant initial reaction involves low-molecular-weight cellular thiols. While this reaction is an important detoxication mechanism, the depletion of the cellular pool of thiols is a primary factor in fungitoxic action resulting in deficiencies in critical metabolites and the inactivation of thiol enzymes by auto-oxidation.

Chlorothalonil (Fig. 1) is effective in controlling a broad range of diseases on field crops, fruits, vegetables, ornamentals, and turf. Although the chemistry of this compound is different from that of captan, the mechanism of fungitoxicity is quite similar. Initial reactions with fungal cells involve soluble thiols, but concurrent reactions with cell-bound thiols continue after the soluble thiol pool is depleted. Thus, the fungitoxicity of chlorothalonil is attributed to the inactivation of low- and high-molecular-weight thiols.

Anilazine is another broad-spectrum surface protectant that acts by a mechanism similar to that of captan and chlorothalonil. It is used mainly for control of turf and vegetable diseases.

Cationic surfactants, such as dodine, are toxic to fungi and bacteria. Their low cost and dependability has kept them on the market despite the availability of more potent fungicides. Dodine is mainly used to prevent diseases of fruit trees. The biological activity of cationic surfactants is dependent on the presence of a charged group and length of the hydrocarbon chain; the charged group is directed to an anionic or polar site while the hydrocarbon chain binds to a nearby hydrophobic region. Normal membrane functions and enzyme actions are likely to be disrupted as a result.

While various organotins are effective antifungal agents, only the triphenyltins are used as agricultural fungicides. They are important in disease control on pecans and a variety of other commodities. Oxidative phosphorylation appears to be a primary target of action, but there are numerous effects in fungal cells indicating multiple sites of sensitivity.

Quintozene (PCNB) (Fig. 1) is used to control a number of soilborne fungal diseases. PCNB and several other fungicides, including dichloran, probably bind to hydrophobic regions of the fungal cell and interfere with a variety of processes such as membrane function and cell division.

III. Systemic Organic Compounds

In the mid-1960s, a new era of plant disease control emerged with the introduction of systemic fungicides (Table II). In contrast to the surface protectants, these chemicals penetrate into a plant, withstand the plant's metabolism, and are more selective in toxicity. A systemic fungicide usually does not control as broad a range of fungi as surface protectants. One of the major advantages of systemic fungicides is that they can be applied after infection has occurred since they are internally therapeutic. This quality makes them very valuable in integrated pest management (IPM) programs. Another feature that differentiates these fungicides from the surface protectants is their increased specificity as far as their modes of toxicity are concerned. These fungicides inhibit one or several related metabolic sites as opposed to the surface protectants, which interact with a number of biochemical sites. While the site specificity reduces the risk of nontarget effects, it increases the possibility of selective resistance development in the fungal population.

The carboxamide fungicides were the first systemics introduced. These fungicides are used primarily on grains for the control of smuts, rusts, and a number of other diseases. Carboxin (Fig. 2) is the best known of this group. These compounds block the transfer of electrons from succinate to ubiquinone in the mitochondrial electron transport pathway and thus interfere with energy production in the fungal cell.

Benzimidazole fungicides are effective against a wide range of fungi. Their disease control qualities are related to surface protection as well as penetration into local tissue. Fungicides in this group include benomyl (Fig. 2) (which undergoes transformation to carbendazim), thiabendazole, and thiophanate-methyl. Benzimidazoles bind to tubulin and inhibit formation of microtubules. Since microtubules are essential in a number of cellular processes such as mitosis and hyphal extension, this inhibition effectively curtails fungal growth.

The dicarboximide fungicides include vinclozolin, iprodione (Fig. 2), and procymidone. They are used to control a number of diseases on vegetables, fruits, and ornamentals. Although laboratory studies have shown they may be translocated in plants, in actual use they are applied as surface protectants. Their primary mode of action is not clear, although several secondary effects have been determined. These include interference with nuclear function, membrane damage, and effects on motile function.

The phenylamide fungicides are specific for control of fungi in the taxonomic class called Oomycetes. Many of the fungi causing foliar, root, and crown diseases are in this class. Downy mildews and late blight are well-known examples. The phenylamide fungicides are composed of three groups: acylalanines (metalaxyl (Fig. 2), furalaxyl, and benalaxyl) oxazolidinones (oxadixyl); and butyrolactones (ofurace and cyprofuram). These compounds are effective through

TABLE II

Systemic Fungicides

Class	Example	Target Site	Primary uses
Carboxamide	Carboxin	Electron transport	Grain diseases
Benzimidazole	Benomyl	Tubulin	Many diseases of wide crop variety
Sterol biosynthesis inhibitor		Sterol biosynthetic pathway	Many diseases of wide crop variety
pyrimidine	Fenarimol		
imidazole	Imazalil		
triazole	Triadimefon		
piperazine	Triforine		
pyridine	Buthiobate		
morpholine	Tridemorph		
Dicarboximide	Iprodione	Not specifically determined	Diseases of vegetables, fruits, and ornamentals
Phenylamide	Metalaxyl	Ribosomal RNA synthesis	Diseases caused by Oomycetes

inhibition of ribosomal ribonucleic acid (RNA) synthesis.

The largest group of systemic fungicides comprises over 30 chemically diverse compounds that interfere with fungal sterol biosynthesis (Fig. 3). Certain sterols, usually ergosterol in fungi, are necessary for proper membrane structure and function. Without these, cell death or inhibition of growth occurs. These sterol biosynthesis inhibitors may be divided into three groups based on their primary site of action in the sterol biosynthetic pathway. These are:

1. Squalene epoxidase inhibitors (no agricultural fungicides are currently available in this group). Naftifine and terbinafine are examples.
2. Sterol C-14 demethylase inhibitors. This group is the largest and includes triforine, triadimefon, propiconazol, bitertanol, buthiobate, fenarimol, imazalil, prochloraz, and flusilazole.
3. Sterol Δ^8–Δ^7 isomerase inhibitors and/or sterol Δ^{14} reductase inhibitors. Tridemorph, dodemorph, and fenpropimorph are examples.

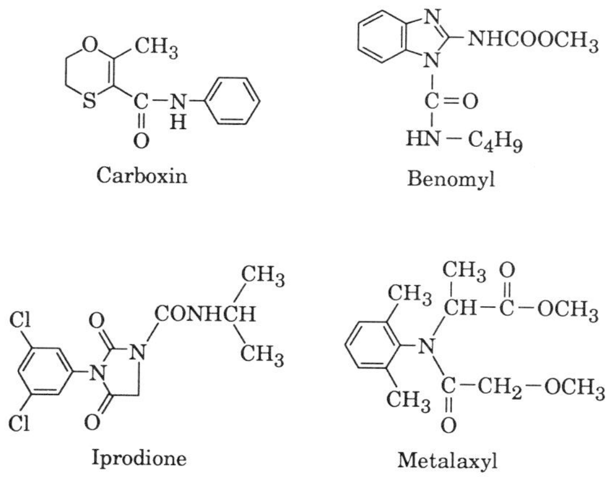

The sterol biosynthesis inhibitors are active against a broad spectrum of fungi which cause diseases in a variety of crops and ornamentals. Growth regulatory action on host plants may occur as a side effect of the use of the C-14 demethylase inhibitors due to inhibitory effects on the plant's gibberellin biosynthetic pathway, particularly when application rates are exceeded.

IV. Nonfungitoxic Compounds

A number of the recently developed antifungal compounds are effective through their impact on disease development (Table III). These compounds generally have little or no effect on the rate of growth of pathogenic fungi *in vitro* at concentrations which control pathogenic activity *in vivo*. They may act directly on the pathogen to interfere with its establishment in plant tissue or with its initiation of the disease process after it has invaded the plant. A third approach is for the chemical to affect the host–pathogen interaction so that host defense mechanisms destroy or halt encroachment of the pathogen.

Several nonfungitoxic disease control chemicals are in a group known as the melanin biosynthesis inhibitors. Although laboratory studies indicate these com-

FIGURE 2 Examples of systemic fungicides.

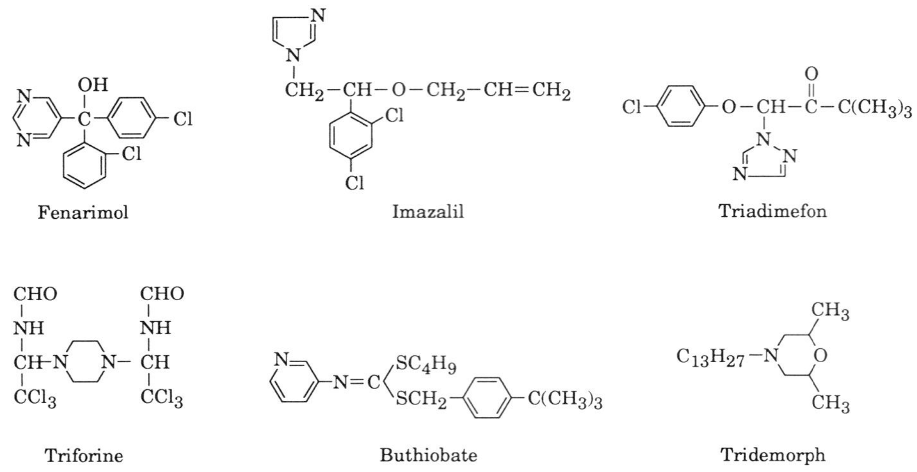

FIGURE 3 Examples of systemic fungicides that inhibit sterol biosynthesis.

pounds block melanin biosynthesis in a variety of Ascomycetes and imperfect fungi, they give practical control only of rice blast disease. Tricyclazole (Fig. 4) is the most thoroughly investigated of this group. This compound blocks certain reductase reactions in the fungal polyketide pathway to melanin, consequently interfering with the process by which the pathogen penetrates the plant. Without melanin, the fungal structure that normally enters the host plant lacks the architecture, rigidity, and force that are required for the penetration process.

Fosetyl-Al (Fig. 4) is the only commercially available fungicide that is known to be transported in a downward direction in plants, thus allowing control of certain root diseases by application to leaves, stems, and trunks. Once inside the plant, fosetyl-Al is degraded to phosphonate (phosphoric acid). This fungicide is an example of an antifungal compound that provides plant protection through direct effects on the pathogen, followed by an enhanced response of the host plant's resistance system to the modified pathogen. Chemical changes caused by this compound on the surface of the pathogen appear to be responsible for inducing enhanced host plant resistance.

A new approach to antifungal action may be seen in compounds that have no direct effects on pathogens but are effective in controlling diseases through their action on host plants. This type of action has been termed systemic acquired resistance (SAR). Probenazole (Fig. 4), which is in this group, controls rice blast disease. Evidence indicates that probenazole promotes the formation of a host-produced chemical barrier to an invading pathogen. Two experimental compounds, 2,6-dichloroisonicotinic acid and its methyl ester derivative, promote SAR in a number of plants by triggering host plant production of chemicals that prevent infection. Although these experimental compounds are phytotoxic and thus will not be commercially developed, they illustrate the type of approach that is likely to be used in future development of fungal disease control chemicals.

TABLE III

Nonfungitoxic Fungicides

Compound	Target site	Basis for disease control	Primary use
Tricyclazole	Melanin biosynthesis	Pathogen cannot penetrate host	Rice blast disease
Fosetyl-Al	Chemical alteration on surface of pathogen	Enhanced host resistance in response to altered pathogen surface	Root diseases caused by Oomycetes
Probenazole	Undetermined	Host formation of chemical barrier around invading pathogen	Rice blast disease
Isonicotinic acid	Undetermined	Modified host physiology leading to disease resistance	Experimental only

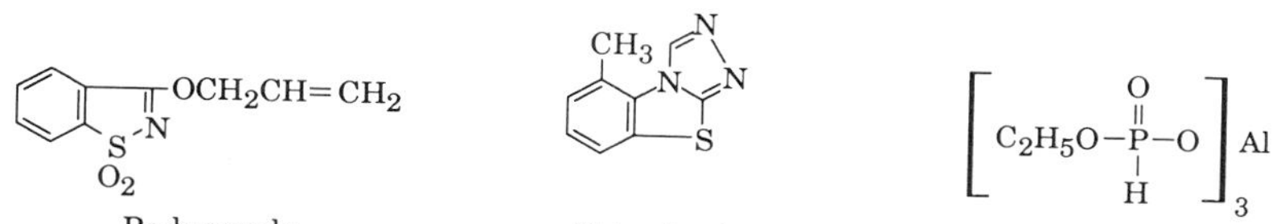

FIGURE 4 Examples of nonfungitoxic fungicides.

V. Fungal Resistance to Fungicides

Biological systems, regardless of their complexity, are very dynamic; changes are constantly occurring during the process of growth and reproduction. In any population of living organisms, a great deal of diversity exists as a result of these changes. Pathogenic fungi are no exception. Various efforts to control plant diseases may be successful for a period of time but are unlikely to be permanent solutions. This may be seen in the development of plant varieties that are not susceptible to diseases, as well as in the use of chemicals to control fungi that cause diseases. These efforts to thwart the disease-causing fungi serve as selection pressure on the fungal population. Fungi in that population which are not susceptible to a given fungicide, or are able to circumvent the host plant's defense system, multiply and may cause disease problems that evade the controls that were previously successful. Failure of various means to control pests is not unique to agriculture; a similar situation exists in the use of antibiotics in human therapy.

The problem of fungal resistance to fungicides became a major consideration in plant disease control following the introduction of the systemic, biochemically specific fungicides. The major factor is the biochemical specificity rather than the systemicity. Fungicides such as sulfur, chlorothalonil, and captan that affect multiple sites in fungal cells are much less likely to experience resistance. On the other hand, failure to control disease in the field has been reported for many of the specific site inhibitors including benzimidazoles, dicarboximides, sterol demethylase inhibitors, and phenylamides.

There are a number of mechanisms by which fungi may demonstrate resistance. Most cases of resistance can be traced to the spontaneous appearance of mutant fungi with a single gene change resulting in biochemical modification of the fungicide target site. This causes a decreased target affinity for the selective fungicide. Other mechanisms may involve reduced fungicide uptake or accumulation, detoxication, and compensation through production of increased amounts of an inhibited enzyme.

The extent of crop loss resulting from resistant fungi is related to the ability of a particular fungal population to increase and become dominant. Factors such as fitness (how one fungal strain competes against another in a particular situation), nature of the pathogen and disease, and the degree of selection pressure influence this process. Frequent, repetitive use of a particular fungicide increases the risk for a loss of effectiveness not only for that fungicide but for all fungicides that have similar modes of action.

Steps can be taken to reduce the possibility of resistance development. These strategies should be undertaken before the problem occurs. Laboratory studies can determine the mode of action of a fungicide and what types of resistant mutants are likely to emerge. With this information, a grower can integrate a number of factors into a disease control program for a given crop. These include alternating or combining fungicides with different modes of action, cultural measures such as removing dead or diseased plants, use of disease-resistant plants, and biological control. Monitoring for resistance will increase the likelihood that measures can be taken to avoid total crop loss. In order for this integrated approach to be successful, a variety of fungicides must be available. Not only should these vary in modes of action, but the combination use of multisite surface protectants with site-specific systemics should be an option.

VI. Environmental Concerns

The impacts of man's activities on the environment are currently a major consideration in legislative and regulatory activities. Farming practices, particularly the use of pesticides, have received a great deal of attention in efforts to lessen the possibility of adverse environmental effects. Investigations of such effects focus on the fate of pesticides in the atmosphere, water, soil, and living organisms. Distribution and fate vary according to the chemical properties of the specific pesticide, such as water solubility and volatility, and local environmental parameters, such as temperature and soil type, pertaining to the pesticide application site. [*See* PEST MANAGEMENT, CHEMICAL CONTROL.]

Quantities of fungicides used are generally less than those of herbicides and insecticides. This factor, in addition to a lack of problems associated with acute toxicity to nontarget organisms, has resulted in fungicides not being as extensively investigated as other classes of pesticides in environmental monitoring programs. Fungicide residues are seldom found in random sampling of soil, water, and air.

From an environmental perspective the greatest concern related to fungicide use is alteration of soil ecosystems. The introduction of a crop system alters the natural soil ecosystem initially. Changes caused by fungicides are most likely to occur in the immediate vicinity of treated plants. The persistence of chemical residues in soil are highly dependent on local conditions and rate of application. Soil ecosystems are quite complex, and fungicide applications may result in beneficial as well as adverse effects. The type and number of microorganisms present can be altered and subsequently affect the persistence of other pesticides. Fungicide applications can adversely impact nontarget fungi, predacious mites, beneficial insects, and earthworms. Particular concern has been expressed about effects on beneficial fungi that are associated with mycorrhizae, morphological structures that are a mutualistic (symbiotic) relationship between fungi and host plants and serve as feeder roots for host plants. Beneficial side effects of fungicide use such as control of parasitic nematodes and mites have also been noted.

Microbial degradation is probably the single most important factor in preventing build-up of fungicide residues in the soil. In some cases the residues have acted as a nutrient source for certain segments of the microbial population and promoted an increase of those segments; this can result in a loss of effectiveness for a particular fungicide if it is degraded too rapidly. On the other hand, if a fungicide persists too long, ecological associations necessary for future crop production may be affected and the chances for fungal resistance are increased by the prolonged selection pressure.

In order to minimize detrimental environmental impacts, attention should be given to fungicide application and disposal methods. The latest technology in these areas is available through the Cooperative Extension Service in each state. Another highly effective approach is the use of IPM. This approach combines the use of chemicals, fungicides in this case, and nonchemical pest control methods. The nonchemical aspects of IPM involve the use of resistant plants when possible, sanitation, managing irrigation and drainage, and crop rotation.

VII. Human Health Concerns

Acute toxicity is not generally a major concern in the use of agricultural fungicides. There are cases indicating that some individuals may develop contact allergies following exposure, but generally fungicides do not cause problems of an acute nature in agricultural workers. Sulfur is the single fungicide most frequently cited as causing skin and eye irritations. Mixing and loading fungicides prior to application offer the greatest potential for worker exposure. Research has demonstrated that use of protective gear and adjustments in working practices as well as in formulations of the active ingredient can reduce or eliminate this exposure potential.

Most concerns about the effects of agricultural fungicides on human health have focused on their potential to cause cancer through exposure in the diet. Because no reliable data exist on human cancer resulting from fungicide exposure, the likelihood of cancer occurrence is based on studies in which laboratory animals, usually rats and mice, are fed fungicides. Unfortunately these estimates are often reported in the media without an explanation of the parameters used in risk assessment methodology, which are highly debatable from a scientific perspective. In examining concerns about the relationship between fungicides and cancer, one should take the following into consideration:

1. Because fungicides are not acutely toxic, large quantities can be fed to animals on a daily basis during long-term studies. In the United States a range of doses is used that is increased to maximum tolerated dose (MTD), the highest dose that results in toxic effects during long-term exposure without causing death and does not decrease body weight by more than 10%. The high doses that greatly exceed the likely human consumption level are usually justified on the basis that at levels comparable to those in the human diet no effects would probably occur.

2. Large quantities of fungicides fed to animals may saturate or inhibit systems within the body that, at levels normally encountered, would break down the chemical or show little, if any, changes. The process of estimating

potential carcinogenicity by extrapolating from the high doses used in laboratory studies to the low doses likely to be actually experienced is highly controversial. The surface protectant fungicides that are the multisite inhibitors appear to be particularly vulnerable to this testing protocol. The systemic fungicides with site of action specificity could also face the same problem depending upon fungal sites of action and whether similar sites are present in the test animals.

3. Extrapolating data from mice and rats to humans is questionable. There are definitely differences between these mammals. Considerable efforts have been made and are continuing to improve the ability to extrapolate between species.

4. Many of the estimations of cancer risk through dietary exposure make the assumption that 100% of the food crop has been treated with the fungicide in question and that fungicide residues are present at the maximum levels allowed. Survey data on fungicide use indicate that not necessarily all of a given food crop is treated. More importantly, an examination of data from a number of residue monitoring programs reveals that residues are seldom detected in food that has been produced using fungicides. In situations when residues are found, they are usually present at levels considerably below those allowed.

Undoubtedly new scientific information about cancer development will ultimately be incorporated into the regulatory procedures associated with risk assessment. When this happens, the estimated long-term effects of exposure to fungicides will probably change. One should keep in mind that these risk estimations are useful for regulatory purposes and for comparing various pesticides, but they definitely do not predict actual human cancer occurrence.

VIII. Future Directions

Fungicides will continue to play an important role in agricultural production. An expanding population will require an increased food supply, and fungicides, as well as other pesticides, will be essential to avoid severe food shortages. Over the last 50 years there has been a noticeable movement in the direction of pest control chemicals that are less likely to cause adverse environmental or human health effects. This trend, which is a result of increased scientific knowledge, will continue as research makes new data available. Compounds will be favored that affect specific sites in targeted fungi. This will result in low use rates which are less likely to have adverse side effects.

Nontarget effects can be minimized by identifying fungicides that do not accumulate in the environment. Compounds that are not toxic to nontarget species will be sought. A comparison with chemicals known to be hazardous will reduce the chances of introducing new chemicals with unfavorable characteristics. An examination of the effects of a candidate fungicide on genetic function can indicate whether potential problems may exist in this area. Costs associated with development of pesticides are substantial. Unless the agricultural use for which a fungicide is developed is large, the financial returns to the developer are insufficient to cover the costs of registration and the additional studies likely to be required to maintain registration. This could have a major impact on the introduction of new fungicides. Some type of legislative or regulatory action may be required to ensure that farmers have the adequate pest control materials for protecting their crops.

Bibliography

Agrios, G. N. (1988). "Plant Pathology." Academic Press, New York.

Delp, C. J. (1988). "Fungicide Resistance in North America." APS Press, St. Paul, MN.

Köller, W. (1991). "Target Sites of Fungicide Action." CRC Press, Boca Raton, FL.

Lyr, H. (1987). "Modern Selective Fungicides." Gustav Fischer, Jena.

Ragsdale, N. N., and Sisler, H. D. (1991). *In* "Handbook of Pest Management in Agriculture" (D. Pimental, ed.), 2nd ed., Vol. 2, pp. 461–469. CRC Press, Boca Raton, FL.

Goat Production

MAURICE SHELTON,

Texas A&M University Agricultural Research and Extension Center

Glossary

Browse Shoots, twigs, or leaves of trees or shrubs used as food for animals, or the act of consuming browse

Cashmere (pashmina) Down or undercoat fiber produced by a number of types of goats. The name derives from Kashmir, a region in the Himalayan mountains of northern India. The fiber is fine and soft and can be made into lightweight and colorful fabrics such as sweaters and shawls. Cashmere is often referred to as Pashmina in India

Domestication To adapt an animal to life in association with and to the advantage of man. Selective breeding during generations of living in association with man

Feral Individual or group of animals which escaped from domestication and became wild for one or more generations

Forb Herb or a plant other than a grass; broad-leaf herb or weed

Herbicide Agent (or a chemical) used to destroy or inhibit plant growth; a selective weed or plant killer

Mohair Fiber produced by an Angora goat; fiber is noted for the production of fabrics of brilliant colors and great durability

Organoleptic Affecting or making an impression upon one or more of the organs of sense

Ruminant Animal which ruminates—characterized by chewing again that which has already been swal-

lowed; animals with a compound or compartmentalized stomach of four compartments, the first of which is known as the rumen

The importance or significance of goat production in meeting mankind's need for food and fiber is highly variable throughout the world, depending on need and the resources available. They seldom serve as the sole source of income to a farm or ranch enterprise. Goat production often serves a role in subsistence types of agriculture in providing an important food source for large numbers of poor people, and to a lesser extent, they form the basis for large-scale commercial enterprises. Goats are often maligned as destroyers of the environment or by others as providing an ecologically sound means of brush and weed control. Some governments actively discourage goat production, while others devote significant resources to improved production from the species. This great disparity in attitudes and in the importance attached to the species provides both an opportunity and a challenge to those who would concern themselves with this species.

I. Origin and Domestication

Goats and sheep are thought to have been among the first species of farm or ranch livestock to have been domesticated by man. Insofar as can be determined, only the dog predates sheep and goats as animals to have been tamed and brought into a beneficial relationship with man. Domestication should not be regarded as a single event occurring at a specific time; however, domestication is thought to have occurred "at least by the eighth millennium B.C.," or at least 10,000 years ago at one or more sites in Asia or Africa. The close chronological relationship between the domestication of the three species mentioned and the transition of man from a nomadic hunter to one who actively manages the resources around him suggest that this event played a role in placing man on the long road to civilization. Over the years, and even to this date, many people are almost self-sufficient because of the products obtained from sheep or goats.

II. World Numbers and Distribution

A consideration of world numbers and distribution of goats is important to any treatment of the contribution or potential of this species. Current world numbers are thought to be on the order of 550 million head. This number is thought to be increasing, but at a slower rate than the human population. Thus, they must be made more productive if their contribution is to be maintained. The total number of goats is disproportionately represented in tropical or subtropical regions, in developing countries, and in the hands of small holder agriculturalists, with the result that their contribution to meeting mankind's needs is more important than indicated by numbers or production alone. The above conditions are interrelated, but should not be interpreted in a simple cause and effect relationship. Over two-thirds of the world's goat population is located within 30° of the equator and they further tend to be concentrated in arid regions as contrasted to the humid tropics. It is reported that 94% of the goat population is in developing countries, with close to 90% (Table I) in Asia (57.8%) and Africa (31.2%). The three countries with the largest number of goats (China, India, and Pakistan) are found in Asia. Total production, especially meat and

skins, is even more concentrated in Asia. The contribution of goats is especially manifest in the rural areas where they are closely associated with the "poorest of the poor." These unique aspects of the distribution and contribution of the goat relate to their adaptation, resource requirement, and in one case (the Indian subcontinent) to the absence of religious taboos against their use. Within individual countries, distribution is often highly localized, dependent largely upon the resources available and past history. For instance, approximately 90% of the goats in the United States are found within Texas, and more specifically, within or adjacent to the Edwards Plateau.

III. Unique Adaptation and Resource Requirements of the Goat

The goat (*Capra hircus*) is a ruminant animal belonging to the family Bovidae and subfamily Caprini, and as such, has a great many traits or features in common with other animals to which they are closely related. However, they do possess some unique characteristics which contribute to their distribution and their use. It has long been common knowledge that goats browse (consume woody plants) more extensively than other domestic livestock species. They also consume a wider variety of total plant species. They do not browse more extensively than certain wildlife species, such as the white tail deer in the United States and a number of African game species. Additionally, goats are tolerant of high temperatures, can travel long distances, and are less dependent on water than most types of cattle and sheep. These factors appear to

TABLE I

Goat Numbers and Productivity (1990)

Region	Goat numbers (1000 head)	% of total	Milk production		Meat production		Skins	
			Metric tons (1000)	Percentage total	Metric tons (1000)	Percentage total	Metric tons (1000)	Percentage total
Africa	173,944	31.22	1,958	22.30	624	24.96	109,139	22.65
N.C. America	13,855	2.49	392	4.46	43	1.72	9.608	1.99
S. America	23,374	4.20	171	1.95	73	2.92	14,229	2.95
Asia	321,973	51.80	4,165	47.44	1,631	65.24	327,511	67.98
Europe	15,448	2.78	1,748	19.90	106	4.24	15,303	3.18
Ocenia	1,956	0.35	—	—	4	0.16	704	0.15
USSR	6,480	1.16	345	3.92	25	1.00	5,290	1.10
Total	557,030	—	8,780	—	2,506	—	481,785	—

Source: Adapted from Acharya and Singh (1992). The Role of the Goat in Conservation of Ecology and Livelihood Security. Proceedings V International Conference on Goats, pp. 81–99. New Delhi, India.

provide an adequate explanation for the concentration in the arid tropics or subtropics. These areas are characterized by limited water supplies and the vegetation generally consists of a sparse covering of low growing woody plants. The limited number of goats maintained in temperate regions is generally maintained to exploit specific economic opportunities or to utilize a specific resource, such as browse or forb encroachment of farmlands or established pastures. Goats are sure-footed, and are notorious for their ability to negotiate precipitous mountainous terrain. This appears to provide an adequate explanation for wild or domestic types being the almost exclusive inhabitants of these areas. Finally, goats tend to be associated with small holder agriculturalists or to the landless poor due to their small size (less resources required), and to some of the characteristics enumerated earlier. One additional trait of importance is the flocking instinct that they possess, along with sheep, which permits them to be herded or managed on unfenced ranges, pastures, or public domain. The practice of grazing goats on public domain can be viewed as one of the negatives for the species. In developing countries, the grazing pressure is seldom effectively controlled and degradation of resources is a frequent result. All domesticated grazing animals (cattle, buffalo, horses, sheep, and goats) may be at fault, but the goat often is blamed because they can survive longer and are last on the scene. They may also be more at fault, because they consume a wider variety of forage species. The real blame for overuse of grazing lands, "the tragedy of the commons," should rest with the human element for failure to exercise proper control.

A disproportionate share of goat numbers are in small flocks. This is due, in part, to limited resource availability of small holder agriculturalists or in developed countries to a large number of flocks which serve the role of hobby, laboratory animals, or pets. In the first instance, they often serve the role of scavengers and are not uniquely matched to the resources available, except in the case of low cost or their capacity to survive. In the latter case, the matching of resources to animal requirements is relatively unimportant because they are often reared under artificial conditions. Most of the goats of the world are utilized for meat production only, and many of these are found in the small-sized flocks. Commercialization of goats on a substantive scale is largely restricted to those kept for milk or fiber, but commercialization of goats for meat production is increasing. Milk production from goats tends to fit into two categories. One of these is for household use by individual families. The other alternative represents commercial scale production. In the latter case, milk production from goats is more expensive than that from cattle largely as a result of higher labor, equipment, and distribution costs when expressed as a function of the small volume produced. Thus, the dominant factor in locating a fresh milk production enterprise from goats is proximity to markets. At the same time, goats kept for milk production must be fed formulated rations to support a high level of milk production, and thus, they are less tied to a particular resource base. The above conditions are less true for processed products such as cheese, but still, markets or marketing are dominant concerns.

This leaves fiber production, particularly mohair production, as the most commercialized phase of the goat industry. In the past, it has not been unusual to find one property or one owner running as many as 25,000 goats. It is this type of enterprise in which type and amount of resources are critical. Since fiber is not a perishable commodity, the industry may be located at any site worldwide where resources are most suitable. In a large measure, this is in areas where brush or browse are found on the range or grazing areas. This relationship can serve either or both of two roles. One of these is to suppress, to some degree, brush invasion of grazing lands. This role is becoming increasingly more important as energy and labor costs place constraints on mechanical control and environmental concerns place constraints on the use of herbicides. They can also serve a role in the suppression of fire. Their second role is to produce a merchandisable product from this type of resource. If sheep are not present on the range, goats may also be used to serve a similar role in suppression of forbs or weeds. It should be pointed out that goats do not consume all types of browse and forbs, but they are more likely to do so than competing species such as cattle. Extensive information is available on the type of plants they will consume, but this tends to be area specific. It is not feasible to treat this on a "world" basis in this discussion. [See WOOL AND MOHAIR PRODUCTION AND PROCESSING.]

In addition to type of resource, goats kept for fiber production tend to be concentrated in arid regions in the lower latitudes. The three major mohair producing countries are located in the 30–40° latitudes. This is, in part, explained by the forage resources in these areas. However, it is obvious that arid regions are more healthy for the goat and that the lower latitudes obviate the necessity for long confined winter feeding periods. Finally, goats are concentrated in certain areas because of historical precedent or because they are the only animals that can survive in these areas. Since these areas are often fragile environments (arid or mountainous lands) matching animal numbers to resources available is very important for the well-being of the animal and the preservation of the resource base. This matching of animal numbers and resources (stocking rate) also tends to be area specific, and should preferably be based on research or long-term experience in the area. In the absence of this information, the effect of the grazing animal on the resource base should be carefully observed. Goats may be compared to other species on a body weight basis but it should be realized that small animals tend to consume slightly more feed per unit of body weight than larger animals. In some situations, animal unit conversions are made to favor the goat due to their consumption of a greater variety of, and in some cases invading, plant species.

IV. Products

The basic products obtained from goats are meat, milk, fiber, and skins. Secondary uses include their use as laboratory animals, as pets, or for the manure they produce. Some wild types of *Capra* or crosses of these with domestic types are often used for sport hunting. In some locations, significant populations of feral goats exist. These are also, at times, hunted or gathered for meat. Some of these secondary uses may warrant elaboration. Their use as a laboratory animal may be for a variety of scientific purposes and one breed or type, the pygmy, is occasionally maintained in laboratory animal colonies. Another use for the dairy type goats is as a replacement for the cow in agricultural research because they can be maintained more economically. In many societies, various species of ruminant livestock are valued for the manure they produce. However, it should be remembered that they do not add back to the land anything more than they received from it. Thus, they serve only as a gathering mechanism in which they are mining grazing lands to provide fuel energy for home use or fertilizer for intensively farmed crops.

The data presented earlier, in Table I, indicate that quantitatively the major product obtained from goats is milk, with approximately 8.8 million metric tons compared to 2.5 million metrics of meat and 481 thousand metric tons of skins. Since both milk and meat from goats are used largely for household consumption, it is unlikely that data on production or

consumption represent a high degree of accuracy. However, in the absence of more accurate information, these data must be used as the basis of our discussion. It is the writers belief that milk is the most important product obtained from goats and that it is most seriously underestimated in reporting. Also, food for human use is produced much more efficiently as milk than in the form of meat. If the dry matter content of meat is estimated at 35% and that of milk at 14.5%, approximately 40% more dry matter is harvested in the form of milk than for meat. It is apparent that a majority of goats are kept only for meat production or that all types of goats produce meat at least at salvage. It is important to recall that milk and fiber can be produced on a reoccurring basis whereas meat and skins are produced only at sacrifice of the animal.

A. Milk

Goats rank below the cow, buffalo, and sheep as a source of milk for human consumption. In market channels only a small part (less than 2%) of world milk production is obtained from goats. Some have alleged that the percentage of people (children) who receive goat milk daily is close to that of cattle. Some individual countries (Niger, Somalia) receive a major portion of their milk supply from goats.

The level of milk production from selected types of dairy goats approaches that of dairy cows when expressed as the basis of body weight or efficiency. However, the labor costs of milk production from goats have been estimated to be as much as four times that of milk production from cows. Further, inefficiencies are encountered in processing and distribution because of the low volumes in market channels. Thus, milk production from goats tends to be concentrated in small farmer or developing country conditions where labor costs are discounted or in upscale markets in developing countries where it may be marketed at higher prices (than cows milk) due to some actual or presumed unique qualities. Many claims are made by promoters or goat enthusiasts for unique or superior qualities of goat milk. Many of these cannot be documented. Chance alone would dictate that goat's milk differs from that of other species just as individuals or breeds may differ within species. Mean differences between the species is within the range of variation within species. The most significant factor contributing to a unique market outlet for goat milk is that it represents an alternative for those people, especially infants, who develop allergies to cows milk.

Estimates of the frequency of infant allergies to cow's milk range from 3 to 8%. It is known that goat's milk tends to be lower in certain types of casein (α s-1 casein) and thus infants with sensitivity to casein should be more tolerant of goat milk. Goat milk also tends to differ from cow's milk in respect to the fat content. The fat globules of goat milk tend to be smaller and to lack the agglutegens that are in cow's milk. The significance of this is that it is slower to separate out and that it may also may be more easily digested. Goat milk also tends to contain a higher proportion of short-chain fatty acids such as capric, caproic, caprylic, and lauric, which can impact taste.

In addition to these unique physiochemical properties of goat milk, which contribute to marketing opportunities, there are on a world basis many traditional products made from goat milk which contribute to potential market outlets.

Record levels of milk production vary by breed, but are as high as 3000 kg per lactation. More typical values are in the range of 700–900 kg per lactation for well-managed flocks under temperate conditions, and 200–400 kg for selected dairy types under developing country conditions, to less than 100 kg for nondescript types under small holder conditions. Thus, the potential for improved production is great, but requires significant inputs to accomplish. [*See* DAIRY PROCESSING AND PRODUCTS.]

B. Meat

Essentially all goats which survive to slaughter age produce meat, and most goats are exploited only for meat production. Most of the world supply of goat meat is produced and consumed in Asia and Africa. It is often the preferred meat in much of Asia, such as India, Pakistan, and Nepal, or with people originated in these areas, regardless of where they currently reside. This is evidenced by a large demand for goat meat in the Caribbean region which has a large number of people of Asian origin. Since goats must be slaughtered for the harvest of meat or skins the efficiency of meat production can be low and is greatly influenced by reproductive rate and death losses prior to market. Meat from goats has some unique characteristics. One of these is that the carcasses have lower fat or higher lean than other species such as cattle, buffalo, sheep, or pigs. This is due to the fact that they are seldom fed the quantity or quality of feed required to permit them to deposit large amounts of fat. Closely related to this is the fact that they are not glutinous feeders even when given an opportunity

and thus fatten less readily. They also tend to deposit more of their fat internally, thus removing it from the carcass itself. Their low fat content can be viewed as a positive by today's fat conscious consumers. Some increase in the fat cover over the carcass would improve appearance and shelf life of the carcass in market channels. Due to their low fat content, yield at slaughter (carcass weight as a percentage of live weight) is low for goats (45 to 48%) as compared to other livestock species. Shown in Fig. 1 is a breakdown of major dress-off items from one slaughter experiment. Another somewhat unique feature is their small carcass size, which makes for easier distribution and consumption of the carcass prior to spoilage where refrigeration is limited. Also, goat meat is thought to have unique organoleptic properties, which make it preferred by some and discriminated against by other groups. In developed countries, primary emphasis is placed on carcass meats, but in developing countries where food or food of animal origin is in reduced supply essentially all the products, including the offal, blood, and skin, may be used for human consumption. Since much of the goat meat is produced and consumed in the latter areas, carcass quality, hygienic considerations, and the cost of processing are of less concern.

Goats tend to be marketed for meat in fairly defined age groups. One of these is the suckling kid (4 to 6 weeks of age) as represented by cabrito production in Mexico. This is a very inefficient production system and can be justified only if a very high price is obtained or if it can be combined with milk production from the does following weaning of the kid. The second age group is that of weanling kid at 4 to 6 months of age. This is the typical market age in North America and much of Europe. A third age is on the

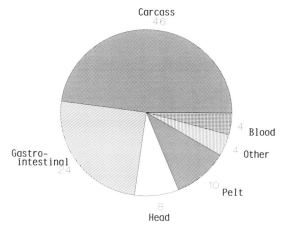

FIGURE 1 Dress-off items in percentage from goat slaughter.

order of 6 months to 1 year of age for animals not suitable for slaughter at weaning. This animal is often used for barbeque. A majority of the animals slaughtered at the above ages would be made up of surplus male kids. The final age group would be culled breeding stock (mostly females) at advanced ages. For the quality conscious consumer this would represent a lower value product, but to many consumer this would be of little concern since the meat would be consumed following thorough cooking and seasoning. One of the major sources of goat meat on the export market are feral goats from Australia and New Zealand, and this likely represents whatever can be caught at a given "round-up." Age is of primary concern through its effect on tenderness of meat served as steaks or roasts after limited cooking. This represents only a small part of the total goat meat consumed. Consumers in developed countries have more interest in the primal cuts (leg and loin) which represent approximately 40% of the carcass (see Fig. 2), whereas less discriminating consumers make little distinction between carcass components.

The major factors affecting efficiency of meat production from goats are reproductive rate and rate of growth or slaughter weight expressed as a function of size of the parental breeding stock. Reproductive rate of goats (percentage kidding and kidding rate) tend to be acceptable under most production conditions, but death losses at or around kidding and weaning tend to be high in many production systems. The end result is that net reproductive rate expressed as kid crop in percentage or total weight weaned or marketed is low in many production systems. In addition, growth rates are often low, reflecting low slaughter weights or delayed marketing necessitating that the animals be kept to advanced ages to reach optimum slaughter weight. The end result of both

these is that efficiency of meat production, expressed as off-take, is low for many goat populations, especially in developing country conditions. It is important that this be improved in light of the extensive and often deleterious effects of goats on forage resources in fragile environments. Technology to change this is largely available, but is often difficult to implement due to socioeconomic constraints in many areas of production.

C. Fiber

Essentially all land mammals are fiber producers to some degree. Fiber apparently serves a function in nature as protection from abrasion, from extremes in temperatures, and to some extent as a sense organ. Many animal species have been utilized for fiber production. These include sheep, goats, rabbits, various species of camilidae, yak, muskox, etc. Sheep are the major producer of harvested animal fiber (wool), and by comparison all other types of animal fibers tend to be luxury or specialty fibers produced in small volumes. The ancestors of the domestic goat tended to be restricted to the colder climates at higher elevations of Eurasia and would no doubt have possessed a well-developed coat for protection from cold. In the present age, only a small percentage of the world's goat population is exploited for fiber production (less than 2% for mohair), but fiber production, especially mohair, is more commercialized and more organized than other types of goat production.

The types or classification of fibers harvested from goats are shown below.

	Approximate total world production, 1990 (1000 kg)	Range in fiber diameter (μm)
Mohair	22,300	25–40
Cashmere or Pashmina	4,500	12–19
Cashgora	50	19–25
Common goat hair	—	>40

Mohair, a product of the Angora goat, is produced in greater quantity than the other types of goat fibers. This is true both on a per-head basis (3–5 kg, annually) and to total world supply. The major centers and current world production are shown in Table II. The two major world centers of production are the Republic of South Africa (RSA) and the United States. Pro-

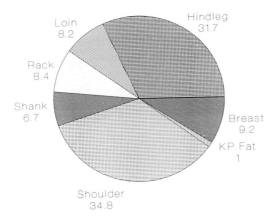

FIGURE 2 Retail cuts of goat carcasses in percentage.

Loin 8.2
Hindleg 31.7
Rack 8.4
Shank 6.7
Breast 9.2
KP Fat 1
Shoulder 34.8

TABLE II

World Production of Mohair, 1984–1991 (in 1000 kg)[a]

	84	85	86	87	88	89	90	91[c]
South Africa[b]	8,227.3	9,181.8	10,454.5	12,500.0	12,727.3	12,045.5	8,636.4	8,000.0
United States	5,090.9	6,045.0	6,363.6	7,363.6	7,136.4	6,818.2	6,818.0	6,818.0
Turkey	3,636.0	3,500.0	3,409.0	3,000.0	2,727.0	1,818.0	1,818.0	1,182.0
Argentina	1,227.0	1,136.0	1,227.0	1,182.0	1,136.0	1,000.0	682.0	591.0
Australia	500.0	545.0	591.0	955.0	1,000.0	1,000.0	682.0	591.0
New Zealand	45.0	90.0	90.0	180.0	454.0	454.0	454.0	318.0
Total	18,726.2	20,497.8	22,135.1	25,182.0	25,182.0	23,045.0	19,318.0	17,500.0

[a] From Mohair Council of America.
[b] Includes Lesotho.
[c] Estimation.

duction in Turkey has shown a downward trend during the last 8 years. Another country with a significant level of production is Lesotho. However, since the mohair from Lesotho is generally marketed through RSA it is included with RSA in the above tabulation. Argentina has long had a significant number of Angora goats but the actual level of mohair production from this country is small and decreasing. Beginning approximately 10 years ago, there has been a rapid rise in Angora goat numbers and mohair production in Australia and New Zealand, but production from both countries appeared to be down since 1990. Production in RSA declined sharply in 1990 and 1991, due in part to dry weather along with severe price breaks for mohair. Production in the United States has tended to remain stable. A number of other countries have taken an interest in Angora goats in recent years, but their impact on world supply is minimal at present. The desirable features of mohair are its strength, durability, and ability to be dyed in lustrous bright colors. The major end uses for mohair are shown in Fig. 3. From this it can be seen that traditionally

mohair was used for hand-knitting yarns. Other uses include mens and womens clothing and woven furnishings. A sharply reduced demand for hand knitting yarns resulted in sharp price breaks for mohair since 1988. Major centers for processing mohair have traditionally been in Europe (U.K., Belgium, France, Germany, Spain, and Italy). In contrast to other types of goat production, Angora goats and mohair production are not found in tropical regions and are not the "poor mans cow." They are used almost exclusively to produce fiber.

Cashmere is the most important fiber (in terms of quality or price) obtained from goats. It is sometimes referred to as pashmina, especially in India. Although cashmere is produced in less quantities than mohair, the price of cashmere is generally higher than that of mohair and at times the total value of the clip as well. Since the amount of cashmere produced per animal is low, usually less that 250 g, the price must remain high in order to generate a meaningful income to the producer. Thus, even more than mohair, cashmere is traditionally a luxury or prestige commodity. The most noted characteristics of cashmere are its fineness and the color, light weight, and insulating properties of garments made from it.

Major world centers of production have traditionally been China, Mongolia, Iran, and Afghanistan. Small amounts are produced in the former USSR, India, Turkey and Pakistan. In recent years, several other countries, most notably Australia, New Zealand, and Scotland, have also taken an interest in cashmere production. However, China remains the major supplier with close to 50% of the world total (Table III). Prices received for cashmere trended upward for over a decade until 1989. These factors are no doubt the explanation for the recent interest in cashmere outside the traditional centers of production, but as of this writing prices are down sharply.

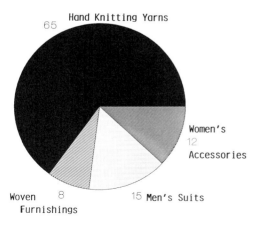

FIGURE 3 World mohair consumption and end use (%).

TABLE III
Estimated World Cashmere Production in 1989 (Metric Tons)

Area/country	Approximate total hair production	Approximate down production
China	3400	1700
Iran/Afghanistan	2400	850
Outer Mongolia	1500	700
USSR/Pakistan/ India/Turkey, etc.	800	300
Australia	65	20
New Zealand	150	45
Total	8315	3615

Source: Hopkins, H. (1989). Proc. Cashmere Goat Conference, San Angelo, Texas, Oct. 26–28.

Animals used to produce cashmere are, more so than the Angora, a multi-purpose animal being used for milk and meat production as well.

Cashgora is a recently coined term for the product which is intermediate in fiber diameter between cashmere and mohair. The total world production is small and largely restricted to New Zealand. Although there must be a use or value for the product which is intermediate between the two well-known fiber types, the use and outlet for this material is not well established at present.

Little information is available and no estimate of production is provided for common goat hair since it is not a major product in trade channels. It may be used for felting, coarse-hair yarns, carpets, blankets, stuffing, etc., and was traditionally used for making tents of desert nomads. Obvious sources of commercial quantities of this product are commercial dehairing of cashmere and that removed from skins in the tanning process.

D. Skins

There is limited published or statistical information on skins from goats. This commodity should be viewed primarily as a co-product or a by-product of animals slaughtered for meat production. However, some skins are obtained from fallen animals, and in many societies, especially in isolated locations in developing countries, goats are slaughtered on the farmstead and the skin is the only cash-earning commodity. It is generally considered that skins represent 15–25% of the value of the animal, but when the skin is processed into end use products its value would be many multiples of that at slaughter. Some breeds or types of goats, especially those of tropical origins, produce reputation skins. These are noted for the lightweight

and fine grain of products made from them. As with goat numbers, the major sources of goat skins are Asia (India, China, Pakistan, and Bangladesh) and Africa (Ethiopia, Sudan, Somalia, and Kenya). In the Americas only Mexico and Brazil produce a significant number of skins. A great deal of technology is required in curing, tanning, and processing of skins, but much of this technology is available in the industry. There are major problems in dealing with the effluent or waste products of tanning of leather, and for these reasons much of this industry has become localized in areas with less stringent regulations. Major opportunities to improve income from skins are to be found in improved harvesting, preservation, and collecting of skins as many are discarded and others are damaged due to cuts or decay before being processed. The major importers of goat skin leather or goat skin products are Europe (Germany, France, and the U.K.), the former USSR, and the United States. [*See* ANIMAL BY-PRODUCTS FROM SLAUGHTER.]

V. Genetic Resources

Within the more than one-half billion head of goats in the world, there is a wide variety of genetic resources. Some have estimated as many as 1000 genotypes or genetic subgroups. Few of these fit very well into any technical definition of breeds. Those which do are largely confined to Europe or North America, whereas most goats are located in the warmer and less developed parts of the world. However, for the purpose at hand, many of these genetic subgroups might be viewed as breeds. There is no complete catalog of these genetic groups, and if such existed, space would prevent its inclusion in this discussion. Some approaches to classification of goats have been made and the most complete effort to list, classify, and describe breeds of goat placed great emphasis on horn shape and ear length. Space does not permit a detailed treatment of this subject at this point. For this reason, the writer has chosen an alternative grouping for the sake of convenience. [*See* ANIMAL BREEDING AND GENETICS.]

(a) The European (Alpine) dairy types. These include such well-established breeds as Saanen, Toggenburg, Alpine, Chamois, Poitevin, etc. These types are largely bred for dairy purposes, but yield meat and skins as secondary products at slaughter. Most originated or were initially utilized in mountainous regions. They have been exported to many places in the world, and genetics from this source are found widespread in goat populations of essentially all countries.

(b) Long-legged, long-eared, roman-nosed goats are found through much of Africa and Asia. Some recognized breed groups are the Nubian, Damascus (Shami), Beetal, Jamnapari, etc. Representatives of this type, or animals showing a resemblance to this type, can be found from the tip of Africa to Southeast Asia, and they obviously derive from a common ancestry. They may be used for meat and/or milk. Their large size suggests their use as a meat type, but limited studies have not shown them to be more productive than many other types. Some types, such as the Jamnapari and Beetal, show extremes in both ear and leg length.

(c) Dwarf types are also found throughout Africa and Asia and likely share a common ancestry, which may well derive from the small type found in tropical (tsetse fly areas) Africa. Recognizable types include the Black Bengal of India and the Pygmy or Nigerian dwarf which has been exported to Europe and the United States. Their small size would suggest to many that they are poor choices for meat production, but in fact, research studies have shown that as a result of early sexual maturity and high reproductive rate, they may actually be one of the more efficient meat producers, especially when bred to larger type males. Dwarf types in Europe or the United States are often used as laboratory animals or pets or in hobby flocks.

(d) Fiber types. The Angora, used for mohair production, is a unique and well-recognized breed of goat. It is the only breed which can be used for mohair production. Although it may well have been derived from other groups, most likely cashmere types, it has benefitted from a long period of selection for mohair production and as a result is distinct. It should not be crossed or intermingled with other types, because this will result in a deterioration in the role each is expected to serve. Cashmere is more properly identified as a product, as contrasted to a breed or genotype. Cashmere is, in fact, the down or undercoat from a dual-coated animal. Goats which produce at least some cashmere are found at many places in the world. However, most of the world's cashmere production occurs in the arid highlands of Asia and the Near East, and the animals in this area do have a great deal in common and differ, at least in some respects, from most other populations. These animals and the product they produce (cashmere, pashmina) appear to derive, at least in earlier periods, more from natural selection than from selection by man. In China there

are a number of recognized breed groups, as well as some wild types which produce excellent cashmere.

(e) Nondescript goats make up a large part of the total found throughout the world. The above defined groups encompass only a small part of the total. The majority of the remainder represent nondescript population or a mixture of the other types. In many areas there are distinct types based on some simple feature such as color or ear length. An example of the so-called breeds based largely on color is found in Northeast Brazil. A breed based entirely on ear length is the LaMancha in the United States. Typical examples of mixed blood types of goats are the "so-called" Spanish goats of the United States and the Criollo or Crioula in Central and South America.

VI. Problems and Opportunities

On the theory that problems or limitations become opportunities when viewed from a different vantage point, these two subjects are being discussed under the same heading.

Clearly, one of the greatest opportunities to improve the contribution of goats is to do a better job of matching the animal numbers and forage resources. There are many areas where feral goats represent uncontrolled populations which are abusing forage resources without providing significant returns. On a larger scale, the goat populations in a number of developing countries or areas exceed the carrying capacity of the resources available. This leads to damage to these resources and reduces productivity of the animals involved. In contrast, the limited numbers of goats in many other countries suggest that the species is not being adequately or appropriately utilized to exploit their potential. This involves their value in multi-species grazing programs. They can be used (a) to increase overall productivity from many of these areas, (b) to assist in control of many undesirable and invading plant species in pastures or range lands, (c) to produce products (meat, milk and skins) which are in demand at some place to feed or provide for the growing world population. There is a specific need to reconsider the place of the goat in the control of many undesirable plant species at a time when human and fossil fuel energy are becoming more expensive and more restrictions are being placed on the use of herbicides to accomplish this task. A prime example of this is the use of goats in leafy spurge control in the western United States. Goats have also been shown to serve a role in prevention or reducing the threat from fire in many ecosystems by removing the forest undergrowth which serves as a fuel for wild fires.

Closely related to the above is the potential to improve the productivity of the large population of goats (over two-thirds of the total) which are found in many developing countries. The productivity of these animals is, in general, very low compared to their potential. In many cases, the offtake is so low that their use or overuse of the resources can scarcely be justified. For example, the record levels of milk production for the dairy breeds in temperate regions range from 2000 to 3000 kg per year of lactation. More typical or more realistic levels of milk production are 800–1200 kg based on milk recording schemes in the United States and Europe. By contrast, production level of native goats under tropical conditions has been reported as low as 136 kg (range 15–450). This can be markedly improved by crossing with established dairy breeds, but the resultant mixed breed animal may well require improved feed and management. In a similar manner, off-take (number of animals marketed per 100 animals in the flock) is often in the range of 10–20 under developing country conditions, compared to over 100 under more favorable conditions or better management.

In tropical or subtropical and especially developing country conditions, the demand for food is great and thus markets should not be a constraint to goat production, although an ability to pay may be a problem. On the other hand, if goat production is to increase in temperate regions (United States and Europe), there must be coincident market development. This could include promotion of the products which are unique to the goat such as fiber (mohair or cashmere), milk (an alternative to cows milk), and meat (the low fat content). The potential is evident, but the realization of this potential may not be so easily accomplished. However, all that is required is that market development keep pace with production.

Control or containment and protection constitute problems in goat production. Some of the options in respect to control or containment represent fencing, herding, and tethering. Protection refers to the need to prevent theft or predation. The degree or nature of these problems and approaches to their resolution vary greatly between countries or areas within countries and are too complex to attempt to discuss at this point.

The availability of technology as related to genetics, nutrition, reproductive physiology, management, and disease and parasite control is generally adequate to support a much greater use or higher productivity from goats. There is a continuous need for genetic improvement and for development or refinement of other technologies. This is especially true in respect to adapting this technology to stressing environments or to developing country conditions. However, technological constrains are dwarfed by socioeconomic constraints to applying this technology under developing country conditions. One should not be overly optimistic in assessing the degree to which this will be accomplished, but the potential and the need are sufficiently great that the task cannot be ignored.

Bibliography

Acharya, R. M., and Singh, N. P. (1992). The Role of the Goat in Conservation of Ecology and Livelihood Security. Proceedings V International Conference on Goats, pp. 81–99. New Delhi, India.

Devendra, C. (1992). Goats and Rural Prosperity. Proceedings V International Conference on Goats, pp. 6–25. New Delhi, India.

Holst, P. J. (1987). World Production and Utilization of Goat Skins. Proceedings IV International Conference on Goats, Vol. I, pp. 145–152. Brasilia, Brazil.

Hoversland, A. S., Parer, J. T., and Metcalfe, J. (1965). The African dwarf goat as a laboratory animal in the study of cardiovascular physiology. *Fed. Proc.* **24,** 705.

Lowenstein, M. (1982). Dairy Goat Milk and Factors Affecting It. Proc. III Int. Conf. on Goat Production and Disease. Tucson, AZ.

Mason, L. (1981). Wild goats and their domestication. *In* "Goat Production." Academic Press, London.

Rao, K. S., and Rao, G. G. (1992). Production, Processing and Export of Goat Skins. Proceedings V International Conference on Goats, pp. 521–533. New Delhi, India.

Rubino, R., and Bourbouze, A. (1992). Problems of Extensive Goat Production on Public Grazing Land: A case study in the Mediterranean. Proc. V. World Conf. on Goats, Vol. II, pp. 16–30. New Delhi, India.

Scholnik, A., Maltz, E., and Gordin, S. (1980). Desert condition and goat milk production. *J. Dairy Sci.* **63,** 1749.

Shelton, M., Snowder, G., and Figueiredo, E.A.P. (1984). Meat Production and Carcass Characteristics of the Goat. Technical Report No. 45, US-AID Collaborative Research Program. Univ. of Calif./Davis.

Valdez, R. (1985). "Lords of the Pinnacles. Wild Goats of the World." Mesilla, NM.

Wilson, R. T., Sharma, K., and Galal, E.S.E. (1992). Small Holder Goat Production Systems in Africa and Asia. Proc. V. World Conf. on Goats, Vol. II, pp. 36–53. New Delhi, India.

Unknown (1981). Breeds. *In* "Goat Production." Academic Press, London.

Government Agricultural Policy, United States

GORDON C. RAUSSER, *University of California, Berkeley*

Glossary

Acreage reduction An acreage set-aside and/or diversion that is generally voluntary; acreage set-aside programs require that participating farmers idle a percentage of their crop base acres to be eligible for other program benefits; acreage diversion programs pay producers a given amount per acre to idle a percentage of their base acres; a farmer's base acres are determined by the production history of the crop

Loan rates (price supports) The Commodity Credit Corporation (CCC) makes nonrecourse loans at established loan rates to farmers for wheat, feed grains, cotton, sugar, wool, tobacco, and honey; the loan, plus interest and storage, can be repaid within 9–12 mo and the commodity sold on the cash market; if it is not profitable for the farmer to repay the loan, the CCC has no recourse but to accept the commodity in full payment of the loan; commodity loans, therefore, are frequently referred to as price support, since national season average prices generally do not fall below set loan levels; local prices, on the other hand, can fall below the loan rate for part of the marketing year

Political–economic resource transactions (PERT) Productive or public interest policies intended to reduce transaction costs in the private sector

by correcting market failures or providing public goods, thus increasing the size of the economic "pie"

Political–economic seeking transfers (PEST) Predatory or special interest policies meant to redistribute wealth from one social group to another and not explicitly concerned with efficiency

Producer subsidy equivalent The ratio of the total value of all public sector assistance to total farmer receipts

Slippage Defined by $s = -[(DY/Y)(P/DP)]$ where Y is aggregate per-acre yield and P is the ratio of land planted to total land, planted and diverted, for that crop

Target prices, deficiency payments In the United States, deficiency payments are paid to farmers to make up the difference between a price determined to achieve a politically acceptable income level (target price) and the higher of the average market price or the loan rate; deficiency payments are made on each farm's actual planted acres and farm program yield; the farm program yield is based on each farm's yield history; target prices were set initially to reflect an average cost of production; specifically, for those who participate, the expected deficiency payment for a particular crop, c,

$$E(d_{ct}) = [P_{ct}^T - Max(P_{ct}^S, E(P_{ct}))](1 - \omega_{ct})L_{ct}Y_{ct},$$

where P_{ct}^T is the target price; P_{ct}^S, the support price; $E(P_{ct})$, the expected average price received by farmers; ω_{ct}, the percentage of land base required to be idled; L_{ct}, the land base in period t; and Y_{ct}, the program yield per unit of the land base

Agriculture policy is a complex web of interventions covering output markets, input markets, trade, public good investments, renewable and exhaustible natural resources, regulation of externalities, education, and the marketing and distribution of food products. At the level of the federal government, these interventions have resulted in enormous budgetary costs; huge surpluses of farm products; major disputes with other countries, distorted international markets, and benefits to special interest groups that are often highly concentrated. The same programs, however, have been part of an agricultural sector the productivity of which, over much of the last century, has been spectacular.

Do these massive governmental interventions correct for market imperfections, lower transaction costs, effectively regulate externalities, and enhance productivity? Or are these programs the results of manipulation by powerful commodity or agricultural interest groups actively engaged in rent-seeking or directly unproductive activities? In this latter perspective, agricultural interest groups are presumed to behave much like the proverbial 800-pound gorilla—they walk where they want, they stand where they want, they sit where they want, and they take what they want.

In the design and implementation of governmental policy in agriculture, conflicts naturally emerge between public and special interests. A conceptual formulation that attempts to explain or, for that matter, prescribe public policy emphasizing only one of these interests is doomed to fail. Frameworks that neglect political forces and the role of special interest groups will have little explanatory power. Similarly, models that attribute all political action to special interests will also face serious limitations as explanatory, predictive, or prescriptive frameworks.

This article argues that agricultural policy in the United States has led to both the enhancement of efficiency through "productive policies" and the transfer of wealth and income to special interests through redistributive or "predatory policies." These two activities can be examined in terms of PEST (predatory or special interest) and PERT (productive or public interest) policies. Political-economic-seeking transfers (PEST policies) are meant to redistribute wealth from one social group to another and are not explicitly concerned with efficiency. In contrast, political-economic resource transactions (PERTs) are intended to reduce transaction costs in the private sector by correcting market failures or providing public goods; these policies have neutral distributional effects, at least in design.

In fact, an examination of public policy in agriculture reveals not only tension between the PERT and PEST roles of the public sector, but also some coordination between these two types of activities. As differ-

ent interest groups access, influence, and pressure the political process, the government trades off PESTs and PERTs in its attempts to acquire, balance, and secure political power. At times this manipulation has led to programs that appear to be incoherent. Examples include conservation, which requires the retirement of vulnerable acreage, and price supports, a transfer mechanism that penalizes premature land retirement and creates incentives for overutilization of vulnerable acreage. These apparent incoherencies, however, are the direct result of institutional arrangements that generate sufficient support for particular types of governmental action. Thus, a rational process generates a government portfolio of productive (PERT) and predatory (PEST) policies. In such a world, the challenge for economists is to design and advocate policies that are both economically productive and politically sustainable.

I. Early Development of United States Agricultural Policies

Federal programs for increasing growth in the agricultural sector began in the second half of the 19th century. The period from 1850 to the early 1900s witnessed the emergence of important institutions aimed at lowering transaction costs in the private sector. The Morrill Act of 1862 offered federal land grants to each state to establish free public higher education through the Land Grant College system. The U.S. Department of Agriculture (USDA), created in 1862, initially focused on research, regulation, and information generation. The Hatch Act of 1887 set up the Agricultural Experiment Station system by providing annual grants to each state for agricultural research. The Smith–Lever Act of 1914 set up the Cooperative Extension Service system of county agents. [See AGRICULTURAL EXPERIMENT STATIONS; COOPERATIVE EXTENSION SYSTEM; EDUCATION: UNDERGRADUATE AND GRADUATE UNIVERSITY; USDA: A NATIONAL SYSTEM OF AGRICULTURAL RESEARCH.]

The grassroots organization represented by the county agent extension system proved to be an effective mechanism for communicating new agricultural technologies and knowledge directly to farmers in a systematic fashion. This organization also became the conduit for communicating back to the USDA and the land grant universities information on farmers' problems that required research. These early federal policies can largely be characterized as long-run institutional development, in which the government was supplying public goods whose associated benefits and costs were widely dispersed.

A major resource promoting agricultural productivity has been the knowledge generated by public sector investments in research. This knowledge generation has repeatedly been shown to have significant influence on agricultural growth. Nonetheless, the striking feature of agricultural research policies has been the overwhelming evidence of underinvestment. As Ruttan has shown, the rates of return to public good investments in agricultural research justify much higher levels of public research support.

Following the emphasis on public research, education, and extension support, legislation turned to the undesirable issues of rural infrastructure and problems of limited information. This legislation covered rural delivery of mail, soil conservation, agricultural credit, rural electrification, rural road building, and many other investments in the physical infrastructure of agriculture. Problems of limited information were addressed by still other legislation regulating different aspects of agriculture and had the purpose of lowering transaction costs, including issues such as fertilizer and seed standards, weights, animal health, and food safety.

In more recent years, the evolution of many United States agricultural policies has demonstrated a distinct pattern. Over the early part of the 20th century, enabling legislation was often justified as a means of correcting market failures and enhancing productivity. However, unlike policies of the prior century, once in place these policies evolved into programs whose benefits were concentrated but whose associated costs were widely shared. Unsurprisingly, much of this legislation became a vehicle for codifying rent-seeking behavior. Striking examples of such agriculture policy evolution include soil conservation, western resource development, farm credit, and environmental pesticide policy.

II. Legislated Redistributive Activities

Early agricultural policies were often justified to some degree by market imperfections, even if they were sometimes manipulated for purposes of redistributing income to the farm sector. However, the institutional structure that emerged from the 19th century and early 20th century efficiency-enhancing legislation (Morrill Act, USDA, Hatch Act, and Smith–Lever Act)—composed of the extension system of county agents, the USDA and generic farm groups—formed the foundation for one of the best organized economic interest groups in the country. The agricultural depression of the 1920s, which foreshadowed the Great Depression, provided the stimulus for this coalition to be more cohesive and effective in redistributing benefits to farmers. Also, during this period, farm interests were able to avoid a number of governmental regulations legislatively through exemptions from antitrust, labor, and tax legislation.

The long history of redistributive agricultural policies began in earnest with the passage of the Agricultural Adjustment Act of 1933, which continues to be revised every 4 yr or so. Following a 1936 ruling by the Supreme Court, these redistributive programs required voluntary participation and offered nonneutral transfer schemes linking government support directly to the amount produced. Since these programs were tied to specific commodities, the generic farmer organizations began to lose influence. In effect, commodity-based groups became the primary vehicles for political expression of farmer interests. At the same time, the USDA began a transformation from an organization that focused largely on research and education to a more conventional government agency, managing programs that provide direct economic benefits to specific interests.

Initially, the major policy instruments for redistributing income to the farm sector were price supports and public storage. Price supports were implemented through government loans to farmers, who put up a certain amount of a commodity as collateral for the period of the loan. If market price fell below the loan rate (price support), the government took ownership of the collateral; if not, the farmer could be expected to pay off the government loan and redeem the commodity. Of course, since price supports were generally set well above market equilibrium prices, storage of the surplus was a necessary by-product. Price support incentives combined with large increases in farm productivity—resulting, in part, from the public investment in research—led to huge surpluses. [*See* CROP SUBSIDIES; PRICES.]

With the commodity redistributive policies came, of course, losses for consumers and taxpayers, gains to farmers, and deadweight losses, the range of which has been estimated for many commodities on numerous occasions. The redistributive support mechanisms range from mandatory production and market controls (tobacco/peanuts), import restrictions (sugar), government rental of land which is then held idle, and other approaches to restrict supplies in the

United States market to *ad valorem* subsidies (wool) and government purchases of commodities (dairy) that increase United States output. Commodity programs that receive the largest federal outlays as well as the most political attention (e.g., grains and cotton) simultaneously combine output-increasing and output-reducing incentives. Table I reports the figures for a representative year over the period 1985–1988. Note that the effects captured in the table underestimate total social losses; for example, they neglect the waste generated from rent-seeking behavior and the deadweight losses associated with tax collections. Further, with the passage of the 1985 Food Security Act, the distribution of burden across consumers and taxpayers shifted dramatically in the mid-1980s, so the net losses computed here fell relative to early periods.

The stylized facts emerging from Table I (not only for the United States but for other countries as well) can be summarized as follows: the redistribution of income to agriculture is greater (1) the richer or the more industrialized the country; (2) the higher the cost of production; (3) the fewer the number of farmers, absolutely and relative to the total population; (4) the more price-inelastic the supply or demand function; (5) the lower the portion of total consumer budget spent on food; and (6) the smaller on world markets the exporting country or the larger the importing country is. The redistributive efficiency increases as

the demand or the supply function becomes less elastic. Moreover, as Gardner (1983, p. 233) has shown, "The efficient method of intervention depends on which function is less elastic. Inelastic demand favors production controls, and inelastic supply a deficiency payment approach."

III. Policy Instruments

Many margins for adjusting behavior are available, the side effects of which seem to continually surprise both policymakers and interest groups. Since the 1930s, attempts to address these adjustments have resulted in a piecemeal proliferation of policy instruments. On the supply side, this change includes the land controls and land conservation mentioned earlier, as well as production quotas; on the demand side, it includes export subsidies and enhancements, concessional foreign sales and food grants, and food stamps. Unfortunately, each additional policy instrument brought its own unanticipated side effects, requiring still additional mechanisms for containing the expanding capacity for commodity production.

Sometimes the side effects seem so obvious that policymakers can only have missed them through sheer myopia. For example, the initial voluntary acreage-reduction programs focused on compliance

TABLE I

Range of Annual Domestic Welfare Gains and Losses from Support Programs under the 1985 Food Security Act, 1985–1988

	Cost (billions of dollars)			
Crop	Consumer loss	Producer gain	Taxpayer cost[a]	Net loss
Wheat	0.24–0.30	2.62–3.22	3.67–4.27	0.69–1.95
Corn	0.68–0.76	7.23–7.62	7.30–8.10	0.36–1.63
Cotton	0.19–0.21	1.20–1.46	1.40–1.60	0.13–0.61
Peanuts	0.36–0.40	0.29–0.35	0[b]	0.01–0.11
Dairy	1.80–2.90	1.50–2.90	1.13–1.72	0.73–3.12
Sugar[c]				
Case I	1.90–2.40	1.50–1.70	0[b]	0.20–0.90
Case II	1.35–1.55	1.15–1.25	0[b]	0.10–0.40
Tobacco	0.20–0.22	0.34–0.38	0[b]	(0.12)–(0.18)[d]

Source: Computed estimates from unpublished U.S. Department of Agriculture data.
[a] Includes Commodity Credit Corporation expenses after cost recovery.
[b] These programs are run at no net cost to the government.
[c] Case I assumes U.S. policies do not affect world sugar prices. Case II takes into account the fact that U.S. policies reduce world sugar prices. The value of sugar import restrictions to those exporters who have access to the U.S. market (that is, value of quota rents) is $250 million.
[d] The tobacco program is estimated to have a positive net domestic welfare gain, because of the large value of U.S. exports allowing domestic producers to extract surplus from foreign consumers.

requirements *for a particular commodity*, neglecting the fact that farmers might substitute and grow other crops; for example, farmers might substitute soybean for corn production. In addition, consumers that had demanded the original crop were sometimes able to substitute a nonprogram for a programmed crop. Of course, if too many restrictions on substitution are placed on farmers, they will choose not to participate.

To understand how farmers can respond to voluntary programs, it is important to describe the mechanics of the income transfers. For some years, the major vehicle for these transfers has been "deficiency payments." The government sets a target price for certain commodities. The target price is set well above the market price, which encourages high program participation. The deficiency payment rate is computed as the difference between the target price (set by law) and the higher of the price support or the average market price received over the first 5 mo of the marketing year. Each farmer participating in the program has a payment base, determined by the land base (essentially how much land they have dedicated to the crop in the past) and "program yield" (based on the individual's or county's past yields). The deficiency payment rate multiplied by the payment base, adjusted for acreage set-aside requirements, determines the total deficiency payment. Thus, the amount of deficiency payments to farmers is influenced through four different channels—target prices, price supports, the land resource base, and productivity.

To receive the deficiency payments, participating farmers must allocate land to a crop in the program or to conservation uses dictated by the USDA. Moreover, until 1990, the enabling legislation generally required farmers to forego present and future program benefits if they harvested crops other than the program crop for which they had a "land base." This feature was intended to prevent a farmer from collecting federal subsidies for not growing one crop, while growing another. This regulation also has the effect of coupling income transfers to the planting and harvesting of program crops. Historically, one of the major barriers to entry into program crop production has been land bases on which acreage restrictions are imposed.

Over the years, more flexibility has slowly been introduced and the amount transferred has become increasingly less dependent on the actions, current and past, of farmers. For example, until the 1986 market year, the expected program yield was determined as a moving average of a farmer's past yields. One provision of legislation in 1985, however, was to assign unalterable program yields. Thus, a farmer could no longer strategically influence this variable.

The incentive to raise production caused by price supports was also dramatically reduced with the 1985 legislation. The Secretary of Agriculture was given discretion in the case of feedgrains and wheat to lower the price support up to 20% below the basic loan rate. For soybeans, the loan rate can be lowered no more than 5%. For cotton and rice, the effective loan rate is set at world market prices. As a result, cotton and rice farmers participating in government programs could first pledge their output as collateral for a loan at the basic rate and, at maturity, repay the loan at the prevailing world market price if it is lower than the basic rate. In the case of land base, current actions can still influence how a farmer's base is computed. A producer of a program crop has an assigned "base" acreage of that crop, which is derived from a 5-yr moving average of plantings of that crop on the farm. As a result, a forward-looking farmer may plant larger acreage in anticipation of future subsidies.

The trend toward lowering entry barriers to production of program crops and the degree of coupling at the margin was continued in the 1990 farm legislation. In comparison to previous legislation, the flexibility provisions allow market signals to play a more significant role in guiding production decisions. These provisions permit 15% of the land base to be planted to any program, any oil seed, or any industrial, experimental, or other nonprogram crop except for fruits and vegetables. This 15% of the total base is not eligible for support payments, but program crops, other permitted crops, or conservation uses are allowed.

In addition to this 15% "normal flex" provision, farmers are also allowed the option of an additional 10% flexibility. Subsidy payments are lost on these acres as well as on the 15% "normal" flex acres, but for the "normal flex" and "optional flex" acres, the land base is protected. Prior to 1990, the allocation of land to any nonprogram or other program crop would have reduced by an equivalent amount that acreage that would enter the 5-yr moving average process for determining land base.

That portion of the actual land base that is idled can be decided by each producer, and each producer will rationally idle the least productive land that he controls (whether as an owner or a renter). This option, along with reconfigured variable inputs on the utilized land (plus the existence of nonparticipants) means that a program that seeks to reduce acreage by a given percentage normally reduces output by a substantially smaller percentage. This phenomenon of increased per-acre yields associated with government acreage control programs has been referred to as "slippage." Estimates of the amount of slippage range from 30% to as high as 60%.

Given the possibilities for manipulating output patterns, predicting government agricultural spending is highly uncertain. Since the target price is set by the legislation, the major sources of uncertainty are the support price, the land base, and the number of farmers who choose to participate. Although it is not surprising, therefore, that the Office of Management and Budget (OMB) and the USDA frequently generate point forecasts for government expenditures that are widely off the mark, it is notable that, compared with other budgetary predictions, agricultural expenditures have been systematically downward biased over the last few decades. One explanation is that strong incentives exist for underestimating expected treasury costs in an area where the transfer recipients are distinctly more powerful and better informed than those who share the burden for the transfers (i.e., taxpayers, consumers).

In an attempt to control government spending, as well as to address goals of distributional equity, deficiency payments are limited to $50,000 per farm. Over the years, however, many loopholes have allowed these payment limitations to be exceeded. The loose definition of "person" has fostered overlapping partnerships and other methods of farm ownership that qualify for multiple payment limits. Accordingly, the number of "farmers" in program-eligible commodities has increased over the last decade, whereas the number of farmers producing commodities ineligible for subsidies has declined.

Despite these attempted limitations, the distribution of program benefits continues to be viewed by many as inequitable. For the 1988 crop year, operating farms with sales above $100,000 received 57.6% of the direct government payments. As shown in Table II, the cumulative distribution of government payments reveals a concentration among the largest farming operations, with the average payment to all farmers having annual sales exceeding $500,000 per year at approximately $40,000. Since many large farms do not produce commodities eligible for government programs (approximately 25% of all farmland in the United States is eligible for government crop programs), participating farms receive considerably more than this figure. In fact, based on sample surveys conducted by the USDA Economic Research Service, the estimates of payments to program-participating farms is $30,598 for the sales category $100,000–249,000, $41,888 for the sales category $250,000–499,000, and $66,037 for the sales category above $500,000.

IV. Implications of Coupled Transfers

Many of the inputs used in agricultural production are joint, producing valuable as well as undesirable outputs. Encouraging agricultural production through coupled transfer schemes while requiring some land to be idled leads to excessive utilization of basic inputs. Residuals of excessive fertilizer and pesticide input applications combine with excess water and are transported into various water sources, an external output. Toxic salts accumulate in agricultural land. Burning crop residues may result in air pollu-

TABLE II
Distribution of All Government Payments by Farm Class, 1988

Farm class[a] (dollars)	Number of farms (thousands)	Average payment (dollars)	Total payments to class (millions of dollars)	Total payments (%)	Total farms in class (%)
<10,000	1,051	559	588	4.1	47.8
10,000–19,999	270	2,368	640	4.4	12.3
20,000–39,999	253	5,821	1,472	10.2	11.5
40,000–99,999	300	11,461	3,444	23.8	13.7
100,000–249,999	220	21,452	4,714	32.6	10.0
250,000–499,999	67	32,484	2,188	15.1	3.1
>500,000	35	40,874	1,435	9.9	1.6
Total	2,195	6,597	14,481	100.0	100.0

Source: U.S. Department of Agriculture. "Economic Indicators of the Farm Sector: National Financial Summary, 1989." ERS, ECIFS 902, Table 30, p. 46.
[a] Annual sales.

tion. Wind erosion contributes to particulate air pollution and has been estimated to cost $4 billion or more in annual damages in the western United States, whereas erosion caused by water runoff has been a major contributor to water pollution, resulting in damages estimated to range from $5 billion to $18 billion annually. These examples illustrate the joint input feature of land, water, pesticides, and so on, leading to multiple products, some subset of which results in the degradation of environmental resources.

Essentially, the land that is allocated to production of program crops is combined with more pesticides and fertilizers than would otherwise be the case. Farmers receive subsidies only on that land that is part of the farmer's program crop base. Thus, a disincentive is created for rotating crops. Because crop rotation is a nonchemical technique for pest control, the coupled transfer programs aggravate pesticide pollution by encouraging the substitution of chemical for nonchemical pest control. In this respect, the experience of the United States is consistent with that of the rest of the world. Countries that tax their agricultural sectors (e.g., Argentina, Thailand) use less than one-twentieth the amount of chemical fertilizer per cultivated acre than highly subsidized countries such as Switzerland. A similar direct correspondence exists between producer subsidies and the use of farm pesticides.

Given the relationship between coupled transfers and the determined land base, acreage that is suitable for the program crops becomes more valuable. These subsidized land values encourage farmers to allocate available land to program commodity production. In some instances, this allocation has included land that is steeply sloped and, thus, highly erodible, as well as wetlands that provide important wildlife habitat. Hence, coupled transfers based on land use have created incentives for farmers to use land in ways that increase adverse environmental impacts. These concerns helped motivate the conservation reserve program of the 1985 legislation and the planning flexibility provisions of the 1990 farm legislation. These most recent farm bills have established a trend toward reducing the linkages between agricultural subsidies and farmers' production and land-use decisions. Accordingly, potential adverse environmental spillovers have been slowly reduced.

The inflexible settings of price supports and target prices in the early 1980s followed the favorable agricultural economic markets of the 1970s. The coupled transfer policies augmented the degree of overexpansion within the United States agricultural sector, making the sector especially vulnerable to the unanticipated interest rate, exchange rate, and growth rate patterns of the early 1980s. One adverse environmental result was the "mining of the soil" that many farmers engaged in during the 1980s to survive financial stress.

Partially because of the nature of the coupled transfers, one production record after another was broken during normal weather years of the 1980s. These high levels of production led to pressure for change. For example, in 1983, commodity-specific certificates were offered in lieu of cash transfers, that is, farmers were offered subsidy in kind rather than cash. This change became a means for releasing public stocks held in the farmer-owned reserve. In 1986, generic commodity certificates were introduced in place of commodity-specific certificates up to the level of available stocks. Governmental expenditures skyrocketed in 1986 because governmental stocks moved onto market through the generic certificate program, driving real prices to record lows for many commodities and, thus, indirectly increasing the level of deficiency payments. As noted earlier, the 1985 Food Security Act also dramatically lowered price supports, computing their levels as a moving average of past market prices with some bounded discretion on the part of the Secretary of Agriculture to set the actual price support at lower levels.

Finally, a number of general equilibrium analyses have been conducted to estimate the intersectoral effects of coupled transfer policies on the balance of the United States economy. One study concluded that the misallocation of resources and capital to agriculture depressed the productivity of other sectors of the United States economy, reducing American manufacturing exports by $7.5 billion and service exports by $3.4 billion. Another study estimated that the removal of all programs that distort agricultural production or constrain input use would increase 1991 GNP by $9.6 billion.

V. United States Agricultural Policies and the Rest of the World

Among the developed countries, the United States is far from unique in its treatment of agriculture. All 24 of the Organization for Economic Cooperation and Development (OECD) industrialized countries have a long and vibrant history of agriculture protection. Numerous studies have estimated gains and losses for other countries as well as for the United States. For the year 1986, it has been estimated that the global deadweight losses of farm policies totaled $40 billion annually. More recent studies by the OECD have suggested that this number is dramatically higher for later periods. These studies, of course, help establish the potential value of multilateral agricultural policy reform, which proved to be the most promising feature of as well as the greatest obstacle faced in the Uruguay Round of the General Agreement on Tariffs and Trade (GATT) negotiations that began in 1986. [See INTERNATIONAL AGRICULTURAL POLICY; MACRO-ECONOMICS OF WORLD AGRICULTURE; TARIFFS AND TRADE.]

Since the United States is a large producer of some commodities on the world market, its price supports and accumulation of stocks can conceivably result in short-run favorable consequences for all exporters of the commodity in question. Specifically, if the internal price supports are so high that they effectively eliminate the export market as a relevant alternative, all the benefits accrue to other exporting countries in the short run. Over much of the post-World War II period, the United States has behaved as a residual supplier on world markets of many major commodities, especially food grains, cotton, and feed grains.

However, to the extent that the price support programs and coupled subsidy transfers discussed earlier, as well as protection against import competition (such as quotas in the United States and variable levies in Europe), all induce greater production, world prices will be depressed. This result is particularly evident when the United States government sells unwanted stocks on the world market at less than the domestic price (through the Export Enhancement Program), makes concessional sales, or simply donates the food as aid (through PL480). These potential effects have been examined in a number of empirical analyses. For example, Roningen and Dixit estimate that eliminating United States agricultural policies would increase world dairy product prices by 23.5%, sugar by 22.8%, coarse grain by 11.6%, wheat by 10.6%, rice by 2.9%, ruminant meats by 3.8%, and nonruminant meats by 3%. This change would lead to corresponding costs for consumers and benefits for producers in the rest of the world.

Anderson and Tyers estimate that multilateral agricultural policy liberalization by all OECD countries would increase the world prices of dairy products by 90%, sugar by 22%, coarse grain by 3%, wheat by 25%, rice by 18%, ruminant meats by 43%, and

nonruminant meats by 10%. Although these price changes would result in costs for consumers and benefits for producers in the developing world, Anderson and Tyers estimate that the net welfare of developing countries would increase by 1%. Simultaneous policy liberalization by developing countries, however, would result in a net increase in developing country welfare of up to 64%.

One justification often expressed in support of price floors and public storage programs in the United States and in other industrialized countries is that these policies stabilize what would otherwise be an unacceptable domestic volatility in basic commodity prices, at least over the very short run. Ironically, these same policies amplify rather than dampen commodity price fluctuations on international markets. One glaring example of this phenomenon is the world sugar market. The European Community (EC) and the United States both protect their domestic sugar producers, for example, in the United States through price supports, tariffs, and import quotas. These policies have been estimated to have increased price instability in the residual world market for sugar by approximately 25%. Moreover, because the United States has been dominant in the world sugar trade, the imposition of import quotas has lowered world sugar prices.

Not surprisingly, European and United States sugar policies have also placed significant burdens of adjustment on many developing countries. The World Bank's 1986 World Development Report has estimated that sugar policies of industrialized countries cost developing countries about $7.4 billion in lost export revenues during 1983 and reduced their real incomes by about $2.1 billion. Given the domestic supply response to sugar and other substitutable products, and the zero treasury provision of the United States sugar program, even those developing countries who currently benefit can expect their quota levels and, thus, their values to slowly vanish. For world wheat prices, it has been estimated that the variability could be reduced by 48% if all countries were to end their subsidization of wheat. Tyers and Anderson, using a model simulating policy reform in more than a half dozen commodity markets, calculated that liberalization of agricultural policies of industrialized countries would substantially reduce the international price variability of major temperate-zone commodities: wheat by 33%, coarse grains by 10%, rice by 19%; sugar by 15%, and dairy products by 56%.

VI. Accounting for Predatory and Productive Policies

One measure of the degree of government intervention across commodity groups can be represented as a "producer subsidy equivalent" (PSE), the ratio of the total value of all public sector assistance to total farmer receipts. As shown in Table III, the degree of government involvement is most dramatic for products for which demand is inelastic, for example, sugar, milk, rice, and wheat. Feed grains have an intermediate level of support, whereas sectors with more elastic demands, such as soybeans and red meats, have the lowest level of support.

The decomposition of the public sector assistance into productive (PERT) and predatory (PEST) forms of government policy is also reported in Table III. The productive category includes all expenditures by the public sector that are expected to lower transaction costs and enhance the rate of economic growth, for example, public-good expenditures, information and marketing services, grades and standards inspections, crop insurance, public research, and extension. For the PEST category, all redistributive transfers from other segments of the economy to agricultural producers, for example, deficiency payments, price sup-

TABLE III

Productive versus Predatory Policy Interventions in U.S. Agriculture, 1982–1986 Average

Product	Producer subsidy equivalents		
	Total (%)	Productive (PERT) (%)	Predatory (PEST) (%)
Sugar	77.4	7.9	92.1
Milk	53.9	7.8	92.2
Rice	45.0	6.4	93.6
Wheat	36.5	13.5	86.5
Sorghum	31.5	14.5	85.5
Barley	28.8	20.9	79.1
Corn	27.1	17.7	82.3
Oats	7.6	61.6	38.4
Soybeans	8.5	74.3	25.7
Beef	8.7	55.5	44.5
Poultry	8.3	65.0	35.0
Pork	5.8	82.5	17.6
Average	24.6	35.6	64.4

Source: U.S. Department of Agriculture, "Estimates of Producer and Consumer Equivalents: Government Intervention in Agriculture." Economic Research Service, ATAD Staff Report No. AGES 880127, April, 1988.

ports, trade barriers, storage subsidies, input subsidies, and subsidized credit, are incorporated.

Note that the products with inelastic demands (sugar, milk, and rice) receive a lower proportion of their public support in the form of productive policies, whereas the products with elastic demand (soybeans and meats) receive a higher proportion of their support in the form of productive policies. The data are consistent with the view that coupled predatory policies are higher in sectors in which demand is inelastic and supply is very responsive to policies, and lower in sectors with highly elastic demand and low supply elasticities. As noted earlier, redistribution efficiency would argue for low supply elasticities, but the joint determination of PESTs and PERTs places more weight on policy-induced supply expansion. For some products that do not appear in Table III, for example, specialty perennial crops (e.g., oranges, lemons, grapes) for which demand is highly elastic but productivity and supply response are low, coupled predatory policies do not generally exist. Instead, for these specialty crops, producer organizations tax their members to finance the provision of local public goods.

For public-good investments and predatory coupled transfers, it has been shown that, if a productivity-enhancing policy harms producers because of highly inelastic demand and responsive supply but producers have more political clout than other interest groups, the amount of public-good investment will be inadequate. However, the political obstruction to public-good investments can be countered with subsidies that are tied to production, thus leading to less underinvestment in public goods than would otherwise be the case. In effect, since productive policies may harm members of special interest groups, compensation through predatory subsidies may offer a means of making the pursuit of the public interest politically viable. Transfers that seem only predatory at first glance may, in certain cases, actually be politically necessary if society is to approach more closely the optimal configuration of productive policies.

Even if demand is elastic and the "representative" producer benefits from the dissemination of an advance, producers are likely to be heterogeneous in new technology adoption. Those producers who make the greatest use of the new technology will gain from its dissemination and the associated equilibrium price decrease, whereas others who make little or no use of the technology are likely to lose. Indeed, nonadopters always lose when the demand curve is anything less than perfectly elastic. In this setting, the key is not the elasticity of demand, but the heterogeneity of producers in their ability to take advantage of technical advances. If sufficient numbers of these heterogeneous producers are harmed by the equilibrium effects of technological changes, then potential political impediments to future technical advances may arise. If so, some promise of wealth transfers from the winning consumers or taxpayers to the losing producers will be necessary to have any advance at all. It has been shown that wealth transfers tied to output may be a more effective means than per-firm lump-sum payments in inducing defection from the coalition of those producers least harmed by the technical change. Price-distorting payments target producers who, although harmed by the technology dissemination policy alone, expand their production the most.

A recent study supporting this perspective has examined PEST transfers and PERT investments in agricultural research for 17 countries. The evidence is revealed in Fig. 1, which shows that the ratio of PERT to PEST transfers unambiguously increases with country income levels. In Fig. 2, productivity measured by value added per agricultural worker is related to the mix of PEST and PERT expenditures. This result suggests that one reason for the record of strong productivity growth in developed country agriculture is that, despite a strong tendency toward increased protection, a complementary tendency exists toward support for agricultural research. The complementary provision of PEST and PERT policies provides a consistent explanation for the distinctly different patterns found in developed versus developing countries. Developed countries typically protect their agricultural sectors while investing more in agricultural research and generating higher levels of agricultural productiv-

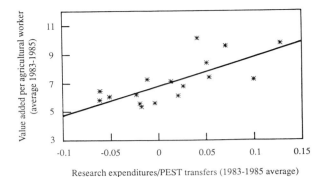

FIGURE 2 Value added per agricultural worker versus research expenditure/PEST transfers.

ity, whereas developing countries typically tax their agricultural sectors, invest little in agricultural research, and experience generally low levels of agricultural productivity.

VII. The Search for Politically Robust Reform

Far too frequently the economics profession has examined PEST policies as though they were separate from other policies, explaining their existence by the relative influence of interest groups or the opaqueness of the policy impacts. For the United States agricultural sector, however, one of the major messages is that policies can be packaged so vested interests may acquiesce to one policy setting in exchange for another. This observation applies not only to United States agricultural policy, but to all types of public-sector activities including privatization with safeguards for some social groups in formerly command economies, urban planning and the granting of zoning variances in exchange for the supply of local public goods, and special worker adjustment compensation for industries facing increased international competition.

The challenge for economists in agricultural policy, as in other areas, is to identify policy reforms that make economic sense and are politically robust. In the past, the best the economic literature has been able to offer in the design of democratic decision-making frameworks is to *separate* the processes for productive and predatory policies. However, whatever the issues of analytical convenience, researchers are now recognizing that political and economic forces must be jointly considered in matters of both design and implementation of public policies. Much

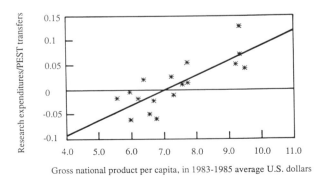

FIGURE 1 Research expenditures/PEST transfers versus per-capita gross national product for 17 countries.

recent investigation has been devoted to theoretical and empirical models of public sector decision making in an attempt to accomplish this task.

Economists have only begun to scratch the surface in the development of operational frameworks for blending productive and rent-seeking policies. In general, work in this area must recognize that these two types of policies go hand in hand; frequently, predatory policies are offered as compensation to those that are harmed as a result of the implementation of productive policies. Just as frequently, productive, or what may only appear to be PERT, policies are structured to mask the redistributive mechanisms put in place by PEST policies, for example, conservation and commodity subsidies, food security and self-sufficiency, instability and subsidized public storage, and so on. Further, PERT policies with concentrated benefits but widely shared cost profiles naturally evolve into PEST policies, especially when the power of the few persists and/or vested interests are relatively homogeneous. Even if the initial conditions do not satisfy these characteristics, policies can solidify and, in some instances, create interest groups whose political influence grows over time. Therefore, of course, the political-economic costs of removing policy distortions can be dramatically different from the cost of their original implementation. These asymmetric costs can result in policy irreversibilities; unfortunately, a consequence is generally swept aside when the original policy intervention is evaluated. Finally, the special advantages offered to those groups seeking PEST transfers that face highly inelastic demand and supply relationships must be tempered by the impact of PERTs on production possibility frontiers.

Operational prescription must recognize not only the economics of various policies, but also how the distribution of political power will affect the sequence of policy steps. The distribution of political power will often be critical in reforming policies to be more productive and less predatory. Situations will arise in which the political timing may be especially ripe, perhaps because of an economic crisis caused by outside factors, to change the institutional structure of agricultural programs. This was certainly true in the mid-1980s when macroeconomic and international phenomena helped spawn a crisis in the United States agricultural sector. In the midst of this crisis, political entrepreneurship emerged that led to some governmental autonomy in the design of the 1985 Food Security Act as well as the subsequent 1990 Farm Act. The lowering of economic barriers and the enhanced planning flexibility introduced by these two pieces

of legislation cannot be explained by the pure rent-seeking or predatory models of governmental intervention found in the literature.

Opportunities for restructuring the tradeoff between the *public* and *special* interests have often appeared greatest during times of economic crisis. However, the sustainability of the restructured tradeoffs and the new mix of productive and predatory policies has been shown time and time again to depend critically on changes in the underlying institutional configuration. In the case of United States agricultural policy, examples of institutional changes that could alter the level and distribution of political power might arise from the recently concluded GATT negotiations. In the Uruguay Round of the GATT negotiations, it was accepted early by all parties that distortionary trade policies in agriculture exist to rationalize internal country policies; thus, both sets of policies should be included in the negotiations. Accordingly, numerous proposals were tabled in Geneva for reducing internal country-coupled PEST policies and substituting PERT policies. For the United States government, this substitution process has been proposed to occur over a 10-yr adjustment period. Therefore, the interest-group configuration after the completion of the GATT negotiations could be dramatically different than the political landscape that has existed over much of the previous 60 yr or so. Agriculture will no longer be compartmentalized. Agricultural sector issues will be linked with other trade issues, thus widening the vested interests that will determine whether a GATT agricultural code is accepted or rejected. If the GATT agreement is accepted by the Congress, the executive branch will, no doubt, lean on the external code as a basis for creditable commitments to achieving more PERTs in exchange for fewer PESTS.

In the grand scheme, the major policy issue is whether society can achieve more PERTs in exchange for fewer PESTs. In the case of United States agriculture, although the PERT/PEST balance over the last two centuries may have been positive, as the years have unfolded it has become increasingly less so. Short of an external GATT agricultural code, the actual process of reversing this trend will depend on those interests that have access to the policy-making process, the space of issues over which those interests can negotiate, the degree of consensus that is sufficient to complete negotiations, and the appropriate course of action if negotiations break down. For example, simply changing congressional seniority rules would significantly alter access power. Many of the commodities that enjoy the greatest amount of PEST transfers can be characterized as southern crops. Changing the relative cost of organizing those who benefit from reforms will increase their responsiveness to changes in their welfare. This will alter incentives for access which, in turn, can be expected to result in fewer PESTs for a given level of PERT expenditures. Creative packaging of PESTs and PERTs can, in effect, change the political technology by demonstrating the feasibility of alternative, more efficient programs of wealth transfer. This change often requires political entrepreneurship, that is, leaders who become essential players by being part of any consensus or admissible coalition supporting reform. In the final analysis, designing mixes of PERTs and PESTs to generate greater efficiency and improved equity will not be sustainable without altering the policy-making process.

Bibliography

Anderson, K., and Tyers, R. (1990). How developing countries would gain from agricultural trade liberalization in the Uruguay round. *In* "Agricultural Trade Liberalization: Implications for Developing Countries" (I. Goldin and O. Knudsen, eds.), pp. 41–76. The World Bank, Washington, D.C.

Gardner, B. L. (1983). Efficient redistribution through commodity markets. *Am. J. Agric. Econ.* **65,** 225–234.

Rausser, G. C. (1974). Technological change, production, and investment in natural resource industries. *Am. Econ. Rev.* **64,** 1049–1059.

Rausser, G. C. (1982). Political economic markets: PESTs and PERTs in food and agriculture. *Am. J. Agric. Econ.* **64,** 821–833.

Rausser, G. C., and de Gorter, H. (1989). Endogenizing policy in models of agricultural markets. *In* "Agriculture and Governments in an Interdependent World" (A. Maunder and A. Valdés, eds.), pp. 259–274. Oxford University Press, Oxford.

Rausser, G. C., and Foster, W. E. (1990). Political preference functions and public policy reform. *Am. J. Agric. Econ.* **72,** 642–662.

Rausser, G. C., and Zusman, P. (1992). Public policy: Explanation and constitutional prescription. *Am. J. Agric. Econ.* **74,** 247–257.

Roningen, V. O., and Dixit, P. M. (1989). "Economic Implications of Agricultural Policy Reform in Industrial Market Economics." U.S. Department of Agriculture Staff Report, U.S.D.A., Washington, D. C.

Ruttan, V. W. (1982). "Agricultural Research Policy." University of Minnesota Press, Minneapolis.

Tyers, R., and Anderson, K. (1986). Distortions in world food markets: A quantitative assessment. Paper prepared for the World Bank, "World Development Report 1986." Washington, D. C., 1986.

United States Department of Agriculture (1988). "Estimates of Producer and Consumer Equivalents: Government Intervention in Agriculture," Report No. AGES 880127. U.S.D.A. Economic Research Service, Washington, D.C.

United States Department of Agriculture (1989). "Economic Indicators of the Farm Sector: National Financial Summary, 1989." U.S.D.A. Economic Research Service, Washington, D.C.

Grain, Feed, and Crop Storage

WILLIAM E. MUIR, *University of Manitoba*

Glossary

Aeration Process of ventilating stored grain with outdoor air to bring the grain to a uniform temperature that is near the ambient-air temperature

Drying front Develops and passes through a layer of grain being dried by passing air through it. The drying front is where grain moisture evaporates into the passing air

Equilibrium moisture content Moisture content of the product when it is in equilibrium with the relative humidity and temperature of the surrounding air

Structural loads On a grain bin are the forces applied to the building structure by the action of gravity on the stored products. Other structural loads include the forces of wind, snow, and the mass of the building itself

Storage ecosystem A bulk of stored material where the living organisms, seeds, fungi, insects, etc., interact with each other and with the nonliving environment; temperature, moisture, oxygen, etc.

Temperature front When air is passed through a grain bulk (e.g. aeration) a temperature front develops where the grain temperature comes into equilibrium with the temperature of the air

The expanding human population throughout the world depends on the safe storage of cereal grains, oilseeds, and legumes for a continuing supply of food between harvests. The stored grain must be adequately protected from the destructive or contaminating action of insects, mites, microorganisms, and rodents. Because biological, chemical, and physical variables all interact in grain storages, an integrated, multidisciplinary knowledge base has been developed by workers in agricultural engineering, ecology, entomology, mycology, mycotoxicology, and plant pathology.

I. Introduction

A. Importance and Need for Crop Storage

The cereal grains wheat, rice, corn, and barley are the major sources for human food and animal feed throughout the world. All cereal grains and oilseeds are harvested at specific, short periods of a few weeks in producing regions of the world. Thus, to maintain a constant supply of food to the consumer, the harvested seeds must be stored for up to 1 year or more. Storage is also needed (1) to maintain seed for the next crop; (2) to maintain the crop as it is transported from producing areas to consumers in cities and in other countries; and (3) to maintain a supply for years when demand exceeds production which may have been reduced due to poor weather conditions.

In the United States and Australia the major portion (e.g., two-thirds in Kansas) of the storage space is in off-farm, centralized storages. While in Canada over three-fourths of the storage capacity is on the producing farms, and this ratio is even higher in subsistence-farming areas of the world such as India and China.

The objective of all storage systems is to maintain both the quantity and quality of the stored product, at as low a cost as possible. The quantity can be reduced when grain is consumed by insects or rodents or when losses occur from human theft, carelessness, or leakage. Quality can be measured by such variables as germination, nutritional value, baking characteristics, odor, flavor, contamination, and appearance. Quality can be reduced by the activity of insects, microorganisms, and rodents in the grain. In developed countries located in temperate climates, storage managers can prevent most storage losses with well-engineered drying and storing systems. Losses, however, can be significant in years having production and weather conditions favorable to insects; e.g., it has been estimated that in 1980, stored-grain insects cost U.S. wheat farmers about $30,000,000. In developing countries the losses may average about 10% and can be close to 100% in some specific situations.

B. The Storage Ecosystem

Any grain bulk, ranging from a 50-kg bag of rice stored in a home in India to a 2500-tonne steel bin of corn in Iowa, can be considered a man-made ecosystem. The living organisms in this ecosystem are the producers (the grain kernels) which are being attacked by consumers (insects, mites, and rodents) and decomposers (fungi and bacteria). These organisms interact among themselves and are affected by the temperature, relative humidity, and gaseous composition (CO_2, O_2, N_2, pheromones, odors, etc.) of the surrounding and intergranular (nonliving) environment. The major objective of the manager of the storage ecosystem is to control the nonliving environment so as to prevent the consumers and decomposers from spoiling the living grain. The remainder of this article describes the components of the storage ecosystem and techniques used to reduce the deterioration of stored crops.

II. Deterioration Processes and Quality Changes

A. Product Respiration

All living aerobic organisms respire. The respiration process of grain consumes stored food in the kernel and oxygen from the air and produces carbon dioxide, water, and heat. To prevent loss of the stored food in the kernel the respiration rate must be kept low by storing the grains at a low temperature and moisture content or for some products a low oxygen concentration. Because the products of respiration—moisture and heat—increase the rate of respiration, the deterio-

ration rate can increase rapidly if respiration is not kept low.

Similarly the respiration of the attacking organisms (e.g., insects and fungi), if unchecked, can cause an exponential increase in temperature and deterioration. For example, due to mold growth the temperature of a moist (23% moisture content) pocket of wheat increases in temperature from 3° to 9°C in the first 10 days, to 20°C in the next 10 days, and then a maximum of 65°C in the next 7 days.

B. Microorganisms

The major decomposers that attack stored grain are fungal species of *Penicillium*, *Aspergillus*, and *Fusarium*. For most of the species to grow, the grain or oilseeds must have a water activity of at least 0.65. Equivalent moisture contents vary according to the crop, e.g., 13% for wheat, a cereal grain, and 8% for canola, an oilseed. Fungi are the most common microorganisms in stored grain because other microorganisms require higher water activities, e.g., most bacteria require a water activity of 0.90 (22% moisture content wheat).

Stored-product fungi such as *Pencillium* spp. can grow slowly at temperatures down to about −5°C while others such as *A. fumagatus* can continue to grow up to about 60°C. Optimum growth occurs at between 20° and 40°C.

Because some fungi can slowly grow and spread throughout a grain bulk even at relatively low temperatures and moisture contents, the length of time the grain is stored significantly affects the rate of spoilage when conditions of the stored grain become favorable for rapid fungal growth. Damage to the seed coat during threshing, handling, or drying opens up fissures where the fungi can readily attack the kernel. Insects, mites, and rodents can increase fungal growth by spreading spores, producing water and heat, and damaging the seed coat.

C. Insects and Mites

Several species of insects attack stored products. Some of the common ones are Indian-meal moth, *Plodia interpunctella* (Hübner); Angoumois grain moth, *Sitotroga cerealella* (Olivier); granary weevil, *Sitophilus granarius* (L.); maize weevil, *Sitophilus zeamais* Motschulsky; red flour beetle, *Tribolium castaneum* (Herbst); and lesser grain borer, *Rhyzopertha dominica* (Fabricius).

Most insect species have an optimum temperature range around 30° to 35°C, a lower threshold for reproduction of about 20°C, and an upper threshold of about 40°C. Most insects die when exposed to temperatures below about −10°C or above about 60°C.

Most stored-product insects can do well in dry grain, e.g., down to about 10% moisture content in wheat. Thus, in dry, warm grain and in tropical climates the main spoilage agent is usually insects; while in moist, cool grain and in colder temperate climates the main concerns are fungal-induced spoilage and mites.

Mites are an important pest of moist, cool grain in the northern grain growing regions of North America, Europe, and Asia. Adult mites have eight legs (insects have six legs) and are usually less than 1 mm long. They consume grain, mold growing on the grain, or other mites. Mite pests such as the grain mite (*Acarus siro*) can feed and reproduce on grain down to 5°C with optimum conditions of about 23°C and 85% relative humidity. Mite populations can increase by 2500-fold per month compared with increases of 10- to 70-fold per month for stored-product insects.

D. Rodents

On a worldwide basis, rodents (rats and mice) destroy 3 to 5% of the grain produced. Rodents also contaminate stored grain with their droppings, urine, and hair and can spread several human diseases.

The number of rats or mice in an area depends mainly on the availability of food, water, and space, i.e., room for nesting and movement. Killing rats and mice by poisons, traps, or cats reduces the population for a short time but it can quickly return to its original level.

The best control procedures are to maintain clean buildings and surroundings and to remove all hiding places for the rodents to nest and live. Stored grains cannot be removed but, if possible, storage structures should be made rodent proof to prevent entrance of the rodents. Spilled grain and other food and water sources in and around storage ecosystems must be removed so as not to attract rodents.

III. Properties of Grain and Grain Bulks

A. Moisture Sorption

The moisture content of stored grains and oilseeds directly affects rates of deterioration by fungi, insects, and mites. Thus, the drying of grain is the most common method of controlling deterioration. Moisture

contents of seeds are usually expressed on a percentage wet-mass basis:

(mass of contained water/mass of dry matter and water) × 100%.

At very low moisture contents (0 to 5%) the moisture is held strongly in the kernel, mainly by chemical binding forces. As the moisture content increases, the water is held by weaker, intermolecular forces such as van der Waal forces. At higher moisture contents, (above about 23% for wheat) the additional moisture begins to act as free water. This free water is still within the kernels but no measurable energy is required to separate the water from the kernel dry matter.

Intergranular air surrounding the kernels will come into moisture equilibrium with the moisture in the kernels. If the kernels are at a high moisture content (above 23% for wheat) at which free water exists in the kernels then the air will come to a relative humidity of 100%. At lower moisture contents the equilibrium relative humidity drops below 100%. For wheat at about 14.5% or canola at about 8% moisture content and 20°C the equilibrium relative humidity is about 70%. Because most fungi and other microorganisms cannot grow when exposed to relative humidities of less than 65 to 70% relative humidity, the moisture content in equilibrium with 65 to 70% relative humidity is considered to be the maximum moisture content for safe storage. Equilibrium relative humidities increase with increasing grain temperatures; thus, moisture contents for safe storage decrease with increasing grain temperatures.

B. Heat and Moisture Movement within Stored Bulks

Stored bulks of grains and oilseeds consist of grain and intergranular air. Heat is transferred by thermal conduction through the kernels and the intergranular air spaces and by free convection within the bulk. In cool regions of the grain bulk cool, dense intergranular air is pulled downward by the force of gravity. In the warmer regions the warm, less-dense air is buoyed upward (like a boat in water) by the cool, dense air being pulled underneath it.

Moisture can move from moist grain to drier grain by molecular diffusion through the kernels and through the intergranular air spaces. The driving force for such movement is the difference in vapor pressure of the water in the wet and dry grain. The resistance to such movement is high and thus this movement is normally considered only for moisture movement within the kernel and between adjacent kernels. The more important mode of moisture transfer is the moisture movement in the free-convection air currents set up due to temperature gradients within the bulk.

C. Monitoring Stored Grain

1. Temperature

The condition of stored grain must be monitored regularly so that incipient spoilage can be detected and preservation treatments can be applied. The best method of monitoring is to regularly sample the grain bulk at several representative points. Extracting grain samples, however, is time consuming and can be dangerous or impossible in large bulks. Experienced farmers and storage managers depend on sensing a change in odor which usually accompanies stored-grain deterioration. This procedure, as with grain sampling, requires the person to enter the storage bins. This can be difficult and dangerous. Instruments which replace the human nose in detecting odor changes are too expensive and unreliable.

Two practical methods of monitoring the stored grain have been developed which detect the products of respiration of the organisms responsible for deterioration. Both fungi and insects respire and produce water, carbon dioxide, and heat. Temperature sensors (thermocouples or resistance thermometers) can be temporarily inserted into the grain bulk or permanently fixed throughout the bin. The sensors can be connected to a centrally located instrument for manual reading or automatic recording.

Temperature measuring equipment is relatively simple and inexpensive. Properly placed sensors can detect the cooling and drying fronts in ventilated bulks. Rapid spoilage throughout the bulk or rapid spoilage at or near the temperature sensor can be detected. Slow spoilage or localized spoilage 50 cm away from the sensor cannot be easily detected because of the low thermal diffusivity of grain. For this same reason, temperature readings are sometimes difficult or impossible to interpret. For example, readings in mid-winter of over 25°C may mean there is active spoilage or, because of the very slow rate of temperature change in an unaerated large bin, the grain is just cooling slowly without any spoilage.

Measurements of the concentration of carbon dioxide (CO_2) in the intergranular air are easier to interpret because any increase above the ambient concentration of 0.03% indicates undesirable respiration somewhere in the bulk. The other major advantage of CO_2 measurement is that the gas readily diffuses throughout the bulk from the spoilage pocket. Thus, many fewer sampling points are necessary than for direct grain sampling or temperature measurement. To sample the intergranular air, small-diameter plastic tubes must be run into the grain bulk. Gas samples can be measured with either a chemical indicator tube or an electronic sensing device.

IV. Physical Methods of Suppressing Deterioration Processes in Stored Products

A. Temperature Control

1. Unventilated Storages

The first factor that affects the temperature of stored grain is the temperature of the grain as it goes into storage. When grain is harvested with combines under sunny conditions the temperature of the grain going into storage can be about 8°C above the ambient air temperature. Thus, even in cool, temperate climates where spring seeded crops can be harvested in mid-August, the initial temperature of the stored grain can be 35° to 40°C. Such temperatures are conducive to rapid deterioration by fungi or insects.

An unventilated bin of warm grain exposed to cool atmospheric temperatures begins to cool from the walls inward. Grain has a low thermal diffusivity (approximately 10^7 m^2/s) which is about one-third of that for the insulating material, glasswool. Thus an equal volume of glasswool would cool by conduction three times faster than a bin of grain. Because of the time lag in temperature change the center of a 6-m diameter, cylindrical bin of grain can be warmer in mid-winter than in mid-summer. For similar reasons the diurnal fluctuations of atmospheric temperatures only affect the temperature of the outer 15 cm of grain. The free convection currents that develop in the intergranular air buoy the air upward in the warm center of a bulk cooling from the outside. This action results in the warmest pocket of grain in winter being located above the geometric center of the bulk, near its upper surface.

Temperatures of unventilated grain are affected mainly by the initial temperature of the stored grain, climatic conditions, bin size and shape, and bin wall material. The initial temperature of the grain may have a significant effect for less than 4 months in a

4-m-diameter bin but the effect can continue for 18 months in an 8-m-diameter bin.

Atmospheric temperature, solar radiation, wind velocity, and soil temperature affect temperatures in a free-standing grain bin. Increased wind velocity increases the rate of heat transfer between the air and the bin wall. Solar radiation causes the temperature of the bin wall to increase above the ambient air temperature. For example, the measured temperature at noon on the south facing wall of a galvanized steel bin filled with wheat rose to 45°C when the ambient air temperature was −10°C.

The diameter or width of free-standing bins of grain can have the greatest effect on grain temperatures. For example, under Canadian Prairie conditions, the temperature of wheat at the center of a 4-m-diameter steel bin stored at an initial temperature of 35°C falls to 0°C within 6 months while at the center of a 10-m-diameter bin the temperature remains above 20°C for 2 years and does not exhibit seasonal cycling.

Most free-standing, cylindrical bins have been manufactured from galvanized steel. Galvanized steel has a high absorptivity for solar radiation but has a low rate of radiant emission at bin wall temperatures. Thus, galvanized steel absorbs solar radiation and warms rapidly during the day but it cools slowly by radiation to the cool surroundings and cold sky when shaded from the sun and at night. Conversely, white paint has a low rate of absorption of solar radiation and has a high rate of radiant emission and thus maintains cooler grain temperatures.

The cooling rate of warm grain that has begun to cool from the walls inward can be increased by turning the grain. Stored grain is turned by transferring it from one bin to another. If, during turning, the grain is well mixed then all of the grain comes to the average grain temperature. The warm grain at the bin center mixes with the cool grain at the bin periphery. There is little heat transfer between the grain and ambient air during the turning process because the movement is usually rapid and the surface area of the grain stream exposed to the ambient air is relatively small.

2. Aerated Storages

Stored grain can be cooled rapidly and uniformly to the ambient air temperature by blowing ambient air through the grain. Grain aeration systems are usually designed for an airflow rate of 1 to 2 (L/s)/m³ of grain. As the air is pushed through the grain, a cooling front develops in the grain. At 1 (L/s)/m³ it can take about 200 h to cool the grain to the temperature of the entering air. Depending on the grain and air conditions the moisture content of the grain may be reduced by about 0.5%. After the cooling front moves through the grain, the fan can be turned off until the temperature difference between the ambient air and grain again increases to 5° to 10°C. In this manner the grain temperature can be maintained near the ambient air temperature. Aeration is normally an excellent means of cooling the grain to reduce the rate of deterioration and insect reproduction. By maintaining uniform temperatures throughout the grain bulk, aeration also reduces moisture migration due to temperature gradients and free convection currents in the intergranular air.

In some locations it is recommended that the grain be warmed by aeration as the ambient temperature rises. This may be necessary to prevent excessive condensation or frost forming on cold grain that is moved out of storage when or where the ambient air is warm and humid. This can occur, for example, when cold grain from the northern United States is moved down the Mississippi River for transfer to ocean-going ships in New Orleans.

In some locations grain is harvested in the spring or early summer when the ambient air temperature remains high. If the grain is harvested dry and at an initial temperature of 35°C or above, insect infestations may be controlled by the high grain temperatures. The reproduction rate of many stored-product insects is limited at such temperatures. Aerating the grain would only cool the grain to temperatures that are optimum for the insects. Grain stored at high temperatures must be inspected frequently; when the ambient air does drop to near 20°C in the late summer or autumn aeration can be used to rapidly cool the grain below the insects' optimum temperatures.

B. Moisture Content Control

1. Principles of Drying

The major method of preventing or reducing the rate of deterioration of stored grains, oilseeds, and other seeds is to dry them to a moisture content at which the growth of microorganisms and seed respiration are reduced to a minimum. Drying will also prevent the growth of mites and some insects. Some crops such as corn grown in midwestern United States are usually harvested at moisture contents above those safe for storage. In some regions where harvesting normally occurs in humid weather, e.g., Scotland, all of the harvested grain must be dried. Other crops, e.g., wheat, and in drier regions, e.g., North American prairie and Australia, the harvested grain is dried less frequently. [See Food Dehydration.]

Drying consists of two transport phenomena: (a) the transfer of thermal energy into the grain bulk and into individual kernels required to evaporate the moisture and, (b) the transfer of water vapor out of the kernels and grain bulk. Before harvest the maturing grain is dried by solar energy heating the kernels on the plant and by wind carrying away the moisture. During harvest many subsistence farmers continue using the same solar drying process. They spread the cut plants or threshed grain on an open, dry surface such as packed soil, brick, or asphalt. In mechanized farming systems, air forced through a layer or bulk of grain is used to carry in thermal energy and carry out the water vapor. Other possible means of supplying the required thermal energy include the use of microwaves or mixing the grain with a preheated granular material, e.g., sand or steel balls. In microwave drying the water vapor is usually removed from the bulk with a vacuum pump. Mixing the grain with a desiccant (e.g., silica gel, bentonite or previously overdried grain) is an alternative method of removing moisture from grain.

The rate of drying is determined by the rates of heat transfer into the kernels and moisture transfer out of the kernels and grain bulk. For the common air drying method these rates are increased by increasing the air temperature, lowering the vapor pressure of the air, and increasing the air velocity. During drying, however, the temperature of the grain must not increase above temperatures that damage the grain quality. Seed viability is damaged above 45°C while corn for milling can be heated to 60°C and corn for animal feed can be heated to 100°C.

2. Drying with High-Temperature Air

Systems for drying grain with high-temperature air consist of fans to move the air through the grain, a high-temperature heat source (usually natural gas, propane, or other fossil fuel burner), and equipment to move the grain into, through, and out of the drier. Batch driers dry a quantity of grain and then the heat is turned off while the grain is cooled with ambient air. After cooling the fan is stopped; the dry, cool grain is unloaded; and then the drier is refilled with a new batch of wet grain. Because the fan is off during the unloading and reloading, the capacity of the drier is reduced. This grain movement frequently requires human supervision. Batch driers, however, tend to be simple, lower capacity, and lower cost than continuous flow driers. In continuous flow driers the grain moves slowly through the drier at an automatically

controlled rate requiring less frequent human supervision.

The simplest driers of both types have the heated air blowing through a layer of grain with the same grain on one side of the layer always exposed to the hot air. This can result in heat damage and increased brittleness of the overheated kernels. In many types of batch driers the grain is recirculated and mixed to provide more uniform drying. In some continuous flow driers baffles are added to mix the grain as it moves through the drier.

The dry, hot grain must be cooled to near the ambient temperature before long-term storage. For cooling to occur in batch driers the heat source must be turned off while the fan blows ambient air through the grain. In continuous flow driers the hot, dry grain passes into a cooling section where ambient air is blown through the grain. The capacities of both driers can be increased by cooling the grain in a separate storage bin. For batch driers the heater and fan are then off only while the grain is being moved in and out of the drier. For continuous flow driers the capacity can be increased by using the cooling section as an added heated-air drying section.

Transferring the hot, dry grain to a bin and immediately cooling it with ambient air can remove up to another 1% moisture from the grain. If the grain is allowed to temper for 10 to 12 h in the bin before cooling, moisture at the centers of the kernels moves out toward the kernel surfaces. If the grain is then cooled, up to 2 or 3% moisture can be removed during this process called dryeration. By removing some moisture in the cooling bin the capacity of the high-temperature drier is increased because the grain can leave the drier at a higher moisture content. An added benefit, particularly with corn, is the reduction in the amount of brittle or broken kernels under the less severe drying conditions. High-temperature drying causes temperature and moisture content gradients within the kernel that result in stress cracks in the kernels. Stress cracking is also a major problem for high-temperature drying of rice. Special driers and techniques have been developed for rice so that the moisture is removed slowly and evenly.

New driers are being designed and built to improve energy efficiencies. Driers are available that recirculate some of the exiting hot air and cooling air so as to reduce the loss of sensible heat energy in the air.

3. Drying with Air at Near-Ambient Conditions

Grain in a storage bin can be slowly dried by blowing outside atmospheric air through the grain. The air is heated about 1° to 3°C as it passes through the fan and therefore is at near-ambient conditions. Sometimes the air is also heated a few degrees by electric heaters, fossil fuel burners, or solar collectors. Under most situations the airflow rate required to dry the grain adequately is at least 5 to 10 times greater than that needed for aeration. Stored grain is aerated with ambient air at 1 to 2 $(L/s)/m^3$ mainly for temperature control rather than for drying.

As drying with near-ambient air begins, two fronts and three zones can develop in the grain bulk. At the entrance of the air into the grain a zone develops where the grain is at the temperature of the air and is at a moisture content in equilibrium with the relative humidity of the entering air. Downstream from this zone is the drying front where thermal energy in the air evaporates moisture from the grain. Then there is a zone in which the grain is in equilibrium with the cooled, moisture-laden air leaving the drying front. There is then a second front, the temperature front, in which the cooled air comes into equilibrium with the initial temperature and moisture content of the grain. In this front, if the grain is initially warmer than the air, the air warms and picks up more moisture which is evaporated by the heat stored in the grain. In this temperature front the moisture content of the grain decreases by less than 1% depending on the grain and air conditions. Downstream from the temperature front the grain is at its initial temperature and moisture content. The temperature front, whose velocity depends mainly on the airflow rate, passes through the grain bulk relatively quickly (e.g., 15 h at an airflow of 12 $(L/s)/m^3$). The drying front moves much slower, taking a few to several weeks to pass through the bulk depending on several factors including airflow rate, the initial moisture content of the grain, and the temperature of the incoming air.

In near-ambient drying the condition of the entering air follows the diurnal and seasonal changes in weather. Although, for this reason, several minor fronts and zones can develop in the grain bulk, they tend to spread and become indistinguishable from the major ones described above. Frequently the conditions of the air entering the grain reduce its moisture content below the maximum limit for commercial sale. Because the grain is sold on a mass basis any moisture loss below this maximum limit represents a direct financial loss to the owner. The owner has less grain (and water) to sell and makes less money even though he is selling a better quality, more dense product that will store without deterioration for a longer period. Continuing to operate drying fans during rain or high humidity weather adds some moisture

back into the overdried grain and this air, dried by the grain continues moving the drying front through the bulk. Except during periods of high ambient relative humidity, adding extra heat to the air with a heater or solar collector usually increases the overdrying with only a small increase in the rate of drying.

The main design variable in planning a near-ambient drying system is the airflow rate. Both the initial capital cost of the fan and motor and the operating cost of the electrical energy consumed increase with airflow rate. The minimum airflow rate is selected to dry the grain before any unacceptable fungal spoilage occurs in the undried layers and within the maximum allowable drying time (determined by marketing plans and storage space). The fan size must be selected on the basis of the harvesting and drying conditions expected during the next several years that the fan will be used. At present, the only practical method of varying the airflow rate for an already installed fan and bin is to vary the depth of wet grain placed in the bin for drying.

4. Computer Models Used for Design and Management of Grain Driers

Mathematical models that simulate the drying of grain have been programmed for use on computers. The initial conditions of the grain are input to the models. The models then accurately predict the temperature, moisture content, kernel damage, and fungal deterioration of the grain based on the varying conditions of the entering air.

Computer models have been used to determine and compare the performance of various types of high-temperature driers. The effects of changes in drier design or operation can be quickly predicted without the long time delay and cost required to build and test different driers. Similar models operating on microprocessors connected directly to the drier provide better control of the drier than either simple thermostatic controls or manual controls.

Computer models of near-ambient, in-bin drying have been used to predict the minimum airflows required to dry grain. Usually the models are used to simulate drying and spoilage of the grain based on historic weather data for the past several years. The minimum airflow to complete drying without spoilage in the worst year can be selected. If some risk is acceptable, then the minimum airflow required to dry in a chosen percentage of the past years could be selected as a design for future years. Such a design based on some level of expected risk requires a well-informed storage manager.

C. Controlled Atmosphere Storage

Controlled atmosphere (CA) storage can limit the growth of insects, mites, and aerobic fungi by reducing the concentration of oxygen (O_2) and increasing the concentration of carbon dioxide (CO_2) or nitrogen (N_2) in the intergranular air. To control the intergranular atmosphere the storage unit must be made airtight and normally either CO_2 or N_2 is injected into the storage unit to displace the O_2.

Controlled atmospheres containing an elevated level of CO_2 (>60%) and a depleted level of O_2 (<10%) at low relative humidities (<50%) and high temperatures (>27°C) are lethal to most insect species that are responsible for losses in stored dry grain. The response may, however, vary depending upon the nature and size of the infestation, the life stages of the insects, and other storage conditions. Insects have the potential to develop resistance to controlled atmospheres, if controlled atmospheres are improperly used. Controlled atmospheres do not have any detrimental effect on functional characteristics of grains and they help to maintain seed germination and viability. Some deterioration of storage structures, especially concrete structures, may be caused by controlled atmosphere gases.

For higher moisture content grain (14 to 20% for wheat), in which the deterioration risk is mainly from microorganisms rather than insects, CA storage can also be somewhat beneficial. The grain viability and food quality can be preserved for several weeks but then anaerobic microorganisms can grow sufficiently to kill the grain and produce a fermented odor and taste. The nutritional value is preserved and animals prefer the higher moisture grain to the same grain stored dry.

V. Methods of Killing Stored-Crop Pests

A. Chemical Treatments

Chemicals have frequently been used to control insect pests in stored products. The two main types of pesticides are fumigants and residual contact pesticides. Fumigants are gaseous compounds that can diffuse through a grain bulk and kill most insects and some mites. The most common fumigant is hydrogen phosphide, PH_3. The fumigant is added to the grain in the solid form of aluminum phosphide which reacts with moisture in the intergranular air to form the toxic gas, hydrogen phosphide. The phosphide tablets are introduced and distributed throughout an infested grain bulk either by insertion directly into the stored bulk or by adding the tablets to the stream of grain as it is moved from one bin to another. Hydrogen phosphide gas is highly toxic to humans and other mammals but probably does not leave a toxic residue on the grain.

For a successful insect kill the infested grain must be fumigated in a gas-tight storage in which the fumigant concentration can be maintained for 10 days when the grain temperature is 5° to 12°C or 3 days when the grain temperature is above 20°C. Fumigants do not prevent reinfestation after treatment.

Residual contact pesticides, e.g., malathion, are sprayed into a stream of grain as it moves into storage. Insects are killed only if they come into contact with treated kernels. The effectiveness of the chemical can continue for several months depending on grain temperature and moisture content. Malathion has a low toxicity to humans and other mammals.

The use of both types of chemicals is declining because of the increasing resistance of insects to the chemicals and the possible risks to human health.

The growth of microorganisms (fungi, bacteria, etc.) on damp or high moisture grain can be reduced or prevented by treating the grain with chemical preservatives. Preservatives that have been used include propionic acid, formic acid, ammonia, and sulfur dioxide. Treating grain with such chemicals eliminates the need for drying or preserves the grain until it can be dried. Normally, treated grain is used for animal feed.

B. Other Treatment Methods

Stored-product insects can be killed instantly by cooling the grain to below −20°C or warming the grain to above 60°C. Temperatures below 17°C stop insect reproduction, and below −10°C stop microorganism growth.

Some subsistence farmers add inert dusts, e.g., diatomaceous earths or activated clays, to control insects. The dusts cannot be completely removed from the grain, leaving a gritty feel or taste, but they are considered nontoxic to warm-blooded animals. The dusts are not suitable for commercial facilities because they can damage grain handling equipment and they can create a dusty environment which is unhealthy for grain handlers. Other natural products that have been used to preserve stored grain include: oils from peels of various fruits, vegetable oils, sorbic acid from the fruit of mountain ash trees, and hot peppers.

Insects in stored grain can be sterilized by passing the grain in a thin layer through a beam of high-energy electrons. Advantages include: no harmful chemical residues, no danger to equipment operators, nutritional value is unaffected, and the grain temperature is increased less than 0.1°C. Disadvantages include: the sterilized insects may continue to live for several weeks, it provides no residual protection for the grain, and the seed is killed. Because of their high capital costs these grain treatment units can be economical only when a steady, high throughput for several years can be expected.

VI. Health Hazards

A. Mycotoxins

Mycotoxins are poisonous substances that are produced by some strains of fungi which grow on stored grains, other foods, and animal feed. The most familiar mycotoxin is aflatoxin which is produced by the fungi, *A. flavus*. Aflatoxin has been most frequently detected on peanuts but has also been detected on corn, rice, barley, and sorghum seeds. Other mycotoxins including vomitoxin, zearalenone, and ochratoxin can be produced by other fungi such as *Penicillium* spp. and *Fusarium* spp. The fungi can grow on grain without producing mycotoxins. Furthermore, the poisons cannot be easily detected or removed from the grain; thus, the best control method is to prevent fungal growth by storing the grain dry and cool.

Extremely low concentrations of mycotoxins can induce a wide variety of symptoms in animals and humans. These include swollen vulvae, shrunken testes, abortions, slow growth rate, liver and kidney damage, and ultimately death.

B. Respiratory Diseases

A recent study of grain farmers in Canada found that 80% had varying forms of respiratory diseases. An earlier study found that about 10% of both farmers and grain handlers had symptoms of Farmers Lung syndrome. The symptoms are similar to those of pneumonia and include a fever, profuse sweating, marked weakness, and breathlessness. These symptoms occur after the person works with or is exposed to dust from moldy grain or hay. The symptoms can last from 2 to 30 days and may require hospitalization.

The symptoms tend to increase with repeated exposure to moldy grain or hay and can occur in persons of all ages. Both fungi and mites in moldy grain trigger the allergic reaction. The disease causes permanent damage to the lung.

Another respiratory hazard of working with dusty grain and feed is called Toxic Organic Dust syndrome. The symptoms are similar to Farmers Lung but most people recover with no permanent damage or increased future risk.

C. Entrapment and Suffocation in Grain Bulks

In the state of Indiana from 1964 to 1978 entrapment and suffocation in grain bulks caused two to three deaths per year and 40% of the accidents involved children less than 15 years old. Victims on the top surface of a grain bulk can be pulled into and become submerged while grain is being emptied out from the bottom of the bin or transport vehicle. Victims, specially young children, can be playing in a bin or in the box of a transport vehicle and be accidently covered with grain during filling.

Persons have survived entrapment and have been successfully extricated. The risk of suffocation can be reduced if the victim can get his hands over his nose and mouth before he becomes submerged. If the accident occurs in a bin with forced ventilation, the fan should be turned on to provide air to the victim. The rescuers must attempt to remove the grain sideways from the victim without pulling the victim further into the bulk. In many storage structures this can be accomplished by cutting openings in the sides of the bin.

VII. Structural Loads Exerted by Stored Grain

A. Static Loads

The structural design of grain storages is based on the loads exerted by wind, snow, and the stored grain. For free-standing, cylindrical bins wind loads on the empty structure can lift and overturn the bin. For rectangular buildings with bulk storage the negative air pressures on the leeward side must be added to the outward pressures of the grain. Snow loads on roofs depend on the predicted snow accumulations and roof shape. [*See* STRUCTURES.]

Stored grain is a granular material that is considered to be a semi-fluid because, like a fluid, grain exerts lateral pressures outward against the walls. Unlike a fluid and similar to a solid grain exerts a vertical friction load on bin walls.

The American Society of Agricultural Engineers has developed a standard procedure for predicting loads in grain bins. The static loads exerted by the grain on the walls and floor are calculated as functions of bin dimensions, grain bulk density, and friction between kernels and between kernels and the wall material.

B. Dynamic Loads

Grain exerts different dynamic loads when the bin is being filled or emptied. Structural loads during filling are similar to static loads; however, loads during emptying can be much larger and can cause the bin walls to fail.

During the emptying of deep bins, where the height of the bin is more than twice the diameter, all the grain moves downward together in plug (or mass) flow. In shallower bins the grain develops a funnel directly above the emptying port. The top surface forms into an inverted cone and the grain flows down the top surface and then down a vertical "pipe" to the outlet. The bin actually empties from the top downward. The dynamic loads during "funnel emptying" are similar to the static loads. A general recommendation is that loads during plug flow can be 1.4 times higher than those during static storage. Some researchers, however, have measured dynamic loads greater than 4 times static loads.

C. Other Grain Loads

Thermally induced loads occur in thin-metal walls of bins when the temperature of the ambient air or bin wall decreases. The metal attempts to contract, reducing the circumference and diameter of the bin. The grain in the bin resists this contraction causing increased lateral pressures against the wall of up to 15% during a 20°C temperature drop per hour.

Grain kernels ventilated with moist air can absorb moisture and expand. The expansion of the kernels and the bulk are restrained by the bin walls and the mass of grain above. Limited experimental work has indicated that the wall pressures may increase by 6 times for a 2% increase in moisture content and 11 times for a 10% increase in moisture content. Such increased loads could cause structural failures; therefore, it is usually recommended that during in-bin

aeration or drying care must be taken to prevent large increases in grain moisture content.

VIII. Integrated Management of Stored Grain

Farmers producing and storing grains and oilseeds must integrate a wide range of knowledge from experts in several different disciplines. When managing stored grain, farmers and other grain storage managers must use knowledge from agricultural engineering, entomology, mycology, chemistry, and economics. The future development of knowledge-based systems or expert systems on microcomputers is one possible method of collecting, organizing, and transferring diverse knowledge from several experts to farmers in a readily accessible and user-friendly format.

Expert systems are computer programs that store both qualitative and quantitative information. Frequently the information is in the form of rules. A simple rule could be: If the date is September and if the temperature of the stored grain is above 25°C and if the weather forecast is for temperatures below 20°C then aerate the grain for 3 days. Thus, an expert system for grain storage managers would be a computer program that provides the manager with the practical, situation-specific information needed in deciding on day to day strategies to manage and operate storage facilities.

A manager using the program would, at the time of filling his bins, input to the program descriptions of his bins, his grain treatment facilities, and the grain put into the bins. The manager would also input his management objectives and quality criteria. These could include expected storage period and use for the grain, final moisture content, and acceptable risk of spoilage. The program would have in its memory such information as historic climate data for the location, performance of available drying fans, characteristics of available pesticides, etc. The computer, through direct connections to weather stations and monitoring instruments in the stored grain, could be continuously recording, in real time, the weather conditions, available weather forecasts, and conditions of the stored grain.

Mathematical models that can simulate heat, moisture, and gas transfer through the grain, insect and mite populations, and grain quality loss could be included in the expert system. Based on the present conditions and on both historical weather data and the weather forecast the models could be used to predict the effects and probabilities for success of various management decisions.

The expert system would compare the various possible scenarios and then use rules to output to the storage manager suggested actions or decisions. One of the important attributes of good expert systems is that the user can then ask the computer to explain or follow through the logic used to arrive at the recommendation. (This type of program is called an expert system because the rules and logic patterns stored in the program are obtained by the computer programmer from experts such as agricultural engineers, entomologists, agricultural extension personnel, and successful storage managers.) The expert system could ask the user for additional information on the present and predicted conditions of the grain, and could indicate the need and timing of future monitoring of the stored grain, and then tell the manager when to next consult the computer program.

As the world recognizes the human and commercial value of stored grain to feed the hungry people of the world, more effort will go into maintaining the quality and quantities of the food grains already being produced each year. The interdisciplinary knowledge needed to economically preserve stored grains, oilseeds, and legumes will have to be developed further and will be transferred to storage managers throughout the world.

Bibliography

Gwinner, J., Harnisch, R., and Mück, O. (1990). "Manual on the Prevention of Post-Harvest Grain Losses." Deutsche Gesellschaft für Technische Zusammenarbeit, Eschborn, FRG.

Jayas, D. S., White, N. D. G., Muir, W. E., and Sinha, R. N. (eds.) (1994). "Stored Grain Ecosystems." Marcel Dekker, New York.

Mills, J. T. (1989). "Spoilage and Heating of Stored Agricultural Products: Prevention, Detection and Control." Agriculture Canada, Ottawa.

Multon, J. L. (ed.) (1988). "Preservation and Storage of Grains, Seeds, and Their By-Products." Lavoisier, New York.

Nash, M. J. (1985). "Crop Conservation and Storage in Cool Temperate Climates," 2nd ed. Pergamon, New York.

Olesen, H. T. (1987). "Grain Drying." Innovation Development Engineering, Thisted, Denmark.

Sanderson, D. B., Muir, W. E., and Sinha, R. N. (1988). Moisture contents within bulks of wheat ventilated with near-ambient air: Experimental results. *J. Agric. Eng. Res.* **40**(1), 45–55.

Sauer, D. B. (ed.) (1992). "Storage of Cereal Grains and Their Products," 4th ed. American Association of Cereal Chemists, St. Paul, MN.

Sinha, R. N., and Watters, F. L. (1985). "Insect Pests of Flour Mills, Grain Elevators, and Feed Mills and Their Control." Agriculture Canada, Ottawa.

Yaciuk, G., Muir, W. E., and Sinha, R. N. (1975). A simulation model of temperatures in stored grain. *J. Agric. Eng. Res.* **20**, 245–258.

Ground Water

SCOTT R. YATES, *USDA-ARS, U.S. Salinity Laboratory, Riverside, California*

MARYLYNN V. YATES, *University of California, Riverside*

Glossary

Aquifer, aquitard, aquiclude Terms used to indicate the decreasing ability of a geologic material (or formation) to transmit significant amounts of water under normal conditions (forces, gradients)

Hydraulic conductivity Rate at which water can move through a soil or an aquifer under a unit hydraulic gradient

Soil root zone Biologically active zone extending from the soil surface to approximately 1 m depth

Storativity Volume of water that a unit volume of aquifer releases from storage when the hydraulic head is reduced by a unit length. For example, the specific storage of an aquifer that releases 0.1 m^3 of water from 1-m^3 of aquifer material after the hydraulic head is reduced 1 m is 0.1 m^{-1}

Transmissivity Rate at which water moves through an aquifer under a unit gradient; equivalent to the product of the hydraulic conductivity and the aquifer thickness

Vadose zone Aerated zone from approximately below the root zone to the upper-most aquifer

Water table Surface of an unconfined aquifer where the water pressure is atmospheric

Ground water is water located in the subsurface in fully saturated porous material. Ground water may occur in a geologic formation, which has confining zones (i.e., thick layers of clay or shale) above and below, where it is termed a confined aquifer, or it may have an unconfined upper boundary where it is

called a phreatic or water table aquifer. It may be located above a layer of soil which inhibits downward movement of water. In this case, the water is perched in a region of porous material that is generally unsaturated. Generally, water moves from the soil surface through the soil-root zone (depth: 0 to approximately 1 m) into the vadose zone. The vadose zone extends from just below the root zone to the ground-water table and is usually unsaturated, although local regions of saturation such as perched ground water may be located inside this zone. Separating the vadose zone and a water table aquifer is the capillary fringe. This is a zone which is at saturation, but the water is under a negative potential as it is in unsaturated soil. The capillary fringe has properties which make it difficult to fit it in either of the vadose or ground-water zones, as the capillary fringe is a transition between partially saturated porous media and fully saturated ground water. Ground water moves from high to low potential energy and from high to low elevation.

I. Importance of Ground Water to Agriculture

Over the past 40 years, the yields of agricultural commodities have risen dramatically. For example, harvests of wheat, soybean, and cotton have risen by as much as 50% and corn by up to 125%. These increases are due in part to improved farm operating procedures, management practices, new techniques for pest control, and more efficient use of water. In arid areas, a significant factor for increased crop yields is a steady supply of irrigation water. [*See* WATER: CONTROL AND USE; WATER RESOURCES.]

Although hydrologists generally focus on water movement in the subsurface, it is recognized that both ground- and surface-water supplies are important and inseparable parts of our water supply system. In arid areas, lack of rainfall contributes to a reduced amount of surface water. Since surface water is often a source of recharge to ground water, the absence of surface water for a long period of time can cause lowering of ground-water tables and a reduction of ground-water supplies. In areas of abundant rainfall, ground water may feed into lakes and streams, keeping the water level in these surface water bodies relatively constant throughout the entire year. Abundant rainfall also provides water, through percolation, that keeps the ground-water level near the surface. It is important to recognize the interaction between ground and surface water when studying the use or contamination of ground water in agricultural areas.

For agriculture, there are two aspects of ground water which are of importance to those whose livelihood depend on growing crops. The first is ground-water quantity. In arid lands, profitability depends, in part, on sufficient amounts of relatively inexpensive water. In areas where there are no large quantities of surface water, ground water may be the principal source of water. To maintain crop yields over long time periods, however, ground water cannot be extracted at too great a rate: if the extraction rate far exceeds the rate of natural recharge, the ground-water resource will be depleted. This will have an effect on both agriculture and the people who live in agricultural areas, since without large surface-water sources nearby, ground water would also be the principal source of domestic drinking water.

The second issue of importance is ground-water quality. During the last 40 years, agriculture productivity has increased significantly, largely due to improvements in pesticides, seeds, fertilizers, equipment, and other management practices. Fertilizers and pesticides, in particular, can help to promote greater crop productivity relative to areas where they are not used. However, the detrimental effects from excessive pesticide and fertilizer use as well as other agricultural-induced effects can cause degradation of the quality of ground water. This can also have a negative effect on the persons using ground water for domestic drinking water. It has long been known that irrigation can cause accumulations of salts in soils, creating highly alkaline soils. Salinity now seriously affects productivity in about 20 to 30 million hectares or about 7% of the world's irrigated lands. The salinization of fertile croplands is between 1 and 1.5 million hectares per year. In the United States, it is estimated that 20 to 25% of all irrigated lands, about 4 million hectares, suffer from salinization. Salts are only one problem; toxic elements in agricultural return waters

can also pose extensive environmental problems. An example of this is the Kesterson Wildlife Refuge in California, where selenium concentrations have accumulated over time and have been detrimental to the fish and other aquatic wildlife. Therefore, management of our ground-water supplies requires the ability to determine quantities of water available for growing crops, the effects of extracting water from the ground-water supplies at the required rate, the cumulative effects on the ground water from pumping water throughout a basin, and determining the effects of agricultural management practices on ground-water quality.

A. Ground Water as a Source of Potable Water

Ground water is recognized as an important worldwide natural resource. In the United States, approximately 50% of the population and more than 90% of rural residents use ground water as their source of domestic drinking water. Ground water is the source for approximately 40% of the irrigation waters used in the United States and it is estimated that the total use of ground water for 1980 was approximately 90 billion gallons a day, triple the usage in 1950. As these figures indicate, ground water is a very important natural resource that will, without doubt, become more important in the future. Due to an extensive ground-water resource and the assumption that the soil would act as a perfect filter for percolating water, there was little concern for protecting the ground-water supply prior to the 1970s. More recently, however, there have been a large number of wells found to be contaminated, which has prompted more and more protective actions for our ground-water supplies. Recently documented problems from agricultural chemicals include nitrate and pesticide contamination of ground water.

II. Equations Describing Ground-Water Flow

Over the past several decades, there has been considerable work to develop a framework within which the ground water can be studied. This work has involved the development of methods for producing useful amounts of water as well as studying the effects of contaminant transport on the quality of ground water. A brief description of the important elements of ground-water flow follows.

It is difficult to study ground-water systems by direct observation. The cost of constructing wells to sample ground water is high. Therefore, mathematical models are used extensively to characterize the subsurface environment. This requires developing a framework in which the state of a ground-water system can be determined from the effects of anthropogenic or natural changes (e.g., due to pumping, transport of pollutants, global climate change, etc.). To achieve this, various relationships to describe the response of the groundwater system to changes in the forces acting upon it are needed.

Hydraulic potential is a way of expressing the energy status of water in porous media. It is easily recognized that water at the Earth's surface will move from higher to lower elevation in response to gravitational forces. This occurs because of differences in potential energy of the water at the higher elevation and movement will always occur from higher to lower potential energy in the same sense that a car with its engine off will roll down a hill. The same is true for ground water. Hydraulic head is a convenient way to express the potential energy of water, since the unit of hydraulic head is length and it can be determined by measuring the height of water above a datum (e.g., mean sea level). Hydraulic gradients represent the difference in the hydraulic potential over a given distance. The gradient indicates the direction and magnitude of the forces moving water.

Ground-water flow depends to a large extent on the local hydraulic conductivities. The hydraulic conductivity relates to the relative ease (or difficulty) with which water moves through the porous medium. Sandy soils are highly conductive, whereas clays have a very low conductivity. The hydraulic conductivity of porous material varies over many orders of magnitude (i.e., many factors of 10, such as from 10^{-10} to 10^{-2} cm/sec). This is a highly variable property of aquifers and this variability markedly affects the movement of water and contaminants contained within.

A. Darcy's Law

A fundamental relationship describing the movement of water is termed "Darcy's Law." Darcy's Law is an empirical description of the quantity of water that will move due to a difference in the hydraulic potential. In the original studies which led to Darcy's Law, a soil column was constructed to study the interaction between the hydraulic potential and the flow of water through a column. Darcy found that the flow of water

was proportional to the gradient of the hydraulic potential. He observed that for some soils water would pass through relatively quickly, for others much more slowly. For a given soil, however, a larger gradient would produce a proportionally larger flow. Doing this for many different soil types, Darcy found that a constant of proportionality could be introduced that would provide an equation that could be used to calculate the flow rate for a given soil type and hydraulic gradient. This constant proportionality is called the hydraulic conductivity and has the units of length per time. Further investigation with different liquids demonstrates that the hydraulic conductivity depends also on the type of liquid used. This relationship is of fundamental importance in characterizing the movement of water in soil and ground water. Darcy's Law is written as

$$q = -K\frac{dH}{dz},\tag{1}$$

where q is the specific discharge (units length/time), which is the amount of water moving through a unit cross-sectional area of a column; K is the hydraulic conductivity (units length/time); and dH/dz is the gradient of the hydraulic potential (unitless).

Using Darcy's Law the specific discharge or the amount of water moving through the porous medium can be determined. Darcy's Law is not particularly useful, however, in determining the areal effects on a large aquifer since this relationship is based on flow through a relatively small "control" volume. Aquifers have a large areal extent, complex geologic features, layers, and boundaries, all of which preclude the use of such a simple relationship to fully characterize the movement of water. One can consider Darcy's Law as an expression relating flow in and through a "control" volume, which has a relatively small size such that the values for the gradient and conductivity are relatively uniform inside the volume and the flow rate is at steady state. An aquifer, on the other hand, is made up of many "control" volumes where locally Darcy's Law is valid. Also, an aquifer is rarely at steady state; therefore, the transient (time-dependent) nature of water movement must be considered. To fully describe the movement of water in an aquifer, a method is needed to combine the control volumes together in a consistent, mass-conserving manner.

B. Mass or Energy Conservation

To derive equations that would allow determining the areal effects on ground water from a pumping water well requires the use of a method for integrating the effects of all the control volumes while maintaining mass conservation. The basic statement of mass conservation is that the time rate of change of any physical quantity is equal to the amount that enters minus what leaves the control volume, minus what is lost from the control volume (i.e., from alteration or extraction), plus whatever is produced in the control volume (i.e., any sources). Generally, for ground-water systems, the only loss mechanism is from ground-water pumping; this could be stated more simply as: the change in storage of water is equal to the water that flows into the control volume minus the water that flows out of the control volume, minus any water pumped from the control volume. Incorporating Darcy's Law into the mass conservation equation produces a partial differential equation which can be solved using initial and boundary conditions to determine the effects of changes in the environmental conditions on ground-water flow:

$$S_s \frac{\partial H}{\partial t} = \frac{\partial}{\partial x}\left(K_x \frac{\partial H}{\partial x}\right) + \frac{\partial}{\partial y}\left(K_y \frac{\partial H}{\partial y}\right) + \frac{\partial}{\partial z}\left(K_z \frac{\partial H}{\partial z}\right). \quad (2)$$

In Eq. (2), it has been assumed that the aquifer and water are both incompressible, that there are no other liquid phases present and that the ground water is under isothermal conditions.

To develop equations which can be used to solve problems, Eq. (2) must be integrated for a specific set of initial and boundary conditions. These conditions are determined by the physical configuration of the aquifer and its initial status. The integration process connects the control volumes together and produces an equation that describes the overall effects throughout the aquifer. A solution to Eq. (2) is said to be unique, that is, there is only one solution for a given set of assumptions (used to produce the governing equation) and initial and boundary conditions (from the physical system).

III. Well Hydraulics

One of the important methods for determining the effects on the ground-water supply from pumping is called the "Theis method." This equation provides a means for determining the draw-down of the potentiometric surface (i.e., the potential water-table level if no confining layer was present) in a confined aquifer due to extracting ground water. To use this equation, certain information such as the storage capacity of the aquifer and the conductivity or the transmissivity of the aquifer must be known. Once this information has been obtained, the shape of the potential water-table profile can be estimated at any radial distance from the well to determine the effects on the potential water-table after pumping begins. The Theis method is a transient solution of the equation governing water flow; therefore, it provides information on the changes in the potential surface with time. This equation could be used to manage the ground-water supplies by limiting the amount of water pumped from ground water, so that excessive draw-downs do not occur. The Theis equation is one particular solution to the governing equation (Eq. (2)) of ground-water flow in aquifers. The Theis equation can be written as

$$h_o - h(r,t) = \frac{Q}{4\pi T}\int_u^\infty \frac{e^{-u}}{u}du = \frac{Q}{4\pi T}W(u) \quad (3)$$

with

$$u = \frac{r^2 S}{4Tt},$$

where $h_o - h(r,t)$ is the distance the potential water table has been lowered, (i.e., the draw-down), h_o is the potential ground-water surface before pumping begins, Q is the pumping rate, r is the radial distance away from the well, S is the aquifer storativity, T is the aquifer transmissivity, and t is the time after pumping begins. The techniques for obtaining this solution are beyond the scope of this discussion, but several assumptions concerning the aquifer configuration and ground-water flow are necessary to solve Eq. (2). It has been assumed that the flow of water is horizontal in the aquifer, the medium is homogeneous and isotropic, the thickness of the aquifer is a constant, the aquifer has infinite horizontal extent and no slope. The well is assumed to fully penetrate the aquifer and be open to the aquifer its entire extent and have an infinitesimal diameter.

Other solutions to the flow equation are available for different geometric configurations or initial and boundary conditions. For example, the Jacob's Straight-Line method can be used for larger times and situations where the confining layer is only partially impervious, and the Hantush-Jacob formula can be used for leaky aquifers with semi-impervious confining layers. Additional methods are available for cases where there is storage in the confining layer or where the well only partially penetrates the aquifer. Generally, as the initial and boundary conditions for the problem become more complex, the equation describing draw-down becomes more complex. For water table aquifers, obtaining equations to determine draw-down are especially difficult. Given sufficiently strict assumptions, however, equations similar to the Theis equations can be developed to determine the draw-down. Another important use of the Theis and related equations is that they can be used to determine the aquifer parameters. To do this, measurements of the draw-down in several observation wells located at different distances from the pumping well are needed. The aquifer parameters are adjusted until the mathematical solution for the draw-down closely matches the observed draw-downs. The aquifer parameters which produce the best fit are retained. A reference containing a complete discussion of pump tests is given in the Bibliography.

A. Draw-down

The simplest example of these concepts is draw-down in a confined aquifer due to pumping. Consider an aquifer, shown in Fig. 1, that is fully confined by impermeable layers above and below the aquifer. The aquifer thickness is $b = 20$ m, it has a hydraulic conductivity of 8.64 m/day (therefore the transmissivity is 172.8 m^2/day), a storativity of 0.001 (i.e., a specific yield of 5×10^{-5}), and initial head of 50 m. After one day, consider the effects of several different rates of pumping: $Q = 100$, 500, and 1000 m^3/day. In Fig. 2, the potential water-table surface, h, is shown as a function of the radial distance, r, away from the well. Clearly, as the pumping rate, Q, increases, so does the draw-down.

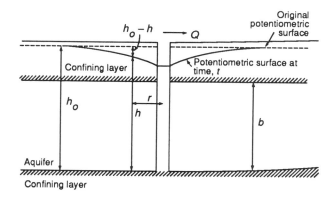

FIGURE 1 Fully penetrating well pumping from a confined aquifer. (Reprinted with the permission of Macmillan College Publishing Company from *Applied Hydrogeology*, 3/E by C. W. Fetter. Copyright © 1994 by Macmillan College Publishing Company, Inc.)

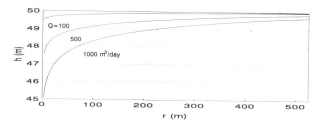

FIGURE 2 Potential water-table surface after pumping.

IV. Ground-Water Quality

Over the last 10 to 20 years, there has been more emphasis on protection of ground-water supplies from contamination than on developing new methods for optimizing ground-water yields. This is due, primarily, to the relatively advanced understanding of the principals of ground-water hydraulics, especially with regard to water extraction. The theory of transport of pollutants to and in ground water, however, is not nearly as advanced. This is due to the complex interactions between the contaminant and the subsurface environment.

Contamination of ground water from industrial and domestic pollutants has been recognized as a serious problem since the mid- to late 1970s. As ground-water monitoring programs have been initiated, more and more incidents of contamination have been reported. Results of EPA's survey of the quality of the nation's drinking water indicated that about 10% of community water system wells and 4% of rural domestic well water contained one or more pesticides; less than 1% of all wells were estimated to contain at least one pesticide in excess of the Maximum Contaminant Level (MCL) or Lifetime Health Advisory Level (HAL). There are several reasons for this. First, each year more waste products are being disposed of which increases the likelihood that contamination will occur. Second, chemical detection methods are constantly being refined which enable smaller and smaller amounts of a contaminant to be detected. For example, during the past few years, chemical analytical techniques were improved so that the concentration of certain chemicals could be detected at concentrations 100 million times lower than a few years before. Currently, some techniques are capable of detecting one part per quadrillion (ppq). This is roughly equivalent to locating a one-inch square stamp in the combined corn-belt states of Ohio, Indiana, Michigan, Illinois, and Wisconsin. Such large changes in the detection limit for a contaminant may give the perception that contamination is occurring more frequently when earlier monitoring studies may have had similar results if current technology had been available.

Generally, the source of the contamination can be classified as originating from a point in space or from a relatively uniform source over a large area; the latter is often termed nonpoint source pollution. Industrial pollutants such as from landfills, containment ponds, leaky storage tanks, injection wells, etc., are considered to be point sources. Agricultural fertilizers and pesticides that are used over large land areas and find their way into surface and/or ground water are classified as nonpoint sources of pollution. The use of agricultural chemicals is one of the most pervasive nonpoint sources of ground-water contamination. Each year approximately 661 million pounds of pesticides (active ingredients; 3.5 billion pounds of formulated pesticides) are used in agriculture. The first reported instances of ground-water contamination by pesticides occurred in 1979 where dibromochloropropane (DBCP) was detected in California and aldicarb in New York. Subsequently, monitoring found DBCP in four additional states. By 1983, ethylene dibromide (EDB) was found in wells located in 16 counties of California, Florida, Georgia, and Hawaii; this prompted suspension of the use of EDB in the United States. Fertilizers are also a large contributors to ground-water pollution: it is estimated that 20.5 million tons of fertilizers were applied to crops during 1988–1989.

Other nonpoint sources of pollution result from household septic-tank systems. Although each septic tank can be considered a point source, when aggregated over a community they have the characteristics of a nonpoint source. Because of the large number (greater than 22 million tanks with more than 1 trillion gallons of waste/year) of septic tanks used in the United States, disease outbreaks caused by these systems and elevated levels of nitrate in ground water caused by septic systems are of great concern.

There are large costs associated with environmental contamination. First, it is very difficult to accurately determine how and to what extent contamination injures an individual's health. Increased numbers of cancers due to exposure to low levels of pesticides have been reported but often it is difficult to determine whether pesticide exposure is the true source of the increased occurrence of cancers. Next, the costs associated with the degradation of the public's health are difficult to determine since it is often unclear whether an illness would have occurred anyway. The costs to remediate contaminated soils and ground water are extremely high. In the case of ground water, remediation may not be technologically feasible or economical. It may be more cost effective to install water purification systems for potable supplies rather than attempting to remediate the contaminated ground water supply *in situ*.

The problem is exacerbated by the large number of chemicals currently in use in the United States and the approximately 1000 new chemicals that are put into use each year. Pesticides, in particular (which include insecticides, herbicides, fungicides, nematicides, rodenticides, fumigants, desiccants, defoliants, growth regulators, and miticides), are composed of between 1200 and 1400 active ingredients, which make up about 50,000 end-use products. Given this number, and the fact that new pesticides are developed every year, it is very unlikely that adequate hazard evaluation will be made on more than few of these. [See PEST MANAGEMENT, CHEMICAL CONTROL.]

There are few studies on the economic impact of ground-water contamination. The few that do exist tend to concentrate on the direct costs of cleanup and neglect confounding issues such as how to put a value on ground water and whether this value is adequately reflected in the market place. It is difficult to determine associated costs such as the short- and long-term health effects, and to evaluate the lost value of the contaminated ground water or the increased cost (i.e., cost to those that must purchase it) of replacement sources of ground water. The Office of Technology Assessment has provided some estimates of the economic costs of contaminated ground water. Their simplified economic analysis included the costs due to losing a well, extension of water supply lines, lost plumbing, lost profits, cost of new well construction, or purchase of water. Even so, the reported losses ranged from 140,000 to 31 million dollars per year. It is likely that the costs would be considerably higher had additional direct and indirect costs been included in the economic analysis.

A. Physical Processes Affecting Solute Transport in Ground Water

Contaminants can enter aquifers by several different avenues. Contamination can occur as water containing contaminants percolates downward from a surface source or from sources in the shallow subsurface, or possibly directly from wells, which may result from a spilling or back-siphoning during chemigation or from pesticide cleaning or handing. Movement from the land surface to ground water can occur through preferential flow paths, such as biochannels (rootholes and wormholes), cracks, joints, and solution channels in the vadose zone. These may be the predominant pathways affecting ground-water contamination in many instances by providing a direct and rapid path to ground water. In some locations, the potential exists for water in contaminated shallow aquifers to move to deeper aquifers through existing improperly sealed or abandoned wells. Also, cross-contamination of adjacent aquifers might take place through the wellbore or outside the well casing in an unsealed annulus. It is difficult to incorporate many of these rapid-pathway mechanisms into models of transport, because of their localized nature, and to develop process models and supporting data for these processes and/or a lack of understanding of the mechanisms involved.

Contaminants in water can be transported great distances to public drinking water supplies or to discharge zones. The processes that affect transport of contaminants are highly complex, and many of them are not clearly understood. The processes can be divided into two groups: those responsible for producing the flux of materials that move through an aquifer and other mechanisms, often compound-specific, that either affect the rate of movement (i.e., adsorption) or reduce the contaminant level (i.e., degradation). *Advection* is one of the primary processes characterizing the movement of contaminants in ground water. Under advective conditions, the contamination is transported along with the ground water moving in the flow system and, in general, the contaminant can be considered to move in the same direction and at the same velocity as the ground water. This may not be true for materials that have vastly different density compared to water, where the vertical movement may be considerably different than water.

Hydrodynamic dispersion is a process that characterizes the spreading of a solute moving through porous material. There are three factors that contribute to the overall dispersion. At low ground-water velocities, the molecular diffusion can be important in the spreading process. At higher velocities, molecular diffusion also occurs but produces a small effect compared to mechanical mixing. At the pore scale, there is a variation in solute velocity depending on the location in the pore; a parabolic velocity distribution forms due to drag exerted on the fluid adjacent to the particle surfaces. Mechanical mixing causes a reduced concentration locally due to mixing of solute and the adjacent carrier fluid as the solute diverges and converges around particles making the porous medium. This occurs since a mass of water that splits and diverges as it moves around soil particles does not converge to the same orientation on the other side of the particles, thus causing the solute to spread. This can be seen in Fig. 3. Dispersion occurs both in the direction that water is flowing as well as transverse to that direction. Dispersion and advection are considered to be interrelated, where the dispersion is related to the variance of the velocity distribution. A consequence of ignoring the velocity distribution is the observance that the dispersion process appears to increase with increasing measurement scale. Even so, because of a lack of information, many times dispersion is assumed to be a constant for a given porous medium. Procedures for including scale-dependent dispersion in current models for simulating contamination transport at field-scale are generally recognized as a limiting factor of current models. There are many possible means for describing the scale-dependent dispersion process but, to date, there is no consensus on the best approach for doing this.

B. Other Contaminant-Specific Factors Affecting Ground-Water Quality

1. Pesticides

When assessing a pesticide's potential to contaminate ground water, both the mobility and the persistence of the pesticide must be considered. If a pesticide is very mobile, and is active for a long period of time, it has a high potential to contaminate ground water. On the other hand, if it is not mobile, and only persists for a short period of time, the potential for ground-water contamination is low (although it may be a candidate to contaminate surface water through runoff).

One of the most important factors determining the mobility of a pesticide is its solubility in water. When a pesticide enters the soil, it will adhere to the soil particles through a process called adsorption, and some will mix with the water that is present in the pores between the soil particles. The solubility of the pesticide determines the amount that will be present in the soil water, and thus be available for leaching. Solubility and adsorption are usually inversely related; therefore, pesticides that have a high solubility will be present in the soil water at a relatively high concentration compared to the amount that is adsorbed onto the soil particles. The affinity of a pesticide to adsorb to the soil can be expressed using the soil adsorption

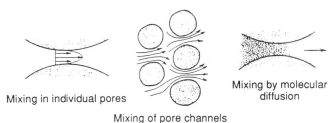

FIGURE 3 Processes of dispersion on a microscopic scale. (R. Allan Freeze/John A. Cherry, GROUNDWATER, © 1979, p. 76. Reprinted by permission of Prentice Hall, Englewood Cliffs, New Jersey.)

coefficient, K_{oc}. The smaller the K_{oc} value, the smaller the amount of pesticide adsorbed to the soil and the larger the amount in the water. Pesticides with small K_{oc} values are more likely to be leached through the soil than those with large K_{oc} values.

The persistence of a pesticide is generally expressed in terms of its half-life, sometimes written $t_{1/2}$. One half-life is the amount of time required for one-half of the mass of the pesticide to be degraded. After two half-lives, three-fourths of the pesticide will have been degraded; after three half-lives, seven-eighths will have been degraded, and so on. Pesticides can be degraded by many mechanisms, including chemical, physical, and biological processes. The half-life of a pesticide is reported in such a way as to reflect the process used to calculate that half-life. Examples include hydrolysis half-life (degradation by the chemical process of splitting the pesticide with water) and aerobic soil metabolism half-life (degradation by oxygen-requiring soil bacteria). The larger the half-life value, the greater the possibility that the pesticide can persist long enough to leach through the entire soil profile and reach the ground water.

In addition to the characteristics of the pesticide, soil properties are very important when determining the vulnerability of a site to ground-water contamination by a pesticide or other contaminant. The soil texture (i.e., the percentage sand, silt, and clay) affects pesticide leaching in two ways. Water, and any materials it contains, moves more slowly through clay soil than through soils with a high sand content. Clay particles also act to slow the movement of some pesticides by providing adsorption sites. Therefore, all other factors being equal, there tends to be less of a concern for ground-water contamination at sites with clayey soils than sandy soils. Also, soils with a high permeability lose applied water quickly through leaching. Pesticides applied to very permeable soils have a greater potential to contaminate ground water than if they are applied to less permeable soils. How-

ever, soils with low permeability have more problems with surface runoff that can lead to surface-water contamination by pesticides.

The organic matter content of soil is positively correlated with the adsorption of pesticides. Soils with high organic matter content would be less vulnerable to leaching than would soils with low organic matter content. Another benefit associated with high organic matter soils is that organic matter is required for microbial growth. Soil microorganisms are important in the degradation of many pesticides.

2. Nitrates

Nitrogen is an essential plant nutrient; thus, its use in agriculture is widespread. Since the 1940s, fertilizer application in the United States has increased from 1.8 million tons per year to approximately 20 million tons per year. Approximately 9 to 12 million tons of nitrogen is contained in the applied fertilizer. Nitrogen can exist in several different forms in the soil: as ammonia, as organic nitrogen, as nitrogen gas (which generally volatilizes out of the soil and into the atmosphere), and as nitrate. Nitrate is the soluble form of nitrogen, and it readily moves through the soil with percolating water. Under aerobic conditions, nitrogen in the soil is converted to the nitrate form. Any nitrogen that is applied in excess of the plant requirements and leaches below the root zone so that it is no longer available to plants has the potential to contaminate the underlying ground water with nitrate.

There are several sources of nitrogen to the soil in addition to agricultural fertilizer application. In certain areas, the geologic deposits are naturally high in nitrate. For example, nitrate–nitrogen concentrations as high as 300 mg liter^{-1} have been measured in the glacial till in the Great Plains of Alberta, Canada. Atmospheric deposition of nitrogen may be as high as 10 to 14 kg ha^{-1} year in some areas. The disposal of waste (human, animal, and crop residue) has been estimated to add 15 million tons of nitrogen to the soil every year in the United States.

The concerns over nitrate contamination of ground water are primarily focused on the susceptibility of very young infants (under the age of 6 months) to high concentrations of nitrate. The stomach of an infant is not as acidic as that of older individuals; thus, certain bacterial species that convert nitrate to nitrite proliferate. Hemoglobin is the molecule in the blood that carries oxygen. In the presence of nitrate, the iron in hemoglobin is oxidized from Fe^{+2} to Fe^{+3}, forming a molecule known as methemoglobin. Methemoglobin is not capable of binding oxygen; thus, oxygen cannot be carried throughout the body. Over time, the skin of the infant turns blue due to the lack of oxygen, thus the term "blue-baby syndrome" or methemoglobinemia. This condition can be fatal without proper medical treatment.

There are other concerns related to high nitrate and high nitrite waters. These concerns are based on the reactions between the nitrogen compounds and secondary or tertiary amines in foods to form nitrosamines. There have been studies in animals that suggest that there may be adverse effects (e.g., cancers, birth defects, reproductive toxicity) associated with exposure to nitrosamines. However, to this date, none of the studies has conclusively demonstrated a link between the consumption of high nitrate waters and these effects in humans.

The U.S. Environmental Protection Agency (EPA) regulates the concentration of nitrate in public drinking water supplies. A maximum contaminant level of 10 mg liter^{-1} nitrate–nitrogen has been established; this level is enforced by either the state or the EPA.

3. Salinity and Drainage

Water management for salinity and sodicity control is very important in agriculture. Salt can affect plant growth from three mechanisms: osmotic effects which result from the total dissolved concentration of salts in the water and soil in the root zone; specific ion toxicity which results from a concentration of an individual ion above a threshold that causes harm to the plants; and poor soil physical conditions such as soil dispersion which result from high sodium or low salinity levels. These effects cause reduced yields of crops and therefore are highly undesirable. One method for controlling these kinds of effects is by flushing relativity clean water through the soil to carry the salts down below the root zone. Continued use of this type of flushing will have a negative effect on the ground water as the salts are flushed down toward

the water table. Even with water of relatively low salinity, salt accumulation occurs over time, since a portion of water applied to the soil surface is evaporated, leaving behind a higher concentration of salt in the remaining water. Over a season, the build-up of salts may increase to a point where extra water is needed to flush the salts below the root zone. As a consequence, over numerous seasons large amounts of salts and toxic ions can be leached to ground water.

For locations where the ground-water table is too close to the soil surface, the presence of a high water table can be harmful to crops growing on the soil surface. When this situation occurs, it may be necessary to install drains to lower the water table to a depth sufficient for the plants to have an aerated soil zone. Many factors affect the need for the use of drains, such as how much rainfall occurs, whether there are impermeable zones, or hard pans, in the soil which restrict water movement out of the root zone.

4. Microorganisms

Microorganisms that can cause disease in humans may be introduced into the subsurface environment in a variety of ways. In general, any practice that involves the application of domestic waste water to the soil has the potential to cause microbiological contamination of ground water. This is due to the fact that the treatment processes to which the waste water are subjected do not effect complete removal or inactivation of the disease-causing microorganisms present. For example, viruses have been detected in the ground water beneath cropland being irrigated with sewage effluent.

Another source of microorganisms to the subsurface is municipal sludge. Land application of municipal sludge is becoming a more common practice as alternatives are sought for the disposal of the ever-increasing amounts of sludge produced in this country. The sludge that is produced during the process of treating domestic sewage contains high levels of nitrogen and other nutrients that are required by plant materials. However, it may also contain pathogenic microorganisms at concentrations sufficient to cause disease in exposed individuals (Table I). Several studies conducted in the late 1970s suggested that viruses are tightly bound to sewage solids and are not easily released into the soil. In a more recent study, viruses were detected in a 3-m-deep well at a site where anaerobically digested sludge was applied to a sandy soil 11 weeks after sludge application (Table II).

The EPA has recently promulgated new standards for the disposal of sewage sludge. Two classes of

TABLE I

Concentrations of Microorganisms in Digested Sludge

| Organism | Type of stabilization | |
| | Anaerobic | Aerobic |
	(No. per g dry weight)	
Enteroviruses	0.2–210	0–260
Rotaviruses	14–485	ND[a]
Salmonella	$3–10^3$	3
Total coliforms	$10^2–10^6$	$10^5–10^6$
Fecal coliforms	$10^2–10^6$	$10^5–10^6$
Shigella sp.	20	ND
Yersinia enterocolitica	10^5	ND
Ascaris	4^b	
Trichuris	1.3^b	
Toxocara	0.4^b	

Source: Adapted from Gerba (1988).
[a] ND, no data
[b] Average of all types of digested sludge, percentage viable.

sludge are defined based on the pathogen reduction requirements. The crop and access limitations to the land are dependent on the class of sludge applied, with the strictest controls on land receiving the least treated sludge.

Another practice regulated by many states is the reuse of treated sewage effluent for the purpose of crop irrigation. In general, the restrictions on the method of irrigation and the crops which can be irrigated are stricter for the use of effluent that has not been highly treated, and less strict for effluent which has been extensively treated.

Some examples of pathogen detection in ground water at sites where domestic waste was applied to the land are shown in Table II.

5. Management Practices

The pesticide, fertilizer, and domestic waste application practices and the irrigation practices at the site

TABLE II

Viruses in Ground Water following Land Application of Waste

Researchers	Site
Goyal *et al.*	27.5 m below cropland irrigated with secondary sewage effluent
Jorgensen and Lund	3 m below sludge application site 11 weeks after application
Vaughn and Landry	402 m down gradient from a sanitary landfill
Wellings *et al.*	12.2 m below a septic tank at a well 32.8 m away

are very important in determining the potential for contamination of ground water. Contaminants that would not be considered to be leachers by virtue of their chemical and physical properties may leach to ground water if the proper management techniques are not used. Conversely, good management practices may result in preventing ground-water contamination by compound that are considered leachers. Following the label directions and using common sense when applying chemicals or domestic waste can help to minimize the potential for ground-water contamination. Irrigation management is also very important, because in general, the more water applied, the more the contaminant will move into and through the soil. Only the amount of water required by the plants should be applied; overwatering is costly and could contribute to contamination of surface or ground water. Preventing contamination of ground water is less expensive and much easier than trying to remediate contaminated sites or closing wells that exceed standards and drilling new ones.

Optimizing management practices to reduce pollution involves balancing opposing forces. There is incentive to reduce water needed to grow crops. This has led to the development of new techniques to increase irrigation efficiency. Along with new irrigation methods there is a need to determine how these new techniques affect the leaching of contaminants below the root zone. Once the important characteristics are identified, management strategies can be devised that minimize the pollution potential of agrichemicals and other contaminants. For example, trickle irrigation can virtually eliminate leaching of water from the root zone. It has been suggested that this will reduce the movement of contaminants to ground water. If over time, however, salt build-up occurs, a large pulse of water will be required to reduce the salt to appropriate levels. During this leaching period, the accumulated contaminants may be transported out of the root zone at a much higher concentration compared to a situation where some leaching occurs continually. The overall effect of these practices on environmental quality needs to be determined.

Bibliography

Council for Agricultural Science and Technology (1991). "Water Quality: Agriculture's Role." Task Force Report No. 119, Council for Agricultural Science and Technology, Ames, IA.

Fetter, C. W. (1980). "Applied Hydrogeology." C. E. Merril, Columbus, OH.

Freeze, R.A., and Cherry, J. A. (1979). "Groundwater." Prentice-Hall, Englewood Cliffs, NJ.

National Research Council (1993). "Ground Water Vulnerability Assessment: Contamination Potential under Conditions of Uncertainty." Committee on Techniques for Assessing Ground Water Vulnerability, National Academy Press, Washington, DC.

Herbicides and Herbicide Resistance

KRITON K. HATZIOS, *Virginia Polytechnic Institute and State University*

Glossary

Herbicide Chemical substance or cultured biological organism (bioherbicide) used to kill or suppress the growth of plants

Mechanism of action Interference of a herbicide with a specific biochemical or molecular process that leads to lethality

Metabolism Sum of biological processes altering the chemical structure of a herbicide within the living cells of a plant species

Mode of action Sequence of events that leads to death following the primary response of a target plant to treatment with a herbicide

Resistance Ability of a plant to withstand herbicide treatment, as a result of selection and genetic response to repeated exposure to a given herbicide

Safener Chemical or biological agent that reduces toxicity of herbicides to crop plants by a physiological or molecular mechanism

Selectivity Ability of herbicides to control, suppress, or kill certain plants without appreciable injury to others

Site of action Sensitive enzyme/protein, metabolic step, or binding site affected by a herbicide

Susceptibility Sensitivity to or degree to which a plant is injured by a herbicide treatment

Synergist Nonherbicidal compound used to increase the phytotoxicity of a herbicide by a physiological or molecular mechanism

Tolerance Ability of a plant to continue normal growth or function when exposed to normal field dosage of a herbicide

Herbicides are synthetic chemicals used worldwide to control weeds in agricultural, industrial, or aquatic environments. Because of their diverse chemistry, herbicides kill plants by affecting several physiological, biochemical, or molecular processes of plants. The widespread practice of chemical weed control is due to the ability of herbicides to suppress the growth of certain plants without appreciable injury to other plants. The ability of crop or weed plants to withstand herbicide treatment is described as tolerance or resistance and is due either to metabolic detoxification or to modifications in the target sites involved in the action of marketed herbicides.

I. Benefits and Risks of Herbicide Use

The use of chemical herbicides in crop production represents the major area of expansion in weed control technology since World War II. Herbicide treatments are widely accepted today because they allow economic control of weeds and cost-effective increases in crop productivity and quality. In addition, herbicides facilitate soil conservation efforts through no-till agricultural practices, wherein herbicides rather than tillage are used to reduce weed populations prior to planting. Most of the current herbicides are effective when applied at low rates and in low volume of water and they permit the selective removal of weeds from crop fields. The cost of using herbicides must not exceed the value gained and the obtained results from their use must be reproducible. Herbicides now lead other individual pesticide groups such as insecticides and fungicides from the standpoint of total acreage treated, total tonnage of pesticides produced, and total dollar value from pesticide sales, accounting for about 60% of all pesticide sales in the United States. [*See* WEED SCIENCE.]

Apart from chemical herbicides, a number of microorganisms causing plant diseases are being tested and/or developed as potential means for controlling weeds. Such microbial agents are known collectively as bioherbicides or mycoherbicides, when the plant pathogens used are fungi. At present, bioherbicides are viewed as supplements to chemical weed control rather than as a technology that will completely eliminate the use of chemical herbicides.

Common problems associated with herbicide use are related to their inherent ability to injure plants when misused. Herbicide misuse could result from either ignorance of herbicidal activity and selectivity or carelessness during application of herbicides. Proper selection, storage, handling, and application of herbicides would eliminate any basis for their misuse. To be commercially successful, a herbicide must be effective at low rates; control selectivity a broad spectrum of weeds; have relatively short residual activity; be economical to manufacture; be safe and easy to handle and apply; and have no adverse effects on nontarget species and the environment.

Marketed herbicides are chemically diverse and exhibit a plethora of mechanisms of action. The exact molecular target sites of herbicides have been identified and characterized only in few cases and some herbicides are known to have more than one site of action. Repeated use of herbicides in agroecosystems exerts a strong selection pressure that has contributed to the development of a growing number of herbicide-resistant weed biotypes. Chemical structure and physicochemical properties have a profound effect on the biological activity and selectivity of herbicides.

II. Classification of Herbicides

Herbicides can be grouped according to several convenient features that we want to emphasize. Thus, according to their general use herbicides can be classified as: cropland herbicides, industrial (noncropland) herbicides, and aquatic herbicides.

On the basis of the coverage of the target area, herbicide treatments are classified as *broadcast treatments* when the herbicide is applied uniformly to the entire area; *band treatments* when the herbicide is applied to continuous, somewhat restricted areas such as on or along a crop row rather than over the entire field; *spot treatment* refers to the application of a herbicide to a restricted area such as scattered individual plants or clumps and small patches of weeds; *directed sprays* refer to the application of a herbicide to a partic-

ular part of weeds (usually the base of the plant stem or trunk).

Based on the degree of differential responses among plants, herbicides are classified as selective and nonselective. A selective herbicide is more injurious to some plant species than to others. Nonselective herbicides are phytotoxic to all species present. Selective control of weeds in crop fields is dependent on the timing of herbicide application and may be considered either as preventive or as remedial. The timing of herbicide treatments may be influenced by the chemical nature of the herbicide and its soil persistence, the crop species and their tolerance to given herbicides, the characteristics of the dominant weed species, the cultural practices employed, and the climatic and soil conditions prevailing in a particular field.

Preventive weed control is based on herbicide applications made to the soil as either preplanting or preemergence sprays rather than to vegetation. To be effective, soil-applied herbicides must be mechanically incorporated or be moved into the soil with moisture so that they come in contact with germinating weed seedlings. Herbicides that are applied to a dry soil surface and remain in that position during seed germination and emergence of weeds or during the growing stages of established weeds are not effective.

Remedial weed control includes postemergence herbicide applications made directly to the leaves or foliage of plants. Interest in remedial weed control systems has increased because of the recent development of several highly effective and selective herbicides for many crops. Once available, remedial weed control systems may provide farmers with the option to treat only those parts of their fields in which weed populations exceed economically damaging levels.

The pathway of herbicide movement in plants and the speed of herbicidal symptom development are additional features used for classification. Contact herbicides damage only those plant parts to which the chemical is applied and they do not translocate appreciably inside the treated plants. Their symptoms of injury are indicative of an acute effect and they are visible almost immediately after treatment. Contact herbicides are effective against annual weeds and uniform coverage is very critical for best control of weeds with these herbicides. Translocated herbicides are absorbed by either roots or aboveground plant parts and are then transported inside the plant to tissues containing their site of action. Translocated herbicides may be either phloem-mobile (moving both upward and downward) or xylem-mobile (moving only upward). Translocated herbicides are effective against all types of weeds, including established perennials, and uniform coverage is not critical for their effectiveness. Translocated herbicides often exert a chronic effect and typical symptoms of herbicide injury may be visible within a week or a month after treatment.

Classification by mechanism of action is another useful and convenient way to group herbicides. The activity of the herbicide is directed at specific cellular processes and molecular sites. In some cases the target process or site is known; in others, although the effect on the plant is known; the actual cause for that effect at the cellular or molecular level has not been determined. In addition, some herbicides may act by more than one mechanism. Based on their mechanisms of action or their effects on plants, herbicides can be classified as photosynthetic inhibitors, disrupters of cell membranes, inhibitors of pigment biosynthesis (bleaching herbicides), growth regulators (auxin-type herbicides), disrupters of mitosis, and specific metabolic inhibitors, (e.g., amino acid synthesis inhibitors, inhibitors of lipid synthesis, etc.).

III. Chemistry of Herbicides

In terms of their chemistry, herbicides are broadly classified as inorganic and organic molecules. Inorganics were the first chemicals used for weed control, mainly in the period preceding World War II. Inorganic herbicides are nonselective, persistent (nondegradable) molecules, causing membrane damage (contact action). A few of them are still used as desiccants (e.g., sodium chlorate) or as synergists of organic herbicides (e.g., ammonium salts).

Organic compounds represent the vast majority of herbicides used in modern agriculture. Organic herbicides are chemically diverse belonging to several chemical families and they act by many mechanisms of action. Most of the organic herbicides are biodegradable (nonpersistent) and exhibit a desirable range of crop selectivity.

During the course of its development and market life, an individual herbicide may be identified by several names. A code name (e.g., MON-0573 for glyphosate) is assigned to a herbicidal molecule immediately after its discovery. A trade name (e.g., Roundup for glyphosate) is assigned to the same molecule at the time of its first introduction to the market. A given herbicide may have more than one trade name depending on the way it is formulated or on its intended uses. Code and trade names are assigned by the staff of the agrochemical company involved in the discovery and/or development of an individual herbicide. A common name (e.g., glyphosate) and a chemical name [e.g., N-(phosphonomethyl)glycine for glyphosate] are proposed by the respective agrochemical company and they have to be approved by specific organizations (e.g., the Weed Science Society of America) before they can be used in the scientific literature.

Organic herbicides are classified chemically as derivatives of aliphatic compounds (straight chains), aromatic compounds (contain a benzene ring), or heterocyclic compounds. The major functional groups that are commonly found as substituents in organic herbicides include (a) ionizable groups uch as $-COOH$, $-OH$, $-NH_2$, and SO_2NH_2; (b) electron-withdrawing groups such as $-Cl$ and other halogens, $-CF_3$, $-NO_2$, $-OCH_3$, $-C=O$, and $-NHCO_3$; and (c) electron-donating groups such as $-CH_3$, $-C_2H_5$, $-C_3H_7$, and other alkyl groups. The general chemistry and the specific functional groups that are present in a herbicidal molecule are key determinants of its physiochemical (e.g., ionization, water solubility, volatilization, stability, etc.), biological (e.g., absorption, translocation, metabolism, action, and selectivity), and toxicological properties. In addition, chemistry and functional groups are very important for determining the type of formulation, application timing (e.g., preemergence versus postemergence), and environmental fate (e.g., adsorption, leaching, soil persistence, photodegradation, etc.) of an individual herbicide. The chemical names of specific classes of herbicides (e.g., triazines) and the chemical structures of representative members within a class (e.g., atrazine) are discussed in the next section of this chapter.

IV. Mechanisms of Herbicide Action

To be effective, a herbicide must reach its cellular or molecular target site in an active form, at a concentration sufficient to promote herbicidal effects. If the injury is of a transient nature the treated plant may recover, but if it surpasses a threshold, then irreversible damage will ensure and the death of treated plants becomes inevitable. The active concentration of a herbicide *in vivo* is influenced by several morphological barriers and cellular processes that determine its foliar absorption or root uptake, translocation, and metabolic detoxification in plants. The mode of action of a herbicide may vary depending on how the herbicide is applied (e.g., soil versus foliar applications). The size of the plant at the time of application is also important and generally, young seedlings are more sensitive to herbicide treatments than older mature plants of the same species.

Knowledge of herbicidal modes and mechanisms of action is important for understanding the principles involved in the chemical regulation of plant growth and finding insights into herbicide selectivity. In addition, information on herbicide mechanisms of action is vital for designing model test systems for screening candidate herbicides.

In determining the mechanism of action of a herbicide, herbicide concentration and the time-course of plant responses to herbicide treatments are of primary concern. The term primary mechanism of herbicide action denotes the primary cellular process or molecular function which is inhibited by the lowest concentration of a herbicide at the shortest time interval after treatment with this herbicide. Information on the mechanisms of action of herbicides can be obtained from various types of experimentation, including application technique, visible injury symptoms, and cytological, microscopical, physiological, biochemical, or molecular observations.

Herbicides induce numerous changes in the growth of plants and their structure. These effects may range from a mere inhibition of growth to gross morphological aberrations and death. Application techniques and visible symptoms of injury are normally known for most herbicides. Common visible symptoms induced by herbicides on plants include chlorosis, albinism, necrosis, desiccation, defoliation, epinasty, and other formative effects such as increased tillering, multiple shoot formation of internodes, decreased internode length (retardation, stunting, dwarfing), thickened leaves, coleoptile and leaf distortions, reduced secondary root formation, and abnormal seedling development. These morphological responses provide us with a basis to classify herbicides as bleachers, contact herbicides or desiccants, photosynthetic inhibitors, growth regulators, mitotic disrupters, or metabolic inhibitors.

Cytological and microscopical observations have been explored to a rather limited extent as sources of information for determining herbicidal modes of action. Data on the accumulation of radiolabeled herbicides may be obtained by either microautoradiography or subcellular fractionation of homogenized tissues. However, preferential accumulation of a herbicide to a subcellular site (e.g., chloroplast) does not necessarily mean that this organelle is or contains

the target site of action of this herbicide. At the molecular level, the main sites of the currently known herbicides appear to belong to the endomembrane system of plant cells. Table I summarizes our present knowledge on mechanisms of action and respective molecular target sites for a number of commercialized herbicides. A brief description of the major mechanisms of herbicidal action is given below. [See PLANT PHYSIOLOGY.]

A. Photosynthetic Inhibitors

The photosynthetic conversion of light energy into chemical energy is a very important metabolic process that is unique to green plants. Exploitation of this process as a target site for herbicides has been remarkably successful and many commercialized classes of herbi-

TABLE I

Major Mechanisms of Herbicide Action

Mechanism of action	Molecular target site	Herbicide class
Photosynthetic inhibitors	D1 quinone-binding protein	Triazines Substituted ureas Triazinones Hydroxybenzoniriles Anilides Biscarbamates
Membrane disrupters	Photosystem I	Bipyridyliums
Carotenogenesis inhibitors	Phytoene desaturase	Pyridazinones Pyridinones Furanones
	Lycopene cyclase	amitrole
	ζ-Carotene desaturase	dichlormate
	unknown	clomazone
Chlorophyll synthesis inhibitors	Protoporphyrinogen oxidase	Nitrodiphenylethers Oxadiazoles N-phenyl imides
Disrupters of mitosis	β-Tubulin	dintiroanilines phosphoric amides
Amino acid synthesis inhibitors	Acetolactate synthase	Sulfonylureas Imidazolinones
	Glutamine synthetase	Bialaphos Glufosinate
	EPSP synthase	Glyphosate
Lipid synthesis inhibitors	Acetyl-CoA carboxylase	Aryloxyphenoxy-propionates Cyclohexanediones
Cellulose synthesis inhibitors	Unknown	Dichlobenil Isoxaben
Folate synthesis inhibitors	Dihydropteroate synthase	Asulam

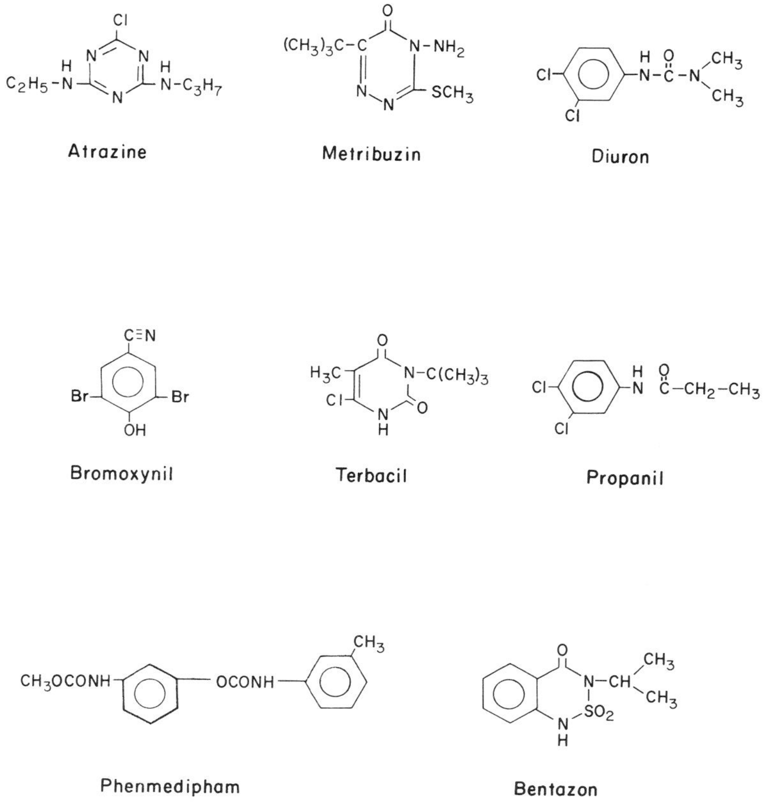

FIGURE 1 Chemical structures of herbicides that inhibit photosynthesis.

cides are known to act as photosynthetic inhibitors. Such herbicidal compounds include anilides (e.g., propanil), benzimidazoles, biscarbamates (e.g., phenmedipham), substituted pyridazinones (e.g., pyrazon), triazines (e.g., atrazine), triazinones (e.g., metribuzin), uracils (e.g., terbacil), substituted ureas (e.g, diuron), quinones, hydroxybenzonitriles (e.g., bromoxynil), and miscellaneous unclassified heterocycles (e.g., bentazon). The chemical structures of representative herbicides that are known to act as photosynthetic inhibitors are shown in Fig. 1. [*See* PHOTOSYNTHESIS.]

Photosynthesis-inhibiting herbicides block photosynthetic electron transport by competing with plastoquinone for binding to the D1, quinone-binding protein (formerly known as the Q_B protein) in the thylakoid membranes of plastids. The native plastoquinone binds to the D1 protein by interacting with its histidine-215 and serine-264 amino acid residues. Consequently, herbicides that act at this site are classified into those of the diuron-type that bind closer to the serine-264 site and those of the phenol-type that bind to the histidine-215 site of the D1 protein.

Triazine-resistant biotypes of several weed species, in which serine-264 has mutated to glycine, have been identified in many locations around the world.

Inhibition of photosystem II electron transport prevents the conversion of absorbed light energy into electrochemical energy and results in the production of triplet chlorophyll and singlet oxygen which induce the peroxidation of membrane lipids. In turn, the herbicide-induced lipid peroxidation destroys the integrity of cellular membranes causing disorganization and desiccation of green plant tissues.

B. Disrupters of Cell Membranes

Bipyridyliums (e.g., paraquat) and dinitrophenols (e.g., dinoseb) are two classes of herbicides (Fig. 2) that act by causing severe damage of plant cell membranes. Paraquat is a nonselective contact herbicide causing a rapid desiccation of green tissues due to photosynthesis-dependent photobleaching. Paraquat competes for electrons with the primary electron acceptor of photosystem I and is reduced by such electrons forming a paraquat radical. The paraquat radical

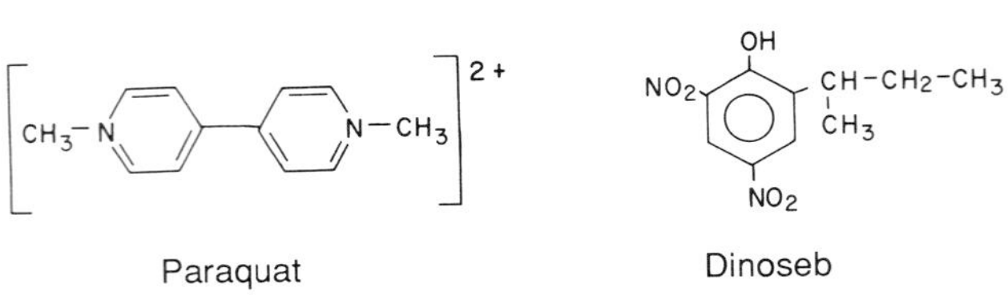

FIGURE 2 Chemical structures of herbicides that disrupt cell membranes.

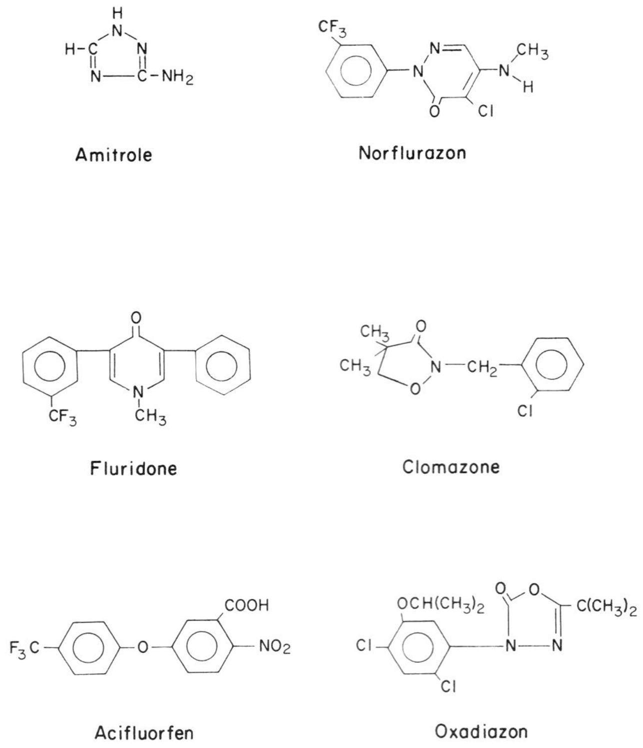

then transfers these electrons to molecular oxygen producing superoxide ion, hydrogen peroxide, and hydroxyl radicals which cause peroxidation of membrane lipids.

Dinoseb and other substituted dinitrophenols are known to act as inhibitory uncouplers interfering with both electron transport and photophosporylation in chloroplast membranes. In addition, these herbicides are known to act as inhibitors of oxidative phosphorylation and as contact herbicides causing membrane damage, when used at high concentrations.

C. Inhibitors of Pigment Biosynthesis (Bleaching Herbicides)

1. Inhibitors of Carotenoid Biosynthesis

Chlorophylls and carotenoids are important pigments in plants and interruption of their biosynthesis by herbicidal inhibitors causes bleaching of cells and plant green tissues. Carotenoids, namely carotenes and xanthophylls, play an essential role in photosynthesis by protecting chlorophyll against photooxidative damage induced by singlet oxygen. A number of herbicide classes inhibiting carotenoid biosynthesis in plants have been developed and include aminotriazoles (e.g., amitrole), substituted pyridazinones (e.g., norflurazon), pyridinones (e.g., fluridone), isoxazolidinones (e.g., clomazone), and furanone derivatives (e.g., flurtamore). The chemical structures of representative members of these classes are shown in Fig. 3. Leaves emerging after treatment of susceptible plants with these herbicides are depleted of all colored plastidic pigments (chlorophylls and carotenoids), and this morphological symptom provides the basis for characterizing these herbicides as bleaching compounds.

The majority of bleaching herbicides inhibit carotenogenesis by interfering with the activity of phytoene desaturase, a membrane-bound enzyme that catalyzes the dehydrogenation of phytoene to form ζ-carotene, a precursor of β-carotene. Amitrole inhibits the cyclization of lycopene, whereas dichlormate in-

FIGURE 3 Chemical structures of herbicides that bleach plants by inhibiting carotenoid synthesis (top four compounds) or chlorophyll synthesis (bottom two compounds).

hibits ζ-carotene desaturase. The mechanism of the bleaching action of the herbicide clomazone is unique, and although its exact target site has not been determined, clomazone seems to inhibit an early step of the carotenoid biosynthesis pathway rather than the phytoene desaturase step.

2. Inhibitors of Chlorophyll Synthesis

A number of herbicides cause photobleaching by mechanisms that are not dependent on photosynthesis. Such herbicides include the p-nitrodiphenylethers (e.g., acifluorfen), oxadiazoles (e.g., oxadiazon) and the N-phenyl imides. The chemical structures of acifluorfen and oxadiazon are shown in Fig. 3. These herbicides inhibit the enzyme protoporphyrinogen oxidase and cause a massive accumulation of protoporphyrin IX, which results from an uncontrolled autooxidation of protoporphyrinogen to protoporphyrin IX. Protoporphyrim IX is a potent photosensitizer that generates high levels of singlet oxygen in the presence of molecular oxygen and light. The accumulation of protoporphyrin IX is mainly extraplastidic and causes a rapid photodynamic damage of cell membranes such as the plasmalemma and the tonoplast.

D. Growth Regulators

Many physiological processes of higher plants are controlled by phytohormones. Several herbicides act by mimicking the activity of natural plant-growth regulators (e.g., auxins) and include the classes of phenoxyalkanoic acids (e.g., 2,4-D), benzoic acids (e.g., dicamba), pyridine-carboxylic acids (e.g., picloram), phenylacetic acids, and quinoline-carboxylic acids. The chemical structures of some of these herbicides are shown in Fig. 4. On the contrary, some classes of herbicides such as phthalic acids (e.g., naptalam) and D-aryloxypropionic acids (e.g., benzoylprop-ethyl) act by interfering with the synthesis or action of naturally occurring auxins and they are known as antiauxin herbicides.

The exact mechanisms by which auxin- or growth regulator-type herbicides initiate growth aberrations of stem enlargement, callus growth, secondary roots, and leaf stunting are not known. It is possible that synthetic auxins, used as herbicides, imitate the action of the natural auxin indoleacetic acid (IAA), but whereas endogenous IAA levels would be controlled *in vivo,* the levels of synthetic auxins are not controlled, overdosing in a sense treated plants. Natural or synthetic auxins are believed to bind to specific receptor proteins, causing an efflux of protons which, in turn, leads to the acidification of cell walls and cell enlargement. Synthetic auxin-type herbicides cause major aberrations in nucleic acid and protein synthesis in the cells of treated plants.

E. Disrupters of Mitosis

Herbicides that are known to severely inhibit or disrupt cell division include dinitroanilines (e.g., trifluralin), phenylcarbamates (e.g., propham), amides (e.g., pronamide), phthalic acids (e.g., DCPA), sub-

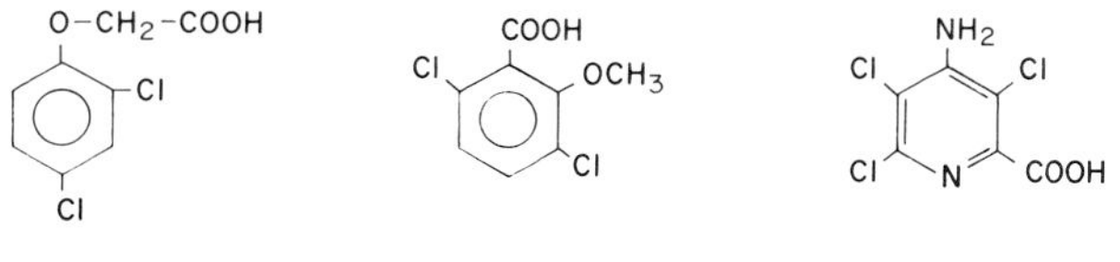

FIGURE 4 Chemical structures of auxin-type herbicides.

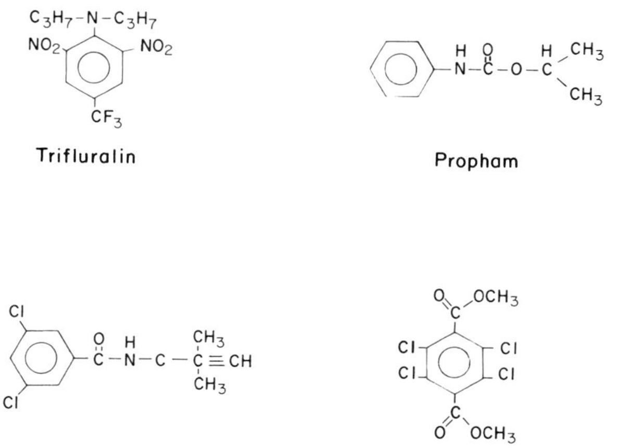

FIGURE 5 Chemical structures of herbicides that disrupt cell division.

stituted pyridine-carboxylates (e.g., dithiopyr), cineole derivatives (e.g., cinmethylin), and phosphoric acids. The chemical structures of representative members of such herbicides are shown in Fig. 5.

Most of the herbicides that inhibit cell division do so by affecting the cellular structure known as microtubules. Microtubules are required for cell division and cell wall formation. Dinitroaniline and phosphoric amide herbicides inhibit microtubule polymerization from the tubulin subunits. Tubulin is composed of an α and β subunit. The β subunit of tubulin has been modified in dinitroaniline-resistant weed biotypes. Dinitroanilines are soil-applied herbicides and the most typical symptom of their injury is a characteristic club-shaped swelling induced by these herbicides in root tips and other structures that are normally elongated.

Pronamide and dithiopyr induce similar effects, except that tufts of microtubules remain at the kinetophore region of chromosomes. Phenylcarbamate herbicides such as propham alter the organization of the spindle microtubules so that multiple spindles are formed. Chromosomes move to many poles and multiple nuclei result. Abnormal branched cell walls partly separate the nuclei.

F. Specific Metabolic Inhibitors

1. Inhibitors of Amino Acid Biosynthesis

The biosynthesis of amino acids is a process unique to plants and bacteria and a desirable target site for herbicide action. As of today, three enzymes of amino acid biosynthesis have been firmly established as primary target sites involved in the action of phosphonate (e.g., glyphosate and glufosinate), sulfonylurea (e.g., chlorimuron-ethyl), and imidazolinone (e.g., imazethapyr) herbicides. The chemical structures of such herbicides are given in Fig. 6.

The enzyme 5-enolpyruvyl-shikimate-3-phosphate synthase (EPSP synthase) converts phosphoenolpyruvate and shikimate-3-phosphate to EPSP, a critical step in the biosynthesis of aromatic amino acids (e.g., phenylalanine, tyrosine, and tryptophan). EPSP synthase is nuclear-coded, but functions mainly in the chloroplast. Glyphosate is the only known inhibitor of this enzyme that has been commercialized as a successful herbicide. Glycophosate acts as a competitive inhibitor with phosphoenolypyruvate, the natural substrate of EPSP synthase and causes a massive accumulation of shikimate in treated plant tissues.

Glutamine synthetase (GS) is the first enzyme involved in assimilating inorganic nitrogen to produce an amino acid. GS converts L-glutamic acid to L-glutamine in the presence of ammonia and ATP. Of the many known inhibitors of this enzyme, only two have been commercialized as herbicides. Glufosinate (also known as phosphinothricin), a synthetic organic herbicide, is marketed worldwide, whereas the tripeptide bialaphos, a fermentation product of *Streptomyces hygroscopicus,* is marketed in Japan as the first-ever commercialized microbial herbicide. In treated plants, bialaphos is hydrolyzed to glufosinate, the actual inhibitor of GS. Glufosinate is an irreversible competitive inhibitor that interferes with the binding of glutamate to GS.

Acetolactate synthase (ALS, also known as acetohydroacid synthase), is a key enzyme in the biosyn-

thetic pathway of branched chain amino acids such as leucine, isoleucine, and valine. The enzyme catalyzes two reactions: condensation of two pyruvate molecules to produce CO_2 and α-acetolactate, a precursor of valine and leucine; and condensation of pyruvate and α-ketoglutarate to form CO_2 and 2-acetohydroxybutyrate, a precursor of isoleucine. Apart from sulfonylurea and imidazolinone compounds, derivatives of triazolopyrimidine sulfoanilides, pyrimidyl-oxy-benzoic acids, nonaromatic imidazolinones, and sulfonylcarboxamides are also known as herbicidal inhibitors of the ALS enzyme. Sulfonylurea herbicides inhibit ALS by slow, tight-binding kinetics and the herbicide molecule binds reversibly to the ALS–FAD–thiamine pyrophosphate–Mg^{2+}–decarboxylated pyruvate complex and also competes for the second pyruvate binding site. Imidazolinones are noncompetitive with respect to pyruvate and there are overlapping binding domains for the different ALS inhibitors at a quinone-binding site. Both sulfonylureas and imidazolinones inhibit ALS *in vitro,* but only imidazolinones decrease the level of extractable ALS.

2. Inhibitors of Lipid Synthesis

Lipid synthesis has been strongly implicated in the mechanism of action of several herbicidal classes such as aryloxyphenoxypropionates (e.g., fluazifop-butyl), cyclohexanediones (e.g., sethoxydim), substituted pyridazinones, thiocarbamates (e.g., EPTC), and chloroacetanilides (e.g., metolachlor). The chemical structures of representative herbicides from these classes are given in Figs. 7 and 8. Direct evidence for the inhibition of lipid synthesis by aryloxyphenoxy-

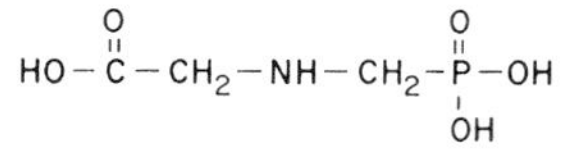

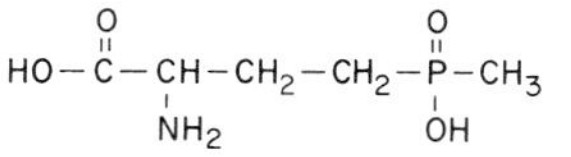

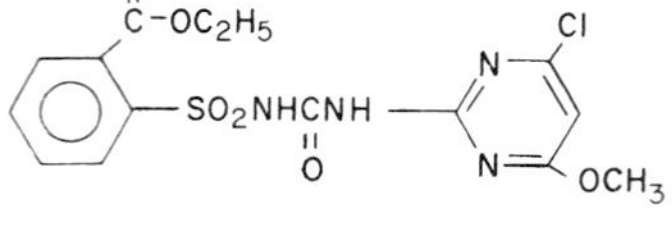

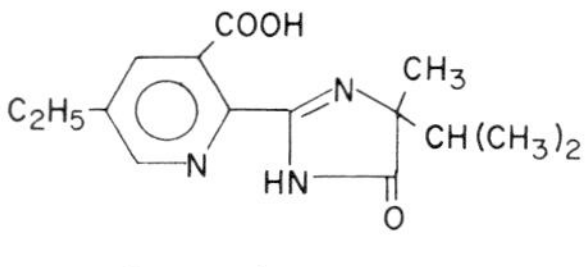

FIGURE 6 Chemical structures of herbicides that inhibit amino acid biosynthesis.

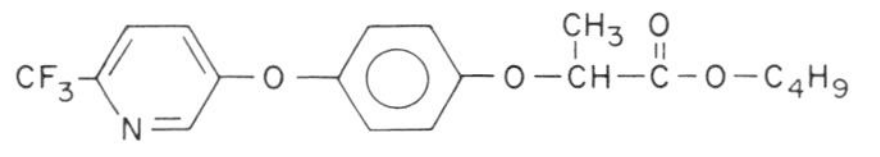

Fluazifop-butyl

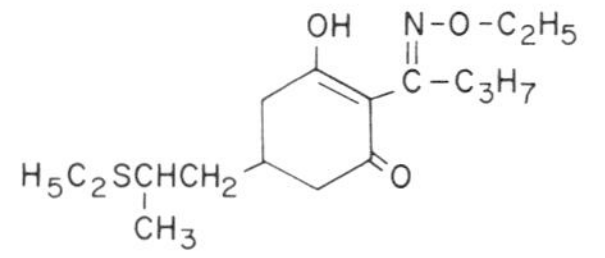

Sethoxydim

FIGURE 7 Chemical structures of herbicides that inhibit aceytl-CoA carboxylase.

propionic acids and cyclohexanediones has been obtained only recently. Both of these classes of herbicides control selectively grass plants, but have no effect on broadleaved plants. The target site involved in their action is the enzyme acetyl-CoA carboxylase, which is found in the stroma of plastids. Aryloxyphenopropionates and cyclohexanediones are reversible, linear, noncompetitive inhibitors of acetyl-CoA carboxylase from grasses and they bind to a common domain on the enzyme.

Selected substituted pyridazinone herbicides inhibit fatty desaturases, which are located in the chloroplast envelope. As a result, treatment with these herbicides decreases the degree of unsaturation of plastidic galactolipids. The exact mechanisms of action of the thiocarbamate and chloroacetanilide herbicides have not been elucidated. Nevertheless, it has been shown that thiocarbamates impair the synthesis of surface lipids (waxes, cutin, suberin) by inhibiting one or more acyl-CoA elongases. These enzymes are not well characterized, but they are associated with the endoplasmic reticulum and catalyze the condensation of malonyl-CoA with fatty acids used in the synthesis of surface lipids. The direct involvement of lipid syn-

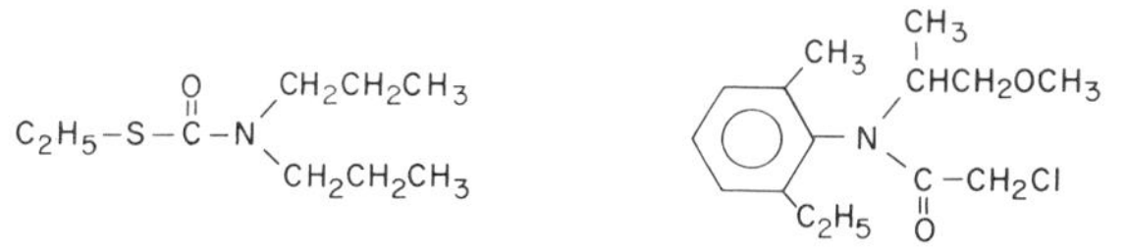

EPTC   Metolachlor

FIGURE 8 Chemical structures of herbicides that may act by inhibiting lipid synthesis.

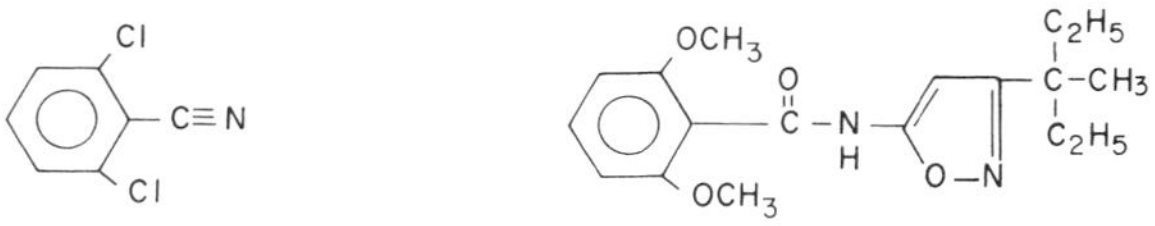

Dichlobenil   Isoxaben

FIGURE 9 Chemical structures of herbicides that inhibit cellulose biosynthesis.

thesis in the herbicidal action of chloroacetanilide herbicides is still unclear.

3. Inhibitors of Cellulose Biosynthesis

Cellulose biosynthesis appears to be a target metabolic process involved in the herbicidal action of dichlobenil and isoxaben (Fig. 9). Treatment of cotton fibers with a photoaffinity labeled analogue of the herbicide dichlobenil showed a specific binding of the herbicide to an 18kDa protein, which has not been characterized. Isoxaben has been shown to inhibit incorporation of glucose to an acid-insoluble cell wall fraction thought to be cellulose. The exact molecular site of both herbicides is currently unknown.

4. Inhibitors of Folic Acid Biosynthesis

The herbicide asulam (Fig. 10) inhibits the biosynthesis of the vitamin folic acid by interfering with the enzyme dihydropteroate synthase. A secondary mechanism of action proposed for this herbicide is associated with inhibition of cell division.

V. Herbicide Selectivity

Selective toxicity of herbicides to weeds but not to crops is one of the most difficult properties to achieve, as might be expected from the biological relatedness of weeds and crops. Selectivity is a function of the physicochemical properties of a herbicide and of the biochemical interactions of the herbicide with the crop and weeds under a given set of environmental conditions. The selectivity of modern herbicides is either based on the differential response of sensitive and tolerant plant species (crops and weeds) to given herbicides (true selectivity) or induced by differential placement of herbicides which maximizes the contact of the herbicide with the weed and minimizes its contact with the crop (placement selectivity). Selectivity is strongly dependent on the dose of the herbicide applied and the timing of herbicide applications.

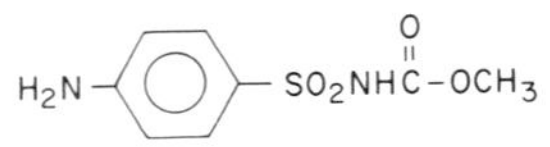

$$H_2N - \bigcirc - SO_2NH\overset{O}{\overset{\|}{C}}-OCH_3$$

Asulam

FIGURE 10 Chemical structures of a herbicide that inhibit folic acid biosynthesis.

A. Factors and Mechanisms Contributing to Herbicide Selectivity

Genetic differences among plants or within a species may vary substantially and can account for selectivity. Cultivars of most crops have been shown to vary in their response to individual herbicides. Young seedlings from seed are generally more susceptible and tolerance increases with age. Rapidly growing plants are generally more susceptible to herbicide treatments. The differential location of the growing point (meristematic regions) in grass and broadleaved plants can also account for the observed crop selectivity of some herbicides. In grass plants, the growing point is not easily exposed to herbicide spraying because it is located at the base of the plant and is protected by the older leaves. Such plants can recover following application of selected herbicides. In broadleaved plants the growing point is located at the top of the plant and is easily exposed to herbicide spraying.

Differential rates or patterns of uptake, translocation, and metabolism of certain herbicides have long been established as major factors accounting for the observed crop selectivity of these herbicides. Differential penetration probably is most important as a selectivity factor among plants of different ages, since cuticle thickness increases as a plant matures. Unless accompanied by differential metabolism, selectivity seldom is obtained by differential translocation alone. Differences in biotransformation or metabolism of herbicide molecules by higher plants represent the most common basis explaining the plant selectivity of most herbicides.

B. Metabolism of Herbicides in Higher Plants

The majority of organic herbicides are transformed by higher plants through activation or deactivation reactions such as oxidation, reduction, hydrolysis, and conjugation. The rate of herbicide metabolism is very much dependent upon the plant species, giving rise to herbicide selectivity. Certain herbicides are much more rapidly degraded or metabolized by tolerant species and in most cases, the metabolic reactions are catalyzed by specific plant enzymes.

Herbicide biotransformations in higher plants involve a combination of enzymatic reactions, which through a series of intermediates result in the formation of soluble or insoluble herbicide residues that are subsequently stored or compartmentalized in plant cells. In general, herbicide metabolism in plant tissues is divided into three phases. Phase I enzymes oxidize (mainly hydroxylate), reduce, or hydrolyze herbicidal substrates, introducing reactive groups that can serve as sites for the subsequent conjugation to endogenous moieties such as glutathione, glucose, and selected amino acids, catalyzed by enzymes of phase II. In turn, phase I and phase II reactions are coupled to internal compartmentation and storage processes that comprise phase III of herbicide metabolism in plants. Cellular storage sites are the vacuole for soluble conjugates and the cell wall for insoluble conjugates. Enzyme classes catalyzing the major transformation and conjugation reactions of herbicides in higher plants include the cytochrome P450-dependent monooxygenases, glutathione S-transferases, UDP-glucosyltransferases, and hydrolytic enzymes (e.g., carboxylesterases and amidases). Selected examples of such plant enzymes and their herbicidal substrates are listed in Table II.

In some cases, differential metabolism changes an inactive compound or proherbicide to an active one and accounts for herbicide selectivity. The most cited example of such a case is that of the β-oxidation of 2,4-DB to 2,4-D by susceptible broadleaved weeds. Small-seeded legume crops are tolerant to 2,4-DB because they are not efficient in converting 2,4-DB to 2,4-D by means of β-oxidation.

C. Role of Other Chemicals in Herbicide Selectivity

The addition of other chemicals can increase or decrease the activity and selectivity of herbicides. Several chemicals called safeners or antidotes have been shown to improve the tolerance of partially tolerant grass crops to herbicides without increasing the tolerance of susceptible weeds. A number of such chemicals are currently marketed either as prepackaged formulated mixtures with their respective herbicides or as seed dressings and protect many of the major grass crops against injury caused by several classes of herbicides. Herbicide safeners seem to protect grass crops by enhancing the levels and/or activities of all classes of plant enzymes that are involved in the metabolic deactivation of herbicides (Table II). In addition, a number of chemicals that are potent inhibitors of

TABLE II

Plant Enzyme Systems and Reactions Involved in Herbicide Metabolism

Enzyme class	Metabolic reaction	Herbicidal substrate
Cytochrome P450-dependent monooxygenases	Aryl hydroxylation	Aryloxyphenoxy-propionates
		Phenoxyalkanoates
		Imidazolinones
		Sulfonylureas
		Substituted ureas
		Bentazon
	N-Demethylation	Substituted ureas
Carboxylesterases	Hydrolysis of carboxyl esters	Aryloxyphenoxy-propionates
		D-Aryloxypropionates
		Phenoxyalkanoates
		Sulfonylureas
Amidases	Hydrolysis of amide esters	Anilides (propanil)
Glutathione S-transferases	Conjugation with glutathione	Triazines
		Chloroacetanilides
		Thiocarbamates
		Triazinones
		Sulfonylureas
		Nitrodiphenylethers
		Carbamates
UDP-glucosyl transferases	N-Glucosylation	Triazinones
		Chloramben
		Anilides
	O-Glucosylation	Phenoxyalkanoates
		Pentachlorophenol
		Bentazon
Malonyltransferases	Conjugation with malonic acid	Phenoxylkanoates
		Triazinones
		Nitrodiphenylethers
		Thiocarbamates
		Chloroacetanilides

herbicide-detoxifying enzymes are known to synergize the action of specific groups of herbicides in given crop and weed species. Additional information on the chemistry, uses, and mechanisms of action of herbicide safeners and synergistics can be found in references listed in the bibliography.

VI. Plant Resistance to Herbicides

In response to agricultural manipulations, weed species, or ecotypes within a species, that are best adapted to a particular practice are selected for and gradually increase in the mixed population of an agroecosystem. Over the past 50 years, repeated use on the same site of herbicides with similar modes of action has imposed selection for increased resistance within or among species that had been previously susceptible.

Although herbicide resistance in weeds has a more recent history than either insecticide or fungicide resistance, herbicide-resistant biotypes of several weed species have become widespread in recent years.

At present, there are over 100 weed species with biotypes known to be resistant to one or more classes of herbicides in various locations around the world. Of those biotypes, more than half are resistant to triazine herbicides. The remaining weed biotypes are resistant to 14 other classes of herbicides including amides (e.g., propanil), arsenicals (e.g., MSMA), aryloxyphenoxypropionates (e.g., diclofop-methyl), bipyridyliums (e.g., paraquat), dinitroanilines (e.g., trifluralin), hydroxybenzonitriles (e.g., bromoxynil), phenoxyalkanoic acids (e.g., 2,4-D), phenylcarbamates, pyridine carboxylic acids (e.g., picloram), substituted pyridazinones (e.g., pyrazon), substituted ureas (e.g., chlortoluron), sulfonylureas (e.g., chlorsulfuron), aminotriazoles (e.g., amitrole), and uracils (e.g., bromacil).

The major characteristics of herbicides and their use that are contributing to a high risk for evolution of herbicide-resistant weed biotypes include: (a) herbicide has a single target site and specific mechanism of action; (b) herbicide is extremely active and effective in controlling a wide range of weed species; (c) herbicide provides long soil residual and season-long control of germinating weed seeds; (d) herbicide is applied frequently and over several growing seasons without rotating, alternating, or combining with other types of herbicides. Most of these characteristics are correlated quite well with the aforementioned classes of herbicides that have been selected for resistance.

Of special concern in recent years is the development of multiple resistance of some weed biotypes to many herbicides. Multiple resistance describes the evolution of weed biotypes resistant to a series of chemically unrelated herbicides with different mechanisms of action. Thus, multiple resistance is different than cross-resistance, where an individual weed biotype resistant to one herbicide is generally resistant to other herbicides with similar chemistry or the same mechanism of action.

In contrast to herbicide tolerance, which is usually the result of differences in herbicide uptake, translocation, and metabolic detoxification, herbicide resistance in weeds is most often due to an alteration of the target site involved in the action of herbicides at the cellular level. Such a mechanism of resistance is definitely involved in most cases of evolved weed resistance to triazine, sulfonylurea, dinitroaniline, nitrile, substituted urea, and uracil herbicides. Weed resistance to paraquat appears to be due either to rapid sequestration of the herbicide, resulting in reduced paraquat levels at the plastidic site of action, and/or to rapid enzymatic detoxification of superoxide and other toxic forms of oxygen due to elevated levels or activities of antioxidants (e.g., glutathione) and protecting enzymes (e.g., superoxide dismutase). The remaining cases of weed resistance to herbicides seem to be due to enhanced herbicide metabolism. Enhanced metabolism resulting in detoxification of several herbicide classes is also the most likely mechanism involved in multiple herbicide resistance that has been detected in some weed biotypes.

The need for recognizing, preventing, and managing herbicide resistance in weeds is imperative for preserving herbicides as tools of agricultural technology. Some of the strategies that have been suggested for managing herbicide-resistant weed biotypes include mixing and/or rotating herbicides and cropping practices, using more cultivation, and controlling seed set by the resistant weed biotypes. Herbicide rotations should be based on herbicides with different chemistries and different mechanisms of action, to avoid problems of cross- and multiple resistance.

Continuing advances in our understanding of the mechanisms and the genetic basis of weed resistance to herbicides coupled with the ever-growing difficulty and increasing costs for discovering new herbicides have stimulated great interest in introducing herbicide resistance into selected crop species. This type of research has many potential benefits as well as risks. Genetic modification of crops to make them resistant to herbicides could improve herbicide selectivity and allow the wider use of effective herbicides that have a broad weed control spectrum, but they lack crop selectivity (e.g., glyphosate). On the other hand, the use of herbicide-resistant crops may present us with two potential problems. The first is related to the potential transfer of herbicide resistance via pollen from a resistant crop to formerly susceptible weedy relatives, as well as the potential establishment of weeds as escapes from a resistant crop. The second potential problem is the selection of resistant weeds with an increased risk of developing cross-resistance to more than one herbicide, leading to the need for applying new herbicides to the weedy populations.

Bibliography

Caseley, J. C., Cussans, G. W., and Atkin, R. K. (1991). "Herbicide Resistance in Weeds and Crops." Butterworth-Heinemann, Oxford.

Devine, M. D., Duke, S. O., and Fedtke, C. (1993). "Physiology of Herbicide Action." Prentice Hall, Englewood Cliffs, NJ.

Hathway, D. E. (1989). "Molecular Mechanisms of Herbicide Selectivity." Oxford Univ. Press, Oxford.

Hatzios, K. K. (1991). Biotransformations of herbicides in higher plants. In "Environmental Chemistry of Herbicides" (R. Grover and A. J. Cessna, eds.), Vol. II, pp. 141–185. CRC Press, Boca Raton, FL.

Hatzios, K. K., and Hoagland, R. E. (1989). "Crop Safeners for Herbicides: Chemistry, Uses, and Mechanisms of Action." Academic Press, San Diego.

Majur, B. J., and Falco, S. C. (1989). The development of herbicide resistant crops. Annu. Rev. Plant Physiol. Plant Mol. Biol. 40, 441–470.

TeBeest. D. O. (1991). "Microbial Control of Weeds." Chapman and Hall, London.

Warwick, S. I. (1991). Herbicide resistance in weedy plants: Physiology and population biology. Annu. Rev. Ecol. Syst. 22, 95–114.

Weed Science Society of America (1989). "Herbicide Handbook," 6th ed. Weed Science Society of America, Champaign, IL.

Heterosis

JOHN A. HOWARD, *Pioneer Hi-Bred International*

Glossary

Dominance Alleles which express the phenotype in the heterozygous state
Heterozygosity Having one or more dissimilar alleles
Hybrid Offspring from genetically dissimilar parents
Inbreeding Mating between individuals of the same genotype
Quantitative traits Traits which show no clear-cut segregation. Phenotypes which show more of a continuous effect, and require the action of several genes to express the variation

Heterosis is a phenomenon where the first generation of offspring show an improvement in the quality of a trait or traits as compared to either of the parents. Heterosis does not refer to any particular mechanism or theory as to how this phenomenon occurs.

I. Introduction

Heterosis is often described as the superior performance of a trait or traits. Herein lies the first problem. How do we judge what is superior? We must first define the trait or traits of interest. In the simplest case, we could focus on one trait, and ideally, we would have a single gene responsible for that trait.

Then, it is necessary to agree that superior quality for one person is the same for another. Therefore, at best, this is a subjective judgment call. After reaching agreement on what improved quality means for a particular trait, we must agree on what improved quality means when dealing with multiple traits. If one individual shows heterosis with one trait and another individual shows heterosis for a different trait, which one shows greater overall heterosis? Because of this dilemma, heterosis is usually measured for one simple trait or a broad quantitative trait which encompasses the overall productivity of the entire organism, such as yield.

As we begin to measure heterosis, we find another subjective dilemma. The heterotic effect may vary dramatically in different environments. Breeders have known for years the effect that environment can have on a particular genotype. This means that a hybrid may show a large effect in one particular location, but it may be greatly reduced in another location. This genotype by environment interaction, therefore, can reduce the heterosis effect or make it more pronounced.

Most of the heterotic effects studied today are not single gene effects. Therefore, in measuring heterosis, we need to deal with complex traits and multiple traits at one time. While there appear to be endless combinations of how to define improved quality of traits, most people have come to some agreement in principle how to define the qualities used to measure heterosis. It is important to note, however, that while there can be agreement, this is not based on an absolute standard. As more and more research is done, the confusion can grow as to what heterosis is unless we get a more specific definition. Heterosis will have value only as it relates to specific traits and agreed upon definitions of quality improvement. Since heterosis does not describe a mechanism, this leaves open many possibilities of the cause of heterosis.

II. Description of the Phenomenon

How did we arrive at the basic concept of heterosis? Like many other areas in science, this has been an evolutionary process. From the definition, one of the first things needed to get the effect is to have a hybrid. Kölreuter in 1876 generally described the effect of superior hybrids. In his original experiments, he crossed nicotiana plants to make hybrids. He observed that the hybrids had an increase in size compared to the parents because the hybrids had larger leaves. These plants were "superior" to their parents. This was the beginning of our current concept of heterosis.

Creating hybrids with improved attributes does not, in itself, mean that you have heterosis. Darwin predicted that bringing in new traits into a species would give the species a better chance of survival under different selection pressures. This theory, however, does not explain why the hybrids should be more vigorous than their parents, only that adding different traits will allow for increased chance of survival.

If it is possible to get improvements in traits into the germplasm, why not just select those genes and develop superior inbred lines? This can be done in some species but not others. One reason it does not always work is because of the phenomenon known as inbreeding depression. With inbreeding depression, to become purer, lines are continually selfed rather than outcrossed. It becomes more difficult in some species to keep these lines vigorous as they become homozygous. This is usually explained by the occurrence of deleterious recessive genes. As inbreeding continues, more and more recessive genes can express their deleterious effect. While this may be unrelated to the heterotic effect for one particular trait, this can lead to a decrease in overall performance of the line. This concept explains why developing hybrids allows new genes into the germplasm without the problems of inbreeding depression. This gets us closer to heterosis as we know it today. Eliminating inbreeding depression alone, however, does not necessarily ensure heterosis.

The accepted definition of heterosis today encompasses these earlier concepts with the addition of one key element. This was first discussed by Shull in 1907. Shull differentiated between a hybrid's increase in performance over inbreds on crosses either made with specific inbreds or produced by random crosses. In his original experiment, he developed pure lines of two different types of corn. He crossed these lines,

and his results are shown in Table I. Shull was able to show the performance of the hybrid corn was much greater than either one of the pure lines. He went beyond this and showed that other hybrid combinations did not give the same effect. He was not just eliminating inbreeding depression or deleterious traits. He was able to show that specific crosses with the pure lines gave better results than were achieved by random crosses of noninbred plants. This extremely important observation discriminated his work from others before. This gives us the accepted concept of heterosis as it is used today.

From this concept, we can derive a simple equation which can determine whether particular lines have a heterotic effect, and if so, how much. This can be defined where H is heterosis value and F_1 is the first generation progeny of a cross between two lines. The equation then is:

H = The mean value of the progeny minus the mean value of the parents
or
$$H = F_1 - (P_1 + P_2)/2.$$

This heterosis value can be defined with either a specific trait or any combination of traits you choose to measure.

There often appears to be confusion between heterosis, yield, quantitative trait loci, and heterozygosity. Heterosis can be linked to all of these different phenomena. It is not synonymous with any of these which causes the confusion.

One common misconception is that an increase in yield means an increase in heterosis. High yielding inbred lines are the norm in some self-pollinating crops such as wheat. Since these are not hybrids, this clearly shows that yield and heterosis are not identical. In addition, a yield increase in hybrid lines does not necessarily require a heterotic effect. Yield of hybrids can be increased by reducing inbreeding depression. As pointed out earlier, heterosis requires more than this.

Heterosis is not normally used in reference to single gene traits but rather complex traits. Quantitative traits are usually those that are difficult to measure without error and appear to be inherited as multiple genes, rather than as single genes. Quantitative traits such as yield and stress tolerance are often the targets for exploiting heterosis. In trying to select for superior performance in these quantitative traits, the degree of heterosis can play the major role. These quantitative traits, however, could be involved in pure-line crops

TABLE I

Average Values in the Families of White Dent Maize Grown in 1910, Grouped According to the Types of Mating of the Parents

Pedigree numbers	Parental grain-rows	Number of stalks	Av. No. of grain-rows	Heights in Dms.	Wts. in lbs average	Yields bu/acre
Families from inbreds selfed						
E1.16	8 Selfed	57	10.0	17	9.8	24.4
E2.19	8 Selfed	83	9.0	18	22.0	29.6
E7.29	10 Selfed	79	11.1	20	18.3	33.9
E9.32	12 Selfed	80	12.3	17	11.4	20.9
E11.34	A(8) Selfed	75	8.8	16.5	9.1	18.1
E19.47	B(14) Selfed	53	12.9	24	7.3	11.0
E24.54	14 Selfed	66	13.8	23	16.3	25.8
E26.56	18 Selfed	82	15.2	19	15.3	22.9
E34.67	22 Selfed	62	17.9	19	11.0	19.2
E36.71	26, 28 Selfed	72	15.2	19	17.5	34.2
	Unweighted averages	71	12.6	19.3	10.7	25.0
Families from inbreds pollinated by sibs selfing prevented						
E1.17	10xsibs	61	10.2	19	13.8	29.8
E2.20	10xsib	75	9.9	18	21.0	39.5
E7.30	12xsib	85	11.0	22	18.3	37.3
E11.35	A(8)xsib	55	9.5	16	7.5	16.0
E19.48	B(12)xsib	54	12.7	24	5.3	7.8
E26.57	18xsib	89	15.8	20	24.5	37.8
E34.68	20xsib	65	17.9	20	15.3	25.6
E36.72	?(fasc.)xsib	73	22.5	20	18.3	35.2
	Unweighted averages	61	13.7	19.2	15.5	28.7
Families from parents given mixed pollen in each generation: selfing prevented						
E3.23	8, 10 crossbred	88	9.5	22	30.8	49.9
E8.31	10 crossed	65	10.3	22	31.0	68.1
E18.46	12 crossed	91	13.2	24	51.0	80.1
E23.53	14 crossed	94	13.7	27	49.0	74.5
E25.55	16 crossed	95	14.9	28	48.8	73.3
E30.63	18 crossed	202	16.0	22.5	76.8	54.3
E33.66	20 crossed	100	18.5	23	35.8	51.1
E35.70	20, 22 crossed	45	20.0	21	26.3	83.3
E37.73	24, 20 crossed	69	24.2	22	24.5	50.7
E40.75	32 crossed	56	19.2	24	22.5	57.4
E40.76	32 crossed	99	26.2	23	39.0	56.3
	Unweighted averages	91.3	16.9	23.5	39.6	63.5

Original data of G. H. Shull showing heterosis in corn. From Shull, G. H. (1952). "Heterosis: Beginnings of the Heterosis Concept" (J. W. Gowen ed.), pp. 14–48. Hafner, New York.

as well as hybrid crops and, therefore, are not necessarily linked to heterosis.

The third area of confusion is heterozygosity. This is often linked directly to heterosis. For practical reasons, this can be a good working model. However, since we are not implying a mechanism for the definition of heterosis, this needs to be a correlation and cannot be used interchangeably. Heterozygosity in referring to the mixture of the chromosomes would allow greater opportunity for heterosis to occur. If, however, in the simple case where we are measuring heterosis of a single trait, we can bring a different form of a single gene which is not superior. In this way, lines could be heterozygous for a particular trait; however, the trait would not show superior qualities, and no heterotic effect would be observed. This logic can also be applied on a larger scale with complex traits.

III. Possible Mechanisms

A. Genetics

Heterosis cannot be explained by simple mendelian genetics nor can it be explained by overcoming inbreeding depression. This has led to different theories to explain the phenomenon based on the ability of recessive and dominant genes to be selected differentiality. First, consider the example of detrimental dominant genes. These will be highly selected against, in nature or under artificial selection, and will be eliminated easily from the germplasm. In contrast, detrimental, recessive genes can remain in the germplasm much longer since they will only be selected against when they are homozygous. This can explain why inbreeding depressing occurs and why hybrids would be beneficial.

A second hypothesis is that heterosis occurs through the accumulation of dominant favorable alleles at different loci. Under this hypothesis, each parent will contribute favorable dominant genes to the hybrid progeny. Because both parents are contributing a different set of favorable genes to the progeny, there is the potential for the effects of the genes at different loci to interact synergistically. This phenomenon is known as epistasis, and there are a number of studies in maize that have shown epistasis to be an important component of heterosis in specific crosses.

A third hypothesis is that of overdominance. This is a very old hypothesis and is based on the premise that heterozygosity *per se* is the cause of heterosis. Recently, there have been some biochemical and molecular data that support the idea that the gene products from a heterozygous locus can interact synergistically by forming enzymes (heterodimers) that out-perform the enzymes produced by the homozygous locus.

There are proponents of both the second and third hypotheses, and the disagreements between the advocates sometimes appear to be religious. It is likely that both mechanisms can be invalid to a greater or lesser extent in any given hybrid that is exhibiting heterosis.

As mentioned earlier, heterozygosity is sometimes confused with heterosis. In practice, however, this is a way to increase the probability of a heterotic response in the germplasm. While the correlation is good, it is not absolute. Using the tools of molecular biology, DNA markers can measure the relative similarities between different inbred lines. In corn, the correlation between heterosis and similarity of parents was 76%. While this is a good correlation, the correlation with yield was 87%. This raises many questions. The simplest explanation is that not all loci have an equal affect on heterosis. Therefore, to obtain a better correlation, some of the loci should be weighted; which suggests it is not the absolute amount of hetero-

zygosity but rather there are key segments of DNA that are critical.

In studying heterosis, we need to look at the cytoplasmic organelles as well as the nuclear genes. In the case of plants, the genetics of chloroplasts and mitochondria can have an affect on heterosis. It is well documented that reciprocal crosses have different effects on yield and heterosis. This is attributed by the fact that the mitochondria and chloroplast are donated only from the female in hybrids. These cytoplasmic genes, however, can have different affects in combination with nuclear genes. In some cases such as barley, the heterosis in mitochondria can be correlated to the overall effect on yield heterosis. However, this does not hold true in all cases.

B. Physiology/Cell Biology

There are many different observations that have been made with heterosis, but it is difficult to determine the cause and the effect. Attempts are usually made to correlate physiological functions with phenotypic traits such as yield or vigor. In all of the cases discussed below, heterosis can be seen for the precise function described. In all of the cases described below, there are exceptions where no heterosis has been observed. Attempts to correlate each function independently with yield or vigor have also shown examples where they correlate and examples where there was no correlation.

One physiological function examined was uptake. It has been shown that hybrids can have increased rates of uptake and utilization of nutrients than their parent inbreds. By assimilating key nutrients, the hybrid could have a competitive advantage if this were rate limiting in development. This could allow the hybrid to obtain an overall advantage. It is not clear that the lines that do not correlate are due to the fact that uptake is not rate limiting in these lines or that there is not a cause and effect relationship.

There are examples where amino acid levels have been shown to be increased in hybrids compared to their parent lines. This could give advantages to the hybrids for protein synthesis or other metabolites that are derived from amino acids. There is no solid evidence on how often either the amino acids or their derivatives can be rate limiting in development. There is good evidence, however, that these can delay development. One simple explanation is that key enzymes that are rate limiting cannot be made without the proper amino acids. This explanation has merit but is not without exceptions. As above, the reasons for the exceptions are unclear.

Protein synthesis has been one of the more studied effects of heterosis. It has been shown that the rates of protein synthesis can be increased in hybrids over that of inbreds. This could be as a result of amino acid levels as discussed above or increased translation rates. In addition, a different set of proteins has been shown to express only in the hybrids. Therefore, in addition to the rate, there may be novel proteins formed that can increase the overall rate of growth. Alternatively, these could also be different forms of the proteins (changes in phosphortation, methylation, etc.) There are no studies, to date, that have been able to show a clear correlation with any of these new or altered proteins with heterosis.

The rates of DNA and RNA synthesis have been shown to increase in some hybrids as compared to their inbreds. In some cases, ploidy level has been shown to correlate with heterosis. In other cases, the histone/DNA ratio has been correlated with heterosis. Clearly, DNA, RNA, and protein levels can be related to each other through the process of transcription and translation, but none of the examples, to date, have been studied in enough detail to differentiate if there is a direct correlation between them.

A key element for plant development is photosynthesis. It should not be surprising that there have been cases where the rates of photosynthesis are greater in the hybrids than in their parents. This has been correlated in some instances with increases in overall performance of the hybrid. Since photosynthesis is key to plant growth, it can be agreed that this is a likely target for heterosis. Alternatively, you may predict that whatever the mechanism of heterosis is, it would ultimately affect photosynthesis. For both theories, cause and affect relationships have not been observed and absolute correlation has not been seen. [See PHOTOSYNTHESIS.]

It was mentioned earlier that there is a genetic correlation with mitochondria heterosis and grain yield. This can also be seen at the physiological level by either an increase in respiration rates or an increase in ATP synthesis for hybrids compared with their parents. These processes would seem to be likely targets to provide the hybrids with more energy. The lack of an absolute correlation would suggest, at least in some cases, that it may be the regulation of energy after it is acquired and not just rate of synthesis of these high energy molecules.

Despite all of these observations, there has been no universal theory; all show exceptions in correlating

heterosis at the whole organism level. Many of these could be related to each other, but no systematic study has been done. The conclusions would suggest that we must look in much more detail to decipher cause and effect relationships. Because of the diversity of results, however, it is likely that any one of these functions could be involved in heterosis in a particular cross. [See PLANT PHYSIOLOGY.]

C. Biochemistry

Since no major function can correlate with overall heterosis, it seems highly unlikely that there is one specific molecule that is responsible. There has been no evidence for a "heterosis factor" that when present, creates hybrid vigor. There have been, however, very useful studies with some key proteins that give insight as to how heterosis may occur if restricted to a specific trait.

There are examples of enzymes showing a heterotic effect. As mentioned above, photosynthesis can show a heterotic effect, and in some cases correlates to heterosis in the whole plant. The enzyme ribulose bisphosphate carboxylase has shown heterosis with respect to its enzymatic activity. This key enzyme could be responsible for the effect in photosynthesis since it plays a key role in photosynthesis. Also, nitrate reductase has been shown to exhibit heterosis in some cases. It has been speculated that this could cause an increase in nitrate assimilation and the overall increase in the rate of growth.

A more detailed analysis of one enzyme such as acid phosphatase may explain how heterosis can occur with enzymes. In this example, heterosis for increased enzyme activity was observed. This could be reflected both in the decrease of K_m values and the increase of V_{max}. Table II shows the values for both the homodi-

TABLE II

Comparison of Biochemical Properties of Acid Phosphatase from F/F, S/S, and F/S Genotypes

Biochemical property	Genotype		
	F/F	S/S	F/S
Specific activity (μm/min/mg protein)	5.55	8.95	12.01
K_m	6.8×10^{-4}	4.0×10^{-4}	3.6×10^{-4}
V_{max}	7.95	11.80	14.60

Source: Trehan, K. S., and Gill, K. S. (1987). Subunit interaction: a molecular basis of heterosis. Biochem. Genet. **25** (11/12).

mer and the heterodimer. Each parent makes a different homodimer, but the optimum K_m and V_{max} are obtained in the heterodimer. This example may explain, in principle, overdominance since the optimum activity requires the synergy of both genes. It has been specified that this is due to a structural change in protein conformation, but detailed studies have not been done.

D. Molecular Biology

Little is known, to date, of the impact of molecular biology on heterosis. While there has been great progress in molecular biology, there has been a relatively small effort, to date, at examining heterosis at the molecular level. There are, however, some possibilities that people have suggested.

One way of regulating transcription is through methylation of DNA. This relatively simple reaction can cause DNA sequences to become inaccessible for transcription. DNA from different sources may be less likely to be methylated or the methylation gene may be less active in heterozygotes. This would allow greater expression of key genes which could increase overall performance. Alternatively, certain key genes could be methylated rather than a random decrease in methylation for all chromosomal DNA.

A more recent observation is that of co-suppression. In this case, when a gene is transformed into a cell with similar genes present, this new gene causes a down-regulation of the other similar gene(s). The mechanism for co-suppression is not yet known. The phenomenon, however, suggests that versions of genes which are different in sequence, but perform the same function, may be at an advantage. The greater the diversity in the gene, the more likely co-suppression would not be a factor. This molecular observation could easily help explain the correlation between heterozygosity and heterosis.

Today we know of many ways of regulating transcription and translation. Any of these mechanisms, in principle, could affect heterosis. A cascade effect, however, could help explain the many different observations seen on a number of different physiological or biochemical events. While it is tempting to speculate, there is no evidence at this time to support this.

IV. Use in Agriculture

To say heterosis has had a profound effect in agriculture would be an understatement. This is not because of extensive research in this area. This has been due to breeding programs designed to improve performance, and in doing so, the heterotic effect has been observed. This has been shown in microorganisms, fish, chicken, cattle, and plants. Many crops are being bred today as hybrids because of the effect heterosis has on performance as shown in Table III. It shows a sample of different crops which are sold as hybrids today. The range of crops suggests that this is a general phenomenon and understanding it should benefit mankind enormously as it could lead to controlling it in a more precise manner.

The most notable heterotic effect has been in corn. Figure 1 shows the effect in corn. The parents show reduced stature and grow slower and less than the hybrid. In addition, the grain produced is much greater in the hybrid. In this example, hybrid grain yields of 175 bushels per acre are common in contrast to the parents with yields of 40 and 60 bushels per acre. This dramatic example explains why heterosis has enormous practical implications for the production of corn. [See CORN GENETICS AND BREEDING.]

There are many different types of breeding regimes used for different crops to produce heterosis. In the case of corn, a popular method is that of the single cross. This is where a pure line inbred is produced and crossed with a second pure line. There can be many variations of this strategy; however, this is the simplest.

There are many advantages in producing hybrids. Foremost, is that the yield of the hybrid can be increased dramatically over the parent lines. In addition, there are other characteristics that are useful: (1) increased stress tolerance, (2) uniformity in offspring, (3) ability to bring in traits from two different parent lines to get the desired phenotype, and (4) elimination of inbreeding depression. It is important to note that while all of these are advantages of hybrids, not all are necessarily due to heterosis. Using various breeding schemes it should be possible to put all of the genes that have desirable phenotypes into one line. If this could be done, by definition, there would be no heterosis. The reason this is not done is there is no way to propagate hybrid lines by seeds without segregating. Once the line starts segregation, uniformity is lost and so is the performance advantage. If all desirable genes were bred into a pure line, then the problems of inbreeding depression could occur.

Taking advantage of heterosis in hybrid lines raises several other issues. The most notable is the increase in cost to produce the hybrid lines. There are several reasons for this. One reason is that two separate lines must be maintained for production purposes rather than one. These lines must be continually selfed and

TABLE III

Past and Potential Introduction of Commercial Hybrid Varieties in Food Crops, Largely Relating to North American Experience

Before 1955		1955–1974		1975–1990	
Crop	Year	Crop	Year	Crop	Year
Field corn (*Zea mays*)[m]	1921	Sorghum (*Sorghum bicolor*)[s]	1955	Asparagus (*Asparagus officinalis*)[d]	1975
Sweet corn (*Z. mays*)[m]	1933	Sugar beet (*Beta vulgaris*)[i]	1957	Celery (*Apium graveolens*)[c]	1975
Eggplant (*Solanum melongena*)[s, a]	1939	Broccoli (*Brassica oleracea*)[i]	1961	Oats (*Avena spp.*)[s]	1980
Summer squash (*Cucurbita pepo*)[m]	1941	Spinach (*Spinacea oleracea*)[d]	1961	Rye (*Secale cereale*)[i]	1980
Tomato (*Lycopersicon esculentum*)[s]	1943	Beetroot (*Beta vulgaris*)[p]	1962	Potato (*Solanum tuberosum*)[c]	1980
Slicing cucumber (*Cucumis sativus*)[m]	1945	Bussels sprouts (*Brassica oleracea*)[i]	1963	Soyabean (*Glycine max*)[s]	1980
Onion (*Allium cepa*)[c]	1948	Carrot (*Daucus carota*)[p]	1964	Haricot bean (*Phaseolus vulgaris*)[s]	1985
Watermelon (*Citrullus lanatus*)[m]	1949	Pearl millet (*Pennisetum typhoides*)[q]	1965	Field bean (*Vicia faba*)[s]	1985
Winter squash (*Cucurbita spp.*)[m]	1950	Coconut (*Cocos nucifera*)[c]	1965	Peas (*Pisum sativum*)[s]	1985
Pepper (*Capsicum annuum*)[s]	1954	Cauliflower (*Brassica oleracea*)[i]	1966	Lettuce (*Lactuca sativa*)[s]	1990
Muskmelon (*Cucumis melo*)[m]	1954	Lucerne (*Medicago sativa*)[i]	1968		
Pickling cucumber (*Cucumis sativus*)[m]	1954	Barley (*Hordeum vulgare*)[s]	1968		
Cabbage (*Brassica Oleracea*)[i]	1954	Wheat (*Triticum aestivum*)[s]	1969		
		Rice (*Oryza sativa*)[s]	1972		
		Sunflower (*Helianthus annuus*)[i]	1972		

Source: Mayo, O. (1987). "The Theory of Plant Breeding: Heterosis," 2nd ed. pp. 138–166. Clarendon Press, Oxford.

Note: a, Andromonoecious; c, cross-fertilizing but self-compatible; d, dioecious; i, self-incompatible; m, monoecious; p, protandrous; q, protogynous; s, self-fertilizing.

not outcrossed until the time F_1 seed is produced for the farmers to grow. In order for the farmer to grow high yielding hybrids, the seed producers must propagate the low yielding inbreds.

To produce pure hybrid seed another increase in cost results from the fact that in a given cross one inbred is designated as male and the other female. Males are used only for their pollen and then discarded. Only the seeds from females are used. The male rows and the potential seed which may be produced would not be acceptable. It would not show the superior quality or uniformity the farmer expects. This also adds the increase of cost production.

One of the most expensive aspects of this type of production rests on the fact that crops such as corn can self-pollinate. If this occurs, an inbred line is produced instead of a hybrid. Because of the dramatic difference in yield between the hybrid and the self, this is unacceptable for farmers. At first, ensuring that no selfs occurred was done by manual detasseling in corn. This method is still in practice today. Manual detasseling, however, is now more likely to be used in crops in combination with mechanical detasseling. This is still labor intense and requires a costly effort to achieve the uniformity and quality farmers expect.

Another method of producing male steriles has been achieved using a cytoplasmic male sterility factor. This factor has been studied extensively using genetics, biochemistry, and most recently molecular biology techniques. Long before it was understood,

however, it was in wide use. To use this in the production of hybrids, you must first breed the factor into the female parent of the hybrid. It is important to obtain near isogenic lines of the inbred such that other performance characteristics of the inbred are unchanged. This new line would be male sterile and, therefore, eliminate/reduce the need to detassel the corn to prevent it from self-pollinating. This saves much of the labor involved in manual or mechanical detasseling methods. In this way, the sterility characteristic can be left out for maintenance of pure lines. However, for production fields, male sterile lines would be used.

Besides corn, many other crops such as sunflower and sorghum have known cytoplasmic male sterility systems. A potential danger occurs if a large majority of growers use the same cytoplasmic male sterility source. This was the case in 1970 when it was discovered that one cytoplasmic male sterility source for corn was linked with susceptibility to a particular disease. Since the majority of the industry used this method, a significant portion of the corn crop was affected. This has led the industry to be more aware of using only a single source of genetic male sterility in their production.

Most recently, a new method of producing male sterility has been demonstrated using recombinant DNA technology. This has some advantages over previous methods used. The new technology involves nuclear genes that are toxic to the cell or eliminate a

FIGURE 1 Heterosis in corn. The plants on the left and right are the parents of the hybrid in the middle which shows hybrid vigor. Grain yield for the parents is typically 40 and 60 bu/acre while the hybrid yields 175 bu/acre.

inbreds much more difficult. This makes breeding much more of a challenge and increases the cost.

Another feature of hybrids is subsequent generations showing an increase in segregation and thus a decrease in overall quality. The farmer cannot save the F_2 seed and plant it the following year without suffering a decrease in yield relative to the hybrid. While this appears to be a disadvantage, this does have some benefits. Companies that produce seed can be assured that farmers will buy new seed every year. This added revenue translates to an incentive to do new research to develop new hybrid lines with improved quality. This has been the case for corn which has shown over a 1% increase in yield on average per year.

V. Future Prospects

Heterosis will continue to be used in agriculture because of its many advantages. While this presents some unique problems, the benefit outweighs the cost in many cases. Recent progress in molecular biology adds new dimensions to how it can be studied. These new molecular tools add to the genetics, biochemistry, and physiology that have been studied previously. It is now possible to bridge the gap between a phenotype and what physiological, biochemical, and molecular event led to this trait. This should make it possible to develop detailed mechanisms for heterosis.

From what we know to date, it is unlikely we will find a single mechanism to describe heterosis. Since heterosis can be described for any trait there may be different mechanisms for different traits. For complex traits such as yield, it is possible that there are several mechanisms. As people start to unravel different quantitative traits with the use of DNA markers, it will help unravel the more complex versions of heterosis as well. Genes are rapidly now being sequenced and mapped; therefore, we should eventually be able to use these to go back and identify which genes are responsible for a specific genetic effect at a particular locus. In doing so, we should be able to understand not only the gene responsible for the genetic component of heterosis, but the biochemistry of the gene itself and how that relates to the physiological function. The tools now appear to be in place; we need only to use them. [*See* PLANT GENE MAPPING; PLANT GENETIC ENHANCEMENT.]

Bibliography

Fisher, R. A. (1965). "The Theory of Inbreeding: The Function of Inbreeding in Animal and Plant Improvement," 2nd ed. Academic Press, New York.

key step in metabolism. These can be controlled by using promoters specific to cells involved with pollen development. These promoters are combined with DNA sequences which can act as a switch to turn the genes off and on. While there are numerous possibilities of genes to use, none are in production today. This, however, seems only to be a matter of time. This technique may also give rise to hybrid crops which were impractical to produce without genetic engineering.

In addition to production, there are other problems involved in developing superior hybrids. By definition, heterosis shows improved qualities that are unexpected based on the parents alone. Therefore, the parents cannot be selected strictly for their ability to perform well in the field on their own. This has led to the use of tester lines. These are lines that must be crossed with the inbreds to see the potential for increasing yield. This makes directly evaluating the

Leonardi, A., Damerval, C., Hebert, Y., Gallais, A., and de Vienne, D. (1991). Association of protein amount polymorphism (PAP) among maize lines with performances of their hybrids. *Theor. Appl. Genet.* **82:**552–560.

Mayo, O. (1987). "The Theory of Plant Breeding," Chapt. 9, pp. 138–166, 2nd ed. Clarendon Press, Oxford.

McDaniel, R. G. (1986). Biochemical and physiological basis of heterosis. *CRC Crit. Rev. Plant Sci.* **4** (3):227–246.

Shull, G. H. (1952). "Heterosis," Chapt. 2. pp. 14–48. (J. W. Gowen, ed.). Hafner, New York.

Smith, O. S., Smith, J. S. C., Bowen, S. L., Tenborg, R. A., and Wall, S. J. (1990). Similarities among a group of elite maize inbreds as measured by pedigree, F_1 grain yield, grain yield, heterosis, and RFLPs. *Theor. Appl. Genet.* **80:**833–840.

Trehan, K. S., and Gill, K. S. (1987). Subunit interaction: a molecular basis of heterosis. *Biochem. Genet.* **25** (11/12).

Horse Industry: Trends, Opportunities, and Issues

ANN M. SWINKER, JAMES C. HEIRD, *Colorado State University*

Glossary

Appaloosa Breed of horse originating in the United States and is easily recognized by their varied coat color patterns; they are used today as stock and show horses

Arabian Breed of horse that originated over 2000 years ago in the mid-East and northern Africa and later in the desert of the Arabian Peninsula; foundation breed for most of today's breeds of horses

Breed associations Association of horse breeders forming a registry in order to record the lineage of their horses and protect the purity of the breed

Colt Youth male horse under 3 years of age

Donkey Small ass or burro; the male is a jack and the female is a jenny

Draft breeds Are usually tall in height, weigh 1400 pounds or more, and primarily used for pulling loads

Farrier Horse shoer

Foal Young horse of either sex up to yearling age

Mare Mature female horse 3 years of age and older

Morgan Breed that originated in the New England States, believed to be of the decent of one outstanding horse, Justin Morgan, an Arabian thoroughbred cross; used for pleasure riding and showing

Mule Cross between a mare and a jack

Paints American breed of horse that is recognized for its coat color patterns of white plus any other color; these horses are utilized today as stock, pleasure, and show purposes

Palominos American breed of horse originating from Spanish extraction; they are golden in color; palominos are used as stock, parade, pleasure, and show horses

Paso Finos These horses originated in Peru, Cuba, and Columbia are known for their paso fino gaits or a broken pace; they are used for pleasure, parade, or show horses

Purebred Bred from members of a recognized breed, without mixture of other blood and over many generations

Quarter Horse Breed of horse originating in the United States; this well-muscled and powerfully built horse is generally used as a stock, race, pleasure, and show horse

Racking Horses Horse that performs the rack gait, a fast, flashy unnatural four-beat gait, also known as the "single-foot"

Saddlebred Breed of horse that originated in the United States and was developed as a general purpose riding horse used on plantations; today they are used as show horses

Setback Space set between a building such as a barn and the neighboring property

Stallion Mature male 3 years of age or older

Tennessee Walking Horse Breed of horse that originated in the United States; known for their easy gaits and running walk; they are used today as pleasure and show horses

Thoroughbred Breed of horse that resulted from the crossbreeding of native British horses with Barb, Turk, and Arabian horses; they are today utilized for flat track racing, jumping, and dressage

Warm bloods Breeds or crosses of horses originating from crosses of hot-blooded horses (Arabians and

Thoroughbreds) with cold-blooded horses (Draft breeds); utilized for dressage, hunter/jumper, and sporting horses

Horses have helped mankind for centuries: in the beginning as a food source, later as draft power and transportation, and today as a recreational resource. The horse has been an integral part of American heritage since colonial days. In the United States, horse numbers reached a peak during the early 1900s and declined until the 1950s. The horse industry regained its popularity in the 1960s and again peaked during the 1980s. Since 1960 the majority of horses in the United States have been kept for recreational purposes.

From the early 1900s until the mid-1960s, horses were considered neither an industry nor a business. Today, horses are a large component of U.S. agriculture. The horse industry, like other agricultural enterprises, is often tied to the ever-changing national economy. The tax law changes created by the Tax Reform Act of 1986 influenced the industry's economic decline. The loss of investment credit, capital gains, depreciation limits, and reduced business expense deductibles drastically affected owners' and breeders' ability to profitably participate in the industry. However, with these economic changes came new industry trends and new opportunities. Today the industry is again growing; however, the direction is different than in the past. This direction will be explained in the following article.

I. Estimated American Horse Population

Various organizations have supplied differing estimates as to the number of horses in the United States today. The American Horse Council (AHC) (1987) estimated there were 5.25 million equine, while the American Veterinary Medical Association (1988) estimated there were 6.6 million equine in the United States. However, a more recent study, AVMA's 1991 study, estimated a decrease to 4.9 million. The AHC survey ranked the leading states in horse numbers, respectively, as (1) Texas, (2) California, (3) Oklahoma, (4) Colorado, (5) New York, (6) Ohio, (7) Michigan, (8) Pennsylvania, (9) Washington, and (10) Kentucky.

Estimating the U.S. horse population is difficult. Horses are no longer a part of the U.S. census. Many horses are kept as pleasure animals used only for recre-

ation. Horses have a long life span and are difficult to count as compared to population figures in other livestock species. Other studies have estimated the U.S. equine population to be higher than the estimates listed above. The United States Equine Marketing Association has estimated that there are 10.6 million head of horses.

II. Registered Stock and Breed Association Reports and Trends

The increase in the horse population numbers seen in the past two decades (Table I) has decreased the price of the average horse. Breeders attribute this to overproduction and to reduced recreational dollars.

The Tax Reform Act of 1986 caused many investors, who were passively involved in horse ownership, to lose the tax advantage incentive in owning horses. These owners quickly liquidated their stock, flooding the market with high-quality but inexpensive stock. As a result of this overproduction and overmarketing, many breeders in several of the light breeds decreased production. This trend can be seen in the stallion reports (reports sent to breed associations by stallion owners reporting the number of mares bred per stallion) from 1987 through 1991 (Table II). During this time, fewer mares were bred, while the number of breeding stallions decreased very slightly. This decrease in production can also be seen in the number of foals and horses being registered. Table III shows these declines.

Several breeds showed increases in numbers during this period. In particular, the number of draft breeds,

TABLE I

United States Horse and Mule Population (in Millions) from 1900 to 1988

1900[a]	21.5
1910[a]	24.0
1920[a]	25.2
1930[a]	18.9
1940[a]	13.9
1950[a]	7.6
1960[a]	3.0
1987[b]	5.25
1988[c]	6.6

[a] *Source*: USDA.
[b] *Source*: Economic Impact of the U.S. Horse Industry, 1987, American Horse Council.
[c] *Source*: American Veterinary Medical Association, 1988.

TABLE II
Breeding Statistics—Stallion Reports Filed

	Arabian		Quarter Horse		Appaloosa	
	Total stallions	No. of mares bred	Total stallions	No. of mares bred	Total stallions	No. of mares bred
1987	10,996	39,590	31,685	188,885	6382	23,655
1988	10,955	35,264	30,722	182,855	5997	22,332
1989	9480	31,000	28,163	157,514	5340	19,704
1990	8578	27,239	27,514	151,389	5101	18,551
1991	7254	22,467	26,779	142,969	4142	15,362

mules, miniature horses, warm bloods, Paints, Paso Finos, Palominos, and Racking Horses have risen or have remained the same. Despite the decline in horse production numbers, memberships and the number of equine activities have increased for the majority of the breed associations (Table IV). It should be noted that some of this increase may be due to recent changes in membership rules that require all owners to be members (such as was the case in the American Quarter Horse Association).

Despite the decline in foals registered during the last few years, the American Horse Council predicts that the American Quarter Horse will remain the largest registered breed of horse in America, with 2.8 million horses registered at the end of 1990. In addition, there are 715,116 Arabians and half-Arabians; 1,204,000 Thoroughbreds; 510,000 Appaloosas; 683,247 standardbreds; 194,981 Paints; 118,839 Morgans; 275,000 Tennessee Walking Horses; 215,096 Saddlebreds; 76,000 purebred ponies; 52,000 mules and donkeys; 23,000 Palominos; 20,000 Pintos; 15,000 Pasos; 357,000 other purebreds; and 844,000 nonregistered horses.

III. People Who Own Horses

The horse industry is made up of a diverse group of approximately 1 million owners. Participants range from those who utilize the horse as a business and investment to those who choose to spend their leisure time riding, driving, or contributing as a volunteer. According to a survey conducted by *Equus Magazine* in 1990, the average American horse owner owns three to five head of horses and is between the ages of 35 and 45 years. Owners have an average family income of $30–75,000 per year. Over 65% are women. The typical American horse owner resides in an open area zoned for agriculture on 10–49 acres

of land. The average horse owner who does not keep his or her horses at home drives 12.3 miles to board their horse.

The average American horse owner is well educated, middle income, and middle aged. He or she is willing to put forth the extra effort and dollars needed to enjoy their horse-related hobby. The average yearly cost of keeping a horse varies from $1000 to $15,000 per year, depending on training and use. Keeping a pleasure horse is a costly undertaking. Boarding a horse (stall space, bedding, and feed) averages from $150 to $250 per month. The cost of keeping a horse in training can range from $300 to $600 + a month. This cost varies with the type of training, quality of care, the success of the trainer, and many other factors. The average horse owner spends about $26 a month for veterinary fees. The average farrier fee can range from $48 to $75 per shoeing. The fee for transporting a horse to and from an event is 25 to 50¢ a mile. The average cost of participation in a horse show event can vary from $100 to $540 per show. Average riding lessons can range from $15 to $65 per hour.

IV. Economic Impact of the Horse Industry

According to previous surveys, horses are a $15.2 billion business in the United States. In addition, U.S. horse owners account for approximately $13 billion in annual investment and maintenance expenditures. They contribute significantly to the feed and seed industries, in addition to equipment manufacturers and retailers across the country. According to *Feed Management* magazine (1990), U.S. horses consumed 102 million tons of commercially prepared feed. [*See* FEEDS AND FEEDING.]

TABLE III

Breed Registration Figures 1960–1991

	1960	1968	1975	1980	1985	1986	1987	1988	1989	1990	1991
Anglo and half arabian	2200	9800	11,351	10,017	9854	6645	6200	6500	4775	4276	4251
Appaloosa	4052	12,389	20,175	25,384	16,189	14,551	12,589	12,317	10,746	10,669	9902
Arabian	2084	6974	15,658	19,726	30,004	28,283	26,421	24,569	21,723	17,676	12,993
Hackney	459	656	999	595	744	791	621	866	779	809	731
Miniatures	0	0	N/A	N/A	N/A	N/A	N/A	3986	4636	5760	5278
Morgan horse	1069	2134	3400	4537	4538	4329	3803	3526	3732	3618	3392
National show horse	0	0	0	0	856	927	1011	987	919	733	624
Paint	0	2390	5896	9654	12,692	11,273	15,518	14,929	14,390	16,153	18,648
Palomino	657	1262	1710	1637	1301	1518	1719	1747	2080	1598	1564
Paso Fino	0	0	380	645	1335	1323	1249	1464	1453	1550	1483
Quarter horse	35,507	65,326	97,179	137,090	157,360	153,773	147,007	128,352	123,294	110,597	101,390
Racking horse	0	0	N/A	N/A	N/A	N/A	N/A	4475	3500	4500	4500
Saddlebred	2329	3589	4064	3686	4351	4363	3918	3811	3708	3569	3570
Standardbred	6413	10,682	12,830	15,219	18,384	17,637	17,579	17,393	16,896	16,576	13,617
Tennessee walker	2663	8493	6591	6854	7812	8750	8712	8983	8850	7972	7852
Thoroughbred	12,901	22,911	28,271	35,679	50,429	51,293	50,915	49,179	48,500	44,000	42,000
Total reg. figures	70,334	146,606	208,504	270,723	315,849	305,456	297,262	382,075	269,981	250,056	231,795

Source: American Horse Council, 1992.

Note: Figures listed are for foals and horses registered in specific years: not a total horse population count.

TABLE IV
Membership in Organizations

	American Endurance Riding Conference	U.S. Dressage Federation	American Quarter Horse Association
1986	1500	4464	141,267
1987	1500	4753	127,706
1988	1500	5357	130,545
1989	1500	5870	255,059
1990	3500	6362	272,085
1991	3500	7159	276,577
1992	3830	7274	276,500

Note: Values represent members who are participating for awards and titles within the association.

Many support businesses benefit from the horse industry. Some professions are involved in the maintenance of horses: veterinarians, farriers, nutritionists, reproductive specialists, trainers, grooms, farm managers, instructors, and so on. There are other industries, such as insurance, equipment, saddleries, medical supplies, magazines, and clothing that deal directly with the horse owner. There are also other nonrelated businesses which are indirectly supported by the horse industry, such as restaurants, motels, gas stations, and other facets of the local economy that benefit from equine events and activities. In addition, there are capital investments in horses, acreage, barns and facilities, stables, arenas, fencing, trailers, tractors, trucks, hay, and other farm equipment.

Horse sporting events have quite a large impact on the communities in which they are located. Horse sports have been known to draw more than 110 million spectators annually. The American Horse Council (AHC) lists approximately 179 race tracks in the United States, located in 35 states. Attendance at U.S. race tracks exceeds 70 million people each year, with annual wagering on horse racing approaching $13 million. Thoroughbred racing alone in 1989 ranked as the nation's number one spectator sport according to the 43rd annual survey on sports attendance, drawing a record 56,194,565 as compared to major league baseball, which drew 55,173,096.

In addition to horse racing, there are 7000 sanctioned horse shows each year with thousands of local unsanctioned events. The attendance at these events is tremendous; the Walking Horse Celebration show in 1992 was attended by 243,120 spectators. Horse shows generate $223 million per year and rodeos alone contribute $104 million. Furthermore, each of these events generates millions of dollars for the local communities' economies. For example, the National Western Stock Show held in Denver, Colorado, with its large professional rodeo, drew more than 500,310 people and it is estimated that $42 million is spent in the Denver metro area by visitors during the show. This total does not include money paid for livestock or transportation to and from Denver. The total economic impact is estimated at $75 million.

A few of the many large shows that annually have economic impacts on the community in which they are conducted are: the Arabian National Horse Show held and sponsored by the International Arabian Association, which alternates between Louisville, Kentucky, and Albuquerque, New Mexico, and has been surveyed to have an economic impact of $26.3 million; and the American Quarter Horse World Champion Show, which impacts Oklahoma City with an estimated value of $16.5 million.

V. Equine Usage

Today's trend in the horse market is toward an athletic horse that the owner/rider/driver can ride and contest individually and personally. The current horse market demands a finished product; owners want to purchase horses that are trained and capable of meeting their needs. Horses that perform in the following events are in high demand for the 1990s.

Dressage. Dressage is a series of movements developed into a test that are designed to show the horse's fitness, suppleness, and obedience. A dressage test is designed to show the horse's capability in performing various maneuvers and gaits individually at differing levels of ability (Fig. 1).

FIGURE 1 Dressage is fast increasing in popularity with the amateur horseman. Margo McAllister Dippert riding Zoro, Dutch warmblood.

Show Jumping and Hunter Jumping. In these events the horse and rider demonstrate their ability, grace, beauty, and obedience while jumping barriers that confront a rider in a cross-country ride or stadium jump course.

Combined Training and Eventing. This is a combined competition demanding the rider to be experienced in all branches of equitation. The horse and rider must compete in a dressage test, show the speed and endurance of a cross-country test, and complete a stadium jumping course.

Driving. This event is designed to test the skill and versatility of a horse and driver, while performing at a walk, park gait (normal trot) and road gait (extended trot) while harnessed to a cart or wagon. Obstacle courses are also utilized in some driving competitions. Single and multiple hitches have increased in popularity over the last decade. Draft horses and mules, as well as light horse breeds, have seen increased participation in this area.

Polo. First introduced in the United States in 1876, this game is played by four mounted players on each team. The objective of the match is to drive a wooden ball utilizing mallets between goalposts at the end of a 300-yard-long field, while mounted on polo ponies.

Gymkhana. These events test the horse's and rider's agility, speed, and maneuverability. These events are races which are usually timed against a clock. The more popular events are pole bending and barrel racing.

Endurance and Competitive Trail Riding. The attraction of competitive trail riding is that any style or breed of horse can be used. However, the horse needs to be well-conditioned, sound, and calm. Both rider and horse train over all types of terrain. In competitive trail riding, the horse must travel a fixed distance within a fixed time while being judged on soundness and condition. In endurance riding, this event is primarily a race, usually over long distances.

Working Cow Horse. This division requires the horse to imitate numerous jobs common to ranch life. The horse must proficiently perform sliding stops, turns, and lead changes while under control. These events bring in a third component to the horse and rider: the cow. Other cattle performance classes which are popular because of the excitement involved and team participation are calf roping, team penning, team roping, and break-away roping.

Reining. The horse follows a prescribed pattern and is required to change leads, turn, stop, and back. The reining pattern is designed to show the horse's obedience and willingness to perform.

Cutting. This stems from one of the oldest practical uses of the western horse on the ranch—sorting cattle. This event is a true test of the horse's "cow sense," requiring a horse to separate a cow and keep it from returning to the herd during 2.5 min of competition.

Recreational Trail Riding. According to the Parks and Recreation Travel Statistical Abstract—1989, United States Bureau of Census, 20.3 million people visit national parks each year and over 8.5% of these participate in horseback riding. Many horsemen pack into the wilderness for a weekend overnight trail ride or spend their vacation packing and outfitting.

In summary, performance horses which can be ridden and entered in competition by the owner/amateur may be the new direction of the United States' horse industry. This new market for the one-horse owner has increased the value of the better performance horses.

The results of several surveys conducted in 1990–1991 by the American Quarter Horse Association, American Paint Horse Association, United States Equine Marketing Association, *Equus* magazine, *Southern Horseman's* magazine, and *The American Saddlebred* magazine, were similar. All agreed that the athletic horse is growing in popularity; however, horse usage can be subdivided as follows: about 2% of the horses in the United States are involved in racing, while 30% participate in show ring events, and nearly 70% participate in other competitive events such as dressage, combined training hunter/jumpers, driving, rodeo, polo, reining, cutting, endurance riding, trail riding, and others.

VI. Imports and Exports of Horses

Another new trend seen in the horse industry is an increase in exportation. During the 1970s and 1980s, the United States imported a high percentage of the horses sold abroad (Table V). Today we are exporting horses all over the world. Registered horse exports account for foreign sales of approximately $200 million annually. Total U.S. exports of registered Quarter Horses for 1989 alone were 4876 head. The majority went to Mexico, Japan, Brazil, and Europe. Total AQHA imports were 2015 head and the majority were from Canada. Exports have increased dramatically over the last decade due to the higher quality of U.S. horses produced and a European interest in our western style of riding. As we proceed into the 1990s this market trend is now beginning to level off.

Figures collected from 12 U.S. slaughter plants by the USDA Foreign Agricultural Services reported that 155,000,417 metric tons of horse meat (valued at $14,934,445) was shipped to Europe for specialty meats. Experts (unidentified sources) believe that these figures may be off by four to five times, and

TABLE V
U.S. Equine Imports and Exports

	Arabian		Quarter horse		Appaloosa	
	Imports	Exports	Imports	Exports	Imports	Exports
1984	422	144				
1987	122	189	N/A	N/A	N/A	97
1988	96	263	1983[a]	4577	N/A	141
1989	43	208	2015[a]	4876	N/A	255
1990	45	242	N/A	5267	N/A	250
1991	41	407	N/A	5418	N/A	260

Note: N/A, not available at the time.
[a] Majority are imported from Canada and Mexico.

the national value might be as high as $500–800 million for 1992. The increase to nearly $1/lb for "killer prices" seen in the 1991–1992 year has been economically healthy for the U.S. horse industry. With the proposed free-trade agreements between the U.S. and Mexican governments, horse exports for meat and breeding are expected to increase drastically in the mid-1900s.

VII. Business and Career Strengths and Weaknesses

With the changing trends seen in the horse industry of the 1990s, many segments of the horse world have become more lucrative and others less popular. The following are just a few examples of trends recently seen in the industry.

The amateur, one-horse owner is one of the new trends seen in the industry. With this new breed of horseman there has become a new demand for the all-around horse. These owners want to show, exhibit, and ride their own animals. As a result, the demand for breeding stock has declined.

Because many of today's owners do not live on a farm or horse property, the boarding stable business around metropolitan areas has seen a large increase. Several of the quality stables have as much as a 3-month waiting list for potential boarders. The demand for riding lessons has also increased. Riding instructions vary in costs from $15 to $65 per hour. More people are becoming interested in learning to ride a horse and they want to learn correct equitation. High cost of liability insurance and labor for the stable owner and riding instructor are limiting factors for assuring a profitable business today. The liability issue has greatly hurt the "horse for hire" rental business.

Breeding farms have reduced the number of foals produced due to lack of demand. Breeding stallion owners have seen drastic reductions in the number of outside mares being bred to their stallions. However, even though there are fewer horses being produced, breeders are producing higher quality stock. Many breed associations have accepted new scientific technology, such as artificial insemination, embryo transplant, and embryo splitting, which allows the production and propagation of the best genetic offspring possible.

The number of horse shows and exhibitors at shows has declined during the late 1980s. Many major shows recorded all time lows in exhibition numbers. A decline in the availability of recreational dollars and the increased cost of traveling are major reasons for the decline. However, events and shows that began to include the more popular events and activities such as dressage, cattle classes, and reining showed increases in numbers of participants.

Many of the support industries, business, and marketing trends fluctuate with the aforementioned horse industry businesses. Support businesses sell supplies or services to horse owners. These areas are feed, tack manufacturers, salesmen, clothing and boot makers, horse transporters, real estate agents, barn, fences and machinery companies, and many other related product producers. Many other professions also are affected by the cyclic nature of the horse industry.

Business opportunities within the recreational fields fluctuate with equine industry trends. Many of these fields include guest ranch employees, dude string wranglers, packers, outfitters, therapeutic riding programs, horse show organizers, photographers, fair and show grounds management, parks and trail management, and rodeos. Within each of these areas are other support fractions. For example, pick-up men, stock contractors, general management staff, working cattle breeders, and concessionaires comprise some of the support employment for the rodeo industry.

VIII. Careers in the Industry

Many areas of the horse industry require specific training. It often takes more than desire and experience; it takes training and perhaps even a college education. The combination of two or more fields is a key to success and employment in the equine career. A combination of management, accounting, business, biology, or nutrition along with a knowledge of the equine industry opens many doors. Employers are looking for potential employees with desire and experience, along with communication, decision, and reasoning skills.

There is a broad scope of careers in the horse industry for individuals who wish to combine their vocational talents with an equine interest. Employment opportunities fall within the following categories: research, applied sciences, communications, education, recreation, support industries, and related fields.

IX. Concerns and Issues Facing the Horse Industry in the 1990s

A large obstacle facing today's horsemen is the growth in land use restrictions and regulations. Due to urban migration to rural areas, there are often conflicts between new and old residents. These conflicts result in adverse zoning, imposed land per animal ratios, increased standards for setbacks for barns, and requirements for minimum acreage. In some areas horses have been banned from parks and trails because of public nuisance concerns regarding safety and animal waste.

An issue that has affected many industries during the last decade has also had a high impact on the equine world: the issue of "liability." Over the years this issue has reshaped horse businesses. Years ago there were many hack stables where anyone could rent a horse. Due to the current liability risks, this is now a thing of the past. Many stables provided riding lessons for clients; however, due to the high cost of liability insurance to cover these riding lessons, many stables have elected to discontinue this service. Several states are trying to pass legislation to help combat this issue of liability. The state of Colorado passed a law that became effective July 1, 1990: the Equine Civil Liability Act, Senate Bill 90-84. This liability law recognized the personal risks involved in equine activities. Under Colorado law, "An equine professional is not liable for an injury to or the death of a participant in equine activities resulting from the inherent risks of this equine activity." Under the law an equine professional must post warning signs in a clear and visible location or near stalls, corrals, or arenas where equine activities are routinely conducted. The passage of this law has reduced the astronomical cost of liability insurance to equine facilities across the state.

Other issues being championed by the horseman are the extremely high cost of workmen's compensation for equine employees and the animal rights and welfare issues, as well as the concern, "Are horses agriculture?" In many states, horses are not being treated the same as other agricultural livestock commodities in the areas of state and federal tax laws and in the areas of support for research and education. This interpretation could have long range negative effects, not only on the horse industry, but on the entire agricultural industry as well. Some of the problems that could be faced if horses are not considered livestock are: feed purchases are subject to state sale tax, and the sale of a foal would be subject to sales tax. Today, none of these taxes are placed on other species of domestic livestock.

Another issue of importance to the horseman is that of open space and trails. According to a national poll conducted by Peter-Hart Research Associates, 77% of the public views outdoor recreation as a priority in their lives. A recent highway bill that became effective December 18, 1991, not only will provide needed funds for the repair and maintenance of trails which benefit horseback riders, but it also created a national advisory committee that will have equestrian representatives.

Horse ownership has grown despite the slight decrease in horses being produced. The equine community is a large and viable part of American's agriculture (as well as sports, entertainment, and recreation) industry.

X. Conclusion

In our future world, we will see horses used for policing our cities, parading in commemorative and celebratory events, as a sports option for entertainment, recreating in our parks, enjoying the outdoors, touring historic areas, as educational purposes for youth, as therapy for the handicapped, and for tree logging operations where teams are used to reduce environmental impact to the forested land aiding in conservation. The horse has been an integral part of America's heritage and continues to play a vital role in maintaining open lands, providing a recreation outlet, and creating income for state economies and individuals interested in the professional side of working with horses.

Bibliography

American Horse Council (1992). "Horse Industry Directory." Washington, DC.

American Quarter Horse Association (1990). "AQHA Annual Report." Fort Worth, TX.

DeWeese, D. (1988). USEMA assembling horse industry puzzle. *Tack 'n' Togs' Merchandising,* **April,** 47.

Equus Annual Report (1990). "Horse Trends." *Equus,* **Nov.,** 33.

Hood, N. C. (1990). Gallup surveys APHA members. *Paint Horse J,* 54.

Policy Economic Group (1987). "The Economic Impact of the U.S. Horse Industry." American Horse Council, Washington, DC.

Schoeff, R. W., and Castaldo, D. J. (1990). Market data, a comprehensive report on livestock and poultry inventories and feed usage potentials. *Feed Management* **41** (12), 10.

Southern Horseman Magazine (1991). Investigation survey results: How do your trainers' fees compare. *Southern Horseman,* 86.

Horticultural Greenhouse Engineering

D. L. CRITTEN, *Silsoe Research Institute, England*

Glossary

Binomial probability distribution If there are N events, each having a chance P_j of occurring, $1 \le j \le N$, the probability p of j events occurring concurrently is:

$$p = \prod_j P_j \cdot \prod_{N-j} (1 - P_j)$$

Condensation/evaporation (latent heat) Heat exchange due to change of state (gas to liquid or vice versa)

Conduction Migration of heat from hot to cold regions of a material, without movement of the material itself

Cost–benefit equation Net income to a grower may be equated to the algebraic sum of the crop value at harvest and the total running costs over the growing period: the latter will include interest on loans, expenditure on heating, cost of horticultural supplies, etc; marketing costs should also be included if they are significant

Convection Carriage of heat from hot to cold regions by heat-bearing material

Fresnel's reflection laws These give accurate values of light reflection at a single interface between two nonabsorbing refracting media; in particular, variation of reflected and hence transmitted energy with incidence angle are obtained

Greenhouse transmission, transmittance, or transmissivity Ratio of irradiance within to that outside a greenhouse

Irradiance Electromagnetic energy arriving per unit area of a receiving surface

Optimal control Control is optimal if the control variables are such that a chosen parameter, usually grower income, is maximized for a given crop and environment either over a specified time period (e.g., lettuce) or on a continuous basis (e.g., tomato)

Radiance Electromagnetic energy per unit area emitted within a solid angle of one steradian

Radiant energy Electromagnetic energy per unit area normal to the sun's rays

Radiation Interchange of heat in the form of electromagnetic radiation between different bodies; if the bodies are at different temperatures, a net exchange of heat results

The performance of a greenhouse as a conventional unit depends on both controllable (e.g., air temperature) and uncontrollable (e.g., light energy input) parameters. Thus, unlike most industrial processes, it is necessary to monitor and allow for the variations in the latter to achieve a given rate or timeliness of crop production. The problem is aggravated by the three-dimensional nature of the greenhouse. Local internal spatial variations are likely to occur, and these can affect the overall performance of the harvest. The spatial nature of the greenhouse surface also strongly affects both the light input and heat loss characteristics. For example, low-elevation sunlight can produce "hot spots" of light energy, due to reflection from the north roof of an E–W-aligned greenhouse, and it is well known that surface area to volume ratio affects heat loss from any object. Clearly then we have a very complicated system to analyze, control, and optimize.

I. Introduction

A. Historical Background

Though the present texts are concerned with state-of-the-art expertise, it is well to set these in the context of their origins. For horticultural engineering development, most of the basic scientific concepts were developed during the period 1750–1850 A.D., and one sees little or no advance then until circa 1950, when modern studies of light transmission, heat conservation, and climate control began. The early engineers developed their technology to the limit of their scientific and numerical abilities, and it was not until computing techniques became available that further progress was possible. Architecturally of course great strides were made during the intervening period. Many elegant and sometimes very complex designs were executed between 1850 and 1950, and engineering improvements in areas such as boiler design were included as they became available. Nevertheless, one can only marvel at the ingenuity and simplicity of the "working" greenhouse designs of the early 19th century. For example, in the Wrest Park walled garden (circa 1840) there is evidence of a south-facing conservatory heating system provided by the flues from fires used for heating the living accommodation on the north side, the flues being contained by a central wall. There is also a ventilating system with a manually controlled exhaust mechanism, delivering air into the wall and then out above the house, there being no apparent need for movement of glass.

B. Scope of the Article

The article discusses concepts directly related to the behavior of a crop under greenhouse cultivation. There are a number of allied topics which may affect the behavior indirectly, but are not discussed: examples are boiler design, greenhouse strength calculations, wind loading capabilities, and internal greenhouse layout. These are strictly heavy/structural engineering topics, or horticultural practice, and are not normally defined as part of horticultural engineering science. The discussion is also restricted to greenhouses with planar cladding as opposed to curved houses, or "tunnels." Most of the topics discussed can be applied in principle to these latter structures, though much basic work needs to be done on the light transmission properties.

Thermal and Optical Performance of the
Greenhouse—Nomenclature

A_c, A_g	areas of cladding and ground, respectively
A_v	total area of ventilator, m²
a, A	elevation and azimuth
A_1, A_o	area, m²
a, b, c	direction cosines of a normal to a plane
a_o	elevation of a plane
a_s	sun elevation
a_{so}	mid-day sun elevation

C_p	specific heat of a gas at constant pressure
E	total energy requirement, J
E_r	radiation energy, W m⁻²
E_j	energy in a light beam, W m⁻²
f_s	fraction of a span
F	factor containing physical terms associated with transmission of light through a sheet of cladding material
h	convective heat transfer coefficient, W m⁻² °k⁻¹
h'	overall effective heat transfer coefficient, W m⁻² °k⁻¹
H	total depth of crop traversed to reach a specified point (m)
I	irradiance, W m⁻²
k	thermal conductivity, W m⁻¹ °k⁻¹
l	typical dimension, m
L_a	leaf area index
L	radiance, W m⁻² st⁻¹
L_H	latent heat W kg⁻¹
l, m, n	direction cosines of a light ray
M	mass of water transpired, kg sec⁻¹
m	mass transfer coefficient, kg m⁻² sec⁻¹
$\bar{n}$	number of touching cylinders representing greenhouse structural elements
n	refractive index
q	heat flux, W m⁻²
Q	rate of heat flow, W
r	average crop reflectivity
R	thermal resistance, m² °K W⁻¹
R_F	average Fresnel reflection coefficient
Δa	greenhouse cladding element size, m²
t	transmission factor
t_s	structure transmission factor
T	temperature °K or °C
v	speed, m sec⁻¹
V	greenhouse volume, m³
w	wind speed m sec⁻¹
x_c, y_c, z_c	coordinates of the center of an element of cladding, m
x_c, h_c	coordinates of the center of an element of a tall crop cross section, m
$X(g, G)$	probability that a leaf has orientations g (elevation) and G (azimuth)
x	absolute humidity kg kg⁻¹ or distance m
Greek	
α_1, α_2	roof slopes
β	coefficient of cubical expansion
γ	fraction of solar irradiance used to produce sensible heat flux in the air
δ	angle between the sun and any point in the sky (degrees)
$\bar{\delta}$	angle between a light ray and a plane normal
σ	Stefan-Boltzmann constant (5.669 × 10⁻⁸ Wm⁻² °K⁻⁴)
σ_{av}	average cross-section of a leaf, per unit leaf area
ρ	fluid density, kg m⁻³
μ	dynamic viscosity, kg m⁻¹ sec⁻¹
ϕ	air exchange rate, hr⁻¹
ε	fraction of absorbed solar radiation used in transpiration
θ	angular setting of vents
$\Phi(\alpha)$	geometric factor defined by multispan greenhouse roof configuration
$\Omega(\Theta)$	required ventilation rate, m³ m⁻² sec⁻¹
v	transmission gain or loss

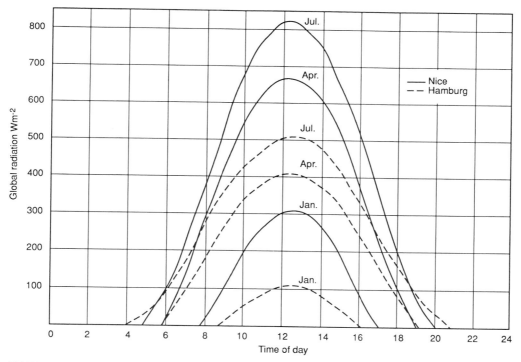

FIGURE 1 Diurnal variation of irradiation. [From Bailey, B. J. (1988). "Principles of environmental control," Chapt. 3. (C. von Zabeltitz, ed.) FAO/CNRE Energy Book.]

II. The Thermal Performance of Greenhouses

A. Energy Sources

Natural radiation may be direct, from the sun itself, or indirect. The irradiance (I) thus varies with latitude, time of year, and time of day, as well as with meteorological conditions. An illustration is given in Fig. 1, for Nice and Hamburg. A distinction is made between total radiation, defined by wavelength band (0.4–2.7 μ) and the photosynthetically active radiation band (0.4–0.7 μ). Heaters are used to make up the heat deficit when solar energy is inadequate, or at night. Convection heaters pass air through a heater and then circulate it around the greenhouse. Convection and radiation heating are obtained when hot water for example is circulated through pipes. Floor and bench heating is often used to heat plants growing in pots or trays.

B. Energy Transfer

1. Conduction

The steady rate of flow of heat (Q) across the greenhouse cladding is given by

$$Q = k_g A_o (T_1 - T_2)/l, \tag{1}$$

where T_1 and T_2 are the surface temperatures on either side of the cladding and k_g is the thermal conductivity of the cladding. An equation of this type can be developed to establish heat flow patterns through the greenhouse floor.

2. Convection

Convection involves the transfer of heat between a solid and a fluid medium. The rate of heat transfer is given by

$$Q = A_o h \Delta T \tag{2}$$

$$\Delta T = T_s - T_f. \tag{3}$$

T_s is the surface temperature, and T_f the temperature in the body of the fluid. The Nusselt number (N_u) is defined by

$$(Q_{convection}/Q_{conduction}) = N_u = hl/k_f, \tag{4}$$

where k_f is the fluid thermal conductivity.

The Grashof number (Gr) is defined by

$$(\text{buoyancy forces/viscous forces}) = G_r = g\beta l^3 \rho^2 (T_1 - T_2)/\mu^2. \tag{5}$$

The Prandtl number (P_r) is defined as the ratio of

momentum diffusion to thermal diffusivity. The Reynolds number is defined

$$R_e = \frac{l v \rho}{\mu}. \qquad (6)$$

Then dimensional analysis shows that

$$N_u = C(G_r P_r)^n \text{ for free convection} \qquad (7)$$

$$N_u = C R_e^m P_r^n \text{ for forced convection}. \qquad (8)$$

Values of C, m, and n, in Eq. (8) for a flat plate in air are shown in Table I. Simplified forms of Eq. (7) are shown in Table II. For forced heat loss due to wind passing over a greenhouse, the following equation for heat transfer coefficient is suggested

$$h = 2.8 + 1.2 w, (0 < w < 4 \text{ msec}^{-1}) \, W \, \text{m}^{-2} \, {}^\circ\text{K}^{-1}. \qquad (9)$$

3. Radiation

For a black body, energy radiated (E_r) is given by the basic Stefan–Boltzman law:

$$E_r = \sigma T^4. \qquad (10)$$

For exchange between two black bodies, the net transfer of energy Q_{12} from surface, area A_1, is given by

$$Q_{12} = A_1 f_{12}(\sigma T_1^4 - \sigma T_2^4), \qquad (11)$$

where f_{12} is the fraction of energy emitted by surface 1 arriving at surface 2 and is calculated for each situation.

Greenhouse/sky radiation exchange is the most significant radiative component; the sky is usually assumed to be black at a temperature of 20°K below outside air temperature. Cloud cover reduces the radiation losses. Typically, for a cylindrical greenhouse $f = 0.818$.

4. Latent Heat

For absolute humidities x_s at a surface and x_a in the air,

$$M = m A_o(x_s - x_a). \qquad (12)$$

TABLE I

Values of c, m, and n for a Flat Plate in Air (Eq. 8)

Re	C	m	n
$<10^5$	0.664	1/2	1/3
$>10^5$	0.037	4/5	1/3

[From Bailey, B. J. (1988). "Principles of environmental control", Chapt. 3. (C. von Zabeltitz, ed.) FAO/CNRE Energy Book.]

TABLE II

Approximate Equations for Free Convection

Surface	Laminar $10^4 < Gr \, Pr < 10^9$	Turbulent $Gr \, Pr > 10^9$
Vertical plane or cylinder	$h = 1.42 \, (\Delta T/1)^{1/4}$	$h = 0.95 \, (\Delta T/1)^{1/3}$
Horizontal cylinder	$h = 1.32 \, (\Delta T/1)^{1/4}$	$h = 1/24 \, (\Delta T/1)^{1/3}$
Horizontal plate		
Heated facing up or cooled facing down	$h = 1.32 \, (\Delta T/1)^{1/4}$	$h = 1.43 \, (\Delta T/1)^{1/3}$
Heated facing down or cooled facing up	$h = 0.61 \, (\Delta T/1^2)^{1/5}$	$h = 0.61 \, (\Delta T/1)^{1/5}$

[From Bailey, B. J. (1988). "Principles of environmental control", Chapt. 3. (C. von Zabeltitz, ed.) FAO/CNRE Energy Book.] *Note*: l is the vertical or horizontal dimension or diameter (m). ΔT is the difference in temperature between the surface and the bulk fluid (K).

By comparing with convection, m can be related to h, the heat transfer coefficient:

$$m = h/C_p. \qquad (13)$$

The transfer of heat is therefore

$$Q = L_H h A_o(x_s - x_a)/C_p. \qquad (14)$$

Evaporation from leaves and from the ground, plus condensation on the cladding inner surface, constitutes the principal contribution of evaporation latent heat to the greenhouse heat transfer. Air exchange may cause a change in humidity, and hence alter the latent heat content of the house atmosphere.

C. Theoretical Energy Exchange in a Greenhouse

Figure 2 shows the various interchanges that occur due to the greenhouse and its contents. Preceding and succeeding suffices with Table III, define the interchanging quantities in the following equations:

$$\text{Air} \quad {}_cQ_p + {}_cQ_f + {}_cQ_r + {}_cQ_h + {}_iQ = 0 \qquad (15)$$

$$\text{Plants} \quad {}_cQ_a + {}_lQ_a + {}_rQ_f \\ + {}_rQ_r + {}_rQ_h + {}_{sr}Q + {}_rQ_s = 0 \qquad (16)$$

$$\text{Floor} \quad {}_cQ_a + {}_lQ_a + {}_rQ_p \\ + {}_kQ_f + {}_rQ_r + {}_rQ_h + {}_{sr}Q \\ + {}_rQ_s = 0 \qquad (17)$$

$$\text{Roof} \quad {}_cQ_a + {}_lQ_a + {}_rQ_p + {}_rQ_f + {}_rQ_h \\ + {}_{sr}Q + {}_cQ_{ea} + {}_rQ_s = 0. \qquad (18)$$

Relevant shape factors, emissivities, thermal transfer

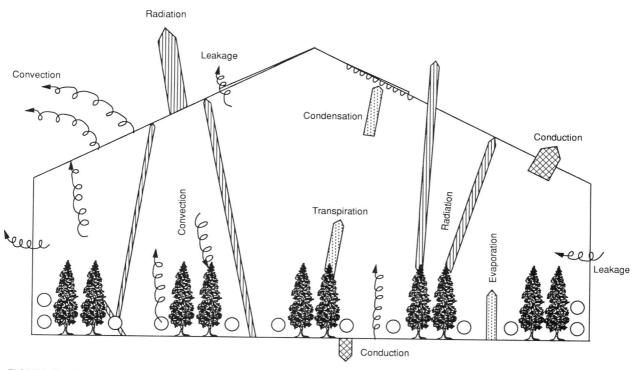

FIGURE 2 Thermal interactions in a greenhouse. [From Bailey, B. J. (1988). "Principles of environmental control," Chapt. 3. (C. von Zabeltitz, ed.) FAO/CNRE Energy Book.]

coefficients, etc., and external conditions all have to be evaluated to solve Eqs. (15–18).

D. Practical Determination of Heat Loss and Boiler Capacity

The loss from a closed greenhouse to the outside is usually approximated to loss by conduction through the cladding, and air infiltration (leaks). Thus, total loss (q) is given by

$$q = q_c + q_i, \tag{19}$$

where q_c is the conductive and q_i the infiltration heat losses. Radiation losses are ignored.

1. Conduction Losses at the Cladding

Conduction heat loss per unit ground area q_c is given by

$$q_c = h_c \frac{A_c}{A_g} (T_i - T_o), \tag{20}$$

TABLE III

Interactions of Thermal Terms in a Greenhouse

| Component | Item with which energy exchange takes place | | | | | | | |
	Int air (a)	Plant (p)	Floor (f)	Roof (r)	Heater (h)	Sun (sr)	Ext air (ea)	Sky (s)
Air	—	c,l	c,l	c,l	c	—	i	—
Plant	c,l	—	r	r	r	sr	—	r'
Floor	c,l	r	k	r	r	sr	—	r'
Roof	c,l	r	r	—	r	sr	c	r

[From Bailey, B. J. (1988). "Principles of environmental control", Chapt. 3. (C. von Zabeltitz, ed.) FAO/CNRE Energy Book.]

Note: c, convection; k, conduction; r', if transmissivity of roof for thermal radiation ≠ 0; sr, solar radiation; l, latent heat; r, thermal radiation; i, infiltration/leakage.

where h_c is the overall heat transfer coefficient of the cover, defined by

$$h_c = \frac{1}{R_i + R_k + R_o}. \qquad (21)$$

R_i, R_k, and R_o are the inner, material, and outer surface thermal resistance. Radiation, condensation, etc., may all contribute to the heat arriving at the inner cladding surface. Typically, $R_i = 0.1$ m^2 °K W^{-1}, and R_k depends on the material, but for 4-mm single glass a value of 0.01 m^2 °K W^{-1} may be taken. R_o is given in Table IV for walls and roofs under different exposure conditions. Hence, h_c can be calculated.

2. Air Infiltration Losses (q_i)
We have

$$q_i = \phi \, V \rho C_p (T_i - T_o)/(A_g \times 3600). \qquad (22)$$

Values of (ϕV) are given in Fig. 3 for different greenhouse types.

3. Total Loss
An infiltration heat loss coefficient can be defined as

$$h_i = \phi V \rho C_p /(A_c \times 3600). \qquad (23)$$

Then q_c and q_i can be combined to give

$$\begin{aligned} q &= A_c (h_c + h_i)(T_i - T_o)/A_g \\ &= h' A_c (T_i - T_o)/A_g. \end{aligned} \qquad (24)$$

h' can be determined from Eqs. (21) and (23) and so q, the design output of the heater, can be determined.

T_i is interpreted as the set point temperature, and T_o the external temperature.

E. Heater Requirements

The heating requirement of a greenhouse per unit area is given by

TABLE IV

Resistance (R_0) of the Outer Surface of a Greenhouse Cover

Exposure	Wall m^2 °K W^{-1}	Roof m^2 °K W^{-1}
Sheltered	0.08	0.07
Normal	0.055	0.045
Exposed	0.03	0.02

[From Bailey, B. J. (1988). "Principles of environmental control", Chapt. 3. (C. von Zabeltitz, ed.) FAO/CNRE Energy Book.]

$$q_h = A_c h'(T_i - T_o)/A_g - It\gamma. \qquad (25)$$

γ depends on the proportion of floor covered by plants and ranges from 0.3 to 0.7. Typical values of h' are shown in Table V for various greenhouse types. The total annual heat consumption can be predicted using Eq. (25), based on local hourly averages, obtained over many years. Hence, fuel requirement can be calculated.

F. Summer Ventilation

The reverse problem occurs in summer, when it is frequently necessary to remove heat to prevent excessive temperature occurring within the greenhouse. Ignoring photosynthesis and floor conduction, the solar radiation absorbed within the house q_{sr} may be analyzed into

$$q_{sr} = q_c + q_i + q_v, \qquad (26)$$

where q_v is the heat removed by ventilation. Also

$$q_{sr} = t(1 - r) I. \qquad (27)$$

Equation (19) can be used to represent $q_c + q_i$. The term q_v can be further analyzed into sensible (q_s) and latent heat (q_l) components,

$$q_s = \Omega \rho C_p (T_i - T_o) \qquad (28)$$

$$q_l = \varepsilon t (1 - r) I. \qquad (29)$$

Thus, from Eqs. (25), (26), to (29),

$$\Omega = \frac{t(1 - r)(1 - \varepsilon)}{\rho C_p (T_i - T_o)} - \frac{A_c}{A_g} \cdot \frac{h'}{\rho C_p}. \qquad (30)$$

It is convenient to define a further nondimensional number $G(\Theta)$, given by

$$\Omega(\Theta) = G(\Theta) w A_v. \qquad (31)$$

For a particular example, regression analysis shows that $G(\Theta)$ may be written as

$$G(\Theta) = .00171 + .0831\Theta. \qquad (32)$$

Θ is in radians. The first term constitutes an experimentally based correction, which is related to leakage, and permits us to set Θ-0 for closed vents. Hence, it is possible to correlate Θ to Ω, at temperature T_i, knowing windspeed w in terms of $G(\Theta)$ and total vent area A_v.

The average total number of hours during which ventilation is needed can be calculated using the energy balance techniques already outlined. For a temperature range T_i of 22°C to 27°C, a change from

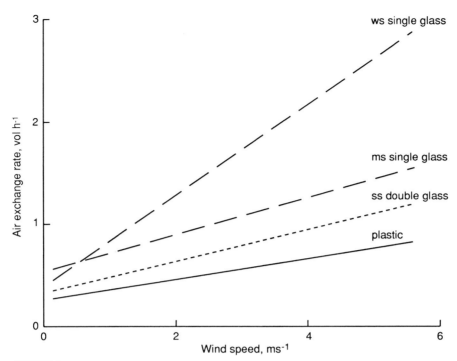

FIGURE 3 Leakage rates in typical greenhouses. ss, single span; ws, wide span; ms, multispan. [From Bailey, B. J. (1988). "Principles of environmental control," Chapt. 3. (C. von Zabeltitz, ed.) FAO/CNRE Energy Book.]

500 to 1000 hr is typically required, based on meteorological data for Hannover, Germany.

G. Thermal Insulation Techniques

Multiple glazing is a well-known technique, and produces considerable savings in heating costs. The actual savings depend critically on the spacing between the layers, and how many there are. For example, a 10-mm gap within a double rigid plastic cladding will increase R_k by an order of magnitude, to a value close to R_i (~0.1 m^2 °k W^{-1}). Some of the benefits of

thermal insulation can be obtained using movable plastic screens, which can be drawn across at night to reduce heat losses, and withdrawn during daylight hours to reduce light losses. Up to 40% of thermal losses can then be recovered, with a penalty of about 4% light loss for the parked screens.

III. The Light Transmission Performance of Greenhouses

A. Light Transmission into the Greenhouse

The transmission of light by transparent cladding materials is governed by the Fresnel laws of reflection at single surfaces extended to cover lightly absorbing materials and multiple surfaces such as the opposite sides of a single sheet of material. It is usual to take white light with an average value of refractive index (n). While it is straightforward in the laboratory to obtain the transmission and reflection properties of samples, in the greenhouse itself it is very difficult to carry out an accurate assessment of light transmission. Recourse to idealized sky and sunlight models, and computer models of the transmission process are

TABLE V

Typical Total Heal Loss Coefficients (wind speed = 4 msec^{-1})

Material		W m^{-2} K^{-1}
Single glass		6.0–8.8
Double glass 9 mm air space		4.2–5.2
Double acrylic SDP 16		4.2–5.0
Triple acrylic S3P 32		3.0–3.5
Double polycarbonate	10 mm air space	4.7–5.0
	16 mm air space	4.2–5.0

[From Bailey, B. J. (1988). "Principles of environmental control", Chapt. 3. (C. von Zabeltitz, ed.) FAO/CNRE Energy Book.]

needed. In this way transmission of idealized structure has been successfully predicted. Even then it is necessary to make some approximations, such as incident light being unpolarized.

For single nonabsorbing sheets, Fresnels' laws which apply to a single interface have been modified by Holmes. For double cladding, these relationships can be replaced by terms of the form $(2R_F)/(1 + R_F)$ and $(1 - R_F)/(1 + R_F)$ for reflected and transmitted light, respectively.

1. Skylight Analysis

We can first dispose of the sun, since its position as a function of latitude, time of year, and time of day is precisely known, and its corresponding average radiant energy is also predictable. For sky light, a number of approximations to real conditions are available. The dull overcast sky at elevation (a) is predictable and we may write

$$L(a) = L_0 (1 + 2 \sin a)/3. \qquad (33)$$

A fairly straightforward relationship for the average sky radiance has also been published and is of the form

$$L(a,A) = C \exp(-\delta/40) + D\left(\frac{5 - 2\sin a}{3}\right). \qquad (34)$$

C and D are constants, δ, is in degrees. Originally C and D were expressed in photometric units, but these are assumed proportional to energy $(\mathrm{W m}^{-2})$.

The dominant presence of the sun in one half of the sky vault prompts an analysis of average skylight into two parts, one symmetric $(L_s(a,A))$ about the E–W line, the other antisymmetric $(L_n(a,A))$, i.e., we write

$$L_p(a,A) = \frac{1}{2}\left(L(a,A) \pm L(a,A)\right). \qquad (35)$$

For the sum s replaces p; for the difference n replaces p.

Note L_n only contributes if an asymmetric transmitting or sensing device is present.

The concept can be extended to a complete harmonic analysis of either an average or an instantaneous sky. Conveniently Legendre polynomials and Fourier harmonics are used in elevation (a) and azimuth (A), respectively. The result is to produce an image of the sky radiance in terms of combinations of harmonics, which can, in principle, be made as precise as one would like. Thus instantaneous sky models can be produced by simultaneous measurements over distinct parts of the sky vault, followed by solving a set of simultaneous equations for harmonic amplitudes.

B. Modeling the Light Transmission Process

To obtain a reliable picture of the internal greenhouse irradiance, the capricious nature of real sky light must be replaced by a definable artificial sky vault. It is also convenient to separate the transparent cladding from the opaque structural members, and use separate techniques to evaluate each. Final transmissions can be subsequently obtained by combination.

1. Transmission of Structureless Greenhouses

Each surface of the greenhouse is divided into small size rectangular elements, each of which has a center at (x_c, y_c, z_c). A ray, incident from either the sun, at position (a_s, A_s), or a sky element, position (a,A), angular width $\Delta a, \Delta A$ is assumed to pass through the center of the element, this ray containing all the elemental incident energy. The equation of rays can be specified in the form

$$\frac{x - x_c}{1} = \frac{y - y_c}{m} = \frac{z - z_c}{n}, \qquad (36)$$

and the greenhouse planes which are intersected by these rays as

$$ax + by + cz = 1. \qquad (37)$$

Angles of incidence are $(\overline{\delta})$ given by

$$\cos \overline{\delta} = al + bm + cn. \qquad (38)$$

Using relationships of this type a reflected ray can be generated by obtaining the coordinates $x'y'z'$ of the reflection of a point on the ray reflected onto the plane under review, and using the relationship

$$\frac{x - x'}{x' - x_c} = \frac{y - y'}{y' - y_c} = \frac{z - z'}{z' - z_c}. \qquad (39)$$

Each incident beam produces a single transmitted beam and a set of reflected beams. Corresponding intensities can be calculated using Eq. (38) in conjunction with the Fresnel reflection law, the order of intersection being known (e.g., by calculating distances along the ray to each surface).

Next, the intersection of the transmitted beam with the ground is examined. If this is within the area of the house, the energy is stored, otherwise it is rejected. Each reflected beam, now of known intensity is treated as a new incident beam, and the whole process is repeated.

After completion of all reflections to any chosen limit, (say the third reflection), the process is repeated until either the entire daily path of the sun or rays all from the sky vault and all the greenhouse cladding surfaces have been evaluated. The resultant distribution over the greenhouse floor represents the transmitted energy. It is often possible to reduce computer run time by taking long or wide houses, ignoring end effects. Programs following these schemes have now been exhaustively tested, and much transmission data obtained. Figure 4 demonstrates both the comparison with experiment and the effect of reflections on the transmission across a single span of transmitting material (perspex), under overcast skies.

2. Transmission of Greenhouse Structure

This can be obtained by the relatively simple procedure of calculating the light blocked out, viewed from any point within the house. It is usual to assume the reflection factor of structural elements is zero.

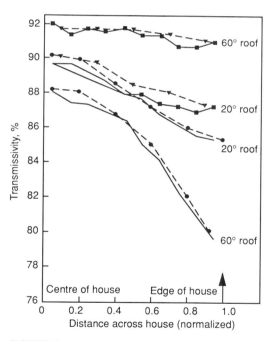

FIGURE 4 Demonstration of the effect of reflections in a single span greenhouse as a function of roof height. Incident beam measured (————) and predicted (---•---). Two reflections measured (--■--) and predicted (--▼--) respectively. (From Critten, D. L. (1983). The evaluation of a computer model to calculate the daily light transmission and transmissivity of a greenhouse. *J. Agric. Eng. Res.* **28**, 545–563.

C. Theoretical Treatment of Light Transmission (Lightly Absorbing Structures) Ignoring Second Reflections

1. The Extended Integral Concept

a. The mean transmittance gain or loss at any point inside or outside an assembly of structures equals the sum of gains or losses at that point due to each structure in isolation.

b. The mean transmittance gain or loss inside an infinite multispan is equal to the integral to infinity (extended integral) perpendicular to the house axis of the gain or loss produced by any single span, the spans being identical, divided by the span width.

The second theorem can be extended to single roof sections, mounted at angles α_1, α_2, to the horizontal, and multispan transmission loss $\nu_{m,\alpha_1,\alpha_2}$ will become,

$$\nu_{m,\alpha_1,\alpha_2} = \int_{-\infty}^{\infty} (f_s \nu_{\alpha_1}(x) + (1 - f_s)\nu_{\alpha_2}(x))\, dx, \quad (40)$$

where f_s defines the fraction of the span covered by the roof section of slope α_1.

To this order of approximation, nonabsorbing vertical walls produce no light loss, Equation (40) therefore represents the transmission of a structureless multispan greenhouse.

2. Elimination of the Product $R_F(\bar{\delta}) \cos \bar{\delta}$

In all calculations relating to light transmission which use averaged Fresnel reflection terms $R_F(\bar{\delta})$, the quantity $R_F(\bar{\delta}) \cos \bar{\delta}$ inevitably arises. To a fair accuracy it is possible to replace this product by a constant between $0 < \bar{\delta} < 90°$ (Fig. 5). If this is done, a dramatic simplification of the light loss term, viewed as the total upwardly reflected radiation, occurs. The average loss from a structureless multispan (ν_m) can be written in the form

$$\nu_m = F\Phi(\alpha)/(\cos \alpha \sin a_{so}). \quad (41)$$

This equation represents multispan transmission as a separable product of a term F, which contains all physical properties of the cladding, plus a geometric term $\Phi(\alpha)$, which depends only on geometry. Figure 6 shows how $\Phi(\alpha)$ varies with α at U.K. latitudes for different seasons. Broadly for E–W houses, when the sun angle a_{so} exceeds 2α, light reflects upwards from the north facing roof in the multispan and is lost. Similarly if $\alpha > \pi - a_{so})/2$ light is recovered from the south roof, though this is of theoretical interest only as neglected multiple reflections have become

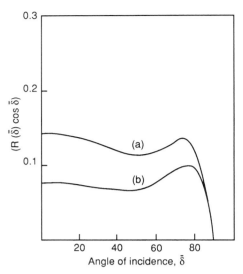

FIGURE 5 Plot of $R_d(\bar{\delta})$ cos $(\bar{\delta})$ for (a) single and (b) double cladding ($n = 1.5$). [From Critten, D. L. (1988). The transmission of direct light by structureless symmetric roofed multispan greenhouses with non-absorbing cladding. *J. Agric. Eng. Res.* **40**, 225–232.]

more important. The description assumes a due E due W path for the sun. The departures from this path create a distortion of the summer curve for $\Phi(\alpha)$. The N–S roof gives a single curve for all seasons.

3. Representation of the Transmission Loss of Structural Members (ν_s)

The following results depend on representing equispaced structural members as arrays of equidiameter cylinders as shown in Fig.7, and also a due E–due West path for the sun.

Defining the ratio of the diameter of each cylindrical element to the spacing of the element as b, then for diffuse light

$$\nu_s = b \ (1.40e = 0.99f), \tag{42}$$

where e is equal to (i) unity for horizontally, and (ii) $(\bar{n})$ the number of touching cylinders, for vertically aligned cylinders. f equals $(\bar{n} - 1)$ and $-(\bar{n} - 1)$ correspondingly.

For direct light at U.K. latitudes

$$\nu_{s,EW} = b(1 + (\bar{n} - 1) \ \omega/\sin a_{so} \tag{43}$$

$$\nu_{s,NS} = b(0.5 + \bar{n}). \tag{44}$$

$\omega = \sin a_{so}$, or cos a_{so} for horizontally or vertically aligned cylinders, respectively.

B. Light Penetration into Tall Crop

Because photosynthesis is nonlinear, its calculation requires values for irradiances on individual leaves. The method to be described recognizes this and produces a range of light intensities at each point, rather than single values. We consider the path of a chosen light beam from a specified sky element at (a,A). A total of 14 sky elements are taken, comprising the sun, plus 13 sky elements, divided into three bands, containing eight elements (lower), four elements (middle), and one element (zenith). Each element is treated as a stationary sun.

1. Transmission through the Greenhouse

We have to consider the transmission of a house in any direction (a,A). The following approximate equation has been derived for a structureless Venlo type multispan:

$$t(a) = 0.9[1 - \exp \ (-a/\bar{a})]. \tag{45}$$

For light generally parallel, perpendicular to the house axis, $\bar{a} = 13°$, 5.7°. Respectively, the changeover from parallel to perpendicular is taken to occur suddenly and given by an azimuth angle A_{cr} determined from

$$A_{cr} = 45 \ (1 - \exp(-a/c)), c = 15°. \tag{46}$$

Losses due to structure can be allowed for, by a second approximate equation. For a Venlo, structural transmission $t_s(a)$ is given by:

$$t_s(a) = \exp[-0.1(1 + 1/\sin a)]. \tag{47}$$

2. Row Crop Penetration by a Single Beam

Using Fig.8, defining the center of an element of crop by (h_c, x_c), then

$$h - h_c = (x - x_c) \tan a_o. \tag{48}$$

If h_c is the crop height, and H the total depth of crop traversed (assuming uniform density), then H depends on how many rows are crossed. Four cases can be defined: if the beam enters the row containing the element, Eq. (49), or the gap next to it, Eq. (50)

$$H = h_c - h_c \tag{49}$$

$$H = \gamma_1 - h_c. \tag{50}$$

γ_1, is the height at which the row is penetrated at the edge.

If N is the number of sides crossed by the beam (two sides per row), then for $N > 2$, odd (51) and even (52)

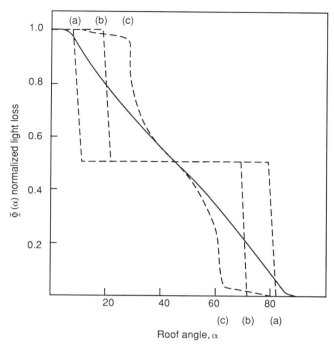

FIGURE 6 Functional variation of the geometric loss factor $\Phi(\alpha)$ at U.K. latitudes (—), N.S.; (---), E.W. oriented houses; (a) 1st February, (b) 21st March, (c) 1st May. [From Critten, D. L. (1988). The transmission of direct light by structureless symmetric roofed multispan greenhouses with non-absorbing cladding. *J. Agric. Eng. Res.* **40**, 225–232.]

$$H = (\gamma_1 - h_c) + \tfrac{1}{2}(N - 2)\,\delta H \qquad (51)$$

$$H = (\gamma_1 - h_c) + \tfrac{1}{2}(N - 2)\,\delta H + h_c - \gamma_N. \qquad (52)$$

γ_1 defines the depth of entry to the row containing

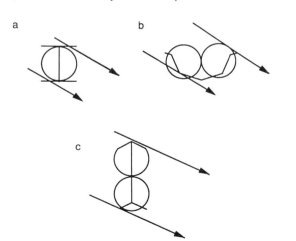

FIGURE 7 The use of equal diameter contacting cylinders to represent various structural greenhouse members: (a) glazing bars, (b) gutter, (c) ridge. [From Critten, D. L. (1987). Light transmission losses due to structural members in multispan greenhouses under diffuse skylight conditions. *J. Agric. Eng. Res.* **38**, 193–207.]

the element at $(h_c x_c)$. Y_N defines the depth of emergence of the ray from the row furthest from the element at $(h_c x_c)$.

δH is the depth of crop traversed in each full row width.

Let the probability P_j that a beam j arrives at $h_c x_c$ be

$$P_j = \exp - (K\,(\partial L_a/\partial h)\,H \qquad (53)$$

$$K = \sigma_{av}/\sin a_j \qquad (54)$$

$\sigma_{av} = \tfrac{1}{2}$ for a spherical distribution. Irradiance I_{lj} on leaf l is given by

$$I_{l,j} = E_j \cos \overline{\delta}_j. \qquad (55)$$

$\overline{\delta}$ is obtained via an equation of the form of Eq. (38), and E_j is calculated from the radiance field.

3. The Total Irradiance due to Multiple Overlapping Beams

We assume a binomial form of distribution to describe the probability that any specific combination of rays will reach (h_c, x_c), thus

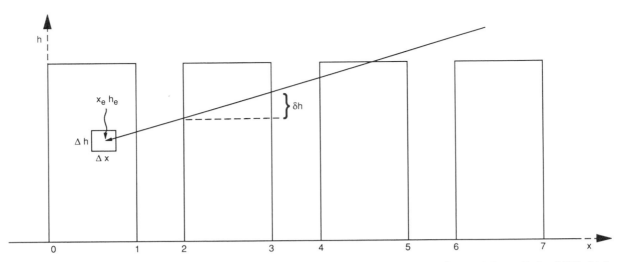

FIGURE 8 A typical path for a ray arriving at an element, center (x_c, h_c) in a row crop. [From Critten, D. L. (1990). Light penetration and photosynthesis in tall greenhouse crops. D.N. 1558, *AFRC Inst. Eng. Res,* Wrest Park, Silsoe, MK45 4HS.]

$$p = \Pi P_j \Pi_{14-j} (1 - P_j). \qquad (56)$$

Then the probability $P_1(g, G)$ that a leaf has angular setting (g, G) and receives the above combination is

$$P_1(g, G) = p \, X \, (g, G). \qquad (57)$$

The corresponding irradiance I_1 is given by

$$I_1 = \Sigma \, I_{1,j}. \qquad (58)$$

By varying j and (g,G) over their entire range, a leaf irradiance distribution can be determined. It is possible to allow for scattered light with the canopy.

Figures 9a and 9b show predicted and experimental irradiance levels and their variance under diffuse overcast conditions in a tomato crop.

IV. Optimal Control

Optimal Control—Nomenclature

$A(\tau)$	adjoint function, cost($£$) per unit rate of change of state variables $X(\tau)$
$B(\tau)$	boundary conditions (e.g., price, $£$)
$\overline{C}$	concentration of CO_2, kg m^{-3}
$C(\tau)$	control variables (e.g., temperature)
C_r	heating costs $£$ J^{-1}
C_w	value of crop $£$ kg^{-1}
D	fixed costs (rent, bank interest) $£$ m^{-2} sec^{-1}
h'	overall heat transfer coefficient, W m^{-2}
H	Hamiltonian function, $£$ m^{-2} sec^{-1}
$I(\tau_h)$	net return at harvest, $£$ m^{-2}
J_o	total incident solar radiation (0.4 − 2.7 μ) W m^{-2}
P_c	photosynthetic rate of a canopy, kg m^{-2} sec^{-1}
P_n	photosynthetic rate of a single leaf, kg m^{-2} sec^{-1}

q_h	heat flux required from the heating system, W m^{-2}
S_i, S_o	average irradiance inside and outside the greenhouse, W m^{-2}
t	average greenhouse transmission factor
T_i, T_o	temperature inside and outside the greenhouse $°$K or $°$C
$V(\tau_h)$	value of crop at harvest, $£$ m^{-2}
W_c	crop fresh weight, kg m^{-2}
W_d	crop dry weight, kg m^{-2}
x_c, h_c	coordinates of the center of an element of a tall crop cross-section, m
$X(\tau)$	vector of state variables
Greek	
α	photosynthetic rate kg (dry matter) J^{-1} (PAR) m^{-2} sec^{-1}
β	CO_2 conversion coefficient kg dry matter kg^{-1} CO_2
γ	heating efficiency of solar radiation
τ	time, sec
τ_h	harvest time

This section brings together the two earlier sections, and gives the greenhouse manager guidance to achieve the highest net income. Most of the work is theoretical, and tests are currently under design and/or execution.

A. The Optimization Problem

The first step is to recognize the existence of a set of definable state variables $X(\tau)$ whose growth with time may influence the growers' income. We write

$$(dX/d \, \tau) = f(X(\tau), C(\tau), B(\tau)). \qquad (59)$$

The vector $X(\tau)$ may contain the dry weight of fruit, or leaf area index (LAI). For maximum crop yield

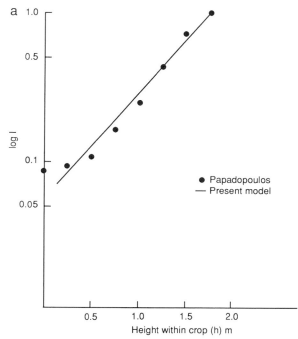

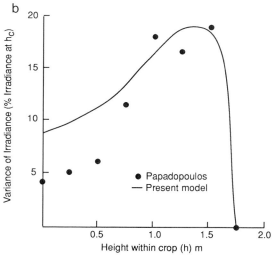

FIGURE 9 (a) Penetration of diffuse light into a rowcrop tomato canopy. (b) RMS variance of the penetration of diffuse light into a row crop tomato canopy. (—) model; (●) measurement. [From Critten, D. L. (1990). Light penetration and photosynthesis in tall greenhouse crops. D.N. 1558, *AFRC Inst. Eng. Res.* Wrest Park, Silsoe, MK45 4HS.]

continuously throughout the year dry weight should be studied. We next select a parameter which, upon optimization, will indicate to the grower the settings required for his control functions $C(\tau)$. Net income (I) is a useful choice, and we write

$$I(\tau_h) = V(\tau_h) + \int_0^{\tau_h} G(X(\tau), C(\tau), B(\tau)) d\tau. \quad (60)$$

$V(\tau_h)$, the value of the crop or harvest may depend on dry weight and price at time τ_h, and hence on $X(\tau_h)$ and $B(\tau_h)$. G is a function defining the total rate of expenditure, whose integral gives the total costs needed to achieve $V(\tau_h)$. For a single harvest (e.g., lettuce) Eq. (60) can be optimized directly. For continual production, the equation should be further integrated over τ_h for the whole growing season, and the resulting total net income optimized, $I(\tau_h)$ then becoming income per unit time instead of income per crop. The function $I(\tau_h)$ can be replaced using the Pontryagin principle by a so-called Hamiltonian function H, which can be maximized instantaneously.

$$H = G(X, C, B) + A(\tau) dX/d\tau. \quad (61)$$

A is known as the adjoint function, and satisfies the relationship

$$(dA/d\tau) = -\partial H/\partial X. \quad (62)$$

To demonstrate the solution process, we assume known boundary conditions $B(\tau)$ and set an initial value of $A(\tau)$.

Then we proceed as follows:
Maximise Equ. (61), to give values for $C(\tau)$, hence use Eq. (59) to update $X(\tau)$, hence use Eq. (62) to update $(A\tau)$.
This sequence is repeated, until $\tau = \tau_h$, using updated boundary conditions $B(\tau)$.

B. Operational Form for *I* and *H*

1. Irradiance Level

For a lettuce crop: $S_i = tS_o$. $\quad (63)$

A leaf photosynthetic rate can now be calculated based for example on the equation

$$P_n = \alpha S_i . \beta \overline{C} / (\alpha S_i + \beta \overline{C}). \quad (64)$$

This is a simple form to represent photosynthesis, neglecting respiration. For a tall crop, I_l in Eq. (58) would replace S_i at point (x_c, h_c). Integration over all possible irradiance levels, followed by integration over all crop area elements then yields the canopy photo synthesis rate (P_c). Integration of P_c with partition of the various products of photosynthesis ultimately leads to W_c, the crop fresh weight at harvest. [*See* Photosynthesis.]

2. Heating Requirement

From Eq. (25),

$$q_h = A_c h' (T_i - T_o)/A_g - J_o t\gamma. \qquad (65)$$

3. Optimization

Using W_c and q_h, Eq. (60) becomes

$$I(\tau_h) = C_w(\tau)W_c - \int_o^{\tau_h} C_r q_h d\tau - D.\tau_h. \qquad (66)$$

If optimization is carried out with respect to dry weight (W_d) only, then from Eq. (61) the Hamiltonian becomes

$$H = A \, dW_d/d\tau - C_r q_h. \qquad (67)$$

$dW_d/d\tau$ may be derived from the canopy photosynthesis, and maximization of H with respect to the control variables at time τ is now straightforward.

C. Optimizing Greenhouse Design

As well as forming the basis for optimizing $I(\tau_h)$ on a dynamic basis an equation of the form of Eq. (60) may also be used to select the best design of house to maximize the growers' return. If we assume blueprint control conditions, $I(\tau_h)$ can be evaluated for different designs. In this way the relative benefits of single and double cladding, single cladding with and without thermal screens, and indeed any new design variant can be studied.

V. The Problem of Control of State Variables in Greenhouses

This section will deal with a control problem of assessing the control valve setting when the state variable varies with position within the controlled zone and also depends on external influences. Two examples are given.

A. Temperature Control

For a fixed set point the deviation will vary with position. It is unpracticable to festoon the greenhouse with sensors, and so we make few measurements, but use models to then predict (in principle) temperatures elsewhere, and hence the best boiler valve setting. It is advantageous to choose measurement sites with care, for example with a piped hot water heating system, monitoring the water temperature as well as

air temperature can be useful in optimizing heating rates. There are a number of external forces affecting the heat supply by the boiler. Windspeed affects heat losses, and sunlight produces heating, and so these too must be monitored. Then models of their effect can be used to predict their influence on the control valve setting from a small number of measurements.

B. Nutrient Film Technology (NFT)

Instead of growing plants in soil, the supply of nutrients to a growing plant assembly (e.g., tomatoes) can be via a fluid (water) contained in a long shallow trough, sloping at about 1° to the horizontal to maintain a slow-moving flow rate, the fluid containing optimal concentrations of the nutrients. The troughs, up to 50 m long, discharge into a reservoir. Concentrations are monitored by measuring pH and conductivity. There are two requirements. First, a model of nutrient consumption along the trough is needed. The modelling problem is aggravated by the existence of stagnant areas within the trough, caused by root matts. Second, the concentration changes of each component must be modeled such that simple pH and conductivity measurements on the returned mixture can be used to restore concentration levels. These examples illustrate the control problem, and much current research is directed toward improving the models, and selecting the best measurements sites. Once the control valve setting is known, techniques common to other control problems can be used, normal practice being to use previous history to predict future requirements, basically an application of Taylor's polynomial expansion of a function. [See TOMATO PRODUCTION IN PROTECTED CULTIVATIONS.]

VI. Greenhouse Structural Design and Location

Since 1950, commercial greenhouses have been constructed with an aluminium frame. In fact Loudon demonstrated in the early 19th century that metal was a better material than wood, because being stronger it caused less light loss. However, steel, favoured by Loudon, has its drawbacks, and it was not until the lighter, durable, easily formed aluminium alloys had been developed that Loudon's proposal could be utilised commercially. [See STRUCTURES.]

Cross sectional views of several modern commercial greenhouse types are shown in Fig. 10. Dimen-

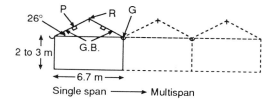

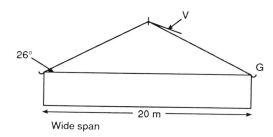

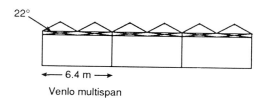

FIGURE 10 Cross-sectional views of typical modern greenhouses.

sions, angles etc are for United Kingdom and/or Dutch designs, and they may vary from country to country. Traditional greenhouses have a common basic besign. The roof is supported at gutter level by vertical stanchions (S). The "backbone" of the structure is the gutter (G), which being large and generally circular has great strength against bending. In single and wide spans, "I" or "T" girders may replace the gutter, which is then relegated to carry rainwater only. The multispan gutter is also used to yield access to the roof, and, traditionally, needs to be capable of taking a heavily clad human foot. The gutter (or girder) supports the roof glazing bars (GB) which are usually symmetrically placed about a ridge (R). Ventilators (V) are normally hinged at the ridge and set in a continuous line, on one, or both sides of the house axis. To eliminate sagging, glazing bars are supported by purlins (P) running axially about half way down the roof slope. Houses with spans greater than 6.4 m may have roof trusses, supported on stanchions, to carry the roof load.

The Dutch Venlo structure, which has been continually refined to improve house performance, is somewhat different in detail. The span is reduced to about half the traditional value, the stanchions being normally placed under alternate gutters. Occasionally, support is provided under each, or every third gutter. To restore light admittance, gutters (not shown) are reduced in overall size, strengthened by using thicker materials, and have a grill placed above them, to provide access. Light admittance is further improved by using a single pane of glass from ridge to gutter, each pane being of 1 m width. Vents (not shown) in total occupy about half the axial length and alternate on opposite sides of the ridge.

In general, stanchions are spaced 3 or 4 metres axially depending on the glass width, where all houses are also strengthened against lateral distortion by transverse girders at gutter level. Roof anchorage is also provided at these stations to hold the roof down.

House alignment is still a subject of debate. Broadly, at high latitudes E–W aligned houses admit more winter light though year round, N–S houses admit slightly more light. It is desirable to have a clear field of view above 10° elevation all round the house, though in the northern hemisphere, some additional loss in the northerly direction can be tolerated (vice versa for the southern hemisphere).

A "good" greenhouse will transmit typically 65–70% of diffuse light incident upon it, as measured under diffuse overcast skies. (Direct light transmission is difficult to include because of measurement scatter due, mainly, to structural shadows.) Broadly, the 30–35% loss is made up of 20% loss due to structure, 10% due to cladding (single), and the remainder due to dust deposit on the glass. Unfortunately, many houses do not reach this level of transmission, and tend to accumulate "clutter" in the roof, for example irrigation pipes, heating pipes, etc. The loss also increases when double cladding is used.

A single clad house will normally consume about 40,000 gallons of fuel per acre, to maintain 6°C internal temperature at temperate latitudes with mild winters (United Kingdom, Holland). Obviously this figure will rise as mean winter temperature falls.

Acknowledgments

The author acknowledges the following: The kind permission of the editors of *The Journal of Agricultural Engineering Research* (Dr. D. J. White) and the FAO/CNRE Energy book (Prof. C. von Zabeltitz) to use material from their published volumes. Staff of the Silsoe Research Institute, especially Dr. B. J. Bailey and Dr. Z. S. Chalabi for reading and commenting on the text, Mrs. T. Stelling for the typescript and Mrs. M. Knaggs for tracing the drawings.

Bibliography

Bailey, B. J. "Principles of Environmental Control," (1988). C. von Zabeltitz (ed.) Chapt. 3. FAO/CNRE Energy Book.

Bot. GPA (1983). "Greenhouse Climate: From Physical Process to a Dynamic Model." Thesis. Landbouwhogeschool, Wageningen, Netherlands.

Critten, D. L. (1987). "Light Transmission and Enhancement in Greenhouses." Ph.D. Thesis, London University.

Critten, D. L. (1991). "Light Interception and Absorption by the Crop."International workshop on greenhouse crop models. Casle of Saumane, Vacluse, France, 26–29 August.

Davis, P. F. (1984). A technique of adaptive control of the temperature in a greenhouse using ventilator adjustments. *J. Agr. Eng. Res.* **29,** 241–248.

Holmes, J. G. (1947). The reflexion factor of glass. *Trans. Illum. Eng. Soc. Lond.* **12,** 108.

IHVE Guide Book A. (1970). Sec. A.

Pontryagin, L. S., Boltyanskii, V, G., Gamrelihdz, R. V., Mishchenko, E. F. (1964). "The Mathematical Theory of Optimal Processes." Pergamon Press, Inc. New York.

Seginer, I., Angel, A., and Kantz, D. (1986). Optimal CO_2 enrichment strategy for greenhouses: A simulation study. *J. Agr. Eng. Res.* **34,** 285–304.

Seginer, I., Shina, G., Albright, L.D., and Marsh, L. S. (1991). Optimal temperature set points for greenhouse lettuce. *J. Agr. Eng. Res.* **49,** 209–226.

Insect Physiology

THOMAS A. MILLER, *University of California, Riverside*

Glossary

Ecdysone Molting hormone, a steroid lipid
Eclosion Act of molting from the egg or pupal case
Fibrillar muscle Specialized muscle that resonates asynchronously with the rate of nervous activation
Myogenic heart Contractile rhythm; a property of the muscle itself
Parthenogenesis Reproduction without fertilization
Poikilotherm Body temperature approximates ambient

Insect physiology is that subsection of entomological science (the study of insects) that deals with the functional mechanisms of insects. It seeks the answer to questions concerning how insects jump, fly, digest food, reproduce, grow, etc., in short, how they work. The study of insect ecology is concerned with how insects interact with the external environment, and physiology is largely concerned with what internal properties allow them to accomplish these interactions. Many of the physiological mechanisms of insects are similar or identical to those of other animals. Because of their ease of rearing at relatively low cost,

insects are valuable tools in the study of general physiological principles.

I. Introduction

Insects are members of the class Insecta, by far the largest group in the phylum Arthropoda. The number of insect species is considerably larger than that of any other group of animals on earth. Indeed, so great are the numbers (estimated at 10 million), and so diverse are the habitats occupied, that we will probably never know all the world's species.

A few insect species spend part or all of their life on or near the surface of the ocean; however, none is known to complete its life cycle in the ocean itself. Despite the paucity of insect life in the ocean, brine midges and other Diptera are known to survive well in lakes and seas with water more saline than the ocean. Thus insects are largely successful specialists who have colonized the land, including the soil, fresh water, and the air, but few or none have reversed the trend and recolonized the ocean, unlike several species of mammal.

Insects play a vital role in pollination of plants and recycling of waste materials in the ecosystem. They also are competitors and parasites of each other and all the other animals. Indeed, some of the most debilitating diseases of mankind are transmitted by insects, such as malaria, trypanosomiasis, and filariasis. Insects have adapted to modern agriculture in all of these same roles, as pollinators, as crop pests and parasites and predators of crop pests, and also as vectors of plant diseases. [*See* ENTOMOLOGY, HORTICULTURAL; ENTOMOLOGY, VETERINARY.]

At one time all six-legged arthropods were grouped in the class Insecta and commonly called Hexapoda (literally six legs); however, it is now accepted that certain of the most primitive hexapods contain features that distinguish them enough from modern insects that they are classified in another arthropod group.

The insect orders are divided between the subclasses Apterygota (wingless insects) and Pterygota (insects that evolved wings). The former now contain only two orders:

1. Archeognatha (Microcoryphia)
2. Thysanura (Zygentoma), bristletails

The Pterygota insects are subdivided further into two groups, the exopterygota and endopterygota. In exopterygota the wings develop externally as wing pads in immature preadult stages:

3. Ephemeroptera, mayflies
4. Odonata, dragonflies, damselflies
5. Plecoptera, stone flies
6. Embioptera, web spinners
7. Dictyoptera, cockroaches, mantids, termites
8. Grylloblattodea
9. Orthoptera, grasshoppers, crickets, phasmids
10. Dermaptera, earwigs
11. Zoraptera
12. Psocoptera, bark lice, book lice
13. Hemiptera, bugs, aphids, leafhoppers, cicadas
14. Thysanoptera, thrips
15. Phthiraptera, lice

The endopterygota develop wings internally during the immature stages and possess a pupal stage. They are considered the most highly evolved of the insects:

16. Megaloptera, dobsonflies, snakeflies
17. Neuroptera, lacewings, ant lions
18. Coleoptera, beetles
19. Mecoptera, scorpion flies
20. Trichoptera, caddis flies
21. Lepidoptera, moths, butterflies
22. Diptera, flies, gnats, midges, mosquitoes
23. Siphonaptera, fleas
24. Hymenoptera, ants, bees, wasps, sawflies

Physiologically the exopterygotes exhibit incomplete metamorphosis during development with relatively small changes from one molt to another, as in the grasshoppers. These insects are referred to as the hemimetabola. The endopterygotes, or more advanced insects, change in appearance dramatically from immature stages to adult, such as from caterpillar to pupa to butterfly. These are called the holometabola.

In further contrast to these two advanced groups of pyterygote insects, the apterygota are called ametabola because there appears to be even less distinction between immature and adult stages of growth. Indeed, the ametabolous Thysanura are known to reach sexual maturity before the last molt, a conditioned called paedogenesis.

II. Growth

Insects have an exoskeleton, or hard outer cuticle. Because of this, growth occurs in a series of discontinuous events, the molt or ecdysis. Ametabolic or hemimetabolic insects molt from one stage, or stadium, to another until an adult stage, or imago, is achieved. The immature forms have been called nymphs. Holometabolic insects are larvae as immatures, then pupae, then adults.

In some rare cases, there may be more than one pupal stage of development, but very highly specialized insects such as the Phylloxera are known to develop through as many as 21 different life-forms in one complete life cycle.

The common aphid parthenogenetically (asexually) develops wingless progeny in the spring and summer, with winged forms appearing only during crowding, which serves as a trigger for dispersal. Sexual reproduction takes place in the fall stimulated by short days and cooler temperatures. These progeny are capable of overwintering to complete the life cycle. In this case the development is closely associated with environmental changes.

At the other extreme of growth, the periodic cicada is known to live in the ground as a nymph for 13 to 17 years. Near the end of this period of time, a given population begins to synchronize development by an unknown mechanism, so that, during a 2-week period, the entire population emerges, molts to the adult stage, and then reproduces. The females lay eggs in small tree branches and then die. The eggs hatch soon after and the young larvae drop and burrow into the ground to begin another 13- or 17-year period of development.

Discontinuous growth occurs in the winter for most insects in temperate climates, which enter a hibernation, known as diapause. There are many different types of diapause, including a summer diapause called estivation. Diapause will be described in a later section.

Outside of the Thysanura and the Ephemeroptera, which are known to molt after reaching the adult stage, all insects stop development as adults and convert their energies to reproduction.

III. Integument and Molting

The integument, consisting of a single layer of epidermal cells and the overlying cuticle, serves many purposes in protecting the insect. It provides a waterproof layer to prevent desiccation, an exoskeleton upon which to attach muscles, and the wings with which insects fly, and is the primary barrier to infection and attack by entomopathic fungi and other microorganisms.

The integument must be transparent over the compound eyes and ocelli to allow light reception and must provide a means by which all other external sensory stimuli are received and translated to nervous impulses, so the information can be sent on to the central nervous system for processing. Sensory perception through the cuticle is accomplished by a series of discrete sensory structures that are specific modifications of the integument. The sensory nervous system and sensory detection are described in Section IV.

The cuticle is composed of a very thin outer epicuticle and an inner procuticle. Dermal glands, interspersed in the epidermal layer, are responsible for secreting and maintaining a cement layer on the outer surface of the epicuticle after it is fully formed. It does this by means of ducts through the cuticle.

Indeed the integument of insects has the seemingly incompatible functions of remaining impermeable to water yet providing access from inside to outside for maintaining the water-proof wax and cement layers on the outer epicuticle in case of abrasions or injury. The cuticle must also be strong and solid, yet be flexible enough to provide movement without damage to the cuticle. The wax layer of the honeybee epicuticle is said to be the same material as that used to construct the honeycomb.

The insect is able, given time, to regenerate body parts at subsequent molts following injury. This suggests that the cuticle is a living structure, not dead or inert. Indeed, the integument that is isolated from trophic nutrients supplied by the hemolymph (blood) quickly becomes brittle, cracks, and breaks off.

The procuticle is composed of protein, lipid, and carbohydrate parts that are recruited by and processed through the underlying layer of epidermal cells. Arthropodin is a term given to the extractable protein of the cuticle, and sclerotin is the term referring to all tanned protein. Although absent in the epicuticle, the main carbohydrate portion of procuticles is the substance chitin, which is related chemically to cellulose (Fig. 1), a main structural component of plants. Chitin is a polymer of N-acetylglucosamine, a polysaccharide.

The procuticle is a laminate structure composed of two major parts, an outer sclerotized (and insoluble) exocuticle and an inner, softer endocuticle (Fig. 2). The endocuticle continues to grow in thickness during an intermolt period as products and precursors are secreted by the underlying epidermal cells.

Long before an insect molts, the new cuticle is prepared beneath the older cuticle. At a certain point the new and old cuticles separate as a discrete event called apolysis. The softer parts of the old cuticle are dissolved and reabsorbed by the epidermal cells immediately before the molt by activation of a molting fluid. When the endocuticle has been dissolved, the insect splits along a dorsal fracture line in the remaining exocuticle and forces itself out of the older exocuticle shell, leaving behind an empty exuvia. Because the tracheal system is composed of cuticle, even the old tracheal lining is pulled out of the spiracles at the time of the molt.

The cuticle of newly molted insect is normally transparent. Within seconds the insect expands the body, usually by swallowing air, to unfold the new cuticle, which begins to darken. This darkening process is called tanning and is accomplished by recruiting phenolic amino acid molecules from the hemolymph and delivering them to the outer aspect of the new

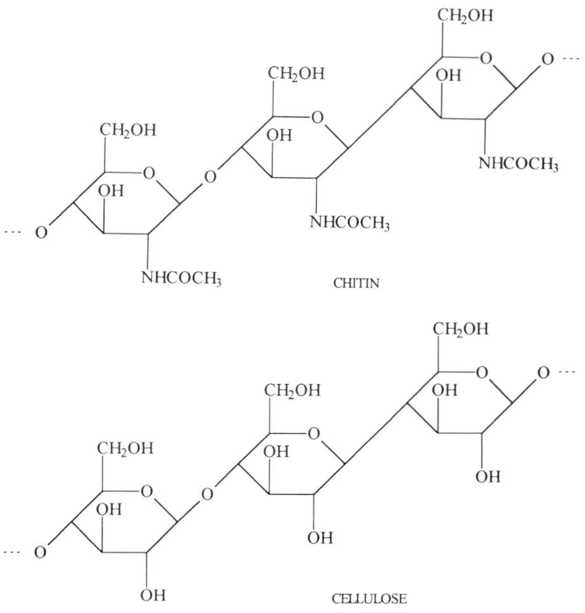

FIGURE 1 The structures of chitin and cellulose. (From Merck Catalogue.)

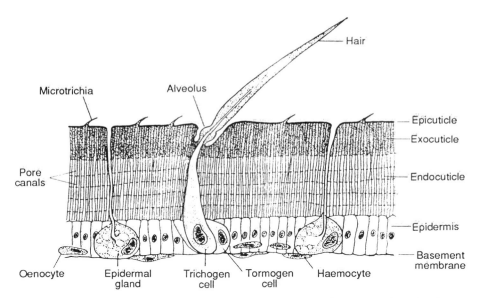

FIGURE 2 Labeled layers of typical insect cuticle: epicuticle, exocuticle, endocuticle, and epidermis. [Reproduced with permission from Davies, R. G. (1988). "Outlines of Entomology," 7th ed. p. 8. Chapman and Hall, New York.]

procuticle via minute pore canals connecting the epidermal cells to the outer cuticle. Once there or on the way, the amino acids are oxidized to quinones by phenoloxidase enzymes. The quinones then react with proteins in the procuticle to form cross-links (Fig. 3). This hardens and darkens the resulting exocuticle, forming stiff sclerites on most of the body segments of adult insects and nymphs and hard head capsules, mouthparts, and claws in most larvae.

This tanning reaction is repeated in the process of repairing wounds in the cuticle. If a wound is not fatal, the restorative processes can be seen to patch and close the open wound in a matter of hours. Coagulating hemolymph proteins and blood cells are eventually tanned as the epidermal cells expand and divide to cover the new area.

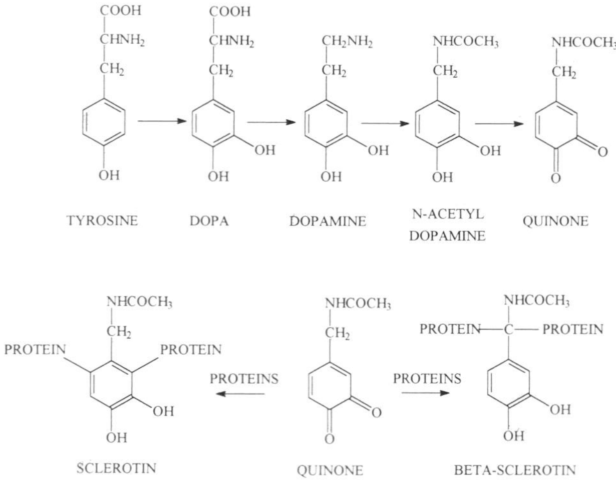

The hard parts of the cuticle of many adult insects vary depending on the species from rock hard to flexible. Specialized cuticle in joints sometimes is composed of a special protein, resilin, that has much of the elastic properties of rubber. Resilin is known to be an important part of the wing hinge mechanism of adult insects that must undergo distortion during flight yet remain stiff to support the wings without permanently changing properties, nor breaking in stress fractures.

The cyclorrhaphan Diptera, such as the common housefly, use a specialized structure during development from larvae to adult stages. Instead of molting from the last larval instar to a separate pupa, the fully developed larva stops feeding, clears the gut, wanders to find a pupation site, then goes through a number of discrete changes. The mouthparts retract and the body becomes rounded owing to contractions of the body wall muscles. Eventually the larval cuticle is tanned in place in a manner similar to tanning of other newly molted insects, but in this case, a puparium is formed. The adult fly then forms inside of the puparium and emerges after completing development.

Certain external and internal cues are given during this cyclorrhaphan development that affect the outcome. For example, if the blowfly larva is placed in

FIGURE 3 Oxidation of Tyrosine and protein linking. [Modified from Mordue *et al.* (1980). "Insect Physiology." p. 39. Halsted Press (J. Wiley), NJ.]

contact with water, pupariation does not occur and further development is stopped until the water is removed. In this manner, a large group of larvae can be induced to synchronize development.

If a larva is tied with a piece of thread or string as a ligature in the middle before completing development, only the front half of the insect pupates. If the ligature is applied further along in development, both halves pupate. This simple experiment and related studies were used to prove that the molt is controlled by hormones that are released at certain critical times during development from tissues inside the insect and circulate in the hemolymph to synchronize the metamorphic changes in all the cells of the body, as described in the following section.

IV. Hormones

The first insect hormone demonstrated by ligation experiments was the brain hormone. Now known as PTTH, which stands for prothoracicotropic hormone, the brain hormone is produced by only one or two pairs of nerve cells located in the lateral parts of the forebrain. When the time for a molt approaches, PTTH is delivered via axons from the cell body of origin to a small nervous gland behind the brain called the corpora cardiaca, where it is released into the bloodstream, or hemolymph.

The trigger to start these events is not well understood, but certain caterpillars are known not to molt until they achieve a certain critical weight. It is not known how the insect weighs itself. In other cases, molting is triggered by a more obvious event, for example, a blood meal in assassin bugs activates stretch receptors in the swollen abdomen, which in term signal brain centers to begin developing PTTH.

One of the main functions of PTTH is to activate the prothoracic gland (PG), which in turn has already sequestered a store of steroid precursor molecules from the diet. There may be a host of other effects of PTTH on other targets within the insect, but activation of the PG is the best demonstrated and understood function. If a ligature string is applied to the neck of the insect before the release of PTTH, the head contains the PG and thus the entire head end of the insect receives a signal to molt and does so, while the body areas away from the ligature receive no signal and remain unchanged. If the ligature is applied after the release of PTTH, the molting process proceeds in both halves of the insect. Thus the time of ligation can be used to demonstrate a "head critical period" during which PTTH is released.

PTTH was first isolated from silkworms. It is reported to be a glycopeptide composed of two identical or nearly identical peptide subunits connected by a sulfide bond. Isolation of the gene responsible for synthesizing PTTH revealed that a propeptide precursor is first synthesized, which is composed of 224 amino acid residues with various subunits bounded by sites at which proteolytic cleavage can occur. The active principle is said to reside in the final 109-amino-acid subunit. When constituted in the whole insect, two 109-residue subunits are cleaved from the precursor peptide and then connected by a sulfide bond and covalently bonded to a glycogen molecule.

In response to PTTH the PG converts its store of steroids to ecdysone, which is then released into the general circulatory system (Fig. 4).

Ecdysone is oxidized by various tissues in the insect body to 20-hydroxyecdysone (20-HE) (Fig. 4), which is the active form of this lipid hormone. The 20-HE then interacts with the nucleus of each cell in the body to bring about cell division. Triggering of synthesis and release of ecdysone is considered a synchronizing event designed to produce a burst of development and cell division in the entire body all at the same time so that molting with or without metamorphosis can proceed.

The prothoracic glands degenerate in most adult insects soon after their last molt. An exception to this is in the Thysanura order of primitive insects in which

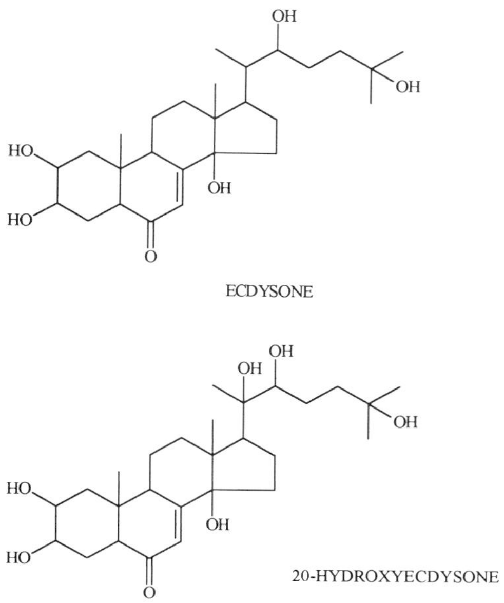

FIGURE 4 The structures of ecdysone and 20-hydroxyecdysone. [Modified from Mordue *et al.* (1980). "Insect Physiology." p. 36. Halsted Press (J. Wiley), NJ.]

the prothoracic glands do not degenerate after the insects reach sexual maturity. Thysanura, however, continue to molt after reaching the adult stage, and thus they are seen to support the generally accepted function of the prothoracic glands as responsible for supporting molting in general. Indeed, ecdysone was originally called the molting hormone.

Located very close to the corpora cardiaca nerve complex behind the brain of insects is another organ called the corpora allata, or CA. The CA differs markedly in structure from the corpora cardiaca in that it is a true endocrine gland. Although the CA receives innervation from the brain and corpora cardiaca, it is not nervous tissue.

After removal of the CA from insects, subsequent molts occur on schedule, but only mature stages are produced as a result. The CA is now known to synthesize and release another hormone called juvenile hormone (JH) that plays a critical role in determining development at each molt (Fig. 5).

So far five JHs have been identified in insects and named JH 0, I, II, III, and iso-JH. Certain of these are more predominant in some insects, such as JH III being the predominant JH in moths and butterflies (Lepidoptera). The epoxide structure of JHs (two carbons and an oxygen atom each bonded to the other in a three-membered circle) is somewhat unusual for an animal hormone. The function of JH during preadult development is widely accepted as providing developmental cues during a molt along with ecdysone.

At each molt, the shape of the subsequent tissues in the body is dictated by a complex interaction of the concentrations of ecdysone and JH immediately preceding eclosion. At one critical time during the synchronized events leading to a molt, if the JH titer in the hemolymph is present, then juvenile features are produced in the subsequent stage. If the titer of JH is absent at this precise time, then mature features are produced. In holometabolous insects, this gives

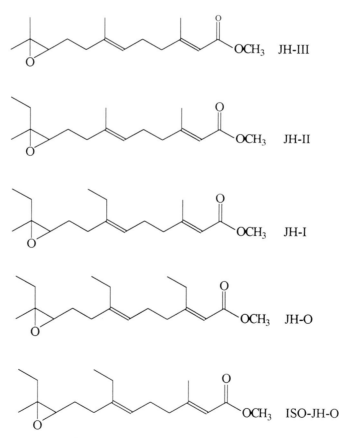

FIGURE 5 Juvenile hormones isolated from insects. [Modified from Downer, R., and Laufer, M. (eds.). (1983). Chemistry and metabolism of juvenile hormone. *In:* "Endocrinology of Insects," Vol. I. p. 58. Alan R. Liss, New York.]

rise to metamorphosis, whereas in hemimetabolous insects, adult development occurs.

A number of other events in the life of insects are coordinated by the release of neurohormones that are synthesized in specific parts of the nervous system. During the initiation of flight in migratory locusts, the substrate used to provide energy for flight shifts in the first 30 min from carbohydrate to fats. The fat reserves are mobilized on signal from a circulating neurohormone called adipokinetic horomone (AKH).

AKH, a peptide 8 or 10 amino acids long, is first synthesized and then released into the general circulatory system, where it activates the breakdown of fat reserves in fat body to diglycerides. AKH also increases the efficiency of diglyceride uptake by the flight muscles from the circulatory system, and probably has several other functions as yet unknown. AKHs have now been described from several insects, and many other neuropeptides that perform trophic functions like AKH are also known.

V. Nervous System

The central nervous system of all insects consists of the brain, located in the head, and several ganglion nerve centers each connected by a pair of nerve tracts or connectives in a string called the ventral nerve cord. Primitively there is one ganglion associated with each of the segments of the body. In most cases ganglia have evolved so that two or more are combined together and are indistinguishable. The extreme case of this condensation of nerve centers is found in advanced Diptera, or flies, in which the central nervous system consists of only the brain and thoracic ganglion masses (Fig. 6).

The organization of a typical ganglion follows a similar pattern. The outer structure is a glial or cellular "perineurium" layer that provides a regulated ionic environment next to the bare axons and also provides an avenue to admit nutrients and eliminate waste products from ordinary metabolism. Beneath the perineurium is a nerve cell body layer, which consists of motor neurons, interneurons, or neurosecretory neurons.

The cell bodies of motor neurons are grouped in discrete locations normally in dorsal and lateral positions in a typical ganglion. These "soma" are almost always monopolar, giving rise to a single process that leaves the cell body as a neurite. The neurites then divide into dendrites and axons. The dendrites ramify into the very center of the ganglion in the "neuropile,"

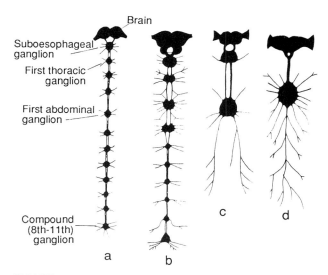

FIGURE 6 Ventral nerve cords from several insects. [Reproduced with permission from Davies, R. G. (1988). Outlines of Entomology, 7th ed. p. 45. Chapman and Hall, New York.]

where they synapse with other axons to receive nervous input. Long axons exit the ganglion and innervate the various muscles of the body segment that the particular ganglion is associated with.

With only a few rare exceptions, all sensory neurons are located in the periphery of each of the body segments. The most obvious are mechanoreceptors that innervate single hair structures or setae of the body wall and are movement sensitive. All sensory cell bodies, or soma, provide axons that penetrate into the ganglia associated with the body segment where the sensory structure is located. In most cases the sensory soma are bipolar or multipolar. They receive stimulatory input at the dendrite end, which is translated into graded electrical potentials. When these generator potentials exceed a given threshold, all-or-none nervous impulses are initiated on the opposite side of the soma and propagate along the axons and into the associated neuropile of the corresponding ventral ganglia via segmental nerve trunks.

In mammals the excitatory motor neurons that give rise to movement are known as cholinergic because the principle neurotransmitter chemical that is synthesized in the neuron and released at the synaptic nerve endings, the neuromuscular junctions, in response to nerve stimulation is acetylcholine (Fig. 7).

In insects, the excitatory neuromuscular transmitter chemicals are thought to be amino acids or peptides; however, many of the sensory neurons that have been studied are known to be cholinergic. This means that the synapses in the neuropile of each of the ventral

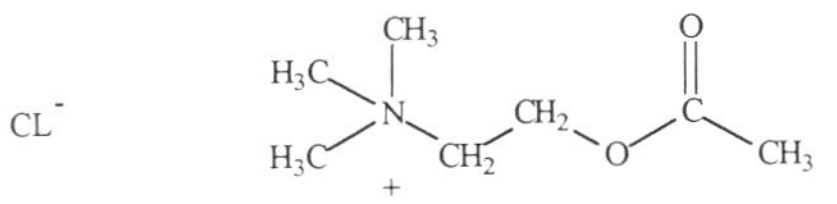

FIGURE 7 The structure of Acetylcholine chloride. (From Merck Catalogue.)

ganglion of the central nervous system that are formed between sensory axons arriving from the periphery and dendrites of interneurons or motor neuron are cholinergic. Cholinergic synapses all characteristically have an enzyme, acetylcholinesterase, that occupies the extracellular space between the incoming axon terminal and the outgoing dendritic nerve.

Any acetylcholine that is released from the presynaptic axon is rapidly hydrolyzed by acetylcholinesterase. Several insecticides owe their activity to either inhibiting the hydrolytic activity of acetylcholinesterase or stimulating or blocking the cholinergic receptor on the postsynaptic dendrite. If the acetylcholinesterase is inhibited, acetylcholine is allowed to build up in the synaptic gap, where it constantly stimulates the postsynaptic cell, leading to convulsions.

Insects contain two types of excitatory motor neurons called fast and slow and one type of inhibitory motor neuron. The fast or slow designation refers to the response of the corresponding muscle to stimulation of the excitatory axons and has nothing to do with speed of propagation. If a given muscle responds with a twitch to a single shock of one axon, the axon is classified as "fast." Slow axons evoke no response to single shocks, but higher frequencies of stimulation evoke a slow graded contraction whose force is directly related to the frequency of stimulation. All slow positional movements of insect limbs are thought to be produced by slow excitatory motor units. Fast axons are used only during vigorous walking or running movements, and therefore the vast majority of motor neurons in insects are slow.

Insects also possess a few inhibitory motor neurons, which have been most thoroughly studied in the thoracic ganglia supplying the legs. Because the inhibitory motor neurons usually send axons to more than one muscle in a given leg, they are called "common inhibitors." Upon stimulation of an inhibitory motor neuron, a simple chemical, called GABA or gamma aminobutyric acid, is thought to be released at the neuromuscular junction from the axon terminal. GABA causes the postsynaptic muscle cell to hyperpolarize or become more stable (the opposite of excitation), and inhibitory motor neurons have been shown to remove "reflex postural tonus" in muscles immediately prior to an escape response.

GABA is also thought to serve as an inhibitory neurotransmitter between neurons in the neuropile of the central nervous system, where it also mediates inhibition analogous to its role in some of the muscles. Indeed, inhibition in the central nervous system is thought to be the principal means of eliminating the multitude of stimulatory signals arriving at the central nervous system from the peripheral neurons.

Many thousands of sensory neurons are located in the antennae of insects. These each separately send axons into a discrete structure at the front of the brain known as the antennal ganglion, or deutocerebrum. All sensory axons synapse in the neuropile of the deutocerebrum with interneurons. Some of the interneurons, in turn, send considerably fewer axons out of the deutocerebrum to higher brain centers. The ratio of incoming sensory axons to outgoing interneuronal axons in the few insects in which this has been investigated thoroughly is about 600 : 1. The principal types of synapse in the neuropile of the deutrocerebrum are thought to be cholinergic and GABAergic, corresponding to the sensory terminals and interneuronal inhibitory connections.

The GABA synapse is an important site of action of another category of older chlorinated hydrocarbon insecticide, the cyclodienes, such as chlordane, endosulfan, toxaphene, and lindane. In addition, the newer insecticide, avermectin, has been shown to act at the GABA synapse as well. All of these materials act by interfering with the postsynaptic membrane by increasing or decreasing permeability. There appears to be no enzyme with a function analogous to cholinesterase at the cholinergic synapse. Instead, excess GABA is removed from the synapse by a very efficient uptake and transport system.

The sensory neurons involved in vision operate in a manner similar to that of all other animals. Indeed, the reaction that translates light energy to electrical information in the rhabdoms of the retinula cells relies on rhodopsin proteins, whose structure bears remarkable similarity across the phyla. The specific physiology of the visual apparatus in insects is unique. Insects possess three discrete types of visual apparati, the well-known compound eyes, the lesser-known stemmatae characteristic of many larval insects, and the least-known ocelli, usually located on the dorsal aspect of the head between the compound eyes of many adult and nymphal insects. In addition, insects are known to respond to light when all the optical structures are covered or removed and this is referred to as a dermal light sense.

The two principal types of compound eye are apposition and superposition. The former is present in most diurnal insects and is characterized structurally by the rhabdom being located adjacent to the specialized lens system formed by the overlying cuticle. The superposition eye is characteristic of most nocturnal insects. It is also called the clear zone eye because the rhabdom is separated from the lens system by tissues that form a transparent rodlike column.

The individual ommatidia of an apposition eye typically accept light within a few degrees of the ommatidial axis. The rhabdoms of nocturnal fliers with superposition eyes, on the other hand, accept light from a very wide angle. This enables the nocturnal fliers to operate in very low light intensities. Light adaptation of the superposition eyes usually involves the migration of pigment in cells surrounding the ommatidia, which acts to shield off-axis light rays, thus superposition eyes can function in conditions of greater light intensity, but apposition eyes are normally unable to function under conditions of low light intensity.

Nocturnal adult insects are thought to have evolved the ability to navigate by starlight or moonlight by keeping the light source at a constant angle with the body. The spiraling flight of an adult insect near a candle or porch light at night is thought to resemble this navigation by a distant light source.

The compound eye of insects is not so much able to discern a given shape as it is sensitive to movement. Indeed, a stationary grasshopper can be approached and touched provided no rapid or jerky movements are made. Because the compound eye is made up of individual ommatidia, seen as hexagonally shaped facets on the surface of the eye, certain insects have evolved ommatidia with specialized functions depending on the location on the eye. Some aquatic insects that float on the surface of water have ommatidia specialized for vision in the air on the part of the eye aimed "up" and ommatidia specialized for vision in the water on the part of the eye aimed "down." Dragonfly larvae and praying mantid adults that ambush prey have ommatidia aimed forward to achieve a binocular effect that enables them to accurately measure distance to the prey before a strike.

The visual acuity of the adult insect eye is sometimes remarkable. This has been measured as a high "flicker fusion frequency" in simple "electroretinogram" electrical potentials obtained from surface electrodes placed on the compound eye in response to

high-frequency light flashes. Individual potential responses are discernible at frequencies typically in the 200 to 300 flashes per second range and are said to depend on nervous connections in the first optical ganglion of the eye. If this ganglion is removed or its function impaired, the flicker fusion frequency is said to drop to 40–60 flashes per second, or more typical of larval or nymphal insects.

Unlike most animals, insects have the ability to discern colors. Unlike the birds or primates that have color sense, insect color vision is based on individual retinula cells being maximally stimulated in either the yellow-green, blue, or ultraviolet portions of the spectrum instead of the more familiar red, green, and blue. Although some insects have been shown to have the ability to see red, most insects are thought, incorrectly sometimes, to be insensitive to infrared. Indeed, many insect behavior studies are conducted under infrared light, which is assumed to be invisible to the insect.

The first evidence for the ability of insects to discern color came from the ability to train honeybees to come to specific colors on the basis of a sugar reward. The ability of insects to discern ultraviolet gradually led to the appreciation that insects "see" different patterns than human beings are able to discern. Indeed, a simple daisy flower that appears pure white to human beings often shows a vivid "bull's-eye" pattern to the honeybee or other insects.

The last property of the insect eye discussed here, the ability to detect the plane of polarization of light, is used by diurnal fliers and walkers for navigation. Because of the nature of light scattering of sunlight by the atomsphere, the direction of the sun can be determined by an animal that can analyze the plane of polarized light. This ability is said to be used by ants and bees and other insects to orient from the nest to an object such as a food source and return to the nest accurately. Honeybees are able to pass on information about the distance and direction of a food source to their hivemates by performing a "waggle dance."

Ants are able to mark the trail to a food source for nestmates with a remarkable system of trail-marking chemicals that are manufactured in various specialized glands. In both bees and ants, the plane of polarized light is thought to be the critical means to discern information about direction from the starting point. Ants can be disoriented and forced take "wrong turns" merely by holding polarizing filters over them as they forage.

Insects have evolved an unusual variety of sensory structures to detect movement. These include airflow, substrate vibrations, and sound waves, including ultrasound. The general category of these sensors is mechanoreceptor, and all can be related back to the typical scolopidium sensory unit, which is composed of a bipolar sensory nerve cell with a scolopale structure of modified cuticle at the dendritic end and an axon formed at the opposite end.

Probably the best-known mechanoreceptor in insects is the campaniform sensilla. These are single-sense cells associated with minute flat areas of cuticle and are said to be directionally sensitive to forces on the cuticle. The wings and halteres on Diptera are well endowed with these sensors.

Besides stretch receptors attached directly to various muscles, the insects have a number of chordotonal organs. Some of the latter have become specialized to detect sound. Three such particular groups of chordotonal sensillae have distinctive names of their own, namely, the subgenual organs, Johnston's organ, and the tympanal organs.

Subgenual (literally below the knee) is a specialized chordotonal organ located at the knee joint usually on the front leg. This structure is present on all insects except, curiously, Diptera and Coleoptera. These organs can pick up substrate vibrations between 100 and 10,000 Hz with amplitudes of 4×10^{-10} cm. They are usually arranged as sensory cell groups stretched over large tracheal tubes.

The flagellum of the adult mosquito and midge is usually attached to a conspicuously swollen or enlarged pedicellus segment. The pedicellus is occupied by a large number of scolopidia that make up a chordotonal organ called the Johnston's organ. In the mosquito *Anopheles aegypti,* there are believed to be 30,000 such scolopidia and in the adult male they are tuned to respond to the 500- to 800-Hz sound of the female mosquito in flight, which evokes mating behavior in the males. All insects are said to possess the Johnston's organ, although in mosquito it may be at its most conspicuous.

Another variety of chordotonal sensillae, the tympanal organs, are present in a number of different insects. Unlike the subgenual organs or Johnston's organ, tympanal organs occur as specializations at a number of different locations, such as the conspicuous "ear" on the thorax of most grasshoppers or the foreleg of Tettigoniidae. Tympanal organs on night-flying insects are said to be sensitive to the ultrasonic pulses used by predatory bats. Best known among these are the tympanal organs on noctuid moths. Tympanal organs are present as paired structures on all noctuid moths, on Geometroidea, Saturniidae,

Bombycoidea, and microlepidoptera, and are said to have evolved during the middle-Tertiary period. Those on Sphingoidea reside in the modified palps, but in other adult moths they are usually located on the metathoracic or first or second abdominal segments.

One tympanal organ of the noctuid *Prodenia eridania* is said to consist of three nerve cells, A1, A2, and B. Since the B cell is nonacoustic, the moth uses only two nerve cells per "ear" to detect the bat cry. This can be considered as another example of Dethier's labeled line neurons because detection of ultrasonic pulses leads to a very conspicuous "escape" behavior on the part of the flying adult moth. Some of the tympanal organs are sensitive to fairly high frequencies of sonar compared to the human hearing range. The tympanal organ in a modified wing vein of the lacewing *Chrysoperla carnea* is said to respond to sonar pulses of 100,000 Hz.

All chemosensory structures of insects have in common one or more pores through the cuticle by which environmental chemicals gain access to sensory dendrite structures. There are two contact chemoreceptors that are better known than any others, the labellar taste hair (on the mouthparts) of the blowflies and houseflies and the tarsal chemoreceptors (on the feet) of flies and other insects, which seem to serve a similar function. When an adult housefly is not fed for a period of time and then allowed to walk on a sugar solution, it extends its proboscis (sucking mouthparts) and attempts to feed. The proboscis extension is a reflex response.

The proboscis response must be evaluated carefully to rule out the situation where the response is to water, not the sugar solution. If care is taken in pretest conditioning of the insects, then the proboscis response can be used to measure threshold sensitivity to sugar. *Calliphora,* the blowfly, is said to be sensitive to sucrose at a threshold of 2.5 mM; the human threshold for detecting sucrose is 20 mM. However, the *Dania* butterflies have a detection threshold of 0.008 mM.

The labellar taste hair of the blowfly is one of the best-described chemoreceptors and one of the simplest to study. Composed of a single large trichoid hair open only at the extreme tip end, the sensor is said to have four nerve cells situated at its base. Because of their responses, these four nerve cells are called the salt, water, sugar, and mechanoreceptor cells.

Young locusts feed on dry bran and fresh grass. The sensory hairs on the palps of the locusts were demonstrated to change electrical resistance during feeding. The increase in resistance of the palps could be induced by injecting hungry locusts with extracts of the storage lobes of the corpora cardiaca. Hemolymph from newly fed locusts also caused an increase in electrical resistance in the palps of hungry locusts. Feeding is thought to desensitize the taste receptors by some neurohormonal influence. In feeding locusts, the anterior part of the foregut is filled last. Cutting the posterior pharyngeal nerves leads to hyperphagia (overeating), sometimes to the point of bursting. A stretch receptor located at the anterior foregut is said to be responsible for signaling the higher nerve centers to inhibit the feeding response.

By far the most-studied chemoreceptors in insects are those on the antennae of male moths that are specific for the sex attractant chemicals, or pheromones, produced by females of the same species. The antennae of silkworm adults and subsequent mating behavior are perhaps as well known as those of any insect. Here the pheromone is a blend of two chemicals (Fig. 8). The large male antenna is filiform and full of branchlets, each with a multitude of minute hairs. Each hair is supplied by a pair of sensory chemoreceptor nerve cells. One of the pair responds to bombykol and the other to bombykal (Fig. 8). All the paired sensory neurons send axons into the deutocerebral ganglion of the brain, where primary information processing occurs.

Attempts to duplicate mating behavior in the laboratory have shown that males have a propensity to respond only at certain times of the day or night, and that the males keep a biological clock to tell the correct time. Females possess, and their behavior is synchronized by, a similar biological clock because the pheromone is not synthesized until near the correct time.

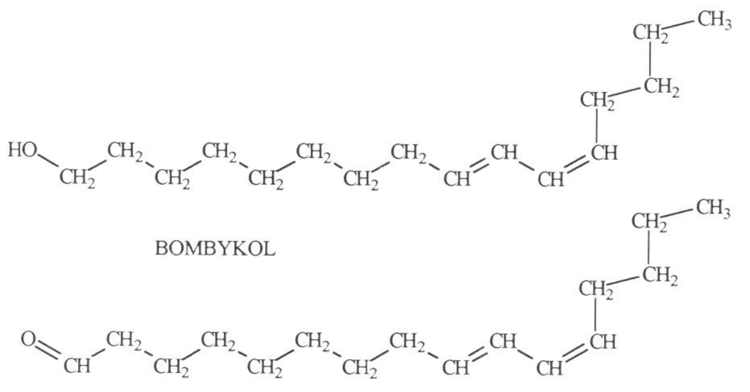

It was recently learned that the signal to induce pheromone synthesis comes from the subesophageal ganglion in the ventral nerve cord of the corn earworm moth. Certain neurosecretory nerve cells there produce a neurohormone (PBAN, pheromone biosynthesis-activating neurohormone) peptide that is released in the terminal abdominal ganglion, which in turn activates a neuroglandular neuron whose nerve impulses stimulate the pheromone gland in the end of the abdomen to begin synthesis and release of the pheromone chemical.

When the response window for sexual attraction occurs, not only is pheromone synthesis triggered, but all accompanying genetically inbred behavior as well, which includes a more or less sophisticated ritualistic recognition response behavior leading to mating. In some insects these behaviors are very complex and involve the release of male pheromones from hair pencil organs on their abdomens to stimulate the females to accept the males.

Genetically fixed behaviors or action patterns reach somewhat of an epitome in crickets. Common male field crickets have evolved specific song patterns to signal territory or warning aggression to rival males, or to attract females of the same species for mating. Females are able to detect the exact song pattern produced by the conspecific male and ignore even closely related cricket songs. The analysis of male cricket song patterns was found to be a superior tool for use in classification of cricket species, many of which appeared to taxonomists to be morphologically identical. As a result of this analysis, the number of field cricket species has doubled in the eastern United States. The cricket song patterns are known to be genetically fixed because interbreeding of very closely related field crickets produced hybrid male offspring each with a new and distinct song pattern. Neither female of the parental strains responded to the hybrid song.

VI. Muscles

All muscles in insects are striated; there are no known muscles analogous to the "smooth" muscle of vertebrates. Certain specific muscles have evolved in insects to perform special functions, such as the fibrillar muscles, which are also called asynchronous muscles.

The maximum contraction and relaxation of ordinary fast (twitch) muscles have been measured in the dorsolongitudinal singing muscles of certain katydid

FIGURE 8 The structures of bombykol and bombykal, pheromones of the silkworm, *Bombyx mori*. [Redrawn from Evans, H. E. (1984). "Insect Biology." p. 118. Addison Wesley, Reading, MA.]

grasshoppers at around 212 cycles per second. This means that a train of 212 nervous impulses per second can produce a single contraction and relaxation, in this case to generate a noise of the same frequency for communication. However, stimulus frequencies artificially imposed above this amount would cause these muscles to remain contracted in tetany and unable to relax between nervous impulses. These are called synchronous muscles because they can only respond to nervous stimuli.

The specialized fibrillar muscles of the flight apparati or tympanal organs of certain insects are unusual. These muscles have evolved the ability to contract many times in response to single stimuli. As a result, they can generate frequencies of contraction far above the 212-Hz limit imposed on ordinary "fast" skeletal muscle fibers.

When a single nervous impulse arrives at a fibrillar muscle, a large electrical wave is generated that quickly spreads to the entire muscle. This electrical wave "activates" the contractile elements of the muscle, which do not develop a force unless under load. If the fibrillar muscle is under a load, or being stretched, when it is activated, it then "vibrates" at a resonant frequency that depends on the amount of load imposed, not on the continued arrival of nervous impulses.

The dorsolongitudinal and dorsoventral opposing pairs of flight muscles in advanced Diptera and some beetles operate in this manner. These opposing muscles are connected either to the front and back of the thorax or to the top and bottom of the thorax. When the wings are unfolded, they are constrained by their thoracic connections into either the wing-up or wing-down positions, which alternately stretches one set of fibrillar muscles of the opposing pair while it relaxes the other and vice versa.

Thus as long as nervous impulses arrive at all the fibrillar flight muscles at a continual low rate of around 10 or more impulses per second, the fibrillar muscles will vibrate at 20 or 30 times this rate owing to their resonant properties. The contractile mechanism is thought to be a property of the myofibrils themselves because the resonant vibrations have been achieved *in vitro* in preparations lacking the muscle membrane and including only the contractile apparatus and energy substrates plus calcium ion. In this manner, the wing beat frequencies of asynchronous fliers can reach several hundred or even thousands of cycles per second.

VII. Respiration

Oxygen diffuses relatively slowly in aqueous medium, therefore diffusion alone can supply tissues no larger than about 1.0 mm in diameter. Larger tissues must evolve mechanisms to facilitate the delivery of oxygen. Insects have evolved the use of hemoglobinlike molecules to carry molecular oxygen to tissues only in low-oxygen environments such as encountered by chironomid midge larvae that live in the silt at the bottom of rivers and lakes and botfly larvae that live in the stomachs of cattle or horses.

Because of the limits imposed on diffusion in aqueous media, insects have evolved a tracheal system that provides an airway from the paired spiracles of the body segments to all the internal tissues. The tracheal tubes are invaginations of the cuticle and are stiffened by the presence of taenidia, which are thickened spiral creases that prevent the delicate air tubes from collapsing under negative pressure.

In some active flying insects such as housefly and honeybee, the trachea are expanded into very large sacs to accommodate an increased air demand by flight muscles. In addition, the tracheal tubes penetrate to all parts of the flight muscles via invaginations as finer branches, the tracheoles, so that all parts of the muscle tissue are close to the air supply.

These active fliers can use 10–50 ml O_2 per gram of tissue per hour, some of the most active tissues known. These high rates can be achieved very rapidly from basal rates of 0.1–0.5 ml $O_2/g/hr$, an increase of 50- to 100-fold instantly. The tracheal system with fast air delivery makes this possible.

In some insects, the ready access of air removes the buildup of carbon dioxide as a product of oxidation; however, facilitated loss of CO_2 also causes undesirable water loss. For this reason the spiracular system appears to be designed in resting insects to remain closed most of the time and open only during discrete bursts of activity to allow rapid exchange of gases, but to conserve water.

Some active adult insects "pump" air through the tracheal system with very obvious telescoping movements of the abdomen, as seen in honeybees visiting flowers. Other adult insects, such as flying grasshoppers, direct air through the tracheal system by controlled opening of the spiracles.

However, for inactive or apparently inert stages such as pupae of Lepidoptera, it was once thought that oxygen was supplied to internal tissues entirely by diffusion and that the ubiquitous presence of the tracheoles solved the physical diffusion problem. More recently, it was shown that even pupae showing little or no overt movement are capable of actively moving air into the tracheal system during the brief periods when a few of the spiracles open to allow directed airflow. There even appear to be redundancies present to accommodate damage to one or more spiracles.

The larval stages of many aquatic insects have a closed tracheal system. In these cases oxygen is supplied by gill structures that facilitate the exchange of oxygen from the surrounding water.

VIII. Circulation

Insects possess a so-called open circulatory system. This means the hemolymph is not confined to a cardiovascular system as in vertebrates, but is bound only by the epidermis and the gut. The circulatory system is composed of the hemolymph and all its contents, and includes all accessory pumps and diaphragms that move or direct the hemolymph. The function of the circulatory system is central to the physiology of the insect because the hemolymph provides the medium common to all tissues.

All digestion products are transported to their destinations via the hemolymph, and all excretion products move by the same route. All products of intermediary metabolism and carbohydrates or lipids needed for energy supply are moved via the hemolymph. Similarly, hormones and neurohormones use this same route. The hemolymph literally provides the "soup of life." When circulation of the hemolymph to the extremities is blocked, the epidermal tissues no longer bathed with a fresh supply of hemolymph soon become brittle, dry up, and die.

Hemocytes are the main repair and defense elements in the insects. Once the outer barriers are breached, a variety of defense mechanisms are mobilized in response. When injury occurs, the hemocytes participate in cuticular repair. In this, insects are truly unique because they can withstand drastic surgical insult and survive with proper care.

Most microcirculation is assisted by accessory pulsatile organs as well as fibromuscular septae in the body of the insect. The accessory organs are usually located at the bases of extremities, such as the better-known antennal or leg accessory pulsatile organs (or

APOs). Both ventral and dorsal diaphragms assist actively in the movement of hemolymph.

Accessory pulsatile organs are usually associated with appendages. Other less obvious mechanisms for the circulation of the hemolymph are suspected to be involved in the movement of hemolymph.

The muscles of the dorsal diaphragm are called alary muscles because of their shape, but they lie wholly within the dorsal diaphragm and are not separate muscles associated with the dorsal vessel. The ventral diaphragm is present only when there is a ventral nerve cord in the abdomen. The ventral diaphragm is always actively involved in either pumping hemolymph past the ventral nerve cord, as in grasshoppers and adult moths, or is actually connected to the ventral nerve cord and actively moves the cord itself, as in some cockroaches. Thus the ventral diaphragm is thought to play a critical role in perfusing the ventral nerve cord with nutrients and carrying away excretory products.

The "heart" in insects is somewhat misnamed. A better name is the dorsal vessel, because it plays a noncritical role in the physiology of the insect. If the dorsal vessel is removed, there is no apparent effect on the continued existence of the insect. This is mainly because removing the dorsal vessel leaves all other accessory pulsatile organs intact and the supply of oxygen to the tissues is not interrupted.

Insects usually have a negative pressure in the hemocoel (body cavity) with respect to the outside air. Pressure pulses occur in all stages of all insects and are produced by simultaneous contraction of all the intersegmental muscles, which implies considerable neural order to the contraction (the central nervous system must coordinate the contraction and production of pressure). In *Tenebrio molitor,* the flour beetle or mealworm larva, the mesothoracic ganglion is thought to be the site of production of the coordinated contraction to produce the pressure. If the mesothoracic ganglion is destroyed, the mealworm pupa survives, continues development, and molts to the adult, but the extremities are necrotized or damaged presumably by poor circulation because the pressure pulses are no longer produced.

At least in pupal stages, the pressure pulses are perfectly coordinated with the brief timed openings of the spiracle valves to exhaust CO_2 and draw in O_2. It is thought that the air movement is greatly assisted by a bellows action of the hemocoel pressure pulses on the tracheal system.

It has been known for some time that arthropods living in the ocean have an unregulated blood ion composition that approximates that of seawater, that is, high in sodium and low in potassium. Because insects evolved from marine forebears, their primitive representatives also have "normal" ionic composition of the blood, recalling that of seawater.

Marine arthropods do not possess impressive ion-regulating mechanisms because their blood ion composition is similar to that of seawater; however, more ion-regulating ability is present in the progression of crab species from wholly marine to estuarine to wholly fresh water, the latter being the most regulated. One may think of insects in this same way, except that moving from the aquatic environment onto the hostile dry land requires even greater energy to maintain the internal milieu.

The cockroach *Periplaneta americana* shows an ionic composition most nearly similar to that of seawater. In marked contrast, the ionic composition of the hemolymph of the larval silkworm is considerably lower in sodium and higher in both potassium and magnesium. The diet of *Bombyx mori* consists exclusively of mulberry leaves. Most plant tissues contain large amounts of potassium, a major cation activating a variety of enzymes and serving to balance the anionic charge of a number of polyanionic molecules present in plants. Potassium readily moves with chloride and water into and out of cells, but as in animal cells, potassium is actively accumulated inside the cell and so is present in large amounts. Magnesium is also present in large amounts in plant tissues and is accumulated to play a role as a major chelator. ATP exists in plant tissues largely as Mg-ATP. Sodium, on the other hand, is anathema to plants. It is actively excluded and when present in the soil in even moderate amounts causes plant damage.

Thus, although the hemolymph composition of plant-feeding insects does reflect the ionic composition of plants, the situation in honeybee, *Apis mellifera,* is somewhat different. Here all the ionic values are not as severe as in *Bombyx mori* larvae and the ionic composition of the adult honeybee is even closer to that of the seawater reference. A similar situation exists between the adult and larval beetle of *Oryctes rhinoceros,* in which the larval values are the most unusual and adult ionic composition is more like that of the primitive insects. Presumably the ionic differences between adult and larvae reflect the food source.

A quick glance at the ionic compositions in Table 1 shows that one would not expect ordinary excitable tissues to function normally. For example, the 46 mM

TABLE I

The Ionic Composition of Seawater and of the Hemolymph of Certain Insects (mM/Liter)

Subject	Na	K	Ca	Mg	Cl	SO$_4$
Seawater	490	9.8	10	54	540	27
Adult cockroach	157	7.7	7.9	10	—	—
Silkworm larvae	3.4	46.0	21.0	87.0	—	—
Adult	7.7	33.0	12.0	40.0	—	—
Honeybee larvae	11	31	18	21	—	—
Adult	47	27	18	1	—	—
Oryctes larvae	15	10	21	160	—	—
Adult	69	14	14	58	—	—

potassium would be expected to depolarize a nerve cell and the 3.4 mM sodium would not be sufficient to support an action potential. Given these unusual ionic compositions, one would expect the nerves to be operating by an unknown or novel ionic mechanism, or to be protected from the unusual ionic bathing medium by some form of barrier or by some other mechanism that provides the proper environment in which to support the electric activity. Evidently, the latter is the case with most nerves.

The situation in muscles is quite different. Muscles do not use sodium electrogenesis to generate the depolarizing reponses during excitation and contraction. Instead they rely on calcium and are, therefore, insensitive to the presence of tetrodotoxin, the specific sodium channel blocker. The resting membrane potential in both muscle and nerve is supported by similar ionic mechanisms. Both may be depolarized by high-potassium solutions (except those insects whose tissues are ordinarily bathed in high potassium already).

The main sugar in insect hemolymph is trehalose. This is a so-called nonreducing sugar and consists of two glucose molecules joined by their reducing carbon ends (and therefore not oxidizable). Any glucose introduced into the hemolymph of insects is immediately converted to trehalose (Fig. 9).

Insects have considerably high levels of amino acids in their hemolymph, accounting for some 50% of the osmotic pressure of the hemolymph. The amino acids also account for about half of the nonprotein nitrogen. The osmotic pressure of the hemolymph is measured as the ability to depress the freezing point; thus the colder the freezing point of the hemolymph, the more constituents present.

The half-life of normal amino acids in the hemolymph is about 2.5 hr; this includes glutamine, lysine, and proline. However, the half-life of glutamate and

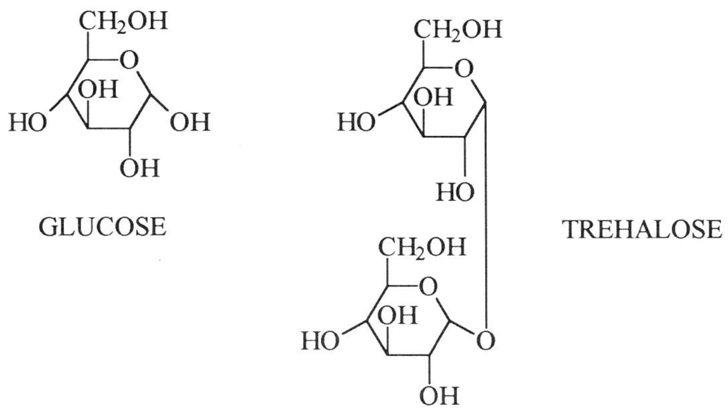

FIGURE 9 The structures of glucose and trehalose. (From Merck Catalogue.)

aspartate are dramatically less than the norm, nominally being 20 min. Therefore most amino acids are constantly turned over at a steady but slow rate so that a given concentration is maintained depending on the insect and the stage.

Glutamate and aspartate are rapidly converted to other products and their concentrations are maintained at or near zero in the hemolymph. Because these substances are thought to be neuromuscular transmitters, it would seem important to maintain low concentrations. If an adult or larval insect is injected with large amounts of glutamate, it can be paralyzed for the period of time necessary to metabolize the injected dose back to subsistence levels. The response to aspartate is absent, suggesting that aspartate is not as critical.

There are two stages in which the amount of glutamate in the hemolymph dramatically increases, namely, the egg stage and the pupal stage in cyclorrhaphan Diptera. Both of these stages are characterized by a lack of muscle activity. Just before eclosion of the neonate larvae, the glutamate concentration decreases to near zero.

Myogenic hearts are defined as those in which the contractions are an inherent property of the muscle (myo). Neurogenic hearts are those in which the contractile activity originates in a cardiac ganglion center that in turn sends motor nerve impulses to the heart muscle. In the latter, the heart muscle has little or no inherent spontaneous contractile activity on its own and the heartbeat character is entirely determined by the amount and timing of arrival of nervous impulses.

Although wrongly classified as neurogenic at one time, the cockroach heart was shown to be myogenic some 20 years ago. Today, all insect heartbeats are considered to be myogenic. Despite its myogenic

character, however, the adult cockroach heart has some 30 or more cardiac neurons scattered along paired lateral cardiac nerve cords that lie on either side of the dorsal vessel. Research has shown that these cardiac neurons are sensitive to stretch, that they are interconnected to one another and to the heart muscle by way of motor axons, and that they are spontaneously active. When the heart muscle begins to relax in its normal activity cycle (start of diastole), the muscle stretches the cardiac motor nerve cells that lie closely apposed to its sides. When stretched, the cardiac neurons begin to produce nerve impulses that increase in frequency as more cardiac neurons become active and as the dorsal vessel is dilated further. The resulting crescendo of nervous activity is shut off immediately when the next systolic contraction of the heart occurs (which coincides with an end to the stretching).

This scenario of the cockroach heart has the cardiac nervous activity occurring during diastole, or the relaxed phase of the heartbeat, and no activity accompanies the early part of systole. In effect, the heart is modulating the activity of the cardiac neurons. The net outcome of this peculiar arrangement is that the dorsal vessel of the cockroach is highly coordinated in its activity, contracting all along its length almost simultaneously, rather than peristaltically as an ascending or descending wave of contractile activity. The peristaltic wave of contraction of the heart is characteristic of those insects lacking cardiac neurons.

The nervous control of heartbeat in insects has been demonstrated in a number of cases. When the thorax of the adult hawkmoth is heated, the heartbeat in the abdomen is low in amplitude and frequency. As the thoracic temperature increases gradually toward 42°C and hovers around this set point during continued heating, the heartbeat increases in amplitude and frequency to a maximum.

From this and other results, it is clear that large night-flying moths have a unique ability to regulate the temperature of the thoracic muscles. The 42°C set temperature mentioned for the hawkmoth is also the temperature at which the thoracic flight muscles function at peak efficiency. The dorsal vessel and ventral diaphragms of these adults combine to transfer blood flow and heat away from the thoracic muscles when the temperature increases above the set point. The circulatory organs decrease their activity when the thoracic temperature drops below the set point. The thoracic ganglia sense the temperature and give rise to cardioregulatory axons that leave the central nervous system and innervate the various circulatory organs in the abdomen. Adult nocturnal insects that do not thermoregulate in some way are generally not active at cooler temperatures. Not all insects appear to regulate the thoracic temperatures as accurately as does the hawkmoth.

The heartbeat of Lepidoptera normally shifts from periods of anteriograde peristalsis (contractile waves moving forward) to periods of retrograde peristalsis throughout the larval period and during adult life. However, for the period of time immediately after adult eclosion from the pupal case and until the wings are expanded, the heartbeat becomes markedly anteriograde peristaltic and very strong. The heartbeat may be under hormonal control for the period of time during wing expansion to cause this change in the nature of heartbeat peristalsis. The role of direct innervation during these events is also unknown.

Soon after eclosion from the pupal case, most adult moths and butterflies eject a conspicuous amount of fluid before completing the last part of metamorphosis and flying away as adults. The evacuation of this fluid is thought to serve two purposes, to eliminate wastes accumulated during the pupal period and to reduce the weight of the adult flying insect to the lowest possible amount. What remains is an insect that has the minimal amount of hemolymph necessary to sustain life.

The small amount of hemolymph remaining in these adults is said to be exchanged with air in the wings in a process called tidal flow of hemolymph (and respiratory gases). The sum total of all organs involved in circulatory movement of hemolymph is said to participate in this tidal movement of hemolymph and air.

During the inspiration part of the tidal cycle, air is pumped into tracheal tubes in the wings in exchange for hemolymph, which is pumped out of the wings into the thorax and abdomen as the blood vessels in the wing veins collapse. During the expiration cycle, this process is reversed. The peristaltic waves of contraction of the dorsal vessel are coordinated with the activity of the ventral diaphragm in the abdomen and both in turn are said to support the appropriate direction of movement of hemolymph during the tidal exchanges of air and hemolymph. Tidal flow of hemolymph suggests a very highly coordinated activity of the autonomic pumps and organs involved in hemolymph movement.

IX. Temperature, Diapause, and Circadian Clocks

Body temperatures dependent on ambient temperature (poikilothermy) are common in all aquatic and many other insects. Endothermy, in which body temperature is determined by the heat generated by the metabolic activity, is common in insects (as in the example given for the adult hawkmoth), but is always periodic and appears to involve shivering thermogenesis and exercise.

The vast majority of insects employ ectothermy in adjusting body temperature as this involves adjusting body temperature based on radiation acquired from the environment. In insects, ectothermy is regulated behaviorally rather than physiologically. The majority of insects are small and as a consequence they are subject to a large surface-to-volume ratio, which makes it difficult to retain heat. Indeed, many of the better examples of endothermy come from larger insects that can more efficiently retain heat and often have layers of hairs or scales to help insulate to this end.

Heat exchange occurs behaviorally in a number of ways. Honeybees are able to regulate the temperature of their hives by endothermy to increase temperature or by wing fanning to cool the hive. Individual bees are known to cool themselves by evaporation from a liquid droplet that they form on their mouthparts.

Acclimation to extremely cold climates often involves special adaptations. *Grylloblatta,* a relatively rare type of primitive cricket, lives at glacier altitudes and is adapted to below freezing temperatures. These insects die when moved to room temperatures. Several mechanisms to survive freezing temperatures are used by insects for survival. These can be as simple as burrowing into the ground to avoid the cool or removing water from the body's tissues. Cold survival might involve increasing the amount of glycerol or sorbitol in the hemolymph as a type of antifreeze, or evolving very specialized proteins that inhibit or prevent ice nucleation or control the rate of nucleation and prevent ice formation from damaging internal tissues.

Possibly the most remarkable adaptation that insects make to adverse conditions is diapause, which is a genetically determined state of suspended development. It is contrasted with simpler quiescence in which dormancy is imposed by external conditions, an example of which is cold stupor that lasts as long as external conditions remain cool, but upon warming the insects recover completely.

Diapause is an inherited trait. In some insects in extreme environments, diapause is always present and the insects simply do not survive without it. In other cases, particularly in more temperate climes or nearer the tropics, the presence of diapause individuals in a population is fractional. In the latter case, diapause is thought of more as a device to bridge a period lacking suitable food sources, for example, rather than due to climatic factors.

Insects can diapause in any life stage—egg, nymph, larva, pupa, or adult. Sometimes more than one diapause stage can occur in a single species during a complete developmental cycle. In addition, the types of diapause vary, some being cold hardy and requiring a definite period of time and chilling to reinitiate development. Indeed, there are so many different forms of diapause, including the unusual summer diapause of many insects (known as estivation) during which a given species might avoid high temperatures, that they are seemingly too complex for analysis.

There is, however, one unifying theme: diapause is triggered as a discrete event, and once triggered the condition involves definite genetic changes that can be thought of as a form of development all its own. The trigger for most diapause is environmental conditions, especially day length, temperature, and food quality. Indeed, insects are so finely attuned to the environment and climatic seasons as to be inseparable from them.

Little is known about the hormonal control of diapause because the complex of hormones present seems to be dependent on the species. The fact that diapause is triggered as a discrete event is interpreted by some to indicate a master or controlling gene or gene sequence that must be activated to induce diapause. So many physiological changes occur during diapause, however, that a symphony of genes must be turned on in a cascade once diapause is triggered.

Insects appear capable of determining the length of a day because diapause is almost always initiated at about the same calendar date each year. Local conditions would modify the exact date, but the impression remains that a species is capable of determining when the day length shortens to a critical amount. Laboratory studies that artificially impose fall conditions at the wrong time of year can induce diapause at will in a given insect.

In addition to being sensitive to day length, insects appear to have an ability to tell time or at least trigger behavior a variable time after an event such as sundown. Many female nocturnal insects, for example, attract mates or lay eggs at specific times of the night. Like diapause, these events are triggered. The female pink bollworm moth produces and releases a volatile pheromone sex attractant chemical between 2 and 3 A.M. in midsummer. The male pink bollworm is insensitive to this odor at all times of the day and night except precisely at the same time it is released.

The window of pheromone release and male response to pheromone, like diapause, is affected by environmental conditions. If the wind speed is too high, or if it is raining during the preset window, no pheromone is released and no mating attraction occurs. Instead, the adults wait for the next window of behavior before trying again. In addition, at least for pink bollworm, the adults are extremely sensitive to temperature. If the ambient temperature cools to 65°F or below during the expected time for sexual attraction and mating, behavior is inhibited in the same manner. Thus the exact local environmental conditions can play a critical role in insect behavior.

X. Nutrition

Given the many habitats of the class Insecta and its successful adaptation across the land and water areas of earth, it is not surprising that diets exhibit the same variety, from very specialized food sources, as found in hyperparasites (parasites of insect parasites), to the generalized omnivorous cockroach that can produce a new generation from a wide variety of foods, including cannibalism. Insects that specialize on wood, such as termites or wood-boring beetle larvae, do not have the ability to digest cellulose. Instead, these insects use symbiotic protozoa that break down cellulose to glucose and supply the host with energy sources. Despite such diversity, a few unifying principles do emerge.

Ten amino acids are essential in the diet: tryptophan, histidine, leucine, arginine, isoleucine, methionine, lysine, threonine, valine, and phenylalanine (or tyrosine). In addition, insects generally require a source of choline and all water-soluble B vitamins except B_{12}. Many suspected cases of nonvitamin dependency were traced to the presence of symbionts. Where symbionts were able to be eliminated from the insect hosts, replacement vitamin diets were always necessary for growth and development. All species requiring ascorbic acid are plant feeders in nature, but not all plant feeders require it. Loss of the ability to synthesize ascorbic acid appears to have occurred many times in adaptation to most plants that are abundant in the vitamin.

Sterols are universally essential for insect growth and in no case has the ability of insects to synthesize the sterol nucleus by squalene cyclization from fatty acid precursors been demonstrated. All suspected cases are shown to lead invariably to the presence of symbiotic organisms providing the sterol precursor. The lack of ability to biosynthesize sterols appears to be related to the ubiquitous presence of sterols as cholesterol and beta-sitosterol in plants. Once acquired, however, insects are fully capable of altering sterols by hydroxylation or oxidation for their own use, such as the vital biosynthesis of ecdysone from dietary sterol precursors. The process of egg development includes accumulation of a wide variety of sterol derivatives that the mother passes on to the offspring.

Use of minerals as dietary requirements is little studied in insects. The midgut is known to possess the ability to sequester and eliminate certain heavy metals as an apparent protective mechanism against poisoning.

In addition to trehalose being the major blood sugar, insects specialize in using either fats, carbohydrates, or proline as direct energy sources or sometimes combinations of these energy substrates. Carbohydrates, being water soluble, are osmotically active and easy to transport in the hemolymph; however, they provide only 0.18 mole of ATP energy molecules per gram of substrate. Fats, on the other hand, provide 0.65 mole of ATP per gram of substrate, but are insoluble in hemolymph (osmotically inactive) and require special arrangements to facilitate transport in the hemolymph. Proline appears to be a compromise; while providing 0.52 mole of ATP per gram of substrate for energy, proline is water soluble and not subject to the same transport problems as fatty acids or triglycerides.

XI. Excretion

Besides elimination of CO_2 as a product of metabolism, which is easily accomplished during respiration, insects have the same problem of nitrogen elimination shared by all animals. Nitrogen is a major by-product of protein metabolism. In insects the final processing of metabolic nitrogen occurs in discrete structures, the Malpighian tubules. These are always present in insects as outgrowths at the juncture of the midgut and hindgut in numbers from 4 to 200 depending on the species.

There are three possible nitrogenous wastes in animals: ammonia is very toxic and water soluble, urea is also soluble and still quite toxic, whereas uric acid is nontoxic but very insoluble in water. Although ammonia might be easily excreted by aquatic animals and is the form of nitrogen waste excreted by dragonfly larvae, mosquito larvae apparently excrete urea or even uric acid, not ammonia.

Excretion and water balance are closely related in the Malpighian tubules. At slightly basic pH in the distal Malpighian tubules, uric acid is predominately in solution and is transported by water uptake toward the gut. At the more proximal end of the tubules near the hindgut, a more acid pH is maintained and the predominate form becomes insoluble urate crystals. The crystals are further transported into the hindgut and then excreted, while the water is reabsorbed from the Malpighian tubules along with sodium and potassium. Bicarbonate ion is thought to play a role in the maintenance of the correct pH in the Malpighian tubules to support the excretion process, but the details are not fully understood.

Reports of "yellow rain" are made on rare occasions. These events are often traced to inconspicuous flights of large numbers of insects, not always obvious from the ground. Migrating insects are known to excrete urates as small yellow globules that could be mistaken for some unnatural event.

XII. Reproduction

The vast majority of insects reproduce sexually, however, asexual forms of reproduction are common. The phasmids or stick insects of the order Orthoptera are thought to be universally parthenogenic (develop from unfertilized eggs) and males are extremely rare. However, ordinary female grasshoppers of the same order can also be forced to lay unfertilized eggs that give rise to viable offspring if they are merely kept in crowded conditions. The honeybees and other Hymenoptera are haploid parthenogenic. Fertilized eggs give rise to diploid females and unfertilized eggs give rise to haploid males.

There are natural reported cases of hermaphrodite moths that contain the morphological properties of both male and female split bilaterally. However, all female insects that develop eggs possess ovaries. Once sexual maturity is reached, all energies are switched to egg development. This reaches extremes in termite queens, which are known to grow into "giants" with distended abdomens and reaching over a foot in length.

Juvenile hormone is thought to play an important role in egg development, and some female mosquitoes are known to be inhibited from taking a blood meal if the corpora allata (juvenile hormone source) is removed. Despite the degradation of the prothoracic glands in most adult insects, ecdysteroids are known to also be sequestered and incorporated into the developing eggs. These undoubtedly originate from other storage locations in the body.

A variety of triggers and inhibitions operate during egg production. In mosquitoes, a blood meal releases neurohormones from the brain and vitellogenin-stimulating hormone (VSH) from the ovary. VSH activates and maintains vitellogenin protein synthesis by the fat body. Vitellogenin protein may be released from fat body into the hemolymph, but uptake by the ovaries for incorporation into egg yolk is a separate process thought to be hormone mediated.

The presence of mature eggs is known to inhibit development of new oocytes until after oviposition allows more space for continued egg development. In some cockroaches that retain egg cases inside the abdomen until near the end of embryogenesis, the feedback inhibition of ovarian development is due to nervous connections between stretch receptors in the abdomen and the corpora allata (juvenile hormone source). Juvenile hormone is also thought to play a vital role in vitellogenesis.

Some adult female insects are known to be monocoitic, that is, they copulate once and are inseminated only once. In Diptera (houseflies, fruit flies, and blowflies) a substance has been found in the accessory gland of the male reproductive system that is transferred in the semen of the males to females during copulation. This substance inhibits the female from acceptance of subsequent males.

This curious phenomenon is important for success of the strategy of insect control known as the sterile insect technique. Adult males, when irradiated with gamma rays to the point of sterility, are still capable of mating and transferring semen. Because the sperm are infertile, females thus inseminated still receive the inhibition message not to copulate a second time, and no offspring are produced. Obviously the strategy would work less effectively the more polygamous the insect.

Bibliography

Chapman, R. F. (1976). "Structure and Function of Insects." Chapman & Hall, London.
Evans, Howard E. (1984). "Insect Biology, Addison–Wesley." Reading, MA.
Wigglesworth, V. B. (1971). "Principles of Insect Physiology." Methuen, London.

Integrated Pest Management

RAYMOND E. FRISBIE, *Texas A&M University*

Glossary

Agroecosystem Relationship of the crop with its living and nonliving environments

Key pest Insect, plant pathogen, nematode, weed, or vertebrate pest that routinely causes economic damage if not controlled

Parasite Animal that feeds in or on another living animal, consuming all or more of the animal's tissues and eventually killing it

Pathogen Disease-producing organism, such as bacteria, viruses, and fungi

Pesticides Pest control substances derived from chemical synthesis or natural products that include herbicides, insecticides, miticides, fungicides, nematicides, and bactericides

Pesticide resistance Condition that results when a pest population becomes, through genetic selection, capable of surviving dosages of a pesticide that formerly controlled it

Pest resistant plants Crop variety or cultivar that is less susceptible to pest damage compared with other cultivars

Predator Animal that attacks and feeds on other animals (prey), which are usually smaller and less powerful; the prey is usually killed and consumed by the predator

Trophic level Position in the food chain, including first level, which are primary producers (plants); second level, which are primary consumers (plant eaters); third level, which are primary carnivores; and fourth level, which are secondary carnivores

Integrated pest management (IPM) is a pest population management system that anticipates and prevents pests from reaching economically damaging levels by using all suitable techniques, such as biological control, pest-resistant plants, cultural controls, and pesticides. IPM seeks to maximize net profits for producers of agricultural commodities while minimizing adverse effects on the environment. IPM systems have been developed for most agricultural commodities in the United States. Additionally, the IPM approach is the central theme for combating pests that affect human and animal health. IPM systems of varying complexity have been constructed for most countries in the world.

The theory and principles supporting IPM have been developed over the last 40 yr. IPM has its foundation in applied ecology. IPM considers not only the pest and natural enemies of the pest, but also the crop and its interaction with its living and nonliving environment. A balanced IPM system involves all major crop pests including insects, nematodes, plant pathogens, weeds, and vertebrates. The scientific basis of IPM is interdisciplinary, including not only the pest disciplines of entomology, plant pathology, and weed science but also the disciplines of agronomy, horticulture, agricultural economics, and agricultural engineering and, in some instances, the disciplines of sociology and human anthropology. This article reviews the environmental and economic rationale for IPM, discusses the ecological basis of IPM, describes how IPM systems are constructed, reviews the essential components of IPM, and introduces basic methods for gaining grower adoption of IPM practices. Although IPM systems have been developed successfully for all classes of pests, for expedience, this article will use insect control as the primary model.

I. Introduction

Prior to World War II, pest control was accomplished primarily through cultural farming practices, such as tillage and rotation, and the mechanical removal of pests. Primitive insecticidal compounds containing arsenic, nicotine, or pyrethrum were used with only mixed success: some pests were controlled, many were not. Directly following World War II, a wide range of new synthetic chemical compounds for the control of pests was introduced to agriculture. Pesticides provided unprecedented control of agricultural pests, particularly of pests that caused human and animal diseases. World War II was the first war in modern times that did not experience more death from typhus fever than from the battlefield. The new insecticide DDT effectively controlled a body louse, the insect carrier of the disease. DDT and other insecticidal compounds came to be used worldwide to control and, in some cases, nearly eradicate malaria and other human diseases carried by insects.

The routine use of insecticides, fungicides, nematicides, and herbicides became a regular part of pest control on farms and ranches beginning in the 1950s. Much of the research effort by public institutions through the 1950s and 1960s was spent perfecting the development and application of pesticides. In fact, farmers became so reliant on pesticides that other forms of control were of little or no consideration. Shortly after the introduction of pesticides, particularly insecticides, negative side effects began to appear. A phenomenon known as pest resurgence began to occur, in which pest populations that were previously controlled with insecticides soared to damaging levels earlier and in greater numbers than previously encountered. Pest resurgence is a result of the destruction of natural enemies including parasites, predators, and, in some cases, pathogens, thus allowing pests unabated by their natural enemies to reach higher populations. Secondary pests, formerly nonpests controlled by natural enemies, became "key pests" requiring the regular use of insecticides for their control. Insects—and later weeds, plant pathogenic fungi, and nematodes—developed levels of tolerance or resistance to pesticides. In the late 1950s, concerns that pesticides were affecting human health and the environment were first raised. These concerns culminated in the regulatory control of pesticides being shifted, in the early 1970s, from the United States Department of Agriculture (USDA) to the Environmental Protection Agency (EPA). [*See* Fungicides; Herbicides and Herbicide Resistance; Nematicides; Pest Management, Chemical Control.]

IPM, first termed "integrated control," was developed and introduced as a concept in California in the late 1950s. Integrated control was developed to bring together chemical (pesticide) control and biological control. The concept was based on the premise that insecticides, if applied at the correct time and at the correct pest population level, could have a minimum impact on the natural enemies of the pest. Although the name was changed from integrated control to IPM, the integration of chemical and biological control remained the major theme of IPM throughout much of the 1970s. As secondary effects, particularly the negative effects relating to human safety and the environment, created greater public concern and as insecticide resistance became more prevalent, IPM became more balanced in its approach. The focus of IPM began to shift to nonpesticidal tactics in the 1980s, including expanded use of cultural controls, pest-resistant plants, and biological control. Although pesticides still play a major role in modern agriculture and likely will continue to do so in the future, the clear trend is that their use is being moderated through IPM. [*See* Pest Management, Biological Control.]

II. An Environmental and Economic Rationale for IPM

Producers of agricultural commodities and the general public have an interest and responsibility to understand and to deal with the nontarget effects of pesticides on the environment. Questions regarding the environmental impact of pesticides were first brought to the public's attention in a significant way in the late 1950s with Rachel Carson's book *Silent Spring*. This book made the public acutely aware of the environmental side effects of the chlorinated hydrocarbon class of insecticides, to which DDT belonged. When the EPA was formed in 1970, one of its first acts was to ban all uses of DDT in the United States. Although DDT was singled out, several other chlorinated hydrocarbon insecticides were considered hazardous to the environment. Chlorinated hydrocarbon insecticides were characterized by their long persistence in soil and water and in food chain products. The concern of the public and policy-makers focused sharply on the negative environmental effects of pesticides, so the stage was set for the development of a rational approach to pesticide use. IPM was viewed as the rational approach.

Farmers, many of whom were concerned about the environmental effects of pesticides, had another concern—an economic concern. Pest resurgence, secondary pest outbreaks, and the failure of insecticidal control because of resistance caused production costs to rise and crop yields to fall. High value crops such as cotton, fruits, and vegetables experienced increasing costs of production because of multiple insecticide and other pesticide applications. Throughout the 1950s and 1960s, insecticides were used on a routine basis regardless of the numbers of pests involved or the damage inflicted. Indeed, the calendar had become the primary criterion used to determine when to apply pesticides.

IPM, as can most fields of science, can point to a landmark study. This research was done by Vernon M. Stern, Ray F. Smith, Robert van den Bosch, and Kenneth S. Hagen of the University of California, and appears in a 1959 *Hilgardia* publication on the integration of chemical and biological control of the spotted alfalfa aphid. This classic piece first proposed that crops could tolerate a certain amount of damage from insects without sustaining an economic loss, in terms of yield reduction or quality. The authors treated insects as populations to be considered over time in relation to the crop and the surrounding environment. Insect populations fluctuated around what was termed a "general equilibrium position," which was defined as "the average density of a population over a period of time (usually lengthy) in the absence of permanent environmental change." Based on the knowledge that insect populations fluctuate naturally, the economic threshold concept was introduced and defined as "the density (of insect pests) at which control measures should be used to prevent an increasing pest population from reaching the economic-injury level." The economic-injury level was defined as "the lowest density that will cause economic damage."

Several economic and ecological principles were included in the development and application of the economic threshold and the economic-injury level. The use of these tactics required that insect pests and their damage be sampled in the field on a regular basis to determine whether an insecticide application was economically warranted. The application of the economic threshold and economic-injury level provided an economic rationale for insecticide use and laid the groundwork for eliminating routine and indiscriminate insecticide applications. From an agroecological perspective, this approach allowed maximum biological and nonbiological mortality of the insect populations to express itself before insecticides were used. The rudiments of a sounder way of making insecticide application decisions were at hand. The IPM approach provided a means to deal with the nagging problems of secondary pest outbreaks and pest resurgence and, of equal importance, IPM provided a way to make insect control decisions based on economic need. Although the theory and practice of economic thresholds and economic-injury levels have evolved and been improved on considerably since 1959, the basic tenets remain. Economic thresholds, sometimes termed action thresholds, were later developed in varying forms for certain species of nematodes, plant pathogens, and weeds.

III. The Ecological Basis of IPM

Pest populations, must be viewed as an integral part of the agricultural ecosystem, termed the agroecosystem. Understanding the relationship of the crop and the pest with their living and nonliving environment is central to IPM. The goal of IPM then becomes the manipulation of the agroecosystem to keep pests below economically damaging levels, to avoid or minimize the disruption of the system, and to reduce negative impacts on the surrounding environment. To achieve this goal, an understanding of the relationships between the pests and their environment is essential.

In trying to achieve a better understanding of the agroecosystem of which pests are a part, one is immediately struck with the amazing complexity of organisms and environmental interactions. Major components of an agroecosystem include the soil substrate and its related biota, crop plants, the physical and chemical environment, and energy provided by the sun and humans. Modifications of the agroecosystem may occur from agricultural, recreational, industrial, and related social activities. During certain periods of crop development, first order consumers, that is, pests, may dominate the system to human disadvantage. In ecological terms, the objective of IPM is to hold the plant community, the crop(s) under consideration, at an early stage of ecological succession and to provide an acceptable crop yield with economically acceptable losses from first order consumers, that is, pests. Pest populations, indeed all populations of living organisms, grow when birth and immigration rates are greater than death and emigration rates. A significant hurdle to overcome in population ecology and IPM is the definition of these rates and why these rates change over time, and of their effects on the dynamics of pest populations, host plants, and natural enemies.

Mathematically based simulation models are important tools used to define and understand relationships within an agroecosystem. Models have been constructed that evaluate multiple-trophic-level interactions. Using insects as the example, the trophic levels under consideration may include the crop plant, the herbivore (insect pest), and carnivores (predators and parasites that attack the herbivore). An examination of energy flow from the sun to the plant and through the plant–insect system under study allows an understanding of the rates of plant growth and senescence as well as population changes among herbivores and carnivores. Models that describe plant growth and development by simulating plant demography, field population ecology, and field validation are fundamentally necessary before developing and linking higher trophic level models.

Plant–pest models serve as conceptual frameworks for understanding the role of pests within an agroecosystem. The selection of the appropriate modeling environment, intrinsic demographic parameters, density-dependent relationships between trophic levels, and physical factors should be considered in constructing simulation models. A particularly important feature in agroecosystem models is that a rigid validation of the model using field generated data be followed. Once the model is capable of accurately reproducing several sets of independent data, it can be used for strategic analysis and planning of IPM systems. Models also can be used to identify relevant parts of the agroecosystem for change and to direct future research.

In addition to strategic models that examine pests within the context of agroecosystems, tactical models that assist in day-to-day decision making have provided some value. Most tactical models rely heavily on the correlation of pest development with an environmental measurement, such as temperature. Insects are capable of development within a fairly specific temperature range. Some temperatures are more optimal for development. By correlating temperature with expected insect development, mathematical models have been useful in determining expected time of occurrence and relative abundance of pests within specific geographic regions. Similarly, models have been constructed based upon temperature and relative humidity, to predict optimal conditions for growth and infection of plant pathogens.

IV. The IPM System Concept

Given an understanding of the importance of ecological considerations for crop production relative to pests, IPM systems can be appropriately constructed. In conceptually designing an IPM system, we restate the IPM goal of selecting and integrating crop production practices that intentionally disfavor pest development. IPM is designed to be practiced. Therefore, how IPM information is to be transferred for implementation on farms or across geographic regions must be incorporated into the IPM design from the outset. In this way, constraints to implementation can be addressed as the system is developed.

Major elements that deserve consideration in designing an IPM system for a single pest on a single crop, for multiple pests on a single crop, or for multiple crops include (1) an understanding of the pest and crop biology and community ecology, (2) an appreciation of the agronomic practices involved in the production of the crop under consideration and of modifying factors of adjacent crops or habitats as they impact on pest development and movement, (3) an understanding of crop/plant susceptibility to the pest(s) and the selection of an appropriate crop variety (cultivar) that may be more or less susceptible to the pest(s) under consideration, (4) knowledge of biological control agents (natural enemies) operating in the system, (5) reliable and practical plant and pest sampling methods combined with established economic thresholds as pesticide treatment decision criteria, (6) recognition of the most effective pesticides for the target pest species that are the least disruptive to natural enemies and other nontarget organisms, (7) consideration of the environmental effects of the proposed system, (8) consideration of any economic policy or social implications that are germane, (9) a well-conceived set of methodologies to efficiently transfer and incorporate the suggested set of IPM tactics into farmers' cropping systems, and (10) both economic and environmental evaluation procedures to track, evaluate, and improve the IPM system as it evolves.

Planning and implementing an IPM system should consider not only the individual elements within the system in relation to pests, production practices, economics, social factors, and the environment, but also the scale or geographic size of the IPM system. Generally, IPM systems have targeted the individual field or farm as the management unit. There is little doubt that the farm as the management unit has been and will continue to be a viable frame of reference for controlling pests. However, because of the high level of mobility as pests move from farm to farm and region to region, pests should be considered, for the most part, "common property," thereby expanding the management unit to the community or regional level. What individual farmers do or do not do relative to managing their pests either directly or indirectly affects their neighbors and, consequently, the entire production region. Producers, whether they realize it or not, share a common responsibility in pest control. Therefore, the design of an IPM system should consider not only the development and implementation of technology for farm-sized management units, but also the possibility of expanding the size of the management unit to the regional (communities within states or clearly defined production regions) or the multiregional (groups of production regions, states, nations, or multiple nations) scale of management. The elements of the IPM system will change, depending on the scale or size of the management unit under consideration.

V. Primary Tactics within an IPM System

A variety of tactics can be directed specifically at pest population reduction in an IPM system depending on the pest's biology and its relationships within an agroecosytem. The primary IPM tactics are cultural controls, including the use of pest-resistant varieties, biological controls, and the safe application of pesticides based on sound biological sampling methods.

A. Cultural Controls

Historically, cultural controls have constituted a major tactic in the suppression of pests. Today cultural controls are considered to be the primary IPM tactic. Cultural controls, if properly selected and deployed, are very successful in "preventing" the pest from causing economic damage. Cultural controls are the baseline for a sustainable IPM strategy. The underlying premise is to grow healthy and vigorous crop plants that are capable of withstanding pest attack and to produce these plants with as little exposure as possible, in time and space, to damaging populations of pests. Cultural controls can include site selection, crop rotation, tillage, fertilization and organic amend-

ments, variety selection, planting time, plant populations, water management, time of harvest, and crop residue management. Selection of specific cultural control tactics will vary, depending on whether one is managing insect, plant pathogen or weed pest, or a combination of pests. [See PEST MANAGEMENT, CULTURAL CONTROL.]

In some locations, pests do not occur or, when they are present, occur in fewer numbers. Susceptible crops can be separated in space from areas that are known to harbor pests, for example, near the pest's overwintering quarters or near another susceptible crop from which migration might occur. Therefore, if possible, the site of planting should be at some distance from a known source of pests. Similarly, crop rotations can be effective in reducing pest populations by rotating a pest susceptible crop with a non-susceptible crop across seasons. Crop rotation, a valuable cultural control tactic for pest suppression, should consider the effects on the target pest(s), natural enemies (such as parasites, predators or competitors), physical soil characteristics, and microbial balance of the soil as well as practicality. Another approach is not to plant (termed fallowing), to remove the host plant from contact with the pest for varying periods. This process can reduce the distribution and abundance of pest species.

Tillage operations can be used to directly destroy the pest or destroy the pest's food sources and harborage. For some crops planted on soils with a low erosion potential, deep plowing is useful in reducing weeds, insects and occasionally plant pathogens. Certain plant pathogenic fungi and bacteria overwinter on plant residues after the crop is harvested. Deep plowing after harvest allows the soil and crop residue to dry for a period, thereby reducing plant pathogen populations. Tillage retains an important role in weed control in combination with herbicides. In addition, tillage increases soil aeration, breaks up crusts on the soil surface, increases the ability of the soil to absorb and retain moisture, and prevents soil erosion. [See TILLAGE SYSTEMS.]

Fertilizers including nitrogen, phosphorus, potassium, and micronutrients in varying concentrations are important to crop productivity and overall plant health. Healthy plants are better capable of dealing with pest attack. A nutrient-stressed plant is more vulnerable to disease than a plant with an optimal nutritional level. Excessive fertilization with nitrogen, however, can promote excessive vegetation and succulent growth, which encourages a microenvironment favorable to plant pathogens and insects. The amount, form, and timing of fertilization have a direct bearing on the incidence and severity of plant pathogen development and disease outbreak. Excessive nitrogen not only affects pests directly, but may increase the length of the growing season and delay crop maturity, thereby putting the crop at risk from pest attack for a prolonged period. Fertilizer use must be a part of overall crop management and must be weighed against other cultural practices. [See FERTILIZER MANAGEMENT AND TECHNOLOGY.]

Selecting a crop variety that is well adapted for the particular production region—given soil, water, temperature, and pest constraints—is successful in insuring plant health and eventual yield and quality. Using a cultivar that is resistant to pests is one of the oldest methods of pest control. Pest resistance in modern crop breeding programs should complement the desire for improved crop yield and quality. Resistant cultivars may require fewer or no pesticide applications. Breeding for pest resistance has been an important component of plant pathogen, nematode, and insect pest management programs for a variety of crops. Resistance is usually viewed in relative terms because a cultivar is considered resistant when it is less susceptible to damage than other cultivars with the same pest population level. Since plant pathogens and insects continue to evolve new races and biotypes, plant breeders must continue to alter plant susceptibility or resistance. The mechanisms of plant resistance to pests vary. For example, the mechanisms employed by the plant for insect resistance are grouped into three categories: (1) antixenosis, (2) antibiosis, and (3) tolerance. Antixenosis is a resistance mechanism that deters colonization by an insect. Insects may orient toward plants, but certain plant characteristics either prevent or reduce colonization, feeding, or reproduction. Antibiosis, on the other hand, is a mechanism used by the plant that adversely affects the insect's development, reproduction, and survival once colonization occurs. Finally, plant tolerance can best be described as the level at which a plant can support an insect, or other pest infestation, without loss in plant vigor or final yield. [See CULTIVAR DEVELOPMENT; PLANT PATHOLOGY.]

Date of planting has proven to be a very successful tactic for avoiding pest damage. Planting before or after anticipated pest population peaks can desynchronize pest populations with susceptible periods of crop development. Planting at the appropriate soil temperature and moisture conditions for optimum seedling vigor and plant development is important. In determining a planting date, it is important to anticipate the population dynamics of pests, plant growth and development, fruiting characteristics, biotic and abiotic factors, and weather conditions. Similarly, plant populations can affect the distribution and abundance of pests. Microenvironmental interactions that contribute to plant pathogen and insect development and survivorship can be influenced by the number of plants per unit area, row configuration, and row orientation.

Water management under irrigated cropping systems or water conservation under dryland, or rain-grown, agriculture can have a direct effect on plant health and pest abundance. Successful water management requires constant observation of the water status of soils and plants and a basic understanding of the interaction of plants to water, climate, and pests. As with fertility, plants have basic water requirements throughout their life cycles. Since plant resources are allocated among roots, shoots, stems, leaves, and fruit, an optimum water balance for plant growth must be maintained. Water stress can occur at any time during crop growth. This stress may make the plant more susceptible to certain insects and plant pathogens.

As discussed earlier, the selection of an earlier maturing cultivar allows escape from late season pest populations. Harvesting the crop immediately is of equal importance to avoid the effects of these pests. Also, crop residues provide harborage for the survival of pests. Sanitation involves the removal of postharvest crop residues that serve as overwintering refugia for the pest. Postharvest sanitation, practiced at the individual farm level or, better yet, area wide, can serve as an excellent nonpesticidal tactic for reducing pests, particularly if practiced yearly.

B. Biological Control

Biological control in the broadest context is the intended use of parasites, predators, pathogens, or competitors to reduce pest populations. Parasites, predators, pathogens, or competitors are collectively termed natural enemies. Biological control approaches for insects are usually divided into three categories: importation (classical biological control), conservation, and augmentation. Also, one or more of these approaches has been successfully deployed against nematodes, plant pathogens, weeds, and vertebrate pests.

Importation, or classical biological control, involves the deliberate introduction of natural enemies into areas where they did not previously occur. This approach has been used successfully against introduced pests of foreign origin when the natural enemies of the pest were left behind in the pest's homeland. In essence, under this form of biological control, the pest's natural enemies are intentionally reunited with the pest at a distant geographic location. Additionally, a natural enemy that historically has never had an association with a pest can be introduced for the purposes of biological control, hence a "new association" of a natural enemy with a pest is established. Importation, to be successful, requires several steps. First, the pest must be correctly identified taxonomically, its native home must be identified, and a search of its native home for natural enemies must be conducted. Once natural enemies are found, they are brought back to the location of intended release and held in quarantine to insure there will be little or no negative effects on unrelated plants or animals where they will be released. After quarantine, the natural enemy numbers must be increased through rearing on the pest host. When the natural enemy is released, a careful evaluation must be conducted to determine the reasons why the natural enemy successfully established itself or, in many cases, why the natural enemy did not establish. The goal is to re-establish population regulation of the pest below damaging numbers.

Many native natural enemies in agricultural systems are effective in regulating pests and preventing damage. A properly deployed IPM strategy seeks to develop ways of conserving these important biological organisms. The value of natural enemies has been seen on many occasions when pesticides are used indiscriminately, destroying natural enemies and resulting in pest resurgence and secondary pest outbreaks. Cropping practices that support natural enemy development and furnish favorable habitats are key to conservation. The use and timing of pesticides that are less detrimental to natural enemies is elemental in conservation. Knowledge of the type and importance of natural enemies is important in conserving this important biological resource.

Even when IPM systems are effective in conserving natural enemies, sometimes pests are not reduced below economically damaging levels. Hence, another option is to augment populations by releasing laboratory-reared natural enemies. The two approaches to augmenting natural enemy populations are inoculative releases and inundative releases. The goal of inoculative programs is to release natural enemies early in the production season when the numbers of existing natural enemies resident in the field are low. The introduced natural enemies will then reproduce and provide pest suppression throughout the growing season. The inundative approach involves periodic releases of relatively large numbers of natural enemies at key times throughout the season. Natural enemies that are released in these inundative programs are not expected to reproduce as they are in the inoculative system. The released natural enemies themselves are expected to provide the biological control. Augmentative releases have been successful, particularly in closed systems such as glasshouses and in perennial cropping systems. Although augmentation has been deployed in several annual cropping systems, more information is needed on the mortality effects of existing natural enemies and the timing and amount of natural enemies that should be released to augment the natural enemy populations.

Although management of plant pathogens has historically relied on cultural controls, including pest-resistant crop varieties, and fungicides and bactericides, potential exists for expanded use of biological control. More recently work has been directed at exploiting the use of nonpathogenic microbial competitors. As more is learned about the type of nonpathogenic or "beneficial" microorganisms available and their competitive ability to colonize and prevent infection by plant pathogens, the more readily this form of biological control will become available. Despite considerable effort to suppress nematodes through classical biological control and inundative releases of antagonistic natural enemies, little success has been achieved. The greatest success has come in the conservation and augmentation of nematode antagonists naturally present in the soil. The biological control of weeds, particularly weeds of rangelands, has enjoyed many successes. The primary biological control tactic used against weeds is classical biological control, or importation of exotic natural enemies.

C. Pesticides and Their Use Based on Biological Sampling

Synthetic organic pesticides are available in several forms: insecticides, herbicides, nematicides, fungicides, and bactericides. Every form of pesticide has several chemical classes. For example, the primary classes of insecticides are organophosphates, organochlorines, carbamates, pyrethroids, and formamidines. Herbicides comprise well over 20 chemical classes, and fungicides and nematicides consist of several classes that are related not only by chemical structure, but also by the mode of action of the particular pesticide against a wide range of pest species. Some pesticides kill pests by direct contact whereas others are systemic, capable of entering and moving through a plant and causing direct mortality to pests (insects, plant pathogens, and nematodes) or, in the case of weeds, throughout the weed pest, interrupting physiological processes and inducing death.

Microbial pesticides, or biopesticides, are natural products produced by microorganisms that induce pest mortality. Bacteria and viruses have been identified and commercialized in the form of biological insecticides. The bacterium, *Bacillus* spp. produce toxins that are not only insecticidal to certain insects, but are also nematocidal. Plant pathogenic fungi have been isolated and reproduced by humans for use as herbicides for controlling certain weed species. Microbial pesticides are highly specific to the target pest and generally nondisruptive to natural enemies.

Regardless of the pest, it is of utmost importance to use a pesticide at the appropriate time, at the correct dosage, and as safely as possible. All commercial pesticides are labeled in the United States by the EPA. The ''label is the law'' regarding the proper and safe use of any pesticide. Although pesticides have proven invaluable in protecting humans, animals, and crops from pests and pest-related diseases, once again improper use of these valuable control agents can cause nontarget effects on natural enemies, livestock, and wildlife.

The selection of the proper pesticide, the dosage, and the time of treatment is governed by the use of a sampling process that estimates pest damage and pest and natural enemy numbers. Pest sampling schemes have been the subject of research for several decades. A great deal of sampling emphasis has been directed toward insect pests to determine whether or not the pest is approaching the economic threshold and whether a remedial action, such as the use of an insecticide, is economically justified as a management option. Also, excellent sampling schemes have been developed for nematodes, weeds, and, in some cases, plant pathogens. If pests and their damage are not sampled on a routine basis, judgments cannot be made on the use of pesticides.

Sampling, from a research perspective, has been a cornerstone in understanding and predicting the distribution, abundance, and interactions of pests with the host crop. Sampling has been used also as the primary approach to gather information to aid in making crop management decisions. The emphasis in this article is on the use of sampling for making informed and reliable pest management decisions. Decision sampling stresses the reliability of a pest population estimation, that is, whether the population is above or below the economic threshold. Highly reliable estimates of a pest population density may not always be necessary to determine if a pest requires control, particularly if the pest density is well above or below the economic threshold. When the sample is taken is important in order to relate pest abundance to a damage susceptible stage of the plant. Where to sample on the plant or in the soil is critical to optimize the chance of discovering pest or damage incidence. The closer the population is to the economic threshold, the more reliable must be the pest population estimate. The number of sample units taken increases exponentially as the density of the pest or its damage approaches the economic threshold.

The size of the sample unit is important in pest management decision making. The ideal sample size is one that best represents the pest population and crop damage but also one that requires the least amount of time or expenditure of effort. The size of a sample depends not only on the ability to discover the pest or pest damage, but also on sample method efficiency and sampler efficiency. The method and the sampler can introduce variability, depending on the crop/pest system under consideration. The frequency of sampling depends on the phenology of the pest species, the rate at which the pest population is increasing (as affected by biotic and abiotic factors), the nearness of the pest density to the economic threshold, and the damage potential and cost of controlling the pest at different crop stages.

Conservation of natural enemies, as discussed earlier, is important in IPM. Although many sampling schemes are in use, a reliable estimate of the impact of natural enemies on a pest population for decision making has not been developed, except for a few species. The role of naturally occurring parasites and predators in reducing pest population has been difficult to quantify for use in a crop management system. Generally ''rules of thumb'' have been applied at the field level where estimates of low, medium, or high numbers of predators or parasites are considered by the decision maker. Whether the decision maker truly understands the complex interactions of the pest with its natural enemies may not be as important as the intent to conserve these biological control agents.

VI. Transferring IPM to Growers

Transferring IPM technology to farmers and ranchers includes virtually all segments of the agricultural industry involved in the production of a given commodity and its protection from pests. As information becomes available from research conducted by universities, state and federal agencies, and the private sector, it must be shared with farmers. Historically in the United States, the Cooperative Extension Service (CES), part of the land grant university in each state, has had the primary responsibility for the dissemination of IPM information to growers and the agricultural industry. [See COOPERATIVE EXTENSION SERVICE.]

Although IPM programs implemented by growers through CES and the private sector have focused on the appropriate combination of cultural, biological, and chemical control methodologies, several other factors must be considered in the appropriate design of an IPM educational approach. The scale or size of the IPM program, the economics of implementation, and the social and environmental setting of the program must be considered before an IPM program is offered to growers. Although the disciplines of agronomy, horticulture, entomology, plant pathology, weed science, agricultural economics, and agricultural engineering are pivotal in developing an interdisciplinary IPM program for growers, the disciplines of sociology, anthropology, and psychology are also important contributors in understanding how growers adopt new technology. Of key importance is the direct involvement of growers in program design. Because the growers are the final recipients, it is vital to gain their perspective and input before developing an IPM educational program for a farm or a region.

Since the implementation of IPM has been a primary educational activity of the CES since 1972, examples of the successful transfer of IPM systems to growers are abundant. CES specialists and county agents have adopted IPM in their educational programs as the primary approach to pest control. Successfully adopted IPM programs have several points in common. A multitactic, multidisciplinary approach must be developed that includes agronomic, pest, economic, and environmental considerations that eliminate the predisposition to pest loss. The elements that most IPM programs consider include a less susceptible plant variety, a planting time and location that separate the development of the crop in time and space from pest populations, fertilization and irrigation practices that disfavor pests, rotation of susceptible crops with nonsusceptible crops to dilute pest populations, computerized models to forecast pest abundance, field monitoring and the use of thresholds in-season, and timely harvest and destruc-

tion of plant residues that serve as pest refugia. Training involving field scouting of the pest and its damage and assessing levels of natural enemies is usually the most visible part of the IPM program. This training is vital to allow growers to recognize pests and damage and to use economic thresholds as the basis for pesticide applications.

A broad range of educational methodologies is used by CES to demonstrate IPM to growers. A powerful method is the use of on-farm result demonstrations. Growers volunteer to use their farms as a model for IPM system implementation, the results of which can be viewed periodically by other growers over the season. Result demonstrations serve as a field laboratory before, during, and after the season. Several result demonstrations distributed across a production region constitute an excellent means of gaining adoption by growers.

Several other educational techniques are widely used, including field days and tours sponsored by CES in collaboration with private agricultural consultants, university and USDA scientists, and, in some cases, agricultural chemical industry representatives. Allowing small groups to engage in learning a particular technique or methodology, field days and tours constitute an excellent way to expose growers to a wide range of field and pest management conditions.

Other teaching activities include the use of electronic and print media. Information on the current status of pests and natural enemies, economic thresholds, pest biologies, and computerized pest forecasts are only a few examples of the type of information that is disseminated routinely through the media to a wide clientele of growers, agricultural consultants, pesticide dealers, pesticide applicators, and financial institutions. Farm journals, newspapers, news magazines, and home and garden magazines are frequent carriers of IPM articles. Most CES IPM programs produce weekly newsletters, an effective method of providing specific local information. Additionally, a wide array of IPM teaching aids such as fact sheets, technical bulletins, crop/pest guidelines, manuals, books, slide sets, and videos has been produced and is available in every state through CES. Computers have been used effectively by CES and private agricultural consultants to store and analyze pest and crop data, develop program summaries, predict damaging pest infestations, and serve a variety of communication functions that are useful at community, state, regional, and national levels.

IPM programs should engage in continual evaluation to identify weaknesses and areas for improvement. Various techniques have been developed to evaluate the economic benefits of growers participating in IPM compared with those of growers who do not. Adoption of IPM techniques reduce production costs and increase net profits to growers. In fact, of the hundreds of evaluations that have been conducted, nearly all have resulted in an increase in net profits to growers through reduction of production costs, usually from reduced pesticide inputs. In some cases, additional net returns have been generated from increased yields experienced through the use of IPM. Because IPM is information intensive, it has been shown to reduce risk, or variability, in crop production. The increased profits and reduced risk for IPM growers have been experienced at the farm, community, state, regional, and national levels.

IPM systems are more sustainable over time. The likelihood of pest outbreaks, pesticide resistance, and environmental disruption is less when using IPM techniques. IPM programs of the future will rely even less on pesticides and more on biologically based techniques such as pest-resistant crop varieties, cultural management, and biological control. Pesticides may become a more limited resource in United States agriculture because of the negative public perception of pesticides, stricter environmental regulations, increasing costs of registering pesticides with the EPA, relatively poor economic returns for pesticide manufacturers in small acreage food crop markets, and pesticide resistance.

Bibliography

Dent, D. (1991). "Insect Pest Management." CAB International, Oxford.

Frisbie, R. E., El-Zik, K. M., and Wilson, L. T. (1991). "Integrated Pest Management Systems and Cotton Production." John Wiley and Sons, New York.

Kilgore, W. W., and Doutt, R. L. (1967). "Pest Control: Biological, Physical and Selected Chemical Methods." Academic Press, New York.

Madden, P. W. (1992). "Beyond Pesticides: Biological Approaches to Pest Management in California." ANR Publication, University of California, Oakland.

Pimentel, D. (1981). "Handbook of Pest Management in Agriculture," Vols. I–III. CRC Press, Boca Raton, FL.

Rajotte, E. (1987). "The National Evaluation of Extension's Integrated Pest Management (IPM) Programs." Virginia Cooperative Extension Service Publication 491-010, Blacksburg.

Stern, V. M., Smith, R. F., van den Bosch, R., and Hagen, K. S. (1959). "The Integration of Chemical and Biological Control of the Spotted Alfalfa Aphid. *Hilgardia* **29 (2)**, 81–154.

Zalom, F. G., and Fry, W. E. (1992). "Food, Crop Pests, and the Environment: The Need and Potential for Biologically Intensive Integrated Pest Management." APS Press, St. Paul, MN.

International Agricultural Research

RICHARD H. BERNSTEN, GLENN L. JOHNSON, *Michigan State University*

Glossary

Basic disciplinary research Research to improve the measurements, theories, and techniques of an academic discipline

Applied disciplinary research Research to apply the measurements, theories, and techniques of an academic discipline

Problem-solving research Addresses a specific practical problem of a specific decision-making unit and is typically multidisciplinary

Subject matter or issue-oriented research Provides a kind of multidisciplinary knowledge useful in addressing a rather well-identified set of problems faced by a rather well-identified set of decision makers: examples include different kinds of sustainability, agronomic, plant breeding, gender, and farm management research

In today's developed countries, the foundations of modern agricultural and rural research systems, along with complementary investments in agricultural education and extension, were laid in the 1700 and 1800s. In the United States and other developed countries, university, governmental, and private sector scientists contributed to building these systems. In developing countries, agricultural research was first supported (early 1900s) by several European powers and the United States, focusing on export crops produced in their respective colonies. Beginning in the 1940s developing countries gave dominate priority to harnessing science and technology to increase food crop productivity. Over the past 50 years, various funding sources have supported these efforts, including foundations, bilateral aid programs, multilateral agencies, and private sector seed and agro-chemical companies. Today, the industrialized countries face problems of overproduction. Yet, the developing countries still face the elusive challenge of increasing food production, ensuring food security, and increasing income with which to buy food—in major part because of the difficulty in balancing technical advances with institutional (including policy) advances, human development, and resource enhancement. Food production technology is a necessary but insufficient condition for overcoming food insecurity and generating income to buy food and other necessities.

I. Agricultural Research in the United States

Key early contributions to agricultural research include Charles Townsend's experimentation on crop rotations in the early 1700s; the establishment of agricultural improvement societies in Great Britain, France, Denmark, Italy, and Germany in the mid-1700s and the first professorship of rural agriculture and economy at Oxford (1790); the founding of the Rothamstead Experiment Station in England (1834); German scientist Justus von Liebig's work on the application of organic chemistry to agriculture (1840); and Gregor Mendel's research on genetics (1866).

In the United States, agricultural research is a part of the larger education–research–extension systems, which incorporated and extended the early discoveries and innovations to meet the needs of modern agriculture and an expanding urban population. Similar systems evolved in industrialized Europe, Canada, Australia, and Japan over the same time horizon, with each country's institutions reflecting its own cultural and historical experiences.

A. Universities

The land-grant university system, which constituted the core of the U.S. agricultural research structure for years, was a response to demands from local agricultural societies for governmental assistance to the farming community. The state of Michigan established the country's first agricultural college in 1855. With the passage of the national Land-Grant Act/ Morrill Act (1862), each state was provided with means to establish a college of agriculture and mechanical arts—marking the beginning of federal support to higher education in agriculture. While focusing largely on technology, the experiment stations soon included some research in farm management (including rural sociology) and, later, included programs in agricultural economics, home economics (human ecology), and agricultural history. Relative to agricultural technology, research on institutional and policy improvements, human development, and the enhancement of natural and man-made resources has been neglected over the years in the U.S. land-grant institutions. More recently some attention has been given to agro-ethics. [See EDUCATION: UNDERGRADUATE AND GRADUATE UNIVERSITY.]

Recognizing the need to strengthen the country's research capacity, Congress passed the Hatch Act in 1887, thereby providing federal support to the states to conduct applied agricultural research (in cooperation with the U.S. Department of Agriculture) at agricultural experiment stations associated with the land-grant colleges. The state of Connecticut established the first agricultural experiment station in 1876. With the passage of the Smith-Lever Act (1914) which established a national, university-based extension service, the basic structure of today's public agricultural research, education, and extension system was in place. [See AGRICULTURAL EXPERIMENT STATIONS; COOPERATIVE EXTENSION SERVICE.]

Currently, the land-grant system supports a broad array of applied and basic biological and physical science research on plants, animals, food, soil and water, agricultural engineering, and rural social and family problems but continues to neglect relatively the non-technical aspects of rural farm, and nonfarm, environmental, social, family, and consumer issues.

Contributions to agricultural and rural research have also been made by institutions outside of the land-grant system. These contributions were often less direct in the form of support for underlying basic physical, biological and social sciences; perhaps because the technical agricultural sciences were both developed and dominated by land-grant universities. The non-land-grant universities made basic advances for agriculture in chemistry, physics, bacteriology, genetics, and microbiology in America as well as in Europe. For example, contributions came from cytologists to the development of hybrid corn—Liberty Hyde Bailey in the United States and Charles Darwin in the U.K. were correspondents. In Germany, Humboldt's studies of the effects of altitude on plant growth and populations were fundamental—this list could be greatly extended. Perhaps because issues and problems to which the social sciences can contribute were neglected in the land grants, the non-land grants were fairly quick in establishing rural social science programs and institutions such as Stanford's Food Research Institute, Henry Schultz's price research program at the University of Chicago, John D. Black's agricultural economics program at Harvard, and later programs centered around T. W. Schultz and D. Gale Johnson at the University of Chicago. Also considerable rural related, disciplinary social science research was done by historians, political scientists, general economists, sociologists, and anthropologists.

More recently competition has developed with respect to both disciplinary and applied research. This competition is between land-grant colleges of agriculture and the non-land-grant universities and, for that matter, between agricultural colleges and the basic biological and physical disciplines of the land-grant universities. As a consequence, pressures have developed to replace the "formula funding" of agricultural research with competitive grant funding open to everyone (especially disciplinary scientists) from outside the agricultural establishment having interests in basic research in the biological and physical science discipline. Non-land-grant colleges lack the technical agricultural expertise and farm land required to mount large-scale efforts to attach many practical multidisciplinary problems and issues.

B. U.S. Department of Agriculture (USDA)

The USDA, established in 1862, was raised to full cabinet status in 1889. Today, agricultural research directly under the USDA is carried out primarily by the Agricultural Research, the National Agricultural Statistical and the Economic Research Services. USDA staff are assigned to USDA headquarters, at regional research experiment stations and at land-grant universities. Very importantly the USDA Cooperative States Research Service (CSRS) coordinates federal budget requests for the support of both federal and federally supported state research. This includes federal support of agricultural experiment stations which accounts for less than one-fourth of the typical station budget. [*See* USDA: NATIONAL SYSTEM OF AGRICULTURAL RESEARCH.]

1. Agricultural Research Service (ARS)

In addition to its regulatory functions, the USDA supported a wide range of activities by the early 1900s, including research on crop and animal production, disease and pest control, soil mapping, extension, and biological surveys. Today's ARS, created in 1953 through a reorganization of research bureaus, directs scientific research in the fields of crops, livestock, soil and water conservation, agricultural engineering, utilization research and development, and human ecology. Organized as multidisciplinary teams involving mainly biological and physical scientists focusing on agricultural technology, ARS scientists carry out research to provide a better understanding of basic processes related to problems of regional or national importance, as well as research focused directly on problems and issues. Overall, ARS research has even neglected the rural social science aspects of technology generation and has grossly neglected rural social sciences research unrelated to technological advances.

2. National Agricultural Statistical Service (NASS)

This agency and its predecessors have been responsible for collecting, processing, and publishing primary data on the agricultural system and rural people and areas of the United States. The basic knowledge generated by this agency is used in developing national income, expenditure, and net income data; in creating indexes of input use, output, and prices; and in analyzing problems and issues. Use of these data in NAS and ERS research has been coordinated with data generation by the U.S. Bureau of the Census to develop a U.S. agricultural data system that is still one of the best in the world despite its increasing obsolescence and neglectful underfunding.

3. Economic Research Service (ERS)

The USDA has conducted economic and related social science research since the turn of the century, including in-depth studies in farm management, data systems, agricultural policy, demography, marketing, and rural societies. Using data from the census and from NASS and ERS and its own predecessor

agencies USDA developed the world's premier data system for agriculture. Rural social science research was institutionalized with the creation of the Bureau of Agricultural Economics (BAE) in 1922. The BAE made major contributions to policy formation and program planning of the Department under the New Deal. The BAE aggressively explored rural social science issues and proposed many controversial policy changes, which led to its abolition in 1953 when it was subsumed temporarily under the ARS. In 1961 the USDA's economics staff was reorganized as a separate service, the ERS, and made responsible for carrying out social (including economic) analyses in support of policy making. Key research areas include analyses in the areas of supply and demand, finance, production, marketing, foreign agriculture, agricultural history, trade, demography, natural resources, and rural development.

C. The National Academy of Science (NAS), The National Science Foundation (NSF), The Board of Agriculture and Renewable Resources (BARR), The National Research Initiative (NRI), and Research on National Needs (RNN)

After World War II, the United States expanded support for basic disciplinary research by supplementing its parastatal NAS with direct financial support for basic biological, physical, and (to a much lesser extent) social sciences via the NSF and National Institutes of Health (NIH) in the conviction that U.S. biological and physical science research had been too applied. This redirection in science policy and increase in basic science programs was accompanied by a widespread shift toward basic disciplinary research in all scientific and academic circles. The rural social as well as biological and physical agricultural sciences lost status in academe. In the mid-1980s, agricultural interests pressured NAS to give more status to agricultural research. This resulted in a compromise in which the existing Board of Agriculture and Renewable Resources (BARR) was reconstituted as the current Board on Agriculture.

However, the imbalance between emphasis on disciplines versus practical problems and issues has shifted back and forth. The NSF developed its Research on National Needs (RNN) program to counter overdisciplinization. Despite such efforts to support research on practical problems and issues, disciplinarians argued for increased "competitive grant" funding for agricultural research. In the late 1980s, the National Research Initiative (NRI) was established in an effort to channel additional agricultural research resources to states through the Cooperative States Research Service (CSRS)—allocated on a competitive basis and open to all nonprofit research organizations. Somewhat paradoxically, as the colleges of agriculture became more disciplinary, opportunities arose for biological and physical scientists in other colleges and in non-land-grant universities to do applied discipilinary work in agriculture. The social scientists at Harvard, the University of Chicago, Stanford, Vanderbilt, and elsewhere who had long been filling needs for applied disciplinary social science work were joined by biological and physical scientists from nonagricultural colleges who were looking for opportunities to do applied disciplinary research in agriculture. Open opportunities for such work increased when agriculturalists shifted their interests to more basic disciplinary research, away from their more traditional concern for practical applied disciplinary and multidisciplinary problems and issues or subjects. Generally, social or biological and physical scientists outside colleges of agriculture have not possessed the land and experimental facilities to do multidisciplinary research on practical agricultural problems and issues that cross the basic biological, physical, and social science disciplines.

In the 1970s and 1980s, unattended and unresearched multidisciplinary practical problems and issues involving the environment, poverty, gender inequality, rural welfare, food chain contamination, drug abuse, AIDS, educational deficiencies, resource sustainability, and the like led to a widespread public disillusionment with the disciplinarity of science and academia. This conviction went beyond activist groups to the general public. With substantial justification, the idea became widespread that practical issues and problems were being neglected by science and academia in favor of disciplinary interests. Disillusionment with the agricultural research establishment (ARE) also set in—The Ford Foundation ceased its support of both traditional and disciplinary agricultural research; at the same time clientele groups in agriculture became less supportive of the ARE as it shifted in the disciplinary direction.

D. Private Sector

Private sector research is carried out by both small firms and large companies. The private sector's major contributions have been in applied research leading to product development, including farm machinery, food processing, crop breeding, herbicides, fertilizers and pesticides, and institutional changes in the agribusiness sector as is evident when one considers recent institutional changes in the poultry, red meat, agricultural credit, fertilizer, and machinery industries. Genetic engineering is an important new focus of private sector research. In recent years, multinational seed and agricultural chemical firms, including Pioneer, W. R. Grace, Cargill, Dekalb, Upjohn, and Montsanto, have launched applied research initiatives in less developed countries.

II. International Agricultural Research

A. Colonial Research Systems

Until the 1950s, the primary source of international assistance to agricultural research came from European countries and the United States as they attempted to expand exports from their overseas possessions. The Netherlands has a long history of support to export crop research in Indonesia and Surinam, as did the United States in the Philippines, Liberia, Cuba, and Puerto Rico. At the turn of the century, British supported an empirewide research network, with export crop research institutes in India, Canada, Australia, and New Zealand and later a system of autonomous interterritorial commodity research institutes in Anglophone Africa. France supported little agricultural research in her colonies prior to WW II, but thereafter set up a network of commodity institutes in Francophone Africa that were centrally controlled by the associated French research center. Belgium, on the other hand, provided little financial assistance to its colonies but rather set up research centers (i.e., INEAC in the Belgium Congo, founded in 1933) that were financed by the colonial states. These research centers, designed to support the commercial policies of European and American powers, generally focused on cash crops such as cotton, sugar cane, natural rubber, tea, coffee, cacao, and livestock, including tsetse fly control. Although food crop research was much less emphasized, stress on export crops had the advantage of generating income with which the colonial populations could purchase food and other necessities. The post-WW II stress on food crop production was probably as imbalanced in the opposite direction as the pre-WW II stress on export crop production.

B. Post-World War II Efforts to Support Agricultural Research

In the early 1940s the industrialized nations recognized the need to increase food production in developing countries and began to set in place the network of domestic and international institutions mentioned above that were designed to provide technical, financial, and educational assistance to increase food production in the Third World. Unfortunately, it was accompanied by neglect of technologies for income-producing export crops.

In 1941 the Rockefeller Foundation sent a team to Mexico, which led to the establishment of a collaborative research program to expand wheat and corn (for food) production. Over the next 50 years, numerous organizations and programs were established in less developed countries to support agricultural research and development oriented to increasing food crop production. The trend began in the mid-1940s with the founding of the Food and Agricultural Organization (FAO) (1945) of the United Nations and the World Bank (1946). The 1950s saw the establishment of the United State's Point-Four foreign aid program (1950); the beginning of Ford Foundation (1950) support to agriculture; and several bilateral assistance programs (initially by Britain, France, Germany, Canada, Australia, and, later, by Japan and OPEC countries). USAID was created in 1961 to promote development; its program to strengthen agricultural universities eventually targeted 40 developing countries. The Inter-American Development Bank was created in 1959. The 1960s saw the creation of the International Rice Research Institute (1961) (the first of 13 such centers), the establishment of regional banks for Africa (1964) and Asia (1966); and the United Nations Development Program (1966). The 1970s saw the establishment of Canada's International Development Research Center (1970), the Consultative Group for International Agricultural Research (1971), the International Fertilizer Development Center (1974), and the Small Ruminant CRSP (1979)—the first of several USAID-funded collaborative research support programs. The 1980s saw the creation of the Australia's Center for International Agricultural Research (1982) and the Special Program for African Agricultural Research (1985). Several key initiatives are discussed below.

1. U.S. Foundations, Non-Governmental, and Private Voluntary Organizations

Both the Rockefeller and Ford Foundations were catalysts in promoting and funding the initial international agricultural research centers (IARCs) and continue to provide modest support to these centers. Winrock International Livestock Research and Training Center (Winrock) initially focused on livestock research, but broadened its mandate to include support to crops, natural resources, and policy analysis in the early 1980s. The Farm Foundation has used its small budget effectively in support of extension education more than research and to support agricultural economics and rural sociology internationally. During the 1960s and 1970s the Agricultural Development Council made a major contribution to training Asian social scientists. In recent years, NGOs have supported research efforts through their work with local organizations to diffuse research to farmers throughout the developing world.

a. Rockefeller Foundation (RF) RF has focused on strengthening the technical agricultural sciences—through its support to the IARCs (see CGIAR system) and by assigning leading U.S. scientists to work in national food crop research programs (i.e., Mexico, India, Colombia). In addition, RF has trained many scientists who have assumed leadership roles in their national research programs. Current RF initiatives include support to biotechnology research on rice throughout Asia; grants to faculty members in Uganda, Kenya, Malawi, and Zimbabwe to conduct problem-oriented research to improve the productivity of small farmer; and support to research on natural resource management in a few countries.

b. Ford Foundation (FF) In contrast to RF, the Ford Foundation has sought to strengthen the social sciences. In the 1950s Ford became the "first major US foundation to set up an international program of multi-purpose grant-making offices overseas, focusing on problems rather than disciplinary subjects." During the 1960s and early 1970s, the FF joined RF to help establish the initial IARCs and supported efforts to create policy analysis capacity and administrative expertise in the agricultural ministries of developing countries. Initiatives to extend the benefits of the green revolution more broadly include the India Intensive Agricultural Districts Program (IADP) during the 1960s, support to universities and government ministries to strengthen their agricultural research and training capacity, programs to better integrate women into development, and interdisciplinary farming systems research—with emphasis on bringing together university, ministries, and NGOs to address farmers' problems. Current initiatives include strengthening the capacity of NGOs to implement grass roots development projects, linking rural NGO's efforts with government-sponsored initiatives, initiatives to insure that government policies support these efforts, and involving NGOs and the public sector in natural resource management—including irrigation and forestry.

c. Private Voluntary (PVOs) and Non-Governmental Organizations (NGOs)

PVOs and NGOs engaged in development work include CARE, Catholic Relief Service, OXFAM, Africare, Norwegian Church, World Vision, Save the Children, and Heifer Project (livestock). Historically, most PVOs/NGOs focused on food distribution in suppport of disaster relief, but increasingly many also support community development projects, applied commodity and farming systems research, and agricultural extension to help insure that research results are made available to limited resource farmers.

2. The CGIAR System

By the early 1950s, agricultural scientists had recognized that new agricultural technologies could not be simply transferred to developing countries, but rather countries must develop their own capacity to generate new technology. [See CONSULTATIVE GROUP ON INTERNATIONAL AGRICULTURAL RESEARCH.]

Building on the success of the program which helped Mexico become self-sufficient in grain, in 1960 the Rockefeller and Ford Foundations joined forces to establish a center in Asia—the International Rice Research Institute—to do the same thing for rice. In the years that followed, additional centers (IARCs) were launched to increase food production in the less developed world, each with a regional or specific commodity mandate: including CIMMYT (1969), located in Mexico which focuses on corn and wheat; CIAT (1967) in Colombia for cassava, field beans and rice, and pastures in the American tropics; IITA (1967) in Nigeria for the improvement of agriculture in the humid and subhumid tropics; CIP (1970) in Peru for potatoes; WARDA (1970) in the Ivory Coast for rice in West Africa; ICRISAT (1972) in India for sorghum, millet, chickpea, pigeonpea, and peanuts; ILRAD (1973) in Kenya for the control of the livestock diseases of sleeping sickness and East Coast fever; ILCA (1974) in Ethiopia for livestock production; IBPGR (1974) in Italy for the conservation of genetic diversity; ICARDA (1975) in Syria for barley, lentil, and faba beans worldwide and wheat, chickpea, pasture and forage crops in West Asia and North Africa; IFPRI 1975) in the United States for policy research to promote food production, distribution, and consumption; and ISNAR (1980) in the Netherlands to assist developing countries to strengthen their research systems.

As the number of IARCs increased, the need to coordinate funding and oversight became apparent. In 1971 the Consultative Group on International Agricultural Research (CGIAR) was established as an informal consortium of governments, international and regional organizations, and private foundations.

Today, the CGIAR constitutes a network of 13 research centers with a mandate to nurture agricultural research to improve the quantity and quality of food production in the less developed countries. In addition, the CGIAR system works with 11 affiliated research centers. Since the early 1970s, the CGIAR has broadened its focus from initially supporting only commodity research, to support of genetic resource conservation, food policy research, and the management of national agricultural research systems.

The IARCs, in collaboration with national research programs, pursue a variety of activities that contribute to crop improvement; including collecting, storing, and distributing germ plasm; breeding new varieties, agronomic and related research; training national scientists; publishing report of the latest research results; and holding workshops and conferences which enable scientists to interact and learn from each other. Since 1971 the CGIAR budget has grown from $20 million to over U.S. $250 million (1992). Major donors include the United States, Japan, Canada, World Bank, EEC, UNDP, and the Rockefeller and Ford Foundations.

3. Bilateral Assistance Programs

The United States, United Kingdom, France, Canada, Japan, and Australia provide a major share of direct assistance to agricultural research. In addition, 24 developed and developing countries support agricultural research through contributions to the CGIAR system and other international organizations.

a. United States

In an effort to alleviate severe shortages of research and extension manpower, USAID enlisted the support of U.S. land-grant universities to build and strengthen agricultural science capacity in Asian, Latin American, and African universities. Forty land-grant universities have been paired as partners with developing country institution—the largest programs involving India, Nigeria, Brazil, and Indonesia. These "institution building projects," implemented primarily from 1952 through the 1970s, helped land-grant universities send their faculty on long- and short-term overseas assignments to assist in developing curricula and research capacity. While greatest priority was given to strengthening undergraduate education, graduate degree and research programs were established. Major fields of training included crop and animal science, with much less emphasis on the social science. In addition, local staff were sent to U.S. universitites for graduate training and technical assistance was provided for campus construction, laboratory equipment, and library facilities. While many of the larger host-country universities continued to support significant levels of applied research, few took on major extension roles or provided leadership to national rural development policy making. While most universities successfully retained their trained staff, many of the faculty now approach retirement. As opportunities for overseas training have declined over the past decade, and their governments face severe financial constraints, many of these universities face an uncertain future.

In the late 1970s, USAID established the Collaborative Research Support Program (CRSP)—a new approach to mobilizing the research capacity of U.S. higher education to implement multidisciplinary, problem-oriented, collaborative agricultural research with scientists in developing countries and the IARCs. The CRSPs, coordinated by a Council of USAID and participating university representatives, link over 700 scientists in 32 U.S. universities and over 80 international research institutions. Each of the 10 CRSPs is guided by a global research mandate, which gives priority to high-payoff problem-solving and issue-oriented research that benefits limited resource producers and consumers in the collaborating countries and U.S. agriculture. The CRSPs provide funding for joint U.S.-based and developing country scientists to plan and carry out long-term research to increase the production, storage, and utilization of neglected crops (beans/cowpeas, peanuts, sorghum/millet) and small ruminants, and address critical research on soil management, fisheries stock assessment, pond dynamics/aquaculture, human nutrition, integrated pest management and sustainable agriculture. In addition, funds are used to train host-country scientists.

Since the early 1960s, USAID has financed several hundred projects to increase agricultural research capacity in developing countries. USAID has limited capacity to implement research projects. Thus, it contracts with U.S. universities, private consulting firms, the USDA, and IARCs to provide short- and long-term technical assistance, train staff, and build research facilities to strengthen government-supported crop and livestock research institutes in developing countries. In response to the "New Directions" Congressional mandate, the mid-1970s saw a refocusing of research to place more emphasis on the needs of the "poor majority." This laid the groundwork for multidisciplinary, participatory, on-farm, farming systems research to better address farmer's needs, and the important roles of women in development, nontraditional crops, and less well-endowed environments. While many USAID-funded research efforts contributed to increased agricultural production, it became increasing clear in the 1980s that technology alone could not increase rural welfare. Without appropriate policy reforms, macroeconomic adjustments, human development, and an expanding resource base, farmers lacked important essential ingredients for using new technologies.

b. United Kingdom Support to agricultural research is funded by the Office of Development Assistance (ODA). Short- and long-term technical assistance activities are implemented by ODA program staff, and via contract to universities, the institutes of the National Research Institute, private consulting firms, and individuals. In contrast to the U.S. model, universities in the U.K. have been far less involved in implementing large institution-building research projects, but do play a important role in training Third World scientists.

c. Australia Established in 1982, Australia's Center for International Agricultural Research (ACIAR) mobilizes Australian's agricultural research capacity for the benefit of developing countries. Similar to the CRSPs, ACIAR implements its mandate by commissioning Australian institutions (especially universities) and individuals, in partnership with developing country research groups, to implement research in Australia and in developing countries. Priority is given to problem-oriented research on animal and crop production, farming systems, land use, fisheries, forestry, postharvest technology, and the socioeconomics of agriculture. Projects are generally funded for 2–3 years with possible renewal. ACIAR's approach emphasizes responding to needs expressed by developing countries, addressing problems of national importance, significant local scientist participation, and problems with a potential to exploit Australia's special research capacity. While most projects involve Southeast Asian and Pacific country scientists, ACIAR support research in other regions with environments similar to Australia.

d. France The Center for International Cooperation in Agronomic Research (CIRAD) was established in 1984, following consolidation of several tropical commodity research institutes formerly under GERDAT. The CIRAD is organized into seven departments, each with a specific commodity/subject matter mandate (i.e., CIRAD-CA for annual crops and CIRAD-CP for cotton). The center supports research, training, and dissemination activities at CIRAD's own centers, within host-country agricultural institutes, universities, and parastatals and in support of development projects. About one-half of CIRAD's activities are funded by the French government and one-half through contracts from the World Bank, FAO, and the European Economic Community. In contrast to USAID which contracts its research projects, CIRAD implements it mandate through its staff of over 1000 senior scientists—approximately 40% of whom work overseas in about 50 developing countries. While private consulting firms and universities play only a minor role in implementing research overseas, two French centers located in Montpellier train agricultural researchers and technicians from developing countries, Europe, and France.

e. Canada The International Development Research Center (IDRC) programs Canada's aid for research in agriculture and natural resources. Established in 1970 to assist developing countries solve pressing problems, it provides direct support to Third World institutions, with minimal reliance on long-term expatriate technical assistance. Projects build research capacity through support to training and studies of locally identified problems. IDRC projects focus on neglected crops grown by the poor (including cassava, millet, and sorghum), ruminant animals, fisheries, forestry, agricultural economics, postproduction systems, human nutrition, and environment and sustainable development. IDRC also sponsors research and information networks that enable Third World scientists to learn from each other. Research projects are guided by a holistic approach and implemented by interdisciplinary teams of scientists.

4. Multilateral Assistance

a. The World Bank Since the late 1960s, the Bank has provided loans to developing countries to strengthen their capacity to generate new technology. Applied and/or adaptive research is the approach emphasized in most projects. Bank loans have financed six types of agricultural research and extension initiatives in over 68 countries—agricultural and rural development projects with adaptive research and extension components, national adaptive research and extension programs, research components in education projects, agricultural research reform and reorganization, special grants to non-CGIAR centers, and financial and administrative support to the CGIAR—channeled to the various IARCs. During the period 1981–1987 the Bank invested about $98 billion in 21 "free standing" research projects and 209 agricultural and rural development projects with research components. The total cost of the research element in these projects was about $2.1 billion. Most "free standing" projects have provided for graduate training fellowships. Where a gap existed between research and extension, projects have included strategies for strengthening linkages between research and extension efforts.

b. The Food and Agricultural Organization of the United Nations While perhaps best known as the sponsor of conferences designed to focus attention on world food and natural resource issues, FAO also plays an important role in supporting agricultural research. These efforts have taken three forms—assistance to projects designed to strengthen national agricultural systems, co-sponsorship of the CGIAR, and the promotion of regional and interregional research networks. Projects have focused on a variety of fields, including sorghum and millet development, sheep and goat production, irrigation, tick-borne cattle diseases, horticulture, integrated pest management, agricultural equipment development, and remote sensing. Most projects include a major training component. Agriculture and trade statistics collected by FAO are widely used in analyzing the state of world agriculture. In addition, FAO has supported campaigns (typically with an applied research component) to increase food production and farmers' income (e.g., fertilizer program, locust control) and eradicate livestock diseases (e.g., rinderpest, foot-and-mouth, African swine fever, and trypanosomiasis), carried out worldwide surveys (e.g., World Food Surveys), and sponsored studies on famine relief, food security, marketing, desertification, agrarian reform, postharvest losses, trade, and environmental issues.

c. Institute of Applied Systems Science Analysis (IASSA) Headquartered in Austria, the IASSA was established by the U.S. and Soviet governments, with several European countries and Canada providing support. Initially, the National Academy of Sciences was the administering U.S. agency. It has carried out research on global models pertaining to natural resources, acid rain, water, energy, food, and agricultural policy.

5. Consulting Firms

Numerous private nonprofit and consulting firms provide technical assistance to agricultural research projects on a contractual basis, through funding from bilateral aid programs or international organizations like the World Bank.

6. National Agricultural Research Systems in Developing Countries

In most developing countries, agricultural research is generally carried out by institutes under the ministry of agriculture or by autonomous research institutes. Few countries have significant private research capacity. Although universities have played a minor role in agricultural research, their undergraduate and graduate training programs have contributed to strengthening research capacity. At the end of the colonial period, most research systems were weak and had insufficient trained personnel to implement research. Over the past 30 years, national governments and donors have invested heavily to strengthen these systems—by both upgrading physical facilities and training scientific manpower. Since independence most countries have given priority to food crop research. Training efforts have emphasized technical agricultural disciplines (e.g., plan breeding, agronomy, veterinary medicine), resulting in a severe shortage of social scientists working in national research programs. Since the mid-1970s, most countries have given greater emphasis to adaptive research including farming systems research. Research capacity varies greatly across national systems. In general, research systems are strongest in Asia and Latin America and weakest in Sub-Saharan Africa. Today, national research systems face a variety of challenges. Rapid population growth, rising incomes, and urbanization will increase the demand for food. Greater recognition of environment issues, resource degradation, sustainability, postharvest problems, and the potential contribution of biotechnology requires that research systems expand their research agendas. On the other hand, national and international resources to support agricultural research are declining in both relative and absolute terms, resulting in staff attrition, shortages in operating funds, and facility deterioration. To meet these challenges, it will be necessary to find ways to increase support to agricultural research, expand social science research capacity, utilize available resources more effectively, promote greater intraregional cooperation, expand the role of private sector research, and reassess the role of CGIAR system to determine how it can best serve national research systems in the future.

III. Lessons Learned

Since World War II, we have learned as a first lesson that progress in and for agriculture, rural societies, and consumers depends on research to achieve reasonable levels and combinations of (1) improved technology, including both food and cash crop technologies, (2) a wide range of human capacities, (3) natural and man-made resources, and (4) private and public institutions including policies, programs, facilities, and infrastructure. Agricultural researchers bear responsibility for researching all four of these "driving forces for progress." Research administrators bear responsibility for maintaining these and several other kinds of balances in agricultural research systems.

If a society allows any one of these four forces to be deficient, the other three are constrained by the deficient one. Technologies without capable people qualified to use them are of little value. Without the adequate support of private and public institutions (including appropriate policies), advanced technology and well-trained people are frustrated. Equally constraining on technologies, institutions, and well-trained people is a lack of resources both natural and especially man-made ones secured by converting natural resources into capital that embodies appropriate improved technologies. Food production without generation of income to buy food and other necessities does not overcome hunger and poverty.

Assessing agricultural research systems is a normative matter. It involves the impacts of a research system's output on such important considerations as the security of food supplies; the distribution of poverty, affluence, and opportunities; the avoidance of food chain contamination and environmental pollution; the sustainability of our natural resources; the maintenance of esthetically pleasing living conditions; the arts; bio-diversity; and health and nutrition. Consequently agricultural research systems need to research the values that guide the development of farm and rural systems and society. Such systems must be concerned with ends or values as well as means as they pursue progress on technology, human capabilities, institutions, policies, and natural and man-made resources. This, then, is a second kind of balance required in our research institutions. Because practical problems require both value and value free knowledge for their definitions and solutions, our agricultural research institutions must have balance with respect to these two kinds of knowledge. The need is for objective knowledge about values as opposed to non-objective advocacy of emotionally held values. Objective knowledge is possible about monetary values and about many nonmonetary values including the value of healthy well-nourished bodies, freedom, biodiversity, gender equality, unpolluted environments, and uncontaminated food chains—the list can be extended almost indefinitely. Further, knowledge is required about exchange or extrinsic values. Prices for instance are values in exchange but we need knowledge of rates of exchange between nonmonetary values as, for instance, when making trade offs between preserving a wilderness area and providing access to it. At other times we need knowledge of more intrinsic values. In appraising agricultural research systems, for instance, we often have to consider the intrinsic value of a human life rather than considering trade offs between human lives and, say, freedom from food safety regulations. Ideally our knowledge about values should also be interpersonally valid and cardinal, not just ordinal.

A third kind of balance is also important in designing, guiding, and controlling the work of agricultural research systems. This is the balance between: (1) direct research on the *problems* of private and public decision makers, (2) research on such *subjects* as resource sustainability, poverty, animal welfare, hunger, food chain contamination, gender inequality, global warming (or cooling?), community development, acid rain, farming systems, desertification, food quality (nutrition and taste), family development, and international trade, and (3) underlying basic *disciplinary* research in such *disciplines* as anthropology, biology, economics, genetics, sociology, chemistry, philosophy, bacteriology, psychology, hydrology, history, physics, geography, geology,—the list goes on. The first two of these three kinds of research are multidisciplinary and holistic due to the nature of the individual practical problems of concern in the first and of the sets of practical problems of concern in the second. The third kind of research considered above was disciplinary which is often highly specialized within disciplines that are themselves specialized. In attaining balance between the above three kinds of research and the four driving forces, value knowledge is crucial. Practical problems are defined and solved using knowledge of values as well as relatively value-free knowledge. Values are also important even for the basic disciplinary work done in agricultural research systems as it is knowledge of values that indicates what kinds of basic research have practical relevance for farmers, consumers, and rural societies. There is a justified expectation that the basic disciplinary research done in agricultural research centers be relevant for farming, rural societies, and/or the consumers of farm and rural products and services.

Site, time, society, and situational specificity decrease in importance as emphasis shifts from problem solving to subject matter or issue oriented and then to basic disciplinary research. So do multidisciplinarity and the importance of values. Similarly, holism decreases in importance while specialization and reductionism become more tolerable and less damaging as the three kinds of research are considered in the above order. Again, a need for balance exists. Specificity with respect to problems must be balanced against disciplinary specificity. In seeking this fourth kind of balance it must be recognized that somewhat paradoxically problem specificity goes along with multidisciplinary holism.

In the history of international agricultural research institutions, it is clear that *both* food and cash crop (income-producing crops) are important. Before WW II the imbalance neglected food crops. Since WW II, cash crops (often for export) have been neglected. As a fifth lession, we have learned that it is important to establish a better balance than now exists between the two.

The above five balances indicate in turn the importance of maintaining a balance in agricultural research systems. This sixth kind of balance is that between the social sciences and humanities, on one hand, and the biological and physical sciences, on the other. A major study of social science agricultural agendas in the late 1980s and early 1990s stresses (1) that maintaining the above five balances requires strong social science programs in agricultural institutions, (2) that most agricultural research establishments neglect the social sciences and humanities, and (3) that most agricultural researchers and administrators are not philosophically oriented to do and administer the objective research on values that is needed to determine those balances. The same study also indicates that our agricultural establishment institutions are increasingly criticized for being imbalanced in the first four respects listed above. These criticisms are in substantial part justified. The criticisms come from ecological movements, hunger activists, nutritionists, animal rightists, feminists, the "greens," humanists, the buisness world, human rightists, community and political leaders, the press, religious communities, consumers, farmers, rural residents, youth, and the like.

Many of these critics have a partially inaccurate view of agricultural research institutions as irresponsible pursuers of technical advance and profits for themselves, farmers, and agribusinesses without regard for the environment, family farms, poverty, equity and justice, animal welfare, gender equality, nutritional values, consumer tastes and perference, health, food chain contamination, Third World farmers, etc. Where and when this perception is true, correcting the difficulties requires more input from the social sciences. Even when such perceptions are untrue, correction of the misperceptions requires social science inputs.

Future Priorities for Agricultural Research Systems (ARSs)

I. Technological advance must continue to have priority in ARSs. However, most ARSs need to place greater relative emphasis on
  A. The generation of new and improved public and private institutional arrangements, policies, infrastructural facilities, and programs including those that do research.
  B. The enhancement, preservation, and maintenance of natural and man-made resources including those man-made resources that embody new advanced technologies.
  C. The generation of a wide range of human capabilities to
    1. Handle and generate new technologies.
    2. Manage and generate new and improved private and public institutional arrangements, policies, infrastructural facilities, and programs.
    3. Manage new and improved human capabilities.
  D. Income generation as well as food production.
II. The philosophic orientations of the ARS personnel (including administrators) need to be broadened and diversified to improve capacity to generate and use knowledge
  A. Both monetary and nonmonetary values.
  B. Intrinsic as well as extrinsic or "in exchange" values. More specifically the need is to go beyond the reductionistic positivistic orientations common among biological and physical scientists to include normative and pragmatic orientations capable of supporting objective work on values and more holistic analyses of multidisciplinary problems and issues dealing with institutions, human capabilities, and resource enhancement as well as technical advances.
III. Many ARSs need to reverse their present trends toward emphasis on basic disciplinary work to the increasing neglect and exclusion of multidisciplinary problem-solving and issue-oriented research
  A. Without abandoning the disciplinary work that is synergistic with and relevant for multidisciplinary problem-solving and issue-oriented research.
  B. To serve farmers, rural people, and societies and consumers better with problem-solving and issue-oriented research results.
IV. Establish more and better interactive/interaction with farmers, rural societies, and the consumers of goods and services generated in rural areas in order to

  A. Improve identification, definition, and resolutions of practical problems and issues
  B. Facilitate participation of relevant private and public decision makers and choosers in:
    1. The preassessment of research projects.
    2. The generation of knowledge both value-free and about values.
    3. Postassessments and evaluation of research efforts and outputs.
V. Develop the social science and human capacity needed to attain the balances called for in I through IV above.

Bibliography

Anderson, J. R., Herdt, R. W., and Scobie, G. M. (1988). "Science and Food: The CGIAR and Its Partners." CGIAR, the World Bank, Washington, DC.

Becker, G. S. (1975). "Human Capital," 2nd ed. Columbia Univ. Press for National Bureau of Economic Research, New York.

Brown, A. W. A., Byerly, T. C., Bitts, M., and San Pietro, A. (eds.) (1975). "Crop Productivity—Research Imperatives." Proceedings of an International Conference, October 20–24, 1975, Boyne Highlands, MI.

Cochrane, W. W. (1979). "The Development of American Agriculture: A Historical Analysis." Univ. of Minnesota Press, Minneapolis, MN.

Encyclopedia Britannica (1990). Agricultural Science (pp. 181–184) and Agriculture (185–207). Encyclopedia Britannica, Chicago.

Evenson, R. (1980). A century of agricultural research and productivity change—Research, invention, extension, and productivity change in U.S. agriculture: A historical decomposition analysis. In "Research and Extension Productivity in Agriculture" (A. A. Araji, ed.). Univ. of Idaho, Moscow.

Johnson, G. L., and Bonnen, J. T. (eds.) (1981). "Social Science Agricultural Agendas." Michigan State Univ. Press, East Lansing, MI.

Johnson, G. L. (1988). Technolgical innovations with implications for agricultural economics. In "Agriculture and Rural Areas Approaching the 21st Century: Challenges for Agricultural Economics" (R. J. Hildreth et al., (eds.). Iowa State Univ. Press, Ames.

Javier, E., and Renborg U. (eds.) (1988). "The Changing Dynamics of Global Agriculture." Proceedings of a Seminar/Workshop on Research Policy Implications for National Agricultural Research Systems. ISNAR, The Hague.

National Academy of Sciences (1977). "World Food and Nutrition Study: The Potential Contributions of Research." Commission on International Relations, National Research Council, Washington, DC.

Pond, W. G., Merkel, R. A., McGillard, L. D., and Rhodes, V. J. (eds.). "Animal Agriculture: Research to Meet Human Needs in the 21st Century." Westview Press, Boulder.

Ruttan, V. (1978). Induced institutional change. *In* "Induced Innovations: Technology, Institutions, and Development" (H. Binswanger *et al.*, eds.). The Johns Hopkins Univ. Press, Baltimore.

Ruttan, V., and Hayami, Y. (1984). Towards a theory of institutional innovations. *J. Dev. Studies* **20**(4), 203–223.

Schuh, G. E. (1981). Economics and international relations: A conceptual framework. *Am. J. Agricult. Econom.* **63**(5), 767–778.

Schultz, T. W. (1961). Investment in human capital. *Am. Econom. Rev.* **51,** 1–17.

Schultz, T. W. (1971). "Investment in Human Capital: The Role of Education and Research." The Free Press, New York.

Irrigation Engineering, Evapotranspiration

Terry A. Howell, *USDA-Agricultural Research Service, Texas*

I. Evapotranspiration and Irrigation Engineering
II. Irrigation Engineering
III. Irrigation Water Management

Glossary

Crop coefficient Ratio of evapotranspiration for a specific crop at a specific growth stage to the reference crop ET for that same time period and climatic conditions

Irrigation capacity Gross flow rate per unit land area irrigated

Irrigation scheduling Systematic determination of the need for irrigation and the timing and amount of irrigation water to apply to a specific crop and/or field with a specific irrigation system

Limited irrigation Planned irrigation management that does not meet the full crop water requirement; also called *deficit irrigation*

Lysimeter A device, generally a tank or container, that defines the soil boundaries, particularly the lower boundary, for measuring the water and/or solute movement and the soil water balance of the enclosed soil

Reference Crop ET Evapotranspiration from a specified crop (most often short grass or alfalfa) which is well supplied with water and has full ground cover (near maximum vegetative cover) and minimum exposed soil

Irrigation engineering is the application of science to irrigation design, management, and operation for the benefit of mankind. Evapotranspiration is the combined processes of water evaporation from soil, plant, or water surfaces and water evaporation from plant tissue (internal plant surfaces) by transpiration. Evapotranspiration influences irrigation design and management. Irrigation design and management directly affect plant growth processes, crop yield, environmental impact of irrigation on soil and water resources, and individual producer net profits.

I. Evapotranspiration and Irrigation Engineering

A. Description

Evaporation is the vaporization process whereby a substance, either liquid or solid, is converted into a vapor. For solids, the process is generally called *sublimation*. In agriculture and irrigation engineering, usually evaporation refers to the water vaporization from soil, plant, or water surfaces, and *transpiration* usually refers to the vaporization of water from plant tissues generally through the stomata of plant leaves. Evapotranspiration is the combined processes of water vaporization from evaporation and transpiration and is also called *consumptive use* in some literature. In addition, water retained in the living tissue is generally ignored since it is such a small amount compared to the mass and/or rates of water vaporization consumed in either evaporation or transpiration. Although evapotranspiration cannot be defined as a single process, it is considerably easier to measure than evaporation or transpiration; hence, its use as both an identifying term and a measured parameter is widespread in the agricultural and irrigation sciences to describe the use of water by vegetation.

Irrigation engineering is a specialized branch of engineering dealing with the application of science to irrigation design, management, and operation. Irrigation engineering is a subdiscipline of the larger agricultural and civil engineering fields. Traditionally, civil engineers specializing in irrigation engineering have been more directly involved with off-farm engineering applications (water supply, dams, canals, drainage, etc.) while agricultural engineers specializing in irrigation engineering have been involved with on-farm applications (application methods, system design, irrigation scheduling, etc.). An overlap of agricultural and civil engineering in irrigation engineering is widely visible. Since this encyclopedia is intended for agricultural sciences, on-farm irrigation engineering will be emphasized. [*See* IRRIGATION ENGINEERING: FARM PRACTICES, METHODS, AND SYSTEMS; WATER CONTROL AND USE.]

B. Measurement and Estimation of Evapotranspiration

1. ET Measurement

Many methods have been proposed and used to measure water use by vegetation. Generally, the lumping of evaporation and transpiration into evapotranspiration does not pose a severe theoretical restriction. However, in some cases the distinction of water use in evaporation and in transpiration (as separate physical processes) is clearly more desirable. For simplicity, the term evapotranspiration will be designated by the symbol ET, evaporation by E, and transpiration by T, henceforth in this chapter (remembering that ET = E + T).

ET can be directly measured by two means—weighing lysimeters and by eddy correlation. ET can be indirectly inferred by water balance or energy balance based on the principle of the conservation of mass and energy, respectively. Weighing lysimeters are devices with a soil container which is mounted on a scale that can precisely determine the change of the soil mass due to the vaporization of water by E and T (Fig. 1). Sometimes the lysimeter soil surface may be covered to eliminate E, and thereby permitting T to be measured. Small lysimeters (called *micro-lysimeters*), usually about 200 mm or less in diameter and 100 to 200 mm deep, have been used to manually measure E over short periods (a day to perhaps 2 or 3 days) for bare soil or beneath crop canopies. This method is basically a simple soil water balance of the surface soil water where most of the soil water evaporation occurs, and the soil water content volume change (measured as mass) is determined by removing and weighing the lysimeter containers and then replacing them back into the soil for evaporation to occur. These micro-lysimeter measurements of E require routine soil volumetric sampling to "refresh" the soil in the micro-lysimeter and to relocate the measurement sites. They cannot be used reliably during rain or irrigation events and may not correctly

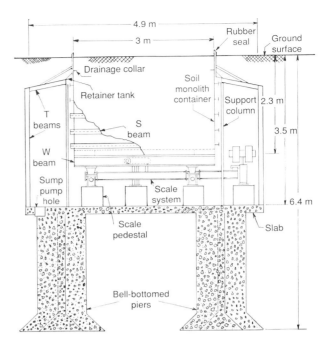

FIGURE 1 Schematic diagram of the weighing lysimeters at Bushland, Texas (USDA-ARS). [From Marek, T. H., Schneider, A. D., Howell, T. A., and Ebeling, L. L. (1988). Design and construction of large weighing monolithic lysimeters. *Trans. ASAE* **31**, 477–484; reprinted by permission of the American Society of Agricultural Engineers, St. Joseph, MI.]

represent the soil drying since plant root extraction is eliminated. Weighing lysimeters (and percolation lysimeters as well) provide a defined water flux at the lysimeter boundary (generally zero; although drainage water can be removed, water can be added to simulate upward flow from a water table, or a constant water table elevation can be maintained).

Eddy correlation measurement of ET requires precise and fast-response instruments to measure the covariance of the perturbations (fluctuations from the mean) of vertical wind and water vapor movements. With higher speed and more accurate portable, DC-powered data acquisition systems, eddy correlation methods are becoming more widely used. Eddies are gusts of wind created by the turbulent flow and mixing of the atmosphere controlled by the forces of momentum, heat, and water vapor transfer.

ET can be determined by a water balance as

$$\mathrm{ET}_i = \overline{\Theta}_i - \overline{\Theta}_i - 1 + R_i + I_i - Q_i - D_i, \quad (1)$$

where ET_i is the water use during period i, Θ_i is the profile soil water content (over some specified depth Z as $\overline{\Theta} = \int \Theta \, dz$ from 0 to Z) at the end of period i, R_i is precipitation, I_i is irrigation, Q_i is runoff (or runon if negative), and D_i is drainage at depth Z (or upward flow if negative) during period i, and all terms are expressed in units of length (usually mm; equated to 1 kg m^{-2} for water). For most agricultural applications Θ, R, and I can be measured by several methods; however, Q and certainly D are more difficult to determine. Often, Q and D can be neglected in certain situations. The ET rate is determined by dividing ET by the period length.

ET can be determined by an energy balance as

$$ET = (Rn - G - H)/\lambda, \qquad (2)$$

where ET is in mm sec^{-1} (positive during evaporation or transpiration), Rn is net radiation in W m^{-2} (positive when incoming exceeds outgoing radiation), G is soil heat flux in W m^{-2} (positive when the soil is warming), H is sensible heat flux in W m^{-2} (positive when the air is warming), and λ is the latent heat of vaporization in J kg^{-1} [approximately 2.45×10^6 J kg^{-1} at 25°C]. Rn can be measured with net radiometers, and G can be measured with soil heat flux plates buried at a shallow depth (usually about 20 to 50 mm deep) and soil calorimetric correction for the thermal energy storage in the soil layer above the plates. H can be measured using profile techniques (micrometeorological methods) or using surface temperature measurements (these are usually made with infrared thermometers). In Eq. (2), ET is determined as the residual [i.e., the remainder of $(Rn - G - H)/\lambda$]. Most often, however, the Bowen ratio method is used where

$$\beta = H/(\lambda ET) = \gamma \, (K_h/K_v) \, [(\Delta T/\Delta e)] \qquad (3)$$

and

$$ET = (Rn - G)/[\lambda \, (1 + \beta)], \qquad (4)$$

where β is the Bowen ratio (fraction), γ is the psychrometric constant in kPa °C^{-1} (approximately 6.6×10^{-4} P, where P is barometric pressure in kPa), K_h and K_v are the eddy transfer coefficients for sensible and latent heat (usually equality between K_h and K_v is assumed), respectively, and ΔT and Δe are the vertical gradients for temperature in °C and for vapor pressure in kPa, respectively. The Bowen ratio method can reduce instrumentation detail required in the micrometeorological profile methods; however, precise measurements of ΔT and Δe are required as well as the assumption that $K_h K_v^{-1} = 1.0$. The Bowen ratio energy balance method cannot be used when β is equals -1.0, which occurs most often at neutral atmospheric conditions before sunrise and late evening after sunset. Often the magnitude of the energy balance fluxes at night are too small to be reliably mea-

sured by the Bowen ratio. The Bowen ratio energy balance method and other energy balance methods require highly accurate measurements of Rn and G, which commonly can contain errors of ±5% or more. These Rn and G errors directly affect the accuracy of H and λET.

Transpiration (T) can be measured using a heat balance method for certain species with a main stem (at least 5 mm in diameter for small plants to over 100 mm for trees). Figure 2 illustrates a heat-balance gauge. The gauge consists of a small heater that is placed in contact with the plant stem and several thermopiles (or thermocouples) that measure the radial and vertical heat migration from the heater. A constant power is applied to the heater and the transpiration flux through the plant stem is related to the heat migration rate along the stem accounting for radial heat dissipation away from the heater. The device is carefully insulated to avoid heat transmissions to or from the environment. The areal transpiration can be computed based on the plant or crop density. In practice, many individual gauges need to be measured and averaged to account for plant to plant variations.

2. ET Estimation

ET (as well as E and T) is influenced by many factors—climatic factors (mainly solar radiation, air temperature, relative humidity, and wind speed), soil factors (i.e., water content, thermal properties, physi-

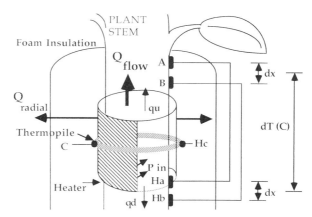

FIGURE 2 Schematic diagram of a stem heat balance gauge used to measure plant transpiration. A, B, Ha, and Hb are thermocouple temperature measurement locations; and C and Hc are radial thermopile temperature measurement locations; P is input power from the heater; qd is the downward heat flow, qu is the upward heat flow, Q_{radial} is the radial heat flow, and Q_{flow} is the net upward heat flow; dx is the increment for upward and downward temperature gradients and dT is the temperature gradient in °C measured as [(A − Ha) + (b − Hb)]/2. [*Source:* Dynamax, Inc., Houston, Texas.]

cal layers, soil strength, and root-zone salinity), and plant factors (i.e., plant density, plant height, rooting depth, leaf area, and stomatal conductance). Crop ET is often characterized for hypothetical crops called *reference crops* (ET for a reference crop will be called ET_r). Short grass (usually a cool season type species) and alfalfa are the most common reference crops. The ET of these crops when "well-supplied with water" and with a "full ground cover" generally defines ET_r. ET_r is often computed using the Penman combination type equation which is given below for a grass ET_r case as

$$\lambda ET_r = [\Delta (Rn - G) + (\gamma\, Ea)]/(\Delta + \gamma), \quad (5)$$

where Δ is the slope of the saturation vapor pressure curve $[\partial e\, \partial T^{-1}]$ in kPa °C^{-1} [usually evaluated at the mean air temperature, T_a, in °C] and $Ea = 74.42$ $(1.0 + 0.53\, U_2)\, (e_a^* - e_a)$ in W m^{-2} for grass reference ET_r, where U_2 is the mean wind speed in m sec^{-1} at a 2 m elevation above the ground, e_a^* is the saturation vapor pressure in kPa at T_a, and e_a is the ambient vapor pressure in kPa. The Penman equation was later modified using resistance factors to apply more generally to any crop or vegetation and is known as the Penman–Monteith equation which is given as

$$\lambda ET_r = [\Delta (Rn - G) + (\gamma\, Ea)]/(\Delta + \gamma^*), \quad (6)$$

where $\gamma^* = \gamma\, (1 + r_c/r_a)$ where r_c is the canopy resistance to vapor transfer in sec m^{-1}, r_a is the aerodynamic resistance to vapor transfer in sec m^{-1}, and Ea is now defined as $Ea = [(m\, \rho_a\, \lambda)/P]\, [(e_a^* - e_a)]/r_a]$ in W m^{-2}, where m is the molecular mass of water vapor to air mass [0.622] and ρ_a is the air density in kg m^{-3}. The aerodynamic resistance (r_a) includes the effect of wind on the evaporation process (note: r_a is inversely related to wind speed). ET_r will be crop specific because Rn will depend on the crop and soil albedo (short-wave or solar radiation reflection ratio) and the crop and soil emissivity (long-wave emittance factor), the effects of the crop on energy flux into the soil (G), the aerodynamic factors of the crop that influence r_a (mainly crop height, crop roughness, and atmospheric stability), and the crop resistance factors that influence r_c (mainly leaf area and stomatal resistance). For time periods of a day, G is often assumed to be negligible; however, for longer periods (weeks or months) or shorter periods (hours) G can be a significant factor and should not be neglected. ET_r is defined in terms of the crop canopy resistance, r_c, for a specific reference condition.

Many other ET_r estimation methods and equations have been developed, particularly for applications where climatic data may be limited and all the parameters required for Eqs. (5) and (6) may be unavailable. A few of the more widely used empirical reference ET equations for grass are given below

Priestley-Taylor $\lambda ET_r = \alpha\, \Delta\, (Rn - G)/(\gamma + \Delta)$ (7)
Jensen-Haise $\lambda ET_r = C_T\, (T - T_x)\, R_s$ (8)
Hargreaves $\lambda ET_r = 0.0023\, R_A\, TD^{1/2}$
$(T + 17.8), \quad (9)$

where α is an empirical coefficient (dimensionless) which is approximately 1.26 for wet surface conditions, C_T and T_x are determined by empirical equations based on site elevation and the warmest month's mean maximum and minimum temperatures, R_s is solar radiation in W m^{-2}, R_A is extraterrestrial solar radiation (solar radiation outside of the earth's atmospheric layer) in W m^{-2}, and TD is the mean monthly temperature difference (maximum minus minimum) in °C. The Priestley-Taylor equation is most often applied to more humid locations; the Jensen-Haise and Hargreaves equations are more appropriate for weekly or longer-term ET estimates. In addition, evaporation pans are widely used as methods to estimate ET_r; however, pan location and the site conditions surrounding the pan can greatly affect pan evaporation.

Empirical crop coefficients are used to compute the crop (or other vegetation as specified) water use as

$$ET = [(K_{cb}\, K_w) + K_s]\, ET_r, \quad (10)$$

where ET_r is the computed reference ET for a specified reference crop in mm d^{-1}, K_{cb} is the basal crop coefficient (fraction), K_w is a water deficit ET reduction factor (fraction), K_s is a soil evaporation factor (fraction), and ET is the actual crop water use in mm d^{-1}. Figure 3 illustrates a generalized crop coefficient curve. Ideally, the empirical factors (K_{cb}, K_w, and K_s) could be developed using Eq. (6) with appropriate

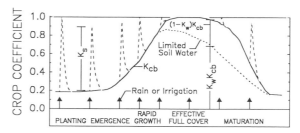

FIGURE 3 Generalized crop coefficient curve illustrating the crop coefficient parameters. [Adapted from Wright, J. L. (1982). New evapotranspiration crop coefficients. *J. Irrig. Drain. Engr. Div. ASCE* **108**(IR1), 57–74. Reprinted by permission of the American Society of Civil Engineers, New York, NY.]

values for r_a and r_c. The basal crop coefficient, K_{cb}, is defined for the case with a "well-watered" crop but dry soil surface (several days after irrigation or rainfall). K_{cb} is determined for a specific crop and for a specific method of determining ET_r. For this reason, the use of published values of K_{cb} must carefully determine the appropriate ET_r and method of estimating ET_r. K_w is defined by the reduction in ET caused by reduced soil water, may be both soil and crop specific, and normally decreases exponentially (or logarithmically) with increased soil drying. K_s is specific for a particular soil and will generally decline exponentially to zero following several days of drying.

II. Irrigation Engineering

Engineering designs for irrigation systems provide detailed information on water supply (rate and volume), application rates, hydraulic design of water delivery components, operation criteria for the systems, and maintenance schedules for the irrigation system. ET impacts the water supply or demand for the irrigation project (field, farm, or entire project on a hydrologic basin or region scale). This chapter will deal only with the effects of ET on irrigation engineering applied to on-farm irrigation design and management; however, the impact of off-farm, district, or project engineering is recognized to impact on-farm irrigation engineering.

A. Irrigation Capacity

Irrigation capacity (IC) is defined as the gross flow rate per unit land area, and it is usually characterized in units of liter $\sec^{-1}$ m^{-2} (or mm s^{-1}) or more commonly converted to mm d^{-1} (mm d^{-1} = 8.64 × 10^4 liter $\sec^{-1}$ m^{-2}). IC includes all the application conveyance losses (only on-farm losses are considered in this chapter). IC should be optimized through the engineering design because IC directly affects the fixed irrigation system costs since the size of the water supply and conveyance structures (pipelines, canals, pumps, valves, power demand costs, power distribution component sizes, etc.) are directly related to IC. IC is an irrigation rate constraint, and it can affect crop growth and yield performance for the particular climatic regime in which the system is intended to function as well as irrigation efficiency (fraction of applied water actually being used by the crop). IC is sometimes indirectly and/or directly constrained by regulations (i.e., well sizing, well spacing, turn-out flow controls). In certain cases, irrigation volume will also be constrained (i.e., water allotments, water depletion regulations). Generally, IC is one of the primary factors affecting variable irrigation costs, particularly when ground water is the main irrigation water supply, through the gross flow rate which is directly proportional to energy consumption where pumping is necessary.

As IC is reduced, the ability of the irrigation system (with its efficiency and uniformity) and irrigation management to meet the full crop irrigation needs is sacrificed. Irrigation capacity in excess of the minimum IC necessary to meet the crop water needs (including any necessary leaching for salinity management) in all years requires additional capital investment for irrigation equipment. Since the irrigation system peak application rate is also directly proportional to IC, runoff from irrigation applications can result if IC is too large; however, the irrigation hydrology (the partitioning of irrigation applications into infiltration, runoff, deep percolation or drainage, and ET) is complex and difficult to predict. The goal of irrigation should be to achieve a high partitioning of irrigation applications into ET (especially T) while minimizing application losses to runoff and drainage resulting in high irrigation efficiency, irrigation application efficiency (defined as the fraction of applied water actually being stored in the crop root-zone), water use efficiency (WUE is defined as the ratio of crop yield to seasonal crop water use (ET) usually expressed in units of kg m^{-3}, where 1 g m^{-2} per mm equals 1 kg m^{-3} or 10 kg ha^{-1} per mm equals 1 kg m^{-3}), and irrigation water use efficiency (IWUE is defined as the ratio of crop yield to total seasonal irrigation amount with the same units as WUE). The optimum IC is somewhat difficult to precisely determine since the acceptable risk level associated with reduced crop yields resulting from soil water deficits depends on the philosophies and financial resources of the individual grower (i.e., a particular design with a specific IC may meet the crop needs in 9 years out of 10, on the average, with a maximum yield reduction of 10%). The grower needs to specify the risk level that is acceptable, and then the IC and system design can then be determined to meet or exceed that criterion. Figure 4 illustrates the simulated effect of net sprinkler IC on corn yields at Bushland, Texas (Pullman clay loam soil), for a specific irrigation management strategy for 28 years of climatic record (1958–1985). This illustration shows for this particular case that a net IC above 8 mm d^{-1} did not improve expected corn yield. However, as net IC declined to

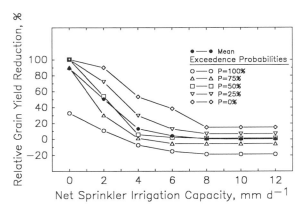

FIGURE 4 Simulated relative corn grain yield reduction for a Pullman clay loam soil at Bushland, Texas, as affected by net sprinkler irrigation capacity for 20-mm applications with a 75-mm allowable soil water depletion prior to irrigation for a 28-yr period. [From Howell, T. A., Copeland, K. S., Schneider, A. D., and Dusek, D. A. (1989). Sprinkler irrigation management for corn—Southern Great Plains. *Trans. ASAE* **32**, 147–154, 160. Reprinted by permission of the American Society of Agricultural Engineers, St. Joseph, MI.]

4 mm d^{-1} the mean corn yield would be reduced about 10% while 1 year in 4 (25% exceedence probability) the corn yield could be reduced almost 30%.

IC necessary to meet the full irrigation needs of a crop is largely based on (1) the maximum crop ET rate over some specified planning interval, (2) the plant available soil water that can be extracted by the crop without any serious yield reduction, and (3) effective precipitation during the planning interval. The first factor is well defined in many sources while the second factor is more difficult to precisely characterize for particular crops and soils. The third factor can be estimated in many ways, but it is influenced strongly by the precipitation pattern (frequency, amount, and intensity), soil factors (slope, surface cover, soil type, etc.), and normal ET rates during the specific time interval. Equation (1) can be rearranged to solve for *I* as the irrigation requirement. IC can be bracketed in several ways. At some soil water content level (Θ_c), the crop cannot take up water from the soil at a rate sufficient to meet the atmospheric demand rate for transpiration (the value of K_w in Eq. (10) will begin declining below a value of 1.0 and the value of r_c in Eq. (6) will begin to increase above the value defined for the reference condition), and the crop will develop a water deficit which will reduce growth (and eventually yield) and ET through mechanisms that regulate the stomatal opening and biochemical processes in the leaves. This critical soil water content is not necessarily the same for these two

processes—normally growth (photosynthesis) will be reduced before ET is greatly affected—and may even vary with several environmental conditions. In addition, if the soil water content is too large, exceeding some value Θ_u, then water more easily moves through the profile resulting in water losses to *D* with its associated nutrient leaching losses and rainfall losses to *Q* may increase.

The irrigation management goal is therefore to maintain Θ within this range ($\Theta_u - \Theta_c$) while minimizing irrigation application losses to *D* and *Q* with *I* constrained by the irrigation design to be $\leq$ to IC$\star T$, where *T* is the design time period in days and IC is in mm d^{-1}. The maximum IC can be estimated as $\int$(ET $-$ R)dt over time period *T* in days, when no soil water ($\Theta_{i-1} = \Theta_c$) can be extracted without reducing crop growth and yield, divided by the irrigation application efficiency (as a fraction). This maximum IC will clearly depend on effective rainfall. In most cases, the expected effective rainfall for short duration planning periods (one week or less) will be zero. As the soil water content increases above Θ_c, available soil water can be extracted by the crop to meet its ET demand without reducing crop growth and yield, thereby reducing the irrigation amount and IC required to meet the crop water needs. Likewise precipitation, groundwater contributions (negative *D*), and water harvesting (negative *Q*) (see Eq. (1)) directly offset ET thereby reducing irrigation needs and irrigation capacity. IC can be estimated using an equation developed by the USDA–Soil Conservation Service given as

$$IC = 0.034 \, (ET_m^{1.09}/AD^{0.09}), \qquad (11)$$

where IC is in mm d^{-1}, ET_m is the monthly mean ET for the peak month in mm month^{-1}, and AD is the allowable soil water depletion in mm between irrigations which avoids crop water deficits.

B. Irrigation Scheduling

Irrigation scheduling (IS) comprises of strategic (long-term) decisions (i.e., selection of methods for detecting plant water needs, planning for seasonal water allotments to specific fields or crops, etc.) and tactical (short-term) decisions that mainly determine when to irrigate and how much irrigation water to apply. In some cases, irrigation applications may be desired for reasons beyond meeting crop water needs (i.e., frost protection, crop stand establishment, salinity management, chemical applications—herbicides or pesticides, etc.). IS needs to consider the crop water needs, irrigation system constraints (IC and application rate), energy conservation, soil water contents, weather and precipitation patterns, and cultural practices like harvesting, fertilizing, etc. IS will directly affect the crop production economics through its effect on crop yield and crop quality and on irrigation costs (labor, energy, and/or water).

IS strategic decisions include the method of crop irrigation need determination, the desired range of single irrigation application amounts for best uniformity and efficiency, and the crop yield goals. Tactical IS decisions include the day-to-day integration of irrigation with other farming practices (planting, cultivation, harvesting, pest control, immediate weather forecasts, etc.).

Figure 5 illustrates a simple example crop production function (relationship between crop yield and applied irrigation water) and irrigation economics. The crop production function is assumed to follow a quadratic function in this example. The middle graph (Fig. 5A) shows a low fixed irrigation cost while the lower graph (Fig. 5B) shows a higher fixed irrigation cost. Both graphs (Figs. 5A and 5B) show low and high variable irrigation costs associated mainly with the costs of irrigation water. These examples assume that income is directly proportional to crop yield and that irrigation costs are linear. Several important points can be illustrated with this simple example. First, as either fixed or variable costs increase, the net profit (vertical distance between the income and cost curves) and range of positive net profits (horizontal distance between the points of intersection of the income and cost curves) decrease. The fixed costs do not greatly affect the optimum irrigation amount that maximizes net profit. The optimum irrigation amount (the point where the slopes of the income curve is equal to the slope of the cost line) decreases with increased variable irrigation costs. An additional point is that maximum net profit is not overly sensitive to the irrigation amount near the optimum irrigation amount (the slopes are relatively low). Of course, relationships like those illustrated here are simplified and do not consider many additional production economic and engineering parameters.

Many irrigation systems are designed and managed to operate near the maximum crop production level and this is usually called full irrigation. As Fig. 5 shows, this may not necessarily be the maximum net profit or the most optimum use of irrigation water; however, it may reduce the production risks that are faced by the grower. As the irrigation amount is reduced from that necessary to produce maximum crop yield, the risks (reduced net profits) increase. In addition, irrigation systems apply water with differing distributions of application amounts called application uniformity, and the application uniformity can affect irrigation economics (both net profit and system capital costs) as well. Traditionally, when lower irrigation amounts from those necessary for maximum crop yield are used, the irrigation management strategy is called limited or deficit irrigation. These strategies rely on avoidance of critical crop water stress, particularly in the sensitive crop growth phases normally associated with reproductive growth (i.e., anthesis in most cereal crops). Figure 5 illustrates that a deficit- or limited-irrigation strategy may not necessarily result in a reduced net profit. Limited- and deficit-irrigation management can be constrained by either volume or rate irrigation constraints. The rate constraint is the IC (or a well spacing or sizing regulation constraint) while a volumetric constraint could be a pumping volume regulation (i.e., so many m^3 per unit land area) or a water right constraint (legal permit).

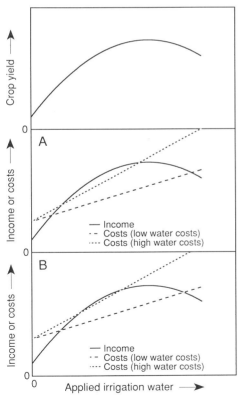

FIGURE 5 A hypothetical example of a crop production function and irrigation economics for linear irrigation costs with both low (A) and high (B) fixed and variable costs (water costs).

Additional legal or regulatory constraints on drainage, runoff, or water quality (both drainage and runoff) can impact irrigation design and management. These later regulations are called nonpoint source discharge regulations. Irrigation system design affects the fixed irrigation costs though the size of pipe size, canal size, pump size, power demand charge, etc., and the variable irrigation costs through the pumping rate, pumping pressure, labor, etc. Irrigation management and IS affect net profit through the resulting crop yield and quality and the variable irrigation costs, which are proportional to the total seasonal irrigation applications.

1. Irrigation Timing

Many methods are used to aid and determine irrigation timing decisions, which are a critical component of IS. IS should be based on plant water needs rather than indirect parameters such as soil water content, etc. However, plant measurements are often less quantitative, more time consuming, and often more difficult to automate. Plant water stress symptoms include visual signs like color changes, growth patterns, leaf rolling or curling, leaf wilting, etc. Often by the time that these visual observations are evident, significant damage to the crop yield potential may have already occurred. More quantitative measures of direct plant water deficits include plant temperature, reflected or emitted radiation, stem diameter, leaf diffusion resistance, leaf water potential, plant transpiration, etc. A major difficulty in using quantitative plant water stress measurements is the separation of the influences caused by the environmental parameters and those caused by plant water deficits. Many times some of the above plant measurements are made before sunrise to determine the rehydrated level of plant water stress. Other daytime measurements of plant water deficit may rely on air temperature, relative humidity (or combined into the vapor pressure deficit), or solar radiation. In some cases, dynamic atmospheric changes (clouds, wind, etc.) greatly affect the plant water status and its measurement. In some instances, a portion of the field may be managed with low soil water deficits to serve as a check or reference field for nearby fields using plant-based IS timing. Plant-based measurements are sometimes unreliable when extrapolated for several days, which may be necessary to schedule or order irrigation water anticipating irrigation needs.

Soil water parameters are often used in IS timing. Soil water can be estimated from simple soil sampling and judgment based on visual and feel methods; gravimetric methods requiring soil samples to be weighed, dried, and reweighed; soil water potential sensors (tensiometers and thermocouple psychrometers); porous block sensors (in equilibrium with the soil of electrical resistance, capacitance, and/or heat dissipation types); neutron attenuation meters (gauges that emit low levels of nuclear radiation and count the slow neutrons that are reflected back from water or other hydrogen elements); or soil dielectric gauges (time domain reflectometry). Several of the soil water sensors can be automated for measurement speed; however, soil contact and placement are major limitations. Soil water content or potential is an indicator of expected plant water stress. Soil water content or potential will usually permit longer-range IS timing forecasts than will plant based measurements. In addition, soil water measurements can be used more directly than plant indicators to determine irrigation amounts necessary to refill the soil profile.

Irrigation timing sensing methods should be viewed as information rather than one method versus another. Each method adds potentially greater collaboration or support for each of the other measurements. The grower or irrigation consultant needs to gather sufficient information, either soil or plant based, to make the irrigation timing decisions. These decisions should be presented in the context of a scheduling opportunity window. The earliest irrigation date in this scheduling window will avoid application losses to drainage and runoff while the later date in this scheduling window will avoid the development of plant water stress and associated future yield reductions.

2. Irrigation Amount

Irrigation amount is largely dictated by the irrigation application method, application efficiency, and the available soil water storage capacity. The irrigation amount is largely constrained by the IC and the frequency of irrigation applications. The irrigation application method will have a specific range of application amounts in which its efficiency and uniformity may be optimized. This optimum range could be about 50 to 100 mm for surface irrigations, 15 to 50 mm for sprinkler irrigations, or 5 to 25 mm for microirrigation (drip, trickle, bubbler, micro-spray, etc.). Available soil water storage dictates how much water could be stored within the soil profile without excessive losses to drainage. However, it may be desirable in many cases, particularly in subhumid and semi-arid climates, to avoid refilling the soil profile to leave potential storage for precipitation to minimize precipitation runoff losses.

III. Irrigation Water Management

On-farm irrigation water management is the combined utilization of irrigation system design with IS to enhance effectiveness of irrigation. Irrigation water management involves the integration of many strategic (long-range) and tactical (short-range) decisions with the farm management decisions (again both strategic and tactical), water supply, and legal and institution constraints.

Farm management decisions of cropping sequence and variety selections affect irrigation management. In addition, farm cultural operations such as tillage, pest control (both weeds and insects), fertility, crop harvesting, and other farming activities must be integrated with irrigation management to achieve the farm production goals. In many cases, these farm and crop management decisions may be more critical than irrigation decisions. In the United States, many times these farm management decisions are constrained by government farm programs or natural resource regulations.

Irrigation water supply has additional management constraints. Off-farm water supply may involve water "ordering" (advance forecast of water demand) from a water district or a water management agency. The ET of the crops being irrigated and the irrigation methods directly affect the water order. In other cases, the control of the water supply is simply the regulation or limit on water pumping, particularly from groundwater sources. These pumping restrictions have many forms from taxes or fees to absolute water withdrawal limits or regulations. For example, in southeastern Texas, groundwater withdrawal in certain areas is subject to fees charged by ground water districts to control and reduce land subsidence; in southwest Nebraska, the local natural resource conservation districts have imposed a fixed limit over a 5-year period on irrigation pumping volume; and in many western states, rigid water right laws control the water allocations for irrigation.

Energy consumption in irrigation also has emphasized the need for integrated management of irrigation with power distribution. In many situations with electrical-powered irrigation water supplies, electrical load management integration with irrigation management is necessary to reduce energy consumption (and therefore reduce irrigation variable costs) or to control the power demand by regulation to "off-peak" time periods. In the United States during the 1970s when energy rates were rapidly escalating, electrical load management became a critical component to preserve and/or maintain irrigation power availability.

Water quality issues have become major irrigation management factors. The impact of irrigation on the sustainability of irrigated agriculture has become important globally. The increased demand for the declining developed, high-quality water resources within the United States is one example of this environmental awareness. This awareness is heightened in areas with conjunctive use of groundwater and surface water for multi-purpose use (irrigation, domestic, municipal, and industrial). For example, groundwater contamination from leached nitrogen beneath irrigated lands along the central Platte Valley in Nebraska has heightened awareness about the necessity to integrate farm fertility management with irrigation management; in the San Joaquin Valley in central California, the leaching of naturally occurring toxic elements such as selenium into drainage waters has caused farm drainage discharge elimination with its associated perched water table creation and land degradation; in the Grand Valley of Colorado, percolating waters beneath irrigated lands leach naturally occurring salts into the Colorado River with many downstream impacts all the way to California and even into Mexico, affecting international treaties and compacts.

Often irrigation management is focused on annual or shorter-term objectives—crop variety or species chosen, crop yield and/or quality, irrigation method, irrigation amount, energy costs, etc. Longer-term objectives for irrigation management include sustainability (water availability), water quality issues, and producer risk. Clearly, irrigation must be profitable or it will no longer remain viable and feasible. ET, irrigation design, and irrigation management affect both the short- and long-term value of irrigation. In many cases, the value of irrigation far exceeds its value to an individual producer extending to local, regional, national, and world economies. It remains increasingly important to conserve limited natural resources both (soils, water, and energy) and to use these resources wisely to insure long-term food and fiber production for a growing world population. Irrigation engineering will continue to serve an important function in meeting this global need.

Acknowledgments

This article is a contribution from United States Department of Agriculture (USDA), Agricultural Research Service (ARS), Southern Plains Area (SPA), Conservation and Production Research Laboratory, Bushland, Texas, and was prepared by a U.S. Government employee as part of official duties.

Bibliography

Brustart, W. (1982). "Evaporation into the Atmosphere." D. Reidel, Dordrecht, Holland.

Cuenca, R. H. (1989). "Irrigation System Design: An Engineering Approach." Prentice Hall, Englewood Cliffs, NJ.

Hagan, R. M., Haise, H. R., and Edminster, T. W. (eds.) (1967). "Irrigation of Agricultural Lands." Agronomy Monograph No. 11, Am. Soc. Agron., Madison, WI.

Hoffman, G. J., Howell, T. A., and Solomon, K. H. (eds.) (1990). "Management of Farm Irrigation Systems." ASAE Monograph, Am. Soc. Agric. Engrs., St. Joseph, MI.

James, L. G. (1988). "Principles of Farm Irrigation System Design." John Wiley & Sons, New York, NY.

Jensen, M. E. (ed.) (1980). "Design and Management of Farm Irrigation Systems." ASAE Monograph, Am. Soc. Agric. Engrs., St. Joseph, MI.

Jensen, M. E., Burman, R. D., and Allen, R. G. (eds.) (1990). "Evapotranspiration and Irrigation Water Requirements." ASCE Manual and Reports on Engineering Practice No. 70, Am. Soc. Civil Engrs., New York, NY.

Monteith, J. L., and Unsworth, M. H. (1990). "Principles of Environmental Physics," 2nd ed. Edward Arnold, London, Great Britain.

Pair, C. H., Hinze, W. H., Frost, K. R., Sneed, R. E., and Schiltz, T. J. (1983). "Irrigation" *formerly "Sprinkler Irrigation."* The Irrig. Assoc., Silver Spring, MD.

Rosenberg, N. J., Blad, B. L., and Verma, S. B. (1983). "Microclimate, the Biological Environment." John Wiley & Sons, New York, NY.

Stewart, B. A., and Nielsen, D. R. (eds.) (1990). "Irrigation of Agricultural Crops." Agronomy Monograph No. 30, Am. Soc. Agron., Crop Sci. Soc. Am., and Soil Sci. Soc. Am., Madison, WI.

Irrigation Engineering: Farm Practices, Methods, and Systems

E. GORDON KRUSE, *USDA-Agricultural Research Service, Colorado*

Glossary

Evaporative demand Amount of water that could be evaporated, if water was not limited, in response to the atmospheric energy available as solar radiation or circulation of warm, dry air masses

Evapotranspiration (ET) Evaporation of water in an area of growing plants, including both transpiration and evaporation of water from soil and other surfaces wetted by rainfall

Infiltration Process of absorption by soil of water applied to the soil surface

Infiltration capacity Measure of a soil's ability to absorb water that is ponded on the soil surface, usually expressed in depth of water per unit of time

Irrigation set Land area, typically a fraction of a field, that can be irrigated at one time by the available irrigation water stream

Transpiration Evaporation of water from the stomata of plants

Water application efficiency Ratio of the average depth of irrigation water stored in the root zone to the average depth of irrigation water applied

Water stress Condition of subnormal plant growth caused by the root's inability to extract soil water at an adequate rate

Water use efficiency Ratio of crop dry matter produced, per unit of land area, to the total evapotranspiration from the area

Irrigation is defined in dictionaries as the artifical watering of land (as by canals, ditches, pipes, or flooding) to supply moisture for plant growth. Irrigation is used for other purposes as well, some of which will be discussed in this chapter. Thus, another definition might be: The application of water to crops, in excess of naturally occurring precipitation or shallow groundwater, to augment their growth and enhance their environment.

I. Irrigation Purposes

A. Plant Water Needs

In order for agricultural crops to be grown productively, they must be able to obtain water from the soil. Individual plants must be able to extract this water roughly in proportion to the rate at which they transpire in response to atmospheric evaporative demand. If water is lacking, plants may wilt and die. If precipitation is too little to maintain soil water levels, even for periods of a few days for some crops and soils, irrigation is needed to prevent stress. [*See* Water: Control and Use.]

B. Other Purposes of Irrigation

Irrigations are often applied to leach salts from the soil, a salinity control measure described in more detail later. The unique thermodynamic properties of water, as it evaporates or freezes, make certain types of irrigation useful for micro-climate control on a field. In hot weather, evaporation of sprinkled water cools heat-sensitive crops. When high value crops are threatened by frost, sprinkled water will freeze on the plant surfaces, releasing heat that protects the vegetation. Sprinkling has been used to keep fruit trees cool during late winter warm spells, so that blossoming is delayed until danger of frost damage is low.

II. Water Supply

Water for irrigation comes from either surface- or groundwater supplies. [*See* Water Resources.]

III. Irrigation Methods

A. Surface Irrigation

Surface irrigation methods are those in which water is made to flow over the soil surface, with a part of the flow infiltrating. Surface irrigation is often called "gravity irrigation," but the latter term is better reserved for irrigation systems that rely on gravity to pressurize field pipelines. Gravity systems can thus include sprinkler or micro-irrigation, as well as surface irrigation.

Engineers, in analyzing surface irrigations, often refer to an advance phase, the flow of irrigation streams from the point of inflow to the far field boundary; the ponding phase, during which the entire field surface is inundated; and the recession phase, extending from the time inflow is stopped until infiltration and runoff cause free water to disappear from the field surface.

Assuming that infiltration conditions are everywhere the same on the field surface (an assumption that is seldom valid), irrigation will be uniform if the intake opportunity time is the same at every point on the field. That is, all parts of the field surface should be inundated for the same length of time. Considering the phases defined in the previous paragraph, intake time will be everywhere equal if the advance and recession phenomena take place at the same rate. Because recession, at least in furrows, is often faster than advance, another way to approach uniform irrigation application is to make the advance phase as short as possible relative to the ponding phase. Surface irrigations will be acceptably uniform if advance takes place in 20 to 25% of the time of ponding. The ratio can be improved by increasing the flow rate onto the field, to speed advance; or to decrease the field length, so a given stream size will complete advance in a shorter time.

Furrow irrigation is a common method of surface irrigation, used with row crops. It is named for the channels that are created parallel to and between crop rows to contain the irrigation streams. Thus, inundation, and infiltration, is confined to a fraction of the soil surface between crop rows. There is little plant impedance to advance of irrigation streams across a field; the seed bed is not inundated, minimizing crusting that might hamper plant emergence; the vegetation is not wetted, an advantage for disease prevention; and irrigation can be limited to every other furrow, speeding watering of a field when water supply is limited. Furrows usually run in the direction of greatest field slope. To irrigate, water is introduced to each furrow, usually by siphon tubes from field ditches or from gated pipe (lightweight aluminum or plastic pipe carrying flow at low pressure, and fitted with adjustable outlets or "gates" at spacing equivalent to the furrow intervals.)

Border irrigation is a surface irrigation method for close growing crops such as small grains, hay, or pasture crops. A field is divided by parallel soil ridges running in direction of greatest slope. Ridges may be on the order of 10 to 20 cm high and spaced at intervals of 5 to 20 m. Spacing should depend on size of irrigation stream, but should also allow easy operation of cultural and harvesting equipment such as, say, hay swathers. Large irrigation streams are introduced at one or more points at the upstream end of each border, by siphon tubes or special water control structures. The stream spreads across the width of border and flows toward the downslope end. Good efficiency is often obtained if inflow is terminated when stream advance has reached about three-fourths to four-fifths the length of the border. The surface flow continues until the entire border length has been covered for an adequate intake opportunity time.

Level or low gradient basin irrigation can be a very efficient surface irrigation method under suitable site conditions. A basin is a field, or portion of field, that has been leveled so as to have no slope, either transverse or longitudinal. Very large streams of water are introduced at one or more points at the perimeter of the basin. The large streams cover the basin surface rapidly, then infiltrate over whatever time is necessary, sometimes long after water inflow has been terminated. Level basins are suited to soils with medium infiltration capacities. Natural land slope must be small, so that too much soil will not have to be moved in levelling and so that unproductive subsoils will not be exposed. Row crops can be grown, either flooded or irrigated by level furrows within the basins.

Wild flooding is a term for surface irrigation methods that use a minimum of land preparation and water control. An example is the irrigation of mountain meadows in the western United States. In these areas water is usually plentiful. Shallow, rocky soils prevent land shaping to form a surface over which water can be distributed uniformly. Value of the crop produced is low and does not justify much expenditure for irrigator's time or physical improvements. Water is turned out at multiple points along unlined ditches and allowed to flow as it will over the soil surface. If water distribution turns out to be somewhat uniform, it is a tribute to the art and experience of the irrigator.

B. Sprinkler Irrigation

Sprinkler irrigation generally involves distribution of pressurized water from pipelines, through devices (sprinkler heads) that cause the water to be sprayed through the air to the soil surface. Sprinkler systems allow greater control of rate and uniformity of water application than most surface methods and therefore can be expected to use water more efficiently. Although sprinkler systems have the potential for efficient water use, they must be well designed and managed if the benefits are to be realized. Plant nutrients and some pesticides can be injected into irrigation water and applied effectively through well designed and managed sprinkler systems. Systems can be classified as set or moving—examples of each are described below and illustrated in Fig. 1.

1. Set Systems

A set sprinkler system is one in which the heads are not moving while they are in operation. In a hand move system, pressurized water is distributed through a network of pipes, usually aluminum, 5 to 15 cm in diameter and 6 to 10 m in length. The pipes are fitted with quick couplers so they can be easily connected and disconnected. Sprinkler heads are mounted in a regular grid on pipe risers from the aluminum pipes. Typically, the network is laid in place, pressurized with water, and allowed to irrigate one portion of the field (a set) until the necessary depth of water has been applied. Water is then turned off and the system is moved, one piece at a time, to the next set, where the process is repeated. The system is called "solid set" if there are enough sprinklers and piping to serve an entire field for multiple irrigations without being moved. Set systems are sometimes used only for seed germination under difficult soil or climate conditions. Surface or micro-irrigation is then used for the remainder of the growing season.

Side roll and tow line systems (Fig. 1) are mechanized variations of set systems. In a side roll, sprinkler heads are mounted on a lateral pipe that also serves as the axle running through the centers of a series of wheels 1 to 2 m in diameter. After the irrigation of one set, the system is dewatered and rolled, parallel to itself, to the next set. The tow line has small wheels or skids at intervals along each lateral so a tractor can be used to tow the lateral from one set to the next.

"Guns" or "big guns" are large sprinkler heads that operate at high pressures and discharge high flow rates. A single gun irrigates a relatively large area and can be moved from set to set manually or mechanically.

2. Moving Systems

The center pivot is a moving sprinkler system, first marketed in the 1950s, and is by far the most common, even in the 1990s. The name derives from the circular movement of the sprinkler lateral about a pivot point in the center of the field being irrigated. Water is supplied under pressure to the lateral through special piping at the pivot. The lateral is carried by wheeled "towers" spaced at 30 to 60 m, at a height sufficient to clear most agricultural crops. Tower wheels on the early center pivots were rotated by a rachet mechanism, activated by hydraulic cylinders driven by the pressurized irrigation water. At present most center pivots use electric motors and gear reduction drive trains to propel each tower. Sprinkler heads, spray heads, or other emitters on the lateral discharge water at a constant rate. The effective rate of application on the soil surface is then controlled by the speed of rotation of the lateral about the pivot. Commonly, the operator controls this speed by setting the ratio of on/off time of the motor on the outermost tower. Mechanisms start or stop intermediate towers to keep the lateral in alignment.

Center pivot laterals can be designed for many field shapes, by varying lateral length or by operating through less than a full circle. The most common "pivot" is 400 m long and waters a circular area of 50 ha within a 65 ha square field, a quarter-section.

Since the outer portion of the center pivot lateral moves faster than the inner portion, rate of discharge per length of lateral must increase continuously from the inner to the outer portion, if application rate is to be radially uniform. This is controlled by increasing size of orifices in emitters or by spacing emitters more closely as radius increases. Computer programs are available to calculate size and spacing of emitters for given lateral lengths and water supply rates, to produce uniform water applications.

To avoid the unirrigated field corners that result from applying center pivots to square fields, "corner systems" have been developed. A corner system consists of an extension (swing boom) to the lateral that folds back and ceases discharge when field radius is short. The swing boom extends and begins to discharge water when a longer irrigated radius is needed. Sophisticated electronic guidance systems direct the

Linear move

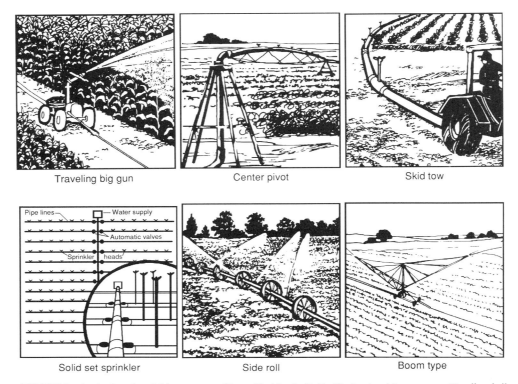

Traveling big gun | Center pivot | Skid tow

Solid set sprinkler | Side roll | Boom type

FIGURE 1 Agricultural sprinkler systems. (From Fischbach, P. E., "Irrigation Management Handbook." Biosystems Engineering Dept., University of Nebraska, Lincoln.)

corner systems around farm buildings or other obstacles.

As methods have been developed to supply water under pressure to a moving sprinkler lateral, attachment to a pivot is no longer necessary. Linear move sprinklers consist of laterals supported by center-pivot-like towers. All towers move at the same speed, however, so the lateral moves parallel to itself while irrigating a rectangular field area. Water supply can be pumped from an open ditch along the lateral's path by a pump and power unit mounted on the sprinkler system, it can be supplied by flexible hose, or it can

be obtained from a series of valved pipeline outlets that the linear system locates, attaches to, opens, then releases after it has attached to the next.

"Travelers" are an adaptation of the big gun sprinklers described earlier. The guns are mounted on a wheeled carriage that is towed slowly across a field, by a cable or by the hose that supplies water. The water supply hose can be flexible or rigid and connects the sprinkler to a pressurized supply. Boom-type sprinklers are similar; a long boom with spray heads substitutes for the big gun. Application rates are high with high volume sprinklers, and the soil's infiltration capacity must also be high if the applied water is to infiltrate as intended and not run off the field surface.

C. Micro-irrigation

Micro-irrigation is a term encompassing several irrigation methods that have been developed since World War II. They have in common the distribution of water under low pressure in plastic tubing. Micro-irrigation methods include drip or trickle (synonymous terms), subsurface irrigation, and mist, spray, or bubbler irrigation.

Surface drip irrigation systems distribute water to the point on the field where it is to be applied to the soil. The water is then discharged through emitters at rates such that it infiltrates immediately. There is no ponding or redistribution of water on the soil surface. Drip systems can be easily automated, allowing small, frequent applications. Nutrients, and sometimes pesticides, can be added to and applied with the water. Disadvantages are expense and maintenance of the network of plastic tubing that distributes the water to each of the emission points, which have to be within a few centimeters of every plant. Commonly one or more drip irrigation laterals will be supplied for every row of trees in an orchard, one for each row in a vineyard, and perhaps one for every one or two rows of specialty crops such as melons or tomatoes.

Perforations in plastic tubing and discrete plastic emitters are two methods that have been developed to dissipate water pressure, such that water drops are released slowly onto the soil and so that the water will be distributed uniformly along drip lines (Fig. 2). The small flow passages in emitters make them subject to clogging by small particles of sediment, organic matter, or chemical precipitates in the water. Thus, drip systems often require complex water treatment and filtration facilities upstream of the emission points. Design of emitters that resist clogging is continually improving.

If the drip system is designed and operated to emit water uniformly, infiltration into the soil will be equally uniform and will not be affected by varying soil properties. Nonuniform water application is caused by variations in the hydraulic properties of emitters, as manufactured, by poor design of the distribution network, or by differential clogging of emitters in the field.

Plastic laterals and emitters, similar to those used for surface drip systems, can be buried in the soil root zone to create subsurface irrigation systems. An alternate to laterals with discrete emitters are those with porous walls, so that pressurized water will ooze through the tubing. Laterals are buried at depths of 5 to 45 cm below the soil surface and emit water directly into the soil. Some subsurface irrigation laterals are placed so as to not be damaged when fields are harvested. Thus, they do not have to be replaced after replanting. A disadvantage of subsurface irrigation is that clogging of buried emitters is difficult to detect and remedy.

Micro-irrigation sprayers or misters have larger flow passages than drip emitters. They operate at slightly higher pressures and discharge water in small droplets over a radius of 1 or 2 m. They are used more for shrubs and ornamentals than for agricultural crops, although sprayers have application in orchards. Bubbler irrigation systems discharge water at low pressures, but relatively high rates. Water then tends to pond on the soil surface, but the ponds can be confined to small basins near the plant to be watered. Bubbler irrigation has been used for orchards and for ornamental plantings.

D. Recent Developments

The LEPA system, an acronym for Low Energy Precision Application, is based on a modification of linear move or center pivot sprinkler systems. Instead of emitting the water through sprinkler heads, the moving lateral is fitted with "drop tubes" at close spacing. An emitter at the end of each drop tube discharges water a few centimeters above the soil surface, at low pressure. Energy requirements are less than for most other center pivot or linear move systems, because of the low pressure discharge. Because instantaneous discharge rates are greater than the infiltration capacity of most soils, small basins, a meter or two long and one row width wide, may be created on the soil surface to hold the irrigation water until it infiltrates. Such basins may also retain precipitation that would otherwise run off the field. Recent LEPA developments include emitters that can discharge a stream or spray water onto the soil or be adjusted to spray water with injected pesticides onto plant surfaces along the path of each drop tube.

Surge irrigation, patented in 1986 by Utah State University, is a modification of furrow irrigation methods and apparatus. Water is applied intermittently to furrows in surge irrigation, perhaps cycled on and off at intervals from a few minutes to an hour or more. In traditional furrow irrigation, by contrast, a stream is applied continuously for several hours.

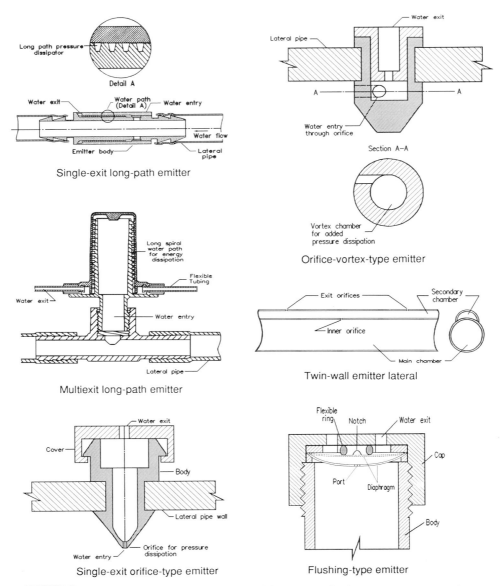

FIGURE 2 Drip irrigation emitters. (From "Trickle Irrigation," Chapter 7, Section 15 of SCS-USDA National Engineering Handbook.)

On many soils, a given volume of water, applied in surges, causes the stream to advance down the furrow faster than if applied continuously. The rapid advance helps obtain uniform infiltration times along the furrow. Several types of apparatus are commercially available to automate surge applications, usually by switching an irrigation stream alternately between two sections of gated pipe.

Subirrigation was one of the early irrigation methods in the United States. It was used in areas where shallow groundwater occurred naturally or where topography and slowly permeable soil layers were such that water seeping from unlined ditches would create perched water tables shallow enough that plant roots could draw water from the capillary fringe. A recent variation is a system referred to as controlled drainage, integrated subsurface drainage/irrigation, or water table management. Used in the more humid, central and eastern parts of the United States, controlled drainage uses ditches and control structures to drain shallow groundwater if levels get high enough to restrict crop growth. During periods of inadequate precipitation, water is ponded in the ditches and seeps from them to raise levels of shallow groundwater, so it will be available to the plant roots. Computer simulations of the water depths and flow patterns allow rational design of the systems. Development is progressing to allow prediction of crop needs and weather so the control structures can be operated to provide nearly constant water table levels during a cropping season.

IV. Selection of Irrigation Method

A. Crop

Most crops can be irrigated by any of the common irrigation methods. Furrow irrigation is used almost exclusively for row crops while border irrigation is used more commonly for close growing crops such as hay or small grains. Beans may be susceptible to disease if the foliage is wet frequently by sprinklers. "Paddy rice," little grown in the United States, is kept inundated during much of its growth cycle, as a method of weed control. Only level basin irrigation can maintain the inundation with acceptable efficiency.

The expense of micro-irrigation systems is most easily justified for high value crops where individual plants are not closely spaced, such as orchards or vineyards. Side-roll sprinklers cannot be moved over tall crops and are most often used on hay, small grains, and low-growing row crops. Permanent sprinkler systems, rather than movable, are used for climate control and in vineyards and orchards.

B. Soil

1. Infiltration

Sprinkler systems, especially center pivot and big guns, are generally suited for soils with high infiltration capacities, so that all applied water is absorbed and there is no runoff. Surface systems, on the other hand, are appropriate for low to moderate intake soils where the stream can complete its advance before excessive infiltration occurs near where water is introduced.

2. Water Holding Capacity

Shallow soils, coarse-textured soils, or crops with shallow root systems may not be able to take advantage of large depths of water applied in a single irrigation. Few surface irrigation systems can apply water

depths of less than about 5 cm practically and efficiently, so sprinkler or micro-irrigation methods are more apt to be appropriate. Because depth of each application is small, the time interval between irrigations must be short if crop water stress is to be prevented. Thus, automated systems are desirable, to eliminate the need for frequent, manual irrigations.

3. Topography

Surface irrigated fields must have a continuous, and preferably uniform, slope from the edge where water is introduced to the downstream end of the field. Very few fields have natural topography conducive to efficient surface irrigation, but many can be made to irrigate well after soil is moved, to create a plane surface. For level basins, unless the initial field slope is very small, considerable volumes of earth may have to be moved to create a surface that is both plane and level. If the cost of moving earth is too great, or if subsurface materials would be exposed that cannot be restored to fertility or otherwise farmed, level basin irrigation methods may not be practical. Erosion can be excessive with surface irrigation on high slopes or erodible soils. Such lands are often suitable for sprinkler systems, if water can be applied at rates that are lower than the soil's infiltration capacity. In the most extreme cases of severe topography and/or low infiltration capacities, some type of micro-irrigation system can usually be designed that will apply water effectively.

Sprinkler systems are suitable for most agricultural lands, except those with low infiltration capacities such that water cannot be applied slowly enough to prevent runoff. On rolling topography, special valving can be provided to compensate for the pressure differences caused by different elevations of sprinkler heads, and thus prevent nonuniform discharges.

V. Management

A. Plant, Soil, Water Relations

The primary purpose of irrigation is to maintain favorable soil water conditions, so that crop growth and production are not restricted. For most agricultural crops, soil water should be kept at high enough levels that plant roots can readily extract it. The soil should not be saturated for prolonged periods, because the roots also need oxygen. Irrigation is managed by determining the water holding capacity of the soil on the field in question, then maintaining water levels within a certain range that depends on that capacity. [*See* SOIL–WATER RELATIONSHIPS.]

The traditional rule of thumb of irrigation management is to maintain soil water levels so that no more than 50% of the water contained between wilting point and field capacity is extracted. The percentage may vary, depending on the sensitivity of the particular crop to water stress.

1. Salinity

All sources of water in nature contain at least small amounts of dissolved salts. Rainfall is, of course, relatively pure. Melting snow packs also furnish good quality water. Streams in the Rocky Mountains may have dissolved solids content, in the spring, on the order of 50 parts per million—very high quality. Groundwaters, on the other hand, often contain minerals that were dissolved as the water percolated through geologic formations. Lower reaches of streams that have collected return flows from one or more irrigation projects, or municipal or industrial users, may contain dissolved solids levels equal to or greater than the recommended limits for human drinking water, 500 ppm.

Evapotranspiration (ET) from irrigated fields removes pure water but leaves salts behind, mostly in the soil and to a lesser extent in the vegetation. If salts accumulate in the soil over a period of months or years, the osmotic pressure of the soil solution can increase enough to restrict plant extraction of water. Effects on the crop are very similar to stresses resulting from low soil water levels. In addition, certain ions, such as those of chlorine and boron, if concentrated enough, may be directly toxic to plants. [*See* IRRIGATION ENGINEERING, EVAPOTRANSPIRATION.]

Good irrigation management can help prevent salt-caused stresses on irrigated crops. If water can drain from the root zone, either naturally or through installed drainage systems, extra irrigation water can be applied to dissolve and transport salts from the root zone in a process known as leaching. Soil may be leached by applying more water than is needed to restore the root zone to field capacity at each irrigation or by special irrigations for leaching before or after the main irrigation season. To maintain a balance of salt in the soil (no long-term increases or decreases), the ratio of the leaching depth to the total infiltrated irrigation and precipitation amounts must equal the ratio of the weighted salt concentration of irrigation water and precipitation to the salt content of the soil water that drains below the root zone. [*See* SOIL DRAINAGE.]

In humid regions, where irrigation water tends to be of good quality, seasonal irrigation applications are small, and precipitation naturally causes leaching, leaching by irrigation may not be necessary. [*See* IRRIGATION IN HUMID REGIONS.]

2. Sodicity

Sodium ions in the soil solution cause clay particles to disperse, decreasing pore volume, and causing infiltration capacity of a soil to decrease dramatically. As the concentration of calcium or magnesium ions increases, the effect of the sodium ions diminishes. A sodic soil, one with a high sodium content, can be difficult to reclaim because the lowered infiltration capacity makes it hard to introduce adequate quantities of leaching water containing beneficial ions. On new irrigation projects, the water quality should be examined carefully, relative to soil characteristics, to assure that sodic conditions are not created by irrigation.

3. Soil Swelling and Cracking

Some soils, by virtue of the clay minerals they contain, shrink as their water content decreases, and large cracks open. These soils, as a result, have high initial infiltration capacities. As the soil wets, the clays expand and the cracks close, sometimes before the desired volume of water has infiltrated. Depending on the soil, the best management technique may be to irrigate lightly and frequently, so that each irrigation infiltrates before the infiltration capacity drops too low; or it may be to irrigate at large time intervals, when cracks have opened to their maximum, and the irrigation application can infiltrate before cracks close.

4. Surface Sealing

As water drops strike aggregated soil particles, or as water flows over them, the aggregates disperse. Soil particles from the aggregates tend to be carried into pores so that the permeability of a thin surface layer, perhaps a few millimeters thick, is reduced. The layer of reduced permeability controls infiltration capacity for the soil as a whole. Large water drops from sprinklers have high impact energy when they hit the soil surface and soil surface sealing is especially severe. Surface sealing can be managed by using sprinklers with reduced drop energy, by providing mulch or vegetative cover that dissipates energy of drops before they reach the soil, or by maintaining high soil organic matter content, which tends to increase the strength with which the soil aggregates resist dispersion.

B. Irrigation Requirement

The irrigation requirement for a crop, in a given area, is the seasonal total ET, reduced by the amount of water that precipitation and shallow groundwater can be expected to provide, and adjusted upward according to the efficiency with which irrigations can be applied. For a project of multiple farms, the irrigation requirement is an area-weighted average for all crops expected to be planted and irrigated.

C. Irrigation Scheduling

Irrigation scheduling is a management practice by which proper time and amount of an irrigation are predicted far enough in advance so that water can be applied to minimize crop stress and maximize water use effectiveness. Many techniques are used for irrigation scheduling, the simplest being the intuition and experience of irrigators, perhaps triggered by changes in crop or soil appearance. A more exacting irrigator may take samples of soil from representative locations in a field and determine its water content by "feel." Irrigations may be scheduled on a more scientific basis by using direct or indirect measurements of plant or soil water content, predetermined relations between daily weather variables and plant water use, or remotely sensed plant canopy temperatures, among others.

A limitation of soil- and plant-based water status measurements for irrigation scheduling is the difficulty in projecting status at the time of measurement to that at the time irrigation will be required. To predict need for irrigations, the measurements may have to be taken at 2- or 3-day intervals, and the trends extrapolated to indicate the desired day of irrigation. A second limitation is the difficulty of selecting one, or a few, plants or soil sampling sites that represent the entire field.

D. Coordination of Irrigation with Farming Systems

Irrigation management involves more than just applying water at proper depths and intervals to prevent plant stress. The grower must also schedule irrigations to avoid those moisture-related conditions that would encourage proliferation of damaging fungi, disease, or insects. Field soils need to be dry enough to allow equipment operation when cultivation, hay cutting, or other cultural operations are necessary. Nutrients and pesticides are increasingly being applied to plants and soils by injection into and distribution with irrigation water, especially with pressurized irrigation. Such applications complicate management, because they need to be made (1) when both the chemical and the water can be used by the crop and (2) so as to minimize detrimental environmental effects.

Soon after applications of soluble nutrients or pesticides, irrigation should be avoided or controlled carefully to prevent leaching of the chemicals below the root zone. Such leaching represents the loss of a costly input and may contaminate groundwater.

VI. Effectiveness of Water Use

A. Application and Water-Use Efficiencies

Water application efficiency is a useful parameter for comparing two irrigation methods or for comparing effects of different management techniques on a given field. It is not the only important measure of irrigation effectiveness. The extent to which root zone soil moisture is replaced by a given irrigation, uniformity of application, the fraction of applied water that runs off the field surface and the fraction that percolates below the root zone can all be quantified to aid in evaluating and improving irrigation technqiues.

Water application efficiencies commonly range from 40 to 85%. Many people, seeing these values, think that much of the applied water is being wasted. This is not necessarily so. If deep percolation or runoff from a given field is not available for any other beneficial use, it is indeed wasted. More commonly, however, surface runoff returns to streams, from which it is diverted by downstream users. In some river systems in the western United States, such return flows are "reused" several times. Surface runoff may be reused on the same farm or even the same field, by pumping collected runoff back to the point of application. Water percolating below the root zone of a field often recharges groundwater aquifers, from which it can be pumped.

Low water application efficiencies are of concern when the water comes from a nonrenewable water supply—perhaps an aquifer that is being mined. They indicate a more rapid depletion of the supply than might be necessary. Also runoff and deep-percolated water, the causes of low efficiencies, are almost always of poorer quality than the water applied, as a result of sediments or dissolved solids picked up from the soil. Water use efficiency is a useful parameter for comparing different management techniques for a given crop on a given site.

VII. Economic Importance

Farmers would not irrigate if they did not expect economic returns. Although the capital costs of irrigations systems are often high, and labor, water, and energy costs may be significant annual expenses, irrigation must provide a net economic return. Irrigation helps to stabilize farm income. Crop failures that might result from water stress are prevented. Knowing that crop production will not be limited by water stress also helps the grower justify expenditures for improved seed, fertilizer, and pest control.

Irrigation has economic importance on a scale larger than that of the individual irrigator. In 1987, farms with some irrigated land totaled 25% of the agricultural land in the United States, but produced 51% of crop sales and 33% of total agricultural sales. Crop sales from farms having even a fraction of land irrigated totaled $30 billion. Total value of irrigation in any region is even greater because of livestock that are fed irrigated crops and the economic multiplier effect that considers benefits to those businesses that supply irrigated farms and pack, ship, and market their products.

Bibliography

Hoffman, G. J., Howell, T. A., and Solomon, K. H. (eds.) (1990). "Management of Farm Irrigation Systems." The American Society of Agricultural Engineers, St. Joseph, MI.

International Commission on Irrigation and Drainage (1967). "Multilingual Technical Dictionary on Irrigation and Drainage." New Delhi, India.

Jensen, M. E., Burman, R. D., and Allen, R. G. (eds.) (1990). "Evapotranspiration and Irrigation Water Requirements." The American Society of Civil Engineers Manual on Engineering Practice No. 70. New York, NY.

Rydzewski, J. R., and Ward, C. F. (eds.) (1989). "Irrigation Theory and Practice." Proceeding of an International Conference at the University of Southampton. Pentech Press, London, England.

Stewart, B. A., and Nielsen, D. R. (eds.) (1990). "Irrigation of Agricultural Crops." American Society of Agronomy Monograph # 30. Madison, WI.

Tanji, K. K. (ed.) (1990). "Agricultural Salinity Assessment and Management." The American Society of Civil Engineers Manual on Engineering Practice No. 71. New York, NY.

Irrigation in Humid Regions

JOE T. RITCHIE, *Michigan State University*

I. Introduction
II. Humid Regions
III. Use of Irrigation in Humid Regions
IV. Conclusion

Glossary

Evapotranspiration Quantity of water used in the combined processes of evaporation from plants (transpiration) and soils (evaporation) for a unit of time, usually 24 hr; potential evapotranspiration (PET) is the maximum evapotranspiration rate possible from freely evaporating surfaces and is expressed in depth of water; typical humid region summertime PET value is 4 mm/day; the PET is calculated from equations using weather data elements of solar radiation, temperature, and, in some cases, wind and vapor pressure deficits

Plant extractable soil water Quantity of water stored in the soil that can be extracted by plant roots; expressed in depth of water (mm) and useful in evaluating how long plants can grow in an initially wet soil before needing irrigation; the potentially extractable soil water is the extractable water for the maximum anticipated rooting depth when the soil is wet to maximum capacity to hold water without rapid drainage; soils in humid regions with low extractable water values of about 40 to 90 mm will need irrigation more than soils with higher values to prevent plant water deficits

Irrigation system Equipment needed to supply and distribute water on a field; distribution can be done by sprinkling, using below ground tubes, surface application, or slow dripping

Irrigation scheduling Determination of when to irrigate a crop during a drying cycle between rainfalls or irrigation. When proper scheduling is practiced, irrigation water is usually conserved; scheduling is done by computing the water balance in the soil, taking account of water inputs (irrigation and rainfall) and outputs (evapotranspiration, drainage, and runoff); usually provides farmers with advance notice of the probable date to irrigate if there is no rainfall; sometimes takes into account a short-term weather forecast

Water use efficiency Ratio of the volume or mass of water used per unit plant biomass growth or the total water used in producing the biomass or economic yield of a crop; water use efficiency of 2.5 g of corn grain yield per kilogram (liter) of evapotranspiration is typical, but the value varies with the climate and yield levels of the crop; is usually higher in humid than in arid regions

Radiation use efficiency Ratio of the mass of biomass produced by plants per unit of light energy intercepted; provides a reasonable approximation for daily or weekly net photosynthesis values; typical values are about 3.5 MJ per gram of plant dry matter growth of plants like corn and 2.5 for plants with less efficient photosynthetic systems like wheat and soybeans; for radiation, use efficiency calculations are expressed as photosynthetically active radiation, which is about half the incoming solar radiation

Net revenue The price of the harvested yield of a crop minus the production costs associated with the irrigation (equipment, interest, fuel, operation) have to be considered; fixed costs that would be the same for irrigated or rainfed crops are not needed although they are important for determining final profitability

Leaching Process of movement of water soluble chemicals out of (below) the soil root zone with the water that drains out of the soil; in humid climates, this leached material (usually nitrates and small amounts of some pesticides) will slowly drain into groundwater, causing possible contamination of the water if the concentrations reach critical levels

Irrigation in humid climates usually enhances crop yield as a supplement to natural rainfall. However, several factors are important for successful and profitable irrigation systems. Variations in climate, soils, topography, and reliable water supplies can determine the feasibility of an irrigation system. Determining the water use efficiency and evapotranspiration rates of the plants and assessing the plant water available in the soil are important when managing and selecting the system.

Crops that provide food, feed, and fiber for the world population require a relatively large supply of water for adequate productivity. Crop yields in humid climates are usually enhanced through the use of irrigation to supplement the natural rainfall, but several factors must be taken into account to assess its value. Irrigation is growing rapidly in many humid regions and will likely continue to grow because of the gradual decline of irrigation in arid regions. In arid regions the demand for water supplies by nonagricultural users is increasing and large irrigated land areas are vulnerable to being lost because of salinization. If policies and economic conditions are suitable, irrigation in humid climates not traditionally irrigated will play an increasingly important role in strategies for raising and stabilizing world food production.

I. Introduction

The belief that humid regions have adequate water for rainfed agriculture comes from the assumption that the annual rainfall provides sufficient water for the plants to grow, given evaporation is occurring. The problem with this assumption is that it does not consider the temporal distribution of rainfall and that large amounts of the water will not stay in the soil long enough to be used by plants. [See SOIL DRAINAGE.]

In temperate climates, the warm season—when crops are growing optimally—usually is characterized by higher than average evaporation rates and lower than average rainfall. Many of the larger rainfall amounts occur when storms produce runoff from the soil, decreasing water infiltration into the soil. When rainfall enters wet soil, large amounts of the water will drain into the subsoil at depths out of reach of plant roots. In most humid regions, water that moves rapidly through the soil will ultimately reach the groundwater. The unpredictable distribution of natural water supplies for rainfed

crops often causes plant water deficits and may be a major factor influencing farm decisions such as selection of the crop species and variety, planting date, plant density, fertilizer amounts, and pest control strategies.

In tropical climates characterized by wet and dry seasons, most crop growth occurs during and immediately following the wet season. During this time the rain will provide most of the water needed to support plant growth. The wet season is also influenced by the same rainfall distribution problems facing temperate humid climates, creating a potential plant water deficit during some part of the growing season. Consequently, crop production in the humid environments of temperate and tropical regions can often benefit from irrigation as a supplemental supply of water for crops.

II. Humid Regions

A humid climate is characterized by having an average annual precipitation of 102 cm, and for the 48 contiguous United States this area includes most of the land east of the Great Plains or approximately the area east of a line bounded by the Minnesota and Wisconsin border in the North to the Texas and Louisiana border in the South. There is a small humid region in the Northwest that includes the western third of Washington and Oregon and a small part of northern California. These areas are characterized by a higher relative humidity, especially during the warm season, and more cloudy days than occur in arid regions. Humid climates often have lower quality soils with several special problems, but the water supply from rainfall is usually adequate for irrigation if properly protected and conserved.

The transition from the humid East to the arid West is a gradual continuum in several elements of the climate. Figure 1 depicts the variations in climates at several locations (Table I) during June, July, and August from east of the Rocky Mountains. Cloudiness causes reduced solar radiation, higher relative humidity (smaller vapor pressure deficits), and lower potential evapotranspiration in humid regions. The 3-month total rainfall minus potential evapotranspiration varies from about zero near the Atlantic Coast to a deficit of about 200 mm near the eastern edge of the Great Plains. To obtain optimum crop productivity, the water supply for this deficiency can come from water stored in the soil before the active crop growing season as well as from irrigation.

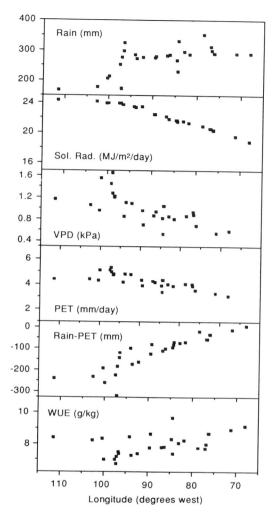

FIGURE 1 Several aspects of the climate and other factors related water supply and demand at various longitudes of the eastern United States during June, July, and August. The locations of the sites used for the graphs are given in Table I.

A. Potential Crop Productivity

The maximum rate of plant growth is larger for most arid climates than that for humid climates because the greater solar radiation provides more light energy for plant photosynthesis. However, the evapotranspiration rates are higher in the arid climates because of the higher radiation and vapor pressure deficit. An index used by agronomists and agricultural climatologists to compare growth and evapotranspiration is water use efficiency. This efficiency index is the ratio of plant growth rates to evapotranspiration rates. The economic yield and total water used by the crop is also a useful water use efficiency concept. [*See* IRRIGATION ENGINEERING, EVAPOTRANSPIRATION.]

Water use efficiency for corn production in the United States can be demonstrated by contrasting climates. A corn yield of about 12 Mg/ha is a relatively common observation for optimum soil water and fertility conditions in the humid Indiana and arid California environments. The crops use about 440 and 600 mm of water, respectively, in evapotranspiration. Conversion of the total season evapotranspiration into an equivalent mass of water, the water use efficiency for these examples is 2.7 and 2.0 g of grain per kilogram of water used for the two climate regions or about a 30% increase in efficiency in the humid region.

To provide a comparison of water use efficiency across the spectrum of climate conditions in the eastern United States, a concept of radiation use efficiency can provide useful insights into this important concept. This efficiency index expresses the mass of crop dry matter produced per unit of radiation intercepted.

TABLE I

A Listing of the Sites and Their Corresponding Longitude and Latitude Used for the Climate and Irrigation Analysis for Fig. 1

City/State	Longitude	Latitude
Little Rock, AR	92.3	34.8
Washington, DC	77.0	39.0
Griffin, GA	84.3	33.3
Springfield, IL	89.6	39.7
Indianapolis, IN	86.2	39.7
Dodge City, KS	100.0	37.5
Manhattan, KS	96.6	39.3
Shreveport, LA	93.8	32.5
Caribou, ME	68.0	46.9
Blue Hill, MA	71.2	42.3
Lansing, MI	84.6	42.7
Saulte Ste. Marie, MI	84.4	46.6
St. Cloud, MN	94.2	45.6
Great Falls, MT	111.4	47.5
Lincoln, NE	96.7	40.8
Syracuse, NY	76.2	43.1
Raleigh, NC	78.6	35.6
Bismark, ND	100.4	47.8
Cleveland, OH	81.7	41.5
Columbus, OH	83.0	39.9
Oklahoma City, OK	97.5	35.5
Stillwater, OK	97.1	36.2
Harrisburg, PA	76.8	40.3
Rapid City, SD	102.6	44.1
Nashville, TN	86.8	36.3
Fort Worth, TX	97.2	33.2
Madison, WI	89.4	43.3

Note: The sites were all inland and represent a cross section of the climates across the United States east of the Rocky Mountains.

It has been found to be a relatively reliable and stable means of predicting crop growth rates. Using a radiation use efficiency value of 1.3 g/MJ and assuming all radiation is intercepted by the crop during the months of June, July, and August, the calculated water use efficiencies for the climate conditions given in the upper graphs of Fig. 1 are given in the bottom graph of Fig. 1. The trend toward higher water use efficiency in the humid regions is also true for other crop species.

III. Use of Irrigation in Humid Regions

Irrigation of crops in humid regions increases crop yields most of the time. The irrigation amounts are significantly less than those needed in arid regions because precipitation provides most of the water needed to meet the crop water demand. In contrast to more arid regions, the higher rainfall in humid regions provides a greater supply of water, its quality is higher, and soil salinization is not a problem. However, several economic, technological, and institutional barriers have prevented irrigation from being introduced on a large scale in the humid regions of the United States and other parts of the world. Although investment in irrigation in humid climates is marginally profitable, there has been a notable increase in irrigated land of the eastern United States. Government census information summarized in Fig. 2 depicts the trend of more irrigated land in humid regions and less for arid regions of the 48 contiguous states. If the trends of the past 15 years continue, the eastern United States will have as much land under irrigation as the

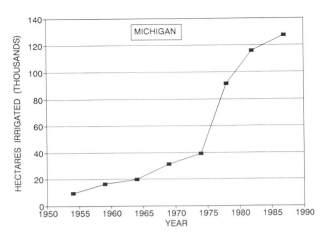

FIGURE 3 Area of irrigated land in Michigan from 1982 until 1987.

western United States within about 50 years. The arid region decline is partly the result of depletion of water from aquifers that are not being recharged. The increasing demand for water supplies for municipal and industrial uses is contributing to the decline in the arid regions.

Trends in irrigated land in Michigan (Fig. 3) show a major increase since the mid 1970s. A major reason for the increase is a rapid expansion of the hybrid seed corn industry in the southwestern part of the state. Irrigation helps to ensure a relatively stable seed supply for the industry. Should there be an increase in the price of other field crops that occupy large land areas, there could be a larger increase in irrigation in humid states like Michigan.

A. Crop Yield Improvement

Significant yield increases of field crops almost always result from irrigation in humid regions. In a 21-year comparison of irrigated and rainfed corn yields in Michigan, it was reported that rainfed yields averaging 7.31 Mg/ha were always lower than irrigated yields. The average irrigated yields were 3.92 Mg/ha higher than the rainfed yields. The yield increases for the irrigated trials ranged from 0.69 to 10.39 Mg/ha, demonstrating the possible differences in rainfall amount and distribution between years. A similar study in the Southeast revealed that irrigated corn yields increased by a range of 1.44 to 4.70 Mg/ha. Another location in the Southeast reported that soybean yield increases ranged from 0.31 to 0.81 Mg/ha, with the optimum yield increases occurring from

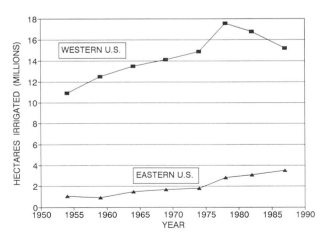

FIGURE 2 Area of irrigated land in the contiguous United States from 1982 until 1987.

irrigation applied at the bloom stage of plant development.

B. Sources of Irrigation Water

The most important requirement of an irrigation system is that it must have a reliable water supply. Water for irrigation may be drawn from surface supplies such as rivers, lakes, streams, and ponds or reservoirs developed for agricultural use, but in some areas lowering aquifer levels that do not recharge annually will limit future water availability for irrigation. This is not a widespread problem in humid regions as much as it is in the Great Plains region. [See WATER RESOURCES.]

C. Types of Irrigation Systems and Their Management

The types of irrigation systems used in arid and humid regions are generally the same, with the size of the system depending upon the crop, topography, field size, and availability of a sufficient water supply. The primary systems used in humid areas of the United States include sprinkler and subirrigation, with the type of system determined by the crop to be irrigated, soil, and land slope. Types of sprinkler systems include center pivot, solid set, linear move, and travelling gun, with center pivot likely to be the most popular because of low costs per hectare and minimum labor requirements. The typical costs of a center pivot system in 1993 is given in the Economic Risks section. Subirrigation systems can include pipes buried just below the tillage zone or irrigation can be done by reversing the flow in drainage pipes. Irrigation by reversing the flow is sometimes referred to as water table management and is becoming popular in several regions where the land is nearly level and the soil has a near impermeable layer below about 100 cm depth. The cost of irrigating by water table management and the energy requirements for pumping water are usually low. A key factor when irrigating with any system is scheduling when water is applied to the crop. Water should be applied when it is needed, and scheduling an irrigation system by computer according to soil type and weather patterns may allow farmers to decrease the overall amount of water applied and lower irrigation costs. [See IRRIGATION ENGINEERING: FARM PRACTICES, METHODS, AND SYSTEMS; WATER: CONTROL AND USE.]

D. Irrigation Amounts and Soil Properties

In humid regions irrigation is a supplement to rainfall. Although water supplies are more abundant in humid regions, it is important to use precipitation as efficiently as possible. The amount of irrigation water required to ensure optimum crop growing conditions primarily depends on the rainfall distribution during the crop growing season and the amount of water plants can extract from the soil before there is a plant water deficit.

Plant roots extract water from soil for use in the transpiration process. Approximations of the effective root depth and in soil water holding capacity are required for determining the time in a drying cycle when irrigation water should be applied. For extraction of water from the soil, roots must grow to within 1 or 2 mm of the soil water. Some of the soil water cannot be extracted because of a large suction caused by the small capillary pores in the soil. The soil water content at this lower limit of extraction is called the wilting point. The pressure potential of the soil water at this degree of dryness is about -1.5 kPa. The water reservoir for root extraction is constantly changing because of root growth into wetter soil regions and drying of the soil where roots already exist.

To evaluate the timing and amount of irrigation, there is an approximate water content above which additional water cannot be held in the soil because the force of gravity is greater than the soil suction. This upper limit of soil water content is often called field capacity. The pressure potential of the soil water at this water content varies with soil type in the range of -0.01 kPa for clay soils to -0.03 kPa for sandy soils. Some soils have poor internal drainage caused by a soil layer with low hydraulic conductivity. When all the pores in poorly drained soils become saturated with water, plant roots will have an extra supply of water because of the lack of drainage. However, soils that are saturated for several continuous days cannot be tilled when needed and the roots of most crop plants will not grow further because of a depleted oxygen supply. These poorly drained soils must be artificially drained to be useful for crop production.

By applying the concepts of root depth and the water content at field capacity and wilting point, the approximate capacity of the soil pores as a reservoir of plant water can be determined. A useful term to describe the apparent capacity of the soil water supply for plants is the potentially extractable soil water (PESW). Most soils considered suitable for crop production have PESW values of about 1.35 mm of water for each 1 cm of effective rooting depth. An exception is sandy soils, which have PESW values between 0.6 and 1.1 mm per centimeter of soil rooting depth. Soils with stones will also have lower PESW values.

Plants growing in soils initially wet to field capacity can go longer without a water deficit during a drying cycle if the PESW is large. The total PESW depends on the effective rooting depth. When annual crop plants reach their maximum rooting depths in a soil, the soil properties influencing rooting depth will influence the PESW values. Rooting in poor soils may be no deeper than 25 to 30 cm in the tillage zone. In good soils, rooting depth may be as much as 200 cm. Thus by using the approximate value of available water as 1.35 mm/cm, the total PESW for soil can vary between 35 and 270 mm.

The effective rooting depth is influenced by the age of a plant and by several physical and chemical soil barriers. A large percentage of the arable soils in the eastern United States has some degree of these barriers. The main physical problem is the existence of rock or compacted zones in the soil that are barriers to optimum root growth. The physical barriers for compacted soils are termed fragipans and tillage pans. The tillage pans are caused by compaction during tillage operations. If these compacted zones are near the surface, deep tillage can help provide a condition for deeper root growth. The deep tillage improvement, however, often lasts only 1 or 2 years.

The principal chemical barrier to root growth is aluminum toxicity. This condition occurs in highly acid soils containing aluminum. Roots will cease growing deeper when they reach this toxic layer. Adding limestone to affected soils helps reduce this problem, but application below 30 cm is often too costly for producers.

Another important factor influencing rooting depth is the lack of oxygen in poorly drained soils that are frequently saturated. Roots of upland crops are sensitive to low oxygen and usually do not extend their new growth to other soil layers. If saturation is likely to occur often, soils of this type need to be artificially drained to allow roots to grow at deeper depths to increase the PESW for times of low rainfall when the soils become dry. The depth of drainage tiles or tubes is usually about 100 cm.

Once rooting depth is known for determining PESW, the timing and number of irrigations can be determined. Only 50 to 70% of the PESW can be extracted by plant roots before the soil dryness will cause a plant water deficiency. Thus for optimum

plant growth, irrigation is required before the roots extract soil water to its lower limit of availability.

The potential evapotranspiration (PET) conditions determine the rate of soil drying. In humid climates PET values are quite diverse because of variable cloudiness. Assuming that an average PET for a humid climate is 4.0 mm per day, a soil initially wet to field capacity with 150 mm of PESW will provide crops with an unlimited supply of water for about 22 days before more rainfall or irrigation is required. For soils initially wet with a variation of 40 and 250 mm PESW, the time of unlimited growth without irrigation is about 6 and 37 days, respectively. This degree of soil variability emphasizes the importance of the soil properties in evaluation of the value of irrigation in humid regions.

In soils that have some restriction of rooting depth, there is usually a high probability that the frequency of rainfall deficits during the growing season will cause some crop growth or yield loss without irrigation. Evaluation of the actual probabilities for irrigation requirements can be done by simulating the soil water balance every day and determining the frequency of times the soil water deficit reaches a level where plants need additional water. The soil water balance can be reasonably simulated when the daily weather variables of solar radiation, temperature, and rainfall are known and when the root depth can be reasonably approximated. Such a water balance is contained in the CERES–Maize crop simulation model for corn. The CERES model simulates the soil water balance, plant growth, and yield. It has been validated in Michigan for both irrigated and rainfed conditions.

Assuming the CERES model is accurate, it is possible to determine some of the required information regarding irrigation needs and risks. Using a 30-year sequence of weather as measured in previous years to represent the probable weather variations in the future, some of the information required for irrigation decisions can be obtained. Weather typical of a site in St. Joseph County, Michigan, provided a simulated record of irrigated and rainfed yield results and irrigation amounts for soils with contrasting PESW values. The irrigation simulations assumed typical conditions for a center pivot sprinkler irrigation system of 25 mm irrigation added each time the water deficit reached the 50% PESW value. The PESW values assumed were 90 and 160 mm, representing relatively low and high water holding capacities. To obtain a cumulative probability distribution of the desired information, yields and irrigation numbers from the

30-year simulation were sorted in ascending order and plotted as a cumulative probability of 1/30.

The simulation revealed that the number of irrigations needed each season (Fig. 4) varied from a low of none for years for the high PESW to 11 (275 mm) for 1 year on the low PESW soil. The average number of irrigations was 4.23 and 5.90 for the two soils, respectively. The predominant number of irrigations needed (60% probability) was in the range of five to seven for the low PESW soil and six to eight for the high PESW soil. Simulated rainfed yields from the lower PESW condition were always lower than the higher PESW condition. With the exception of 1 year, the yields for the irrigated crops were always higher than rainfed crops. The differences in irrigated yields are caused by variations in factors other than the water supply. Variations in the length of the warm season was the primary cause of the year-to-year yield differences.

Most of the eastern United States is likely to have similar variations in year-to-year irrigation amounts as the results shown in Fig. 4. Even for the contrasting soils with the same weather conditions, the variation in the two cumulative probability distributions of irrigation numbers was quite similar, and only the averages changed. The seasonal variation in rainfall for much of the humid United States is similar to that for southwestern Michigan, with only the mean values changing with the location. The mean irrigation requirement for various locations is likely influenced by the soil PESW and the seasonal difference between rainfall and PET. The average irrigation amount for the low PESW soil of Fig. 4 was 148 mm (5.9 irrigation applications of 25 mm). The 3-month average difference between PET and rainfall for two locations shown in Fig. 1 north and south of St. Joseph County, Michigan, was 93 mm (Lansing, MI), and 100 mm (Indianapolis, IN). An approximation of the average amount of irrigation water required for various sites in the United States would be about 50 mm more than the average difference between PET and rainfall for low PESW soils and about 10 mm more for higher PESW soils (Fig. 1).

E. Economic Risks

The question of whether to irrigate in humid regions is a strategic decision that impacts the farm business for many years to come. A strategy is devising plans to reach a goal. When the goal is to improve or reduce variability of net income, the financial impacts should be evaluated before investing in an irrigation system. Since yield increases are almost always possible with irrigation and yield variability is reduced, the price the increase in yields is expected to bring and the costs of the irrigation system are required to project net income generating capacity. In addition to the cost and price information, more intensive management is required with irrigation than with rainfed farming. Yield increases expected for the farm soil type, such as those provided in Fig. 3, provide critical information for the economic evaluation. A price for the increased yield must be assumed along with the annual ownership costs associated with the investment and the increased variable costs due to increased seeding rates, fertilizer, fuel, electricity, and labor.

The principles needed to develop an economic assessment of irrigation systems in humid regions are illustrated by the production of corn in southwestern Michigan with the low and high PESW soils. The irrigation system is a center pivot that will irrigate 52.6 ha (130 acres). The yield information from Fig. 3 and an assumed price of $80.28/Mg ($2.50 per bushel) for grain provides the gross income. The yield

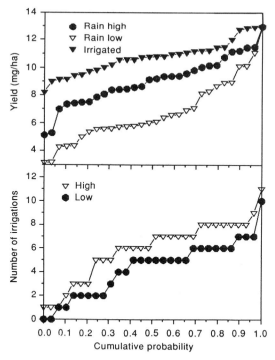

FIGURE 4 The cumulative probability distribution (bottom) of the number of 25-mm irrigations required for optimum corn production in St. Joseph County, Michigan, for a soil with low and high PESW values; and (top) the cumulative probability distribution of rainfed yields for two contrasting soils and for irrigated yields.

dependent costs (transportation and drying) were assumed to be $11.22/Mg. The annual ownership cost for the example is $9470. The ownership cost assumes a 10-year life of the system and a 10% interest rate. The system costs $60,300; 42% of which is the well, pump, and power supply. The distribution system is 58% of the cost. The assumed variable costs (seed, fertilizer, pesticides) for an irrigated system were $18,620 and $15,491 for the rainfed system. These differences are primarily caused by the need for more fertilizer since there will be a greater expected yield and more seeds per hectare are planted. The cost per 25 mm irrigation is $600. Other fixed operational costs are not required for this assessment because they are the same for both irrigated and rainfed conditions.

The net revenue from the 52.6-ha area for irrigated and rainfed conditions of the two soils is depicted as cumulative probabilities in Fig. 4. In this case, if the goal is to maximize net revenue, the goal is best reached with the rainfed crop on high PESW soil. However, for the low PESW soil, the net returns for the irrigated crop are larger only about 50% of the time. The variability of net returns is reduced by irrigation. The bottom of Fig. 5 depicts the revenue

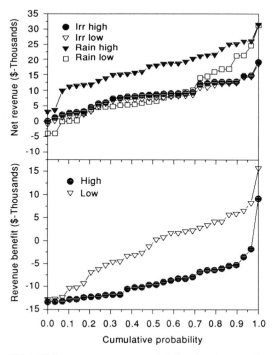

FIGURE 5 The cumulative probability distribution of net revenue for irrigated and rainfed conditions of Fig. 4 (top) and for the revenue benefit (irrigated returns minus rainfed returns) of irrigation (bottom).

benefit (irrigated minus rainfed) from irrigation. Only 1 year in the 30 was an extreme drought year with a revenue benefit for the high PESW soil. The low PESW soil had a benefit half the time. Although the greatest benefit was for the low PESW soil, the net revenue was lower because it required more irrigation. As a scenario to demonstrate the sensitivity of an analysis like this to the price of the crop, if the price for the grain was doubled and the other costs remain the same, the average net revenue for the irrigated crops would increase about $45,000 and about $38,000 and $28,000 for the high and low PESW soils under rainfed conditions.

The yield benefit, prices, and costs for an economic analysis can be obtained from agricultural experiment station trials, validated simulation model results, and farmer experience. Experiment station trials should be used with caution because of the difficulty of extrapolating them from one soil, climate, and management system to another. Simulation results should agree with experimental results and farmer experience. Simulation usually does not take into account pest or other yield reducing factors except for water and nutrients. Farmer experience is very helpful, especially in areas with comparable soils and climate. It provides a reality check of practical management. However, caution should be used because there may not be a valid comparison of irrigated and rainfed yields over several years, as done by experiment stations. Good managers should use a combination of all three sources of information when deciding about investing in an irrigation system for humid regions.

Irrigation may be beneficial to crops, but it also increases the potential for environmental contamination. As environmental concerns increase, this dimension of managing irrigation systems will become more critical. Therefore, the decision to minimize possible contamination of the environment should be linked with the goals of maximizing economic returns. The principal environmental degradation that may increase with irrigation includes nitrate and pesticide leaching into ground water and the runoff of agricultural chemicals and topsoil into surface water. [See GROUND WATER.]

The primary concern about nitrate leaching into ground water is the public health concern. Nitrate poisoning in humans is rare, but there have been reports of infant deaths due to methemoglobinemia, a condition caused by a high nitrate content in drinking water. The U.S. Public Health standard for nitrates in drinking water is 10 parts per million or less. This is a limit well below where any problems with methemoglobinemia have been identified. The concentration of nitrates in several aquifers in humid regions used for public water supplies has been increasing in the past 2 decades, creating concern for the future use of nitrogen fertilizer in those regions.

Leaching occurs when water soluble compounds (such as fertilizer) flow below the root zone with the excess water that drains out of the soil. This happens when the soils become saturated due to heavy or frequent rainfall. In humid regions the drainage is likely to be greatest during spring and autumn if the subsoil does not contain a barrier to downward water flow. For soils that are artificially drained, the equivalent leaching losses will end up in surface water from tile drain outlets.

Irrigation usually ensures that crop yields will not be reduced by water deficits. However, with higher yields, there is a greater demand for fertilizer nutrients. The larger fertilizer applications will temporarily cause higher concentrations of nutrients in the soil before being used by plants. However, leaching losses are usually small during the growing season because there is seldom excess water that is not used in evapotranspiration. The main problem is that any excess nitrates not used by plants after nutrient uptake ceases are vulnerable to leaching losses. These losses are usually greatest in sandy soils or where there is a large annual flow of water through the soil.

To minimize nitrate leaching, fertilizer amounts need to match the plant requirement as close as possible. One method that usually helps minimize nitrate leaching losses and improve nitrate uptake is to apply the fertilizer on two or more occasions during the active nutrient uptake period. For annual crops, one small fertilization is usually beneficial at planting time. The other application can be applied about 2 weeks before anticipated plant deficiencies might occur. These methods are more management intensive, but greatly decrease the probability of leaching from heavy rains that might occur if a single application is applied on or before planting. The multiple or split fertilization procedures are more management intensive and costly, but provide the best way to minimize leaching losses. [See FERTILIZER MANAGEMENT AND TECHNOLOGY.]

Irrigation provides a good possibility for reducing nitrate leaching because yields have less variability in the amount of nutrients required than rainfed crops. For rainfed crops, the weather conditions of the near future are not known, making the nutrient requirements of the crop more uncertain. Farmers who apply larger fertilizer amounts anticipating a good weather year may have greater leaching losses in years when water deficits reduce yield.

On land that is vulnerable to soil erosion and nutrient losses, irrigation can enhance these losses because of the increased use of chemicals needed for crop production. In humid regions of the United States, the most vulnerable time is likely to be in the spring when the chemicals have been applied to the bare soil before being needed by the plants, and chemicals are at a higher concentration. The center pivot sprinkler irrigation systems are more likely to be used on a large field area of marginal land such as steeper slopes. On land with steeper slopes, there may be erosion problems during irrigation application at the end of the distribution pipeline because the application rate may exceed the water infiltration rate. Terracing and use of grassed strips can help overcome this problem in the same way that it does for rainfed systems.

IV. Conclusion

The use of irrigation in humid regions will likely continue to increase as pressure from a growing population increases the need for food production and as the area irrigated in the traditional arid regions declines. The supply of irrigation water from aquifers and surface sources is usually adequate in humid regions and its use, if planned carefully, should not cause great societal or environmental problems. There are large areas in the U.S. humid regions that can be potentially irrigated without causing major problems. When the value of the crops produced is high enough, the introduction of irrigation into a region can greatly enhance the regional economy. If decisions are made to invest in an irrigation system after experiencing a low probability drought year, there is a good chance that the investment will result in financial losses. Therefore it is important to consider carefully the weather, soil type, and management requirements before investing in expensive irrigation systems.

In humid regions there is a long history of nonagricultural water use and a short history of irrigation. In irrigated arid regions, the opposite is usually true. Thus, priority for allocation of water for agricultural use in humid regions is usually low. Development of water supplies in humid regions, unlike the arid regions, is usually left to the individual. Federal policies in the United States have made it possible for tax dollars from humid regions to be expended on water development for irrigation in the arid regions. Even taxes for application of municipal waste water on land in humid regions has been devoted to the clean up of the water rather than viewing it as a source for irrigation water. Thus we should anticipate the need for new government policies as irrigation increases in the humid regions. These policies will likely be related to water supplies for irrigation as well as public health issues. New research will be required to overcome the technological problems unique to humid regions.

Bibliography

Alocilja, E. C., and Ritchie, J. T. (1993). Multicriteria optimization for a sustainable agriculture. *In* "Systems Approaches for Agricultural Development." (F. Penning de Vries, P. Teng, and K. Metselaar, eds.), pp. 381–396. Kluwer Academic, Dordrecht, Netherlands.

Boggess, W. G., and Ritchie, J. T. (1988). Economic and risk analysis of irrigation decisions in humid regions. *J. Prod. Agric.* **1,** 116–122.

Camp, C. R., Sadler, E. J., Sneed, R. E., Hook, J. E., and Ligetvari, F. (1990). Irrigation for humid regions. *In* "Management of Farm Irrigation Systems." (G. J. Hoffman, T. A. Howell, and K. H. Solomon, eds.), pp. 551–578. Am. Soc. of Agric. Engineers, St. Joseph, MI.

Cassel, D. K. (1983). Effects of soil characteristics and tillage practices on water storage and its availability to plant roots. "Crop Reactions to Water and Temperature Stresses in Humid, Temperate Climates." (C. D. Raper, Jr., and P. J. Kramer, eds.), pp. 167–186. Westview Press, Boulder, CO.

1987 Census of Agriculture (1989). "Geographic Area Series, Part 51 United States Summary and State Data," Vol. 1. U.S. Dept. of Commerce. Superin. of Documents, U.S. Govt. Print. Office, Washington, DC.

Hergert, G. W. (1986). Consequences of nitrate in groundwater. Solutions: *J. Fluid Fertil./Ag. Chem. Industry* **30,** 24–31.

Parsch, L. D., Cochran, M. J., Trice, K. L., and Scott, H. D. (1991). Biophysical simulation of wheat and soybean to assess the impact of timeliness on double-cropping economics. *In* Modeling Plant and Soil Systems. Agronomy. (J. Hanks and J. T. Ritchie, eds.) Vol. 31, pp. 5–29. ASA, Madison, WI.

Ratliff, L.F, Ritchie, J. T., and Cassel, D. K. (1983). Field-measured limits of soil water availability as related to laboratory-measured properties. *Soil Sci. Soc. Am. Proc.* **47,** 770–775.

Ritchie, J. T. (1986). The CERES–Maize model. *In* "CERES–Maize: A Simulation Model of Maize Growth and Development," (C. A. Jones and J. R. Kiniry, eds.), pp. 3–6. Texas A&M Univ. Press, College Station, TX.

Ritchie, J. T., and Amato, M. (1990). Field evaluation of plant extractable water for irrigation scheduling. *Acta Horticult.* **11,** 595–615.

Schwab, G., and Black, J. R. (1989). "Irrigation: Economic Considerations You Should Make before Investing." Agricultural Economics Staff Paper 89-35(V3R). Michigan State University.

Skaggs, R. W. (1991). Drainage. *In* "Modeling Plant and Soil Systems." Agronomy. (J. Hanks and J. T. Ritchie, eds.), Vol. 31, pp. 206–243. ASA, Madison, WI.

Sneed, R. E., and Patterson, R. P. (1983). The future role of irrigation in a humid climate. *In* "Crop Reactions to Water and Temperature Stresses in Humid, Temperate Climates." (C. D. Raper, Jr., and P. J. Kramer, eds.), pp. 187–200. Westview Press, Boulder, CO.

Tanner, C. B. (1957). Factors affecting evaporation from plants and soils. *J. Soil Water Conserv.* **12,** 221–227.

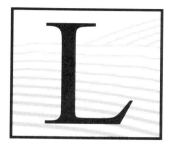

Labor

LEO C. POLOPOLUS, *University of Florida*

Glossary

Annual earnings Total income received from farm and nonfarm work in a calendar year

California Agricultural Labor Relations Act A compromise piece of legislation passed in 1975 by the California state legislature to provide legal boundaries for collective bargaining for farm workers in the state; it provides for secret ballot elections for union representation and an Agricultural Labor Relations Board, but specifically exempts farm labor contractors from employer status

Collective bargaining Involves the determination of wages, hours, and working conditions between employers and an organization of workers; the organization of workers is commonly called a labor union

Farm labor contractors Independent employers of agricultural labor who recruit farm workers and pay these workers for their services; these employers may contract with farmers, intermediaries (bird dogs), processing plants, or packing houses to execute certain prescribed functions of the farming operations

Hired labor Workers paid for hourly work or for work done on a piece rate basis

Hourly wage rate A common method of payment for agricultural tasks performed; farm work is exempt from federal overtime hour provisions of the minimum wage law

Immigration Reform and Control Act Passed in 1986 at the federal level to provide mechanisms for providing special agricultural workers (SAWS), replacement agricultural workers (RAWS), sanctions for employing illegal workers, temporary foreign agricultural workers (H–2A), antidiscrimination provisions, and other objectives

Labor in agriculture The human resource component of the agricultural sector of the economy

Labor demand Derived from the demand for agricultural products; assuming production technology is constant, an increase in the demand for the product increases the demand for agricultural labor

Labor productivity Usually measured in terms of the annual average percentage change of output in relation to man hours of physical work; has achieved dramatic upward growth for several past decades because of the division of agricultural labor and the combination of biological and mechanical innovation in agriculture

Labor supply Relates to the number of persons willing to work in agricultural pursuits for various levels of wage rates; in general, more people are willing to engage in agricultural work as wage rates increase, and vice versa

Migrant labor Workers who leave their permanent place of residence for at least one night are considered migrant agricultural workers; usually intrastate migrants or interstate migrants

Minimum wages The Fair Labor Standards Act of 1935, as amended, established minimum wage rates for agricultural workers that are now identical to minimum wage rates for nonagricultural workers; small farmers with highly seasonal employment patterns may not be required to pay their workers minimum wage rates; the federal minimum wage law also prescribes stringent rules for employing children in agricultural work

Occupational Safety and Health Act (OSHA) A federal program that seeks to assure a safe and healthful working environment for workers; farmers hiring fewer than 11 employees are exempt from OSHA; however, any farm employer may be subject to citation for serious, willful, and repeated violations of OSHA rules

Piece rate A method of payment to agricultural workers based on the number of units (boxes, trees, rows, flats, bushels) harvested or worked; hourly wage rates can be estimated from piece rates if data regarding the number of units worked and the length of time involved are known

Unemployment insurance A federal–state program that provides eligible farm workers with reduced income payments when workers are laid off through no fault of their own; although differences in benefit provisions exist from state to state, unemployment compensation covers essentially all but the small employers; the cost of this program is born by employers, who pay taxes based in large part on their experience rating; although workers do not contribute to the unemployment insurance fund, occasionally unemployed workers are provided "extended" benefits from federal funds

Unpaid family labor Family members who engage in farm work for zero cash remuneration at the time of labor, but may share in the profits of the farm firm, if any, at the end of the season or crop year

Workers compensation Each state usually provides workers coverage for work-related injuries and diseases; costs for these programs generally vary depending on experience rating and the particular language of state laws

In its broadest context, labor in agriculture refers to the human resource component of the agricultural sector of the economy. These "laborers" include hired workers as well as unpaid farm operators and family members. The skill levels in American agriculture vary widely from airplane pilots, biotechnologists, and computer programmers to seasonal hoe hands and fruit and vegetable pickers.

Science and technology have reduced the number of manual laborers utilized for many agricultural operations, although in the past, most farms were too small to develop new technologies on their own. The research and development for agriculture is supported by government research agencies, input suppliers, and industry organizations. Thus, personnel trained at the M.S. and Ph.D. levels in the agricultural sciences tend to be employed by nonfarm, but agriculturally related, organizations. These personnel, although extremely important, represent only a minor fraction of the total number of persons engaged in agriculture.

Farm operators represent the largest human resource base in agriculture. Whether individual proprietors or integrated into a family farm corporation, farm operators receive their compensation as a residual return or profit from engaging in the risks of agricultural enterprises. Not only must these farm operators increasingly have sound scientific training in agricultural production, but also business management.

Focus of any discussion of labor in agriculture, however, is on the hired farm worker. These hired workers represent a significant portion of total farm expenditures, particularly for fruit, vegetable, and other horticultural crops. Moreover, considerable attention is placed on the "hired" portion of the farm work force because of the complex set of public policies enacted at the state and federal levels.

I. Introduction

Labor involves physical and mental work. Although considerable mental work is associated with most agricultural tasks, the focus is on the amount of physical work or time needed to perform given agricultural labor jobs. Labor also represents one of the three major factors of agricultural production, the other two factors being capital and land.

Labor productivity in agriculture has achieved remarkable upward growth trends over several decades because of two basic tenets: (1) the division of labor and (2) biological and mechanical innovation in agriculture. Specialization and division of labor are the bases of economic development of industrialized societies. Efficiency gains occur in part from the enhanced dexterity acquired by repetition of particular tasks. Technological improvements in agriculture have also tended to reduce the man hours and drudgery of many agricultural jobs.

The demand for agricultural labor is derived from the demand for agricultural products. If we assume constant technology, an increase in the demand for agricultural products increases the demand for agricultural labor. However, increases in product demand have not necessarily been accompanied by increases in the demand for agricultural labor, because of labor-saving technology on farms, as well as innovations in the harvesting, handling, and packing/processing of agricultural products.

The supply of agricultural labor relates to the number of persons willing to work in agricultural pursuits for various levels of wage rates. In general, more people are willing to engage in agricultural work as the wage rate increases. Supply of farm labor is also affected by wage rates and working conditions in nonfarm labor sectors and by immigration policies. As the general economy worsens and/or enforcement of immigration laws slackens, the supply of farm labor increases.

II. Changing Patterns of Labor Use

For the United States as a whole, the persistence of family farms has meant that unpaid family labor represents the largest component of the farm labor force. Hired farm workers, however, continue to receive public attention in terms of social welfare legislation and other programs designed to improve the working conditions of seasonal and migrant farm workers.

Jobs performed by seasonal and migratory farm workers tend to be narrowly defined, because they generally involve a single specific task such as harvesting fruit or vegetables. The employee–employer relationship tends to be casual, with essentially no preferences for rehiring in successive years. The worker–job relationship also tends to be casual, rather than a continuing relationship that might develop into more skilled work categories.

Although seasonal farm work has attracted the dominant share of public and private attention over the past few decades, numerous semi-skilled, skilled, supervisory, and management jobs have evolved on large-scale commercial farms. These jobs have their origin in the application of modern science and technology to agriculture and to the emerging management structure on industrialized farms.

Despite the application of science and technology to agricultural production processes, the specter of seasonality has not been obviated or eliminated. In some cases, mechanization and other scientific developments in agriculture have actually shortened the seasonality of labor requirements. Seasonality of agricultural production has the effects of disrupting the flow of wage earnings to farm workers, skilled and unskilled, and of lowering annual earnings below those received in nonfarm jobs. Finding a solution to the problem of seasonality in agriculture has been the desire of many forward-thinking agribusiness firms.

For example, some large farm employers have been able to select crops, schedule plantings, and otherwise arrange operations to employ crews throughout the year. This change has permitted high rates of retention of employment from year to year, higher annual earnings, and increased productivity of the farm work force.

A. Unpaid Family Labor versus Hired Labor

In the United States in 1990, there were on average two unpaid family farm workers for every hired farm worker. There is also seasonality of farm work. In 1990, for example, the total farm work force (hired and unpaid family) ranged from 2.5 million in January, to 2.7 million in April, to 3.3 million in July, and back to 3.0 million workers in October. The hired farm work force is relatively more important in the summer month of July with 33% of the total, compared with the winter month of January with 28% of the total farm work force. [See FARMING SYSTEMS.]

California and Florida, two of the three largest states in terms of hired farm workers, both have relatively large components of *hired* farm workers compared with unpaid family farm workers. In these states, the ratio of hired workers to unpaid workers is approximately two *hired* workers for every *unpaid* worker, just opposite the situation for the United States as a whole.

Over time, the total number of farm workers has dropped substantially, from 13.5 million in the 1910s to 3.0 million in the 1990s. Most of this decrease is due to the gradual but persistent reduction in the number of farms in America, which caused the number of unpaid family workers to decline from 10 million in the 1910s to 2 million in the 1990s. The hired farm work force has also decreased over this same time span, but only from 3 million in the 1910s to approximately 1 million in the 1990s. Of course, seasonality affects hiring of farm workers each year, varying from 700,000 hired workers in January of 1990, for example, to 1.1 million hired workers in July of 1990, a spread of 400,000 workers.

The decrease in farm employment, whether hired workers or unpaid family workers, has been related to increased productivity from mechanization and other technological innovations. Mechanization, higher yielding crops and livestock, and improved fertilizers, pesticides/fungicides, and irrigation equipment have reduced the labor input per unit of output while permitting aggregate agricultural output to expand. In the period between 1945 and 1990, which witnessed a reduction in total farm employment from 9.8 million to 2.9 million, farm production increased 90%.

B. Migrant Labor Patterns

Migrant farm workers constitute a small but important subgroup of the domestic hired farm work force. Migrant laborers are defined as persons who temporarily leave their home county and stay away from home overnight to engage in farm work. The reason for migrant workers in agriculture is, particularly, the seasonality of farm production and harvesting. The seasonal demand for labor in agriculture gives rise to incentives for people to migrate for agricultural work. The economic and physical conditions surrounding these workers has been of considerable social concern.

Migration is the result of a response by individuals to potential wage differentials, that is, those for whom migration would result in higher earnings are more likely to migrate than others. Certain government programs, such as unemployment insurance for farm workers, act as depressants of farm labor migration. Also, public policies toward undocumented workers can significantly affect the incidence of migration of domestic farm workers. A lax policy on enforcement of illegal immigrants tends to reduce the stimulus for domestic worker migration, whereas tight enforcement encourages more migration of domestic workers.

Migrants supplement the local labor force during peak use seasons when the demand for farm workers frequently exceeds the supply of farm workers living in the local area. Their work is greatly affected by weather conditions, variations in crop yield, and availability of local labor. Vegetable, fruit and nut, and horticultural specialty farms are most likely to employ migrant farm workers.

The number of domestic migrant farm workers has decreased from almost one-half million in 1959 to less than 200,000 in 1985. Their relative importance has also fallen from 13% of the total hired farm work force in 1959 to 6% of the total in 1985. The decrease in the aggregate number and relative importance of domestic migrant farm workers reflects the general trend toward increased mechanization. Migrant laborers have, however, continued to be relatively important for those commodities for which mechanical harvesting is either not economically feasible or not conducive to quality fresh produce.

Because of the emergence of an unknown number of documented illegal aliens employed in American agriculture in the late 1980s and early 1990s, the statistical validity of migrant worker data is questionable. These workers, for example, may show local addresses and may be defined as domestic nonmigrant farm workers, only to migrate back to Mexico each year and live briefly in their real native home area.

Historically, three major routes have been taken by migrant workers in search of farm work. One route leads from the Caribbean and southern Florida up to New England. Another route leads from northeastern Mexico and southern Texas up to Michigan. The third route leads from northwestern Mexico and southern California up to the state of Washington. Corresponding to each route is a group of migrants: the Atlantic Coast stream, the Midwest stream, and the Pacific Coast stream. Although public interest centers on these *interstate* migrant workers, most migrant farm workers are really *intrastate* migrants.

C. Contract Labor

Growers have increasingly looked to labor contractors to deliver a supply of labor sufficient to meet their highly seasonal labor needs. Growers also depend on labor contractors to manage the work performed by seasonal farm employees. Labor contractors also permit growers to disengage from the details of field labor management and to avoid the problems associated with recruitment, retention, productivity, payroll, transportation, meals, and housing. This permits the grower to treat labor like any other input.

Labor contractors are particularly advantageous when workers are likely to be foreign-born, migrant, illegal, unskilled, uneducated, and unorganized. Workers with these characteristics face difficulties in finding jobs and, consequently, rely on informal networks of friends, relatives, and contractors for employment information.

Labor contractors have become indispensable to seasonal labor markets because of their extensive contacts with farm worker communities and migration networks. They also have bilingual skills that bring non-English-speaking workers into seasonal agricultural job markets. Their networks also provide entry possibilities for undocumented workers and workers with little or no previous farm work experience in the United States.

Contract labor in agriculture is particularly prominent in California, Florida, and Texas. Of the $1.8 billion expended for farm contract labor in the United States in 1987, $1.04 billion (over 50%) occurred in these three states. Moreover, the bulk of farm labor contractor expenditures was tied to fruit and vegetable operations in California, Florida, and Texas.

Labor contractors provide harvest labor options not only for growers, but also for other owners of agricultural commodities, for example, processors, packing houses, and independent buyers. As labor contractors increase their size of operations, they behave like other entrepreneurs in terms of labor organization and management, that is, they hire crew leaders for the supervision and management of two or more crews, handle payroll, tax, and insurance matters; and increasingly perform assembly and transportation functions. Compensation rates paid to labor contractors reflect the functions performed by them.

III. Productivity of Agricultural Labor

Technology, not land or labor, is the cornerstone of the productive capacity of United States agriculture. The massive increases in agricultural output in America over the past 200 years have been accomplished by successive changes in the technological base of agricultural production. Just prior to the Civil War of the 1860s, *horse power* replaced *hand power*. The tractor became the symbol of the *mechanical power* era, which came into prominence after World War I. After World War II, however, the major impetus behind increases in agricultural productivity became *science* based. The two components or phases of science power involved the *chemical* and *biological* revolutions in agriculture.

The chemical revolution in agriculture involves the proper application of fertilizers, insecticides, herbicides, and fungicides in agricultural production. These applications are intended to increase yields. However, because of environmental and other concerns, focus in recent years has shifted to the application of *biological* science to increase yields of plants and animals. The biological revolution in agriculture includes such diverse fields as genetics, plant and animal breeding, animal nutrition, sanitation, biological disease control, and other biotechnological sciences.

The gradual historical transition from hand power, to horse power, to mechanical power, and finally to science power has had a profound effect on labor in agriculture. These technological advances over time have permitted agricultural output to increase dramatically with fewer and fewer agricultural workers. In effect, capital investments in the form of tractors, other machinery, farm chemicals, and new breeds of

TABLE I

Labor Productivity in Agribusiness, 1948–1980

	Average annual change in output per man hour (%)		
	1948–1963	1963–1973	1973–1980
Farming	5.7	8.0	7.0
Food stores	5.3	1.8	−1.2
Food processors	3.7	2.5	1.8

Source: Polopolus (1986).

livestock and new plant varieties have *increased* agricultural output per unit of agricultural labor.

The labor productivity of American agriculture is measured by an index number that defines the ratio of agricultural output, expressed in constant prices, to man hours of input. Historically, farm worker productivity doubled between 1810 and 1880, doubling again by the early years of World War II. Since 1950, farm worker productivity has more than doubled. However, the rate of labor productivity growth in farming has tended to decline in recent years.

Compared with other sectors of the American economy, the labor productivity growth record of the farming sector has been phenomenal. Within the agribusiness economy, labor productivity growth in farming is considerably higher than the labor productivity growth rates for food stores or food processing (Table I). Labor productivity growth rates for food stores and food processors have actually declined over the 1948–1980 period. The negative labor productivity rate for food stores in the 1973–1980 period suggests that output per man hour decreased in absolute terms. In contrast, labor productivity growth for American farms is at a relatively high level. [*See* PRODUCTION ECONOMICS.]

IV. Changes in Location of Agricultural Production

Locational adjustments of agricultural production have occurred frequently over time. These locational shifts are caused by many factors including changes in international trade policies, domestic farm policies, product and/or farm input prices, and consumer demand. The irony of locational adjustments of agricultural production is that both "winners" and "losers" are created almost simultaneously. For example, trade liberalization policies can have the effect of reducing agricultural production of oranges in the United

States, for example, but increasing orange production in Mexico. This change could translate into fewer citrus jobs in the United States, with an increase in citrus jobs in Mexico, assuming technology remains reasonably constant. Any unemployed American citrus workers are not expected to travel to Mexico to seek the new jobs because of the huge disparity in wages and benefits in the United States and Mexico.

Adjustments in the location of agricultural production can occur from interregional competitive factors *within* a country or from *international* competitive factors. Domestic farm policies tend to insulate regions from competitive and volatile world markets. However, these programs were not sufficient to prevent cattle and broilers from becoming leading agricultural commodities in the South, displacing cotton and tobacco as the top commodities in this region in terms of cash farm receipts. Because of the specialized nature of agricultural jobs, although many are in the unskilled category, changes in agricultural production patterns cause changes in the nature and structure of agricultural employment. Thus, farm labor is affected not only by technological changes, but by the vagaries of interregional and international competition.

V. Evolution and Development of Federal Policies Regarding Farm Workers

From almost complete exclusion in the 1930s, farm labor is now covered under most social and protective federal programs. In some cases, parallel state laws exist to protect farm workers. Thus, farm workers are now covered on approximately the same basis as nonfarm workers in such program areas as social security, minimum wage, child labor, unemployment insurance, workers' compensation, occupational safety and health, and immigration reform.

The closing of the gap between farm workers and nonfarm workers on social legislation, as well as the increased average size of agricultural production firms, permits the hypothesis that farming in America has become "industrialized." In reality, considerable differences remain between agricultural and "industrial-manufacturing" production systems. The notable distinctions involve the seasonality and perishability of agricultural production processes. Agricultural production is a biological, rather than a mechanical, production process. The production units are spatially dispersed. Weather effects—such as severe freezes, floods, hurricanes, or excessive drought—can cause unexpected financial losses to farm employers and farm workers.

Nevertheless, large-scale agricultural employers have become increasingly attuned to the need for wage rates, fringe benefits, and working conditions roughly comparable to those provided by nonfarm employers. However, in periods of excessive farm labor supply, the economic incentives for closing the gap in wages, fringe benefits, and working conditions between farm and nonfarm industries are lacking.

A. Social Security

The objective of the federal Social Security program is to provide monthly cash benefits to replace a part of the earnings lost through an employee's retirement, death, disability, or hospitalization.

Essentially all farm employers must comply with federal Social Security regulations. To avoid employer coverage, farms in America in 1990 would have to pay an employee less than $150 in cash wages during a calendar year or pay total wages of less than $2500 per year to all employees. Employers and employees contribute to the tax base. In 1990, employers withheld 7.65% of an employee's cash wages up to a limit of $51,300 in annual wages. Employers also were required to add 7.65% of cash wages as the employer's contribution to the program.

The Social Security program prescribes an assortment of forms to be filed and data to be recorded. When labor contractors are involved, a farm operator may be held liable as a joint employer if the labor contractor fails to pay the Social Security tax.

B. Fair Labor Standards Act

This federal act is more commonly known as the Minimum Wage Law. It generally is concerned with the minimum standard of living in terms of minimum wages, equal pay, overtime pay, record keeping, and child labor. Farm employers are exempt from the overtime pay provisions of the act, whereas the minimum wage of $4.25 (1993) is required of farm (and nonfarm) employers covered under the statute.

Farmers who use more than 500 man days of labor during any calendar quarter (approximately 7 full-time employees working 5 days a week) must comply with the provisions of the Minimum Wage Law. Family members (parent, spouse, child) are excluded from the minimum wage requirement, as well as from the 500 man day test. Also, the act permits teenagers between 16 and 19 years of age to be employed at wage rates somewhat below the minimum wage.

The federal law establishes 16 as the minimum age for working in agricultural jobs declared hazardous by the Secretary of Labor and for working during school hours. Children 14 and 15 years of age can be employed in any nonhazardous agricultural occupation outside school hours. A child 12 or 13 years of age can also be employed outside school hours if she/he has written consent of parents or if the employment is on the same farm where his/her parents are employed.

The primary issue of the Minimum Wage Law is its impact on farm jobs. Historically, each movement upward of the minimum wage has had the net effect of displacing farm jobs with the lowest skill requirements, because many unskilled farm jobs are paid at hourly rates at or very near the minimum wage. Thus, increasing the minimum wage has had the effect of increasing the adoption of capital-intensive or labor-saving technology on farms. The minimum wage requirement is also a factor causing the number of hired farm workers to decline over time, particularly in the southern region of the United States.

C. Unemployment Insurance

Although considerable variation exists from state to state in employer coverage and worker benefits, the overall purpose of unemployment insurance is to provide a partial and temporary income supplement to persons who lose their jobs through no fault of their own. Minimum federal coverage standards of agricultural employers are established, but individual states may have more extensive coverage.

Covered farm employers are required to pay a federal tax and a state tax. The state tax is usually variable and dependent on the experience rating of the particular employer. In Florida, for example, a farm is required to participate in the program if its farm payroll is at least $10,000 in any calendar quarter or if the farm has 5 or more employees for some portion of a day in 20 or more weeks of the year.

To be eligible to receive unemployment insurance benefits, an unemployed farm worker would generally have to be unemployed, be able to and available for work, not be subject to disqualification, and to have sufficient wage credits under state law. Once meeting the benefit eligibility requirements, claimants are entitled to receive weekly benefits of some percentage of the weekly average wage, but not more than some maximum defined by state law. Farm

workers, however, can be denied unemployment compensation if they, among other factors, voluntarily quit their job without good cause, are discharged for misconduct, fail to apply for or accept suitable work, or are illegal immigrants.

A feature of the unemployment insurance program that is somewhat misunderstood is the burden of taxes. *Employees do not pay any part of these taxes.* Costs are borne by the employer, except for extended federal benefits which are subsidized by the federal treasury.

The equity issue is key here. Relatively small farms do not have to pay the unemployment insurance tax, whereas larger farms must pay the tax. This can increase average unit production costs for the larger farm units, other factors being equal. From a public relations standpoint, however, workers tend to prefer being employed by farms that provide unemployment insurance benefits. This factor could improve the quality of labor available for open positions at farms covered with unemployment insurance.

D. Immigration Reform

Immigration reform policy is focused on the provisions and administration of the Immigration Reform and Control Act (IRCA) of 1986. IRCA makes it unlawful for any employer in the United States to employ an alien not legally entitled to work in the United States. It requires that farm employers carefully monitor Form I-9 for completeness, making this form available to officers of the U.S. Immigration and Naturalization Service or U.S. Department of Labor for inspection on advance (3 days) notice.

In addition to record keeping and I-9 requirements, IRCA has a broad array of provisions that include (1) imposition of civil and criminal sanctions or penalties for knowingly hiring illegal immigrants, (2) violation of the law for improper discrimination in hiring or recruiting individuals on the basis of nationality or citizenship status, (3) a broader program (H-2A) for obtaining temporary foreign agricultural workers, (4) a Special Agricultural Worker (SAW) program that provides opportunity for eventual United States citizenship of previous illegal immigrants working in United States agriculture, and (5) a Replenishment Agricultural Worker (RAW) program to replace perishable crop agricultural workers (SAW) who do not qualify for legalization or who leave agriculture for other jobs.

Heavy penalties are imposed by IRCA on persons knowingly hiring illegal immigrants. The maximum penalty is $10,000 for each unauthorized worker employed. IRCA also provides additional funds for enforcement to bar illegal entry into the United States. At the time of the enactment of IRCA, most economists predicted that this new immigration law would have the effect of legalizing a large number of previously illegal workers. Many of these SAWs fraudulently certified themselves to be agricultural workers but were not involved in agricultural employment. Many of the bona fide agricultural workers with SAW status were expected to abandon seasonal farm work for year-round nonfarm work, given their new American citizenship status. With stronger enforcement at the borders and with a dwindling supply of farm workers, the initial expectation was that farm labor supplies would tighten after 1986 and farm wage rates would escalate.

This preliminary analysis of the likely impact of IRCA on farm labor markets turned out to be incorrect. What actually happened was that new waves of illegal immigrants entered the United States seeking farm work, after the passage of IRCA. In many cases, these illegal workers simply purchased documents to portray themselves as legalized workers. The "documented illegals" have had the effect of increasing the supply of farm labor and keeping wage rates from rising above the inflation rate.

E. Workers' Compensation

While each state has its own rules and regulations regarding workers' compensation, some states do not provide farm worker coverage. Where coverage is provided, workers compensation protects workers that receive job-related injuries or diseases.

Coverage for agricultural firms is applicable to the medium-sized to larger employers. In Florida, for example, agricultural employers of 6 or more regular employees are required to purchase workers' compensation insurance. Farms that qualify for coverage must purchase workers' compensation insurance from an insurance carrier, qualify as a self-insurer, or join a group self-insurer fund. Cost of insurance varies depending on employment activity and experience rating of each employer.

A significant policy issue has arisen from a recent United States Supreme Court case. In the Adams Fruit Company case, the Supreme Court held that injured agricultural workers may sue their employer for damages under the Federal Migrant and Seasonal Agricultural Worker Protection Act, as well as receive benefits for work-related injuries under a state workers' compensation law. This decision erodes the doc-

trine of exclusivity of workers' compensation remedies which allow for quick, no-fault relief for workplace injuries in exchange for foregoing expensive private lawsuits.

The Adams case also exposes employers to double liability in workers' compensation cases. Certain farm employers must now pay the insurance premium for the state workers' compensation program, as well as provide additional liability insurance coverage in the event that state insurance does not provide sufficient relief to workers seeking even larger benefits for workplace injuries.

Some effort is being made in Congress to reverse the thrust of the Adams Supreme Court decision through new legislation. These efforts are designed to restore state workers' compensation laws as the exclusive remedy for workplace injuries.

F. Occupational Safety and Health Act (OSHA)

The OSHA program seeks to insure a safe and healthful working environment, as well as preserve human resources. Although this federal law covers every employer engaged in a business that affects interstate commerce, farmers hiring 10 or fewer employees are exempt from OSHA inspection and all subsequent rules and penalties. However, serious, willful, or repeated violations by any farm employer are subject to citation.

For farm employers of 11 or more workers, OSHA imposes several requirements, such as (1) informing employees of safety regulations and displaying posters; (2) reporting serious accidents within 48 hr; (3) maintaining up-to-date records of all occupational injuries and illnesses; (4) posting summary of prior year's occupational injuries and illnesses; (5) complying with special agricultural standards for anhydrous ammonia, slow-moving-vehicles emblems, roll-over protection structures, and field sanitation; and (6) instructing each employee on safe operation and servicing procedures for tractors and the handling of hazardous materials.

Although worker's compensation and OSHA programs both relate to accidents and illnesses in the workplace, their reporting requirements are different. There is also a difference in coverage or applicability. OSHA regulates only the larger agricultural employers, whereas workers' compensation covers medium- and large-sized employers.

G. Overall Impact of Labor Laws and Regulations

Labor laws and regulations usually have a differential impact on the two major groups of participants—employers and workers. *Farm employers* affected by these laws and regulations usually are burdened or adversely affected by the (1) additional and excessive paper work; (2) complexities of dealing simultaneously with parallel, but not identical, programs of federal and state governments; (3) inequity among farmers for identical programs (larger farmers covered whereas smaller farmers not covered); (4) lack of uniformity of criteria for employer coverage across labor programs; (5) difficulty in utilizing labor programs for enhancing individual worker productivity; and (6) weak enforcement of existing labor programs.

Overall, many farmers in the United States view federal and state labor laws as a required form of bureaucracy or a nuisance. However, enlightened farmers have increasingly softened their opposition to labor programs over time. The real issue then is how to improve the effectiveness of existing programs, while diminishing the inequities.

Farm workers are generally pleased that such programs as social security, minimum wage, unemployment insurance, and workers' compensation have become increasingly available to them. Gaps in worker coverage still exist, however, particularly for workers of relatively small farms.

For larger farms that also provide opportunities for year-round employment, attracting good quality labor has not been a problem. Many of the larger dairy farms, for example, provide benefit packages that include paid vacations, health insurance, and free housing for regular or year-round employees.

For many farm employers caught in adverse competitive situations in product markets, the costs of mandated labor programs may have contributed to marginal or negative profits, leading to the closing down of farm operations altogether. Thus, the long-term effect of providing increased labor program benefits to farm workers has been better and larger benefits for fewer workers over time. If the industrialization of agriculture continues, those remaining agricultural workers are likely to have labor program benefits essentially equal to those of nonfarm workers in the future.

VI. Collective Bargaining in Agriculture

Collective bargaining represents a conflict resolution process in which workers organize collectively to negotiate wages and working conditions with their employers. Because labor–management conflicts can erupt into physical violence and chaos for workers and employers, federal labor relations legislation was enacted in 1935, including the Wagner Act to establish the basic rules of behavior for dealing with labor–management relations. However, this act and its subsequent amendments excluded farm workers.

Originally, farm workers were excluded from coverage under the National Labor Relations Act (NLRA) on the basis that they were not employees within the meaning of the act. Farms were considered family and household enterprises. Also, strikes at harvest time could jeopardize the national food supply. In 1935, however, Congress intended to provide coverage for farm workers at a later date.

The original Wagner Act of 1935 was excessively pro-labor. It protected the rights of workers to organize. However, the Taft–Hartley Amendments of 1947 constrained labor union behavior. For example, these amendments prohibited secondary boycotts by labor unions. The Landrum–Griffin amendments of 1959 further constrained and proscribed union behavior.

All attempts by the Congress to provide NLRA coverage to farm workers unions have failed. The 1960s experienced flurries of proposed legislation, hearings, and debate. Through the years and until 1969, the arguments of farm labor and farm employers were quite stable and predictable. Organized labor and pro-labor supporters argued that farm worker exclusion was discriminatory. On the other hand, farm employers argued that if farm workers had the protection of NLRA, they would organize unions. These farm labor unions would, in turn, strike at harvest time and jeopardize the nation's food supply.

Since 1969, the positions of farm workers and farm employers have been reversed. Farm labor unions, positively influenced by the impact of secondary boycotts on California table grapes in the 1970s, have come to view exclusion of farm workers under the amended NLRA as beneficial to their cause. On the other hand, farm employers have tended to argue that national uniformity of farm worker coverage under the NLRA is preferable to state-by-state coverage.

A. The California Experience

In 1975, California enacted the Agricultural Labor Relations Act (ALRA). This state legislation differed from the national labor relations law because it focused on the provisions for and administration of farm worker elections. Whereas the NLRA constrained against secondary boycotts for any purpose, the state law permitted *certified* unions to use secondary boycotts to obtain and maintain collective bargaining agreements. The California law, however, severely restricts strikes and boycotts prior to the establishment of a certified bargaining agent.

One of the distinctive features of the California ALRA is its special provision regarding the seasonal nature of agricultural employment. For example, ALRA permits elections to be held during periods of peak employment. The state law, however, does exclude farm labor contractors from consideration as farm employers.

In the first year following passage of the California ALRA, 429 elections involving approximately 50,000 workers occurred. The United Farm Worker (UFW) union won 82% of its organizing attempts, whereas the Teamsters' Union won 57% of its organizing efforts. Election activity greatly diminished after July 1, 1976.

In 1976, California voters soundly rejected Proposition 14, which would have increased funding for the Agricultural Labor Relations Board and, more importantly, would have given labor unions rights to access farm property to organize farm workers.

B. The Hawaii Experience

Although California's experience with collective bargaining in the 1970s received national attention, Hawaii has included agricultural workers in its labor relations act since 1945. In 1945, the International Longshoremen's and Warehousemen's Union (ILWU) signed an agreement with the Hawaiian sugar industry. This agreement was signed without any violence; it has also been a durable collective bargaining agreement over the decades.

C. The Potential For Farm Worker Organization

Several factors inhibit extensive collective bargaining in the farm labor market in the United States, whether or not coverage is provided under federal or state laws. First, most farm laborers in America are unpaid family workers. In many regions, the seasonal hired farm work force is heavily tilted toward students and housewives. These workers are certainly poor candidates for collective bargaining units. In other regions, seasonal hired farm workers have only a casual attachment to the farm labor market and are quite mobile. Workers are also geographically dispersed, making communication with organizers difficult. A piece-rate system of payment for harvesting crops also diminishes the potential effectiveness of farm labor unions.

When the increasing role of independent farm labor contractors is added to the increasing supply of "doc-

umented" illegal workers available for farm work, the potential for greatly expanding the influence of farm labor unions in America becomes dubious. Unless subsidized by outside sources, farm labor unions need to maintain their viability by collecting dues from members in excess of the aggregate expenses required to organize workers and pay for the union's financial commitments. Since hired farm workers tend to be seasonal workers—unattached, mobile, geographically dispersed, culturally divergent, and relatively poor—the chances of developing viable farm labor organizations become quite slim.

D. Impact of IRCA on Labor Organizing

Many labor advocates theorized that when slightly over 1 million unauthorized workers gained legal status under IRCA, these workers would attempt to improve their wages and working conditions even further by getting involved with collective bargaining efforts. However, the overall surplus of agricultural workers since the passage of IRCA in 1986 has worked against widespread labor organizing efforts in American agriculture. The proportion of farm workers covered by union contracts declined throughout the 1980s. This trend also occurred for nonfarm workers.

Several major factors explain the decline in the importance of labor unions, both within and outside of agriculture. These factors include the surge of foreign imports and the increasingly competitive international economic environment, a less hospitable political environment for labor unions, a shift in population base toward the Sun Belt states or states with right-to-work legislation, and a growing perception that unions do not necessarily provide workers with better wages and working conditions.

Given the excess of farm labor supply and the relative ease of worker entry, the threat of strikes diminishes greatly. Thus, it is not surprising that collective bargaining in agriculture has declined in the 1980s and 1990s.

VII. The Farm Labor Market

Of course, in many sectors in American agriculture year-round employment is available. These sectors include poultry, egg, dairy, beef, and, to some extent, ornamental horticulture industries. In many of these industries, a fairly stable employment relationship exists between farm employers and their workers. However, the total employment represented by these sectors is small relative to the total employment of the seasonal agricultural industries.

Seasonal agricultural employment is characterized by casual employment relationships between the worker and the employer. Very frequently, seasonal farm workers do not know the names of their employer, whether they are farmers or labor contractors. Since the great majority of this work is performed at piece rates, neither the contractor nor the farmer hires these workers as individuals.

Although the employer now usually provides these workers with coverage for such benefits as unemployment insurance, social security, and workers' compensation, the employer is not concerned with whether a crop is picked by 10 people or 100, as long as it is harvested in a timely manner. Similarly, little concern exists on the part of the employer with whether those who pick the crop today are the same individuals who harvested the crop last week or last year, as long as sufficient hands are available to harvest today's crop on time. Thus, not only is the seasonal job market casual, but it encourages considerable entry and exit of workers within a given season.

A. Wage Rate Trends

Nominal wage rates for United States farm workers have risen from about $2.25 per hour in 1975 to $5.57 per hour in 1991. Considerable variability in wage rate trends occurs over crop and region. In relation to the nonfarm sector, hourly farm earnings are persistently only 50% of nonfarm hourly wage rates.

In terms of *real* United States farm hourly wages, wage rates have been flat or declining since the passage of IRCA. For example, real United States farm hourly wages decreased 2% for the 1986–1991 period, compared with a 4% per annual increase in *nominal* wages over the same period.

Regional data show substantial differences in wage trends. Between 1986 and 1991, *real* wages for hired farm workers decreased by 13% in California and by 8% in the Southern Plains region. There was no change in Florida and a slight increase in the Pacific region.

A long-term view of United States trends in *real* farm wage rates show that these wage rates rose steadily throughout the 1950s and 1960s, peaking in 1969. *Real* farm wages then fell briefly, rising again until 1977. They then fell for 8 yr, increasing in 1986. *Real* farm wage rates have sloped gently downward in the post-IRCA period. Based on an analysis by the Commission on Agricultural Workers in 1992, farm wages have followed the same overall patterns as nonfarm wages since 1948.

When comparing recent wage trends for the employees of farm labor contractors and farm workers hired directly by farmers, real wages of contractors' employees dropped 16% over the 1989–1991 period, compared with no change in real wages for employees of farmers over the same period.

Looking to the future, it is unlikely that wage rates for hired farm workers will outpace the rate of inflation as long as new streams of documented illegal workers enter the United States farm labor market. Stricter enforcement of the present IRCA legislation and/or any new federal program to tighten illegal immigration could have the effect of increasing both nominal and real farm wage rates in the United States.

B. Annual Earnings of Hired Farm Workers

The eminent scholar on farm labor, Varden Fuller, succinctly summarized the income status of farm workers with the following statement:

> The people have not become poor from working in agriculture; they have become agricultural workers because they were already poor. (Fuller, 1968, p. 434)

As an occupational category, farm laborers and supervisors have, for many years, ranked second only to domestic household workers at the bottom of the income scale. The low earnings of hired farm workers result from the short or intermittent nature of farm work, as well as from low earnings on the job. Even farm workers who also performed some nonfarm work achieved near rock-bottom annual income levels.

Agricultural work is considered one of the last employment opportunities remaining for the redundant unskilled labor pool. Some of these workers, unable to obtain permanent employment, try to meet year-round economic needs by patching together a sequence of seasonal jobs, sometimes including migratory work. These jobs are of low productivity and are low paying. Thus, these workers achieve low annual earnings—not because they work in agriculture, but because they are a part of a pool of low skilled or unskilled laborers who are in surplus supply throughout the nation.

C. Changing Demographics of Seasonal Workers

In years past, the non-Hispanic Caucasian worker was the dominant seasonal farm worker in the United

States, except in certain Southern regions where the African-American worker was dominant. This was during the era when students, housewives, and underemployed local individuals formed the basis of the seasonal hired farm work force. Beginning in the West and Midwest in the 1960s, however, a growing number of Mexican and Mexican-American workers has entered United States agriculture. With Hispanic workers now fully diffused in eastern United States farm labor markets, the "Latinization" of the seasonal United States farm labor force is now fairly complete.

By the late 1980s, Mexicans had become the largest single ethnic group among seasonal farm workers throughout the country. Their presence in the farm labor force, in contrast to that of United States citizens, has been increasing since many employers prefer to hire young, highly productive workers willing to work for lower wages. The shift to Mexican-born workers has also been accompanied by a decrease in families and older workers, since new arrivals are more likely to be young men and, at least initially, without families.

1. California

In the second half of the 19th century, Chinese immigrants provided needed labor for California agriculture. The Chinese were succeeded by the Japanese, Hindustanis, and Filipinos. Mexican and Mexican-American workers, however, have provided most of the labor for California agriculture since the beginning of the 20th century.

In 1983, nearly three-fourths of the California farm labor force was born in Mexico. The next largest group of workers (10%) was composed of Mexican-American workers born in California and other southwestern states. What has changed in recent years is the increasing proportion of workers from Indian towns and villages in Mexico, primarily Mixtecos from Oaxaca.

2. East Coast

Until recently, east coast agriculture had relied on its own sources of farm laborers. European immigrants, for example, were employed extensively in New Jersey truck farming in the 1920s. Appalachian whites were recruited for the New York apple harvest, whereas southern-born African-Americans made up the bulk of the farm labor force in Delaware and Maryland. Puerto Rican workers replaced many of these groups.

The large-scale penetration of Mexican-born workers into eastern United States labor markets did not begin until the 1960s. Although influxes of Haitian workers took place in the early 1980s and Guatemalan workers appeared in the mid-1980s, Mexicans had become the largest single immigrant group in South Florida and much of the East Coast by the end of the decade.

The increase of Mexican and Mexican-American farm workers in the East coincided with the dramatic decline in the number of United States-born African-American farm workers. African-Americans who choose to stay in farm work have found increased competition for their long-held jobs by relatively recent immigrants from Mexico and Central America.

VIII. Concluding Remarks

Human labor resources will continue to be crucial to the agricultural production process. Although some labor scarcity may occur in the future for year-round management, scientific, and technical positions, the supplies of labor for positions at the lower paying and lower skill levels will continue to be more than ample. Latinization of the seasonal farm labor work force will be essentially complete by the beginning of the 21st century.

The biotechnology revolution in American agriculture will gradually reduce the demand for human labor per unit of agricultural output. These technological innovations will, however, shift upward the training and skill requirements of agricultural workers over time. The largest structural changes in the farm labor market will occur if and when effective enforcement of United States immigration laws occurs. A stricter enforcement program would cause farm wage rates to rise. This, in turn, would bring into play enhanced technological innovation to reduce manual labor demand in United States agriculture.

As farm employment becomes somewhat more concentrated into the hands of relatively large-scale growers and/or labor contractors, the social benefit package for farm workers will improve. This "industrialization" of the farm work force will lead to increased parity in wages and working conditions between farm and nonfarm workers, although a gap in favor of nonfarm workers will continue to exist. The economic and social conditions necessary for increased collective bargaining in United States agriculture will not be present in the near future.

Bibliography

Emerson, R. D. (1977). Farm workers and labor organization. *In* "Florida's Farm Workers: Toward a Responsible Public Policy," Institute for Social Policy Studies, Tallahassee.

Emerson, R. D. (ed.) (1984). "Seasonal Agricultural Labor Markets in the United States," Iowa State University Press, Ames.

Fuller, V. (1968). Hired farm labor in the West. *In* "Rural Poverty in the United States," President's National Advisory Commission on Rural Poverty, Washington, D.C.

Fuller, V. (1991). "Hired Hands in California's Farm Fields," Giannini Foundation Special Report. California Agricultural Experiment Station, University of California, Berkeley.

Hayes, S. E. (1984). The California Agricultural Labor Relations Act and national agricultural labor relations legislation." *In* "Seasonal Agricultural Labor Markets in the United States," (R. D. Emerson, ed.), Iowa State University Press, Ames.

Holt, J. S. (1984). Introduction to the seasonal farm labor problem. *In* "Seasonal Agricultural Labor Markets in the United States,"(R. D. Emerson, ed.), Iowa State University Press, Ames.

Polopolus, L. C. (1977). Farm Labor in Florida. *In* "Florida's Farmworkers: Toward a Responsible Public Policy," Institute for Social Policy Studies, Tallahassee.

Polopolus, L. C.(1986). Labor productivity and agribusiness. *Agribusiness Int. J.* **2,** 269–277.

Polopolus, L. C. (1989). "Agricultural Labor in the 1990s," Staff Paper #367. Food and Resource Economics Department, University of Florida, Gainesville.

Polopolus, L. C., and Emerson, R. D. (1991). Entrepreneurship, sanctions, and labor contracting. South. J. Agric. Econ. **23,** 57–68.

U.S. Commission on Agricultural Workers (1992). "Report of the Commission on Agricultural Workers," U.S. Government Printing Office, Washington, D.C.

U.S. Department of Agriculture (1991). "Farm Employment and Wage Rates 1910–1990," Statistical Bulletin Number 822. National Agricultural Statistics Service, Washington, D.C.

U.S. Department of Labor (1991). "Findings from the National Agricultural Workers Survey (NAWS) 1990: A Demographic and Employment Profile of Perishable Crop Farm Workers," Research Report No. 1, Office of Program Economics, Washington, D.C.

Lactation

R. MICHAEL AKERS, *Virginia Polytechnic Institute and State University*

Glossary

Alveolus Milk producing unit of the mature mammary gland, composed of a hollow sphere of secretory epithelial cells surrounding a lumen

Caseins Major class of specific milk proteins made by the mammary secretory cells, account for 82% of milk proteins, packaged into colloidal micelles for secretion

Colostrum Thick, straw-colored secretion, rich in immunoglobulins, which accumulates in the mammary alveoli late in gestation

Ducts Hollow tubes made of a double layer of nonsecreting epithelial cells which direct secretions from the alveolar lumen to the teat or nipple

Galactopoiesis Maintenance of lactation

α-Lactalbumin Specific milk whey protein, induced by prolactin, part of the enzyme lactose synthetase necessary for production of lactose (the primary milk carbohydrate)

Lactogenesis Last stages of biochemical and structural differentiation of the alveolar epithelial cells during the periparturient period, required for onset of copious milk secretion

Mammogenesis Growth and morphological development of the mammary gland

Myoepithelial cells Elongated, stellate cells which form a mesh-like network of cells around the secretory cells of the alveolus. In response to oxytocin the myoepithelial cells contract to intitiate milk letdown

Transgenic Usually refers to an animal containing a stable foreign gene inserted into its genome

For all mammals in the wild, lactation is the culmination of the reproductive cycle. While specific strategies for successful rearing of young vary depending on the particular species, milk of all mammals contains variable ratios of proteins, carbohydrates, and lipids in an aqueous medium. These macronutrients serve to support the growth and development of the offspring, and in the case of the dairy animals, support the nutritional needs and food desires of millions of *Homo sapien* consumers. The purpose of this article is to provide an overview of development of the mammary gland, describe the biochemical and structural differentiation of the milk synthesizing mammary epithelial cells, define physiological factors influencing cyclic mammary function, and finally to speculate concerning the role new techniques of molecular biology might have on the future of milk production.

I. Mammary Development

A. Ductular and Alveolar Formation

Derived from the embryonic ectoderm, mammary epithelial cells, with impetus from secretion of estrogen and progesterone postpubertly, prolactin and growth hormone, and placental hormones during pregnancy, proliferate to form the mammary alveoli. Connected via a terminal duct to progressively larger ducts and ultimately the teat or nipple, the epithelial cells of an alveolus synthesize and secrete milk. Secreted milk is stored in lumenal spaces of the alveoli and ducts between milking or suckling episodes (Fig. 1). There is also storage of milk in the gland and teat cisterns of those animals with mammary glands organized into an udder (cattle, sheep, goats, and other ruminants). With the exception of a few of the epithelial cells which line the terminal duct directly leading into the alveolus, all milk is synthesized by the single layer of epithelial cells which line the internal

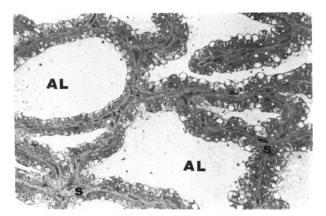

FIGURE 1 Light microscope view of section of mammary tissue from a lactating cow. Several alveoli cut in cross-section are illustrated. Lighter stained areas are alveolar lumena. Secretory cells form a single layer around the periphery of each alveolus. Because of accumulation of secretions within the lumenal spaces, alveoli are closely packed together with little apparent stromal or vascular tissue. Approximate magnification 180×. The following abbreviations are used in the figures: AL, alveolar lumen; S, stromal tissue; F, fat droplets; SV, secretory vesicles; G, Golgi apparatus; ER, rough endoplasmic reticulum; N, nucleus; MYO, myoepithelial cell.

surface of the alveoli. Thus, the multicellular alveoli are the functional milk synthesizing structures of the fully developed mammary gland.

With preparation of the mammary gland for milking or stimulation by the young, oxytocin from the posterior pituitary is released into the blood stream. Oxytocin binds to receptors on the myoepithelial cells surrounding the alveoli, inducing these stellate cells to contract, reduce the volume of the alveolar lumena, and force milk into the mammary ducts for removal. Successful lactation requires that the mammary gland acquire a large number of milk secreting cells. Simply stated, abundant milk production is directly related to the number of potential milk producing alveolar cells in the mammary gland and the functional capacity of these cells. Not only must alveoli be abundant in the mature gland, the epithelial cells must differentiate during the periparturient period such that the biochemical and cytological machinery necessary for synthesis and secretion of milk is highly developed. The importance of these processes is illustrated in comparative studies of mammary development in first gestation beef and dairy cattle reared and managed under identical conditions. Specifically, reduced milk production in beef cows is only partially a consequence of failure of mammary alveolar cells to proliferate. Not only are there fewer potential milk producing cells at the end of gestation in beef heifers, but

those which enter lactation exhibit less biochemical and structural differentiation than alveolar cells of the dairy heifers.

During gestation it is believed that the combined synchronous secretion of estrogen and progesterone (and placental lactogens in some species) is responsible for the rapid, exponential increase in mammary growth. Early gestation is associated with elongation and branching of mammary ducts, mid-gestation with formation of alveoli, and the later third of gestation with final proliferation and differentiation of the secretory cells. Hormone ablation/replacement experiments in rodents indicate that estrogen is especially important in stimulation of ductular growth while progesterone induces morphological differentiation to form alveoli. An observed increase in mammary progesterone receptors in association with lobulo-alveolar formation in sheep suggests the role of progesterone is similar in rodents and ruminants. While some species exhibit continuing growth of the mammary gland during lactation, i.e., rats exhibit as much as 40% of total mammary growth during lactation, it is believed that for most dairy animals mammary growth is complete shortly after parturition. This does not however, mean that it might not be possible to stimulate additional mammary growth during lactation with appropiate treatments or physiological circumstances. In goats, unilateral inhibition of milk secretion results in a compensatory increase in milk production by the remaining gland. Based on nuclear magnetic resonance imaging of goat udders there is also evidence that the mammary gland continues to grow during early lactation, particularly in primiparous does. It has also been reported that inhibition of milk removal of two mammary glands of lactating beef cows induced increased tritiated thymidine incorporation (an indicator of cell proliferation) into alveolar epithelial cells of the lactating glands. [See ANIMAL REPRODUCTION, NONPREGNANT FEMALE; ANIMAL REPRODUCTION, PREGNANCY.]

B. Tissue and Cell Interactions

Although most mammary growth occurs during pregnancy (48 to 94% depending on the species), the epithelial precursors which make alveolar formation possible depend on ducts which arise during the peripubertal period. Based primarily on studies with rodents, neonatal mammary growth involves proliferation and branching of a primary ductal sprout into underlying mesodermally derived stromal tissue. Rate of mammary growth continues in proportion to body growth (isometric) until just before puberty, when the rate is increased relative to the body (allometric). During the allometric phase, ducts rapidly elongate and fill the fatty stroma with subsequent secondary branching of existing ducts. Thus, mammary development involves intimate interaction between the epithelial cells, stromal fibroblasts, and adipocytes. In mice, ductular elongation requires the penetration of the fat pad by a highly specialized structure, the terminal end-bud. These club-shaped structures are 0.1 to 0.8 mm in diameter and form at the proliferating ends of ducts. Between 4 and 8 weeks, the end-buds extend through the fat pad and occasionally bifurcate to create new growth points. Elongation continues until the end-buds reach the margin of the fat pad where they regress. Consequently, at the end of the puberty associated allometric growth phase, the mammary fat pad is filled with ducts waiting for signals to initiate development of side branches and subsequently alveolar structures during gestation.

The situation in ruminants is less well defined. There is no compelling evidence that the end-bud structure exists; neither is the entire area of the mammary stromal tissue completely filled with ducts during the peripubertal period. Regardless, certainly in most species, allometric mammary growth associated with puberty is abolished by ovariectomy and restored by replacement therapy with estrogens. In addition, nutrition and management practices which modify animal development generally also influence development of the mammary gland. As a specific example, mammary growth and subsequent milk production can be markedly reduced by high energy feeding during a seemingly critical interval of several months prior to puberty in dairy heifers. There is also evidence that exogenous growth hormone can stimulate mammary development during the same interval.

A major boost to understanding of cell type interactions in mammary development has been the introduction of cell culture methods which allow long-term culture of isolated mammary epithelial cells. In particular, introduction of techniques using collagen and other extracellular matrix proteins has revitalized mammary cell culture. A number of workers have demonstrated that mammary cells from numerous species are capable of prolonged growth, formation of duct-like or alveolar-like structures, and synthesis and secretion of specific milk constituents. A related technique has been the development of lines of immortalized mammary epithelial cells. Initial reports suggest that data from these methodologies approximate cellular events in natural mammary development and thus support use of these techniques as

model systems for study of mammary cells. Parallel development of cell lines of mammary stromal cells and of myoepithelial cells offers the possibility of creation of functional mammary tissue in the controlled environment of the culture dish.

C. Secretory Cell Differentiation

Lactation requires at least three distinct events: (1) the prepartum proliferation of alveolar epithelial cells; (2) biochemical and structural differentiation of these cells; and (3) synthesis and secretion of the milk constituents. During lactation the alveolar cells synthesize and secrete copious amounts of carbohydrate, protein, and lipid. Lactation places dramatic physiological demands on any mother, but especially so on the high-yielding dairy cow. To emphasize, uptake of glucose and acetate by the mammary gland may account for 85 and 45%, respectively, of quantities available to the body during peak lactation. It has been calculated that high-producing dairy cows must mobilize adipose and tissue nutrient reserves energetically equal to one-third of the milk produced during the first month of lactation. Such animals generally remain in a net negative energy balance until several weeks after peak lactation (about 60 days postpartum). Certainly, dramatic adjustments in control of intermediary metabolism are necessary to support the demands of the mammary gland. Despite this apparent "native" demand, sustained increases (10 to 40% depending on stage of lactation) in milk yield are consistently observed in high-yielding cows given exogenous growth hormone. Increases are associated with improvements in mammary blood flow, enhanced tissue mobilization (initially), increased appetite, increased secretion of insulin-like growth factor one (IGF-I), and improved nutrient absorption from the intestinal tract. Such observations suggest that despite great increases in average milk production among dairy cows in the last 25 years, ultimate average capacity may be much greater, and thus even greater efficiency of milk production can be realized.

Although it is evident that biochemical differentiation of the alveolar epithelial cells must precede lactogenesis, it must also be appreciated that the cells must acquire the structural machinery for packaging and transport of milk constituents (Fig. 2). The ultrastructure of the mammary alveolar cells is dramatically altered during the interval just prior to parturition. When the alveoli first develop during mid-gestation, the cells exhibit few of the organelles necessary for copious milk component biosynthesis and secretion.

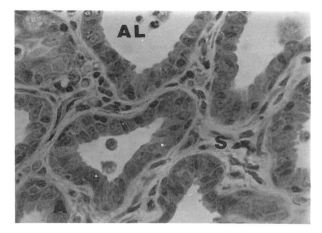

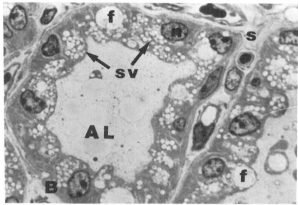

FIGURE 2 (A) Mammary tissue taken from a first gestation heifer approximately 4 months prepartum. Several alveoli are shown. Secretory cells are poorly differentiated with no evidence of secretory activity. (B) Mammary tissue from the same heifer taken 1 week postpartum. Illustrated are parts of two alveoli. The secretory cells are well differentiated, basal areas of the cells are darkly stained, and apical regions have a distinct lacy appearance because of the presence of numerous secretory vesicles and lipid droplets. Approximate magnification 350 and 900×, respectively.

The cells are characterized by a sparse cytoplasm with only scattered polyribosomes, free ribosomes, a few strands of rough endoplasmic reticulum, rudimentary Golgi elements consisting of dictyosomes adjacent to the cell nucleus, scattered mitochondria, and a few scattered vesicles. Individual cells often contain large lipid droplets, and nuclei are most often irregular in shape and occupy most of the cell area. Soon after the alveoli develop, the alveolar lumen begins to accumulate fluid and progressively increased amounts of serum and cell-derived proteins. These secretions subsequently result in formation of colostrum which is rich in immunoglobulins. For many species the passive immunity provided to the suckling young as a result of ingestion of the colostrum is essential for

survival of the offspring. As parturition approaches the cells undergo a dramatic structural transformation. Poorly developed cells characteristic of gestation are rarely observed. The cell nuclei become rounded and positioned in the basal area of the cell. The areas lateral and basal to the nuclei become filled with rough endoplasmic reticulum, and small lipid droplets (Fig. 3). The apical cell area is populated with Golgi membranes with budding secretory vesicles and enlarged lipid droplets destined for secretion through the apical plasma membrane into the alveolar lumen. These changes are evident even in the light microscope. The basal area of the cell becomes darkly stained (the ergastoplasm), the nuclei rounded, and the apical region lacy in appearance because of the abundant secretory vesicles (Fig. 2B). The mature cell thus takes on a polarized appearance, with the basol-lateral area of the cell dedicated to uptake of precursors from the blood stream and synthesis of proteins and lipids and the apical area with its Golgi apparatus dedicated to carbohydrate biosynthesis, glycosylation of proteins, and packaging of proteins and lactose for secretion from the cell.

Control of differentiation depends primarily on secretion of prolactin and glucocorticoids. Mammary tissue explants from pregnant donors of essentially all species tested exhibit biochemical and structural differentiation of the alveolar cells when tissues are incubated in media containing insulin, glucocorticoids, and prolactin. While insulin appears to be necessary for maintenence of mammary explants in culture, for most species the key hormones necessary to induce differentiation are glucocorticoids and prolactin. Experiments in which inhibition of prolactin secretion during the periparturient period reduces milk production provide additional evidence of the requirement for prolactin in lactogenesis. Finally, it is also clear that adequate removal of secretions is needed to insure copious milk production as well as removal of inhibitory influences of progesterone.

II. Milk Synthesis and Secretion

A. Milk Composition

Across species there are dramatic differences in milk composition. Milk from Holstein cows (the source of the majority of milk for human consumption in Western societies) has about 3.2% protein, 3.4% fat, and 4.6% lactose. In contrast, hooded seals produce milk with about 6.0% protein, 50% fat, and virtually no carbohydrate. Much of the variation likely reflects

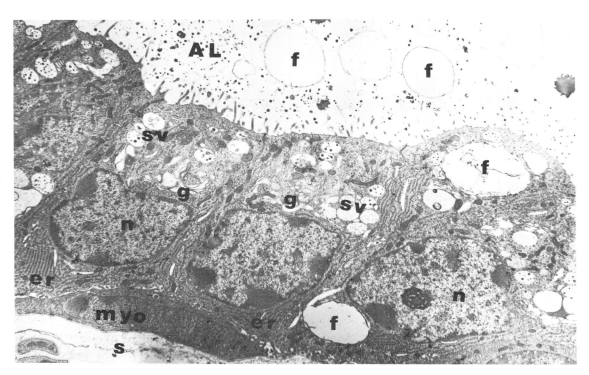

FIGURE 3 Transmission electron microscope view of mammary alveolar cells taken from a lactating cow 2 days postpartum. The profile of three epithelial cells illustrates a stage of intermediate structural differentiation of the alveolar epithelium as copious milk production is initiated. Compared with cells prior to parturition, cell nuclei are more rounded and basally displaced, secretory vesicles appear juxtapositioned to the Golgi, and the basal area of the cells contains many strands of rough endoplasmic reticulum. Numerous casein micelles (black particles) and fat globules are present in the alveolar lumen. Approximate magnification 6000×.

evolution-induced effects which provide the best stratagem for offspring survival. In the case of the hooded seal, pups are born on potentially unstable pack ice and must rapidly gain sufficient strength and insulation to survive. In fact, the mothers suckle their pups for only 4 days but during this period pups may increase their weight from about 20 kg at birth to more than 40 kg on Day 4. While the hooded seal has the shortest lactation of any known mammal, the high-fat milk provided to the pup supplies the energy and metabolic water necessary for an abrupt introduction into a polar environment.

B. Biosynthesis of Proteins

Total protein content of milk varies among species, but the two major groups of proteins are the caseins and whey proteins. A large number of other proteins usually present in trace amounts include serum proteins (immunoglobulins, albumins, and enzymes) and proteins from the fat globule membranes. The caseins are phosphoproteins and in cow's milk are empirically defined as those proteins which precipitate from skim milk when it is acidified to pH 4.6. As a consequence of the hydrophobic nature of the caseins in milk, these proteins form complex colloidal particles called micelles. These micelles are not only nutritionally rich sources of amino acids but additionally allow large amounts of calcium and phosphorous to be maintained in a stable form in milk. Proteins which remain in solution when milk is acidified are collectively referred to as whey proteins. As standardized to cow's milk, there are four major types of caseins: α-S1 and S2, β, κ, and γ. These classes account for approximately 38, 36, 13, 10, and 3% of total caseins, respectively. Under normal circumstances all of the caseins combined account for 82% of the total protein in milk and the whey proteins for about 18%. Major mammary cell specific proteins of the whey fraction include α-lactalbumin and β-lactoglobulin. All of the specific milk proteins are synthesized from amino acids taken up from the blood stream by the alveolar epithelial cells.

Autoradiographic studies with radiolabeled leucine show that amino acids are rapidly taken up from the vasculature or culture media into the rough endoplasmic rich baso-lateral area of the alveolar cells. Within 3 to 15 min, label in the ergastoplasm falls with concurrently increased labeling in the apical Golgi region of the cell and peak labeling 30 to 60 min postexposure. Thereafter, radiolabeled proteins appear in secretory vesicles and in the alveolar lumena. Elaborate studies have since demonstrated that all of the specific milk proteins are synthesized with short amino acid extensions (signal peptides) which direct the transfer of nascent peptides into the cisternal space of the rough endoplasmic reticulum and consequently the Golgi and secretory vesicles for release from the cell. In ultrathin sections prepared for the electron microscope, secretory vesicles appear as membrane profiles with scattered dense granules. These densely stained particles are the casein micelles and the space around the granules is a result of presence of lactose packaged in the same secretory vesicles. The individual caseins begin to assume their tertiary structure and aggregate into rudimentary casein micelles as vesicles bud from the Golgi. Mature micelles form as the vesicles are transported to the apical plasma membrane. Transport of lactose and protein containing secretory vesicles is believed to be at least partially directed by microtubules and other cytoskeletal elements. In cells from lactating glands, numbers of microtubules increase and orient themselves along the longitudinal axis of the cells. This orientation likely directs movement of secretory vesicles to the apical plasma membrane. In addition, drug-induced disruption of microtubules reversibly blocks milk secretion. Once positioned near the plasma membrane the vesicles fuse with the plasma membrane and the contents are released via exocytosis from the cell. Groups of vesicles may also fuse in chains simultaneously with the plasma membrane and release the contents of multiple vesicles at once.

C. Biosynthesis of Lactose

Composed of glucose and galactose, the disaccharide lactose is unique to the mammary gland. The enzymes necessary for lactose synthesis are located in the Golgi apparatus. The whey protein α-lactalbumin when combined with Golgi membrane bound galactosyltransferase forms the active enzyme lactose synthetase. This means that lactogenesis is closely linked to the initiation of synthesis of α-lactalbumin. Prolactin is especially important in activation of the α-lactalbumin gene and thus synthesis of lactose. As the α-lactalbumin is transported from the rough endoplasmic reticulum to the Golgi, lactose production begins. Because lactose cannot pass across the secretory vesicle membranes, water is drawn osmoti-

cally into the secretory vesicles. This explains the ultrastructural appearance of the secretory vesicles of the mammary cells compared with other protein secreting glands, i.e. pancreas, pituitary. With exocytosis of the secretory vesicles, lactose is released into the alveolar lumena to become part of milk. Like the secretory vesicles, cell membranes do not transport lactose; thus, the osmotic gradient is maintained and water remains in milk. It is relevant to note that marine mammals which produce little lactose also produce very thick, rich secretions with little water.

D. Biosynthesis of Fat

Lipid synthesis is intitiated in the eragastoplasm of the alveolar cells and is first evident in appearance of small lipid droplets. These droplets appear to combine and otherwise enlarge, and move to the apical region of the cell. Mature droplets begin to protrude from the cell pushing an envelope of plasma membrane. The droplets are progressively surrounded by the membrane and the droplets are released into the alveolar lumena. Consequently milk fat droplets appear in milk as membrane-bound globules. Exact mechanisms responsible for transport of the growing droplets to the apical plasma membrane are currently an active area of study. However, it is believed that proteins which associate with the surface of the fat droplet as it matures in the cell are involved in control of transport through the cell and direction of the droplets for interaction with sites on the apical plasma membrane.

A comparison across species demonstrates that lipid is the most variable general component of milk. The fat content of human and cow's milk is about 4%, 6–12% for many rodents, but 50% for many aquatic mammals. A general inverse relationship between lactose content and fat content of milk may reflect a need for the mother to conserve water by minimizing lactose production (thereby limiting the osmotic draw of water into milk) while providing the suckling young with high energy. Of the lipids in the fat globules, triglycerides account for 97–98%. However, the degree of saturation of the long chain fatty acids is variable as is the relative proportions of short, medium, and long chain fatty acids. Milk lipids are derived from uptake of fatty acids absorbed from the diet and as well as lipids mobilized from tissue stores. In addition, the mammary gland synthesizes fatty acids from precursors. In nonruminants, glucose provides the carbon skeleton for fatty acid synthesis, but in ruminants acetate and β-hydroxybutyrate provide the starting materials. Because of rumen fermentation of dietary carbohydrates, glucose needs must be satisfied by extensive gluconeogenesis in the liver via conversion of rumen-derived propionate. Much of the available glucose is utilized in the synthesis of lactose. The striking difference between ruminants and nonruminants comes about by the inability of ruminant mammary cells to convert glucose to acetyl-CoA in the mitochondria for transport to the cytoplasm (the site of fatty acid synthesis). Consequently, ruminants utilize abundant amounts of acetate from rumen fermentation for synthesis of ATP and fatty acids in the mammary cells. [See ANIMAL NUTRITION, NONRUMINANT; ANIMAL NUTRITION, RUMINANT.]

III. Regulators of Mammary Function

A. Proliferation vs Product Formation

Coordination between proliferation and differentiation is governed by complex interactions among hypophyseal, adrenal, ovarian, and placental hormones. Moreover, it is increasingly clear that effects of many of the classic mammogenic hormones are modulated or mediated by a plethora of growth factors via endocrine, paracrine, and/or autocrine modes of action. As examples, IGF-1 directly stimulates proliferation of mammary epithelial cells and the number of IGF-1 receptors in the mammary gland change in correspondence with rates of proliferation. Increased growth of mammary tissue in response to exogenous growth hormone or placental lactogen in cattle appears to depend on local production or uptake of IGF-1 by the mammary gland. To add to the complexity, local tissue synthesis of IGF binding proteins (IFGBPs) likely alters the biological activity of this potent mammary mitogen. Epidermal growth factor (EGF) and transforming growth factor-α (TGFα) also stimulate mammary cells and can enhance the effect of IGF-1.

B. Role of the Endocrine and Nervous Systems

Lactogenesis—the onset of copious milk production in concert with parturition—is driven by coordinated action of prolactin, growth hormone, estrogen, glucocorticoids, and progesterone. Maintenance of elevated serum concentrations of progesterone and of progesterone receptors in the epithelial cells during gestation serve to prevent premature onset of milk component biosynthesis. As parturition approaches, serum concentrations of progesterone decrease with a consequent reduction in inhibition. During the same interval, enhanced secretion of estrogens serves to increase prolactin receptors in the mammary gland and prolactin and glucocorticoid concentrations increase. Thus, lactogenesis relies on increasing positive stimulation and removal of inhibition. In particular, prolactin has been shown to increase mRNA synthesis of milk protein genes (α-lactalbumin and caseins) and promote differentiation of the epithelial cells, while glucocorticoids enhance structural differentiation of the alveolar cells and increase the half-life of mRNAs for the milk proteins. Galactopoiesis or maintenance of milk production requires delivery of vital precursors (glucose, animo acids, fatty acids, acetate) and trace nutrients to the alveolar epithelial cells and removal of waste products. In most species studied, secretion of prolactin during lactation is critical for galactopoiesis, since experiments which reduce serum prolactin concentrations markedly reduce or even stop milk production. By contrast, in cattle, circulating concentrations of prolactin are certainly not limiting in that neither reductions in prolactin concentrations to very low levels nor administration of exogenous prolactin appreciably alters milk production. Circulating concentrations of growth hormone, however, are closely associated with maintenance or enhanced milk production. For example, genetically superior dairy cattle exhibit increased basal circulating concentrations of growth hormone and capacity to secrete growth hormone. There is also ample evidence that administration of exogenous growth hormone increases milk production. Such increases are associated with parallel increases in mammary blood flow, increased nutrient mobilization from body stores, increased voluntary feed intake, and greater efficiency of nutrient absorption from the intestinal tract. The marked physiological adjustments needed to sustain high levels of milk production in superior dairy animals are dramatic and regulated by actions of the endocrine system.

C. Local Tissue Regulators

While the ovary is a primary regulator of mammary development via its production of estrogens and progesterone, increasing evidence suggests that at least some of the effects of the classic mammary mitogens (estrogens, progesterone, prolactin, and growth hormone) are mediated indirectly. Specifically, production of IGFs and their binding proteins within the mammary gland likely modulate mammary development via paracrine and/or autocrine modes of action. Production of IGFs is believed to be associated with stromal cells and the binding proteins associated with the epithelial cells. Especially in rodents, EGF and TGF-α appear to be naturally important mammary mitogens. The number of EGF receptors changes in correspondence with mammary growth (i.e., highest in mid-gestation, lowest in lactation). Furthermore, apparent number of EGF receptors is increased in the distal areas of elongating mammary end-buds. TGF-α mRNA has been localized in ductular and alveolar epithelial cells in mammary tissue from rats and humans.

Mammary growth ultimately depends on a balance of positive growth stimulators and growth inhibitors which act to prevent inappropriate proliferation. A number of proteins with growth inhibiting properties have been described. These include the transforming growth factor-β family (TGF-β), interferons, and tumor necrosis factor (TNF). A protein referred to as mammostatin, isolated from mammary cell culture media, has been shown to inhibit the proliferation of a variety of both normal and tumorgenic mammary epithelial cells but not other types of cells. Another 13-kDa inibitory protein—mammary-derived growth inhibitor (MDGI)—has been isolated from the bovine mammary gland. The protein is structurally distinct from known growth factors and tissue concentrations of MDGI are high in tissue from lactating cows but low in tissue taken after cessation of milking. A reduction in concentration of the inhibitor would be consistent with the need for proliferation of mammary cells to begin a subsequent lactation following a nonlactating period. TGF-β, which consists of five closely related polypeptides, was first described on the basis of the ability of the molecules to promote anchorage independent growth of rat kidney cells. Since that time, TGF-β2 has been isolated from cows' milk and expression of mRNAs for TGF-β1,2, and 3 have been studied by *in situ* hybridization in bovine mammary tissue. Greatest amounts of TGF-β1 were in the alveolar cells, with lesser expression in subepithelial areas. Unlike TGF-β1 and 3, TGF-β2 was expressed only in the epithelial cells of the mammary gland. Experimentally, local implants of TGF-β1 reversibly inhibit proliferation of end-buds in rodents and proliferation of mammary cells in culture.

IV. Molecular Biology, Transgenic Animals, and Milk Production

A. Mammary Gland as Bioreactor

Likely no single aspect of biotechnology has elicited a greater array of hopes, concerns, wishes, and promises than the opportunity of engineering "new and improved" animals. One aspect of this speculation specific to lactation is the use of the mammary gland as a bioreactor for the biosynthesis of important proteins. Production of recombinant proteins via activation of foreign genes in bacterial cell cultures is a reality for several structurally simple proteins (insulin, human and bovine growth hormone, interferons, EGF, etc.). However, bacterial cells lack the ability to process (glycosylation, secretion) other clinically or economically important complex proteins because these cells lack the biochemical machinery. This has resulted in a search for other systems to make these proteins. In some cases cultures of mammalian cells are successful but on a large scale such systems are technically difficult to maintain. The mammary gland with its pronounced capacity to synthesize and secrete a variety of proteins in a manner for easy harvest (milk) is an apparent alternative. Simplistically, the idea involves production of a cDNA containing the gene of interest, linking it to a promoter region for one of the specific milk proteins, delivering the hybrid gene construct to the fertilized egg (most often by microinjection), incorporation of the gene construct into the embryonic genome, breeding, induction of lactation in female gene recipients, and testing of milk to determine if synthesis of the gene product is directed into milk. Given the uncertainties of successful incorporation of constructs following microinjection and subsequent mammary expression, production of transgenic cattle is sure to be an expensive, patience requiring activity. Regardless, successful production of pigs producing human protein C and sheep expressing human α-1-antitrypsin in their milk forecasts the practical generation of dairy ruminants producing recombinant proteins in their milk. [*See* TRANSGENIC ANIMALS.]

B. Molecular Mechanisms of Milk Synthesis

A secondary consequence of biotechnology applied to lactation will be an explosion of knowledge concerning details of mammary function. It will be a challenge to integrate facts derived from model systems, determine relevance to animal agriculture, and to design strategies for a positive impact on production. Although likely few dairy producers will be directly involved in efforts to supply transgenic proteins, related efforts to modify normal milk constituents could have widespread impact. Reduction of lactose content of milk (less water to transport, improved cheese-making capacity), suppression of β-

lactoglobulin synthesis for milk destined for infants, and modifications of fat content or composition are appropiate targets. Other possibilities might include: increased activity of mammary desaturase enzyme to increase unsaturated fatty acids in milk, secretion of protectors against proteolysis or lipolysis to improve storage of milk, or activation of receptors for immunoglobulins in the mature gland to improve the immune competence of milk. It might also be reasonable to direct the secretion of known growth factors or other biologically active proteins into milk to promote the development or performance of suckling young or to prepare milk for a specific therapeutic need.

Although lactation can be viewed as simply the end of the reproductive cycle, it is clear that the mammary gland and its activity provide a fertile ground for numerous scientific specialists. Tumor biologists, immunologists, and microbiologists seek to control breast cancer and mastitis. Endocrinologists, cell biologists, and the newly arrived molecular biologists scurry for the Rosetta Stone to interpret the language of the chemical milieu that drives mammogenesis, lactogenesis, and galactopoiesis. It is somehow fitting that the mammary gland, long the symbol of nurturing and care, should fill this scientific role and perhaps, as a consequence of

biotechnological intervention provide even more than food to human society.

Bibliography

Akers, R. M. (1990). Lactation physiology: A ruminant animal perspective. *Protoplasma* **159**, 96–111.

Cowie, A. T., Forsyth, I. A., and Hart, I. C. (1980). "Hormonal Control of Lactation." Springer-Verlag, Berlin.

Forsyth, I. A. (1991). The mammary gland. *Baillier's Clin. Endocrinol. Metab.* **5**, 809–832.

Mepham, T. B. (1983). "Biochemistry of Lactation." Elsevier, Amsterdam.

Neville, M. C., and Daniel, C. W. (1987). "The Mammary Gland." Plenum, New York and London.

Peaker, M., Vernon, R. G., and Knight, C. H. (1984). "Physiological Strategies in Lactation." The Zoological Society of London, Symposium Number 51, Academic Press, Orlando.

Sheffield, L. G. (1988). Organization and growth of mammary epithelia in the mammary gland fat pad. *J. Dairy Sci.* **71**, 2855–2874.

Topper, Y. J., and Freeman, C. S. (1980). Multiple hormone interactions in the developmental biology of the mammary gland. *Physiol. Rev.* **60**, 1049–1106.

Tucker, H. A. (1987). Quantitative estimates of mammary growth during various physiological states: A review. *J. Dairy Sci.* **70**, 1958–1966.

Land Use Planning in Agriculture

MARLOW VESTERBY, HENRY BUIST, *USDA-Economic Research Service*[1]

Glossary

Agricultural land Rural land including farmland, non–Federal rangeland, and any other lands that can be used for crops or pasture, such as portions of wildlife refuges; agricultural land excludes some rural land such as forest land, parks, roads, and wildlife refuge areas not in crops and pasture

Easement Agreement held by an individual or public trust that entitles the holder to certain rights, typically in exchange for payments

Farmland Land in farms, including cropland, pasture, and land that is part of a farm but idle; in 1987, the U.S. Census of Agriculture defined a farm as any place generating agricultural sales of $1000 or more

Infrastructure Roads, sewers, schools, hospitals, and other facilities that provide services to a community

Land trust Organization established to hold property for special uses

Market values Prices at which both buyers and sellers are willing to do business

Rural land All land not classified as urban, including agricultural land, farmland, cropland, rangeland, and forest land; it includes land owned by local, state, and Federal governments

Urban land Land for residential, commercial, industrial, institutional, transportation, communications, utilities, and other built-up uses

Urbanization The conversion of rural land to urban uses

Land use planning, in a broad sense, is the collection of Federal, state, and local government financial, production, regulatory, and other activities that influence the location, amount, and rate of change of major land uses. Policy instruments used under the rubric of "planning" include the public provision of infrastructure, tax laws, subsidy programs, zoning, impact fees, and development rights purchases, to name a few. The purpose of the policies is to address problems caused by conflicting land uses. Land use planning in the United States is left mostly to the states which usually delegate it to counties, cities, and towns. States may provide enabling legislation to help local planning efforts. While the Federal government manages land use on Federally owned lands, it seldom participates directly at state and local levels. However, Federal law does encourage U.S. agencies to find alternatives when their actions might result in damage to important agricultural lands. For example, plans might be changed to relocate a Federal facility to avoid using "prime" agricultural land.

Only limited attempts have been made to coordinate land use policies across and within the three levels of government, to reconcile conflicts in the objectives of urban and rural planning, or to establish a coherent system of rights and entitlements between developers, land-owners, current and future residents, and their political representatives. For brevity, this article focuses on land use policies that specifically apply to rural communities where the principle concern is the protection of farmland against conversion to urban uses. Some attention is given to the relation between agricultural planning and broader land use problems.

[1] The views expressed are the authors' and do not necessarily represent policies or views of the U.S. Department of Agriculture.

I. An Inventory of Major Land Uses

The classification of land into its various uses and how these uses change over time provide the background to planning issues. There are about 2.3 billion acres of land in the United States (Table I). In 1987, 56 million acres were urban (residential, industrial, commercial, institutional). Rural land (everything not urban) encompasses forest land, rangeland, cropland, and pasture, and other uses such as roads, parks, and swamps. Less than one-half of rural land qualifies as land in farms according to the U.S. Bureau of the Census definition of farms. There were 964 million acres of land in farms and 1.2 billion acres of other rural land. "Land in farms" does not include public rangeland grazed on a permit or most forest land.

A. Urban Land

From 1960 to 1990 urban land increased by 119%, from 26 to 56 million acres (Table II). Despite the large rate of increase, urban land occupied less than 2.5% of total land area in the United States in 1990. The rate of expansion decreased from 37% in the 1970s to 18% in the 1980s.

B. Range

From 1950 to 1987, grassland pasture and range (which excludes cropland used only for pasture and

TABLE I
Major Uses of Land in the United States (1987)

Major land use	Land in farms[a]	Other rural land	All land
	Million acres		
Urban		56	56
Rural	964	1245	2209
Range	410	181	591
Cropland and pasture	443	21	464
Farmsteads and roads	7	0	7
Forest[b]	80	651	731
Other rural land[c]	24	392	416
Total U.S. land[d]	964	1301	2265

Sources: U.S. Department of Commerce (1989). "1987 Census of Agriculture," AC87-A-51. Daugherty, A. B. (1991). "Major Uses of Land in the United States: 1987," AER-643, Economic Research Service. USDA.
[a] "Land in farms" must generate at least $1000 in product sales according to the Bureau of Census definition of a farm.
[b] Includes timber land and reserved timber land, both Federal and non-Federal; parks; wildlife areas; and other special use areas.
[c] Includes areas used for transportation, recreation, defense, swamps, bare rock areas and deserts.
[d] Includes Alaska and Hawaii.

TABLE II
Urban Land Area in the United States

Year	Total	Rural	Urban	Urban area percentage increase
	Million acres			
1990	2263	2207	56	18%
1980	2265	2218	47	37%
1970	2264	2229	35	36%
1960	2266	2241	26	—

Sources: Frey, H. T. (1983). "Expansion of Urban Area in the United States: 1960–80." Staff Report AGES830615. U.S. Department of Agriculture, Washington, DC. U.S. Department of Commerce (1992). "Population and Housing Units by Urban and Rural." U.S. Department of Commerce (1988). "Statistical Abstract of the United States: 1988," 108th ed.

grazed forest land) decreased from 701 to 591 million acres, 16%. Over 90% of all rangeland is west of the Mississippi River. When grazed forest land and cropland pasture are included with grassland pasture and range, the combined use accounts for over one-third of the total land area in the United States, including Alaska and Hawaii. [*See* RANGELAND MANAGEMENT AND PLANNING.]

C. Cropland and Pasture

Since 1945, cropland and pasture in the United States have remained stable, at about 460 million acres (Fig. 1). However, although cropland and pasture stayed roughly constant for 42 years, other land in farms, primarily range and woodland, decreased by 15% from 1945 to 1987. Some variation occurs in cropland actually used for crops each year because of changes in government commodity programs such as the Acreage Reserve Program and the Conservation Reserve Program. In 1992, all Federal programs idled about 63 million acres of cropland. [*See* U.S. FARMS: CHANGING SIZE AND STRUCTURE.]

D. Forest Land

Forest land decreased from 773 to 731 million acres from 1959 to 1987. Forest land includes timberland and special use land in parks and wildlife areas. Land in special uses increased while timberland decreased.

E. Other Rural Land

Other rural land includes special and miscellaneous uses such as rural transportation, defense areas, marshes, open swamps, bare rock areas, deserts, and

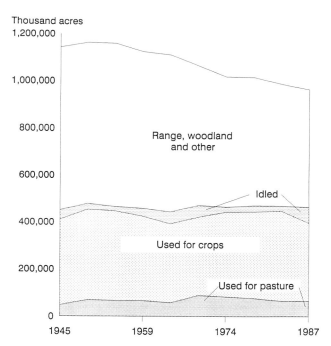

FIGURE 1 Use of land in farms in the United States 1945–1987. [*Source:* Daugherty, A. B. (1991). "Major Uses of Land in the United States: 1987." AER-643. Economic Research Service, U.S. Department of Agriculture. Krupa, K. S., and Daugherty, A. B. (1990). "Major Land Uses." Data product 89003. Economic Research Service, U.S. Department of Agriculture.]

recreation and wildlife areas not included as forest land. Other rural land increased from 1959 to 1987 from 389 to 416 million acres (7%), primarily due to increases in recreation and wildlife areas.

II. Dynamics of Land Use Change

Most land is in the same use from the beginning to the end of a decade. However, some land uses do change. Furthermore, changes are dynamic in the sense that a use such as cropland may lose and gain area over the same period. Cropland may convert to range, and range may convert to cropland; the same dynamic process happens with forest land. In contrast, shifts to urban land are essentially irreversible—once urbanized, land seldom converts back to a rural use.

A. Land Use Change Studies

Several studies examine land use change in the United States. The Economic Research Service (ERS) of the U.S. Department of Agriculture (USDA) has docu-

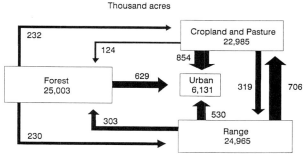

FIGURE 2 Shifts in major land uses: fast-growth counties, 1970–1980. Numbers in boxes are 1970; numbers along arrows are changes from 1970 to 1980. Cropland and pasture include feed lots, orchards, ornamentals, and other miscellaneous agricultural land. Forest includes wetland. About 250,000 acre of miscellaneous minor uses that converted to urban are not shown. [*Source:* Heimlich, R. E., Vesterby, M., and Krupa, K. S. (1991). "Urbanizing Farmland: Dynamics of Land Use Change in Fast-Growth Counties," AIB-629. Economic Research Service, U.S. Department of Agriculture.]

mented land use changes in the fast-growth counties of the 1970s. Counties qualified as fast growth if they had at least 25,000 residents and a 25% increase in population over the decade. There were only 139 such counties in the 1970s (4.5% of all 3100 U.S. counties), but these fast-growth counties accounted for about 50% of the 1970s' population increase in the United States. Shifts in major land uses, shown by the arrows in Fig. 2, depict changes to and from each use over the decade.

B. Large Urban Increases Small Rural Decreases

The ERS study showed that the residential component of urban land increased by 50%, the largest gain of all categories (Fig. 3). Commercial land claimed the second largest increase, 35%, during the decade. Gains for one major land use mean losses for another. Forest, cropland, pasture, rangeland, and wetland all had net losses during the decade. Because rural categories had large beginning bases, percentage losses were small—3.9% for cropland and pasture and 2.8% for forest land.

Land in a use category at the beginning of a decade tended to stay in that category during the decade. The ERS study showed that over 90% of all major land uses in 1970 were still in the same land use in 1980 (Table III). Residential land was especially immutable, remaining over 99% urban from the beginning to the end of the decade.

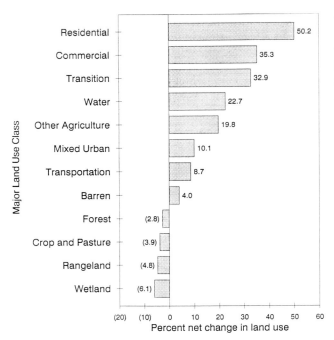

FIGURE 3 Net changes in major land uses. [*Source:* Heimlich, R. E., Vesterby, M., and Krupa, K. S. (1991). "Urbanizing Farmland: Dynamics of Land Use Change in Fast-Growth Counties," AIB-629. Economic Research Service, U.S. Department of Agriculture.

C. Rates of Urban Conversion

Estimates of rural to urban conversion rates vary depending on the sources of data for a particular study and the definitions used. The ERS study estimated rural to urban conversion in the United States at 740 thousand acres per year during the 1970s. Using the U.S. Bureau of the Census definition of urban area, the annual rate of urbanization was 913, 1269, and 861 thousand acres in the 1960s, 1970s, and 1980s, respectively. An estimate derived from the National Resources Inventory conducted by the Soil Conservation Service of the USDA showed 726 thousand acres per year urbanized from 1982 to 1987.

Urban conversions of rural land depend on demographic and economic factors. The ratio of land use change per household is a more useful relationship for analysis and projection than change per person, since most decisions about new residential development depend on households, not each individual. According to the ERS fast-growth study, the amount of land consumed by each additional household was 0.47 acres (Table IV). In a similar study of rapidly growing counties in the 1960s the rate was almost the same, 0.46 acres. However, these coefficients vary by locality depending on previous urbanization, land costs, and infilling of urbanized areas.

D. Urban Expansion Greatest in Southern States

The ERS study found that the Southeast and Southwest had the greatest urban expansion during the 1970s, 43 and 44%, respectively. The Southwest had the greatest percentage increase in households, 73% (Fig. 4). The North had the smallest increase, 28%. The results reflect difference in the stages of economic development in the South and the North and may reflect a "sunbelt" shift of population from colder northern climates to warmer southern states.

TABLE III
Distribution of Land Use: Fast-Growth Counties (1970s)

1980s land uses	Urban	Cropland and pasture	Range	Forest	Other	Total
1970s land uses			Percent[a]			
Urban	<u>98.8</u>	0.3	0.7	0.1	0.2	100
Cropland, pasture, and range	4.3	<u>93.4</u>	1.4	0.5	0.4	100
Range	2.8	2.8	<u>92.5</u>	1.2	0.7	100
Forest	3.2	0.8	0.9	<u>94.9</u>	0.3	100
Other	1.7	1.4	2.3	0.7	<u>93.8</u>	100

Source: Vesterby, M. (1988). "Land Use Change in the 1970s." Data Product 88018. Economic Research Service, U.S. Department of Agriculture.
[a] The diagonal (underlined numbers) shows percentage of land remaining in its use through the 1970s. The off-diagonal shows the percentage of 1970 land uses (left column) that converted to land uses in the 1980s (top row).

TABLE IV
Demographic and Land Use Change: Fast-Growth Counties, 1960–1980

Year and category	Population	Households	Persons per household	All urban Total	All urban Per household	Residential Total	Residential Per household	Nonresidential Total	Nonresidential Per household
	Million	Million	Number	1000 acres	Acres	1000 acres	Acres	1000 acres	Acres
1960s study[a]									
1960	11.1	3.1	—	2748	—	1454	—	1294	—
1970	16.3	4.8	—	3523	—	1918	—	1605	—
Difference	5.2	1.7	—	775	—	464	—	311	—
Average									
1960	—	—	3.54	—	0.87	—	0.46	—	0.41
1970	—	—	3.37	—	0.73	—	0.40	—	0.33
Marginal[b]	—	—	3.06	—	0.46	—	0.27	—	0.18
1970s study									
1970	24.2	7.5	—	6485	—	3854	—	2631	—
1980	35.2	12.5	—	8865	—	5728	—	3136	—
Difference	11.0	5.1	—	2380	—	1874	—	505	—
Average									
1970	—	—	3.23	—	0.87	—	0.51	—	0.35
1980	—	—	2.81	—	0.71	—	0.46	—	0.25
Marginal[b]	—	—	2.18	—	0.47	—	0.37	—	0.10

Sources: Heimlich, R. E., and Vesterby, M. (1992). Farmland Loss to Urban Encroachment No Threat to U.S. Agriculture. "Rural Development Perspectives." **8**(1), 2–7. Economic Research Service, U.S. Department of Agriculture. Zeimetz *et al.* (1976). "Dynamics of Land Use in Fast Growth Areas," AER-325. Economic Research Service, U.S. Department of Agriculture.
[a] Fifty-three counties with greater than 20,000 population gain and at least 30% increase between 1960 and 1970.
[b] Net change in urban land divided by the change in household numbers.

III. Legal and Economic Context of Agricultural Land Use Planning

What justifies land use planning? Why not let the free market allocate land into competing uses over time? Most economic arguments supporting intervention claim to have identified "market failure," the inability of markets to achieve efficient allocations of goods and services. The following hypothetical scenario captures many aspects of market failure argument as it pertains to the rural–urban land conversion problem.

Recent public investments in roads and sewers by a nearby urban government have greatly increased the market values of a nearby community of farms. Farm owners next to the urban area are faced with the choice of selling to developers and realizing substantial capital gains or holding out, either in anticipation of higher land values or because of personal reasons. These personal reasons may be sufficiently strong to encourage farmers to form a temporary alliance against selling out. However, in time, some farmers do sell all or parts of their farms. Those remaining suffer increased urban congestion and complaints about unpleasant odors and noises associated with farming. Eventually, the character of agriculture changes in response to demands from new urban residents. Remaining farms, that once raised hogs, chickens, livestock, small grains, and hay crops, shift to intensive agriculture—fruits, vegetables, and nursery products. Because of the changes, some local farm supply dealers leave the area or go out of business. Others begin supplying lawn and garden products to new urbanites or specialize in supplies needed for the new intensive agriculture. In the long run, many of the farms on the rural-urban fringe convert to urban uses.

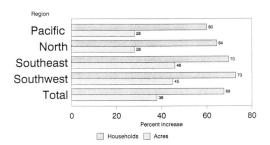

FIGURE 4 Household and urban area increase: Fast-growth counties, 1970–1980. [*Source:* Vesterby, M. (1988). "Land Use Change in the 1970's." Data Product 88018. Economic Research Service, USDA.

Many variations of the scenario exist, but the above example illustrates the main points of contention. The problem begins with public infrastructure investments for roads and sewers. When these investments result in a gain or loss to others who had no financial interest in the activity, we have what economists refer to as an externality or entitlement problem. Beneficial and adverse externalities accrue to farmers who did not finance construction of the infrastructure. Reduced land values may occur for some farmers further from the new urban center. Other farmers, closer to the new development, experience increased land values caused by new urbanization. When some land sales occur the alliance of farmers fails, resulting in potentially numerous conversions. Economics of agglomeration draw economic activities together, creating urban areas. As farms are sold, the old interdependence among farmers' production supply and marketing activities changes, causing a restructuring of agriculture in the area.

How do writers of U.S. land use policies attempt to resolve the economic conflicts exemplified in the scenario? The Tenth Amendment to the U.S. Constitution gives the states powers not delegated to the Federal government. Enabling legislation from state governments endows thousands of local jurisdictions in the United States with considerable autonomy over zoning plans, property taxes, and the provision of public goods and services. Local powers may be constrained by Federal laws and statutes, such as the takings clause of the Fifth Amendment to the U.S. Constitution, or a state law, such as Proposition 13 in California. (The Fifth Amendment of the U.S. Constitution states, in part, ". . . nor shall private property be taken for public use without just compensation." Proposition 13 places limits on property tax assessments.) This decentralized approach to land use policy is decisively American: the expression of societal preferences necessarily strikes some balance between equity, efficiency, and liberty (autonomy). In land market allocations, U.S. institutions seem to favor autonomy, sometimes at the expense of efficiency and equity. For example, in the scenario, a regional planning agency may have recognized the effect that the new infrastructure would have had on the farm sector and could have suggested an alternative plan (although there is no guarantee that they would). The process of deciding land use in the United States seldom includes selling development rights. To achieve equity and efficiency gains, a redistribution or trading of development rights may be one possible alternative.

IV. Objectives of Agricultural Land Use Planning

Governmental entities plan land use for many reasons. In agricultural areas, a common reason cited is to maintain the Nation's capacity to produce food and fiber. This and other reasons are discussed below.

A. Maintenance of Open Space

Preservation programs sometimes purchase land or development rights to provide open space for esthetic and environmental reasons. Urban dwellers often enjoy visiting rural areas as a respite from central city living.

B. Environmental Protection

Areas protected from development may help preserve and improve water and air quality. Undeveloped watersheds, for example, can buffer streams and rivers from soil sediments, pesticides, and other residues. Vegetative planting, the construction of dams and diversions, streambank stabilization, and other measures preserve or restore water and air quality in watersheds.

C. Prevention of Urban Sprawl

Urban sprawl denotes scattered, "buckshot," or "leapfrog" development erratically spread through a predominantly rural area. The nuisances associated with urban sprawl—such as congestion and crime—and the nuisances of agricultural production—such as odor, dust, and pesticide usage—often render urban and rural land uses incompatible. Various planning devices, such as zoning and agricultural districts, are designed to separate land uses to avoid conflicts.

D. Controlling Infrastructure Costs

By keeping development within growth boundaries that delineate eligibility for public services, the costs of providing roads, schools, and hospitals are lower than if spread over wider, less densely populated areas. This planning tool occasionally faces legal challenges similar to those faced by exclusionary zoning.

E. Preserving the Local Farm Economy

Some farming locales may specialize in the production of crops grown exclusively in the area or that have

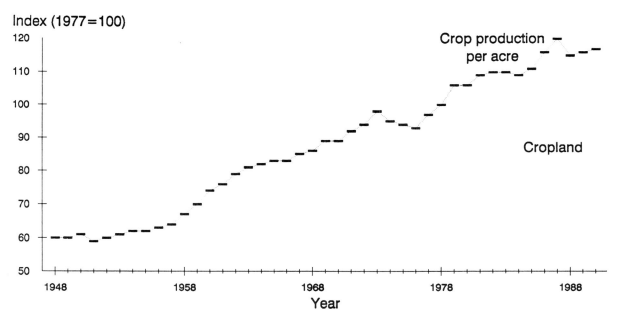

FIGURE 5 Cropland and productivity: United States, 1949–1990. [*Source:* Heimlich, R. E., Vesterby, M., and Krupa, K. S. (1991). "Urbanizing Farmland: Dynamics of Land Use Change in Fast-Growth Counties," AIB-629. Economic Research Service, USDA.]

unique brand names or slogans. Managing the rate and location of urbanization may prevent cases where interdependent farm sectors lose viability due to the high property taxes based on urban development potential, the loss of supporting farm businesses, and the nuisance of road and neighborhood congestion. [*See* RURAL SOCIOLOGY.]

F. Assuring Food and Fiber Production

The preservation of cropland to maintain the capacity of the Nation or a region to produce food and fiber has been a strong motivation for public efforts to save farmland, particularly, prime agricultural land. Nationally, however, protecting food and fiber production has no real urgency. Cropland productivity in the United States doubled since 1949 and will likely increase in the future with productivity gains from new technology (Fig. 5). While urbanization converts about three-fourths to one million acres per year of rural land, only about one-third of that is from cropland and pasture, which is partly replaced by conversion from forest and range lands. Government programs designed to reduce surpluses, by setting aside cropland in acreage reserves, and encouraging agricultural exports through export enhancements, reveal the basic strength of the U. S. agricultural sector. In the unlikely event of a food crisis, reserved crop land

could quickly be brought back into production if needed. Regionally, however, some areas, such as the Northeast, have lost substantial farmland acreage. Several programs have been developed to protect against further losses.

V. Agricultural Planning Tools and Legislation

Losses of rural land to urban uses became a major concern of public policy during the mid-1970s, and in response, a variety of new legislation started to appear. Private conservation initiatives—such as the establishment of special land trusts—also have been developed in an attempt to save farmland and to achieve land use policy objectives. Public initiatives to protect rural lands have originated at all three levels of government—Federal, state, and local—but never have been coordinated into a cohesive national policy.

A. Direct Federal Role in Farmland Protection

1. As part of the 1981 omnibus farm legislation, the Farmland Protection Policy Act encourages Federal agencies to identify adverse effects of programs on farmland conservation and to minimize the extent to

which Federal programs contribute to unnecessary farmland conversion.

2. Section 170(h) of the Internal Revenue Code enables taxpayers to claim income tax deductions for charitable contributions of development rights easements to qualifying nonprofit organizations. Such tax advantages provide an incentive for participation in private farmland protection programs, such as the American Farmland Trust or similar regional and local land trusts.

3. The Farms for the Future Act, a small part of the 1990 omnibus farm bill, established the Agricultural Resource Conservation Demonstration Program. This program provides Federal guarantees and interest rate assistance for loans made by lending institutions to state trust funds that invest in the protection or preservation of farmland for agricultural purposes. For example, an authorized agency of a state government could use the loans to purchase development rights on farmland. [*See* GOVERNMENT AGRICULTURAL POLICY, UNITED STATES.]

B. Indirect Federal Role

Besides these three explicit Federal laws, there are several indirect Federal tax regulations that influence land use. The impact of these regulations on the amount and value of farmland preserved is largely unknown. However, for some regulations, it is possible to surmise whether the impact tends to favor or dissuade farmland preservation.

1. Capital gains are taxed on realization instead of accrual under current U.S. law. Farmers who would receive real estate capital gains by selling to an urban developer have an incentive to postpone selling so that farm real estate values can continue to accrue without the penalty of capital gains taxes that would be levied at the time of sale. In short, the "*lock-in effect*" applies to real estate just as it does to any other capital asset and results in an inadvertent contribution to farmland protection.

2. The *deductibility* of debt interest payments and state and local taxes from income that is Federally taxable also influences a farmer's sell or hold decision. For example, deducting local property taxes is analogous to a farm sector investment tax credit or depreciation allowance (taking into account that the former is a deduction from income and the latter a direct tax credit). The deductibility of property taxes provides an incentive for employing investment capital (such as farmland) resulting in lower user costs of capital

and higher investment in the farm sector compared to the case in which no deductibility is allowed.

3. A potential offset to the above farmland protection benefit, however, is that the urban sector receives the same deductions. The deductibility of mortgage interest payments and local property taxes to a whole community of new urban dwellers would likely overwhelm the same deductibility value to the single farm owner–dweller whose land could be used to build the new community. Thus, the deductibility provisions in the Federal tax code can impart a bias for urban use over less dense rural uses of land, since urbanites have an indirect incentive to raise their bid for farmland.

This bias is intensified in a subtle way. Federal tax laws provide capital gains tax *exclusions* to homeowners who sell their existing homes and "trade-up" to more expensive ones. To the extent that urban dwellers trade-up by giving developers market signals to increase the urban boundary, the urban-valued bids for farmland capitalize the tax breaks and make the increased bids more attractive to the farm owner. The people who lose by the shifting of tax benefits are the urban and rural residents who are averse to increasing urbanization and the disamenities it can bring, such as congestion, or who enjoy the direct amenities provided by farm living on the urban fringe.

4. While the lock-in, deductibility, and exemption features of the Federal tax code have an ambiguous net influence on farmland preservation, the Federal farm programs should retard conversions of farmland to urban uses to the extent that recipients of program benefits are located in urbanizing areas. In 1990, farmers received $9 billion in direct government payments for participating in Federal commodity and soil conservation programs. The farm subsidies average about $10,000 per year for each farm that participates in the programs. However, farms at the rural–urban fringe probably tend to be smaller than average and concentrate more on nonprogram crops, such as fruits, vegetables, and nursery products. Government program subsidies for these farms are likely much less than the National average. Nevertheless, the Federal farm programs can financially assist farmers to remain in farming despite competing urban pressures.

C. State and Local Farmland Protection

There are several state and local farmland protection programs.

1. Use Value Assessment (UVA)

Aiken's survey of state laws up to 1989 revealed that all 50 states have enabling legislation that permits the portion of market or urban value that exceeds agricultural use value on farms to be exempt from local property taxation. By 1988, 27 states authorized the taxing jurisdiction to recover deferred taxes ("roll-back" penalties), and many of these states allowed interest to be charged on the deferred taxes. Six states required the landowner to enter an explicit agreement to restrict land use (easement). State laws enumerate which lands are eligible for the program, how to calculate market and use values, what interest rates and capitalization rates to use, and what rollback penalties apply after shifting into nonfarm uses.

A benefit of UVA is that it lessens the farmers' liquidity problem. If urban pressures increase property values, taxing the farmer on actual instead of use value could force the farmer to sell to an urban bidder just to pay taxes. In addition, Federal laws require payment of capital gains taxes on realization, not on accrual of value. In contrast, in the absence of UVA at the local level, property taxes would be based on accrual. Finally, the pattern of accrual is not easily observable by tax assessors unless transactions take place, but then it is too late to preserve the farmland. Of the many criticisms of UVA, four of the most common criticisms are:

a. The local tax burden shifts from the urbanizing farm sector to other areas, including other farmers who have not realized a gain in property values and cannot benefit from UVA. In other words, the tax burden is shifted to others who do not or cannot participate in a UVA. However, rollback provisions may ameliorate some of the shift.

b. The tax breaks decrease the holding costs of land speculation, providing pressure for more urban conversion.

c. The tax breaks can benefit any owner of agricultural land and not just farm owner–operators.

d. The value of the tax break is small compared to potentially large capital gains, so the farmer might sell even if there were no local taxes. The penalties are often not severe enough to prevent conversion to nonagricultural uses.

In view of these issues, many argue that UVA does not work to protect farmland from urban development and that it results in unintended and even regressive income redistribution. Other criticisms could be based on how UVA is administered, such as the selection of ad-hoc capitalization rates that are used in income-capitalization formulas and the ways farm income is estimated.

Many states have adopted rollback provisions that require payment of all or part of the taxes deferred by UVA when the farm is sold. These penalties are an attempt to remedy some criticisms just itemized. First, the unintended tax shifting is redressed if the farmer has to pay deferred taxes when he sells or converts to nonfarm use. Second, by charging the rollback, selling becomes less profitable since some of those profits are paid in back taxes, presumably strengthening the local property tax lock-in effect that aids farmland protection by lengthening the farmer's holding period. However, the last argument is true only if the farmer has committed to the UVA program and if the program has a mandatory rollback provision. Prior to participation, UVA with a full rollback (with interest on the deferred taxes) will make the farmer "holding-period neutral": the farmer's after tax rate of return on farmland as an asset would not depend on the holding period if UVA had a full rollback. In practice, most states only have a partial rollback, which is a futile compromise between wanting to create a local lock-in effect but not wanting to deter participation.

The objectives of protecting farmland from urbanization and having a sensible and equitable local property tax system do not appear to be jointly achievable. The farmers' liquidity problem may be softened by UVA, but rollback provisions, which are analogous to Federal capital gains tax laws, are used to more evenly distribute tax burdens. Otherwise, the beneficiaries of property value appreciation do not compensate the community for the public investments that helped create the urban land value nor do they repay the tax breaks provided. In fact, more states are moving to the use of rollbacks to recoup deferred taxes even though such penalties can weaken the local lock-in effect and undermine farmland protection.

2. Purchase of Development Rights (PDR)

By 1991, about 14 states, mostly in the Northeast and mid-Atlantic regions, had established purchase-of-development-rights programs, to go beyond UVA's ability to control farmland losses. Under these policies, state and local governments can acquire easements which transfer the rights to develop land from private to public ownership in exchange for payment. Landowners retain ownership of the residual land use rights. Administration of PDRs occurs mostly at the state level and sometimes entails cost-sharing with local jurisdictions. The eligibility of land depends on the trade-offs inherent in such factors as the cost of the easements, the degree of development pressure, soil types of the land, the specific land use, and others. Methods of funding include issuing bonds, collecting real estate transfer taxes, and earmarking general revenues for the programs. The price of an easement is equal to the approximate difference between the farmland's estimated market and agricultural use value.

Unlike zoning, which sometimes conflicts with the takings doctrine of the Fifth Amendment, PDR programs are based on voluntary participation by farmers who are compensated for separating and transferring the development rights of their land from the broader bundle of rights associated with land ownership. Since only the margin of market value above use value has to be paid, PDR programs demand fewer public funds than would be needed for a program which purchases land outright. An advantage the PDR program has over UVA is its ability to target threatened farmland without providing benefits to all parcels.

PDR programs are also subject to criticisms.

a. The programs are expensive and can be difficult to budget, especially when state and local governments are having fiscal problems.
b. Despite some advantages over UVA, PDR programs also have the targeting problem. The farmers with the least opportunities to convert have the most to gain by voluntarily coming forward to negotiate an easement. In contrast, the farmer who is simply ready to retire and take his pension as a capital gain may not volunteer for an easement.
c. Like squeezing a balloon, placing easements on some parcels merely increases the urbanizing pressure on unprotected parcels and can result in leapfrog development that is even more incoherent than would have resulted without interference.
d. Estimations of market and use values are as prone to inaccuracies as they are in UVA.

The effectiveness of both PDR and UVA is not independent of the characteristics of a particular parcel nor even the socioeconomic characteristics of the farm-owner. The path of development can depend on such things as the location of existing infrastructure, and the timing of development can depend on such things as the farm-owner's age and income.

3. Other Methods of Farmland Protection

Local governments or regional bodies implement exclusive and nonexclusive zones where development is restricted and farming is the preferred use. These *land use regulations and zoning* laws include state comprehensive planning requiring counties and municipalities to prepare and execute land use plans and ordinances. State or regional land use regulations may have many goals, but primarily focus on controlling growth associated with large developments that have multi-jurisdictional effects. States usually delegate regulation and zoning authority to local governments. About thirty states had such regulations as of 1991.

Transfer of Development Rights (TDR) programs have been used to compensate farm-owners who have had the urban value of their land zoned away. Under the program, developers must buy development rights from a landowner in an agriculturally preserved area and exercise it in an area in which development is permitted. TDRs are also used, in essence, to facilitate the "sale" of zoning variances. The price of the zoning variance is the cost of having to buy compensating development rights.

Like PDRs, TDRs avoid conflicts with the takings doctrine of the Fifth Amendment by providing compensation to land owners who are subject to regulations. However, TDR programs have problems of their own. Under TDR programs, the costs of farmland protection shift to developers and can provide a significant savings to the public budget. However, developers face having to double-pay. They buy land in the urban zone and pay the urban premium and then pay another premium by purchasing development rights off other land in the preserved zone. These costs can be partly or completely shifted as higher housing prices to new residents. Thus, developers and new residents may pay for farmland preservation in other zones. Other criticisms challenge the optimality of a prespecified land-use plan, point out the difficulties of matching developers and the holders of development rights, and question the ability of TDR programs to compensate all land-owners who have had urban land value zoned away.

To briefly enumerate the remaining planning policies, every state has *Right-to-Farm laws*, which endow farmers with protection against nuisance suits in cases where farm and nonfarm interests collide. States also organize *agricultural districts* to administer farmland retention programs (such as current use assessment), require modifications to local regulations to encourage farming as a preferred use, and restrict local government authority to regulate farm structures or acquire farmland by eminent domain. Fifteen states had such programs in 1991. State *legislative or executive orders* declare the importance of agriculture to the state, address the rate and causes of farmland loss, and order state agencies to reduce or restrict activities that would convert farmland. Sixteen states have legislative or executive policies.

VI. Summary

Farmland preservation at local and state levels is an important means of maintaining open space, preventing urban sprawl, and controlling infrastructure costs. At the Federal level a primary reason cited for Federal participation in farmland preservation programs is to ensure adequate farmland for the production of food and fiber. However, urban land constitutes less than 3% of all land in the United States. Even though urban expansion has been rapid, the decrease in farmland has been small, less than 4% per decade for the 1960s and the 1970s, and the decrease was primarily from farm woodland and rangeland, not cropland. There has been no net decrease in cropland in the United States since the early 1940s.

Federal, state, and local policies directly and indirectly influence the conversion of rural lands to urban uses. Direct Federal participation in farmland protection has been small compared to state and local governments, while indirect Federal influences through tax laws could be stronger. Administration of farmland protection programs occurs at state and local levels and includes tools such as use value assessment, purchase of development rights, transfer of development rights, establishment of agricultural districts, zoning, and right to farm laws. Even though local governments have the most direct control of land use regulations, the sometimes hidden interdependencies among the policies of the three levels of government suggest that a more coordinated and comprehensive approach to land use planning stands as a serious alternative to the decentralized approach. Alternatively, policy conflicts could be mitigated within the decentralized framework by amending the appropriate laws.

Bibliography

Aiken, J. D. (1989). "State Farmland Preferential Assessment Statutes." RB-310. Agricultural Research Division, University of Nebraska. Lincoln, NE.

Bushwick, N. (1988). State and local concerns: Information needs and local actions for protecting agricultural land. *In* "Land Use Transition in Urbanizing Areas, Research and Information Needs" (R. E. Heimlich, ed.). Economic Research Service and the Farm Foundation, Washington, DC.

Bills, N. L. and R. N. Boisvert. (1988). The agricultural district approach. *In* "Land Use Transition in Urbanizing Areas, Research and Information Needs" (R. E. Heimlich, ed.). Economic Research Service and the Farm Foundation, Washington, DC.

Clark, R. T. (1977). Transferable development rights: Some problems in evaluation. *In* "Economic Issues in Land Use Planning" (D. M. Sorensen and H. H. Stoevener, eds.) WRCDC Report 3. Western Rural Development Center, Corvallis, OR.

Daugherty, A. B. (1980). Preserving farmland through federal income tax incentives. "Nat. Tax J. **33**(1), 111–115.

Dillman, B. L. (1990). A framework for evaluating land retention programs. *In* "Land Use Transition in Urbanizing Areas: Research and Information Needs" (R. E. Heimlich, ed.). Economic Research Service, U.S. Department of Agriculture and Farm Foundation, Washington, DC.

Fischel, W. A. (1982). The urbanization of agricultural land: A review of the national agricultural lands study. *Land Econom.*. **58**(2), 236–59.

Gardner, D. B. (1977). The economics of agricultural land preservation. *Am. J. Agric. Economi.* **59**(5), 1027–1044.

National Agricultural Land Study (NALS) (1981). Final Report. U.S. Government Printing Office. Washington, DC.

Public Law 97-98, 95 Stat. 1329, Title XV, Subtitle I, Farmland Protection Policy Act. Dec. 22, 1981.

Public Law 101-624, Subtitle E, Chapter 2, Farmland Protection, Nov. 28, 1990.

U.S. Department of Agriculture, Soil Conservation Service and Iowa State University Statistical Laboratory (1987). "Basic Statistics, 1982 National Resources Inventory," SB-756.

U.S. Department of Agriculture, Soil Conservation Service and Iowa State University Statistical Laboratory (1989). "Summary Report, 1987 National Resources Inventory," SB-790.

Vesterby, M. and Heimlich, R. E. (1991). Land use and demographic change: Results from fast growth counties. *Land Econom.* **67**(3), 279–91.

Vesterby, M., Heimlich, R. E., and Krupa, K. S. (1994). "Urbanization of Rural Land in the United States." Agricultural Economic Report 673. Economic Research Service, U.S. Department of Agriculture.

Williams, N. L. and Bills, N. (1991). Protecting farmland: State funded purchase of development rights (PDR) programs in the Northeast. *Policy Issues in Rural Land Use,* **4**(1). Cornell Cooperative Extension, Ithaca, NY.

Livestock Pests

S. E. KUNZ, *USDA-Agricultural Research Service, Texas*

Glossary

Ectoparasites Those arthropod species that feed or oviposit their eggs on the external body parts of the host; these parasites obtain nourishment by piercing the skin and feeding on blood or by feeding on skin debris, hair, or body secretions

IPM Combination of a number of control technologies such as use of insecticides, biological control organisms, practice of sanitary procedures, and the practice of cultural procedures integrated in such a way to cause a decrease in the pest populations

Livestock (veterinary) entomology Science of dealing with insects, ticks, and mites, that parasitize or otherwise affect a number of domestic animals, especially those livestock raised on food produce systems; the study of biological distribution, economics, and control of these pests on animal husbandry

Mange Condition caused by the feeding of several species of mites on the host. Mites feed on the surface or burrough into the skin and, while feeding, cause secretions to be produced under which they may survive and continue to reproduce

Resistance Mechanism by which an insect protects itself against pesticides applied for parasite control or mechanisms built up by the host which prevent damage of the host by a parasite or by lowering the acceptability of the parasite to the host so that parasite damage possibilities are decreased

Vector Arthropod that is capable of transmitting disease organisms from host to host causing the disease to be transferred from an infected animal to a healthy animal; some vectors are simply mechanical in nature by transferring blood cells on their mouth parts from an infested host to a healthy host, but other vectors allow the disease organisms to undergo development within the vector species for transmission to other hosts at a later time

Livestock ectoparasites include a number of insect, tick, and mite species which can cause economic damage to livestock. The study of these pests to determine their biology, ecology, and control is usually carried out by individuals trained in livestock or veterinary entomology. In many countries outside of the United States this function is often carried out by veterinarians. Ectoparasites are those pests which infest the outside of the host as compared to endoparasites which inhabit the internal system of the host, usually the digestive system.

I. Role of Ectoparasites in the Efficiency of Livestock Production

A. Type of Damage

Arthropod pests affect the efficiency of livestock production. Ectoparasites inflict damage by taking blood, transmitting diseases, and causing irritation which impedes the feeding or resting of the host. These parasites can also cut holes or otherwise blemish the hides of the animals which devalues finished leather products. They decrease weight gains and milk production as well as reduce production of wool and mohair. Some pests can predispose animals to secondary infestations by other insects or infections by other disease-causing organisms. They can cause paralysis, abortion, unthriftiness, and in severe cases cause death.

B. Production Losses

Bloodsucking flies, often called "biting" flies, attack cattle and interfere with normal feeding and resting activities. This feeding results in the loss of blood, reduced weight gains, and increased susceptibility to diseases and even death of cattle in extreme situations. These pests may also spread diseases such as anaplasmosis, anthrax, tularemia, and bluetongue. The most important biting flies are the horn fly, *Haematobia irritans,* found on cattle in pastures, and the stable fly, *Stomoxy calcitrans,* primarily found on cattle in confinement. [*See* Animal Diseases.]

The horn fly is considered the most important and economically damaging pest of range cattle and can cause weight losses up to 14%. Although losses can occur on mature cows, these animals probably compensate for this loss after the fly season. However, the weights of calves from cows experiencing fly control can be about 6 kilos per head heavier at weaning time than similar calves weaned from cows infested with horn flies. This increased gain in weight of young calves is considered to be due to increased milk production of the cow. Exact economic population thresholds for horn flies are difficult to determine. Populations in Canada of less than 100 flies per head have been said to be an economic level whereas populations of 300 to 500 flies per head are responsible for economic losses in the southern areas of the United States. [*See* Beef Cattle Production; Dairy Cattle Production.]

Stable flies on beef cattle can reduce average daily gains by about 0.25 kilos per calf in a feedlot situation. Stable flies can also reduce milk production in dairy cattle. Although stable flies have generally not been considered to be a problem on range cattle, in recent years there are more reports of the stable fly moving out into range situations. Stable flies feeding on cattle in the United States will cause economic damage and there are reports of *S. nigra* infestations in Africa causing death to animals due to exsanguination by very large numbers of flies.

Horse flies cause considerable annoyance to animals. The "bite" of a horse fly is much more irritating and the loss of blood per feeding is greater than for other biting flies. Horse flies are also vectors of anaplasmosis which results in considerable weight losses and death if left untreated. Oftentimes large numbers of horse flies or mosquitoes will feed on livestock. Generally, chemical controls provide little protection from horse flies or mosquitoes so weight gain losses and milk production losses from these pests can be expected although little specific data have been developed.

Nonbiting flies also adversely affect cattle. The face fly, *Musca autumnalis,* causes little direct damage, but contributes to the spread of pinkeye caused by *Moraxella bovis* which can result in considerable losses to range cattle. Losses attributable to face flies transmitting pinkeye are estimated at 15 kg per head in young calves at weaning time. Face flies have also been incriminated in the spread of eye worms (*Thelazia* spp.).

Cattle infested with the northern cattle grub, *Hypoderma bovis,* and the common cattle grub, *H. lineatum,* suffer considerable damage in finished carcasses as a result of the need for excessive trimming of the damaged carcass. More serious damage can occur, resulting in the downgrading of finished hides. Hide losses due to grub damage can range from $10 to 25 per head and upward to $42 losses per 1000-lb. animal from carcass trim. Weight gain losses are insignificant when compared to hide and trim losses.

Prior to 1970, cattle in the southwestern United States were attacked by the screwworm fly, *Cochliomyia hominivorax,* but a highly successful eradication campaign has eliminated this pest from the United States and Mexico. Benefits from this program are estimated at billions of dollars.

Cattle are typically infested with a number of species of lice. Cattle lice cause irritation, unthriftiness, and anemia and are most prevalent in the cooler months of the year. Losses of 0.02 kg per head (average daily gain) have been observed. Nutritional levels of the host animals will greatly affect these losses with little or no loss caused from light to moderate infestations on well-nourished animals.

Cattle are also infested with scabies and mange mites that live on or in the skin and cause severe dermatitis in the host. Losses by these parasites are limited to the colder periods of the year and not found in all states.

Cattle are parasitized by several species of ticks that feed on the blood of their host. These ticks inject toxins while feeding that can cause paralysis, damage to hides, irritation, and disease transmission. The most common ticks in the United States feed only periodically and cause limited damage. *Boophilus* ticks (Texas cattle fever ticks) have been eliminated from the United States, but threats to the United States cattle industry remain with their continued presence in Mexico and the Caribbean. These ticks are the vectors of Texas cattle fever (*Babesia bigemina*) which can cause serious losses if infected ticks are allowed to become established in areas in which ticks have been previously eliminated and animals have lost immunity to the Texas cattle fever disease. *Amblyomma variegatum*, a tick present in the Caribbean, is a vector of heartwater fever and a threat to United States cattle production. Damaging populations of endemic ticks in the United States are limited by seasonal activity. High numbers of ticks can cause economic losses due to blood loss, irritation, and decrease in milk production which can result in weight gain losses to young calves.

Sheep and goats are parasitized by arthropods that feed on blood, skin scales, hair, or wool. Some invade tissues or inhabit the nasal chambers. These pests cause decreased production of wool and mohair and can decrease the value of pelts. Sheep are infested with lice, sheep keds, and mites. Larvae of the sheep nose bot fly, *Oestrus ovis,* live on the mucous surface of the nasal passages and sinuses of sheep. The biting fly, *Culicoides variipennis,* transmits bluetongue in sheep. [*See* GOAT PRODUCTION; WOOL AND MOHAIR PRODUCTION AND PROCESSING.]

Swine in the United States are parasitized by hog lice, *Haematopinus suis,* and mange mites, *Sarcoptes scabiei suis.* These pests cause irritation, decreased weight gains, and stunted growth. Table I summarizes the potential damage of these ectoparasites. [*See* SWINE PRODUCTION.]

II. Insect Pest Management (IPM) in Livestock Pest Control

A. Principles of Control

The principal reasons for controlling ectoparasites on livestock are to reduce or to prevent losses to the

TABLE I

Potential Losses due to Ectoparasites of Cattle in the United States[a]

Pest	Total losses ($ millions)
Horn fly	876
Stable fly	432
Face fly	123
Horse fly	190
Mosquitoes	50
Cattle grub	560
Lice	38
Scabies	250
Ticks	104[b]

[a] Losses do not include cost of chemical controls and labor.
[b] Does not include quarantine cost of *Boophilus* ticks.

supply of food and fiber for humans. Since the late 1940s the main technology used to control these pests has been the application of pesticides. Generally, pesticides have been inexpensive, effective, and safe to use. It is only within the last three decades that there has been increased public concern about the possible effects of toxic substances in the environment. These concerns have brought about changes in pest control practices. Insect pest management (IPM) has resulted from these concerns and has brought about changes in control practices. In IPM programs many factors are considered before toxic chemicals are applied to animals. The ability to establish and observe economic thresholds can reduce the number of pesticide applications required to maintain pest populations at acceptable levels. In control programs, it is necessary to correctly identify the pest species in question and the magnitude of damage being done. Using information available about the biology and behavior of the pest species in question may alleviate the need for pesticide application. [*See* INTEGRATED PEST MANAGEMENT.]

Oftentimes cultural or mechanical control procedures can be initiated to eliminate the source of the infestation. Waste management, including the drying of accumulated manure in feedlots or other livestock facilities, prevents the development of several fly species and reduces or eliminates the need for pesticide application. Animals rotated away from pasture along waterways where horse flies and mosquitoes are prevalent during the summer season can reduce the intensity of feeding by these insects. [*See* ANIMAL WASTE MANAGEMENT; PEST MANAGEMENT, CULTURAL CONTROL.]

Mechanical traps can be used to trap insects such as horn flies from the backs of animals. Although developed 50 years ago these traps have been redesigned to be more efficient and can be used especially in situations where animals have access to them on a regular basis. These traps are most efficient in areas where animals are compelled to use them on a daily basis such as in paths to and from water or feed.

Biological control consists of the use of one life form to suppress populations of another. Common biological control organisms include parasites, predators, and pathogens. Under certain conditions such as confined poultry units, the release of parasites has been effective. The use of parasites in feedlot operations in the midwestern United States has not been successful in controlling house flies and stable flies. A significant problem in biological control has been one of quality control practiced by the providers of the parasitic species. Oftentimes releases are made of inadequately known species, or of species not designed to control a particular pest species. In some cases, adequate care is not taken in the rearing of a particular parasite species whereby contamination by another species resulted in the displacement of the desired parasite. Generally, pest control resulting from parasite releases in other than some confined instances is inadequate. In some field conditions, natural competition by other insect species can reduce horn fly populations by as much as 90% but the remaining 10% survivorship is sufficient to create extremely large populations. Although biological control should be considered as part of an IPM system, it in itself has generally not been satisfactory to control the pest species of most livestock. [*See* PEST MANAGEMENT, BIOLOGICAL CONTROL.]

It has been observed that certain breeds of livestock and also certain individuals within breeds are more or less refractory to ectoparasites. This observation has resulted in crossbreeding Zebu × British breeds in Australia resulting in a tick-resistant crossbreed. It has been demonstrated that many species of animals develop antibodies to ectoparasites. This observation has led to research to develop vaccines for some ectoparasites. Vaccines to provide immunity of hosts to their parasites offers long-term prospects for controlling ectoparasites on livestock without the use of toxic chemicals.

Although the promising results with crossbred animals, vaccines, biological control, and the use of mechanical and cultural procedures are all important parts of an IPM program, the basis for most ectoparasite control on livestock currently remains centered around chemical control. Insecticide use has evolved considerably since the first use of DDT in the 1950s and 1960s. Although more toxic, but less long-lived, the organophosphates replaced DDT and continue to be used today. A newer class of compounds, the pyrethroids, have replaced some of the organophosphates. Other insecticidal chemicals used for ectoparasite control are known as insect growth regulators (IGR) which mimic hormones regulating the growth of insects. The application of IGR's results in the failure of the insects' ability to complete its development. Other compounds of this nature produce chitin-inhibiting hormones that block the proper formation of the insect exoskeleton. [*See* PEST MANAGEMENT, CHEMICAL CONTROL.]

Insecticides for control of livestock pests can be applied by many different methods. These include topical sprays, dusts, dips, pour-ons, spotons, feed additives, injections, and self-applicating methods such as dust bags, back rubbers and insecticide treated ear tags. The self-applicator methods are used primarily on range or pastured animals. For maximum effectiveness, dust bags and backrubbers should be employed in a forced-use situation. A common way to achieve this is to design fences and gates so that cattle must pass the self-applicator in order to obtain water or feed. Plastic ear tags containing insecticide have been in use for about 10 years to control horn flies. This technology was so well accepted and its use was so widespread that large populations of horn flies were exposed to continuous use of pyrethroid insecticides. After about 3 years use, horn flies became resistant to these compounds so that now horn fly resistance to pyrethroids is present to some degree in all major cattle producing areas of the United States and Mexico. This problem also extends into central Canada.

Sprays are used to some extent on pastured cattle but sprays are practical only on small herds or when larger herds are being transferred from pasture to pasture. Insecticides applied as sprays do not provide control for long periods of time but are effective against some pests.

Insecticidal dips are used for the control of ticks and to a lesser extent cattle grub, cattle lice, or scabies. Dips are used extensively in areas where *Boophilus* ticks require treatment on a periodic basis such as in Mexico or in some areas of the Caribbean. Dips are not extensively used in the United States outside of limited tick control areas along the Texas–Mexico border.

Systemics are insecticides that are absorbed through the skin. Systemics remain in the animals system for 24 to 72 hr during which time it is toxic to feeding insects. Systemics can be applied topically in various ways or as feed additives and were first developed to control the cattle grub.

III. Resistance Management

Insect pests are very capable of surviving adversity. One of those adversities is exposure to pesticides. Currently over 500 species have developed resistance to one or more chemicals. Insects and ticks of livestock are listed among this group and have developed resistance at various levels to several compounds on a worldwide basis. In the United States, livestock producers were relatively free of the resistance problem until recently. With the development and use of ear tags in the early 1980s, U.S. producers encountered their first resistance problem.

The frequency of resistance in a pest population is in large part a result of selection pressure from pesticide use. Strategies to manage resistance aim to reduce this pressure to the minimum yet accomplish control. Recommended strategies involve the use of tactics designed to increase the useful life of a pesticide and to decrease the interval of time required for a pest to again become susceptible to a given pesticide.

Some of the most important issues impinging on the development and selection of management tactics to prevent, delay, or manage resistance to pesticides are the biology of the pest and the type of pesticide and application used, the dynamics of resistance, and the lack of supporting data and field validation of data.

The rate at which pesticide resistance develops is extremely variable among species. Such factors as the rate of reproduction, pest movement, and relative fitness of resistant members all contribute to the dynamics of resistance.

Resistance is not absolute throughout a pest's range, and susceptible populations of some pests continue to exist. Furthermore, in an area where resistance has occurred, continued use of a pesticide may be required to control other pests that are still susceptible which confounds management attempts.

Generally, insects resistant to an insecticide in a given stage will also, to a lesser or greater extent, be resistant in another life stage. With the bolus formulations, there is a risk of introducing resistance in the larval stage to a different class of chemicals. Boluses provide long-term continuous treatment and thus could cause resistance in adult insects if not monitored and managed properly. A benefit of the bolus treatment, however, would be that the treatment would not kill migrating susceptible adults so that the interbreeding effect of susceptible adults with resistant flies would be fully utilized as an alternate method for managing pyrethroid resistance.

By using variations in dose or rate of application, resistance may be delayed or minimized by preserving a sufficient population of susceptible individuals. Lower rates of a given pesticide can be used so as not to select in favor of heterozygotes where resistance is recessive. However, a higher dose or more toxic, long-term pyrethroid treatment (ear tag) administered to a resistant population may provide some very short-term control but the resistant population will become only more resistant in time. In hindsight, the highly selective continuous dose provided by pyrethroid ear tags is no doubt responsible for pyrethroid resistance. However, intensified use of any compound by any method of application that simulates ear tag intensity can and will cause a resistance problem.

Fewer or less frequent applications, which reduce the selection pressure over time, should decrease the rate and probability of resistance development. Because of their inefficiency and the lack of maintenance, the dust bag or oiler applications did not provide the same persistent pressure as ear tags. Even where these systems were well maintained their use was not so widespread as to eliminate all susceptible individuals from an area. Any application that is less frequent and less persistent will discourage the development of resistance and restore a less resistant population.

Control of a pest with a particular pesticide in a single field or site, rather than over a large area, will leave untreated insects in surrounding areas to aid in deterring resistance development. Susceptible individuals will move into previously treated areas, thus diluting the frequency of resistant genes. The success of this tactic may vary with insect species, refugia, and other factors. Anything that will reduce the overwintering population should also delay spring treatment. Although treatment of the overwintering generation would reduce the numbers available for reproduction in the spring, it will not reduce the frequency of the resistant genes in that population. Anything done to achieve late season control of resistant pests would probably also help reduce the spring population of these resistant pests. If susceptible insects in untreated refugia were available in the spring then their effect in diluting resistant genes would be greatly increased.

The delay of pesticide applications until an economic threshold is reached reduces the selection pressure for resistance. Economic threshold levels will vary with regions. Even within regions, these levels will vary from producer to producer. For example, a producer with a purebred herd of show cattle may have his acceptable threshold level at 0 parasites whereas another producer with aged animals without calves may tolerate 200 or more pests per animal.

The selection and use of pesticides or formulations having a lower biological persistence can be a useful tactic for managing resistance. Insecticides with short residual levels tend to slow the development of resistance due to reduced exposure. This is probably the single most important factor causing the current resistance problem in horn flies because pyrethroids became a long-lasting compound in ear tag formulations. A return to more conventional procedures in applying pesticides, if not the pesticides themselves, could result in reversion to a more susceptible population.

The use of pesticides of differing classes or modes and sites of action in rotation, alternation, or sequence to control the same pests has been much studied and is accepted as a valid strategy to avoid resistance. It assumes that the number of generations or length of time between uses of any one material is sufficient to allow the level of resistant genes to decline below a critical frequency. A bolus formulation used against resistant horn flies leaving the pyrethroid-susceptible adult fly population intact would be useful. The alternative chemistry of the bolus formulation would have its full effect against the larval stage but would leave the adult population free to interbreed with susceptible flies. As with some of the other tactics, voluntary compliance or enforceability often prevents the general use or success of this tactic in management of resistance.

Excessive use of pesticides for short-term gains can be the least desired practice in the long term because it can lead to the permanent loss of valuable, efficient, and often irreplaceable pesticides and convenient delivery systems.

IV. Important Pest Species of Livestock

A. Horn Fly (*Haematobia irritans*)

The horn fly is a severe pest of cattle and is found in all cattle producing areas of the world. *Haematobia irritans* is a species found throughout Europe and North and South America. *Haematobia irritans exigua*, commonly known as a buffalo fly, is found in Australia. Horn flies were introduced into North America on cattle shipped from Europe and were first collected in New Jersey in 1887. By 1898 the pest had spread throughout the United States and Canada. Although horn flies can feed on a variety of hosts, cattle are the only host on which reproduction can take place since the larvae develop in fresh bovine dung. Horn flies remain on the animal continuously with the exception of the time females leave the host to oviposit. Each female may produce 20–24 eggs per oviposition cycle with a total of up to 400 eggs per lifetime. Eggs usually hatch within 24 hr and depending on the temperature conditions, adults can be produced within 8 to 16 days after oviposition. Very large numbers of adult flies can occur on cattle, with two population peaks common in the southern United States, occurring in early and late summer. In the more north-ern reaches of the distribution a single population peak occurs in midsummer. Since numbers can range from 500 to several thousand flies per head on grown cows, significant blood loss and irritation can result as the horn fly feeds 20 to 30 times per day and both sexes pierce the skin to feed.

B. Stable Fly (*Stomoxys calcitrans*)

The stable fly is the only *Stomoxys* species occurring in North and South America. In Africa, *S. nigra* is a very important species. Stable fly eggs are deposited in animal fecal matter mixed with soil, straw, hay, or silage. They can also be found in wet straw or hay, grass clippings, and fermenting algae on sea coast beaches. Recently, breeding sites have been associated with refuse collecting around the base of round hay bales. This situation has caused stable flies to become more of a pasture pest. Incubation of eggs ranges from 1 to 3 days with the life cycle being completed in 2 to 3 weeks depending on moisture and temperature conditions. The adult stable fly can be distinguished from other flies of its size by their distinct biting mouth parts which appear as a bayonet protruding from under the head. The adult stable fly, both males and females, is a persistent feeder and can cause considerable irritation to host animals. Stable flies generally feed only once a day but those flies feeding early in the morning may feed a second time later in the day. The average life of an adult stable fly is approximately 2 to 3 weeks.

C. Face Fly (*Musca autumnalis*)

The face fly was introduced into North America in 1951 and spread from Nova Scotia south to South Carolina and west to California. The adults feed on body secretions and become especially annoying to animals as they feed on facial secretions such as tears, nasal mucous, and saliva. Flies also feed on other body discharges such as blood and milk from which they obtain their protein source for development of their eggs. Face flies spend only a short period of time on the animals with the remainder of time being spent in bushes, trees, and other vegetative and stationary objects. Adult face flies can be found on cattle in pastures from March to November depending on the locality in the States. Face flies lay their eggs on the surface of fresh cattle dung deposited on pasture and range land. Larvae burrow into and feed in the dung and after maturation they disperse into surrounding soil when they pupate. Developmental times for eggs, larvae, and pupae depend on environmental conditions with average time from eggs to adult requiring 12 to 20 days. Adults have a life span of 2 to 4 weeks. Adult face flies are strong flyers capable of transfer between widely separated herds of cattle. Diapause occurs in the adult stage where clusters of overwintering face flies can be found inside buildings and other man-made structures. The effects of face flies on cattle are both direct and indirect. Feeding flies can damage eye tissue which enhances the transmission of the bacterium *Moraxella bovis* the etiological agent of "pinkeye" (infectious bovine keratoconjunctivitis). Face flies also vector nematode eyeworms in the genus *Thelazia* for which they serve as a necessary alternate host in North America.

D. House Fly (*Musca domestica*)

House flies are generally associated with livestock fed in confinement. The fly feeds on a variety of animal excreta and garbage and provides very little direct irritation to cattle. Eggs are laid as clusters within cracks and crevices in moist decaying organic substrates. Egg developmental time varies with temperature conditions with about 3 to 8 days to complete the larval period. The pupal stage lasts from 3 to 10 days, with the adult stage lasting for 3 or more weeks. House fly populations can become very large near poorly managed livestock facilities and may become a public annoyance. In this regard, they are one of the insect species most important to livestock production as an increasing number of producers have suffered legal action when they have failed to adequately control house flies. This is especially important as housing developments encroach on livestock operations.

E. Tabanids (Numerous Species)

The biting flies in the family Tabanidae are a large and cosmopolitan family of bloodsucking flies, commonly known as horse flies or deer flies. Tabanids can range in size from 6 to 10 mm in the smaller species up to 25 mm in the larger ones. They are strong flyers and serious pests of cattle, horse, deer, and other warm-blooded animals. At times the genus *Chrysops* can be particularly persistent to man. Only the females take blood meals but the mouth parts are bladelike and function as cutting instruments which cause a very irritating wound. The breeding habits are aquatic or semi-aquatic although some persistent species can be terrestrial. Most Tabanid species have

one generation per year; however, some species may require 2 or 3 years to complete a generation. Although Tabanids may be involved in the transmission of protozan, helminthic, bacterial, or viral diseases of animals, in most cases the transmission is merely mechanical. Two of the more important diseases transmitted in cattle are anaplasmosis and anthrax.

F. Mosquitoes (Numerous Species)

Mosquitoes are a large group of biting flies consisting of approximately 3000 species worldwide. As in all dipterous insects there are four stages in the life cycle of mosquitoes, the egg, larvae, pupae, and adult. The life cycles and behavior of individual species vary considerably, but most can be placed into one of three representative groups typical of those found in the genera *Aedes, Anopheles,* or *Culex*. *Culex* mosquitoes lay their eggs side by side formed into a "raft" that generally contains between 100 and 300 eggs. When these eggs mature, they will hatch regardless of the availability of water. *Anopheles* mosquitoes lay eggs singly on the water surface and can produce over 200 eggs per oviposition cycle. These eggs usually hatch within 2 to 3 days with development continuing in the water. *Aedes* lay their eggs on moist substraits where they mature and await adequate moisture to stimulate hatch. In some cases, such eggs remain viable for up to 3 years if hatching conditions are unfavorable. The larvae of all mosquitoes are aquatic and occur in a wide variety of habitats. These include permanent ponds and marshes, flooded pastures, tree holes, indentations in the ground, and an assortment of water-holding artificial containers. Only the female mosquito feeds on blood and most species require a blood meal before oviposition can occur. Female mosquitoes take several blood meals and can produce multiple batches of eggs. The females that oviposit on water are capable of hibernation and may live for 6 months or longer. Female mosquitoes are also good flyers and can migrate long distances of up to 20 miles. Mosquito populations vary greatly in numbers and can reach large populations under suitable conditions. Mosquitoes are vectors of Venezuelan, Western, and Eastern equine encephalitis in horses.

G. Simulium (Numerous Species)

A number of species commonly known as black flies, buffalo gnats, or turkey gnats are included in this group. Female black flies deposit their eggs on the surface of objects near water where they are kept moist. Some species occurring along rivers often lay eggs on the surface of moving water. These eggs will eventually sink to the bottom and as the larvae hatch they will become attached to stones, branches, plants, or other debris in swift-flowing water. The duration of the larval period varies from a few weeks to almost a year depending on the species. Pupal development ranging from several days to several weeks is followed by adult emergence. The females of most black fly species are blood feeders and some species may attack domestic animals. *Simulium vittatum* often feeds on the ears of horses and cattle causing pain, scabbing, and irritability. The southern buffalo gnat, *Cnephia pecuarum,* attacks livestock and can reach such large population levels that livestock are sometimes suffocated.

H. Culicoides (Numerous Species)

The primary genera of biting gnats, *Culicoides,* contains species that are pests of livestock. These biting gnats are almost exclusively aquatic in the larval stages and will occur in a variety of habitats including the margins of streams and lakes, ponds, salt marshes, swamps, and rice fields. Species of *Culicoides* are distributed widely throughout the United States and feed principally on livestock in the early evening and nighttime. Livestock maintained outdoors may be exposed to nocturnal attacks throughout most of the summer. Numerous viral pathogens have been isolated from *Culicoides* and these include the important livestock diseases bluetongue, Eastern equine encephalitis (EEE), Venezuelan equine encephalitis (VEE), and bovine ephemeral fever.

I. Screwworm (*Cochliomyia hominivorax*)

There are several species of flies that cause myiasis or the infestation of organs and tissues of animals by fly larvae where they feed upon either the live or dead tissues or on the ingested food of the host. There are three species of flies that produce obligate myiasis, *Cochliomyia hominivorax, Chrysomya bezziana,* and *Wohlfahrtia magnifica. Cochliomyia hominivorax* screwworm is the primary screwworm (NWS) distributed throughout the Americas. The New World screwworm (NWS) is strongly attracted to the wounds and sores of animals and can inflict damage to an animal suffering from a wound as small as a tick bite. Eggs are attached to the host immediately surrounding the

wound and incubation takes place in less than 24 hr under suitable conditions. Larvae may feed from 3 to 5 days after which the mature larvae fall to the ground and pupate. The pupal stage lasts about 7 days followed by adult emergence. Egg to egg development time usually requires about 3 weeks under optimal conditions. The NWS has been eliminated from the United States and Mexico by releasing sterile flies to mate with fertile native females. This cross-mating between the sterilized male and the wild female results in sterile egg production, thus eliminating or controlling this species. In the old world, *C. bezziana* occupies a position similar to that of the NWS. They mostly attack domestic animals or cattle but as is the case with the NWS any warm-blooded animal can be infested including man.

J. Cattle Grub (*Hypoderma* spp.)

There are two species of cattle grub that exist throughout North America and Europe. The common cattle grub, *Hypoderma lineatum,* is present in the southern United States and Canada whereas the northern cattle grub, *H. bovis,* is present in the northern half of the United States and Canada. These two species are host specific, and under normal conditions infest only cattle. The adults (heel fly) of these two species have mouth parts which are nonfunctional; thus, they only live 2 or 3 days. The female heel fly is capable of laying eggs immediately upon emergence from the puparium once she is fertilized. Eggs are oviposited on the hairs, usually on the legs of animals with 500 to 800 eggs being produced by one female. These larvae hatch in 4 to 5 days and crawl down the hairs of the animal and enter the skin. Upon entering the animal the common cattle grub arrives in the gullet after about 2 months of migration. The northern cattle grub migrates to the tissue surrounding the spinal column. At these sites the larvae feed for a variable length of time after which they migrate to the back of the animal where they cut holes in the hide and complete development for an additional 2 or 3 months. These grubs cause warbles, a condition visible on the backs of animals, usually occurring between September and February depending on the locality. Upon completion of the development cycle, the third instar larva drops from the back of the animal and pupates in the soil. The adult emerges in 1 to 2 months. Although there can be considerable irritation caused by the first instar larvae penetrating the skin or by the adult fly in her efforts to oviposit on the animal, most of the damage is done by the larvae cutting holes in the hide. There are no known effective cultural controls for this pest but many of the systemic pesticides registered for use are efficient in the control of these pests.

K. Sheep Bot Fly (*Oestrus ovis*)

The sheep bot fly, *Oestrus ovis*, commonly infests sheep and goats. The adult bot flies have nonfunctional mouth parts resulting in very short life periods. Females are active during the heat of the day from late spring to autumn. They deposit newly hatched larvae near the nostrils of the host. These first instar larvae crawl into the nasal passages and feed on mucous secretions. Larvae finally reach the upper nasal passages and sinuses where they attach and complete their development. Mature larvae crawl out of the nostril, drop to the ground, and pupate in the soil. Although animals are seldom killed by these flies, the larvae cause inflammation of the nasal membranes which is annoying to the sheep and interferes with normal grazing habits.

L. Horse Bot Fly (Numerous Species)

There are three species of horse bot flies, *Gasterophilus intestinalis* (horse bot fly), *G. nasalis* (throat bot fly), *G. haemorrhoidalis* (nose bot fly), which can cause considerable annoyance to horses. As the adult mouth parts of these species are nonfunctional, the duration of the adult stage is relatively short. The adults mate shortly after emergence and the female begins ovipositing almost immediately thereafter. Eggs are attached to hairs on the host's body and the newly hatched larvae penetrate the soft tissues of the mouth where they remain approximately 3 weeks. After this time the larvae migrate to the stomach or small intestine where they become attached to the walls. Upon completion of the larval cycle which lasts several months, the full grown larvae pass out with the feces. Pupation takes place in the soil and adults emerge 2 weeks to 2 months later depending on climatic conditions. The horse bot fly may oviposit 500 to 1000 eggs per female. Incubation period for horse bot fly eggs is about 5 days after which they can be stimulated to hatch by the warmth and moisture from the host's tongue. This fly usually attaches its eggs to the inside of the fore legs but may also attach eggs to the outside of the legs and the flanks. The throat bot fly attaches its eggs to the host beneath the jaw. These eggs may hatch within 4 to 5 days without a required external stimulus. The newly hatched larvae crawl along the skin to the horse's mouth where they penetrate the soft tissue. This species attaches itself to the pyloric region of the stomach or to the upper portion of the duodenum. The nose bot fly attaches its eggs on the upper and lower lips of horses. Hatch occurs in approximately 2 days and the larvae burrow into the tongue or lips where they remain for about 6 weeks. After migration, they attach themselves to the pyloric region of the stomach or to the duodenum.

Reactions of horses to ovipositing female bot flies may be so violent that they injure themselves. First instar larvae cause irritation and pus pockets when burrowing in the oral tissue. The attachment of larvae to the stomach and duodenum walls interferes with digestion. Although chemical treatments are effective, sponging the eggs of these flies while attached to the hair of the horses can induce hatching after which the larvae may be washed away thus reducing the worm burden on the animal.

M. Ticks and Mites

Ticks and mites belong to the order Acarina and almost all terrestrial vertebrates are subject to attack by these pests. The Ixodidae or hard ticks attach to their hosts for long periods of time and are the ones most often seen on livestock. The Argasidae or soft ticks feed for short periods and primarily at night. Ticks feeding alone, even without the transmission of pathogens, can cause damage to livestock. Ticks can cause anemia and irritation from their presence on the animal. Host nutrition influences ticks feeding success. It has been noted that animals on low protein diets produce more ticks than animals on proper diets, with cattle in a weight loss situation producing more ticks than those in a gaining stage. Blood losses are accompanied by some toxicosis caused by the ticks salivary secretions. Toxicosis and paralysis from tick bites are two serious conditions of tick feedings. Dermatosis, exsanguination, and disease transmission are effects of tick feedings. Because ticks are persistent bloodsuckers, their slow feeding on a wide range of hosts and their longevity make them especially important as vectors of diseases. The reproductive potential of ticks is great as some species may deposit up to 20,000 eggs. All tick species pass through four stages as eggs, larvae, nymphs, and adults. Time required for complete development from egg to adult is from several weeks to 3 years. Larval ticks emerging from eggs on the ground commonly climb onto

grasses or other low vegetation from which they are picked up by grazing or passing animals. Ticks can be classified as one-, two-, or three-host ticks. When feeding is completed on one animal, as in the case of *Boophilus annulatus*, it is a one-host tick. In *Rhipicephalus evertsi*, a two-host tick, the larvae and nymph will feed on one host and a second host is required by the adult to feed and complete its development. *Dermacentor andersoni* is an example of a three-host tick. The larvae engorges on small mammals after which it drops to the ground to molt. The nymphal stage feeds on other small mammals and then drops to the ground, molts, and then becomes an adult. As an adult, the tick requires a third host upon which it feeds and then returns to the ground where the female lays her eggs. There are about 660 species of hard ticks. The species most commonly found are *Ixodes scapularis* (black legged tick), *Amblyomma americanum* (Lone Star tick), *A. cajennense* (cajenne tick), *A. maculatum* (Gulf Coast tick), *D. albipictus* (winter tick), *B. annulatus* (cattle fever tick), and *B. microplus* (southern cattle tick). *Amblyomma variegatum* is an African species which has been introduced into the Caribbean from Africa and is a threat to cattle production in the Southern United States as it is a vector of heartwater fever. *Boophilus microplus* and *B. annulatus*, officially eradicated from the United States, are both found in Mexico and continue to be threats to the United States cattle producers as these ticks are vectors of the Texas cattle fever. Strict quarantine procedures are in effect to prevent these species from being imported on live animal shipments from Mexico. *Boophilus microplus* is also a serious pest of cattle in Australia, Central and South America, and Africa.

Closely related parasites of livestock are species of mites which can affect the health of animals by causing dermatitis, loss of blood or other tissue fluids, transfer of pathogenic agents, and strong allergic reactions to their host. *Psoroptes ovis* (sheep scab mite) and *P. bovis* are found on sheep and cattle. The life cycles can be completed entirely on the host animal. The parasitic stages do not burrow into the hosts' skin but the host may become covered by scab formations caused by the feeding of this pest. Infestations on sheep generally affect the body parts most densely covered with wool. The irritation causes the wool to become rough and matted at the site of infestation. These mites are usually at their highest population peaks during the winter months. Sheep scab has been eliminated from U.S. flocks. *Psoroptes bovis* scab on cattle is related to the mite found on sheep and is still present in the United States. Severe dermatitis can result in the death of the animal if left untreated.

Females of the itch mite (*Sarcoptes scabiei*) burrow into the outer layers of skin depositing eggs as they do so. Larvae and nymphs may burrow also but are most frequently found in hair follicles in the skin and reaction of the host caused by the burrowing activity results in intense itching. This often is complicated by secondary infections known as sarcoptic mange subsequent to the scratching. One of the more important species belonging to this group is *Sarcoptes scabiei* variety *suis* which occurs on swine.

Chorioptes bovis, the chorioptic mange mite, spends its entire life cycle on its host which includes cattle, horses, sheep, and goats. These mites do not burrow into host skin but the mouth parts are used to prick the skin as the mite feeds. The resulting mange is usually confined to certain areas of the body such as the neck, tail, or lower legs.

V. Role of Introduced Pest Species in U.S. Production

Many of the livestock pest species present in the United States today are species that have been introduced from other countries as demonstrated by the horn fly and face fly which were introduced from Europe. *Boophilus* ticks and the New World Screwworm as well as sheep scabies have been eradicated from the United States. However, since these species all still reside in land masses near to or adjacent to the U.S. mainland, the possibility of reintroduction continues. The tropical bont tick, *Amblyomma variegatum*, is present in the Caribbean and poses a threat to U.S. livestock production especially in the southeastern states. All of these species are capable of reducing the efficiency of animal production in the United States and strict quarantine procedures to prevent their introduction are carried out by U.S. regulatory agencies. United States producers need to be aware of the threat of the reintroduction of these species and must report any suspect pest species to regulatory agencies. To guard against importation of these species, animal imports should be certified free of these pests upon departure from the exporting country. Upon arrival in the United States they should be adequately inspected for pest species and treated with appropriate prophylactic insecticides. Upon treatment, animals are held in quarantine facilities prior to their transport to final destinations in the United States.

Bibliography

Harwood, R. F., and James, M. T. (1979). "Entomology in Human and Animal Health." Macmillan, New York.

Kettle, D. S. (1984). "Medical and Veterinary Entomology." CAB International, Wallingford, England.

Pimental, D. (ed.) (1981). "Handbook of Pest Management in Agriculture," 2nd ed., Vol. 1. CRC Press, Boca Raton, FL.

Williams, R. E., Hall, R. D., Broce, A. B., and Scholl, P. J. (eds.) (1985). "Livestock Entomology." Wiley, New York.